Applied
Business
Mathematics

13th Edition

Robert A. Schultheis

Professor of Management Information Systems
and
Professor of Business Education
Southern Illinois University
Edwardsville, Illinois

Raymond M. Kaczmarski

Supervisor of Business Education
Detroit Public Schools
Detroit, Michigan

Roswell E. Fairbank

Professor Emeritus of Business Education
State University of New York at Albany
Albany, New York

M47TE
PUBLISHED BY
SOUTH-WESTERN PUBLISHING CO.
CINCINNATI, OH   WEST CHICAGO, IL   DALLAS, TX   LIVERMORE, CA

This teacher's edition of APPLIED BUSINESS
MATHEMATICS, thirteenth edition, consists of
two parts. The first part is the teacher's
manual, which contains general and specific
teaching suggestions; step-by-step solutions
to the textbook problems; and answers to the
pretests, unit tests, and semester examinations. The second part is the student's
textbook, which includes answers to most
drills and problems.

ISBN: 0-538-28468-4

1 2 3 4 5 6 7 8 9 Ki 7 6 5 4 3 2 1 0 9

Printed in the United States of America

Contents (Teacher's Manual)

GENERAL TEACHING SUGGESTIONS

SOLUTIONS SECTION

General Teaching Suggestions

INSTRUCTIONAL MATERIALS AVAILABLE FOR STUDENTS

Instructional materials for APPLIED BUSINESS MATHEMATICS, Thirteenth Edition, that are used by students include a textbook, a workbook, a spreadsheet applications diskette, a test package of pretests and unit tests, and a booklet containing answers to selected problems.

Textbook. APPLIED BUSINESS MATHEMATICS, Thirteenth Edition, Stock No. M47, is recommended for a one-year course. The textbook contains the narrative and problems for the topics included in the text. The textbook also contains:

1. *Calculator Clinics* that show students how to use a hand-held calculator to solve problems in the text and workbook.

2. *Computer Clinics* that allow students to use popular spreadsheet programs to solve business problems similar to those found in the textbook. The Computer Clinics require the use of the Spreadsheet Applications Diskette and one of many popular spreadsheet software products.

3. *Supplementary Problems* that can be used for review assignments, as a source of test questions, for remedial work, or for additional work for those students who finish the regular problems quickly.

4. *Drills for Accuracy and Speed* that should be used to develop and reinforce basic arithmetic skills.

5. A glossary of *Business Math Terms* that includes brief definitions of important terms used in the text and in business.

Workbook. The workbook for APPLIED BUSINESS MATHEMATICS, Stock No. M471, contains problems and drill materials that supplement those in the textbook. Although the workbook practice materials correlate with those in the textbook, different problems are presented.

The workbook is a valuable supplement to the textbook because it provides many learning activities that are not included in the textbook. For example, the workbook contains a variety of blank forms that are similar to those used in business activities such as banking, buying, and selling. These forms are to be used by students to solve workbook problems.

The workbook also contains:

1. A *Vocabulary Review* for each unit. The vocabulary review is a matching exercise that covers the vocabulary terms introduced in the textbook.

2. An *Integrated Project* for each unit. The integrated projects provide students with opportunities to review and apply the arithmetic skills and concepts learned in each unit.

Tests. A series of tests are available for the Thirteenth Edition of APPLIED BUSINESS MATHEMATICS (Stock No. M473). These tests are available in printed form and as MicroEXAM testing diskettes. Both packages include:

1. Four *Pretests,* one for each of the first four units. These first four units review the fundamental arithmetic processes: addition, subtraction, multiplication, division, fractions, decimals, and percents. The pretests allow you to measure student readiness for these units.

2. Seventeen *Unit Tests,* one for each unit of the text. Each test is designed for a 50–55 minute class period and consists of basic skills or arithmetic operation questions and word problems drawn from the unit.

3. Two *Semester Tests,* one covering Units 1–8 and the other covering Units 9–17. Each test is designed to take two class periods and consists of four parts: Part A, which is a series of multiple choice questions covering terms and concepts; Part B, which is a series of basic skill problems; Part C, which is a series of word problems; and Part D, which requires that forms be completed.

Spreadsheet Applications Diskette. A diskette containing 26 spreadsheet templates allows students to complete the *Computer Clinics* in the textbook. The templates are designed so that students do not need to understand how to create a spreadsheet or how to enter formulas into cells. Students only need to know how to enter data into the templates. The computer problems help students understand how a computer spreadsheet can help in decision making by allowing students to play "what if" games with the arithmetic data.

Spreadsheet Application Diskettes are available for use with many popular spreadsheet programs.

Answers to Selected Problems. A booklet, Stock No. M47J, containing many answers that are not shown in the textbook is available for distribution to students if you so desire.

INSTRUCTIONAL MATERIALS AVAILABLE FOR TEACHERS ONLY

Materials available for the teacher only include the teacher's edition of the textbook and workbook.

Teacher's Edition of the Textbook. The teacher's edition of APPLIED BUSINESS MATHEMATICS, Thirteenth Edition, Stock No. M47TE, consists of the student's edition of the textbook with overprinted answers; a teacher's manual, which you are now reading; and the solutions for the textbook, pretests, and unit tests.

Teacher's Edition of the Workbook. The teacher's edition of the workbook, Stock No. M471TE, is a combined workbook and key, consisting of the student's edition with overprinted answers and solutions. The teacher's edition of the workbook also contains *transparency masters,* drawn from illustrations and examples used in the text and teacher's manual.

GENERAL DESIGN OF THE TEXTBOOK

APPLIED BUSINESS MATHEMATICS is written for a one-year course in business mathematics at the high school level. Early in the textbook, students comprehensively review the arithmetic fundamentals that are most likely to have been studied previously.

Throughout the book students use their arithmetic skills to solve a variety of business problems that demonstrate how widely arithmetic is used in the business world. The range of topics covered also provides students with a broad introduction to the business content and terminology that they will study in greater detail in advanced business classes.

Although the majority of the problems that students solve deal with business applications, personal applications are used frequently to make the material more meaningful to students.

Organization of Subject Matter. The subject matter of APPLIED BUSINESS MATHEMATICS is presented in seventeen units. Each unit is divided into sections, arranged in logical order, that present specific problem situations or arithmetical processes.

Order of Presentation. Throughout the text, each topic within a section is based on the preceding topic, and each section and unit is in large measure based upon the knowledge and skills developed in preceding sections and units.

Because of this approach, it is strongly recommended that you present each section and unit in the order in which it appears in the textbook. If the order is changed, both you and students may encounter difficulties, since important knowledge and skills may not have been developed prior to the time they are needed.

For example, in **Unit Seven, Borrowing Money,** the calculations and concepts involving interest become progressively more challenging as students deal with:

1. Finding interest for time periods stated in years, months, and days.

2. Discounting notes and finding interest on demand notes.

3. Calculating finance charges, installment payments and schedules, and annual percentage rates.

Before students are required to make these interest-related calculations, they will have already studied in the previous six units the necessary basic operations involving addition, subtraction, multiplication, division, fractions, percents, and rounding.

Further, the principles of interest are subsequently used in sections dealing with savings accounts and certificates, mortgages, and distribution of partnership income.

Student Objectives. The opening page of each unit lists the competencies to be achieved by students during the study of the unit. The degree to which competencies should be met is not stated, so you are free to tailor the competencies to meet the specific requirements of your course, school, community expectations, and student achievement levels.

Arithmetic Fundamentals. A review of fundamental arithmetic processes is provided in the first four units through concurrent work on these three related groups of problem material:

1. Introductory business problems requiring the use of a fundamental operation are presented in a section that precedes the formal review of the fundamental operation. This approach shows students how a basic arithmetic

process is applied in the business world and gives them a practical reason for studying the operation again.

2. Fundamental operations (addition, subtraction, multiplication, division, fractions, decimals, and percents) are presented in sections that immediately follow the presentation of introductory business problems.

3. Review assignments at the end of each section provide a recap of the business problems and the fundamental operations covered in that section and in previous sections.

After the study of fundamental operations is completed in Unit 4, two groups of problem materials are used in the remainder of the textbook: (1) business problems and (2) *spaced review* of both business problems and fundamental operations. The spaced review of both business problems and fundamental operations allows students to maintain the skills they have learned as they progress through the course.

The concurrent development of business problems and fundamental operations and the continuous spaced review of both are distinguishing features of APPLIED BUSINESS MATHEMATICS.

Five-Step Teaching Pattern. In APPLIED BUSINESS MATHEMATICS, a five-step plan is used to develop understanding and mastery of each type of business problem or arithmetical process. This plan includes:

1. A simple, concise introductory discussion, which provides essential background information for understanding the problem situation.

2. An example of the problem.

3. A model solution of the example and an explanation of the solution.

4. An exercise for immediate practice and initial mastery, consisting of problems like the one in the example.

5. A systematic program of spaced review at planned intervals to ensure retention.

This five-step teaching pattern is similar to methods used by many teachers. Steps 1, 2, and 3 correspond to the presentation phase of a lesson; Step 4 to the practice phase where students apply what they have learned; and Step 5 to the maintenance of skills.

By using this teaching pattern throughout the book, the burden of lesson planning is reduced to a minimum.

Maintenance Program. In the Thirteenth Edition of APPLIED BUSINESS MATHEMATICS, a systematic maintenance program is provided by the section reviews that are found at the end of each section of the text, starting with Section 2. In these reviews, each fundamental arithmetic process and business problem is repeated frequently at intervals throughout the text.

In teaching business mathematics, constant attention must be given to the effects of disuse or forgetting. Unless newly learned skills are recalled soon after they are first learned, they will be quickly forgotten.

We know from the psychology of learning that forgetting occurs very rapidly at first and less rapidly later. To counteract this process, students must recall or review newly learned items frequently at first and less frequently later to make the acquired skill permanent.

This program of systematic recall, review, or application is called a maintenance program. Its purpose is to provide an effective plan for "over-learning" information so that it will be permanently retained by the student.

Reading Level and Vocabulary. The Thirteenth Edition of APPLIED BUSINESS MATHEMATICS is written to be well within the reading abilities of business mathematics students. Sentences are short, the syllabic intensity is low, and general vocabulary consists of familiar words.

Technical business terms are included in the text because students who wish to enter business need to be able to read, understand, write, and say technical terms. Use of technical vocabulary, however, is limited to terms essential to the introduction or explanation of business or mathematical concepts.

Vocabulary Development. To help students acquire the vocabulary related to solving business problems, terms are emphasized in these four ways:

1. New terms are shown in boldface when first used.

2. These terms also appear in section review assignments in which students are required to match the terms with appropriate statements.

3. These terms also appear in unit vocabulary review exercises in the workbook.

4. The terms are presented again, with definitions, in a glossary, **Appendix D: Business Math Terms.**

Other important, but less essential, terms are shown in italics within the text and may also be found in **Appendix D,** depending on the relative importance of their general usage.

This way of presenting and reviewing terms is designed to strengthen student vocabulary skills and to emphasize that understanding certain words and terms is essential to mastery of the subject matter of business mathematics.

Metric and Customary Measurements. Because business firms in the United States compete in an international market, many schools include metrics in their business mathematics courses of study. The extent to which metrics are studied varies among schools.

The metric system of measurements is presented in Unit 5 of APPLIED BUSINESS MATHEMATICS. Four metric measures are included: length, area, capacity, and weight.

The unit on metrics is designed so that it may be included or excluded, as preferred. Problems that maintain skill in using metric measures are provided in review assignments throughout the text. These metric problems may also be used or omitted as desired.

For the foreseeable future, at least, all or most students entering business mathematics probably will have had prior instruction in Customary measurements, whether or not they have been taught metrics. For that reason, most problems in this textbook are based on Customary measures.

Zero With Decimals. In this text, a zero is used to indicate the absence of a whole number value in all decimal expressions, as shown in this example:

5 tenths is written as 0.5
5 hundredths is written as 0.05
5 cents is written as $0.05
One-half percent is written as 0.5%

Expressing decimal values in this manner is preferred with the metric system and is used increasingly with all values in the Customary system. Also, zeros before the decimal point usually occur in calculator displays and often appear in computer printouts. In a sense, the zero before the decimal is used as a place holder to show that the value is correct and that a significant (non-zero) digit before the decimal point has not been inadvertently omitted.

PRACTICE MATERIALS IN THE TEXT AND WORKBOOK

Exercises. The presentation of each new problem or process is followed by an exercise for immediate practice to gain mastery (Step 4 of the Five-Step Teaching Pattern). Each exercise is numbered and is designated in the heading as an oral or written exercise.

Oral exercises require students to solve problems mentally and give the results orally. Problems should be solved without the aid of written calculations. Oral exercises are supplied primarily for classroom work, rather than for out-of-class assignments.

Written exercises require students to prepare written solutions to each problem and show all calculations involved. Problems in written exercises are arranged in graded sequence, with the simplest problem presented first.

Written exercises may be used for classroom work. However, they may also be used for homework assignments. Suggestions for the latter use are found under the heading *Homework Assignments* in the **Presenting Subject Matter in Business Mathematics** section of this manual.

Problems with Guide Answers. Beginning with Exercise 2 in Section 4 of the textbook, answers, printed in color, are given for one or more problems in most of the written exercises. The answers are given so that students may know whether they solved the problems correctly, and so they avoid practicing incorrect methods.

In general, in an exercise where guide answers are provided, an answer is given for the first item in a tabular problem, the first word problem, and for any subsequent item or problem where there is a major change in the pattern of the solution.

The student's use of guide answers is explained in a footnote at the bottom of the page on which the first guide answer appears. Suggestions for your classroom use of guide answers are described under the heading *Using Guide Answers* in the **Presenting Subject Matter in Business Mathematics** section of this manual.

Problems Containing Nonessential Information. In most business mathematics problem situations, students are given only the information essential to solving the problems. They are not asked to eliminate information given in the problem that is not useful to solving the problem. In the real world, however, no such tidy presentation of problem information occurs. Students must learn to identify the information they need to solve a problem and to discard information that is not needed.

This edition of APPLIED BUSINESS MATHEMATICS provides instruction in analyzing problems to help students develop skill in identifying information essential and not essential to solving business problems. Techniques for analyzing problems are presented in Section 5 and problems that include more information than is needed for solution are provided in almost every section thereafter for the remainder of the text.

Problems Requiring Estimation. This edition of APPLIED BUSINESS MATHEMATICS includes increased emphasis on developing student estimation skills. Students are taught to estimate answers to problems as a check on the accuracy of their solutions.

Estimation methods are introduced in Section 9 and one estimation problem is included in nearly every section throughout the remainder of the text. Constant use and reinforcement of estimation skills is designed to thoroughly instill estimating skills and habits in students.

It is important to understand that estimation, by definition, does not produce one, and only one, correct answer. For example, students estimating the answer to an interest problem may generate several different, and totally correct, answers. Suppose that students are to estimate the interest on a loan of $990 for one year at 12%. One student might round off the principal to $1,000 and the interest rate to 10%. The estimated answer: $100 interest. Another student may round off the principal to $1,000 but not feel the need to round the rate of interest. The estimated answer: $120 interest. Both estimated answers allow the student to verify the placement of the decimal point in the answer and to avoid accepting incorrect answers that are substantially out of line with the correct interest amount.

Estimated answers provided in the text and in the solutions have been derived usually by rounding each amount in a problem to the last number on the left. Thus, a principal of $990 becomes $1,000 and an interest rate of 12% becomes 10% for estimation purposes.

When students' estimated answers differ from those provided in the text or solutions, students should be asked to explain how they estimated the answers so you can be assured that the procedures they used are appropriate to the problem they were asked to solve. Having students share the solutions to their estimated answers in class discussions is important. Students benefit when they learn how others use different methods to estimate answers.

Challenge Problems. Certain topics, exercises, and problems that are optional or relatively difficult are marked with a ‡ (double dagger) in the textbook. These materials are challenging and should have special appeal to students who like the study of business mathematics a great deal.

Section Reviews. The reviews at the ends of sections play a major role in helping students preserve their math skills as they progress through the course. Reviews are located at the end of each section and the word problems are numbered to correspond with the section in which they first appear. Reviews may have three parts.

The *Terms* part of the review consists of a vocabulary matching exercise for the terms presented in the section. In a few instances, there are so few new terms introduced within a section that these terms are included in the review of the following section. Problems involving abstract computational skills and number relationships are found in the *Skills* part of the exercise. The rest of the review is *Problems*. The problems are practical word problems that parallel those just covered in the section and others that were taught in earlier sections.

The reviews may be used for classroom work or for homework. Since they involve only the application or review of principles, problems, and processes already learned, they are particularly suitable for homework.

For each word problem included in the section review, the number of the textbook section in which the word problem was introduced is provided in the teacher's edition so that the teacher may refer students back to that section for help.

For maximum effectiveness, each review should be used in the exact order in which it is presented in the text, and no review should be skipped. If it is necessary or desirable to skip a particular topic or section in the text, you should examine each subsequent review and omit any problem connected with the skipped material. The rest of the problems in these reviews should be used in the usual way.

Calculator Clinics. This edition of APPLIED BUSINESS MATHEMATICS provides direct instruction for students in the use of the hand-held calculator to solve business problems. In selected sections of the text, calculator clinics are provided to show students how to use the calculator to solve the problems in the sections. Students are shown not only how to use the ordinary keys of calculators, but they are also shown calculator shortcuts and the use of special calculator keys, such as the percent key and the memory keys.

The directions for the calculator clinics have been written for the hand-held calculators commonly used today. However, calculators vary greatly in how they function, in the kinds of special keys available, and in what functions the keys perform. In general, the calculator clinics have been written so that the procedures described can be performed on any calculator. That is, the first part of the calculator clinics shows how to solve the problem in such a generic way that any calculator can be used.

If the use of special function keys might cause problems on some calculators, the procedures for using these keys have been described in the *Saving Time* sections of the clinics. For example, the use of the percent key is often described in this section so that it can be skipped if there is no percent key on the calculators students use or if the percent key on those calculators performs differently than those in common use.

If your school provides students with calculators, you should test the brand you have by solving the problems in the calculator clinics before assigning the clinics to students. You should especially check your calculator with the procedures described in the *Saving Time* section of the calculator clinics.

Usually, no problems are provided in the calculator clinics. Instead, the student is directed to solve problems in the section with the calculator. Some teachers will have students solve all problems in the text using their calculators. Others will have students only use calculators to solve problems after they have already been solved manually. Other teachers may choose to combine these approaches. Suggestions for using calculators in Business Mathematics are found under the heading *Use of Calculators* in the **Teaching Suggestions** section of this manual.

Computer Clinics. Personal computers have become commonplace in businesses and other organizations. One of the most popular uses of personal computers is providing support for decision making, and one of the most commonly used software packages for decision support is the spreadsheet. Many firms today expect their employees to know what spreadsheet software is and what it can do.

This edition of APPLIED BUSINESS MATHEMATICS provides instruction in the use of computer spreadsheets for the solution of common business problems. Computer clinics are placed throughout the text to allow students to understand how spreadsheets can be used in the decision-making process. The clinics place particular emphasis on how computer spreadsheets can be used to play "what if" games with arithmetic data.

When the first computer clinic occurs in Section 3, computer systems are briefly reviewed and spreadsheet software and templates described. The first template is very simple, involving the keeping of a weekly cash payment record similar to the cash payment summary that students complete manually in Section 3.

The computer clinics should be used in conjunction with the Spreadsheet Applications Diskette. The diskette provides the spreadsheet templates needed to complete the computer clinics. Students do not need to know how to create a spreadsheet or how to create and enter formulas into cells. Basically, students need only know how to: turn on the computer; place the program and data diskettes into the drives; boot the program; load a spreadsheet file; and use the cursor keys so that the correct data can be entered.

Many teachers will not teach business mathematics in a classroom equipped with computer systems. However, many will have access to one computer system that can be used for demonstrations, to a few computer systems that can be used by teams of students, or to a computer laboratory available for individual student use.

The computer clinics have been designed to require a minimum of teacher instruction and supervision. Individual students or small teams of students should be able to complete assignments using a computer with little or no help from the teacher. However, it is suggested that the teacher demonstrate both machine basics and how the problems in each computer clinic are solved before students are permitted to work alone or in teams.

You may wish to assign the computer clinics only to selected students, such as those who finish other work early. You may wish to form small teams of two students each and assign the teams to complete the clinic problems. If you have a few computers in your room, these teams could be assigned the use of the computers on a rotation basis.

Completion of the computer clinics requires that you have a computer system that will run AppleWorks®,* or one of its clones, or Lotus 1-2-3®,** or one of its clones, or MicroTools. There are numerous spreadsheet programs that can read and use Lotus 1-2-3 spreadsheet files. Any of these programs will allow your students to use the Spreadsheet Applications Diskette available for MS-DOS equipment.

Drills for Accuracy and Speed. Many of the exercises in this text pertain to fundamental operations with whole numbers, fractions, decimals, and percents.

To acquire and maintain satisfactory skill in these operations, the student must be drilled on each operation frequently throughout the course. To help you provide review of fundamental operations, drills similar to the original exercises are provided in **Appendix A.** Suggestions for using the drills are found later in this manual starting under the heading *Warm-up Drill* in the **Presenting Subject Matter in Business Mathematics** section.

Supplementary Problems. Supplementary problems similar to those found in each section are provided in **Appendix B.** These problems are classified by units to correlate with the text. Suggested uses of these problems are described at various points in the manual.

For each supplementary problem, the number of the textbook section in which the problem was introduced is provided to aid the teacher in identifying the problems that relate to a certain section and in referring students to a section for help.

---

*Appleworks is a registered trademark of Apple Computer, Inc.
**Lotus and 1-2-3 are registered trademarks of Lotus Development Corporation.

Workbook Exercises. The workbook provides many additional, supplementary problems that parallel those found in the text. The workbook also provides problems that include the completion of business forms, such as promissory notes. Space is provided in the workbook for students to answer each problem.

Integrated Projects. At the end of each unit of the workbook, a business or personal situation is provided that allows students to apply the principles and procedures they have learned throughout the unit. These integrated projects allow students to review what they have learned through a practical, real-life setting.

Vocabulary Reviews. At the end of each unit in the workbook, a matching exercise is provided for the terms that were shown in boldface print in the text. The vocabulary reviews are designed to assess student understanding of important terms introduced in the unit.

FORMAT FEATURES OF THE TEXT

Several format features are used in the text to help students and teachers locate or identify certain items and make the text easier to use. These useful visual references include:

1. *Unit Openers.* Each unit begins with an opening page. This page contains a list of student objectives for the unit.

2. *Use of Margins.* Text material is contained within defined areas of the page. Space in the margin is used in many ways, including as a location for the headings for exercises. Notes also appear in the margin to give students helpful hints, clues to problem solutions, important facts, or capsule definitions of key terms.

3. *Illustrations.* Illustrations of items such as checks, stock certificates, and utility bills are included to enhance text explanations of business terms and concepts.

4. *Boldface Print.* An important term appears in boldface print when it is introduced in the text. Boldface print is also used for paragraph headings to focus student attention on the topic to be discussed in the paragraph.

5. *Color.* Answers to selected problems appear in color. Marginal notes, in most cases, are also printed in color to further highlight them. Example problems are covered with a color mask so that students can spot example problems at a glance.

6. *Reminders to Estimate and Check.* Beginning with Exercise 2 in Section 1, and repeated at intervals in the written exercises and review assignments, students are reminded to check their work. These reminders are intended to encourage the student to work toward accuracy in all calculations.

7. *Challenge Problem Identifiers.* More difficult or optional topics and problems are identified by a ‡ (double dagger).

GENERAL INSTRUCTIONAL STRATEGIES

Teachers use a variety of instructional strategies for teaching new subject matter in business mathematics. Their strategies differ considerably with respect to how new subject matter is presented and the degree to which directed study is used during the class period. Strategies may range from a thorough teacher presentation of the new matter followed by directed study, to a strategy that uses neither presentation nor directed study. The following strategies represent common variations.

Strategy 1. *Presentation.* New subject matter is thoroughly presented by the teacher in two steps. In the first or preparatory step, knowledge that students already have is related to the new subject matter. In the second step, the new topic is developed by the teacher through discussions, explanations, and chalkboard or overhead projector demonstrations to provide the initial understanding of the new problem and the method of solution.

Directed Study. Students silently read the textbook presentation of the new subject matter and prepare solutions to the problems in the exercise immediately following the presentation.

Out-of-Class Assignment. None given.

Strategy 2. *Presentation.* This consists principally of the preparatory step indicated in Strategy 1 with little if any development of the new subject matter.

Directed Study. Careful study of the textbook presentation of the new subject matter is followed by the preparation of solutions to the problems in the textbook exercise.

Out-of-Class Assignment. None given.

Strategy 3. *Presentation.* None.

Directed Study. As in Strategy 2.

Out-of-Class Assignment. None given.

Strategy 4. *Presentation.* As in Strategy 1.

Directed Study. None. The students' work on the new subject matter is done outside of class.

Out-of-Class Assignment. Students read and study the textbook presentation and prepare solutions to the exercise problems in the textbook.

Strategy 5. *Presentation.* As in Strategy 2.

Directed Study. None.

Out-of-Class Assignment. As in Strategy 4.

Strategy 6. *Presentation.* None.

Directed Study. None.

Out-of-Class Assignment. As in Strategy 4.

In schools where no special provision is made for supervised study during a normal class period, Strategies 1 through 3 may be applied by adopting a divided-period procedure. In this case, the first part of the period is used for the presentation of new subject matter and the latter part for directed study.

In schools that provide for supervised study by scheduling a double period for the subject or by lengthening the normal class period, Strategies 4 through 6 would not apply.

In passing from Strategy 1 through 6, students become progressively less dependent upon you and more dependent upon themselves and the textbook for their initial understanding and mastery of the new subject matter. The strategy that you might use on any one occasion will depend upon the grade placement of the subject, the ability of the group, and the nature of the subject matter in the new lesson. Even with a superior group, or a group in the upper grades of the senior high school, Strategy 1 should be used at the beginning of the course for a few weeks. As the class gains confidence and as you become better acquainted with the capabilities of the class, you may try one or more of the other strategies. Experiment and experience will determine which strategy is best adapted to the group under various conditions.

APPLIED BUSINESS MATHEMATICS is designed for use with any of the six instructional strategies. Even with Strategies 3 and 6, students who have the ability may progress successfully by their own efforts with a minimum of dependence on you. In the text, any type of business problem that is at all complex has been divided into elementary topics presented in graded sequence. Each topic has been treated as a separate problem situation, with its own presentation and exercise for initial practice and mastery. In this way the text provides a step-by-step development of topics from the simple to the complex, a necessary factor to insure success with any instructional strategy requiring independent study of the textbook by the student.

PRESENTING SUBJECT MATTER IN BUSINESS MATHEMATICS

In business mathematics there are, in general, two distinct types of subject matter to be presented and practiced more or less concurrently throughout the course:

1. Business problems

2. Fundamental operations

Presenting a New Type of Business Problem. To help students acquire new knowledge, you should have your students recall old knowledge related to the new material. The new problem can then be presented using discussions, explanations, demonstrations, and references to textbook illustrations or other materials to help students understand the problem and the method of solving it.

Although you probably will have to do a lot of "telling," appropriate questions should be asked of students to keep their attention and ensure their participation in the learning process. The effectiveness of the presentation can be tested by conducting a short oral recitation on the first two or three problems in the related exercise in the text, during which all students explain *how* the problems should be solved. Deficiencies that students have should be cleared up immediately through reteaching of the concepts.

Teaching a New Fundamental Operation. Although any of the six instructional strategies described earlier in this manual may be used to teach a new type of business problem, Strategy 1 is usually the most effective for teaching a new fundamental operation.

As referred to here, a new fundamental operation is one that is formally treated in the textbook for the first time, even though students have had previous instruction in arithmetic fundamentals in the preceding grades.

In teaching a new fundamental operation, you should review old knowledge through a chalkboard demonstration of the new process. The presentation should be followed immediately by a five- to ten-minute practice period. During this time, the students should practice the new operation by working out the problems in the related exercise in the text or in the correlated drill in **Appendix A, Drills for Accuracy and Speed.**

In some cases, a minute or two of oral drill on certain parts of the process should precede the practice period. For example, before starting the written practice in multiplication involving decimals (*Written Exercise 5* in *Section 9*), you might ask students to tell how many places should be pointed off in the products of the problems in both *Written Exercise 5* and *Drill 4* in **Appendix A.**

If the results of the written practice show that additional practice is needed, the practice period should be repeated on the next and succeeding days, as necessary. A few minutes of intensive practice on two or three successive days is usually more effective than a long practice on one day.

A homework assignment containing a long list of abstract problems on one type of operation is usually boring for students and should be avoided. Spaced practice in addition to that provided by section reviews, however, should be provided for each type of fundamental operation as part of the general maintenance program.

Directed Study. The directed study part of the class period follows the completion of your presentation of new material. During this part of the period, students work out the solutions to the problems in the textbook exercise or to drill work they have been assigned.

If the textbook presentation of the new problem contains amplifying material that was not included in your presentation, the directed study assignment should call for a careful reading of the textbook before work begins on the problems. If you feel you have adequately covered the textbook material, students may be directed to begin work on the problems at once.

During the directed-study period or in any period of independent work, you should move around the room, checking the students' work and giving help where it is needed.

Some students may finish the work before the end of the directed-study period. If their work is correct and otherwise acceptable, those students may be assigned to solve certain additional problems, such as those found in the supplementary problems provided in **Appendix B.** They can also study the next topic in the textbook and start solving the problems in the exercise connected with it, or begin work on the homework assignment. They may also be asked to help the less able students with their work.

Using Guide Answers. Under the directed-study strategy, the written exercises provide desk work that is done in the classroom under your supervision.

The guide answers in the book are especially helpful at this time. Without a guide answer, a student might solve the problems incorrectly and practice the wrong method before you can check on the way the problems are being done. The class should understand they should signal you for help if, after carefully going over the work, their answers to the first problem do not agree with the guide answer given in the book.

You may find it helpful to give students additional guide answers, with the number provided, depending on the complexity of the problems and the ability of the group.

Warm-Up Drill. To give needed practice for maintaining and improving skill in the fundamental operations and in mental arithmetic, you should provide a five- to ten-minute warm-up drill every day, if possible, or at least three times a week as a minimum. Although the ideal would be to provide such a drill every day, it is usually impossible to do so because of the frequent need to use the whole class period for other activities.

The warm-up drill should consist of problems selected from the **Drills for Accuracy and Speed** provided in **Appendix A.**

The best time for the warm-up drill is usually at the beginning of the class period. Before the class assembles, you should write the assignment on the chalkboard. Ordinarily, you should assign more work than can be completed in the time allotted for the warm-up drill to encourage all students to work rapidly. A sample warm-up drill assignment is shown below.

Warm-up Drill Assignment

1. Drill 18, Problems 1 to 5
2. Drill 4, Problem 7
3. Drill 2, Problem 1d: copy and subtract
4. Drill 1, Column (a), items 1 to 10; copy and add
5. Drill 18, Problems 6 to 10
6. Drill 4, Problem 8
7. Drill 2, Problem 2a; copy and subtract
8. Drill 1, Column (b), items 1 to 10; copy and add

Usually the warm-up problems are arranged in reverse of the order in which they were taught, with the first problem representing the most recent operation. In the sample warm-up drill assignment, note that items 5 to 8 are of the same type as items 1 to 4. By limiting the number of drill types, the slower students will have time to complete at least the problems in the first group of four items. The second group of four items will usually be completed only by the faster students.

When they arrive in the classroom, students should immediately start work on the assignment. While the work is in progress, you are free to take attendance and do other routine duties.

At the end of the time set for the drill, you should stop the work. The papers may be exchanged, scored, and collected as desired. The results may be used for diagnostic and remedial purposes, or the scores may be used in determining term marks.

When properly administered, a five- to ten-minute drill of this type is a valuable learning exercise and an effective device for overcoming straggling and any tendency toward disorder at the beginning of the period. Students soon discover that to get good scores they must report to class promptly and get to work at once; the earlier they get started, the more time they have for the work.

Spaced Recall Pattern in the Warm-up Drills. To counteract forgetting, you should use each drill for accuracy and speed in the warm-up assignments in a systematic pattern. One such pattern calls for the initial use of a given drill on two or three successive days. One day is then skipped and the drill is repeated on the next day; then two days are skipped and the drill repeated; and so on, until a maximum of ten to twelve days are skipped between each use of the drill. This pattern of spaced recall is shown in the following diagram:

Days:	1	2	3	4	5	6	7	8	9	10	11	12	13	14	15	16	17	18	19
Use:	I	R	R		R			R				R					R		

The numbered squares represent successive school days. The letter "I" in the first square represents the initial use of the drill. Each "R" represents a repeated use of the drill.

In a class record book or on other paper, a schedule of drills for the assignments can be prepared like the sample shown below. The "x's" in a given column indicate the drills that are to be included in the warm-up assignment for that particular day.

Week	3					4					5					6				
Day	1	2	3	4	5	1	2	3	4	5	1	2	3	4	5	1	2	3	4	5
Drill 1	x		x					x					x						x	
2		x		x			x				x						x			
3	x		x			x							x					x		
4	x	x	x		x			x				x							x	
5		x	x	x				x					x			x				x
6			x			x	x					x					x			
7								x	x			x		x					x	
8									x	x	x		x				x			
9											x	x	x			x		x		

By working out the schedule for a day in advance and inserting the "x's" where they belong, you can see at a glance which drills are due for tomorrow's assignment. If the warm-up is to be omitted tomorrow, a vertical line may be ruled throughout the length of the column for that day and no "x's" entered in it. The correlated drill that you may start using with each section is stated in the manual.

Warm-up Assignment. As has been pointed out, the schedule of drills indicates the particular drills that should be included in the warm-up assignment being planned for the next day's lesson.

The next step in planning the assignment is the selection of problems in each of the scheduled drills. In selecting problems, you may want to follow these suggestions:

1. Ordinarily, select only one problem in each of the scheduled drills between Drills 1 and 17, inclusive. At the beginning of the year, when only the first two or three drills are usable, several problems should be selected from each drill in order to have an assignment of adequate time length. As more drills become available for use, the number of problems selected from the beginning drills should be reduced.

2. Select not less than four or more than five consecutive problems in each of the scheduled drills beyond Drill 17.

To set up the assignment, list the problems in the reverse of the order in which they were taught, as noted under the sample warm-up drill assignment described previously. In this way, students who work slowly and are unable to do all the selected problems in the time allowed for the warm-up assignment will be able to practice on the most recent operations.

Also follow the format of the sample warm-up assignment and provide additional problems, selected from the same drills and listed in the same order, to provide a challenge to the faster students and to keep them busy for the entire warm-up period.

Ordinarily the problems in each drill should be used in the order in which they are numbered. When the list of problems in a given drill is used up, the problems may be used again in any order desired. Usually, the time interval between the first use and the second use of the same problem or group of problems will be long enough that students won't remember the answers.

Comment on Drill 1. In using Drill 1 (long-column addition), it is suggested that you use the first six or eight addends in the first two or three warm-up assignments, then one more addend in the next two or three assignments, then one more in the next two or three assignments, and so on, to provide a gradual increase in the number of addends students have to handle.

Homework Assignments. The problem material that the teacher assigns for homework will depend on the instructional strategy being used. Teachers who emphasize directed study usually assign only problems of the types that have been initially mastered in class or problems that involve only the application of principles with which the students are already familiar.

The section reviews are particuarly suitable for homework since they involve only the application and review of principles and processes already studied.

If the class work has not reached the review in the current section, the homework may consist of seven or eight problems selected from the seven or eight most recent class exercises, including one problem from the exercise used during the directed-study phase of the current day.

TEACHING SUGGESTIONS

Daily Lesson Planning. Classroom activities should be carefully planned in advance to avoid confusion and waste of time during the class period, and to get maximum cooperation from the students and effective results from teaching. Planning involves considering activities such as:

Preliminary warm-up drill
Correcting and discussing homework
Reteaching problems inadequately mastered
Special drills
Reviews
Testing
Presenting new subject matter
Providing for directed study
Making directed-study and homework assignments

All these activities will not necessarily be included in each class period. The activities and the class time devoted to each will vary daily.

In planning the work for the period, you should list the major activities to be accomplished in the order of their occurrence, with an estimate of the time required for each. Adequate time should be allowed for each activity, and no more should be planned than can be done during the class hour. Since time cannot be estimated exactly, more time rather than not enough time should be allowed, and one or two supplementary activities should be planned for use if extra time is available.

The lesson plan should be written. It should show the planned activities in the order in which they are to occur and in sufficient detail to be used by a substitute teacher.

Arrangement of Written Work. Problem solving is largely a matter of visualizing the problem situation, deciding what steps to use, quantifying the steps, and checking the work.

To increase accuracy, you should insist upon neatness, legibility, and an orderly arrangement of the solution. To encourage this kind of work, and to make it easier to check students' calculations, a uniform arrangement of calculations and answers is recommended.

In one type of form, the student rules a paper vertically to provide a one-inch wide column at the left and a similar column at the right, with space in the center of the paper. The problem identification is written in the column at the left, the solution in the center column, and the answer in the column at the right.

Students may also be told to set up their solutions vertically under three headings: "Given," "Find," and "Solution." This is especially helpful with problems involving fractional and percentage relationships.

Use of Oral Drill. Oral drill is effective when every student gives active attention to each problem. These procedures may be used to secure and maintain student attention during oral drills:

1. State the problem number first; pause briefly to give each student time to think; call on the student who is to answer.

2. Call the problems in random order, not in their numbered order in the exercise or drill. Otherwise, students may look ahead to the next problem instead of paying attention to the present problem.

3. Call on students in random order.

4. Call on inattentive students often.

Use of Calculators. Some schools provide hand-held calculators for use in the Business Mathematics classroom. Many students own hand-held calculators and may want to use them in class. Some teachers may want to require students to use calculators for some or all of their calculations. To minimize problems, the teacher should formulate a clear policy concerning calculator use before the course begins. Here are some ideas to consider in deciding on a policy:

1. You may fear that using calculators will reduce student skills in the manual solution of problems. However, the operations to be performed on numbers are only one aspect of problem solving. The identification of the procedures or steps needed to solve a problem and the selection of the correct information are equally important in problem solving. Also, if *manual* warm-up drills on fundamental operations are required *daily* (see the suggestions for warm-up drills described previously in this manual), students will develop and maintain their skills regardless of whether or not they use calculators in class for other problem work.

2. Because calculators are used widely in homes or in business, you may feel that instruction *must* be given in using them to solve problems. So, once students have demonstrated proficiency in the fundamental operations, you may present both the manual and machine solutions to word problems and require students to become proficient in both methods.

3. You cannot control the use of calculators for out-of-class assignments. If homework is given, students cannot be prevented from using calculators.

If students are to develop mental and manual skills in fundamental oper-tions through the use of drills, the *drills should not be assigned for out-of-class work.*

4. If problems are assigned for *manual*, out-of-class solution, students should show complete solutions to every problem, including pencil "carry-overs" for addition and subtraction problems, and all work for multiplication and division problems. After all work is shown, students may be allowed to use a calculator to check their work.

5. You may permit calculators to be used for classwork as an incentive to develop mental and manual skill in the fundamental operations. You may permit students to use calculators in class only after they have become proficient in doing the fundamental operations mentally and manually.

6. Students may use calculators to reduce the drudgery of lengthy multipli-cation and division problems, such as those involved in solving real prop-erty tax problems. Using calculators in such problems does not eliminate the need to know what operations are required or how those operations are sequenced, but it does eliminate the work and errors involved in mul-tiplying and dividing large numbers.

7. Calculators may be used to teach multiplication and division by 10, 100, or 1,000. You may have students do repeated multiplication and division by these numbers to "discover" principles for moving the decimal point to save time in calculating.

If students are permitted to use calculators in class, calculators will have to be furnished for those students who do not own or cannot buy them, and for stu-dents who forget to bring their machines to class. Some of these problems can be eliminated by teaching business mathematics in a room where calculators are present, such as that used for accounting instruction. A cart may also be used to transport calculators to the business mathematics classroom.

If calculators are used in classwork, daily oral and written drill should be provided to maintain skill in mental and manual operations. Also, from time to time, a "no calculator" day should be announced, without prior notice, so that students must solve all problems without calculators.

Another justification for the use of calculators is their ability to motivate students and provide more time to practice problems in class because of the speed with which problems can be solved. Thus, important concepts and pro-cedures can be taught and practiced more efficiently without the boredom and error that arise out of making repeated calculations.

Developing Vocabulary. The size and nature of student vocabularies are criti-cal factors in students' abilities to read and comprehend text and problem material in business mathematics. Careful attention to the development of ap-propriate business vocabularies by the teacher will help to increase student success in school work.

This edition of APPLIED BUSINESS MATHEMATICS provides two activi-ties designed to increase student business vocabularies: a *terms* part of the sec-tion reviews in the text and a *vocabulary review* exercise for each unit in the workbook. The terms part of the section reviews provides a brief matching problem for those terms that are shown in boldface print in the section. The vocabulary review exercises are matching exercises provided in the workbook that include terms from an entire unit. You may wish to make transparencies of these reviews so they can be used quickly and also more than once during the term. The review exercises make excellent class starters. They may also be given at the end of the class period if time is left or if students have finished their work early. The exercise may also be used solely for practice, or it may be used for grading purposes.

The vocabulary reviews require that students write the terms as their answer. This practice insures that they learn to spell the term as well as recognize its meaning. If the exercise is used only for practice, having the students write the term two or three times gives them greater practice in spelling.

In addition to having students complete the *terms* portions of the sectional reviews and the vocabulary reviews, vocabulary may also be developed in these ways:

1. Each important term should be written on the chalkboard or overhead projector when it is first used in the presentation of new material. These terms are printed in boldface type in the textbook. Once these terms are written or projected, they may be pointed to when they are used in the presentation. Students may also pronounce each term as it is written or projected by the teacher, and they may write the new term several times at their desks. Daily practice in spelling and pronouncing the most recent new terms may be done for the duration of the unit.

2. Students may be required to use a new term in a short sentence. They should respond with a complete, grammatically correct sentence, either orally or in writing. This activity can be easily inserted into the regular classroom plan if new terms are placed on the board when they are introduced. During the class period, you can call on students to use the terms you point to in a sentence.

BASIC CONCEPTS OF MATHEMATICS

In many schools, the concepts emphasized in what had been called the "new math" have been integrated into traditional approaches for teaching math at all grade levels. This integrated approach emphasizes greater understanding of number operations and relationships. The ways in which addition, subtraction, multiplication, and division are performed have not changed for this approach.

Some of the more pertinent, relatively simple, and easily understood of those concepts are used in APPLIED BUSINESS MATHEMATICS, Thirteenth Edition. A brief overview of those concepts is provided here.

Number and Numeral. In today's arithmetic approach, a distinction is made between a number and a numeral. A number is an abstraction or an idea that exists only in the mind. To write about numbers and to record number facts we use number words and number symbols.

For example, if a package contains a pencil, a pen, and an eraser, we use the number word "three" to express the number idea associated with the objects in the package. We express the same number idea associated with the number symbol "3," which we call a numeral. A numeral is often referred to as a name for a number. Thus, 3 is a name for the number three.

For simplicity, we often speak of "the number 3," "the number 15," and so on. We mean, of course, "the number named by the numeral 3," or "the number named by the numeral 15."

Every number has many names or numerals that represent it. For example, 8, 5 + 3, 10 − 2, 16 divided by 2, and $\frac{24}{3}$ are just a few of the many numerals that can be used to name the number eight. The simplest numeral, 8, and the most commonly used, is sometimes referred to as the *standard* or *basic numeral* for the number eight. Similarly, 0 is the standard numeral for the number zero; 1 is the standard numeral for the number one; 2 is the standard numeral for the number two; and so on.

Number Sentences. The idea of having many names for the same number has two important applications in today's arithmetic programs. One application is the work with fractions, decimals, and percents. The other is connected with number sentences.

To show that two numerals are names for the same number, we may write an equals sign between them. For example, we may write 5 + 3 = 8. We call "5 + 3 = 8" a **number sentence.** The sentence 5 + 3 = 8 states that the numeral 5 + 3 names the same number as the numeral 8, and represents a true statement.

A number sentence such as $N + 4 = 11$ is called an **open sentence.** As it stands, the sentence is neither true nor false. It is, however, incomplete in that there is a missing numeral, represented by the letter N. We complete the sentence by replacing N with a numeral that makes the sentence true. The numeral is obviously 7; so we may write 7 + 4 = 11, which is a true sentence.

Solving Open Sentences. Practice in solving number sentences is an effective means for improving the student's ability to interpret number relationships. Interpreting relationships correctly is a key to success with all types of problems. *The work with number sentences should not be omitted.*

As you have probably noticed, a number sentence is also an equation. In fact, the number sentence idea is used as an informal and intuitive approach to the formal study of equations in arithmetic programs in middle schools and high schools. In APPLIED BUSINESS MATHEMATICS we call it a number sentence, not an equation, because the term "equation" is suggestive of algebra and implies the use of the rules of equality in arriving at a solution. We want the student to find the numeral that N stands for, not by means of a rule, but rather by simple reasoning from the number relationship expressed in the sentence. Observe how the numeral for N can be determined by simple reasoning in the following typical sentences:

$$N + 6 = 15 \qquad 4 \times N = 28$$
$$N - 8 = 20 \qquad N \div 6 = 4$$

In $N + 6 = 15$, the 15 results from adding 6 to the missing number. So, the missing number must be 6 less than 15, or 9. Substituting 9 for N gives 9 + 6 = 15, which is a true sentence.

In $N - 8 = 20$, the 20 results from subtracting 8 from the missing number. So, the missing number must be 8 more than 20, or 28. Substituting 28 for N gives 28 - 8 = 20, a true sentence.

In $4 \times N = 28$, the 28 results from multiplying the missing number by 4. So, the missing number must be 28 divided by 4, or 7. Substituting 7 for N gives 4 × 7 = 28, a true sentence.

In $N \div 6 = 4$, the 4 results from dividing the missing number by 6. So, the missing number must be 6 times 4, or 24. Substituting 24 for N gives 24 ÷ 6 = 4, a true sentence.

Special Objectives of Number Sentence Practice. After numerals and number sentences are presented, students solve open sentence problems in exercises and reviews. Particular attention should be given to the type of sentence represented by $4 \times N = 28$. Practice with sentences of this type anticipates the more formal, unknown factor method of solution where the number represented by N, which is the unknown or missing factor, is found by dividing the product, 28, by the known factor, 4.

The unknown factor method is used in connection with fractions and percents for finding the value of N in number sentences such as $\frac{3}{4} \times N = 24$ and 75% of $N = 24$, and in solving word problems involving similar number relationships, where the whole is to be found when a part or percent of it is known.

Number sentences are used also for explaining some of the principles of the basic arithmetic operations presented earlier in the text; and sentences such as $N = 74 + 0$, $N = 8 - 0$, $N = 1 \times 9$, $N = 0 \times 7$, $16 \times N = 16$, and $15 \div N = 15$ are supplied in exercises to provide practice in recognizing the special properties of 0 and 1.

Principles of the Fundamental Operations. Through prior study, some students may be familiar with the terms "commutative property," "associative property," and "identity number," and may be able to recall and apply these terms. Other students may be familiar with the concepts represented by these terms, but probably not by name.

They know that $5 + 3$ gives the same sum as $3 + 5$ and that 5×3 gives the same product as 3×5. These are illustrations of the *commutative property* of addition and multiplication. This principle means that the order in which we add or multiply two numbers has no effect upon the sum or product.

Note that subtraction and division are *not* commutative in that $3 - 5$ does not give the same difference as $5 - 3$, and 3 divided by 5 does not give the same quotient as 5 divided by 3.

Students also know that in adding or multiplying more than two numbers, the way in which we group or associate the numbers together does not affect the sum or product. Thus, $2 + 5 + 8$ may be thought of as $(2 + 5) + 8$ or $2 + (5 + 8)$; and $2 \times 5 \times 8$ may be thought of as $(2 \times 5) \times 8$ or $2 \times (5 \times 8)$. This is called the *associative property* of addition and multiplication.

Subtraction and division are *not* associative. Note that $(24 - 8) - 3 = 16 - 3 = 13$; whereas $24 - (8 - 3) = 24 - 5 = 19$. Also, $(48 \div 6) \div 2 = 8 \div 2 = 4$; whereas $48 \div (6 \div 2) = 48 \div 3 = 16$.

Students likewise know that adding 0 to or subtracting 0 from a number does not change the number, and that multiplying or dividing a number by 1 does not change the number. Thus, $5 + 0 = 5$, $5 - 0 = 5$, $1 \times 5 = 5$, and $5 \div 1 = 5$. Because the number in the result and the number operated on are identical, 0 is called the *identity number* for addition and subtraction; and 1 is called the *identity number* for multiplication and division.

EVALUATION

Good testing and effective use of information gained from careful analysis of test results is essential to successful teaching. To provide you with a thorough and diversified testing program, APPLIED BUSINESS MATHEMATICS offers you a printed test package (Stock No. M473) and MicroEXAM testing diskettes that include pretests, unit tests, and semester tests.

Unit Pretests. Pretests for Units 1 through 4 are provided in printed form, ready for use with students, or on a MicroEXAM diskette. These tests are designed for a 55-minute class period.

Unit Tests. Printed unit tests and MicroEXAM unit tests are provided for Units 1 through 17. They are designed for a 55-minute class period and are ready for use with students.

Semester Tests. Two semester tests are provided in printed form in the test package and on the MicroEXAM testing diskette. The semester tests are carefully designed to measure student achievement in all major aspects of the course, including terms and principles, business forms, fundamental processes, and problem solving. These two tests are designed to be administered in two class periods, or parts of each test may be administered in several periods if more time is needed.

Each test is divided into four parts so that you may alter the length and content of the test to fit the length of your class period and your course content or emphasis. The four parts are: Part A, multiple-choice questions covering concepts and terminology; Part B, skills in basic arithmetic operations; Part C, word problems; and Part D, business forms.

SUGGESTED TIME SCHEDULE

A suggested time schedule for the Thirteenth Edition of APPLIED BUSINESS MATHEMATICS is provided. The schedule is designed for a 36-week, 180-day, or one-year course covering Units 1 through 17 (Sections 1–110).

The schedule assumes that the unmarked (‡) textbook sections and problems, section reviews, workbook problems, calculator clinics, integrated projects, and vocabulary review exercises are included in the course. It also assumes that the unit test is given at the end of each unit. Finally, it assumes that the challenge problems (‡), computer clinics, supplementary problems, and appendixes are optional, and are assigned as needed.

The time schedule is a suggestion only and will need modification to fit the special factors present in each classroom setting. These factors include: student ability; grade level; length of school year; length of class period; and state and local course requirements.

SUGGESTED SCHEDULE

Unit	Sections	Approximate Days
1	1–6	9
2	7–12	9
3	13–20	13
4	21–29	16
5	30–32	4
6	33–42	17
7	43–51	16
8	52–54	4
9	55–62	14
10	63–66	6
11	67–73	12
12	74–79	9
13	80–86	12
14	87–91	8
15	92–98	12
16	99–105	12
17	106–110	7

Teaching Suggestions by Units and Sections

The rest of this manual contains specific teaching suggestions for each unit and section of the textbook.

Unit 1. Money Records

Unit 1 reviews addition (including horizontal addition) and subtraction, with emphasis on cash receipts, cash payments, and checking account records. Students learn to complete deposit slips, checks, and check registers and to prepare bank reconciliation statements. The unit also includes instruction in reading and writing numbers in the decimal system, the use of the hand-held calculator for addition and subtraction, and solving problems that contain extraneous information.

Student learning objectives for Unit 1 appear on the Unit 1 opener page in the textbook.

Pretest for Unit 1. Before starting Unit 1 you may want to find out how well your class can add and subtract and how much they already know about cash and checking account records. The pretest for Unit 1, included in the test package (M473) and the MicroEXAM package, is designed for that purpose. Solutions for pretests are included in this manual.

Problems 1 through 4 of the pretest are abstract problems measuring student skills in addition and subtraction. Students who are slow and inaccurate with these problems will have difficulty in later lessons unless their skills are improved. To improve these students' skills, you may want to use *Mental Drills 1 and 2* found in **Appendix A** of the textbook and Exercises 2, 3, and 4 in the workbook.

Problem 5 presents the arithmetic common to check registers. Problem 6 presents open sentence problems, which are covered in Section 2 of the textbook. Problem 7 tests student skills in horizontal addition.

Problems 8 through 12 of the pretest are designed to measure student knowledge of cash records and elementary banking problems and to find out how well students can apply their skills to the solution of related problems.

Integrated Project for Unit 1. A project that integrates the skills and knowledge presented in Unit 1 is provided in the workbook. *Integrated Project 1* allows students to complete a check register, deposit slip, check, and bank reconciliation statement for an individual; to identify outstanding checks, and to update the check register after the reconciliation statement has been completed.

Vocabulary Review for Unit 1. A vocabulary exercise, *Vocabulary Review: Unit 1*, is found at the end of Unit 1 in the workbook. The exercise reviews 20 of the vocabulary terms included in Unit 1. In the review students are asked to complete the exercise by writing the terms, rather than merely listing a matching letter or number, in order to give students practice in spelling the terms. Suggestions for using the vocabulary review as well as the Terms part of each section review are presented in this manual under the heading **Developing Vocabulary.**

Supplementary Problems for Unit 1. Twelve word problems similar to those provided in the exercises for Unit 1 are presented in the *Supplementary Problems for Unit 1* section of **Appendix B.** These problems include cash receipts problems; cash payments problems; gross, net, and related problems; and bank reconciliation problems.

Transparencies for Unit 1. A number of transparency masters drawn from Unit 1 are provided in the teacher's edition of the workbook (M471TE). The transparency masters include the number drill shown in this manual under *Section 1 Oral Drills,* and forms for a deposit slip, a check, and a check register.

Test for Unit 1. A review, or posttest, of Unit 1, designed to measure student achievement of the objectives of Unit 1, is provided in the test package (M473) and the MicroEXAM package. The review test does not measure the objectives included in the calculator or computer clinics.

Careful analysis of group and individual student performances on this test will provide you with data for determining the need for further review or remediation. Special attention should be given to detecting lack of knowledge of basic number facts, or the digital combinations students need to know to perform addition and subtraction. If fundamental skills are satisfactory students will increase their speed and accuracy in these skills, and in problem solving, as they progress through the course.

Solutions for Unit 1. Solutions to all text problems, the pretest, and the unit test are included in this manual. Solutions to all workbook problems are included in the teacher's edition of the workbook.

Additional Resources for Unit 1. There are many resources you may use to enrich or support the instruction offered in Unit 1. For example, elementary school teachers for Grades 3–6 may provide you with many useful suggestions about how to improve the fundamental addition and subtraction skills of your students. Elementary arithmetic textbooks may also provide you with a rich source of supplementary drill materials in the fundamental processes.

Many banks provide interesting instructional materials (which they make available to their customers) pertaining to keeping checking accounts and to the process of bank reconciliation. You should check with the banks in your area to see if they can provide you with materials about checking accounts and bank reconciliation. Also, office supply stores stock many examples of cash receipts forms, cash payments forms, and cash payments columnar journals. These forms may be used to supplement those found in the text and workbook.

There are also some resources, specific to the topics included in Unit 1, which you may wish to examine. For example:

1. Bank Services for You and Personal Money Management, The American Bankers Association, 1120 Connecticut Avenue, N.W., Washington, DC, 20036, no date.

2. Sargent, Patsy, and Mary Ward, Security First Bank — A Banking Customer Simulation. South-Western Publishing Co., 5101 Madison Road, Cincinnati, OH 45227, 1986. This package contains two reconciliation problems and check writing activities.

3. Doehring, Gene, Cashier Clerk, South-Western Publishing Co., 5101 Madison Road, Cincinnati, OH 45227, 1983. This is a text-workbook presenting the competencies needed to operate a cash register.

4. The Story of Checks, Federal Reserve Bank of New York, Public Information Department, 33 Liberty St., New York, NY 10045, no date.

5. Your Checking Account, American Bankers Association, 1120 Connecticut Avenue, N.W., Washington, D.C. 20551, no date.

There are some materials that you can use to improve your students' skills in addition and subtraction. For example:

1. Muncaster, Barbara F., and Susan L. Prescott, Learning Basic Math and Business Math Using the Calculator, South-Western Publishing Co., 5101 Madison Road, Cincinnati, OH 45227, 1985.

2. Gossage, Loyce C. Mathematics Skill Builder, South-Western Publishing Co., 5101 Madison Road, Cincinnati, OH 45227, 1985. A text-workbook that provides instruction in the fundamental processes and in some applications in business and consumer mathematics.

There are also some audiovisual and computer-related materials that you may find useful for Unit 1. For example:

1. Basic Math Facts Competency Lab, Chaselle, Inc., 9645 Gerwig Lane, Columbia, MD 21046, no date. Ten audio cassettes, 30 copies of each of 10 lessons, 10 reproducible posttests, and a teacher's guide.

2. Bank Reconciliation, Micro Learningware, Highway 66 South, P.O. Box 307, Mankato, MN 56001, no date. This set of microcomputer materials allows students to prepare bank reconciliation statements given the current balances, checks written, outstanding checks, and charges.

3. Business Education Package 1, Micro Learningware, Highway 66 South, P.O. Box 307, Mankato, MN 56001, no date. This package contains four microcomputer programs: loan amortization, bank reconciliation, stock market simulation, and depreciation.

4. The Math System, Opportunities for Learning, 20417 Nordhoff St., Dept. 9F, Chatsworth, CA 91311, no date. A comprehensive and interactive software package providing testing, diagnostics, and instruction in addition, subtraction, multiplication, division, fractions, decimals, ratios, percents, and negatives. Five instructional diskettes, a diagnostic testing diskette, a class records diskette, and a data storage diskette are provided.

SECTION 1. CASH RECEIPTS RECORDS

Comments and Suggestions. When students begin a course in business mathematics they have some knowledge and skill in addition, but most students need to review and drill on addition facts to build their skills in adding swiftly and accurately. Students, however, do not usually enjoy isolated drill in addition without seeing some purpose or application for their work. For these reasons, APPLIED BUSINESS MATHEMATICS uses cash receipts records as a functional means to review addition. This approach is designed to interest students by showing them practical uses for addition in personal and business situations and by setting the stage for addition drills that will improve student speed and accuracy.

The terms **cash receipts record, addition, sum, total,** and **reverse addition** are explained simply. These terms are then included in the Terms section of Review 2. The method by which vocabulary words are treated is explained in detail in this manual under **Developing Vocabulary.** If you have not already read this section of the manual, you will find that it contains numerous suggestions for developing the vocabulary skills of your students.

Because home and business computers have become commonplace, computer-related examples are used in the text to provide students with experience in reading and interpreting computer formats in business and personal mathematical problems. In Section 1 computer screens and computer printouts serve as practical examples of how data processing technology is used. You may wish to distribute examples of computer printouts containing columnar addition in class or display them on a bulletin board.

Adding Faster. Exercise 2 in Section 1 of the text allows students to practice the techniques (described on that page) for adding faster. You will want to stress to your students that addition is included in much of the work involved in business mathematics and that it is very important for them to develop speed and accuracy in adding. Make it clear that drill is needed to build speed and accuracy and that drill early in the course will help them progress successfully throughout the term.

To keep students interested and to avoid monotony, use oral, dictated, and written drills. Drill periods should be short; no one type of drill should be continued for more than ten minutes.

Oral Drills. For oral drills Exercise 2 in Section 1 of the text may be used. Also, the following drill provides excellent practice and is useful in developing student concentration. Write the digits 0 to 9 on the board as shown at the left.

2	
8	7
6	5
1	4
3	9
0	

With a pointer, go rapidly from one digit to another, asking students to name the sum of the group of digits to which you have pointed. Do not go beyond the sum of 30 at first. Call on individual students to give the sum each time you stop. A transparency master of these numbers is provided in the teacher's edition of the workbook (M471TE).

Dictated Drills. Many calculation errors are the result of poorly written figures or careless column arrangement. Students should frequently take addition problems from dictation to practice writing numbers in a neat, legible, and well-arranged fashion. Exercises 3 and 4 may be used as dictated drills.

Dictate slowly at first, increasing your dictation speed on each drill each day so that students will develop skill in writing figures neatly and rapidly. Stress the vertical alignment of the numbers.

Written Drills. Exercise 3 may be used for written practice as well as for dictation. The students should be told to copy the numbers and find the sum. As you did in the dictated problems, stress the importance of writing neat figures rapidly and properly arranging the figures vertically.

	Here is another type of written drill. Write two numbers, such	
32	as 32 and 25, in a column on the board as shown on the left.	32
25	Then tell your students to copy and add the numbers, writing	25
57	the sum, 57, under 25. Then have students add 57 to 25 and	57
82	write the sum, 82, under 57, and so on until a column of six	82
139	numbers is reached. Tell students to find the sum of all six num-	139
221	bers. You can check the accuracy of their work by multiplying	221
556	the fifth number by 4 (4 × 139 = 556).	360
		581
	Later, students may carry the addition to the point where ten	941
	numbers are reached, as shown on the right, and they can find	1,522
	the sum of all ten. You can check their work by multiplying the	3,960
	seventh number by 11 (11 × 360 = 3,960).	

Checking Addition. Checking addition by reverse addition is practiced in Exercise 3 on page 4. This is the time to stress the importance of 100% accuracy in all arithmetic work and the use of reverse addition to ensure that addition is correct. Students are not likely to check their work, because it is "just for practice" and because checking takes time. To insure that students have checked their work by reverse addition, require students to show the pencil "carries" at both the top and bottom of selected addition problems that they hand in to you.

Calculator Clinic. The use of hand-held calculators to solve addition problems and to check addition is explained at the end of Section 1 in the calculator clinic. You may wish to integrate instruction in the use of calculators when you teach manual addition. If so, you should assign the reading of the calculator clinic that describes using the calculator for addition.

There are several approaches you may use to include hand-held calculators in Section 1. You may choose to have students complete the section manually. Then you may instruct students in the use of the calculator and have them redo selected problems in Section 1 using the calculator. On the other hand, you may wish to have students complete all exercises labeled "oral" without the aid of the calculator and complete all other exercises using the calculator. A number of suggestions for the use of calculators in the business mathematics class are presented in the **Use of Calculators** section in this manual.

Correlated Drill for Accuracy and Speed. *Mental Drill 1* in **Appendix A** correlates with Exercise 3 in Section 1. Use Drill 1 for the warm-up assignments described on pages 13–14 of this manual to provide spaced practice in long-column addition.

It is suggested that the first six or eight numbers be used in the first two or three warm-up assignments, then one more number in the next two or three, and so on, to provide a gradual increase in the amount of numbers handled at one time by the students.

The directions at the beginning of the drill tell the student to place the edge of the paper under the last line of the selected numbers and to write the sum on the paper without copying the items. Sometimes you may have students copy the numbers on their answer paper and then add to provide them with additional practice in writing numbers neatly and in correct vertical alignment.

Exercise 4. This exercise provides a review of cash receipts records, combining numbers to add faster, and checking by reverse addition.

Background Information. Addition is related to counting because the sum of two numbers can be obtained by counting. For example, to add 44 and 39 by counting, you could count out 39 items and then counting forward from 44. Call the first item 45, the second 46, and so on, until you reach the number 83 with the thirty-ninth item. The number 83 would represent the sum of 44 and 39.

You can find the sum easier and faster, however, by figuring it with numerals. You can think of addition, then, as a shortcut of counting forward by ones.

SECTION 2. CASH PAYMENTS RECORDS

Comments and Suggestions. Section 2 applies the review of addition to cash payments records for individuals, families, organizations, and businesses. The cash payments record used contains only one column. Special columns for classifying expenses are described in Section 3.

Numerals. Section 2 introduces numerals and number sentences. Before presenting this material to your students, you may wish to reread the topics **Number and Numeral** and **Number Sentences** in this manual.

Stress the fact that a numeral is not a number but the symbol or name for a number. If you want to emphasize the meaning of number you can use an explanation like that found in the first two paragraphs under **Number and Numeral** in this manual.

The idea of a number sentence follows logically from the fact that there are many different numerals that name the same number. Emphasize that the equals sign between two numerals means that the two numerals are names for the same number.

In Exercise 2 of Section 2 many of the number sentences are in the general form of $2 + 6 = 4 + 4$; that is, on neither side of the equals sign is the numeral in the simplest or standard form, such as 8. The more difficult form is used here because it makes students examine closely the numeral on each side of the equals sign rather than just the numeral on one side.

Incomplete number sentences, or **open sentences,** are also presented in Section 2. Before assigning Exercise 3 you may wish to provide oral practice. Using sentences like those listed below on the chalkboard, call on students to give the numeral that should be substituted for the letter to make the sentence true.

$$N + 6 = 15 \qquad 16 - 10 = N \qquad N + 5 = 12 - 4$$
$$N - 8 = 20 \qquad 18 + N = 28 \qquad 5 + 10 = 20 - N$$
$$N + 7 = 12 \qquad 22 - 10 = N \qquad N - 6 = 20 + 4$$

You may wish to demonstrate the procedure for solving the first two open sentences by using the explanations below the second paragraph under **Solving Open Sentences** in this manual.

Reading and Writing Numbers in the Decimal System. Section 2 also reviews reading, writing, and analyzing numbers in the decimal system. The decimal system of numeration has been emphasized in math courses in earlier grades, so students in business mathematics are usually familiar with the basic ideas of the decimal system. However, a review of the system will help students recall and strengthen those basic ideas and sharpen their skills.

An important characteristic of the decimal system is the idea of place value. The number represented by any digit in a numeral depends on the face value of the digit and the place value of the position the digit occupies. For any whole number shown in the decimal system, the place value of the first position at the right is one, the place value of the second position is ten times one (ten), the place value of the third position is ten times ten (one hundred), and so on. In other words, the place value of each position is ten times the value of the position to its right. So, in the numeral 654 the 6 stands for 6 hundreds, or 6×100, which is 600. The 5 stands for 5 tens, or 5×10, which is 50. The 4 stands for 4 ones, or 4×1, which is 4. The number represented by the complete numeral is the sum of the numbers represented by the individual digits. Thus, $654 = 600 + 50 + 4$. That is, the numerals 654 and $600 + 50 + 4$ are names for the same number.

Emphasize the name of the place value of each position in numerals, at least to the sixth place, or 100,000. You may choose to dictate numbers to students so they will receive additional practice in writing and spelling the names of these numbers. Ordinarily, when numbers are written out commas are used to separate thousands from hundreds. Also, hyphens are usually included between the words for numbers between twenty-one and ninety-nine. Thus, 164,298 would be written out as one hundred sixty-four thousand, two hundred ninety-eight.

Exercise 4 in Section 2 provides students with practice in analyzing numbers according to place value and in writing these numbers in words.

Background Information. From the modern point of view, addition, subtraction, multiplication, and division are considered to be operations on numbers; that is, we add, subtract, multiply, and divide numbers, not numerals. The numbers themselves are abstract, but we can get the result of an operation on the numbers by processing the numerals representing the numbers.

The number expression $42 + 6$, for example, symbolizes the addition of the numbers represented by the numerals 42 and 6. Also, $42 + 6$ is itself a numeral that names the number that is the sum of the two numbers. As a name for the sum, however, it is not in the simplest or most usable form. By processing the numerals according to the rules of addition, we get 48 as the simplest or standard numeral for the sum.

By processing the same numerals in a different way, we can get the difference of the numbers, in another way the product, and in still another way the quotient. The way we process numerals for an operation is called the algorithm for that operation. In this way we have the addition algorithm, the subtraction algorithm, the multiplication algorithm, and the division algorithm.

Addition Algorithm	Subtraction Algorithm	Multiplication Algorithm	Division Algorithm
42	42	42	7
$+\ 6$	$-\ 6$	$\times\ 6$	$6\overline{)42}$
48	36	252	

Computation. Computation refers to the manipulation of numerals, with pencil and paper or by other means, according to the principles and algorithms of the operations involved. We make computations to change one numeral or number expression to an equivalent one in simpler or more usable form. The cost of 6 handkerchiefs at 99 cents each, for example, is represented by the expression 6×99 cents, but the preferred form is $5.94, which we get by processing the numerals for the multiplication algorithm.

In other words, computation is primarily concerned with replacing one numeral or number expression with one that is simpler or more usable.

Review 2. This is the first of many reviews that normally occur at the end of a section. This review follows a pattern used in each of the subsequent reviews. A question including matching important terms is usually included and is followed by a series of abstract number problems designed to maintain student skills. The number problems are then followed by a series of word problems.

Problem 1 in the review is a review of the terms that appear in boldface in Sections 1 and 2. Students should write the letters *A* through *H* in a vertical column at the left side of their papers and then match the terms with the statements. They should write the terms next to the correct letters on their papers.

You may prefer to have students write both the letters and the statements, followed by the matching terms, to reinforce the association of terms and statements.

Encourage your students to complete the vocabulary exercises on their first try, without looking at the text. Students should then check their answers against the text narrative or by using **Appendix D, Business Math Terms.**

Several other suggestions for developing vocabulary and using the Terms part of the reviews are presented in this manual in the **Developing Vocabulary** section.

Problem 2 provides a review of addition using whole and decimal numbers. Students are asked to combine numbers that total 10 to speed their addition. They are also asked to check their work by reverse addition. You should require students to show the pencil "carries" above and below these problems to insure that students have added both ways.

Problems 3 through 6 provide students with a review of cash receipts and cash payments problems.

SECTION 3. COLUMNAR CASH PAYMENTS RECORDS

Comments and Suggestions. Cash payments records with special columns used in this section provide a realistic setting for horizontal addition. Students are often confused by the terms *horizontal* and *vertical*. You will want to stress these terms, using synonyms such as *across* and *up and down*. Students will also tend to resist adding horizontally without rewriting the figures in a vertical column. You will want to watch their work habits closely at this point.

Stress the method of proving the final total by taking a horizontal total of vertical totals and a vertical total of horizontal totals. When students use this method they can be sure their final answer is correct. Students should understand that using a corner or grand total proof, or *crossfooting*, is common in record keeping and bookkeeping, and they will frequently encounter business forms using the corner or grand total proof.

Review 3. Problem 1 reviews the new terms from Section 3. You may wish to remind students to try to answer the questions without looking at the text and to check the text for the meanings of the terms only after they have finished the question.

Problem 2 reviews solving open sentences.

Problems 3 and 5 review finding the total cash receipts.

Problems 4 and 6 review finding the total cash payments.

Calculator Clinic. The calculator clinic for Section 3 presents the use of the memory register for addition. Students are shown how to add amounts from the calculator display to the memory register and how to recall and clear the amounts in the memory register. This knowledge is useful in using the hand-held calculator to complete the columnar cash payments records included in the section.

Computer Clinic. The use of electronic spreadsheets for the solution of common problems in business mathematics is introduced in Section 3. The computer clinic begins with a brief introduction to important terms and concepts pertaining to computer hardware and software. The use of electronic spreadsheets to complete cash payments records is then explained.

The student is asked to boot the spreadsheet software used in the class, load the template, call the appropriate file, and enter the data listed in the problem. The payment column totals and weekly row totals are computed automatically.

Students are asked to provide answers to several questions after the spreadsheet has been completed. These questions are designed to focus student attention on the results of the spreadsheet. Some teachers may choose to collect and grade these questions rather than have students print out their completed spreadsheets. Others may require students to hand in both the answers to the questions and a printout of the completed spreadsheets.

SECTION 4. CHECK REGISTER RECORDS

In this section students learn how to complete deposit slips, checks, and check registers. Check registers rather than check stubs are included because check registers have become so common.

Each check listed on a deposit slip is usually identified by the ABA (American Banker's Association) transit number of the bank on which it is drawn. This number is the numerator of the fraction-like symbol in the upper right-hand corner of the check and deposit slip illustrated in the section. The lower part of the fraction-like number is a routing symbol used by bank clerks to expedite the sorting and forwarding of checks to the various Federal Reserve and correspondent banks. For example:

$$\frac{10\text{-}670}{210} \qquad \begin{array}{l}\text{transit number}\\[4pt]\text{routing number}\end{array}$$

When identifying a check on a deposit slip, the depositor should ordinarily use only the transit number. Some individuals and businesses prefer to list checks on the deposit slip by the name of the drawee rather than the transit number.

Guide Answer in Exercise 2. The correct answer is printed in color in the Final Balance column of Problem 2, Exercise 2. This is the first guide answer in the text. The footnote at the bottom of the page explains the guide answer to the students. More information for the teacher about the purpose and use of guide answers is provided on page 6 of this manual.

Electronic Funds Transfer. Banks and many firms are increasingly moving towards greater use of the electronic transfer of funds by computers instead of physically writing and transferring checks and deposit slips.

In addition to the examples described in the text, many companies who regularly do business with one another automatically transfer funds between themselves using computer systems. This avoids the need to prepare, mail, verify, and deposit checks. No paper checks or deposit slips are used at all.

Some students may know friends or relatives whose companies deposit their paychecks directly into their bank accounts. Others may know friends or relatives whose social security checks are deposited directly into their bank accounts. Ask these students to describe their experiences and discuss the advantages of electronic funds transfer.

Subtraction. Subtraction is closely related to addition. In both addition and subtraction, you must deal with three numbers: two addends and their sum. In addition the two numbers are given and you must find the sum. In subtraction the sum and one number are given and you must find the other number.

In this text subtraction is called the reverse of addition because the term *reverse* is commonly understood by students. In technical literature the term inverse is frequently used instead. Point out to your students that they do many things each day which are the reverse or inverse of each other. For example, they put on and take off their coats, turn lights on and off, and open and close books.

Some of your students, because of their earlier instruction, will use the additive method of subtraction, while others will use the "take away" method. Although a uniform procedure for solving problems may be desirable, it is usually unwise to try to change the established habits of students.

Checking Subtraction. You should emphasize the need for 100% accuracy in subtraction. To emphasize this important objective you may require students to show that they have proved their subtraction problems on selected homework and class papers that they turn in to you. Two ways students might show their proofs are:

$$
\begin{array}{r}
256 \\
-104 \\
\hline
152 \\
+104 \\
\hline
256 \quad \text{check}
\end{array}
\qquad
\begin{array}{r}
256 \\
-104 \\
\hline
+152 \\
\hline
256
\end{array}
$$

Gross and Net. The terms **gross** and **net** occur frequently in business and personal situations. The terms are presented in the text in the general sense that *gross* is a larger figure from which an amount is subtracted to find a *net* or smaller figure.

In Exercise 6 gross and net appear as gross and net weight, gross and net bill, gross price and net amounts, gross and net work hours, gross and net wages, and gross and net sales. At this point students should be expected to understand only the meaning of the general terms, *gross* and *net*. As students encounter the terms again throughout the text, they are given formal definitions and extensive practice with each specific use of gross and net. In this way students progressively increase their understanding and mastery of the terms.

Related Problems. The arithmetic procedures used in maintaining a check register (adding to and subtracting from an original balance) are used frequently in many business and personal situations. Exercise 7 provides students with opportunities to see how these arithmetic procedures can be applied to solve related problems. Throughout the reviews in the text, additional related problems that use these arithmetic procedures are presented.

Correlated Drill for Accuracy and Speed. *Mental Drill 2* in **Appendix A** can be used to provide spaced practice in subtraction. This drill correlates with

Exercise 5 and can be used as a warm-up assignment, as described in the **Warm-Up Drill** section of this manual. As soon as Exercise 5 has been covered in class, Problem 1a in Drill 2 should be used in the next day's warm-up assignment, then Problem 1b or 2a in the next assignment, and so on.

The directions at the beginning of the drill tell students to place the edge of the answer paper under the problem and write the difference on the paper. This saves the time of recopying. You may prefer to have students copy the figures on their answer papers and then subtract to provide opportunities for reinforcing neatness and proper alignment.

Review 4. Problem 1 reviews the vocabulary terms shown in bold in Section 4. Problem 2 provides a review of subtraction using abstract problems. Problem 3 reviews cash receipts operations. Problem 4 reviews cash payments operations. Problem 5 reviews gross and net concepts. Problem 6 reviews finding the ending balance in a check register. Problem 7 reviews finding the total of a deposit.

Using Calculators. The use of hand-held calculators to solve subtraction problems and to check subtraction is presented in Section 4. The presentation follows the same pattern as the section on using hand-held calculators for addition.

If you have not already read it, the **Use of Calculators** section of this manual provides a number of suggestions for using hand-held calculators in the business mathematics classroom.

Background Information. Earlier in this manual addition of whole numbers was described as a process of counting forward. Since subtraction is the reverse of addition it may be described as a process of counting backward.

Unlike addition, subtraction is neither commutative nor associative; $5 - 3$ is not equal to $3 - 5$ and $(24 - 8) - 3$ is not equal to $24 - (8 - 3)$. We can interchange two addends or subtrahends in a problem, but we cannot interchange a minuend and a subtrahend, or change a subtrahend to a minuend, or vice versa. So, $5 + 3$ is equal to $3 + 5$ because the two numbers are addends in both expressions. Also, $24 - 8 - 3$ is equal to $24 - 3 - 8$ because both 8 and 3 are subtrahends in both expressions.

However, $5 - 3$ does not equal $3 - 5$ because 5 was changed from a minuend in the first problem to a subtrahend in the second, and 3 has been changed from a subtrahend to a minuend. Nor is $(24 - 8) - 3$ equal to $24 - (8 - 3)$ because 8 was changed from a subtrahend in the first problem to a minuend in the second.

When a problem contains many subtractions, as in $54 - 21 - 15 - 5$, we may subtract the subtrahends in any order. We may subtract any one of them first, then either of the other two from the first difference, and then the third one from the second difference.

We may also add the subtrahends and subtract them in one amount. Thus, $54 - 21 - 15 - 5 = 54 - (21 + 15 + 5)$. This principle is used often in business mathematics. An example seen in the text (Section 5) occurs when students add outstanding checks and subtract them in one amount from the bank balance on a reconciliation statement.

SECTION 5. PROVING THE CHECK REGISTER BALANCE

Comments and Suggestions. This section explains the preparation of reconciliation statements including only service charges, interest earned, and outstanding checks. Other adjustments are explained in Section 6.

Usually, if there are no errors in the bank statement the bank statement balance needs to be adjusted only for the outstanding checks. If there are no errors in the depositor's check register the checkbook needs to be adjusted only for the bank service charge and any interest the account has earned. The service charge and interest credit appear on the bank statement, but not in the check register, because the bank records these amounts directly in the depositor's account without immediately notifying the depositor that these changes have been made. The depositor usually finds out about these amounts by looking at the bank statement, where amounts labeled "SC" for service charge and "IN" for interest are shown. Many banks also include debit memos for the service charge and credit memos for the interest earned in the envelope with the canceled checks.

Many banks now pay interest on checking account balances. Learning how to compute this interest is not the purpose of this section and would complicate the instruction.

Problems Containing More Information than Is Necessary. In the real world students do not confront problems that offer only the absolute minimum amount of information necessary to solve the problems. Rather, they must learn to identify the relevant facts in a situation in order to solve the problem. Exercise 2 provides students with an opportunity to solve reconciliation problems in which more than the necessary information is presented. You may wish to have students read these problems and report orally what information is not needed and what information is needed to solve the problems before you let the students attempt the exercise on paper.

Review 5. Problem 2 reviews horizontal addition and proving horizontal addition. Problem 3 reviews addition of money amounts for deposit slips. Problem 4 reviews gross and net concepts. Problem 5 reviews related problems. Problem 6 reviews the reconciliation statement including service charges and outstanding checks.

‡SECTION 6. SPECIAL RECONCILIATION PROBLEMS

Materials Marked with a ‡. The narrative and problems included in this section are marked with a ‡. Narrative and problems marked in this way are optional and are provided to allow you to meet the need for individual differences among students in your classes.

The review problems in Review 6, however, contain only one problem that is marked. Thus, Problems 1–9 of Review 6 may be assigned to all students even though they were not assigned or did not complete Section 6.

Comments and Suggestions. Besides an adjustment for outstanding checks, the bank statement balance may need adjustment for an omitted deposit or a deposit made too late to appear on the bank statement.

Some banks close early in the afternoon to give tellers enough time to complete their records of the day's transactions. However, many of them have drive-in windows and automatic teller machines so that customers may continue to make deposits or withdrawals. Most banks also receive deposits after hours through a late deposit box and through the mail. Banks record these deposits as of the next business day rather than on the day on which the deposits were made. For example, if a customer made a late deposit on January 31, the deposit would appear as the first deposit on the February statement.

Preparing a reconciliation statement with special types of adjustments is developed through the text exercises in three steps:

1. ‡Exercise 1. Adjustment of the bank statement balance for omitted deposits and for outstanding checks. Omitted deposits are an addition to the bank statement balance and outstanding checks are a subtraction.

2. ‡Exercise 2. Adjustment of the checkbook balance for errors and omissions that are additions and subtractions to the checkbook balance.

3. ‡Exercise 3. Adjustment of both the checkbook and bank statement balances that combine the adjustments in both 1 and 2, already discussed.

Review 6. No new terms were introduced in this section.

Problem 7 reviews the reconciliation statement with outstanding checks, service charges, and interest earned.

Problem 8 reviews cash payments records and Problem 9 reviews finding the balance of a check register.

Problem 10 is an optional problem in preparing a reconciliation statement with a late deposit, service charge, outstanding checks, and interest earned.

Unit 2. Gross and Average Pay

Unit 2 reviews the fundamental operations of multiplication and division, primarily through gross pay and average pay calculations. Emphasis is placed on the use of multiplication and division short cuts and rounding techniques to estimate products and quotients. Students also receive instruction in the use of the calculator for problems involving multiplication and division.

Student learning objectives for Unit 2 appear on the Unit 2 opener page in the textbook.

Pretest for Unit 2. A pretest is included in the test package (M473) and the MicroEXAM package so you can find out how much students already know about basic multiplication and division operations, rounding of numbers, and calculations using averages and gross pay word problems.

Problems 1–5 are abstract problems that measure students' skills in multiplication, division, and rounding. Since these are basic skills that students will use frequently as they study business mathematics, any deficiencies that students have should be remedied by the drills suggested for each section of study.

Problems 6 through 11 require students to find gross pay, simple average, weighted average, a missing item in a series, and piece-rate pay.

Integrated Project for Unit 2. A project that integrates the gross pay concepts in Unit 2 is provided at the end of Unit 2 in the workbook. In *Integrated Project 2*, students figure gross pay for hourly rate and piece-rate workers in a department and update a year-to-date wage summary report.

Vocabulary Review for Unit 2. A vocabulary exercise, *Vocabulary Review: Unit 2*, is found at the end of Unit 2 in the workbook. The exercise reviews 20 of the vocabulary terms included in Unit 2 of the textbook. To practice spelling key terms, students should complete the exercise by writing the terms rather than listing a matching letter or number.

Supplementary Problems for Unit 2. Eight word problems similar to those provided in the exercises for Unit 2 are presented in the *Supplementary Problems for Unit 2* section of **Appendix B.**

Test for Unit 2. A review test for Unit 2 is provided in the test package (M473) and the MicroEXAM package. The test is designed to measure student achievement of the learning objectives of Unit 2, except for those objectives dealing with optional calculator and spreadsheet topics.

Solutions for Unit 2. Solutions to all text problems, the pretest, and the unit test are included in this manual. Solutions to all workbook problems are included in the teacher's edition of the workbook.

Additional Resources for Unit 2. There are many other resources that you can use to support or supplement the instruction in Unit 2. Elementary school teachers can provide you with additional drill material or teaching suggestions for use with students who are weak on the fundamentals of multiplication and division.

Local business firms are able to provide you with real local wage and salary rates, sample time cards, payroll policies that deal with workers who are late in arriving at work, and overtime regulations and pay rates. State and local surveys of employment demand and trends also give wage information.

There are also some published materials that relate to the content of Unit 2 that you may wish to examine. These include:

1. Gossage, Loyce C., <u>Mathematics Skill Builder</u>, South-Western Publishing Co., 5101 Madison Road, Cincinnati, OH 45227, 1985. A text-workbook that provides instruction in the fundamental processes and in some applications in business and consumer mathematics.

2. Muncaster, Barbara F. and Susan L. Prescott, <u>Learning Basic Math and Business Math Using the Calculator</u>, South-Western Publishing Co., 5101 Madison Road, Cincinnati, OH 45227, 1985.

SECTION 7. FINDING GROSS PAY

Comments and Suggestions. Most students are interested in how employees are paid and how their pay is calculated. For that reason, gross pay problems are used to review multiplication. The wage calculations in the early part of this section involve only the multiplication of whole numbers so that students can concentrate on the process used in figuring gross wages. Students calculate gross pay on an hourly rate, salary, and piece-rate basis. The distinction between regular and overtime wages is not presented until Unit 3. The difference between gross pay and take-home pay is presented in Unit 4.

Although students are asked to calculate gross pay in most problems, be sure to point out that other terms such as gross wages, total earnings, and total pay are also used to express the same idea.

The overall purpose of Exercise 1 is to show how gross pay is found when the hourly rate of pay and the number of hours worked are known. In Exercise 2 students find the gross pay of salaried employees and figure equivalent wages. Demonstrate to students how equivalent wages for any time period may be figured.

Three problems in Exercise 3 present gross wage calculations of piece rate employees in a business context and help to establish the idea that employers pay the wages of employees. Students also figure wages on a graduated piece rate basis and on the net items produced.

Correlated Drill for Accuracy and Speed. Drill 3 in Appendix A involves the multiplication of whole numbers and can be used to provide extra practice. Although the directions ask that the product be proved, this may be considered optional, since the topic of checking multiplication is not covered until Section 8.

Review 7. Make sure students understand the difference between the meaning of gross pay, which represents the total amount of pay received by hourly rate employees, and the meaning of hourly rate, which represents the rate of pay per hour. Both terms are included in the Terms section of the review.

Problem 2 reviews number sentences using only addition and subtraction. Number sentences using multiplication and division are included in reviews later in this unit.

Problems 3 and 4 review computing the gross pay for workers using an hourly rate, weekly rate, and monthly rate. Problem 5 reviews the calculation of gross pay using the piece rate basis. Problem 6 is a related problem in which the cash remaining is found by taking the difference between cash receipts and cash payments.

Calculator Clinic. The use of hand-held calculators to solve multiplication problems is explained at the end of Section 7 in the calculator clinic. Follow the pattern you used when presenting the use of the calculator for solving addition problems.

Since procedures may vary slightly for solving different aspects of wage problems, it may be helpful to demonstrate the process for finding equivalent wages and calculating piece rate wages.

Computer Clinic. The student is asked to load Sec7 and enter the listed data into the payroll record. The total hours worked by each employee, the totals of the hours worked on a daily basis, and gross pay are calculated by formulas already in the template. Students are asked to provide the answers to several questions after the spreadsheet has been completed.

SECTION 8. MULTIPLICATION

Comments and Suggestions. Multiplication of whole numbers is usually viewed as a short way of adding two or more equal numbers. It may also be interpreted in terms of counting.

Addition may be thought of as a shortcut way of counting forward by ones. Multiplication, since it is related to addition, may then be thought of as a shortcut method of counting forward by numbers greater than one. To find the product of 5×8, we could count forward five times with eight — 8, 16, 24, 32, 40 — arriving at 40 as the result. The longer process is avoided by memorizing the multiplication table. Success in multiplication requires being able to recall the multiplication facts.

Exercise 1 is effective for drilling on common multiplication facts. Student weakness in dealing with certain combinations can readily be identified. Have students drill orally by calling the row and column numbers randomly and by reversing the combinations. Students can also be teamed to drill each other on the combinations for more practice. This exercise can be repeated frequently throughout the year.

In Exercise 1 multiplication by 1 is omitted because the product is simply equal to the factor that is multiplied by 1. Multiplication by 10 is also omitted from this exercise since the procedure for multiplying by 10, as well as 100 and 1,000, is covered in Section 9.

The term *factor* is used in the text for both multiplication and division. If students learn to use this term, they will be better able to handle later problems that require them to find an unknown factor in multiplication or division. In presenting multiplication problems on the chalkboard, identify the elements of multiplication by writing the words *factor* and *product* or $F \times F = P$ over the corresponding numbers. Students should also label their work with these terms until they show that they have mastered the concept.

Checking Multiplication. Students should develop the habit of checking their multiplication by doing their calculations again or by reversing the factors and multiplying again.

Checking multiplication in these ways will produce an exact check of the number combinations. In working with decimals, though, mistakes can occur in how the numbers are combined and in where the decimal point is placed. The following method may be used to check the reasonableness of an answer in working with whole numbers and decimals:

1. When both factors are greater than 1, the product must be greater than either factor. Thus, in $3 \times 52 = 156$, the product is greater than 3 or 52. When both factors are smaller than 1, the product must be smaller than either factor. In $0.2 \times 0.6 = 0.12$, the product is smaller than either 0.2 or 0.6.

2. When one factor is smaller than 1, the product must be smaller than the other factor. Thus, in $0.3 \times 52 = 15.6$, the product is smaller than the second factor, 52.

The problems in Exercises 3 and 4 can be used to demonstrate these principles. The chalkboard may be divided into sections to represent these variations, and students may then classify each problem and write it in the appropriate section.

Rounding Numbers. Several situations exist where students will have to apply rounding principles. These include:

1. Rounding the factors to the first figure on the left to estimate a product.

2. Rounding a product or quotient to the nearest cent.

3. Rounding a quotient representing an average cost to the nearest tenth or hundredth of a cent.

4. Carrying a quotient, such as a decimal rate, to the nearest tenth, hundredth, thousandth, etc.

5. Rounding numbers to the nearest 10, 100, 1,000, etc. for use in plotting graphs.

The process of rounding is first demonstrated by the rounding of money amounts. The example problem where amounts are rounded to the nearest cent demonstrates a half-or-greater rounding method. The amount is increased to the next highest cent if the digit to the right of the cents place is one-half cent or greater. The amount is not changed if the digit to the right is less than one-half cent. This method of rounding is sometimes referred to as the "Rule of 5" method, and will be used to round numbers in Section 9 for estimation purposes.

Students use rounding principles to solve the problems in Exercise 5. Be sure that all students are familiar with the way in which money figures are written with either a dollar or cents sign to represent the same amount.

Emphasize to students that rounding is a process of accepting a less than precise or mathematically accurate answer, and that inaccuracies caused by rounding should not be compounded by multiplying them. Also emphasize that, in rounding, you look only to the *first* digit to the right of the place you want; considering more than the first digit may cause a wrong result.

Correlated Drill for Accuracy and Speed. Drill 3 in Appendix A can be used for additional practice in multiplying numbers and checking the accuracy of products by reversing the factors and multiplying again. The products obtained can also be used to provide practice in rounding to various places.

Background Information. The rule for placing the decimal point in the product is given in this section. We may think of the derivation of the rule in this way: In multiplying 2.63 by 3.5, the product is 9,205 before counting off the decimal point. This is the same as the product of 35×263. By doing this, we have ignored the decimal points and have treated the numbers as whole numbers. The decimal point was moved two places to the right in 2.63 and one place to the right in 3.5 to change those decimals to whole numbers. To compensate for these changes in the factors, we must count off a total of three places to the left in the product, 9,205, to arrive at the correct answer, 9.205.

Review 8. Problems 2 through 6 review horizontal addition, horizontal subtraction, and selected multiplication facts. Problem 7 provides a review of the principles of rounding to tenths, hundredths, cents, and thousands. Number sentences are reviewed in Problem 8, while Problem 9 reviews finding a net weight. In Problem 10 students are to prepare a reconciliation statement involving a service charge, interest earned, and outstanding checks.

SECTION 9. MULTIPLICATION SHORTCUTS

Comments and Suggestions. The work in this section emphasizes the use of shortcuts in multiplication as a way of saving time and the estimation of products as an aid to checking the reasonableness of answers, thereby increasing accuracy.

Estimating the Product. Three different methods of estimating the product are presented. Both the round-down method and the round-up method are used primarily to provide practice in rounding factors to produce an estimated product. The third method, the rule-of-five method, parallels the rounding procedures that students used in the previous section to round money amounts, decimals, and whole numbers. The rule-of-five method is recommended for use throughout the textbook. However, teachers who have students who are having difficulty in rounding factors for estimation purposes should use the round-down or round-up methods. Either method may be easier for students because less judgment is required in arriving at rounded factors.

Multiplication by 10, 100, or 1,000. Multiplication by 10, 100, or 1,000 is accomplished by moving the decimal point in the multiplicand. Examples in the textbook show problem situations and the results of multiplication. To help students understand the concept, demonstrate on the chalkboard how moving the decimal point produces the same result as multiplying in the usual way and then counting off the total number of decimal places in both factors.

$$
\begin{array}{r} 9.42 \\ \times\ 10 \\ \hline 94.20 \end{array}
\qquad
\begin{array}{r} 9.42 \\ \times\ 100 \\ \hline 942.00 \end{array}
\qquad
\begin{array}{r} 9.42 \\ \times\ 1{,}000 \\ \hline 9{,}420.00 \end{array}
$$

Point out that in each case the final position of the decimal point in the product is as many places to the right of its original position in the second factor as there are zeros in the factor, which is a 10, 100, or 1,000. So, we can multiply by 10, 100, or 1,000 mentally, without written calculations, by simply shifting the position of the decimal point in the second factor.

A two-step related procedure involving multiplication by multiples of 10, 100, or 1,000 is also presented. The first step involves multiplying by the amount of the multiple. In the second step, the decimal point in the product is moved to accomplish multiplication by 10, 100, or 1,000. The first step in this process is disregarded when no multiples are involved because we would be multiplying by the number 1. Since a number is not changed when it is multiplied by 1, there is no need to multiply.

Multiplying Numbers That Have End Zeros. Be sure that students understand the effect of end zeros on the value of a whole number and a number containing a decimal point. Also note that the procedure described in the textbook as a shortcut method of multiplication is most appropriately used when both factors contain zeros.

Multiplying by 1¢ and 10¢. In this manual, two methods were described that can be used to check the reasonableness of an answer. These methods also apply to written work involving multiplication by 1¢ and 10¢. If a student writes "35 articles at 10¢ = $350," show how unreasonable is the result. Point out that since one factor, 10¢, is smaller than $1, the product must be smaller than $35.

Correlated Drills for Accuracy and Speed. Drill 18 and some parts of Drill 21 correlate with Exercise 6. Drills 5 and 6 may be used with Exercise 8. Selected problems from Drill 27 may be used with Exercise 9. The problems from Drill 19 correlate with those of Exercise 10.

Because of the number of problems that are available for student practice, the use of these problems should be spaced over a period of several days, either as a warm-up activity or as a way of maintaining skills.

Review 9. Problem 2 reviews multiplication by $0.01, $0.10, 10, 100, and 1,000 and multiples of those numbers. Problem 3 reviews estimating products to check exact products by using values that make it possible to multiply by multiples of 100.

Problem 4 reviews rounding principles. Problem 5 reviews finding the amount of a deposit. Problem 6 reviews finding the gross earnings of an hourly rate employee.

SECTION 10. FINDING AVERAGE PAY

Comments and Suggestions. The presentation and calculation of simple and weighted averages revolve around wage problems to maintain the continuity of the unit. In Problem 5 of Exercise 2, a related type of problem is used to show that there are reasons for finding averages other than for wage-oriented calculations. Students will solve additional related problems of this type as they progress through the textbook.

In presenting simple averages, use as many descriptions as possible to stress that only like items can be arithmetically averaged by this method. Indicate that the items must have the same weight or importance, or that they count as much as any other item even though the values may be different.

In calculating weighted averages, it is important to stress that some items have more weight or importance, or that they count more than other items.

Since most students are familiar with how their grades for a course are figured, they know that some tests such as a final exam count more than do other tests. The following illustration dealing with test averaging may be placed on the chalkboard to help introduce the weighted average topic.

Test	Score	Weight	Points	
1	75	1	75	
2	80	1	80	
3	83	1	83	
Final	91	2	182	
		5	420	420 ÷ 5 = 84 average

Point out the error that would result from averaging the tests by adding the four scores and dividing by 4. By using the simple average method, the student test average would be incorrectly calculated as 82.25 instead of the score of 84 found through the weighted average method.

Finding an Unknown Item in a Series. Before showing students how to solve for unknown items in a series, remind them that if they know both the total cost of the items and the number of items, they can calculate the average. Conversely, if they know the average and either the number of items or their total cost, they can find the missing element. Recognizing this aspect of averages will help students solve for missing items.

An unknown or missing item in a series can be found by subtracting the sum of the known items from the sum of all the items, known and unknown. Exercise 3 provides practice in finding missing items while applying the concept of averages.

Review 10. Problem 2 reviews multiplication shortcuts and rounding principles. Problem 3 continues the review of number sentences using multiplication. Problems 4 and 5 review simple and weighted averages using related problems. Problem 6 is another related problem that reviews finding the unknown item in a series.

Calculator Clinic. The use of hand-held calculators to solve division problems through finding averages is explained at the end of Section 10. When finding weighted averages, the M+ key is used to complete the multiplication of factors and add the result into the memory register. Those students who may have difficulty with this procedure may first press the equals key to do the multiplication and then the M+ key. If it is suitable to do so, discuss with students the procedure for using the calculator to find an unknown item in a series.

SECTION 11. DIVISION

Comments and Suggestions. This section formally introduces the meaning of division, the ways it is shown, identification of factors and products, placement of the decimal point in the quotient, division to a stated number of decimal places, and procedures for checking the results of division.

In this section multiplication and division are described as reverse or opposite operations. Point out that this relationship is applied when we multiply the divisor and the quotient to check division. Thus, if dividing 405 by 27 yields a quotient of 15, the work can be checked by multiplying 27 by 15 to yield a product of 405.

Remind students that addition and subtraction are also reverse operations and that this idea is used when subtraction is checked by adding the difference to the number being subtracted.

Exercise 1 may be used to drill students on frequently used division combinations. It may be used in the same way as Exercise 1, dealing with multiplication facts, was used in Section 8.

Number Sentences. A formal method for finding N, in a problem such as $4 \times N = 28$, is introduced in this section. The method is based on the fact that the unknown factor of a product can be found by dividing the product by the known factor. Since the product and factors must be correctly identified, special attention should be given to Exercises 2 and 3.

In Exercise 2, have the student first identify the product. Once the product is identified, the other numerals or letters must be factors. Emphasize that the dividend represents a product, and that the divisor and quotient are factors of that product.

A number sentence in the form of $4 \times N = 28$ will be encountered in later work, especially since this form represents a problem where the whole is to be found when only a part or percent of the whole is known. Sentences such as $\frac{4}{5} \times N = 12$, $0.15 \times N = 60$, and $35\% \times N = 175$ will be encountered when students begin the work on fractions, decimals, and percents.

Using a Remainder to Show an Exact Quotient. An exact quotient results when the divisor is contained in the dividend an exact number of times with no remainder. If the problem asks students to find an exact quotient with no qualification, division should be carried out until there is no remainder. Remind students that for most problems they will be directed as to how the quotient should be rounded or told if a remainder is to be shown.

Point out to students that many division problems result in a remainder. In some cases the remainder must be shown because of accuracy requirements. In the example problem, students are directed to find an exact quotient to the ones place. This also means that any remainder is to be shown as a fractional part of the divisor. When the remainder in a quotient is to be shown as a fraction, students should know that they stop dividing after they use all of the digits in the dividend. They should not bring down zeros to continue dividing as they would do in dividing to a stated number of decimal places.

Fractions in the remainder are usually shown in lowest terms. Since the formal review of simplifying fractions is not presented until Unit 3, the problems of Exercise 8 are designed to result in fractions that require no simplification. The discussion of simplifying fractions should be deferred until the topic is discussed in Unit 3.

Checking Division. Emphasize to students the need for developing the habit of checking the accuracy of their computations. They should either do their work again, or multiply the divisor and the quotient and add the remainder, if any, to that product.

Estimating the quotient to verify the placement of the decimal point in the quotient is not presented in the text until Section 12. There is a rough check, however, which the students should be in the habit of using to reveal gross errors in division. This rough check is based on the following principles:

1. When the divisor is greater than 1, the quotient will always be smaller than the dividend. For example, $84 \div 4 = 21$. Since the divisor, 4, is greater than 1, the quotient, 21, is smaller than the dividend, 84.

2. When the divisor is smaller than 1, the quotient will always be greater than the dividend. For example, $48 \div 0.3 = 160$. Since the divisor, 0.3, is smaller than 1, the quotient, 160, is greater than the dividend, 48.

Demonstrate these principles to the class and review similar principles relating to multiplication that were presented earlier in this manual. The review should show that the error-detection principles for both multiplication and division are related, but in an inverse manner. Thus:

If a given number is multiplied by a number greater than 1, the product will be greater than the given number. Since division is the reverse of multiplication, if a given number is divided by a number greater than 1, the quotient will be smaller than the given number, or dividend.

If a given number is multiplied by a number smaller than 1, the product will be smaller than the given number. Since division is the reverse of multiplication, if a given number is divided by a number smaller than 1, the quotient will be greater than the given number, or dividend.

Follow up the demonstration with oral drill based on the problems in Exercise 5 in the text and Drill 8 in Appendix A. Call on students to state whether the quotient in each case should be greater or smaller than the dividend—for example, whether the quotient in Problem 1 of Exercise 5 should be greater or smaller than the dividend, 1,640. Impress upon students how useful this rough check is for spotting at a glance a result that is ridiculously large or small.

Correlated Drills for Accuracy and Speed. Drill 7 in Appendix A provides practice in the division of whole numbers where the quotient is a whole number and there is no remainder. Problems from Drill 7 may be introduced in the preliminary warm-up assignments as soon as Exercise 4 has been covered in class. Exercise 6 correlates with Drill 8.

Background Information. There are two common definitions of *division*. In one definition, division is described as the opposite or reverse of multiplication. In the other definition, it is described as the process of finding the other factor of a product when one factor and the product are known.

Since multiplication may be thought of as repeated addition, its reverse, division, may be thought of as repeated subtraction. For instance, to divide 17 by 5, we can repeatedly subtract 5 from 17, as shown at the right, until there is a final difference of 0 or a number less than 5. At the right we have subtracted 3 fives with 2 left over; that is, in 17 there are 3 fives and a remainder of 2.

$$\begin{array}{r} 17 \\ -\ 5 \\ \hline 12 \\ -\ 5 \\ \hline 7 \\ -\ 5 \\ \hline 2 \end{array}$$

The use of the division process would involve the following computation

$$\begin{array}{r} 3 \quad \text{(fives in 17)} \\ 5\overline{)17} \\ \underline{15} \\ 2 \quad \text{(remainder)} \end{array}$$

In the division algorithm we subtract the 3 fives in one amount, 15, instead of subtracting them individually.

It is important to note that division, unlike multiplication, is neither commutative nor associative. So, $5 \div 3$ does not equal $3 \div 5$, and $(48 \div 6) \div 2$ is not equal to $48 \div (6 \div 2)$.

The expression $5 \div 3$ does not equal $3 \div 5$, because 5 has been changed from a dividend in the first expression to a divisor in the second, and 3 has been changed from a divisor to a dividend. Also, $(48 \div 6) \div 2$ is not equal to $48 \div (6 \div 2)$, because 6 has been changed from a divisor in the first expression to a dividend in the second.

Both addition and multiplication are commutative and associative, but their reverse operations, subtraction and division, are not.

Review 11. Problem 2 asks students first to identify the factor and product, then to find the unknown factor in a number sentence. Problem 3 reviews multiplication and division. The finding of a quotient rounded to the nearest tenth is required in Problem 4.

Problem 5 reviews finding the check register balance when deposits are made and checks drawn. Problem 6 reviews finding a weighted average.

SECTION 12. DIVISION SHORTCUTS

Comments and Suggestions. In this section students review several important aspects of division. They estimate quotients and use shortcut methods of multiplying by 10, 100, or 1,000, and their multiples.

Estimating the Quotient. Encourage students to estimate the quotient to check the position of the decimal point and detect any gross error in their calculations. To give students practice in maintaining their skills in estimation, you should periodically give oral drills or written practice in estimating quotients by using Exercises 1, 2, and 3. Drills 7, 8, and 9 may also be used to provide additional practice.

There is no one acceptable method of estimating the quotient. The answers that students get will vary, but the students will achieve the purpose of obtaining an estimate. To aid students and the teacher, the exercises in this section are designed to generate similar responses from most students, thereby helping to establish a pattern for solution. However, any method of rounding is acceptable that results in the correct location of the decimal point in the quotient.

Division by 10, 100, or 1,000. A shortcut method for dividing by 10, 100, or 1,000 is introduced in this section. Demonstrate the derivation of the rule by showing the division of 24.6 by 10, 100, and 1,000 by the ordinary division process, as follows:

```
        2.46             0.246              0.0246
   10)24.60        100)24.600         1,000)24.6000
      20               20 0               20 00

       4 6              4 60               4 600
       4 0              4 00               4 000

         60               600                6000
         60               600                6000
```

Point out that in each case the position of the decimal point with respect to the digits in the quotient is as many places to the left of its position in the dividend as there are zeros in the divisor. So, we can divide by 10, 100, or 1,000 mentally, without written calculations, by simply shifting the position of the decimal point in the dividend.

Remind students of the rule for multiplication by 10, 100, or 1,000. Point out that the rule for division is the opposite of the rule for multiplication; that is, the decimal point is moved in the opposite direction. This follows the definition of division being the reverse of multiplication.

Correlated Drills for Accuracy and Speed. Drill 20 correlates with Exercise 4. Use four or five problems at a time in the warm-up assignment. Usually the use of this drill should be discontinued when Drill 21 is started. The use of Drill 21 should begin as soon as most students show evidence of mastery of the work in Drills 18 and 20.

Drill 9 correlates with Exercise 5. The problems in these drills should be used one at a time in the preliminary warm-up assignments.

Review 12. Problems 1–3 review number sentences in a variety of ways: identifying factors and products, finding unknown factors and products, estimating the quotient, finding the exact quotient, and rounding. Problem 4 reviews finding a weighted average. Problem 5 reviews finding gross annual income from weekly and monthly salaries. Problem 6 is an optional problem that reviews the preparation of a reconciliation statement that includes outstanding deposits, an error in check recording, outstanding checks, and unrecorded service charges and earned interest.

Unit 3. Regular and Overtime Pay

In Unit 3 the student learns to figure regular-time pay and overtime pay at time-and-a-half and double-time rates. These topics provide an introduction to the extensive review of fractions, ratio, proportion, and mixed numbers.

Student learning objectives for Unit 3 appear on the Unit 3 opener page in the textbook.

Pretest for Unit 3. A pretest is included in the test package (M473) and the MicroEXAM package to measure how much students already know about basic work with fractions and fractional relationships and wage calculations involving both regular and overtime pay.

Problems 1–5 are problems that review basic skills. Problem 6 requires students to figure gross pay for regular and overtime work. In Problem 7 students must determine the overtime pay rate and regular and overtime hours worked to figure gross pay. Problem 8 asks students to find the part that one number is of another. Problem 9 is a ratio problem.

Integrated Project for Unit 3. A project that integrates the wage calculation concepts and the study of fractional relationships in Unit 3 is provided at the end of Unit 3 in the workbook. In *Integrated Project 3*, students figure gross pay from time cards and prepare a management report that analyzes the current payroll and also compares the data from the current payroll period to a previous payroll period.

Vocabulary Review for Unit 3. A vocabulary exercise, *Vocabulary Review: Unit 3*, is found at the end of Unit 3 in the workbook. The exercise reviews 21 of the vocabulary terms included in Unit 3. As before, students write the matching terms to gain practice in spelling them.

Supplementary Problems for Unit 3. Ten word problems similar to those provided in the exercises for Unit 3 are presented in the *Supplementary Problems for Unit 3* section of **Appendix B.** These problems primarily require some type of wage calculation or a fractional comparison of wage items.

Transparencies for Unit 3. A transparency master of the time card found in Section 13 is included in the teacher's edition of the workbook.

Test for Unit 3. A review test for Unit 3 is provided in the test package and the MicroEXAM package (M473). The test is designed to measure student achievement of the learning objectives of Unit 3, except for the objective dealing with the optional calculator topics.

After the test results are determined, a careful analysis of the student answers will provide a basis for determining the amount of review or remediation that may be needed.

Solutions for Unit 3. Solutions to all text problems, the pretest, and the unit test are included in this manual. Solutions to all workbook problems are included in the teacher's edition of the workbook.

SECTION 13. REGULAR-TIME AND OVERTIME PAY

Comments and Suggestions. In this section students learn how to figure time worked from a time card record and to find gross pay given regular time and overtime pay rates.

The easy work with the fractions $\frac{1}{4}$, $\frac{1}{2}$, and $\frac{3}{4}$ in this section provides an introduction to the thorough review of fractions in Sections 14 and 15. How well students work with fractions in this section may give some idea of the kind and amount of review of fractions needed in the subsequent sections.

In the examples and problems dealing with time card records, fractional parts of less than $\frac{1}{4}$ hour are not counted in figuring time worked, and no penalty is charged for arriving 3 minutes late or leaving 3 minutes early. In figuring time worked in actual business situations, however, practice varies considerably among different firms. Some firms ignore any part less than one quarter of an hour. Others figure wages to the nearest quarter hour, ignoring any fraction less than one tenth or figuring time worked to the nearest tenth. Some figure time worked and wages for the exact number of minutes or hundredths of an hour indicated by the time card.

Either you or your students may ask relatives or friends about the payroll practices of various firms and report the findings to the class. You might get samples of time cards showing typical time clock recordings to display on the bulletin board. You might also get data on local hourly and piece-rate pay schedules and develop problems with these data to give students extra practice.

In the overtime problems of this section, overtime rates are given. Calculation of overtime rates is done in Section 17.

Review 13. Problems 3 through 6 review various wage calculations. Problem 3 asks students to find gross pay when the worker is paid a graduated piece rate. Problem 4 asks students to find gross pay when a piece rate is based on the net items produced. Problem 5 reviews finding gross pay when regular-time and overtime hours and the regular-time and overtime rates are given. Problem 6 asks students to find the equivalent pay for a month and a year, given a weekly salary. Problem 7 reviews weighted averages.

SECTION 14. FRACTIONS

Comments and Suggestions. Fractions were briefly and informally introduced in the time card problems of the previous section. The formal review of fractions begins in this section and concludes in Section 15.

The term "fraction" is used throughout this book in preference to the term "common fraction" and with a meaning clearly distinct from "decimal fraction."

The basic idea of fractional numerals, or fractions, as symbols or names for fractional numbers is presented early in this section. In your discussion of the basics of fractions, you may want to emphasize these points:

1. The symbol or numeral that names a fractional number is called a fractional numeral or, briefly, a fraction. A fraction is a numeral, not a number.

2. Fractions may be used to name whole numbers as well as fractional numbers. Because a fraction shows the division of one number by another, the quotient of $2 \div 1$, even though a whole number (2), may be written as $\frac{2}{1}$.

3. Since a number is not changed when it is divided by 1, point out that every whole number can be expressed as a fraction with a denominator of 1. So, $1 = \frac{1}{1}$; $2 = \frac{2}{1}$; $3 = \frac{3}{1}$, and so on.

Make sure students understand the facts about equivalent fractions since they are important for doing some of the computations involving fractions. Note that we get an equivalent fraction if we multiply or divide the numerator and denominator of the fraction by the same number. It should be understood, of course, that zero is excluded. Multiplying the numerator and denominator by zero has no meaning because zero cannot be used as a denominator.

When fractions are simplified they are stated in lowest terms. Students should understand that simplifying a fraction means just replacing it with the simplest fraction in the set of equivalent fractions to which the fraction belongs. In simplifying $\frac{12}{42}$ to $\frac{2}{7}$, for example, we are finding the simplest fraction in the set of equal fractions consisting of $\frac{2}{7}, \frac{4}{14}, \frac{6}{21}, \frac{8}{28}$, and so on, of which $\frac{12}{42}$ is a member. The simplest fraction, or fraction in lowest terms, is often called the *basic fraction* of that set of equivalent fractions.

Although students may use the phrase "reducing fractions" in the same context as "simplifying fractions," it should be made clear that reducing implies that you are making the fraction smaller, while simplifying implies that you are making the fraction equivalent, but in lower terms.

When discussing the simplification of fractions through cancellation, point out that cancellation is a process of dividing numerators and denominators by common factors before multiplying. Cancellation results in easier calculations and products that are often in lowest terms.

As you discuss mixed numbers, explain that a mixed number indicates the addition of a whole number and a proper fraction with the plus sign omitted. For example, the mixed number $2\frac{1}{4}$ is read "two-*and*-one-fourth" and means $2 + \frac{1}{4}$, but it is generally written without the plus sign.

To help with the understanding of mixed numbers, a number line similar to the one shown here may be drawn on the chalkboard. Each interval may be divided into the units shown in the diagram (or into any other number of units) and the division points marked with a dot. As you point to the various dots in random order, call upon students to state the mixed number associated with each dot.

A number line on the chalkboard such as the one shown here will help point out the relationship between a mixed number and the improper fraction from which it is derived.

Emphasize that $2\frac{1}{4}$ names the same number as $\frac{9}{4}$; and that $2\frac{1}{2}$ names the same number as $\frac{5}{2}$ and $\frac{10}{4}$; and so on. This means that we may use either the mixed number form or the fractional form in making computations, depending on which is more convenient to use. In multiplying $2\frac{1}{4}$ by $3\frac{1}{2}$, for example, we may find it more convenient to multiply $\frac{9}{4}$ by $\frac{7}{2}$.

If you prefer, the discussion and explanation of mixed numbers, including that of the number line, can be postponed until you reach Section 18, where mixed numbers are extensively reviewed.

Correlated Drill for Accuracy and Speed. The first two columns of problems in Drill 30 correlate with Oral Exercise 6.

Background Information. Since a fractional symbol expresses the ratio of the numerator to the denominator, numbers that can be named by fractions are frequently called *rational numbers*. The word *rational* is derived from the idea of a ratio. Some of your students who have studied modern math may use the term *rational numbers* rather than *fractional numbers* or *whole numbers*.

The term *rational numbers* applies to whole numbers as well as fractional numbers, since any whole number can be expressed in fractional form by writing it over 1. For example, 0 may be written as $\frac{0}{1}$, and 1 as $\frac{1}{1}$. This does not mean that a whole number must be expressed in fractional form to be called a rational number. The fact that it can be so expressed, not that it must be, is what places a whole number in the class of rational numbers. Thus, the numbers represented by the numerals 0, $\frac{2}{3}$, $\frac{1}{1}$, $\frac{5}{4}$, 2, $\frac{4}{2}$, and 5 are all rational numbers because each one either is or can be expressed in fractional form.

Whole numbers and fractional numbers are classified as rational numbers to distinguish them from numbers that cannot be expressed in fractional form. The square root of two ($\sqrt{2}$), for example, cannot be expressed as a fraction, because there are no two numbers whose ratio or quotient is equal to the square root of two. The same is true of the square root of any number that is not a perfect square, the cube root of any number that is not a perfect cube, and so on. In fact, there are countless numbers that cannot be expressed as fractions. Such numbers are called *irrational numbers*, meaning "not rational" or "not expressible as a ratio."

In the literature of modern mathematics, a numeral such as $2\frac{1}{4}$ is variously referred to as a mixed number, mixed-number notation, mixed-number form, mixed-form, mixed-numeral, mixed-fraction, and mixed-fraction form. Traditionally, it has been called a mixed number, and we have used that term in this text.

Review 14. Problems 2 and 3 review multiplying fractions by fractions, simplifying fractions, canceling to simplify multiplications, and changing improper fractions to mixed numbers.

Problem 4 reviews finding gross pay when regular time hours, overtime hours, and regular time and overtime pay rates are given. Problem 5 reviews finding equivalent pay for a year and a week. Problem 6 reviews finding a missing item in a series by using an average.

SECTION 15. MORE FRACTIONS

Comments and Suggestions. The formal review of fractions that was begun in Section 14 is concluded in this section.

Emphasize to students that the multiplication of a fraction and a whole number provides a short method of repeated addition of the fraction. Point out that $13 \times \frac{3}{8}$ means $\frac{3}{8} + \frac{3}{8} + \frac{3}{8}$ and so on for thirteen of the fractions, but that it is easier to find the result by multiplication.

Stress the procedure for finding the product when the whole number is a multiple of the denominator of the fraction. In $44 \times \frac{3}{4}$, for example, the product is $\frac{44 \times 3}{4}$. Divide 44 by 4 before multiplying by 3. In other words, think of $44 \times \frac{3}{4}$ as $\frac{44}{4} \times 3$.

Encourage students to apply these two rough checks on the product to avoid an illogical answer to a multiplication problem:

1. The product of a whole number and a fraction will be less than the whole-number factor if the fraction represents a number less than 1. So, $12 \times \frac{3}{4}$ yields a product of 9, which is less than 12.

2. The product will be greater than the whole-number factor if the fraction represents a number greater than 1. So, $12 \times \frac{4}{3}$ yields a product of 16, which is greater than 12.

The addition and subtraction of like fractions and the process of raising a fraction to higher terms are presented to lead into the addition and subtraction of unlike fractions.

Before discussing the raising of fractions to higher terms, remind students that equivalent fractions for a given fraction can be found by multiplying both the numerator and denominator by 2, 3, 4, 5 and so on. Involve the students in setting up on the chalkboard the first six fractions in the sets represented by $\frac{3}{4}$, $\frac{5}{6}$, and $\frac{5}{8}$, as follows:

Point out that, to add $\frac{3}{4}$, $\frac{5}{6}$, and $\frac{5}{8}$, students can examine the rows until they find the fractions that have a common denominator. In this case, the fractions are $\frac{18}{24}$, $\frac{20}{24}$, and $\frac{15}{24}$, respectively. Since they are like fractions, their sum is $\frac{53}{24}$. So, the sum of $\frac{3}{4} + \frac{5}{6} + \frac{5}{8}$ is $\frac{53}{24}$, or $2\frac{5}{24}$.

Show that if we want to find the sum of $\frac{3}{4}$ and $\frac{5}{6}$, we add $\frac{9}{12}$ and $\frac{10}{12}$. If we want to find the sum of $\frac{3}{4}$ and $\frac{5}{8}$, we add $\frac{6}{8}$ and $\frac{5}{8}$. If we want to find the sum of $\frac{5}{6}$ and $\frac{5}{8}$, we add $\frac{20}{24}$ and $\frac{15}{24}$.

Now present the method of raising fractions to higher terms with common denominators. Point out that this process is a shortcut method of selecting the like fractions from sets of equal fractions without having to make the sets. Emphasize that the numbers represented by the fractions are not changed; only the names of the numbers are changed.

In Problem 2 of Exercise 7, you may want to point out the following shortcuts that can be used in some of the problems. Remember that a shortcut may take longer unless students are skilled in its use.

1. When the dividend and divisor are the same fraction, as in Problem 2d, we know at once that the quotient is 1, since the quotient of any number divided by itself is 1. For example, $3 \div 3 = 1$. $\frac{1}{3} \div \frac{1}{3} = 1$.

2. When the denominators are the same, as in Problem 2b, we may ignore the denominators and divide the first numerator by the second. For example, $\frac{3}{8} \div \frac{5}{8} = 3 \div 5 = \frac{3}{5}$.

3. When one denominator is a multiple of the other, as in Problem 2c, raise one of the fractions to higher terms so that the denominators will be the same; then divide the first numerator by the second. For example, $\frac{1}{2} \div \frac{1}{4} = \frac{2}{4} \div \frac{1}{4} = 2$.

4. When the divisor is a whole number and the numerator of the fraction is a multiple of the divisor, as in Problem 2e, divide the numerator by the divisor and write the result over the denominator. For example, $\frac{8}{11} \div 4 = \frac{2}{11}$.

5. When the divisor is a whole number and the numerator of the fraction is not a multiple of the divisor, as in Problem 2a, write the numerator over the product of the denominator and the divisor. For example, $\frac{3}{5} \div 3 = \frac{3}{5 \times 3} = \frac{3}{15}$, or $\frac{1}{5}$.

Encourage students to apply these two rough checks on the quotient to avoid giving an illogical answer to a division problem:

1. When the divisor is greater than 1, the quotient will be less than the dividend. For example, $8 \div 2 = 4$. Also, $\frac{8}{9} \div 2 = \frac{4}{9}$.

2. When the divisor is less than 1, the quotient will be greater than the dividend. For example, $2 \div \frac{1}{3} = 6$, and $\frac{2}{5} \div \frac{1}{3} = \frac{6}{5}$.

Correlated Drills for Accuracy and Speed. Drill 29 correlates with Exercise 6. The last two columns in Drill 30 correlate with Problem 2 of Exercise 7.

The use of Drill 31 should begin as soon as most students show mastery of the work in Drills 29 and 30. The use of Drills 29 and 30 should ordinarily be discontinued when Drill 31 is started.

Review 15. Problem 4 reviews finding weighted averages using average weekly receipts. Problem 5 reviews multiplying with fractions. Problem 6 is a related problem. It asks students to find the balance or amount remaining and it is related to finding the ending balance of a check register. Problem 7 reviews graduated piece-rate pay.

Calculator Clinic. The use of the calculator for multiplying and dividing fractions is presented at the end of Section 15.

SECTION 16. RATIO AND PROPORTION

Comments and Suggestions. In business mathematics the principal use made of ratios is in separating a quantity into two or more parts according to a given ratio, as in Problems 1 through 4 in Exercise 2. These are sometimes called problems in *partitive proportion*, although the proportion principle is not involved in solving them.

The quantity to be separated can be thought of as being divided into the number of equal parts represented by the sum of the terms in the ratio. If $3,000.00 is to be divided among three persons in the ratio $3:2:1$, the total amount can be thought of as being divided into 6 equal parts, of which the first person will receive 3 parts, or $\frac{1}{2}$ of the total, the second person 2 parts, or $\frac{1}{3}$ of the total, and the third person 1 part, or $\frac{1}{6}$ of the total.

Unitary Analysis Method of Solving Problems. The topics and exercise dealing with proportion are marked with a ‡, and they are provided for teachers who want to demonstrate this method of solving the problems or whose courses of study require the proportion method.

Problems in business mathematics that can be solved by proportion are usually solved by the method of *unitary analysis*. For many students, unitary analysis is simpler than the proportion method, and you may want to have your students use this method in solving the problems in Written Exercise 3.

In the process of unitary analysis, the first step is to find the weight of <u>one</u> foot of rope, the number of miles driven in <u>one</u> hour, the number of gallons of gasoline used in driving <u>one</u> mile, the amount of pay received for <u>one</u> hour, and so on. This result is then multiplied by the number of feet, hours, or miles in question.

In the use of the unitary analysis method, the solution of the problem in the example for finding the unknown term in a proportion would be:

$$\$64 \div 8 = \frac{\$64}{8} \text{ rate per hour}$$

$$24 \times \frac{\$64}{8} = \$192 \text{ would earn in 24 hours}$$

‡**Proportion Method of Solving Problems.** While solving the problems in Written Exercise 3 by the proportion method, students may have difficulty in setting the ratios correctly. A mechanical procedure that will usually assure correct ratios follows.

In every problem involving two ratios there are two kinds of quantities. In the example for the proportion topic, the quantities are numbers of hours and dollars of earnings. The ratio of the numbers of hours equals the ratio of dollars of earnings. To get the ratios, follow these steps:

	Hours	Earnings
1. Write "Hours" and "Earnings" as the headings of the two columns as shown at the right	**Hours**	**Earnings**
2. On the first line below the headings, insert the number of hours and the earnings of the first ratio.....................................	8	$64
3. On the second line, insert the number of hours and the earnings of the second ratio. Since the earnings are missing, insert *N* for the earnings.....................................	24	*N*
4. Draw a fraction bar between the numerals in both columns and insert an equal sign between the two ratios...................................	$\frac{8}{24}$ =	$\frac{\$64}{N}$
5. Write the cross products and find the missing factor	$8 \times N$ = $8N$ = N =	$24 \times \$64$ $\$1,536$ $\$1,536 \div 8,$ or $\$192$

When this procedure is used, the columns and lines do not have to be in the order shown. The columns or lines, or both, may be interchanged. The ratios may not be the same, but the cross products will be equal and the answer the same.

Review 16. Problem 4 reviews ratios by using common sizes, $3\frac{1}{2}$ and $5\frac{1}{4}$ inch, of microcomputer diskettes. Problem 5 reviews finding equivalent pay for the year and month. Problem 6 reviews weighted averages, and Problem 7 is an optional problem involving proportion.

SECTION 17. FIGURING OVERTIME PAY

Comments and Suggestions. In this section students learn how to figure gross pay on an hourly-rate and weekly-rate basis and to figure overtime rates and overtime hours. The calculations in this section use the mixed number of $1\frac{1}{2}$ to figure overtime rates and to lead into the thorough review of mixed numbers in Section 18.

These points should be emphasized:

1. Depending on the agreement between the employee or the union and an employer, the employee may be paid at an overtime rate or rates for time worked each week over a stated number of weekly hours, or for time worked each day over a stated number of daily hours.

2. Overtime is often paid at $1\frac{1}{2}$ times the regular hourly rate.

3. Some overtime may be paid at double-time rates.

In this textbook, where overtime is paid at the time-and-a-half rate, the overtime pay is figured by multiplying the number of overtime hours by the overtime *rate*, which is $1\frac{1}{2}$ times the regular hourly *rate*. Fractions of a cent in a time-and-a-half rate are *not* rounded or dropped. Double-time work is paid for at 2 times the hourly *rate*.

Another way of figuring overtime pay is to multiply the regular hourly rate by $1\frac{1}{2}$ times the number of overtime hours worked. Either way is acceptable, but students may become confused if you attempt to teach both ways of solving the problems.

Throughout this text, pay has been calculated to exceed the minimum prescribed by federal law at the time the textbook was printed.

Review 17. Problems 2–5 review selected fundamental skills. Problem 6 reviews the calculation of gross pay including overtime hours and overtime pay; Problem 7 reviews ratios. Problem 8 reviews weighted averages. Problem 9 is an optional problem in proportion.

Calculator Clinic. At the end of Section 17, students are shown how to use the memory feature of their calculator to figure total pay when overtime pay is involved. Point out that the calculator's memory is frequently useful for storing intermediate results or separate calculations that are combined to provide a total.

SECTION 18. MIXED NUMBERS

Comments and Suggestions. Section 18 is a review of the basic operations associated with mixed numbers.

The first example shows the computation of the product of $6\frac{5}{7}$ and 17. Multiply 17 by $\frac{5}{7}$ and 6 separately and add the results, because $6\frac{5}{7}$ represents $6 + \frac{5}{7}$ with the plus sign omitted.

In Written Exercise 1 the factor that is more convenient to use may be used as the multiplier, because multiplication is commutative for fractional numbers as well as for whole numbers.

To add mixed numbers, many of the students may have been taught the computational form shown at the right, or one similar to it. Students need not change to the form given in the text. The form in the text requires a little less writing and offers less chance for adding one of the denominators in finding the sum of the numerators.

$$
\begin{aligned}
4\tfrac{3}{4} &= 4\tfrac{6}{8} \\
+3\tfrac{3}{8} &= 3\tfrac{3}{8} \\
\hline
7\tfrac{9}{8} &= 8\tfrac{1}{8}
\end{aligned}
$$

The method of subtraction shown in the example for the solution of $120\frac{1}{4} - 6\frac{7}{8}$ is known as the *decomposition method*. Since we cannot subtract $\frac{7}{8}$ from $\frac{2}{8}$, we take 1 away from the whole-number part, 120, and add it as an equivalent fraction to the $\frac{2}{8}$. In other words, we rewrite $120\frac{2}{8}$ as the equivalent numeral, $119\frac{10}{8}$.

Some of your students may have been taught another method of subtraction, the *equal additions method*. This method is based on the principle that adding the same number to both the minuend and the subtrahend does not affect the difference. For example, $8 - 5 = 3$, and $(8 + 1) - (5 + 1) = 9 - 6 = 3$. The difference is the same because both the minuend and the subtrahend were increased by the same number, 1.

The solution of $120\frac{1}{4} - 6\frac{7}{8}$ by the equal additions method is shown at the right. We add 1 in the form of $\frac{8}{8}$ to $\frac{2}{8}$, giving $\frac{10}{8}$. We then offset this increase by adding 1 to the 6 in the number we are subtracting, giving a result of 7.

	8ths
	10
120	$\cancel{2}$
7	
$-\ \cancel{6}$	7
113	$\frac{3}{8} = 113\frac{3}{8}$

If your students have been taught this method, there is no need for them to change to the method in the text unless your syllabus requires it. One method is as good as the other.

The material that deals with changing mixed numbers to improper fractions prepares the student for upcoming work with multiplying or dividing with mixed numbers.

Correlated Drills for Accuracy and Speed. Drill 10 correlates with Exercise 2. One or two problems at a time would ordinarily be used from this drill for warm-up assignments.

Drill 11 correlates with Exercise 3, Drill 12 correlates with Exercise 5, and Drill 13 correlates with Exercise 6. One or two problems at a time would ordinarily be used from these drills for warm-up assignments.

Review 18. Problem 1 reviews the fundamental processes pertaining to fractions that have been covered in Unit 3 so far. Problems 2 and 3 review writing and using ratios to solve business problems. Problems 4 and 5 involve wage computations. Problem 4 reviews using a time card to find gross pay, and Problem 5 provides a review of piece-rate wages. Problem 6 is a bank reconciliation problem.

SECTION 19. FRACTIONAL RELATIONSHIPS

Comments and Suggestions. These four of the more common and less difficult types of problems involving fractional relationships are presented in Section 19:

1. Finding a part of a number.

2. Finding a number that is a part greater or smaller than another.

3. Finding what part a number is of another.

4. Finding what part a number is greater or smaller than another.

These two other types of fractional relationship problems are presented as optional material in Section 20:

1. Finding the whole when a part is known.

2. Finding the whole when an amount that is a part greater or smaller than the whole is known.

Mastery of the four (or six) types of problems in fractional relationships will increase understanding and reduce difficulties with the same kinds of problems in dealing with percent relationships in Sections 26 and 27.

Throughout Sections 26 and 27, many of the examples and problems are pay problems. Where other types of problems are used, they are well within the understanding and experience of students.

While teaching students to find a part of a number, you must stress the meaning of expressions such as "$\frac{1}{4}$ of," "$\frac{1}{3}$ as much as," "$\frac{3}{4}$ as great as," "$\frac{1}{5}$ larger than," "$\frac{2}{3}$ more than," "$\frac{1}{3}$ smaller than," "$\frac{1}{4}$ less than," "increased by $\frac{2}{3}$ of itself," "decreased by $\frac{1}{4}$ of itself," and so on. Each expression implies the multiplication of some number by the fraction.

Emphasize that the answer to every problem involving fractional relationships should be checked by showing that it satisfies the conditions expressed or implied in the statement of the problem.

For example, if 18 is the computed answer to the problem, "What number is $\frac{3}{4}$ of 24?," the answer would be checked by comparing 18 with 24. If the comparison shows that 18 is $\frac{3}{4}$ of 24 ($\frac{18}{24} = \frac{3}{4}$), the condition stated in the problem is satisfied. The correct answer, therefore, is 18.

If 80 is the computed answer to the problem, "What number is $\frac{2}{3}$ greater than 48?," the answer may be checked by showing (1) that 32 is $\frac{2}{3}$ of 48, the condition stated in the problem, or (2) that 80 is $\frac{5}{3}$ of 48, the condition implied in the problem.

Point out to students the similarity between the first and second types of problems. That is, finding a number that is a part greater or smaller than another is simply a problem in finding a part of a number, then adding that part to the number or subtracting that part from the number.

In finding what fractional part one number is of another, students often select the wrong numbers to represent the numerator and denominator. This is especially common when the problem consists of comparing one number to a smaller number. The tendency of many students is to use the smaller number as the numerator in all situations, regardless of the statement of the problem. Extensive practice should be provided in interpreting such problems and in expressing correctly the fractional relationships that the problems imply. In this connection, give particular attention to the material that explains checking the reasonableness of answers and to the problems of Exercise 5.

Finding what part one number is greater (or smaller) than another number is basically the same as the problem of finding what part one number is of another. It differs in that the difference of two numbers is compared to one of them. Emphasize the need for careful interpretation of the problem in order to select correctly the number that should be used as the denominator of the fraction.

Review 19. Problems 2 through 5 review the four fractional relationships introduced in Section 19. Problem 6 reviews simple averages. Problem 7 is an optional problem reviewing the topic of reconciliation statements with unrecorded checks and unrecorded deposits.

SECTION 20. MORE FRACTIONAL RELATIONSHIPS

Comments and Suggestions. This optional section is a continuation of problems in fractional relationships that were introduced in Section 19. These two types of problems are treated here:

1. Finding the whole when a part is known.

2. Finding the whole when an amount that is a part greater or smaller than the whole is known.

Students frequently have difficulty with these types of problems. Often students will solve these types of problems incorrectly because of inadequate analysis and failure to sense the relationships which such problems express or imply. Many students multiply when they should divide to solve these problems. Considerable emphasis should be given, therefore, to the examples and oral exercises of this section, because the students must know whether to multiply or divide the given number by the given fraction.

Impress on the students that the two types of problems presented in Exercises 3 through 7 are essentially problems in finding the unknown factor of a product. Show, for example, the basic similarity of problems such as "If $\frac{3}{4}$ of a number is 96, what is that number?" and "If $\frac{3}{4}$ of a day's pay is $48, what is the day's pay?" to the easy problem, "If 3 days' pay is $210, what is one day's pay?"

Exercises 5, 6, and 7 are a review of all six types of problems in fractional relationships. These exercises include some optional problems, so all of the exercises are marked optional. Appropriate problems should be used with all students. Use mental as well as oral drill with Exercise 5. Work on both exercises should be repeated to the point of mastery. Mastery of the six types of fractional relationships will aid students greatly in also mastering the related types of percent problems that are presented in the next unit. Furthermore, when the percent has a simple fractional equivalent, the problem is usually solved as a problem in fractional relationships by substituting the fraction for the percent.

Review 20. Problem 2 reviews how to find a weekly salary equivalent to a given monthly salary. Problem 3 reviews graduated piece-rate wages. Problem 4 requires the students to find a fractional part of a number.

Problems 5 through 8 are optional problems which review the two types of fractional relationships introduced in this section: finding the whole when a part is known, and finding the whole when a part greater or smaller is known.

Problems 9 and 10 are also optional problems. Problem 9 reviews reconciling a check register when a check and a deposit have not been recorded. Problem 10 reviews proportion.

Unit 4. Net Pay, Fringe Benefits, and Commission

In Unit 4 students learn to figure a variety of income problems, including computing FICA taxes, withholding taxes, and net pay; finding straight and graduated commissions; and computing salary and commissions. They also learn to compare jobs on the basis of fringe benefits and job expenses. These problems provide the setting and the practical application for learning how to solve six types of percent relationship problems, parallel to the six types of fractional relationships learned in Unit 3. A set of student objectives for the unit are found on the unit opener page.

Pretest for Unit 4. A pretest for the unit is provided in the test package (M473) and the MicroEXAM package.

Integrated Project for Unit 4. A project that integrates many of the skills and ideas presented in Units 3 and 4 is provided at the end of Unit 4 in the workbook. *Integrated Project 4* uses a small architectural firm as a vehicle for integrating the concepts discussed in the unit. The project includes a payroll sheet, a series of percentage analyses pertaining to employees and payroll, and a net job benefits comparison for one of the employees.

Vocabulary Review for Unit 4. A vocabulary exercise that reviews the terms discussed in Unit 4 is included at the end of Unit 4 in the workbook.

Supplementary Problems for Unit 4. Word problems similar to those found in Unit 4 are presented in the *Supplementary Problems for Unit 4* section of **Appendix B.**

Transparencies for Unit 4. Three transparency masters that may be used to illustrate important concepts in Unit 4 are provided in the teacher's edition of the workbook.

Test for Unit 4. A review, or posttest, for Unit 4 is provided in the test package (M473) and the MicroEXAM package.

Solutions for Unit 4. Solutions to all text problems, the pretest, and the unit test are included in this manual. Solutions to all workbook problems are included in the teacher's edition of the workbook.

Additional Resources for Unit 4. There are many useful sources of information pertaining to payroll taxes, wages, fringe benefits, and other related topics available to you from companies, organizations, and governmental agencies in your area.

1. The personnel manager for your school district and personnel offices of major firms in the community may provide current information on fringe benefits and job expenses which are commonly used in your area. Personnel offices at large firms typically provide employee-orientation brochures explaining payroll taxes, fringe benefits, union dues, and other matters to new employees. Ask for copies of these brochures.

   Developing a small library of these orientation booklets will prove useful. Students may browse in the library for career and job information. Also a business teacher in your building may give assignments which use the library to improve student knowledge pertaining to fringe benefits.

   These same sources may also provide copies of selected pages from payroll publications to provide current withholding tables and FICA tables for problem work.

2. Job counselors for the state employment service may be invited to class to discuss job comparisons with students. The job counselors will also have a great deal of first-hand knowledge of current job benefits and costs in the area.

3. The local office of the Social Security Administration is a good source of information pertaining to social security tax rates, maximum income taxed, and FICA tables.

4. The area office of the Internal Revenue Service is a good source of information pertaining to withholding taxes and withholding tax tables.

5. Local real estate and collection agencies are good sources of information pertaining to commission, including rates and graduated sales amounts.

6. Fuller, Robert W., Payroll Procedures, Ninth Edition, South-Western Publishing Co., 5101 Madison Road, Cincinnati, OH 45227, 1985. A text-workbook with many problems in computing payroll from time cards and completing the various forms for payroll.

7. Gossage, Loyce, Mathematics Skill Builder, South-Western Publishing Co., 5101 Madison Road, Cincinnati, OH 45227, 1985. A text-workbook which provides instruction in the fundamental processes and percentages.

8. Herr, N., Decimals and Percent—A Math Practice Booklet, New Jersey Vocational-Technical Curriculum Laboratory, Rutgers—The State University, Building 4103 Kilmer Campus, New Brunswick, NJ 08903, no date. A text-workbook covering the four operations, decimals and percents, the relationships among decimals, percents, and fractions, and the application of percents to interest and discount problems. The materials are primarily exercises and quizzes.

9. Percentages Tutorcourse, Opportunities for Learning, 20417 Nordhoff St., Dept. 9F, Chatsworth, CA 91311, no date. A software package which teaches about percentages, proportion, and ratio.

SECTION 21. DEDUCTIONS AND TAKE-HOME PAY

Comments and Suggestions. The deductions for federal withholding tax, social security tax, and some other common payroll deductions are covered in this section.

Students should know that the amount of withholding tax depends on one's marital status, total earnings, and the number of allowances claimed. The withholding tax table used in this section is for married persons who are paid weekly. The Internal Revenue Service (IRS) provides tables for varying pay periods, including biweekly and monthly, and for different marital statuses including single, married, and head of household. Most employers in your area have such tables. You may wish to obtain copies of pages from several tables to display on a bulletin board or to make into transparencies for discussion purposes.

Students should also know that the withholding tables are changed whenever the government changes the income tax rates. The table used in this section was taken from the tax-rate schedule in effect at the time.

It is also important that students recognize that the social security tax or FICA tax rate changes from time to time, as does the maximum amount of pay per year subject to the tax. The rate (7.65%) and base ($45,000) used in this section were in effect when this text was published. To be sure about both the withholding tax and FICA tax, you should check with your local IRS and Social Security offices.

Computer Clinic. The use of a spreadsheet to calculate total pay, deductions and net pay for a small department is presented in Sec21. The template contains the number of withholding allowances and other deductions for each employee. Students enter gross wages and federal income taxes using the table in

Illustration 21–2. The template also contains the formulas necessary to compute automatically the FICA tax deduction, total deductions, and net wages.

After students have entered the data and computed net wages, they are asked to answer a series of questions. They are also asked to enter a new amount for the FICA rate. The important point for students to realize is that the template allows them to play "what if" games with the FICA rate. That is, students can determine the impact of a change in the FICA rate on the department payroll quickly and easily. You might also point out that the template could be designed to treat factors other than the FICA rate as variables. For example, the hourly-wage rate may be treated as a variable.

SECTION 22. DECIMALS

Comments and Suggestions. The decimal rate of the FICA tax is used to introduce the section on decimals.

Students should recognize that a decimal is a number and that the decimal equivalent of a fractional numeral or a whole number numeral is just another way of expressing the original number. For example, 0.75 and $\frac{3}{4}$ name the same fractional number. Each is a numeral, but in different form. Also, 2.0 and 2 differ in form, but they name the same number.

A number line like the one that follows will help convey the idea that equivalent numerals name the same number.

You should explain that decimals are substitutes for fractions and are used to simplify calculations. It is simpler to find the cost of 345 tubes of toothpaste at \$1.28 by multiplying 345 × \$1.28 than multiplying 345 × \$$1\frac{28}{100}$, or \$$1\frac{7}{25}$. Also, we often get a better idea of the size of a number when it is shown as a decimal rather than a fraction. For example, if a ball player gets 73 hits out of 269 times at bat, the batting average is more clearly shown as 0.271 than $\frac{73}{269}$.

The important thing for students to understand is that equivalent numerals, although different in form, name the same number, and may be put into whatever form is the most convenient or best suited to the work that has to be done.

Multiplication by 0.1, 0.01, or 0.001. You might demonstrate on the chalkboard the derivation of the rule for multiplying by 0.1, 0.01, or 0.001 by showing the multiplication of 38.27 by 0.1, 0.01, and 0.001 by the regular multiplication process.

38.27	38.27	38.27
× 0.1	× 0.01	× 0.001
3.827	0.3827	0.03827

Point out that in each case the decimal point in the product is as many places to the left of the decimal point in the factor being multiplied as there are decimal places in the other factor. Use Exercise 4 in Section 22 for two or three days. Then regularly include multiplication by 0.1, 0.01, and 0.001 in the warmup drills through the use of Drill 22 in Appendix A.

If your class is using hand-held calculators, you may wish to demonstrate the movement of the decimal point when multiplying by 0.1, 0.01, and 0.001

by having students multiply 4,321 by all three decimal numbers. You may also wish to have students discover how to move the decimal point by having them multiply many several digit numbers first by 0.1, then by 0.01, and then by 0.001. When they are finished, students should be asked if they now know how to get the answer to such problems without using a calculator.

Division by 0.1, 0.01, or 0.001. Use the discussion in Section 22 of the text as a model to demonstrate the derivation of the rule. Show the division of 0.1234 by 0.1, 0.01, and 0.001 by the ordinary process of short division. Point out that the position of the decimal point in the quotient is as many places to the right of the decimal point in the dividend as there are decimal places in the divisor. Use Exercise 6 in Section 22 and Drill 23 in Appendix A the way Exercise 4 and Drill 22 were used.

Multiplication and Division by 10, 100, or 1,000 and by 0.1, 0.01, or 0.001. Students frequently become confused when the operations of multiplication and division by 10, 100, 1,000 and by 0.1, 0.01, and 0.001 are contained in the same problem, as they are in Drill 25 in Appendix A. Many students will move the decimal point correctly for multiplication by 10, 100, and 1,000 but they will make errors in the other three operations.

Students are more likely to choose the correct procedure if they keep these principles in mind:

1. A number is increased in value when the decimal point is moved to the *right*.
2. A number is decreased in value when the decimal point is moved to the *left*.
3. When the factor is more than 1, the product must be greater than the number being multiplied. Thus, when multiplying 34 by 10, the product (340) must be greater than 34. So, the decimal point must be moved to the right (see 1 above).
4. When the factor is less than 1, the product must be less than the number being multiplied. Thus, when multiplying 34 by 0.1, the product (3.4) must be less than 34. So, the decimal point must be moved to the left (see 2 above).
5. Since division is the reverse, or opposite, of multiplication, (when you divide by 10, 100, and 1,000 or by 0.1, 0.01, and 0.001) do the opposite of 1–4 above.
6. When the divisor is more than 1, the quotient must be less than the dividend. Thus, when you divide 34 by 10, the quotient (3.4) must be less than 34. So, the decimal point must be moved to the left.
7. When the divisor is less than 1, the quotient must be more than the dividend. Thus, when you divide 34 by 0.1, the quotient (340) must be more than 34. So, the decimal point must be moved to the right.

Calculator Clinic. The use of a hand-held calculator to convert fractions to decimals is covered at the end of Section 22 in the calculator clinic.

Correlated Drills for Accuracy and Speed. Drill 22 in Appendix A correlates with Exercise 4 in Section 22. Drill 23 correlates with Exercise 6. These drills can be discontinued when Drill 24 is started.

Drill 24 in Appendix A provides a review of multiplication and division by 0.1, 0.01, and 0.001. The use of Drill 24 should begin as soon as most students show mastery of the work in Drills 22 and 23.

Drill 25 in Appendix A provides a review of multiplication and division by 10, 100, and 1,000, and by 0.1, 0.01, and 0.001. The use of Drill 25 should begin as soon as most students have mastered the work in Drills 21 and 24. The use of Drills 21 and 24 is usually discontinued when Drill 25 is started.

SECTION 23. FRINGE BENEFITS AND JOB EXPENSES

Comments and Suggestions. This section provides instruction in calculating the fringe benefits and expenses associated with a job and comparing one job with another on the basis of the net job benefits of each job.

Students should recognize that the dollar value of some fringe benefits and some job expenses cannot be calculated exactly and must be estimated. For example, when a field sales representative is provided with a company car, the representative might calculate the value of this fringe benefit in at least two ways. First, the value of the fringe benefit might be determined by finding the cost of operating the salesperson's other car, if there is one. Next, the cost of leasing a comparable car might be calculated and used as the value of the fringe benefit.

It is also important for students to understand that gross pay is an inaccurate basis for comparing one job to another, because both the value of fringe benefits and the expenses associated with a job may be substantial. Students are taught to use the total job benefits less job expenses, or the net job benefits, as the basis for comparison. Students should also understand that comparing one job to another on the basis of economic value alone is insufficient. Other features of the jobs may be much more important; for example, job security, job duties, and the chances for promotion and raises may have a great deal of influence on total job value.

Students often will be surprised at the substantial value of fringe benefits. You should point out that these fringe benefits are a cost to the employer. The cost of fringe benefits must be recovered by raising the price of the products sold or by reducing the profit of the owners. One result of higher prices might be that sales fall and that employees are laid off. Another result might be that not enough profit is available to reinvest in the business to keep it modern. The business may then lose its competitive advantage and fail.

Exercise 1 provides problems in which fringe benefits and total job benefits are computed. Exercise 2 provides problems in which job expenses and net job benefits are found. Exercise 3 provides problems in which jobs are compared in terms of their economic value.

Computer Clinic. The use of a spreadsheet to compute the net job benefits for two jobs is presented at the end of Section 23. Students enter the hourly rate of pay, the pension rate, and the dollar amounts for other job benefits and job expenses. Once students complete Question 3a, they are asked to find what hourly rate of pay for Job #1 would bring the net job benefits of Job #1 to within $1.00 of the net job benefits of Job #2 (Question 3b). Then they are to enter a different hourly rate of pay for Job #1 (Question 3c) and a different pension rate for Job #2 (Question 3d). The simplest way to accomplish this task is to have students repetitively enter hourly rates of pay until they reach their goal.

Once again, students should recognize the real power of a spreadsheet: the ability to make changes in the data and see the impact of those changes immediately. You should point out that when students enter the new hourly and pension rates, they are simulating different job conditions. Thus, *the spreadsheet allows you to simulate a variety of job conditions to help you make a job decision.*

SECTION 24. PERCENTS

Comments and Suggestions. Percents are sometimes more useful and convenient than fractions and decimals. Students' grades, salespersons' commissions, interest rates, discounts, and other numbers are often expressed as percents rather than fractions or decimals.

You may find the following number line helpful in showing students the equivalence of fractions, decimals, and percents.

Stephen J. Cutney, who teaches at Mt. Vernon High School in New York, uses the conversion box shown below to review how to convert fractions, decimals, and percents. Students are asked to find the two elements in each problem that are missing. The box helps students review the conversion rules and recognize that each of the three elements represent the same number differently. The first problem is completed to provide an example for students.

		Conversion Box		
No.	Fraction		Decimal		Percent
Ex.	$\frac{5}{8}$	=	0.625	=	62.5%
1.		=		=	12%
2.		=	0.8	=	
3.	$\frac{3}{4}$	=		=	
4.		=	1.5	=	
5.		=		=	8%

Each conversion operation described in Section 24 of the text is introduced according to the principle that a percent represents a fraction with a denominator of 100. So, fractions and decimals are changed to percents by expressing them as fractions with denominators of 100. Likewise, percents are changed to decimals and fractions by expressing the percents as fractions with denominators of 100. Once this concept is shown, the shortcut procedures for each type of conversion are presented.

The theory underlying changing a percent to a decimal is presented by showing that $25\% = \frac{25}{100} = 0.25$. In practice, we use the shortcut method; that is, we drop the percent sign and move the decimal point two places to the left.

When teaching students how to change a fraction to a percent, you should point out that any fraction, even if its denominator is a factor of 100, can be changed to a percent by dividing the numerator by the denominator. So, instead of showing $\frac{4}{5}$ as the fraction $\frac{80}{100}$ to get 80%, 4 may be divided by 5, and the resulting decimal, 0.8, may be changed to 80%. The student should use the method that is most convenient.

Changing a percent to a decimal is important to the first topic in Section 25, finding a percent of a number, because a percent numeral cannot be used as a factor. We have to replace the percent with an equivalent decimal or fraction before we can figure the product.

The use of percents in calculating is limited. We can add, subtract, multiply, and divide percents. However, we usually have to change a percent to decimal form to use it as a factor or divisor. This is one of the reasons students must learn how to convert percents to decimals.

Calculator Clinic. The use of a hand-held calculator to change fractions to percents is covered at the end of Section 24 in the calculator clinic.

Correlated Drills for Accuracy and Speed. Drill 32 in **Appendix A** correlates with Exercise 2. Drill 33 correlates with Exercise 5. Problems 1–10 in Drill 34 correlate with Exercise 6 and Problems 11–20 correlate with Exercise 7.

SECTION 25. MORE PERCENTS

Comments and Suggestions. Finding what percent one number is of another has many applications in business mathematics. This skill should be mastered by students. Basically, it is the same as finding what part one number is of another, but with the fraction expressed as a percent.

Emphasize the fact that the numerator may be greater than the denominator and the result greater than 100%. The number line shown in the manual under **Comments and Suggestions** for Section 24 will be helpful in developing the idea of percents greater than 100%.

Special emphasis should be given to Exercise 2. Students should be drilled frequently on the problems in this exercise.

The fractional equivalents of parts of 100% shown in the table in Section 25 are useful only if they are memorized and can be recalled immediately. If the fractional equivalent of $37\frac{1}{2}$%, for example, cannot be recalled, there is no point in computing it and then multiplying by the resulting fraction, $\frac{3}{8}$. It is simpler to multiply at once by the decimal equivalent, 0.375. Drill 35 in Appendix A can be used to provide students with practice in using each of the fractional equivalents shown in the table.

Stress doing all multiplication by 1%, 10%, 100%, and 1,000% mentally, placing the answer on paper only.

Emphasize the difference in the meanings of $\frac{1}{4}$ and $\frac{1}{4}$%. Show that the fraction and the fractional percent represent two different numbers. For example, $\frac{1}{4} = 0.25$; $\frac{1}{4}$% means $\frac{1}{4}$ of 1%, or $\frac{1}{4} \times 0.01$, or 0.0025. Point out that $\frac{1}{4}$ is 100 times the number represented by $\frac{1}{4}$%.

Exercise 6 and Exercise 8 should be repeated several times for initial mastery. Drills 36 and 38 in **Appendix A** can then be used regularly in the warm-up assignments.

Calculator Clinic. How to use a hand-held calculator to find a percent of a number and to find what percent a number is of another is presented at the end of Section 25. The calculator practice assignments are designed so students will not have to multiply or divide by a percent that contains a fraction that does not convert evenly into a decimal. If you wish to have students complete all of Exercise 3, explain to them how to state answers such as 16.666666% and 33.333333% ($16\frac{2}{3}$% and $33\frac{1}{3}$%).

If you want students to complete Column 2 of Exercise 5, you must show them how to multiply or divide by percents which contain fractions that are not evenly converted into decimal form. For example, in Problem e in Column 2 of Exercise 5, students are asked to multiply $36.75 by $166\frac{2}{3}$%. Students must enter 166.67, or 166.66666, or 166.66667, and round off the answer to the nearest cent. The answers will be 61.251225, 61.249997, and 61.250001, respectively. In other words, because students must enter an approximation of one factor, they will get an approximation of the correct product.

Alternatively, you might teach students to solve the problem exactly. To do this, students must complete several steps: (1) multiply by 166 and add the result to memory, (2) multiply by 2 and divide that product by 3, (3) add the result to memory, and (4) display the contents of the memory register.

Correlated Drills for Accuracy and Speed. Drill 35 in **Appendix A** correlates with Exercise 4. Drills 36 and 38 correlate with Exercises 6 and 8, respectively.

Drill 37 relates to the work on percents, but it is not correlated with any problems in the text. It requires the use of the short method of multiplying by 1, 10, 100, and 1,000 in the multiplication of percents. In each case, the percent is mentally changed to a decimal, and the decimal is then multiplied mentally by $1, $10, etc. When there is a fraction in the percent, the student should mentally substitute 5 for $\frac{1}{2}$, 25 for $\frac{1}{4}$, etc., then move the decimal point mentally and write the answer, rounded to the nearest cent. Use this drill as a warmup assignment.

SECTION 26. PERCENT RELATIONSHIPS

Comments and Suggestions. Finding the percent of increase or decrease is a problem students will encounter often in business situations. In comparing amounts from different periods of time, students should know that the amount from the earlier period is usually the base. This week's sales, for example, would usually be compared with last week's sales, not last week's sales with this week's.

Problems that ask students to find a number that is a percent greater or smaller than another number (for example, what is 25% more than 32?) can be solved more quickly by adding or subtracting the percentages to or from the base and multiplying. For example, to find what number is 25% greater than 32, students could multiply by 1.25. To find the number that is 25% less than 32, students could multiply by 0.75. Alternative methods were purposely not presented in this section so that students would not be confused. These methods are presented later in the text. If you think your students can handle more than one method for solving these types of problems, you may wish to present them in Section 26.

Calculator Clinic. The use of a hand-held calculator to find a number which is a percent greater or smaller than another number, and to find what percent one number is greater or smaller than another number, is presented at the end of Section 26.

‡SECTION 27. MORE PERCENT RELATIONSHIPS

Comments and Suggestions. This entire section is marked as optional. The use of material marked with a double dagger is explained in the **Challenge Problems** section found in **The Textbook Plan** portion of this manual.

Finding a number when a percent of it is known often gives students trouble, because they multiply the number by the percent regardless of the relationship which the problem states or implies. To help students overcome this trouble, you should emphasize the principles of percent relationships discussed on the first page of Section 27.

Exercise 1 provides intensive practice in deciding if you should or should not multiply the known number by the percent. This exercise should be repeated often to impress the fact that only the number which is the whole may be multiplied by the percent.

Problems of this type are usually solved by the unknown factor method; that is, students divide the product by the known factor. However, some students may find the method of unitary analysis easier to understand. This method consists of two steps. First, students find 1% of the unknown number. Next, students multiply that result by 100 to find 100% of the number. Using this method, the first problem in Exercise 2, "25% × ? = $120," would be solved this way:

Step 1   1% of the unknown number = $120 ÷ 25 = $4.80
Step 2   100% of the unknown number = 100 × $4.80 = $480

Exercise 6 provides a review of all six types of percent relationships, including the two optional types. After it has been used for drill, Exercise 6 can be used as a test. A five to ten minute test should be given on this exercise every week or two, and one should also be given on the related exercises reviewing the six types of fractional relationships (Exercises 5 and 6, found at the end of Section 20). When using Exercises 5 and 6 in Section 20 as tests, you may have the students solve the problems mentally and write only the answers on their papers, or you may have them show their calculations so you may diagnose their difficulties.

SECTION 28. COMMISSION

Comments and Suggestions. This section provides practical applications to the students on the ideas presented in the preceding sections on percent relationships. Commission rate problems provide an application for finding a percent of a number. Problems that involve finding the rate of commission provide a practical setting for finding what percent one number is of another. Finding the amount of sales, given the commission and the rate of commission, is a practical application of finding the whole when a percent of it is known.

Point out that graduated commissions serve as incentives to salespeople to increase sales, since higher sales levels carry higher rates of commission.

Emphasize that the rate of commission is always based on sales. So, the rate of commission is found by dividing the amount of commission by the amount of sales. The amount of commission is the product of the rate of commission and the sales. So, when the amount of sales is an unknown factor, the amount of the sales equals the commission divided by the rate of commission.

Calculator Clinic. The use of a hand-held calculator to find gross wages from salary plus commission and from graduated commissions is presented at the end of Section 28.

SECTION 29. AGENT'S COMMISSION

Comments and Suggestions. The work with agent's commissions provides additional practical applications of percentage concepts. The section provides nothing new arithmetically.

Computer Clinic. The application of a spreadsheet to a real estate sales chart is presented. Students learn to enter sale prices and vary commission rates to compute individual and total gross sales, commissions, and net proceeds.

Unit 5. Metric Measurement

In Unit 5, students review the system of metric measures that they have learned through previous study. In their review of metrics, students do not have to make conversions to either system, metric or Customary. As with other topics in this text, problems using metrics are integrated with subsequent units in the text and are included in review assignments. Students who have not had a chance to study metrics will find the material easy to follow, because an introductory approach that develops basic concepts is used.

Basic Metric Concepts. Although each metric measure has its own basic unit, there are several general items that apply to the measures of length, area, capacity, and weight.

1. The symbols for metric names are written with a small letter, except for the liter, which uses the symbol L.

2. A space, instead of a comma, is used to divide groups of three numerals in the metric system, including numbers less than 1 (Examples: 24 000 m or 0.446 5 L). (Note that a zero precedes the decimal point to show the absence of a significant digit to the left of the decimal point.)

3. The subdivisions of the basic units in the metric system are consistently designated by the Latin prefixes **milli, centi,** and **deci;** the multiples are designated by the Greek prefixes **deka, hecto,** and **kilo.**

4. The metric system is a decimal system, so conversion from one unit to another can be done easily by moving the decimal point. Addition, subtraction, multiplication, and division of metric values can be processed in the same way as decimal values.

5. Students should learn the simple equivalencies given in the text to gain an understanding of how metric measures relate to the more familiar Customary measures.

Integrated Project for Unit 5. A project that utilizes the various metric measurements is provided at the end of Unit 5 in the workbook. In *Integrated*

Project 5, students read sample office supply catalog entries and make calculations involving metric measurements.

Vocabulary Review for Unit 5. A vocabulary exercise, *Vocabulary Review: Unit 5*, is found at the end of Unit 5 in the workbook. The exercise reviews 16 of the vocabulary terms presented in Unit 5 of the textbook.

Supplementary Problems for Unit 5. Eight word problems similar to those provided in the exercises for Unit 5 are presented in the *Supplementary Problems for Unit 5* section of **Appendix B.**

Correlated Drills for Accuracy and Speed. Drills 14 through 17 in Appendix B provide extra practice in addition, subtraction, multiplication, and division of metric values. If you select specific problems within the drills, the students may partially complete them after each section. The drills may also be used as a comprehensive review after the study of Unit 5 has been completed.

Test for Unit 5. A review test for Unit 5 is provided in the test package (M473) and the MicroEXAM package. The test is designed to measure student achievement of the learning objectives for Unit 5.

You can determine the amount of post-test review or remediation necessary through a careful analysis of the student answers to test questions.

Solutions for Unit 5. Solutions to all text problems and the unit test are included in this manual. Solutions to all workbook problems are included in the teacher's edition of the workbook.

Additional Resources for Unit 5. Various mathematics textbooks contain information on metrics. Helpful information about metric measurements and activities can be found in these sources:

1. Metric Guide for Educational Materials, American National Metric Council, 1625 Massachusetts Ave., N.W., Washington, D.C. 20036, 1977. A handbook for educators on the metric system.

2. Think Metric in Business Education, Illinois Business Education Association, 1976. Contains ideas about teaching metrics and a listing of film and print materials on metrics.

3. Think Metric, South-Western Publishing Co., 5101 Madison Road, Cincinnati, OH 45227, 1975. A text-workbook on the metric system for secondary students.

SECTION 30. LENGTH

Point out to students that, as is also true in the Customary system, only certain units of length are commonly used. These include the millimeter, centimeter, meter, and kilometer.

To help students think in metric terms, you might have them list the various places where they have seen measures of length stated in metric terms. Students may also measure their height, or the length and width of a book cover, sheet of paper, desk, door, or classroom, to gain an understanding of metric measures of length.

Other general approximations may also be given to the students. For example, you can tell them that the wire in a paper clip is about 1 millimeter in diameter. A paper clip is about 1 centimeter wide, and an aspirin tablet is about 1 centimeter in diameter. A yardstick is slightly less than a meter long, and a kilometer is about $\frac{5}{8}$ of a mile long.

SECTION 31. AREA

The basic metric concepts also apply to measures of area. Students should know that the common measures of area used are the square centimeter and the square meter. For large areas of land, students should use hectares for acres and square kilometers for square miles.

To build student confidence in using the metric system, you must continue to relate metric and Customary measures. To do this, you might have students measure familiar surfaces using metric and Customary rulers and find their area. You will also need to explain and stress the use of the exponent "2" to designate square measures. The fact that metric square units are 100 times, or one-hundredth of, the next unit of measure will also require explanation.

SECTION 32. CAPACITY AND WEIGHT

The basic metric concepts also apply to measures of capacity and weight. To help students think in metric terms, you may give them these approximations: a gram is a little more than the weight of a paper clip; a kilogram is about 2 pounds; a metric ton is about 10% larger than a short ton, which represents a weight of 2,000 pounds; 5 milliliters make up one teaspoon; a liter is slightly larger than a quart.

As an optional assignment, students could locate and list items sold in stores where capacity and weight measures are given in metric as well as Customary terms.

Unit 6. Budgeting and Buying

In Unit 6, students learn a variety of ways in which they can spend and buy more effectively. For example, they learn about budgeting and they learn how to figure the totals of sales slips, electric bills, gas bills, water bills, and phone bills. They learn to compare prices for products and to compare the costs of renting and buying products. They also learn to find the net savings and payback periods for many energy reduction products and procedures.

The specific objectives for Unit 6 are listed on the unit opener page.

Integrated Project for Unit 6. The integrated project for Unit 6 lets students see how a young couple might complete a spending plan, figure energy costs, figure the savings on energy-saving devices, check bills, compare prices, and compare renting against buying.

Vocabulary Review for Unit 6. A vocabulary exercise that reviews the terms in Unit 6 is included at the end of Unit 6 in the workbook.

Supplementary Problems for Unit 6. Word problems similar to those found in Unit 6 are presented in the *Supplementary Problems for Unit 6* section of **Appendix B.**

Transparencies for Unit 6. Several transparency masters drawn from the illustrations in Unit 6 are provided in the teacher's edition of the workbook.

Test for Unit 6. A review test for Unit 6 is provided in the test package (M473) and the MicroEXAM package.

Solutions for Unit 6. Solutions to all text problems and the unit test are included in this manual. Solutions to all workbook problems are included in the teacher's edition of the workbook.

Additional Resources for Unit 6.

1. Community salespeople and business owners can be useful sources of sales slips and invoices that are used in the community. These invoices can be duplicated for use in exercises or for display in class. Community businesses may also provide copies of sales tax tables that are used at local sales counters.

2. Cooperative education students who are using cash registers on the job or cash register operators might be invited to address the class about making change, using cash registers, encountering problems with customers, and learning about careers in retail sales.

3. Your water, telephone, and power companies usually provide brochures explaining their bills, how to read and check them, and how to reduce the cost of their services by conserving energy, conserving water, or telephoning at the right time. These brochures are excellent reading material for students. Also, the companies will usually furnish representatives to address the class on energy- and cost-saving measures. For example, local offices of the Illinois Power Company provide a variety of materials, including National Energy Watch brochures, that explain energy bills and show the average cost of using various appliances.

    Local telephone companies usually provide many educational resources for teachers at no cost. These resources may include classroom speakers, teaching aids, computer simulations, decision-making activities, and career awareness programs. Contact your local telephone company for a description of the services available in your area.

4. Money Management Institute of Household International, 2700 Sanders Road, Prospect Heights, IL 60070. The Institute provides brochures, booklets, and many other resources concerning wise buying and budgeting.

5. Consumer Reports, Consumers Union of U.S., Inc., 256 Washington St., Mount Vernon, NY 10553. This is a monthly magazine featuring articles relating to budgeting and buying. The subscription department's address is Box 53009, Boulder, CO 80321.

6. Selected U.S. Government Publications, Superintendent of Documents, U.S. Government Printing Office, Washington, D.C. 20402. This is a catalogue of government brochures and books, including materials on budgeting, buying, telephone use, and energy conservation and costs.

SECTION 33. PLANNING A BUDGET

Comments and Suggestions. The monthly cash record summary shown in Illustration 33–2 is related to the cash receipts and cash payments records discussed in Unit 1. The monthly summary provides information for budget planning, so introducing it at the beginning of Section 33 will allow you to take a logical approach to a discussion of budget planning and the problems which follow.

When discussing budgeting with students, you may want to emphasize that budgeting is a relatively simple process of looking back and ahead, then converting needs and wants into plans expressed in dollars and/or percents. Budgets should be designed to maximize a person's needs and wants and to help people and organizations get the most out of their income. Budgets need not be standardized, but they should be designed to fit the needs of each person or business.

The problems in Exercises 1 and 2 focus on typical personal or business situations. They are problems which require finding a fraction or a percent of a number, or finding what fraction or percent a number is of another.

Computer Clinic. The computer clinic for Section 33 uses a template that automatically generates dollar amounts for all payments once the dollar amount of net income and the percents for each payment are entered. Students are asked to enter these data and answer questions about the completed budget. They are then asked to vary net income and some percents.

SECTION 34. CHECKING SALES SLIPS

Comments and Suggestions. In this section the methods of calculating and checking extensions, subtotals, sales taxes, and totals on sales slips are presented. An explanation of making change is also presented. The extensions included in the problems require students to multiply by whole numbers and decimals. The method of finding extensions with fractions is presented in the next two sections.

Students should understand that sales slips and the terms used on the slips vary from firm to firm and location to location. Students might be asked to bring one or more sales slips from local stores to class. If transparencies of selected sales slips are made and shown to the class, students can compare the various forms of sales slips. They may also be asked to identify which sales slips are the easiest and the most difficult to read. You should also discuss various abbreviations used for quantities, such as doz., pr., rm. (ream), and gr. (gross).

Students should also understand that sales tax rates vary with location and may be changed by a government at any time. Students should recognize that some levels of government levy sales taxes on all sales while others charge a sales tax on only certain types of products. Some levels of government charge a sales tax on services; others do not.

Sales clerks are usually provided with sales tax tables. Copies of these tables may be obtained from local stores and displayed in class. You may even want to duplicate the tables and have students use them to solve the problems in Section 34.

Ordinarily, clerks count change to customers beginning with the smallest denomination. However, when electronic cash registers are used and the amount of change is displayed by the register, clerks may count change beginning with the largest denomination and continuing until the amount of change given equals the amount shown in the register display.

You may wish to have students with some retailing work experience share with the class their experiences with making change, writing sales slips, making errors, and observing the habits of customers.

Calculator Clinic. The calculator clinic is designed to show students how to use the memory key to store extensions. This function makes it possible to obtain the subtotal automatically as a by-product of finding the extensions. You should make certain that students understand they must round off any extensions that contain fractions of a cent. To do this, students should round off mentally and key the rounded amount into the calculator before adding it to the memory register.

While this calculator clinic only shows students how to check sales slips, the calculator can also be applied to Exercises 1–3 and 5–6 in Section 34. However, these exercises only require students to find extensions, sales taxes, and totals. They do not require students to check a complete sales slip. Additional practice in this skill can be found in the workbook.

SECTION 35. FIGURING EXTENSIONS

Comments and Suggestions. This section continues to develop the topic of figuring and checking extensions, emphasizing extensions in which (a) the quantity is a fraction of a unit, (b) the quantity is a mixed number, and (c) the price is for a large quantity. These three types of problems are practical applications of the fraction, mixed number, and decimal concepts that have been reviewed in previous sections.

When fractions are used in quantities or prices, the cost of the purchase often ends in a fraction of a cent. This fraction of a cent is treated in various ways. Many store owners treat any fraction of a cent as an additional cent. Many others take the additional cent only if the fraction is one half or greater. These store owners assume that in the long run, losses suffered from rounding down will be offset by the gains made from rounding up. Students should be reminded that in this text, all answers and all extensions of individual items on sales slips are rounded to the nearest cent.

Multiplying by mixed-number quantities requires that the student multiply the price by a fractional quantity and a whole-number quantity. Students may need to review Section 18 if they are having difficulty with mixed numbers.

Many commodities are priced by the hundred or thousand, the hundred pounds (hundredweight), and by the Customary and metric ton. Finding the cost of goods priced in these quantities is a business application of the principles of dividing by 10, 100, and 1,000 that were presented in Section 12.

To find the price of purchases in large quantities, students must understand the meanings of the special symbols used for those quantities. Students may find that knowledge of the origin of these symbols may be helpful in recalling them. The capital C is the Roman numeral for 100, and the M is the Roman numeral for 1,000. In the abbreviation for hundredweight (cwt), the "c" stands for 100 and the "wt" is for weight.

Correlated Drill for Accuracy and Speed. Drill 28 in Appendix A provides practice in finding the cost of items priced in large quantities.

SECTION 36. SHORTCUTS TO FIGURING EXTENSIONS

Comments and Suggestions. In Section 36, the use of exact fractional parts of $1.00 to figure extensions is presented. Exact fractional parts of 100% were presented in Section 25, so the ideas are not new to students. However, you may want to emphasize the nature of exact fractional parts of both $1.00 and 100%; that is, $1.00 and 100% can be divided by these parts exactly, with no remainder.

Exact fractional parts of $1.00 and 100% can be very helpful to students when they are figuring extensions multiplying by fractions. The parts usually permit the calculation of an answer mentally. However, the parts are only useful if the student can quickly recall these fractional equivalents.

The exact fractional parts included in Illustration 36–1 are those that are most common and useful in business operations. Sixths, twelfths, fifteenths, and sixteenths are not included in the table.

Some students may prefer to use the following steps to think through extensions using exact fractional parts of $1.00:

$$12\tfrac{1}{2}\cent = \tfrac{1}{8} \text{ of } \$1$$

$$16 \times \$1 = \$16$$

$$\tfrac{1}{8} \text{ of } \$16 = \$2$$

Correlated Drills for Accuracy and Speed. You may wish to use the exercises in Section 36 as part of your daily drills during coverage of later sections. Additional drill materials on exact fractional parts of $1.00 are provided in Drills 39–43 of Appendix A. Also, Drill 44 provides practice with combinations of exact fractional parts of $1.00.

SECTION 37. FIGURING UNIT PRICES

Comments and Suggestions. Section 37 presents the problems surrounding finding unit prices when items are priced as a group, or sold in fractional or mixed number quantities. Section 38 applies what has been learned in this section to comparison shopping.

Students should understand that buying in large quantities usually results in the lowest unit cost. However, sometimes they may find that buying two or more small quantities of an item is less expensive than one large quantity. The wise shopper does not assume that large size means the best buy; the wise shopper always compares unit prices. Problem 4 in Exercise 3 provides students with an example of a small quantity of an item having the lowest unit cost.

Many stores, especially food stores, are posting unit prices on their shelves so customers can easily compare prices of one product against others. When unit prices are not posted, however, the buyer has to figure the unit price. Also, when special sales or coupons are provided, the buyer should calculate the unit prices to ensure that these special sales and coupons have been reflected in the unit prices shown on the shelf listings.

The procedure for figuring unit prices is simple: divide the price by the quantity, whether the quantity is a whole number, a fraction, a decimal, or a mixed number. Calculations are often made difficult, however, by the odd amounts in which goods are packaged, such as 42 oz., 1 lb. 2 oz., and so on. The terms often used by sellers to describe package sizes, such as "giant," "family," or "economy," are unreliable guides to unit cost or value.

When figuring unit prices from group prices, students must round any remaining fraction to the next cent because, by custom, that is what most merchants will do. When figuring unit cost for prices given in fractions, decimals, or mixed numbers, however, round to the nearest cent.

You may wish to have students bring ads for products priced as a group, or for products sold in fractional or mixed number quantities that they find in the local newspapers. These ads can be placed on the bulletin board or displayed on the overhead projector. Students can then use the ads to compute the unit prices of real products.

Metrics. Much of the work in this section is designed to apply the procedures for using fractions and mixed numbers that students have previously reviewed. Because fractions and mixed numbers are seldom used with metrics, most of the quantities in this section are stated in Customary measures.

SECTION 38. BUYING WISELY

Comments and Suggestions. Section 38 applies what has been learned in Section 37. Buying wisely usually means comparing prices, and comparing prices often means finding the unit prices of each item.

You may wish to have students bring to class ads that show items selling at reduced prices or at discounts. Ask students to figure the percent of discount on the items. The percent saved in buying at reduced prices is a percent of the original price before the reduction is taken. To figure the percent saved, the savings should be divided by the higher, or original, price.

If any students have after-school jobs or cooperative work-experience jobs, ask them if they get an employee discount. Have your class use the information about employee discounts to figure savings on items available for sale at the place where the students with jobs work. Student discounts and senior citizen discounts also could be discussed and illustrated with one or more problems if students are interested.

Have students compare the cost of renting or buying items such as TV sets, chain saws, and motorcycles by using local newspaper ads to get information on renting and buying these items.

Computer Clinic. The computer clinic for Section 38 uses a spreadsheet that accepts data for weekly, daily, and hourly rental fees, and the cost of an item. The template generates the number of weeks, days, and hours of rental fees needed to equal or exceed the cost of the item. Students are asked to enter data for a snowblower and then answer questions about the information generated. They are then asked to enter new data for the fees and item cost and answer more questions.

SECTION 39. CHECKING ENERGY COSTS

Comments and Suggestions. Many power companies apply a fuel adjustment rate to the total number of kilowatt-hours used by an electricity customer. Most of the fuel adjustment rates used in this section reflect increased fuel costs to the company and result in an increased electric bill. If you are in an area in which companies do not charge fuel adjustment fees, you may wish to eliminate this step from the problems.

Many power companies also charge gas customers on the basis of the heat they supply in therms, rather than the gas they supply in cubic feet. Again, if power companies do not use therms in your area, you may wish to have students omit this step in the problems.

Gas and electric rates vary with the type of customer, such as business customers, residential customers, and other special customers. Special discounts are often given for senior citizens, after-hours usage, and different seasons of the year. Also, some companies charge a facilities-use fee for the use of their equipment and lines. To help students learn about the rates of their own companies, you should ask them to bring in copies of their families' power bills for discussion or display.

Power companies have rate schedules that they will give you on request. These local power schedule rates may be used as substitutes for the rates given in the problems.

You may wish to have students read the electric and gas meters at their homes or at school.

SECTION 40. REDUCING ENERGY COSTS

Comments and Suggestions. Students should understand that saving energy does not have to cost anything. In fact, many of the most effective energy-saving measures involve simply changing the way energy is used—changing habits. Turning down the thermostat to 68 degrees in the winter or up to 78 degrees in the summer saves an estimated 3% of fuel costs for each degree that the thermostat is reset. Of course, a variety of energy-saving products can be bought or products which use wind, solar, coal, or other forms of energy can be used.

This section contains problems involving no-cost measures as well as the purchase of energy-saving materials and equipment. When products are bought, students are taught to evaluate their economic effectiveness by using a net savings approach and an economic payback period approach.

Students should understand that year-to-year comparisons of energy usage are difficult because weather plays such an important part in the consumption of energy. Longer periods of time, such as ten or fifteen years, provide a more accurate basis for comparison.

Your local power company will usually provide you with pamphlets and brochures on energy-saving practices and products that the class might find helpful. These materials frequently provide estimates of the savings to be gained from the practices and products. Also, the U.S. Department of Housing and Urban Development, 451 Seventh St., S.W., Washington, D.C. 20410, provides a brochure, entitled "Be An Energy Miser in Your Home," that explains how a building owner may reduce energy bills through conservation and wise purchasing.

Computer Clinic. The computer clinic for Section 40 uses a spreadsheet that computes the amount saved and the payback period when data on the estimated energy costs, the estimated percent saved, and the cost of the energy device are entered. The spreadsheet can be used to provide answers for the questions and to compare the payback periods of many products that are advertised locally.

SECTION 41. CHECKING AND REDUCING WATER COSTS

Comments and Suggestions. You may wish to have students bring in actual water bills for discussion. You can then substitute the rates from these local bills for some of the rates used in the text.

You might also obtain brochures on saving water from a local water company for display or class discussion. Alternatively, you may have students report on water-saving practices used in their homes.

SECTION 42. CHECKING AND REDUCING TELEPHONE COSTS

Comments and Suggestions. The cost of telephone service has become more complicated to compute since the user today has a wide choice of equipment and service companies. As a project, have students bring in newspaper ads that show telephone equipment for sale. Get the local telephone company's monthly rental rates for a variety of rotary, push-button, and specialized telephones. Have students compare the cost of the telephones for sale with the monthly rental rates for similar equipment.

You might also bring into class the long distance rates from some of the common carriers competing with the local Bell Telephone company. Students can then compare the costs of calls made to various places for various lengths of time.

You should review the concepts of payback period and net amount saved over time already introduced in Section 40, **Reducing Energy Costs.**

Unit 7. Borrowing Money

The purpose of this unit is to acquaint students with the major problems and processes of borrowing money, making installment purchases, and using credit cards. Student learning objectives for the unit are listed on the unit opener page of the text.

Integrated Project for Unit 7. The integrated project for Unit 7 allows the student to make decisions concerning whether to finance a major purchase by discounting a note at a bank, using a credit card, buying on the installment plan, or borrowing money on an installment loan.

Vocabulary Review for Unit 7. An exercise that reviews the terms in Unit 7 is included at the end of the unit in the workbook.

Supplementary Problems for Unit 7. Word problems similar to those found in Unit 7 are presented in the *Supplementary Problems for Unit 7* section of **Appendix B.**

Transparencies for Unit 7. Several transparency masters drawn from the illustrations in Unit 7 are provided in the teacher's edition of the workbook. These include day tables and APR tables.

Test for Unit 7. A review test for Unit 7 is provided in the test package (M473) and the MicroEXAM package.

Solutions for Unit 7. Solutions to all text problems and the unit test are included in this manual. Solutions to all workbook problems are included in the teacher's edition of the workbook.

Additional Resources for Unit 7. There are numerous sources of information and materials about loans, installment purchasing, and credit card systems. Some suggestions include:

1. The loan departments of the commercial and savings banks in your community might provide a wealth of information, pamphlets, and forms regarding bank loans, discounting, and interest computations. Ask them for information pertaining to auto loans, vacation loans, small business loans, home equity loans, collateral loans, and installment loans.

2. The credit unions and finance companies in your community should provide a greal deal of information, pamphlets, and loan forms pertaining to installment loans.

3. Your own credit card company(s) may provide information pertaining to cash advances and the interest and fees charged to holders of the cards. The local banks in your community that offer credit card services also may supply this information.

4. The credit departments of local department stores are a useful resource for information, forms, brochures, and other materials pertaining to installment purchase plans and store credit cards.

Some reading materials that may prove helpful are:

1. Murphy, John, Sound Cash Management and Borrowing, U.S. Small Business Administration, P.O. Box 15434, Fort Worth, TX 76119, no date.

2. Using Our Credit Intelligently, National Foundation for Consumer Credit, Inc., 1819 H Street, N.W., Washington, D.C., 20006, no date.

3. Consumer Handbook to Credit Protection Laws, Board of Governors of the Federal Reserve System, Washington, D.C., 20551, no date.

4. The Story of Consumer Credit, Federal Reserve Bank of New York, Public Information Department, 33 Liberty St., New York, NY 10045, no date.

5. CUNA Yearbook, Credit Union, National Association, Inc., P.O. Box 431, Madison, WI 53701, current year. The Yearbook describes the services of credit unions and last year's operations of the Association.

6. What Truth in Lending Means to You, Board of Governors of the Federal Reserve System, Washington, D.C. 20551, no date.

7. Facts You Should Know About Borrowing, Better Business Bureau of New York, Inc., Educational Division, 220 Church St., New York, NY 10013, no date.

SECTION 43. INTEREST-BEARING NOTES

Comments and Suggestions. The material in this section covers the basic principles of promissory notes and simple interest. The section provides a background for the work in interest and discount presented in the rest of the unit.

You may wish to show to the class promissory note and collateral note forms from local lenders such as banks, finance companies, credit unions, or automobile dealerships. You may also wish to ask an employee of a local lender to address the class about the opportunities and dangers pertaining to home equity loans.

SECTION 44. EXACT AND BANKER'S INTEREST

Comments and Suggestions. The formula method of finding interest is presented in this section through both the exact interest formula (365-day year) and the banker's interest formula (360-day year).

These points should be emphasized:

1. Unless stated otherwise, a rate of interest is always an annual rate, or a rate for one year.

2. The interest rate is always based on the principal, or face, of the note. So, the principal is multiplied by the rate to find the interest for one year.

3. Since the rate of interest is always based on the principal, the rate of interest is found by dividing the interest for one year by the principal. If the interest is for a period other than one year, the students must convert the interest to an equivalent annual amount before dividing.

4. The basic interest formula is $P \times R \times T = I$.

5. T (time) may be based on a 365-day year (exact interest) or on a 360-day year (banker's interest).

Numerous problems involving computing interest are incorporated into review assignments throughout subsequent text.

Formula Method. The formula method of finding interest is presented first as it relates to the relatively simple times of years and months. The formula method is applied next to finding interest for days in a 365-day year, or exact interest. Students are then taught the banker's interest method, which uses the easier 360-day year.

The method of finding the rate of interest is also included in this section.

Calculator Clinic. The calculator clinic shows students how to compute exact interest when the time is in years, months, and days. Students are shown how to solve the problems first without using the percent key. Students are shown how to use the percent key in the Saving Time section.

SECTION 45. INTEREST TABLES

Comments and Suggestions. In this section, the students learn to use an exact interest table as an alternative to finding exact interest by formula. The section includes part of a simple interest table. Tables for varying amounts of time and interest rates can be obtained from local banks or from the Financial Publishing Company, 82 Brookline Avenue, Boston, Massachusetts, 02215.

Students may use the table in the book for many different interest rates and times. The text describes how the table can be used for rates and times other than those in the table. Problems using the table for rates that are easy combinations of those found in the table are provided. If students are interested, you may also show them how to use the tables to find interest with rates less than those found in the table. For example, you may show them how to find interest at 4% (divide the 8% table amount by 2), or 6% (multiply the table amount for 8% by $\frac{3}{4}$).

Also, point out to students that when a problem involves a time in days that exceeds the days found in the table, they can often multiply rather than add table amounts to make the problem easier to solve. For example, the interest in the text example on page 243 ($250.00 for 45 days at 8% exact interest) can be found by finding the table amount for 8% interest for 15 days and multiplying by 3 ($0.3288 × 3 = $0.9864). Then the result can be multiplied by 2.5 ($0.9864 × 2.5 = $2.47).

SECTION 46. DUE DATES AND TIMES OF NOTES

Comments and Suggestions. In this section, students learn how to find the due date, or maturity date, of a promissory note when the time is expressed in months or in days. When the time is in months, the date of maturity is adjusted only when the computed date does not exist in the month of maturity. This occurs only in months with less than 31 days.

Demand notes are used to provide a practical business introduction to finding the number of days between two dates. Finding the number of days between two dates is first presented as a manual calculation. The use of a table for finding the days between dates is then presented.

The interest problems in this section use the 365-day year.

SECTION 47. DISCOUNTED NOTES

Comments and Suggestions. Section 47 explains how to calculate the proceeds when borrowing from a bank by discounting one's own non-interest-bearing note. Because bank discount is subtracted in advance, students should recognize that they are paying a higher rate of interest than it might appear. The method of figuring the real rate of interest paid by the borrower when the note is discounted is presented to show how discounting increases the real rate of interest paid.

The interest problems in Section 47 all use time expressed in months to simplify student calculation of discount.

SECTION 48. INSTALLMENT LOANS

Comments and Suggestions. These points should be emphasized:

1. A borrower who gets a personal loan usually receives the face amount of the loan.

2. When the face of a loan is repaid in equal monthly installments plus interest on the unpaid balances, the total finance charge is the sum of all the monthly interest payments.

3. When uniform monthly payments are made to repay a loan and the interest, the total finance charge is the difference between the face of the loan and the sum of all the monthly payments.

4. When monthly finance or interest charges are figured, the result of the multiplication of the rate by the unpaid balance does not have to be adjusted for time because the finance charge is stated as a monthly rate.

You might point out to students that they can convert a monthly rate to a yearly rate by multiplying by 12. For example, a 1.5% monthly finance charge is equivalent to an 18% annual rate of interest.

SECTION 49. MORE INSTALLMENT LOANS

Comments and Suggestions. When an installment loan is obtained from a lender, interest may be figured on the original principal at an annual rate for the entire term of the loan. Exercise 1 provides students with practice in finding the amount of the finance charge and the amount of each monthly payment.

It should be noted that the finance charge usually includes interest, service charges, and any other charges that the borrower *must* pay to obtain credit. Exercise 2 provides students with practice in finding the finance charge when service charges are added.

True Interest Rate or Annual Percentage Rate. The true interest rate a borrower pays on an installment loan is always much higher than the rate used in finding the finance charge, because the borrower does not have the use of the original principal for the whole time of the loan. The average principal over the term of the loan is only a little more than half of the original principal. So, the true interest rate is nearly double the original interest rate.

Under the Truth in Lending Act, the lender must disclose the true rate of interest, or **annual percentage rate.** Calculating the annual percentage rate involves a complicated formula, but the rate can be found easily from available tables. Two small sections of the tables are illustrated in this section.

When using the tables, students first must figure the finance charge per $100 of the amount financed. The amount financed is the amount of cash or credit that the borrower receives from the lender. The method of figuring the finance charge per $100 is explained and Exercise 3 is provided to give students practice in finding the finance charge per $100.

Knowing the finance charge per $100 and the number of monthly payments, the students can find the rate in the table of annual percentage rates. The use of the table is explained and Exercise 4 follows to provide students with practice in using the tables.

An approximate annual percentage rate can be calculated for level-payment loans, without the use of the tables, through the *constant ratio formula:*

$$APR = \frac{24 \times \text{Amount of Finance Charges}}{\text{Original Principal} \times (\text{Number of Payments Per Year} + 1)}$$

If you apply this formula to Problem 2 in Exercise 4, in which Zeb borrows $1,300, the APR would be 13.07%. The tables provide a rate of 12.75%. Likewise, Problem 3 is 13.8%, versus the table's 13.5%; Problem 4 is 13.69%, versus the table's 13.25%.

The constant, 24, is used when monthly payments are involved. Use a constant of 104 if weekly payments are made. The constant ratio formula is used in the spreadsheet template in the computer clinic for Section 49.

Comparative Costs. You may wish to assign your students a series of problems in which they compare the availability, services, and costs of loans from several local lenders such as a commercial bank, credit union, finance company, and auto dealership.

Computer Clinic. A computer clinic that allows students to use a spreadsheet to estimate the annual percentage rate charged on a loan is provided. The spreadsheet uses the constant ratio formula for estimating APR. Students should recognize that the actual APR computed using the tables may be slightly different. They should also understand that the Truth in Lending Act does not allow lenders to estimate or approximate APR.

SECTION 50. INSTALLMENT BUYING

Comments and Suggestions. The provisions of the Truth in Lending Act apply to installment sales as well as installment loans. The seller of an article on the installment plan must disclose the annual percentage rate represented by the finance charge. The same method and general tables are used for determining the annual percentage rate as for determining the rate on an installment loan. Another section of the tables is given in Section 50 for student use in solving the problems in Exercise 4.

An approximate annual percentage rate on an installment purchase can be calculated in the same way as an approximate rate on an installment loan, as explained previously, by using the constant ratio formula.

As in the case of the lender of an installment loan, the seller is not permitted to use the approximate rate in stating the annual percentage rate for an installment sale.

SECTION 51. CREDIT CARDS

Comments and Suggestions. Both storeowners and customers incur costs from the use of credit cards. The cost of credit cards to the business person is presented first in this section. This discussion provides the background for the presentation of the cost of credit cards to the consumer.

Many businesses will pass on to the consumer, in the form of a lower price, all or part of the credit card fee that is saved if the consumer pays cash instead of using the credit card. Some businesses subtract the fee from the price to give a discount for paying cash. Others add the fee to the cash price if the customer uses their credit card to pay for the merchandise.

Students may find it helpful if you make a transparency of a recent credit card statement. Of course, you should first eliminate the account number and customer name. The transparency can be used to teach students how to read the statement, especially the information pertaining to daily finance charge fees, minimum payment amounts, and the account balance.

You might describe to students the advantages as well as the disadvantages of using credit cards. While the textbook outlines the disadvantages of a possibly higher cost of merchandise and the added cost of owning the card itself, you might point out the advantages of being able to pay a bill without having cash in an emergency, being able to take advantage of temporary price reductions at sales, exercising precaution by not having to carry cash, and preparing taxes more easily through the help of credit records kept by the companies.

You may also wish to discuss with students the safe use of credit cards, such as refusing to give out the number over the telephone, keeping the card in a zippered pocket of a purse or wallet, and refraining from lending the card to others. You may also mention that many homeowner insurance policies cover against loss from unauthorized credit card use and that there are companies that, for a fee, will keep track of your card numbers and notify the credit card companies if you lose the cards.

Students should understand that a monthly credit card interest rate of 1.5% is equal to 18% per year.

Calculator Clinic. The calculator clinic in this section describes how to use a calculator to multiply a number by a percent. The text then goes on to relate this method to finding the savings from a cash purchase. For those students whose calculators have the percent function, the clinic also reviews how this function can be used to save time.

Unit 8. Saving Money

In Unit 8, students become acquainted with the concepts and calculations essential to learning to figure interest on savings accounts and to compare different types of savings plans.

Student learning objectives for Unit 8 appear on the unit opener page in the text.

Integrated Project for Unit 8. This project integrates the savings and interest concepts presented in the textbook. It is found at the end of Unit 8 in the workbook. In *Integrated Project 8*, students are given information about the savings plans of different banks and are asked to make savings decisions based on interest calculations.

Vocabulary Review for Unit 8. A vocabulary exercise, *Vocabulary Review: Unit 8*, is found at the end of Unit 8 in the workbook. The exercise reviews eleven of the vocabulary terms presented in Unit 8 of the text. To complete this exercise, students write the terms, rather than listing a matching letter or number. This provides them with an opportunity to practice spelling key terms.

Supplementary Problems for Unit 8. Nine word problems similar to those provided in the exercises for Unit 8 are presented in the *Supplementary Problems for Unit 8* section of **Appendix B.**

Transparencies for Unit 8. Five transparency masters that may be used to illustrate important concepts are provided in the teacher's edition of the workbook.

Test for Unit 8. A review test for Unit 8 is provided in the test package (M473) and the MicroEXAM package. The test is designed to measure student achievement of the learning objectives of Unit 8, except for the objectives dealing with optional calculator and spreadsheet topics.

Solutions for Unit 8. Solutions to all text problems and the unit test are included in this manual. Solutions to all workbook problems are included in the teacher's edition of the workbook.

Additional Resources for Unit 8. There are many other resources that you can use to support or supplement the instruction in Unit 8. Local banks, credit unions, savings and loan associations, and stock brokerage houses may provide you with brochures that describe the features and requirements of passbook savings, time-deposit, and money-market accounts. Based on this information and a common set of assumptions, students can make interest calculations and comparisons, including the penalty for early withdrawal of funds from time deposit accounts.

The local or regional Federal Reserve office can provide information on federal regulations pertaining to banks. Because of deregulation in the banking industry, very few restrictions apply to such items as interest rates and interest penalties on time-deposit accounts. These rates and penalties are competitively set by banks, and customers must compare the offerings of banks to find the plan best suited for particular situations.

SECTION 52. PASSBOOK SAVINGS ACCOUNTS

Comments and Suggestions. Because of deregulation in the banking industry, clear-cut distinctions between institutions that offer financial services no longer exist. In this section and in the remainder of Unit 8, emphasis is placed on banks as the primary offerer of savings plans because they are the most familiar savings institution. Other savings alternatives should be discussed with students as you deem appropriate.

Passbook Savings Accounts. Some banks, as well as credit unions and savings and loan associations, do not use a passbook system in which the teller manually records transactions as they occur. Instead, these banks use a computer to prepare statements that summarize account activity, usually monthly, and they mail these to their customers. So they can keep a record of transactions and figure account balances between statements, customers are given a savings register, which is similar to a check register. With each transaction, bank customers are given a printed receipt to serve as an official record of the transaction. Customers use the receipts to keep their own savings registers and to check against the statements they receive. Interest reported on bank statements must be added to the savings register by the customers.

Some banks may charge a service fee for small accounts, usually for those with balances of less than $100. The service fee may be a fixed amount, such as $6 per quarter, to encourage customers to meet the minimum deposit requirement. Other banks restrict the number of withdrawals allowed from savings accounts during a certain period to discourage frequent withdrawals that add to the bank's cost of servicing such accounts. When the number of withdrawals exceeds a stated maximum, some banks add a per withdrawal service fee.

When students figure interest on savings accounts, they must be reminded to use the entire principal amount and not to round intermediate results. Only the final answer, the amount of interest for the period being calculated, is rounded to the nearest cent.

Practices for calculating interest on savings accounts differ among financial institutions. This text uses the simple method of calculating interest on the smallest balance during the period. Local practices, such as figuring interest on the average daily balance, can be discussed if you so choose.

Calculator Clinic. Students are shown how to use a hand-held calculator to figure simple and compound interest in the calculator clinic at the end of Section 52. In compounding interest, the periodic interest amounts are rounded to the nearest cent and added to the previous balance to form a new balance on which interest is then figured. To save steps, students could add the unrounded interest amount to the previous balance. The final balance and total interest figures may differ by a few cents from those calculated by rounding periodic interest.

To provide additional calculator practice, you should demonstrate the procedure for determining interest on new account balances and minimum balances where deposits and withdrawals are made within the interest period. This should be done prior to student use of the calculator to complete Exercises 4 and 5.

SECTION 53. COMPOUND INTEREST

The concept of compounding interest was introduced in Section 52. In this section, students will use compound interest tables to find the compound interest earned on deposits.

There are many ways in which savings institutions calculate compound interest, and the formulas they use are complicated. To reduce the amount of calculations that students must do, the table method is used to find compound amount and compound interest. The daily interest portion of the compound interest table shown in Illustration 53–1 of the textbook is based on a 360-day year. The 365-day values represent an additional five days interest beyond the 360-day. Many published financial tables continue to maintain a tie to the banker's year.

The marginal illustration on the first page of this section may be used to dramatize the effect of more frequent compounding on total interest earned by a deposit.

Compound interest tables for the value of $1 at various rates and compounding periods may be obtained from financial publications and may be substituted for the values in the textbook to provide additional practice. Students who are proficient in math may also wish to use a calculator to compose their own compound interest tables as an extra-credit assignment.

SECTION 54. SPECIAL SAVINGS PLANS

Comments and Suggestions. Special savings accounts are popular because they offer customers of financial institutions a chance to earn higher rates of interest than are paid on regular passbook accounts. To open special savings accounts, most institutions require a minimum deposit, usually in the $500 to $1,000 range.

Students should know that many of the rules governing special savings accounts, especially those dealing with the penalty for early withdrawal, are written to encourage long-term savings and to ensure that the savings institution has a fixed period of time for which they can use a customer's money. Customers who frequently move money into and out of savings accounts should open regular passbook accounts.

Although the money-market account is presented in the textbook as a fixed-term investment, financial institutions may also offer money-market accounts that are similar to passbook accounts but carry a higher interest rate. Such accounts may have restrictions on the number of withdrawals that may be made and on the minimum balance that must be maintained. When a minimum balance is not maintained, the accounts may earn only the passbook rate.

Computer Clinic. The student is asked to load Sec54 and enter the listed data into the appropriate cells. Although the spreadsheet is intended to provide a comparison of regular passbook accounts and time deposit accounts, it may also be used to do most compounding problems. While using the spreadsheet, students are asked to enter the number of compounding periods the money is kept on deposit instead of the number of months on deposit. The spreadsheet may also be used to try out several "what-if" types of situations relating to changes in interest rates or frequency of compounding.

Unit 9. Investing Money

In Unit 9, students become acquainted with alternative ways to invest money. The investment areas presented include corporate bonds, U.S. Savings Bonds, stocks, mutual funds, and rental property.

Student learning objectives for Unit 9 appear on the Unit 9 opener page in the text.

Integrated Project for Unit 9. This project integrates the investment options presented in the textbook and is found at the end of Unit 9 in the workbook. In *Integrated Project 9*, students are given information about four investment plans and are asked to answer questions about the plans. Students also compose an answer to two questions involving an investment recommendation.

Vocabulary Review for Unit 9. A vocabulary exercise, *Vocabulary Review: Unit 9*, is found at the end of Unit 9 in the workbook. The exercise reviews 25 of the vocabulary terms presented in Unit 9 of the textbook. In completing this exercise, students write the terms, rather than listing a matching letter or number, thereby getting practice in spelling key terms.

Supplementary Problems for Unit 9. Thirteen word problems similar to those provided in the exercises for Unit 9 are presented in the *Supplementary Problems for Unit 9* section of **Appendix B.**

Transparencies for Unit 9. Three transparency masters that may be used to illustrate important concepts are provided in the teacher's edition of the workbook.

Test for Unit 9. A review test for Unit 9 is provided in the Test Package (M473) and the MicroEXAM package. The test is designed to measure student achievement of the learning objectives of Unit 9, except for the objectives dealing with optional spreadsheet topics.

Solutions for Unit 9. Solutions to all text problems and the unit test are included in this manual. Solutions to all workbook problems are included in the teacher's edition of the workbook.

Additional Resources for Unit 9. Some specific resources that may also be used by the teacher follow:

1. A representative of a stock brokerage house usually has many brochures and pamphlets available for use in class or for bulletin board displays. The representative may also be willing to speak to students about investing bonds, stocks, and mutual funds.

2. The trust departments of local banks also can provide information about investment opportunities, especially investing in bonds.

3. The Securities and Exchange Commission and the New York Stock Exchange are both organizations that provide brochures and pamphlets suitable for use in this unit.

4. Barnes, John, What Investing Is All About, South-Western Publishing Co., 5101 Madison Road, Cincinnati, OH 45227, no date. A text-workbook designed for adults.

5. Work of the Stock Exchange, Coronet Films, Inc., 65 East South Water Street, Chicago, IL 60601. A 16-minute film of the exchanges.

SECTION 55. BUYING BONDS

Comments and Suggestions. Corporation bonds may be of two types: secured and unsecured. **Secured bonds** are backed by a claim to some asset of the issuer, usually real property. If the bond issuer fails to make interest payments when due and to repay the money borrowed at maturity, the issuer may be considered insolvent. If this happens, the secured bondholders are considered creditors and may take over or sell the property pledged as security.

Unsecured bonds are backed by the reputation and ability of the corporation to earn enough income to make interest payments and pay back the face value of the bonds when due.

Corporation bonds usually come in $1,000 denominations, but they may be issued in larger denominations such as $5,000 or $10,000, primarily to reduce the paperwork costs of the issuing company. Other bonds may be issued in smaller denominations to give them more appeal to small investors.

Remind students that bond quotations are stated as a percent of par value, and that this is an example of the importance of being able to convert mentally percents to decimals and to use equivalent fractions.

Remind students that the regulations governing U.S. Savings Bonds vary with changes in money markets. Such bonds are similar to unsecured corporation bonds in that the bonds are supported by faith in the U.S. government to repay its debts.

SECTION 56. BOND INCOME

Comments and Suggestions. When an investor buys a bond between two inter-est dates, the interest that has accrued from the last interest date to the date of purchase must be paid in addition to the price of the bond and the commis-sion. On the next interest date, however, the buyer receives the full interest for the period, and so is reimbursed for the accrued interest. To make student so-lution of problems simpler, the concept of accrued interest is not incorporated into the exercises in this section.

Students should be encouraged to bring to class a bond quotation table from the financial section of a current newspaper and one about a month old. By comparing price data for the same bond, students could then see that items such as volume and price fluctuate. Items such as the maturity date and the interest rate of the bond remain the same because these are fixed at the time a bond is issued.

You may also point out to students that brokerage houses may carry an inventory of bonds as part of their investments, and sales to customers may be made from inventory rather than through a bond exchange.

Computer Clinic. In the computer clinic for Section 56, students are asked to compare the yields of two bonds.

SECTION 57. BUYING STOCK

Comments and Suggestions. It is important that students understand the dif-ference between bondholders and shareholders (stockholders). Bondholders are creditors of a corporation while stockholders are owners.

Trading on stock exchanges is done in *round lots* of 100 shares. Any order of less than 100 shares is known as an *odd lot* and is handled by an odd-lot dealer. Although odd-lot dealers charge a fraction of the stock price for their service, this cost differential is assumed to be included in the stock price for all problems in the textbook that deal with odd lots.

Whenever a broker buys or sells stock for a customer, the customer is given a written notice of the transaction that lists the name of the stock, the number of shares bought or sold, unit price, total market value, commission, any other charges or fees, and the net amount owed the broker or due the cus-tomer. Special charges or fees occur when stocks are sold. The seller pays a small Security and Exchange Commission fee and, in some states, a transfer tax. Also, some brokerage firms add a separate charge to cover the cost of post-age and clerical handling of the transaction.

Students may be interested in knowing that an industry-wide, standard commission structure used to exist. That standard was abandoned in 1975 and each brokerage house now sets up its commission rate charges, independent of other brokers. The so-called "discount brokers" charge lower commission rates because their costs of operation are lower than "full-service brokers" who pro-vide broad research and advisory services.

SECTION 58. STOCK INCOME

In this section, students solve problems to find the annual income from divi-dends for stock investments. When the total dividend due a shareholder in-cludes a fraction of a cent, the dividend amount is rounded to the nearest cent.

When students are solving dividend problems, you should remind them that the rate of income earned on an investment in stock is always stated on an annual basis. If a dividend is stated as being paid quarterly or semiannually, the total dividend paid for a *year* must be found to calculate the correct rate of income.

SECTION 59. SELLING STOCK

Comments and Suggestions. All textbook problems assume that the stock is purchased outright and not on a margin basis, so the cost of borrowing is not a factor in figuring the net gain on a transaction.

The net profit or loss on a purchase and sale of stock is the difference between the total cost of the purchase and the net proceeds of the sale. Since any dividends received represent a gain to the shareholder, they are added to the profit to find the total gain from ownership of the stock or subtracted from the loss to find the net loss. If the dividends exceed the loss on the sale, there is a net gain on the entire transaction.

Computer Clinic. In the computer clinic for Section 59, students find the net profit or loss and net gain or loss from a stock investment. Students are also asked to respond to a series of "what if" questions dealing with changes in stock prices and their effect on the profitability of a stock investment.

SECTION 60. MUTUAL FUNDS

Students should be made aware that investments in bonds and stocks require careful study to avoid possible loss of income or capital. Point out to students that mutual funds have become popular investments because they offer diversification of risk with a single purchase. However, as with other investments, the mutual fund company must be selected carefully to also minimize the potential risk of capital loss.

Although mutual funds pay out dividends and share capital gains with shareholders, these topics are not discussed in the textbook. These topics may be discussed with students if questions arise about the management of the mutual fund's portfolio. Also indicate to students that load funds are bought through brokers who share in the commission charge. No-load funds are bought directly from the investment company that manages the mutual fund.

SECTION 61. BUYING REAL ESTATE

Comments and Suggestions. In figuring the annual net income from an investment in real estate, an allowance for the depreciation of the property should be included in the annual expenses. Although a property may advance in price because of price inflation and market demand so that its current market value may be more than its original cost, depreciation is present, nevertheless, and it is reflected in the relative market value of the property.

For example, it may now cost $110,000 to build a house identical to one that cost only $35,000 when built 15 years ago. The old house will not now sell at its reproduction cost, however, because it is old and has depreciated. A prospective buyer will not pay $110,000 for the old house if an identical house can be bought brand new for the same price. The current market value of the old house may be $90,000, or some lesser amount.

In problems students will solve, depreciation is assumed to affect buildings only, rather than both land and buildings.

For enrichment purposes, a local realtor could be invited to meet with students to discuss current real estate trends and the value of buying property for investment purposes. Students could also research the real estate section of the local newspaper for articles dealing with tips on buying real estate.

Computer Clinic. In this computer clinic, students are asked to enter annual rental and expense data in order to find rental income for a property investment.

SECTION 62. REAL ESTATE INCOME

Comments and Suggestions. Point out to students the relationship between the general level of interest rates and the rate of income that can be earned on real estate investments. Higher returns may be achieved through real estate investments than can be earned by leaving money on deposit in a bank, primarily as a reward or incentive for taking risks. Real estate owners who set unreasonable income goals and charge rental prices that are out of line with general market prices will not be able to reach the occupancy level needed to reach investment goals.

The Computer Clinic. The student is asked to enter the data listed into a spreadsheet to find the monthly rent to be charged for a property investment given the cash investment, annual expenses, and a desired rate of income. The spreadsheet may also be used by students to check their answers to the problems in Exercise 1.

Unit 10. Home and Transportation Expenses

In Unit 10, students become acquainted with and develop skills in solving a wide variety of problems concerned with home ownership and home rental. In addition, the costs of owning and leasing cars or trucks are also discussed.

Student learning objectives for Unit 10 appear on the Unit 10 opener page in the text.

Integrated Project for Unit 10. In this project, students review the processes for analyzing the costs of buying and renting homes and buying and leasing cars. In *Integrated Project 10*, students are given information about the home and car buying plans of a family. They then complete tables that summarize the data presented. Students analyze the summarized data, answer questions, and make recommendations.

Vocabulary Review for Unit 10. A vocabulary exercise, *Vocabulary Review: Unit 10*, is found at the end of Unit 10 in the workbook. The exercise reviews 10 of the vocabulary terms presented in Unit 10 of the textbook. In completing this exercise, students write the terms rather than listing a matching letter or number, thereby getting practice in spelling key terms.

Supplementary Problems for Unit 10. Eleven word problems similar to those provided in the exercises for Unit 10 are presented in the *Supplementary Problems for Unit 10* section of **Appendix B.**

Transparencies for Unit 10. Two transparency masters that may be used to illustrate important concepts are provided in the teacher's edition of the workbook.

Test for Unit 10. A review test for Unit 10 is provided in the test package (M473) and the MicroEXAM package. The test is designed to measure student achievement of the learning objectives of Unit 10, except for the objectives dealing with optional spreadsheet topics.

Solutions for Unit 10. Solutions to all text problems and the unit test are included in this manual. Solutions to all workbook problems are included in the teacher's edition of the workbook.

Additional Resources for Unit 10. Students may learn about the mortgage plans offered by local lenders in several ways. They may visit in small groups one or more lenders, such as banks or savings and loan associations, and ask about the types of plans offered and obtain promotional material. They may also write to various lenders in the area and ask them for the same information. It may also be possible for a loan officer from a local financial institution to speak to the class about mortgages.

New car dealers and independent leasing companies may provide data about leasing costs. Similar information may also be found in advertisements for new cars that give purchase prices as well as leasing prices and terms.

To provide extra practice, you may change the interest rates and terms in problems if students have access to amortization tables other than the partial table printed in the book. More extensive tables may be available from local real estate brokers or lenders. Libraries will also have mortgage payment table books, usually in the reference section. Specific materials that may be useful follow:

1. Comprehensive Mortgage Payment Tables, Financial Publishing Company, 82 Brookline Avenue, Boston, MA 02215, no date.

2. Financial Mortgage Loan Handbook, Financial Publishing Company, 82 Brookline Avenue, Boston, MA 02215, Fifth Edition, 1983. This publication contains tables that show the monthly payment needed to amortize a loan.

3. Thorndike, David, Thorndike Encyclopedia of Banking and Financial Tables, Warren, Gorham & Lamont, 210 South Street, Boston MA 02111, no date. Contains numerous financial tables relating to savings, investments, loan payments, and amortization.

4. Life Rates and Data, The National Underwriter Company, 420 East Fourth Street, Cincinnati, OH 45202, no date. This reference guide contains rate and insurance information.

5. N.A.D.A. Official Used Car Guide, National Auto Dealers Used Car Guide Company, 8400 Westpark Drive, McLean, VA 22102, no date. Contains cur-

rent used car prices for most automobiles and trucks. May be used to calculate the amount and rate of depreciation on cars and trucks.

SECTION 63. BUYING A HOME

Comments and Suggestions. In the first part of this section, students solve problems that require them to find down payment amounts, the total amount of closing costs, and the percent that closing costs are of the purchase price of the home. On the unit opener page, a distinction is drawn between the appraisal value of the home, which states a theoretical price for a home, and the market value, which is the price at which the home is actually sold. Make sure that students are able to select the correct value for making calculations.

The nature and amount of closing costs vary from state to state. In some states a transfer tax may be included. In many localities, lenders will charge *points* to a borrower. These points are actually prepaid interest and are based on the amount of the mortgage loan. For example, a lender may charge a 12.7% annual rate of interest on a $60,000 mortgage loan. In addition, the lender may charge three points on the amount of the loan that must be paid at the time of settlement. These points are really percentages. Three points charged on a $60,000 mortgage would be 0.03 × $60,000, or $1,800.

Be sure to discuss Illustration 63–1 and the complete amortization table found in Appendix E. Remind students that interest calculations are done with the formula $I = P \times R \times T$. So, for the $40,000, 13% mortgage, the interest cost for the first month is $9.15 ($40,000 × 0.13 × $\frac{1}{12}$).

Lenders also usually require that the home be inspected for termites and that life and title insurance be purchased for the amount of the mortgage. The buyer may want to have a professional company inspect the property for structural problems or building code violations that may exist. The life, or mortgage, insurance is made payable to the lender in case of the borrower's death. The title insurance protects the financial institution and the home buyer in case the seller did not have a clear title to the property that was sold to the buyer.

Although there are a wide variety of mortgage payment plans available to home buyers, only the fixed-term, level payment plan is presented in detail to develop the concept of amortization. Although this type of plan is the most commonly used mortgage plan, students should be introduced to variable rate, or adjustable rate, mortgages.

The terms of variable rate mortgages vary substantially among lenders. For example, one lender may offer a "balloon" loan for one year at the current rate of interest. They may guarantee in writing that they will refinance the loan at the rate in effect when the loan is due. While the balloon loan is written for only one year, the monthly payments may be based on a 20-, 25-, or 30-year mortgage plan. Another bank may offer a 25- or 30-year variable rate mortgage in which the rate of interest may be changed at certain mortgage anniversary dates; for example, they may be changed after one, three, or five years. If the interest rate increases, some banks will keep the monthly payment the same and add the interest that is not covered by the payment to the principal of the mortgage. They may also keep the payments the same and extend the term of the loan. Other banks will simply raise the monthly payment to cover the increase in mortgage costs.

The issue of refinancing mortgage loans is covered in this unit. When interest rates fall, many borrowers refinance their old mortgages with mortgages at the newer and lower rates. Some banks will refinance their old mortgages with new ones at lower rates. Other banks will charge closing costs again before refinancing. It is important that students learn that the entire offer in regard to interest rates, points, or refinance charges must be studied before a loan is refinanced. The differences between lenders in the same locality can be substantial.

Some states do not permit lenders to charge prepayment penalties if a borrower pays off a mortgage before the due date. Some states do permit this practice. Typically, mortgage documents in these states will have a prepayment clause which reads something like this: "That there will be a 3% penalty if the loan is repaid in the first year, a 2% penalty if the loan is repaid in the second year, and a 1% penalty if the loan is repaid in the third year. No penalty is charged if the loan is repaid after the third year." These can be substantial penalties. If you repaid a mortgage of $60,000 in the first year because you could get better financing elsewhere, your penalty, under the prepayment clause, would be 0.03 × $60,000, or $1,800.

Computer Clinic. In the computer clinic for Section 63, students find the monthly payment needed to pay off a mortgage, and they calculate the total interest paid. Students change the interest rate and term of the loan to study the effect of these variables on monthly payments and total interest paid.

A mortgage factor is included as output. The mortgage amount divided by that factor gives the monthly payment needed to amortize the loan. The factor is unique for a given interest rate and term of a loan.

SECTION 64. OWNING A HOME

Comments and Suggestions. Depreciation is treated as an expense of home ownership to reflect the relative loss in home value that takes place as homes deteriorate through use and aging. As new homes increase in price, older homes may also show price appreciation, but for a lesser amount due to the depreciation that has taken place. The straight-line method is often used to estimate depreciation, with the rate of depreciation ranging from 1% to 4%, on the average.

Although tax laws may change, at the time this text was written taxpayers who itemized were able to take a deduction for interest on home mortgages and for property taxes. This reduction in overall income taxes is included in the problems that involve calculating the net cost of home ownership. The actual amount deducted for these expenses, of course, is only a part of the total amount eligible for deduction. For simplicity, students are given the amount of the tax savings.

In several of the problems in this section, the expenses of home ownership are *estimated* since they can only be guessed at before they actually occur. For example, a problem may be written in this way:

Laura is planning to buy a home for $45,000. She *estimates* her annual costs of home ownership to be: taxes, $1,100; depreciation, 2% of the purchase price; maintenance, $400; insurance, $180; interest expense, $3,000; loss of income on the down payment at 8%. What is her total annual cost of home ownership?

Although the question raised in the problem should technically ask students to find the *estimated total annual cost*, that phrasing might confuse the students into rounding to arrive at an estimate, or approximation, as the problem solution, which is the incorrect procedure for this problem. This situation will also occur when the operating costs of cars and trucks are projected, or estimated, by a potential buyer.

Investors who buy real estate to rent to others expect to receive income from their investments. These investments are called *income-producing investments*. Investors do not include loss of interest income on the investments as an expense since the rental income serves as the income in place of any income the investments would have earned in securities, savings, or other properties. People who buy a home for their own use receive no income on their investments. So, the home is called a *non-income producing investment*. These owners lose the income that their money would have earned had it been invested in other ways. For this reason, this loss of income should be included as an expense of owning the home.

Computer Clinic. In the computer clinic for Section 64, students compare the costs of owning and renting a home. Students make changes in selected items to study the effect on the total cost of renting and owning.

SECTION 65. DEPRECIATING A CAR OR TRUCK

Comments and Suggestions. Depreciation as an expense of car and truck ownership is presented in this section. It should be stressed that the exact amount of the total depreciation cannot be determined until the car or truck is sold or traded in, so the yearly expense or rate of depreciation can only be estimated.

In the presentation of car or truck depreciation, the straight-line method is used. Students should be made aware of the high rate at which cars and trucks depreciate, particularly in the first few years they are owned.

Computer Clinic. In the computer clinic for Section 65, students figure a car's total, average annual, and rate of depreciation. Students make changes to selected variables and discover that the average amount and rate of depreciation are greater when the car is newer.

SECTION 66. COST OF OPERATING A CAR OR TRUCK

Comments and Suggestions. A car or truck bought for personal use is another example of a non-income producing investment. Since the owner of the car or truck could have earned income by investing the money paid for a car or truck in some other way, the annual operating expense should include an allowance for interest on the investment, in addition to the depreciation and the expenses of license fees, repairs, upkeep, state inspections, etc.

Exercises 2 and 4 deal with related types of problems. Exercise 2 contains a variety of problems pertaining to owning and using a car, such as finding the cost of license plates, figuring the operating cost per mile or kilometer, and calculating the distance traveled per gallon or liter of gas.

In these problems, both Customary and metric measures are given to provide teachers with their choice of systems. Teachers may use either or both systems of measurement, as preferred. If both systems are used for a problem, however, the converted answers may not agree exactly because approximate, rather than equivalent, values have been used to make the problems somewhat easier to solve in either system.

Exercise 4 contains problems that involve making buying decisions. Some address aspects of cost not covered previously.

The costs of owning and operating a car or truck vary greatly according to locale and time. You may want to change values in some problems to bring them in line with local and current costs.

When discussing leasing of cars and trucks, you may want to discuss reasons for leasing: no down payment required, tax advantages for business use, and lower monthly lease payments than the amount usually paid monthly for car loans. The lease plans used in the text are of the *closed-end* type, in which the customer does not have the option of buying the car or truck at the end of the lease. Point out that some leasing companies may require a security deposit and one month's lease in advance. Also, the customer is liable for excessive wear and tear on the car when it is turned in at the end of the lease.

Computer Clinic. In the computer clinic for Section 66, students compare the costs of leasing and owning cars. As students work with the spreadsheet, they should find that the least expensive solution, leasing or owning, depends a great deal on assumptions made by consumers.

By entering zero values for unrelated items, students may also use the spreadsheet to calculate independently the cost of leasing or the cost of owning, as desired.

Unit 11. Taxes

In Unit 11, students learn about property, sales, excise, social security, and income taxes. Also presented are the calculations for finding or estimating the benefits to be received from various social security programs. Specific learning objectives for students are listed on the opener page at the beginning of the unit.

Integrated Project for Unit 11. A project that integrates property taxes, social security taxes, and federal and state income taxes for a head of household and one dependent is provided.

Vocabulary Review for Unit 11. A vocabulary exercise that reviews the terms in Unit 11 is included at the end of the unit in the workbook.

Supplementary Problems for Unit 11. Word problems similar to those found in Unit 11 are presented in the *Supplementary Problems for Unit 11* section of **Appendix B.**

Transparencies for Unit 11. Several transparency masters drawn from the illustrations in Unit 11 are provided in the teacher's edition of the workbook.

Test for Unit 11. A review test for Unit 11 is provided in the test package (M473) and the MicroEXAM package.

Solutions for Unit 11. Solutions to all text problems and the unit test are included in this manual. Solutions to all workbook problems are included in the teacher's edition of the workbook.

Additional Resources for Unit 11. A great deal of useful information can be secured from federal and state taxing agencies responsible for income taxes.

1. The Internal Revenue Service provides a federal tax kit to teachers containing information, forms, and instructions for students to complete basic federal income tax forms. A teacher's manual and key is provided with the kit. Call your local Internal Revenue Service office and ask for copies of these teaching materials.

2. Your local Social Security office will send you brochures describing benefit programs and forms that can be used by students to estimate the benefits from Social Security programs.

3. Contact your state revenue service, or a similar agency, to obtain brochures about state income taxes and withholding tables and also about state sales taxes and sales tax tables.

4. Bernstein, Allen, Tax Guide for College Teachers and Other College Personnel, Academic Information Services, Inc., P.O. Box 6296, Washington, D.C. 20015. Published annually, this paperback book provides readable and practical hints for completing federal income tax forms.

5. Year-End Tax Planning Guide, a brochure published annually by A.G. Edwards, One North Jefferson St., St. Louis, MO 63103, 1986. The brochure explains amendments to the tax act and helps you plan for your taxes.

6. Your Federal Income Tax, Publication 17, Internal Revenue Service. This brochure provides explanations of many tax items and is available from your local IRS office.

7. Bower, James, and Harold Langenderfer, Personal Income Tax Procedures, South-Western Publishing Co., 5101 Madison Road, Cincinnati, OH 45227, 1987. While this text-workbook is designed for adults, it provides helpful information about income taxes useful to the teacher.

8. Your 199X Income Tax Handbook for 199X Income, National Research Bureau, Inc., Employee Communications Division, 424 North Third St., Burlington, IA 52801, 1987. This is a detailed brochure about the tax laws published annually and distributed through local savings and loan associations and other banks.

9. Employer's Tax Guide, Publication 15, Circular E, Internal Revenue Service. This booklet, which you can obtain from your local IRS office, provides information to small businesses on employment tax deductions they must collect from their employees and those that they must pay as employers.

10. Your Social Security Handbook, National Research Bureau, Inc., Employee Communications Division, 424 North Third St., Burlington, IA 52801, 1987. This is a booklet describing the social security system and the benefits available to workers distributed through your local savings and loan or other banks.

11. Estimating Your Social Security Retirement Check, U.S. Department of Health and Human Services, Social Security Administration, Baltimore, MD 21235. Obtainable through your local Social Security Administration office.

12. <u>What You Have to Know About SSI</u>, U.S. Department of Health and Human Services, Social Security Administration, U.S. Government Printing Office. This is also obtainable through your local Social Security Administration office.

13. <u>What You Should Know About Your Social Security Now</u>, The Research Institute of America, Inc., 589 Fifth Avenue, New York, NY 10017.

14. <u>Your Social Security Rights and Responsibilities</u>, U.S. Department of Health and Human Services, Social Security Administration, Baltimore, MD 21235. Obtainable through your local Social Security Administration office.

15. <u>Applying for a Social Security Number</u>, U.S. Department of Health and Human Services, Social Security Administration, Baltimore, MD 21235.

SECTION 67. PROPERTY TAXES

This section presents problems pertaining to the computation of property taxes. Assessed valuation is also presented. Property tax problems include those with rates expressed in mills and cents per $1 of assessed value and rates per $100 and $1,000 of assessed value.

You may want to bring to class clippings from the real estate section of the local newspaper describing the location and value of properties. The clippings can be made into transparencies for display in class, or photocopied for distribution to students. You may alternatively wish to obtain pages from a local real estate agent's multiple listings book. These pages are more useful because they provide a photo of the properties. Then, using local rates of assessed value and local property tax rates, students can determine the annual taxes on the properties.

You may also wish to have a team of students visit the local assessor's office to find the following:

1. How the community assesses property in the area.

2. What the property tax rates are in the area.

Instead, you may ask a representative from the local assessor's office to visit the class and explain how the local community calculates and collects taxes, and how these tax funds are spent.

SECTION 68. PROPERTY TAX RATES

Students often have difficulty with converting one tax rate into another, especially converting tax rates into mills per $1. Emphasize that to convert the decimal rate to a rate in mills per $1, students must multiply the decimal rate by 1,000 because there are 1,000 mills in $1.

The class discussion can usually be made very interesting if the local school or town budgets and the assessed valuation of property in these taxing districts are used for the initial explanation of property tax rates.

SECTION 69. SALES AND EXCISE TAXES

If retail sales taxes are in effect in your community, you may wish to supplement the problems in the textbook with problems based on the local tax rates, or you may wish to have students use local tax rates to solve the problems in the textbook.

You may wish to get a copy of a sales tax chart, similar to the one used in the textbook, from a local store for students to use in class. Many stores tape these charts to the cash registers.

To provide interesting problems, you may bring to class newspaper ads that contain prices for items that students in your class would like to buy. Then, you can display the ads on an overhead projector and have students compute the sales tax of each item and find the total purchase price. Often, students do not realize how much money sales taxes add to the purchase price of items they want to buy.

SECTION 70. SOCIAL SECURITY TAXES AND BENEFITS

When this text was prepared, a social security tax rate of 7.65% on the first $45,000 of annual earnings was in use. The tax rate and maximum taxable earnings amount are changed frequently by Congress, so you may wish to contact the nearest social security office for the most recent rates and taxable earnings amount.

Social security benefits are presented in this section so that students have some understanding of the possible benefits the social security system may provide. The partial table of benefits used in the text is comprised of extracted data from the voluminous tables in actual use. Students should understand that the nature and amount of benefits are changed often by Congress and that the tables cannot be used to predict accurately what a worker will receive. Determining the precise monthly benefits for a person who retires is a complex task that requires extensive knowledge of the worker's employment history and current social security laws and procedures. Computation of actual benefits is now done by computers used by the Social Security Administration.

Students are shown how to adjust the benefits they might receive at 65 if they retire early by using percentages for ages 64, 63, and 62. You might wish to teach them how to estimate benefits if they retire in any month prior to age 65 by using this formula:

$$\frac{180 - \text{Months}}{180} \times \text{Table Amount} = \text{Monthly Benefits}$$

The number "180" is a constant, Months is the number of months you retire prior to reaching age 65, and Table Amount is the amount of monthly benefits you would receive at age 65 (shown in the table in Illustration 70–1). Thus, if a person retired 12 months before reaching age 65 and had average covered monthly earnings of $200, the monthly benefits would be:

$$\frac{180 - 12}{180} \times \$180 = \$168$$

This is the same amount you would get by reducing the monthly benefit in the table by $6\frac{2}{3}\%$. The advantage of the formula is that you can compute benefits at any month between ages 62 and 65.

Students should understand that FICA taxes are paid by both employees and employers. These taxes increase the cost of each employee to employers. Students should recognize that the true cost of an employee is salary or wages plus fringe benefits, which include FICA.

SECTION 71. FEDERAL INCOME TAXES

This section provides students with an understanding of the basic arithmetic procedures involved in computing federal income taxes: finding gross income, adjusted gross income, and taxable income, and using tax tables to find the tax due. While federal tax laws, rates, and tax tables change frequently, these basic procedures remain unchanged, and they will help students understand how to compute their federal tax liability regardless of constant amendments to federal tax law.

This textbook uses simplified amounts for exemptions and for the standard deduction. The actual amounts allowed for exemptions and the standard deduction change each year. However, the arithmetic processes associated with exemptions and deductions do not. You may wish to have students substitute current amounts for those used in the text problems.

If you want to provide your students with more extensive experiences in figuring federal income taxes, contact your nearest IRS office for information about their federal income tax teaching kits (see *Additional Resources for Unit 11*). These kits are well-designed, understandable, and appropriate for beginners. Alternatively, you may wish to have students complete some of the text problems using the actual federal income tax forms appropriate to the problems.

Students should understand that it is important to report all income because income amounts are routinely reported to the government by employers and institutions from whom income may be received. Besides keeping records of income, taxpayers should also keep records of expenses that qualify as deductions.

Many people have their tax returns prepared professionally. Students should be cautioned that liability for their return *rests with them*, even if the return is prepared by others.

Students should also understand that the amount withheld by employers or the estimated taxes paid quarterly by self-employed persons seldom corresponds exactly with the amount of taxes owed. Taxpayers must file an income tax return at the end of each year so that the actual tax liability and the underpayment or overpayment may be reported.

SECTION 72. MORE FEDERAL INCOME TAXES

Comments and Suggestions. Many students have part-time jobs and should complete tax returns to obtain refunds of the amounts withheld from their wages during the year. However, some students never file returns because they believe that filing a return means paying more taxes or because they do not understand the process. It is important for these students learn how to file a return and receive their refunds.

When this book was prepared, the most appropriate tax form for most students to use was Form 1040EZ. You may wish to have students complete one or more of the problems in the section using Form 1040EZ, or its current equivalent. Using the actual forms heightens student interest.

The federal income tax teaching kit described in *Additional Resources for Unit 11* provides the current forms, additional problems, and other materials that will help you teach students how to complete Form 1040EZ.

Ask students who are working part-time to bring to class their own complete W-2 and 1099 forms. Show students how these forms are used in the completion of the appropriate federal tax forms.

Computer Clinic. The computer clinic in Section 72 provides students with a spreadsheet they can use to compute federal income taxes for dependents who work part time. The tax spreadsheet assumes that the taxpayer is claimed as an exemption on another's tax return and that the filer will take the standard deduction. The standard deduction is assumed to be a minimum of $500, the amount of earned income, or $3,000, whichever is appropriate. The tax table provided in the spreadsheet stops at $700 of taxable income. (If students are using MicroTools, the tax table will appear on the screen. Students will manually fill in the appropriate tax.) If you wish to increase the table, or update the table for changes in the tax law, the table appears in the spreadsheet between cells A30 and B59. If you change the number of lines on the table, you will also have to change the cell range included in the LOOKUP formula located in cell B17. To update the template, you will need to unlock the spreadsheet.

SECTION 73. STATE AND CITY INCOME TAXES

State and city income taxes may be based on the same taxable income used in the federal tax returns, or adjustments in taxable income may have to be made. States and cities treat some types of income and some types of deductions in different ways.

State and city tax computations are relatively simple when a flat tax rate is used. The tax rates used in Illustration 73–1 are typical of the graduated tax rates used in many communities. You may want to supplement the material in this section with problems based on the rates applicable in your state or city.

Unit 12. Insurance

In Unit 12, students become acquainted with four areas of insurance that protect against the financial risks that arise in everyday living. These areas include life, health and accident, property, and automobile insurance.

Student learning objectives for Unit 12 appear on the Unit 12 opener page in the text.

Integrated Project for Unit 12. This project integrates the insurance concepts applicable to the four areas of insurance presented in the textbook. The project is found at the end of Unit 12 in the workbook. In *Integrated Project 12*, students are given information about a family's insurance coverage and how circumstances may affect a family's insurance needs and force them to look at alternatives to insurance programs currently in effect.

Vocabulary Review for Unit 12. A vocabulary exercise, *Vocabulary Review: Unit 12*, is found at the end of Unit 12 in the workbook. In the exercise, the vocabulary terms presented in Unit 12 of the textbook are reviewed. As in previous vocabulary reviews, students write the matching terms to gain practice in spelling key terms.

Supplementary Problems for Unit 12. Thirteen word problems are provided in the *Supplementary Problems for Unit 12* section of **Appendix B** to provide students with additional practice.

Transparencies for Unit 12. Five transparency masters that may be used to illustrate the use of tables relating to insurance are provided in the teacher's edition of the workbook.

Test for Unit 12. A review test for Unit 12 is provided in the test package (M473) and the MicroEXAM package. The test is designed to measure student achievement of the learning objectives of Unit 12, except for the objectives dealing with optional spreadsheet topics.

Solutions for Unit 12. Solutions to all text problems and the unit test are included in this manual. Solutions to all workbook problems are included in the teacher's edition of the workbook.

Additional Resources for Unit 12. A number of local and industry resources may provide material that may be used to supplement the textbook.

1. Local insurance agents may be available as guest speakers. The agents may also be able to provide sample policies, life expectancy tables, brochures explaining the different types of policies, forms for planning the amounts and types of insurance needed, fire risk loss tables for buildings, and a variety of other materials that can be shared with students in class, used for supplementary problem work, and displayed on the bulletin board.

2. The Insurance Information Institute, 110 William Street, New York, NY, 10038, is also helpful in providing information and materials as background reading for the teacher and for use in class. Items that may be obtained from the Institute include:

    a. A free newsletter entitled *Insurance Insights: A Report to Educators on Property and Casualty Insurance*. This covers such topics as recent changes in the law, recent court cases, and suggestions for filing claims.
    b. The brochure, *Every Ten Minutes*. This explains the types of auto insurance and concludes with a brief test at the end of the brochure.
    c. *Insurance for the Home*, a brochure explaining the types of insurance available for homes, also concluding with a brief test.
    d. The book, *How to Protect What's Yours*, providing information on insurance and giving tips on buying insurance and managing personal finance matters.

3. A Consumer's Guide to Life Insurance, American Council of Life Insurance, 1859 K Street, N.W., Washington, D.C. 20006, no date.

4. Greene, Mark, Insurance Checklist for Small Business, U.S. Small Business Administration, Management Assistant Support Services, P.O. Box 15434, Fort Worth, TX 76119, no date.

5. <u>Life Insurance — What It Means and How It Works</u>, Institute of Life Insurance, 277 Park Avenue, New York, NY 10017, no date. A 20-minute film.

6. <u>Life Insurance Teacher's Guide</u>, American Council of Life Insurance, 1859 K Street, N.W., Washington, D.C. 20006, no date. A resource booklet on life insurance for teachers.

7. <u>Teacher's — Speaker's Guide, Health Insurance</u>, Educational Services, Health Insurance Association of America, 1850 K St., N.W., Washington, D.C. 20006. A resource booklet for teachers on health insurance.

8. <u>Casualty Insurance</u>, Encyclopedia Britannica Films, Inc., 1150 Wilmette Avenue, Wilmette, IL 60091, no date. A 20-minute film.

SECTION 74. LIFE INSURANCE PREMIUMS

In this section, students calculate the premiums to be paid for three types of life insurance issued at varying ages and dependent on the sex of the insured. Relate to students that the premiums charged females are lower than those charged males to reflect the longer expected lifespan of females.

Emphasize that the premium figures in the table in Illustration 74–1 are for units of $1,000 of life insurance. Also point out that the actual rates companies will quote may vary from those shown in the table. After mortality tables are considered, insurance rates are based on the size of the policy, rate of return promised in the policy, expenses of the insurer, lifestyle of the customer, and other features designed to make the policy unique.

Students should know that the premiums on life insurance policies that pay dividends are higher than those of policies that pay no dividends. However, over the life of the policy, the dividends received actually lower the net premium. The net cost of insurance is the total premiums minus the total of the dividends and the cash value of the policy.

SECTION 75. LIFE INSURANCE BENEFITS

All life insurance policies pay death benefits. In addition, some policies accumulate cash value and offer several options to the policyholder. The cash value table shown in Illustration 75–1 illustrates the potential use of accumulated cash value. Point out to students that this feature of cash value policies provides the flexibility needed by an insured to change insurance coverage to match changing needs.

At the time the policy is issued, some companies may offer the insured the option of declaring how dividends will be treated. Dividend notices are later sent to the policyholder, but for information purposes only.

Endowment policies are not treated in this edition because they are not popular and have been replaced by other types of policies, such as universal life. Universal life policies are not covered in this text because they can take an almost unlimited number of forms that are subject to change during the life of the policy.

SECTION 76. HEALTH AND ACCIDENT INSURANCE

Because of rising health care costs, many companies are competing in the health insurance field by offering health care options that aim to reduce premium costs. The benefits and costs of various health care plans may be examined by students as a class project. As group health plans are discussed, students should be made aware that this fringe benefit is a major business expense of employers.

Coordinated benefits clauses usually appear in health and accident insurance policies. This ensures that benefits and payments for services are not duplicated if parents and family members are covered by competing insurance plans.

SECTION 77. PROPERTY INSURANCE

Insurance policies are fairly standard from one company to another in terms of basic coverages. The actual terms, such as the amount of the deductible and coinsurance rates, will vary among companies. For example, the coinsurance rate for renters insurance at some companies is 100%, requiring property to be insured at its full value. A bulletin board display may be made of homeowners and renters policies obtained from a local agent.

In addition to other factors, insurance rates are based on the geographic location of homes and their access to aid in the event of fire. Students may research the rates charged in different communities and discuss other reasons for the rate differences.

In actual practice, the premiums charged on property insurance are rounded to the nearest dollar, and that practice has been adopted in this text.

SECTION 78. COLLECTING ON PROPERTY INSURANCE

Comments and Suggestions. This section presents the various ways in which owners may collect on their policies for losses. Make certain students understand that they will not collect more than the amount of insurance they carry.

Although homeowners may insure their property with only one insurer, business firms that require large coverage and that have a high risk of exposure from the standpoint of the insurer may have to insure their property with several insurers. Any loss that occurs will have to be divided among the insurers after they agree on the amount of the loss.

Replacement cost policies have become more popular with homeowners because they are automatically adjusted for inflation and do not make deductions for depreciation. These policies pay the current replacement cost of the property insured, up to the face of the policy, provided the owner has met the minimum insurance coverage provisions of the policy.

Computer Clinic. The student is asked to load the Spreadsheet Applications Diskette and call up the file Sec78 and enter data relating to a loss of property to find the amount of the loss that an insurer will cover. The spreadsheet can be used for standard coinsurance problems as well as those based on replacement cost.

SECTION 79. AUTOMOBILE INSURANCE

The textbook problems are based on separate rates for bodily injury, property damage, collision, and comprehensive coverage. As pointed out in the textbook, some states combine bodily injury and property damage into a single limit coverage per accident. One premium is charged for this combined coverage.

Car and truck insurance rates vary widely, so you may want to supplement the textbook problems with problems based on rates in your area. You may also want to have the problems in the text solved on the basis of your local rates. Insurance agents are able to provide information about local rates from which you can prepare tables similar to the one in Illustration 79–1 of the textbook.

In states with *no-fault* insurance, additional charges are made for uninsured motorists, medical payments, and work loss benefits insurance. Optional insurance coverage may provide for use of a rental car if an insured vehicle has been damaged and is being repaired.

Unit 13. Finding and Distributing Business Income and Loss

In Unit 13, the students work with forms and problems related to the balance sheet and income statement. Students also learn how to distribute net income or net loss to the owners of a sole proprietorship, partnership, or corporation. The distribution of the assets of a bankrupt business is also covered.

Student learning objectives for Unit 13 appear on the Unit 13 opener page in the textbook.

Integrated Project for Unit 13. This project integrates the concepts and procedures involved in working with balance sheets, income statements, distribution of income to owners, and bankruptcy. The project is found at the end of Unit 13 in the workbook. In *Integrated Project 13*, students are given a balance sheet and an income statement for a partnership and are asked to distribute income. Questions are also asked about the impact on income distribution if the partnership incorporates. The financial status of a bankrupt competitor of the partnership is also investigated.

Vocabulary Review for Unit 13. A vocabulary exercise, *Vocabulary Review: Unit 13*, is found at the end of Unit 13 in the workbook. The exercise reviews 23 of the vocabulary terms presented in Unit 13 of the textbook. Following the pattern established in earlier units, students write the terms, rather than list a matching letter or number, thereby gaining the opportunity to practice spelling key terms.

Supplementary Problems for Unit 13. Fifteen word problems similar to those provided in the exercises for Unit 13 are presented in the *Supplementary Problems for Unit 13* section of **Appendix B.**

Transparencies for Unit 13. Three transparency masters that may be used to illustrate important concepts are provided in the teacher's edition of the workbook.

Test for Unit 13. A review test for Unit 13 is provided in the test package (M473) and the MicroEXAM package. The test is designed to measure student achievement of the learning objectives of Unit 13.

Solutions for Unit 13. Solutions to all text problems and the unit test are included in this manual. Solutions to all workbook problems are included in the teacher's edition of the workbook.

Additional Resources for Unit 13. The financial pages of the daily newspaper and other financial publications frequently report corporate earnings and dividend payments. The material in those resources may be correlated with textbook examples and problems to show their application to everyday business activities. Here are two additional resources:

1. Information and materials pertaining to the preparation of an analysis of financial statements may be obtained by writing the American Institute of Certified Public Accountants, 1211 Avenue of the Americas, New York, New York, 10036. The Securities and Exchange Commission in Washington, DC also provides similar information.

2. Single copies of annual reports may be obtained by writing to major corporations. The reports contain financial statements and often contain a percentage analysis of the statements.

    Stock brokerage offices may also have copies of corporate annual reports and may be able to provide teachers with sample stock certificates and brochures explaining how to read and interpret financial statements.

SECTION 80. THE BALANCE SHEET

It is not essential that students memorize the format of the balance sheet. However, they should thoroughly understand the meaning and relationship of assets, liabilities, and capital. Knowledge of the balance sheet will help them understand the problems in bankruptcy that are presented in Section 86.

All of the examples and problems in this section are based on small businesses. You may want to extend your instruction to include discussion of assets, liabilities, capital, and the balance sheet as they apply to personal finance.

To show the application of balance sheets to personal and business use, obtain the balance sheet forms used by local banks for loan applications. Share them with students through classroom presentation or a bulletin board display.

SECTION 81. FINDING PROFIT AND LOSS

This section introduces students to the logic, terms, and procedures of figuring profit and loss in merchandising businesses. This is done as preparation for study of the formal income statement in Section 82. It is important for students to master the concepts in this section because they relate to the subject matter presented in the units dealing with purchasing and selling for a business.

You may find it helpful to put the following diagram on the chalkboard to show the relationship of the component parts of net sales. Note that the diagram is not drawn to scale.

By referring to the diagram, show that the net sales minus the cost of merchandise sold equals the gross profit; that the cost of merchandise sold plus the gross profit equals the net sales; that the gross profit minus the expenses equals the net income; and that the expenses plus the net income equals the gross profit. Also show that the net sales is equal to the sum of the merchandise sold, the expenses, and the net income.

You may want to illustrate the effect of increases and reductions in operating expenses on net income and net loss, assuming a given gross profit on sales.

The process of finding the cost of merchandise sold may be the most difficult item in this section for students to understand. Remind the students that they have already worked similar problems beginning with the related problems in Section 4. Demonstrate how the solutions for those problems are related to the procedure for finding the cost of merchandise sold.

Be sure to emphasize that gross profit on sales is essentially the difference between the amount of money received for a quantity of goods valued at selling prices (net sales) and the same quantity of goods valued at cost prices paid to buy the goods (cost of merchandise sold). Any inventory losses caused by deterioration, damage, theft, and other causes are assumed to be reflected in the ending inventory amount.

SECTION 82. THE INCOME STATEMENT

This section focuses on three topics: the income statement, percentage analysis of the income statement, and merchandise turnover rate.

A formal income statement is presented for a retail store, Lynn's Book Place. Point out how the elements of the income statement and the procedures for finding net income and net loss are related to the material studied in the previous section.

Because banks require business borrowers to complete an income statement, that form may also be obtained from a bank and shared with students.

As students calculate the percentage analysis for an income statement, point out that this is a common business practice that allows management to make internal and external comparisons. Percentages are used because they show relationships better by providing a constant reference to a net sales base, which is always 100%. Actual dollar amounts vary considerably and cannot be compared directly very easily.

The procedures for calculating the merchandise turnover rate are relatively simple, requiring students to figure only a simple average and then to divide the cost of merchandise sold by that average and to express the rate as an annual or yearly rate. Emphasize that a turnover rate indicates a *number* of stock turns, and that turnover rates are highly variable among businesses.

SECTION 83. DISTRIBUTING PARTNERSHIP INCOME

Two points need special emphasis: (1) Partners may agree, and should agree in writing, to any way of sharing profits and losses that is acceptable to all parties; and (2) In the absence of an agreement, profits and losses are shared equally by all partners. The distribution of partnership profits in proportion to investments is a practical application of the principles of ratio and proportion that were introduced in an earlier section.

SECTION 84. MORE ABOUT DISTRIBUTING PARTNERSHIP INCOME

Other methods of distributing partnership income are presented in this section. These include paying interest on investments and distributing income according to fixed ratios or stated percents.

SECTION 85. DISTRIBUTING CORPORATE INCOME

The information about stock issued by corporations that was presented in Section 57 should be reviewed with students before presenting the new material in this section. Emphasize to students that owners of preferred stock are usually given preference in the distribution of dividends. So, when solving problems involving payment of dividends, students should figure dividends on preferred stock first, then on common stock.

SECTION 86. BANKRUPTCY

The study of bankruptcy presents another business application of the concept of ratio. Settlement with each creditor in a bankruptcy is made on the basis of the ratio of the cash available to pay creditors to the total of the creditors' claims. The rate that results from dividing the cash assets by the total claims may be expressed as a decimal, as a percent, or as cents on the dollar.

Unit 14. Purchasing for a Business

Some of the common buying problems of retailers are included in Unit 14. These include figuring purchase invoice extensions; adjusting for purchases returns and allowances; and finding trade, series, and cash discounts.

Student learning objectives for Unit 14 appear on the Unit 14 opener page in the text.

Integrated Project for Unit 14. In this project, students figure the single discount equivalent to a series of discounts to check an invoice for accuracy. They use the terms of the invoice to figure the discount period and credit period.

After a credit memorandum is applied to the invoice price, the cash price is figured. Students also calculate the amount that could be saved by borrowing to take advantage of the cash discount.

Vocabulary Review for Unit 14. A vocabulary exercise, *Vocabulary Review: Unit 14*, is found at the end of Unit 14 in the workbook. The exercise reviews 17 of the vocabulary terms presented in Unit 14 of the text. As they have done before, students write the terms, rather than listing a matching letter or number to complete the review, thereby gaining practice in spelling key terms.

Supplementary Problems for Unit 14. Fourteen word problems similar to those provided in the exercises for Unit 14 are presented in the *Supplementary Problems for Unit 14* section of **Appendix B.**

Transparencies for Unit 14. Three transparency masters that may be used to illustrate important concepts are provided in the teacher's edition of the workbook.

Test for Unit 14. A review test for Unit 14 is provided in the text package (M473) and the MicroEXAM package. The test is designed to measure student achievement of the learning objectives of Unit 14, except for the objectives dealing with the optional spreadsheet topic.

Solutions for Unit 14. Solutions to all text problems and the unit test are included in this manual. Solutions to all workbook problems are included in the teacher's edition of the workbook.

Additional Resources for Unit 14. There are many other resources that you can use to support or supplement the instruction in Unit 14. For example:

1. Community salespeople and small business owners are a useful source of information pertaining to typical trade discount and cash discount practices.

2. Various marketing textbooks and trade publications will provide information on traditional profit margins for various lines of merchandise that may be used to equate to rates of trade discount.

3. Students may inquire at local financial institutions about the practice of short-term borrowing by retailers and others to pay bills that may be coming due. The concept of line of credit may also be explored.

SECTION 87. PURCHASING MERCHANDISE

To stimulate student interest, display on the bulletin board some actual copies of purchase invoices that contain cash and trade discounts.

The multiplication of unit prices of $1 and fractional equivalents is presented in this section and initial practice is provided by Exercise 3. A few minutes of drill on Exercise 3 should be provided each day for two or three days. Then the process should be included regularly in the warmup drills through the use of *Drill 44* in **Appendix A.**

SECTION 88. TRADE DISCOUNTS

A chalkboard diagram, like the one following, may be used to show graphically the solution to the first example problem in this section, and to emphasize the relationship of list price, trade discount, and invoice price or cost. Point out that, whether expressed in terms of dollars or percents, the following relationships exist: (1) the invoice price equals the list price minus the trade discount; (2) the trade discount equals the list price minus the invoice price; (3) the list price equals the sum of the trade discount and the invoice price.

A blank transparency master may be used to provide more practice in figuring the amounts and percentages of various trade discounts and invoice prices, given a list price.

If they can be obtained, show an actual discount sheet and catalog with list prices to the class.

Chalkboard diagram of list price, trade discount, and invoice price.

| List Price $200 100% | Trade Discount $80 40% |
| | Invoice Price $120 60% |

SECTION 89. SERIES DISCOUNTS

Trade discounts in a series are also called chain discounts. Such discounts are used in several ways. If the market price of an article changes frequently, the manufacturer may establish a list price and a series of discounts. Price adjustments to changing market conditions would be made by allowing an additional discount or by changing or eliminating the last discount. So, if a seller's current discounts on an article are 30%, 10%, and 5%, the price can be lowered by allowing a fourth discount or raised by eliminating the third discount of the original three.

Often, in marketing consumer goods, the manufacturer's list price is the advertised or suggested retail price, with a discount of perhaps 35% allowed to the retailer and discounts of perhaps 35% and 15% allowed to the wholesaler. This allows a profit of 15% for the wholesaler on the selling price to the retailer, and a profit of 35% for the retailer on the regular selling price to the consumer.

Show students how to use the table of invoice price equivalents in Illustration 89–1. The horizontal line of rates at the top of the table lists a single rate and may be thought of as representing the first discount in a series. The rate(s) at the left of the table represent the remaining discount(s) in the discount series. The point at which the rates intersect is the single discount equivalent.

Be sure to stress that a single discount equivalent to a series of discounts cannot be calculated by adding the discounts.

SECTION 90. CASH DISCOUNTS

A chalkboard diagram similar to the one used for trade discounts can be used to show the relationship of the invoice price, cash discount, and cash price.

The logic of discounts for cash payments may also be extended to consumer purchases where a differential is charged for cash and credit purchases. This is done to stimulate cash purchases so that the seller receives money for goods that may be used, in turn, to pay the seller's suppliers.

Cash discount is always figured on the invoice price, before any special charges are added. If the seller has paid the shipping charge and has added it to the invoice, the cash discount is figured on the amount of the invoice before the charge was added. The buyer is not permitted to take a discount on the shipping charge.

SECTION 91. MORE ABOUT CASH DISCOUNTS

Comments and Suggestions. Although retailers may borrow money to pay an invoice to get a cash discount, they do so only when the amount of the discount is greater than the interest expense on their loan. Point out to students that money may also be borrowed to take advantage of a special purchase or discount offered by the wholesaler or manufacturer.

Computer Clinic. Students are asked to call up the file Sec91 and enter the data given. The spreadsheet program will figure the amount of cash discount, the interest on money borrowed to take advantage of the discount, and the net amount saved by borrowing.

Unit 15. Selling for a Business

In the previous unit, students learned many of the arithmetic tasks associated with purchasing goods for businesses. In this unit, students will learn arithmetic tasks associated with selling goods for a business. These tasks include proving cash with a cash register, keeping customer accounts, figuring discounts and prices, finding profit on unit sales, and pricing goods using sales and cost prices for a basis.

Integrated Project for Unit 15. A project that integrates many of the pricing, costing, and other selling activities found in retail and wholesale businesses is included in the workbook at the end of Unit 15. The project lets students review cash proofs, customer accounts, discounting stock for quick sale, finding gross profit, finding profits on unit sales, finding the highest cost price to be paid for a given rate of markup on the selling price, finding the selling price based on cost, and finding the rate of markup based on selling price.

Vocabulary Review for Unit 15. A vocabulary review exercise that reviews the terms in Unit 15 is included at the end of the unit in the workbook.

Supplementary Problems for Unit 15. Word problems similar to those found in Unit 15 are presented in the *Supplementary Problems for Unit 15* section of **Appendix B.**

Transparencies for Unit 15. Three transparency masters that illustrate important concepts in Unit 15 are provided in the teacher's edition of the workbook.

Test for Unit 15. A review test for Unit 15 is provided in the test package (M473) and in the MicroEXAM package.

Solutions for Unit 15. Solutions to all text problems and the unit test are included in this manual. Solutions to all workbook problems are included in the teacher's edition of the workbook.

Additional Resources for Unit 15. Much useful information about the selling and pricing activities of businesses can be obtained by contacting area business firms and organizations. For example:

1. Community salespeople and owners are a useful source of information pertaining to common markup, markdown, trade discount, and cash discount practices. They are also a useful source for selling and pricing forms, such as sales slips, invoices, credit memos, cash proof forms, and account forms. These forms can be used to solve class problems or as a display on a bulletin board.

2. Area equipment manufacturers or distributors can be contacted to display and/or demonstrate cash registers, bar code printers, bar code readers, and various customer accounting systems.

Helpful, first-hand information may be obtained from students in the cooperative education program at your school, if you have one. For example:

1. Cooperative education students who are using cash registers on the job might be invited to address the class on making change, using cash registers, proving cash, and dealing with customer problems.

2. Cooperative education students who are serving as retail sales clerks may be invited to address the class on pricing schemes and tools.

SECTION 92. CASH SALES RECORDS

Comments and Suggestions. In some firms, the change fund is removed from the cash drawer before cash is proved. If so, the gross amount to be accounted for at the end of the work period is the total cash received less the total cash paid out.

Electronic cash registers perform many functions and produce many different types of records and reports. Students should be encouraged to report about registers they have seen or used. You may wish to obtain colorful brochures explaining the features of cash registers from cash register or office equipment companies.

Many supermarkets and fast food stores provide proof of cash forms for their cashiers and daily and weekly cash summaries for their managers. You may wish to obtain samples of these forms from area stores for classroom discussion.

Computer Clinic. Spreadsheet Sec92 is a cash proof form. The student enters data pertaining to the change fund, the register readings, and the cash on hand. The spreadsheet provides the amount of cash that should be on hand and the amount of any cash short or over.

You may wish to have students use the spreadsheet to complete the cash proofs found in Exercise 1 in Section 92.

SECTION 93. CHARGE SALES RECORDS

Point out to students that a seller's sales invoice is a purchase invoice to the buyer. You may wish to obtain sample invoices, account forms, and credit memos from area firms for bulletin board display or classroom discussion.

SECTION 94. FIGURING DISCOUNTS AND PRICES

A chalkboard diagram like the one that follows can be used to show the relationship of the marked price, discount, and selling price. The figures used in the diagram are those used in the first example problem from Section 94.

Point out that, whether shown in dollars or percents, the selling price equals the marked price minus the discount, and the marked price equals the sum of the discount and the selling price.

Discount is the difference between two quantities and is always based on the larger of the two. So, in problems such as those in Exercise 2, the discount should be based on the gross value of the goods or services received. In Problem 1, for example, the discount is the amount by which the cost of five tapes at the regular price exceeds the cost of five tapes at the special sales price.

Chalkboard diagrams will aid students in understanding the solutions to problems in which they are to find the marked price when the selling price and rate of discount are known. The diagrams can also be used by students to check their work. To make a diagram of the second example in Section 94, use this procedure:

1. Make 3 rectangular diagrams, labeling them "Marked Price," "Discount," and "Selling Price."

2. Now insert the known data into the rectangles:
   a. 100% in the rectangle for the marked price, since the marked price is always the base, or 100%.
   b. $24.80 in the selling price rectangle.
   c. 20% in the discount rectangle.

3. Find the percent for the selling price by subtracting the discount percent (20%) from the market price percent (100%). Enter the result (80%) in the selling price rectangle. Now the selling price rectangle shows that 80% of the marked price equals $24.80.

4. The marked price is now figured by the unknown-factor method, and the result, $31, is inserted in the marked price rectangle.

5. Find the amount of the discount (multiply the marked price by 20%). Enter the amount of the discount ($6.20) in the discount rectangle. Check your work by subtracting the amount of the discount from the marked price. The result should be $24.80, the amount of the selling price.

To make the problems in this section realistic, you might ask an area retailer or buyer to address the class on price lines of merchandise, discounts, and selecting a competitive selling price. You might also ask cooperative education students who are working in retail stores to visit the class and discuss pricing, discounts, and marked prices.

SECTION 95. FINDING PROFIT ON UNIT SALES

Chalkboard diagrams like those used in Section 94 should also be used in Section 95 to show graphically the relationship between selling price, cost, gross profit, operating expenses, and net income. Emphasize the three elements constituting the selling price: cost, operating expenses, and net income. Show that in a profitable business the selling price must be large enough to cover the cost, operating expenses, and a reasonable net income.

SECTION 96. PRICING GOODS—SALES PRICE BASIS

Comments and Suggestions. Diagrams can help explain the solution to the problems in this section. For example, the following diagram illustrates the solution for the first example problem in Section 96.

To make the diagram, follow this procedure:

1. Make and label rectangles for selling price, markup, and cost price.

2. Insert the known data into the rectangles:
    a. 100% in the rectangle for the selling price, since the problem states that the markup is based on the selling price.
    b. $50 in the selling price rectangle.
    c. 40% in the markup rectangle.

```
┌─────────────┐      ┌─────────────┐
│             │      │   Markup    │
│             │      │    40%      │
│             │      │    $20      │
│ Selling Price│      └─────────────┘
│    100%     │
│    $50      │      ┌─────────────┐
│             │      │ Cost Price  │
│             │      │    60%      │
│             │      │    $30      │
└─────────────┘      └─────────────┘
```

3. Since the markup is based on the selling price, the amount in the selling price rectangle is multiplied by the percent in the markup rectangle. Insert the product, $20, in the markup rectangle.

4. Subtract the amount in the markup rectangle from the amount in the selling price rectangle and insert the result, $30, in the cost rectangle. This amount is the answer to the problem.

5. Complete the diagram by inserting 60% in the cost rectangle. Prove your answer by multiplying the selling price by the rate of cost (60%).

Computer Clinic. Spreadsheet Sec96 is a pricing spreadsheet for a company that uses the sales price as a basis for pricing. It is designed to provide either the highest cost that should be paid, when the selling price and markup are known, or the selling price, when the cost and markup are known.

When the selling price and markup are known, the student enters these data into Column B of the spreadsheet, "Cost Price Missing." The spreadsheet computes the markup and cost in dollars and the cost in percent.

Column C is designed for those students completing the optional topics in the section. When the cost price and markup are known, students enter these data into Column C of the spreadsheet. The spreadsheet computes the selling price and markup in dollars and the markup and cost in percents.

You may wish to have students use the spreadsheet to complete Exercises 1 and 2 in Section 96.

SECTION 97. PRICING GOODS—COST PRICE BASIS

Using the cost price as the base for markup is simpler, more direct, and more easily understood than using the selling price as the base. It is still used by some businesses. Basing markup on cost, however, can easily lead to under-pricing of stock and gross profits too small to cover operating expenses and net income.

Diagrams similar to those described for the previous sections may be used to explain the problems in the section. The diagram that follows illustrates the solution to the example for "Finding the Selling Price You Need to Give You the Rate of Markup You Want on the Cost."

‡SECTION 98. SPECIAL PRICING PROBLEMS

All of the material in this section is optional. The following diagram may be used to explain the example that demonstrates how to find a markup based on cost that is equivalent to a markup based on selling price.

Students should develop an understanding of the reason why, to yield a given amount of markup, the rate of markup on cost must be greater than the rate of markup based on selling price.

Selling Price
100%
of selling price

Markup
20% of selling price
25% of cost

Cost Price
80%
of selling price

Unit 16. Manufacturing and Office Costs

In Unit 16, students learn how to identify and figure some of the costs that are associated with manufacturing and office activities. Many of the arithmetical problems in the unit are similar to those in previous units except that they occur in different settings.

Integrated Project for Unit 16. A small manufacturing company is used as the setting for the project. The project allows the students to review most of the word problems included in Unit 16.

Vocabulary Review for Unit 16. A vocabulary exercise that reviews the terms in Unit 16 is included at the end of the unit in the workbook.

Supplementary Problems for Unit 16. Word problems similar to those found in Unit 16 are presented in the *Supplementary Problems for Unit 16* section of **Appendix B.**

Transparencies for Unit 16. Several transparency masters drawn from the illustrations in Unit 16 are provided in the teacher's edition of the workbook.

Test for Unit 16. A review test for Unit 16 is provided in the test package (M473) and the MicroEXAM package.

Solutions for Unit 16. Solutions to all text problems and the unit test are included in this manual. Solutions to all workbook problems are included in the teacher's edition of the workbook.

Additional Resources for Unit 16. There are many sources that can be helpful to you in teaching Unit 16. Some examples include:

1. The National Association of Manufacturers provides a variety of publications with information about the manufacturing process, common problems of manufacturers, and other information.

2. Area bookstores provide tax books, sold to individuals to help them prepare their tax forms, that contain the latest information pertaining to the tax laws for depreciation.

3. The nearest office of the Internal Revenue Service will provide the business teacher with a booklet listing various types of plant and equipment assets and the recommended number of years over which they should be depreciated.

4. The area chapter of the Data Processing Management Association will be a helpful source of information on computing costs. The same information may also be available from the data processing department of the school district, if the district has one.

5. Area chapters of the Association of Information Systems Professionals, the Administrative Management Society, and the Association of Records Managers and Administrators can be helpful sources of information pertaining to office costs and office productivity. These chapters will also prove helpful in obtaining speakers for your classroom.

6. Recent editions of college accounting textbooks will provide a discussion and many examples of computing acquisition, maintenance, and operating costs of plant and equipment. The purchasing department or business manager for the school district may also be a helpful resource.

7. Area parcel post, freight, and express offices will usually provide rate schedules that can be used in classroom problems. These offices also may have forms that are used to help clerks or customers calculate total shipping costs. The use of local rate schedules and actual forms to calculate shipping costs makes the unit much more interesting to most students.

8. *Financial Cookbook* is a software package providing 32 programs for computing solutions to business problems such as depreciation, mortgage interest, savings, and credit. It is created by Electronic Arts and published by South-Western Publishing Company, 5101 Madison Road, Cincinnati, OH 45227, 1986.

SECTION 99. FACTORY COSTS

Records of the costs of raw materials, direct labor, and factory overhead are kept for the factory as a whole. Periodic reports of these records provide information to managers pertaining to the costs of goods manufactured during the period.

In manual record keeping systems, a cost sheet may be used. This sheet follows each order as it passes through a factory. On the cost sheet, a record is kept of the cost of the materials and direct labor used to produce the order.

Factory overhead, on the other hand, usually must be estimated because these expenses are for the factory as a whole, not a particular order or a particular department. In addition to the methods used in the problems in the exercises, overhead may be estimated by taking a percent of one of the direct costs attributed to an order, such as direct labor or raw materials. Sometimes the percent is taken on the total direct costs.

Recently, many manufacturing plants have begun to automate the process of recording manufacturing costs through computer software. The software is often referred to as MRP software, or manufacturing resource planning software. This software often is used to keep track of raw materials, direct labor costs, and other cost accounting events.

SECTION 100. FINDING THE BREAK-EVEN POINT

In presenting how to figure gross profit and net income, you may wish to use a diagram similar to that suggested for Section 81 to show graphically the relationship of selling price, cost, gross profit, selling and administrative expenses, and net income.

The presentation on finding the break-even point is designed to help students understand the basic concept of breaking even by controlling costs and setting selling prices.

SECTION 101. DEPRECIATION COSTS

Comments and Suggestions. Four types of depreciation are presented in this edition: straight-line depreciation in Section 65; the declining-balance method, the sum-of-the-years-digits method, and the modified accelerated cost recovery system (MACRS) in Section 101. The modified accelerated cost recovery system method is optional and is intended for the more able and interested student.

Students should recognize that the straight-line method results in the same amount of depreciation each year. They should also recognize that the declining-balance and sum-of-the-years-digits methods provide a more realistic picture of the value of assets as they usually occur. The MACRS is usually mandatory for depreciating many types of assets for income tax purposes under IRS regulations.

You may want to present another method of depreciation, called the *unit of performance* or *production-unit* method. In this method, depreciation is figured on the number of hours a machine has operated, how many products or units it has produced, or how many miles it has run. For example, airplane and boat motors are often depreciated on the basis of how many hours they have been flown or driven, and factory cutting tools are often depreciated on the basis of the number of items they have cut.

To figure the depreciation for one year, you divide the actual numbers of hours, miles, or units that occurred in that year by the estimated number of hours, miles, or units the machine is expected to last. The resulting decimal is multiplied by the depreciable cost of the machine (original cost less salvage value).

SECTION 102. OFFICE COSTS

Many of your students will eventually work in offices, so they should know the value of time, equipment, and supplies in office work.

You may wish to ask a word processing supervisor or an office manager from an area office to address the class on the topics of work measurement, work standards, office productivity, or office costs. Such an address will not only provide students with current data pertaining to costs, but it will also demonstrate to students the importance business firms place on productivity.

Office supply firms in your area also provide a rich source of information about the cost of office equipment and supplies. You may wish to visit or call several of them to obtain copies of their catalogs.

SECTION 103. PAYROLL COSTS

Comments and Suggestions. The work with payroll registers and employee earnings records in this section continues the work with time cards in Section 13 and with figuring deductions in Section 21. You may wish to review briefly the use of time cards and the use of FICA and withholding tables.

The payroll register and employee earnings record require horizontal addition. Both these forms permit accounting clerks to cross-check their totals, providing an internal check of accuracy. Students should understand the need for internal accuracy checks when handling and accounting for money.

Payroll taxes paid by employers are a large expense of many business firms. The employer's responsibility for FICA, FUTA, and state unemployment taxes (SUTA) are presented in this section to help students understand business practices and appreciate the cost of employees to businesses. To complete the discussion, you may wish to review with students some of the fringe benefits that also add to the cost of employees.

You may wish to have a payroll clerk from an area accounting office address the class on the clerk's duties, responsibilities, typical work problems, and forms used for payroll and payroll taxes in the office.

Computer Clinic. A payroll register is presented in the computer clinic. Students are asked to enter payroll data and answer questions about the completed register. They are also asked to enter changes in the overtime hours worked and to assess the differences in total net pay that changes generate.

The spreadsheet may be used by students to complete other problems presented in the text.

SECTION 104. SHIPPING COSTS

When the terms are f.o.b. shipping point, the seller may send the shipment collect or prepay the shipping charges and add the amount to the invoice. The latter procedure is always used for parcel-post shipments since the U.S. Postal Service will not accept a parcel-post package unless the postage is paid in advance.

The distinction between express and freight service is not always clear in the real world. In general, express service is considered to be a relatively faster service than freight service.

When shipping goods, you should check on the relative costs and services of parcel post, express, and freight so that the most satisfactory service may be used in each case. Usually, it is more economical to send heavy shipments by freight and light shipments by express or parcel post. The cost of express service is sometimes less than parcel post, and sometimes more. When speed is more important than cost, air express, air freight, and express mail are available. Shipping arrangements for delivery overnight, same-day, next-day, or two-days can be made, but the rates will be more expensive.

Pictures, folders, other printed material, and rate information can be obtained from local express and freight agencies and your area post office.

Rates charged for shipping and the types of services offered change frequently because competition between the various carriers is high.

SECTION 105. COMPUTER COSTS

This section provides students with problems pertaining to the costs of buying and leasing computer hardware and software, developing software, and computer storage. Other costs of computer systems, such as computer supplies, have been included in other sections.

Computer costs are highly volatile. The costs used in this section were costs commonly charged at the time this text was prepared. However, the basic arithmetic and problem-solving principles presented in the section are useful to learn regardless of the changes in prices.

You may wish to stress that computer systems are comprised of both hardware and software, and that the total cost of the system must include installation costs. You may also point out that with microcomputer systems, software costs may easily exceed hardware costs, especially for systems with a large number of applications.

While the costs of computer hardware have been falling, the costs of software development have not. Recently, firms have turned to using higher-level programming languages, called fourth-generation programming languages, to improve their programmer productivity. Many firms that use fourth-generation programming languages claim that the average lines of code produced per day is as much as five times what it was using conventional programming languages.

Students should understand that programmers can write much more than 20–40 lines of code each day. However, after a programmer tests, debugs, revises, and documents the code that has been written, national studies show that 20–40 lines of "finished" code per day is a very good output per programmer.

You may wish to get printouts of computer program codes for display in class. You may also wish to have students contact or visit local computer dealers to compare prices of equipment and software.

Unit 17. Business Statistics and Graphs

In Unit 17, students become acquainted with various ways of presenting and interpreting numerical data. Students first study various ways to figure averages and probability. They then learn to read and prepare different types of graphs relating to business applications. Commonly used statistics published by federal agencies about consumer prices and unemployment in the labor force are also introduced.

Student learning objectives for Unit 17 appear on the Unit 17 opener page in the text.

Integrated Project for Unit 17. In this project, students assume responsibility for preparing graphs to be used in a management report of unit sales and unit production. In addition, students prepare a report on employment and the effect of cost-of-living raises on total costs.

Vocabulary Review for Unit 17. A vocabulary exercise, *Vocabulary Review: Unit 17*, is found at the end of Unit 17 in the workbook. The exercise reviews 21 of the vocabulary terms presented in Unit 17 of the text. In completing this exercise, students write the terms, rather than listing a matching letter or number, thereby gaining an opportunity to practice spelling key terms.

Supplementary Problems for Unit 17. Ten word problems similar to those provided in the exercises for Unit 17 are presented in the *Supplementary Problems for Unit 17* section of **Appendix B.**

Transparencies for Unit 17. Ten transparency masters that may be used to illustrate important concepts are provided in the teacher's edition of the workbook.

Test for Unit 17. A review test for Unit 17 is provided in the test package (M473) and the MicroEXAM package. The test is designed to measure student achievement of the learning objectives for Unit 17.

Solutions for Unit 17. Solutions to all text problems and the unit test are included in this manual. Solutions to all workbook problems are included in the teacher's edition of the workbook.

Additional Resources for Unit 17. Some specific resources that may also be used by the teacher follow:

1. *Statistical Abstract of the United States*, U.S. Bureau of the Census, Washington, D.C. 20233. This annual publication contains statistical data for a great number of areas. Of particular interest is statistical data relating to the Consumer Price Index, purchasing power of the dollar, inflation, and employment.

2. *Consumer Price Index Detailed Report*, U.S. Department of Labor, Bureau of Labor Statistics, Washington, D.C. 20212. This monthly publication provides information on both the general level of consumer prices and by various categories of goods and services purchased. Price information is also given on the individual items that make up the "market basket" of goods and services usually bought by consumers.

3. *Employment and Earnings*, U.S. Department of Labor, Bureau of Labor Statistics, Washington, D.C. 20212. Detailed statistics about employment at the national and state levels are provided in this comprehensive publication.

4. *Chances are . . .*, Insurance Information Institute, 110 William St., New York, New York, 10038. A programmed instruction book on probability.

5. *Sets, Probability, and Statistics*, Institute of Life Insurance, Education Services, 277 Park Avenue, New York, New York, 10017. A booklet on the application of probability and statistics to life insurance.

6. Johnson, Dale M., *Probability and Statistics*, South-Western Publishing Co., 5101 Madison Road, Cincinnati, OH 45221, 1989.

7. Business magazines and newspapers provide examples of bar, line, and circle graphs pertaining to business topics. The articles accompanying graphs also provide students with an example of how statistical data are interpreted.

SECTION 106. MEASURES OF CENTRAL TENDENCY

As students study the mean, median, and mode as measures of central tendency, they should soon learn that the term "average" may be misleading. Depending on the measure used, computed averages may vary widely even though the same base data are being used to make computations. For example, labor unions and the management of a company may calculate the average pay of employees and arrive at amounts that differ greatly.

As a project, have students look for tables or statements that present an average. Newspapers, magazines, and books are common sources of statistical data.

SECTION 107. PROBABILITY

You may wish to have a coin-tossing experiment performed in class to compare the results with the theoretical expectation of equal heads and tails. Have each student flip a coin once on the desk top. By a show of hands, determine how many came up heads and how many tails, and list the results in two columns on the chalkboard. Repeat the tossing ten or fifteen times. Show the cumulative totals at the end of each trial and the percent of heads in each total. Assuming there are thirty students in the class, the results of the first three trials might appear as shown at the right.

Trial		Totals		%
H	T	H	T	H
18	12	18	12	60
16	14	34	26	57
13	17	47	43	52

SECTION 108. BAR AND LINE GRAPHS

Many business data are presented in graph form rather than, or in addition to, table form. The problems in this section and in Section 109 require students to (a) interpret data represented in graph form, and (b) prepare graphs showing business data.

By referring to the illustrations in the text, point out to students these general characteristics of good graphs:

1. The heading and the scales clearly identify the data being presented.

2. Increments are used to make the graph easy to read; spacing of increments is constant.

3. In bar and line graphs, the horizontal line or axis shows time or other fixed items; the vertical line or axis shows the variable(s).

4. The possibility of misinterpretation is minimized.

Emphasize to students that, although many data may be appropriately graphed in several ways, these guidelines are generally used:

1. A bar graph is used to show the comparative size of two or more quantities or values.

2. A line graph is used to show fluctuations in one or more quantities or values over a period of time.

3.   The rectangle or circle graphs presented in Section 109 are used to show the relationship of parts to the whole and to each other.

Many other business-oriented graphs can be found in annual reports. These materials can be used for classroom discussion and analysis, and for preparing informative displays. You may want to stress graphs showing general economic data and data pertaining to local activities or interests such as farming, fishing, manufacturing, or marketing.

Before students begin constructing graphs, be sure to review procedures for rounding, especially when rounding to amounts such as the nearest $1,000, $2,000, $10,000, and so on. Students will have to round data to some whole number as they complete the exercises in Sections 108 and 109.

SECTION 109. RECTANGLE AND CIRCLE GRAPHS

If students do not have a compass, they may use a round object, such as a can or the lid of a jar to draw a circle. Also, they may construct a rough protractor by drawing a line to divide a circle in half. The half-circle of 180 degrees may in turn be divided in half to form two 90-degree parts. Repeatedly dividing the parts into halves and labeling the degrees they represent will allow students to use this "protractor" to at least produce an approximation of a graph marked in degrees.

SECTION 110. ECONOMIC STATISTICS

Commonly used measures of inflation and unemployment are presented in this section. The rates and amounts in this text may vary slightly because government agencies use different methods or definitions to compile the data that go into their final report. For example, one source may figure the difference between data for January 1 of successive years and calculate the annual percentage change that took place. Another source may analyze data monthly and determine annual rates by averaging monthly data.

In discussing the Consumer Price Index, students may be told that the CPI is a measure of a typical "market basket" of goods and services purchased by consumers across the country. Prices are collected and then compared with previous data.

The value of the current index tells how much prices have changed from the base period to the present. When comparing time periods after the base period, such as from year to year, the following process may be used to calculate the percent change.

Current CPI	312.0	Change	12.0
Less previous CPI	300.0	Divided by previous CPI	300.0
Change	12.0	Equals	0.04
		Times one hundred	0.04×100
		Equals percent change	4%

Beginning with the data for January, 1988 as reported in February, 1988, most Consumer Price Indexes have a new base of 1982–84. The former 1967 base and data relative to that base were retained in this text to simplify the explanations for the historical data presented. Samples of CPI tables with the new base may be shown to students to reinforce the concept that the base is always equal to the index 100.

UNIT 1 • MONEY RECORDS

Section 1. Cash Receipts Records

Exercise 1, page 2

1. $4,385.69   2. $612.38   3. $1,029.19   4. $22,429.98

Exercise 3, page 4

1. $62.70   2. $222.47   3. $250.26
4. $282.00   5. $220.20   6. $227.03

Exercise 4, page 4

1. $23,582.81   2. $1,066.76   3. $3,055.33   4. $770.40   5. $53,713.42

Section 2. Cash Payments Records

Exercise 1, page 9

1. $348.82   2. $1,172.10   3. $11,209.53   4. $1,241.71   5. $956.90

Exercise 3, page 11

1. $5 + 4 = 4 + 5$ 5. $6 + 3 = 9$ 9. $9 - 6 = 7 - 4$
2. $8 + 7 = 7 + 8$ 6. $4 + 5 = 7 + 2$ 10. $3 + 12 = 15$
3. $19 - 4 = 6 + 9$ 7. $8 - 3 = 2 + 3$ 11. $1 + 6 = 9 - 2$
4. $18 - 9 = 4 + 5$ 8. $8 + 5 = 7 + 6$ 12. $3 + 9 = 14 - 2$

Exercise 4, page 12

1. a. 3
   b. 4
   c. 9
   d. 6
   e. 7
   f. Thirty-four thousand, nine hundred sixty-seven

2. a. 6   3. a. 2,000
   b. 1   b. 500
   c. 8   c. 70
   d. 5   d. 1

4. a. 5,000
   b. 300
   c. 80
   d. 9
   e. Five thousand, three hundred eighty-nine

5. **a.**
```
   900
    80
+   7
   987
```
b.
```
 3,000
   500
    10
+    2
 3,512
```
c.
```
 7,000
   600
+    5
 7,605
```
d.
```
 9,000
    80
+    7
 9,087
```

e.
```
 1,000
    70
+    8
 1,078
```
f.
```
10,000
 2,000
   800
    80
+    3
12,883
```
g.
```
20,000
+ 5,000
25,000
```
h.
```
50,000
 6,000
   700
    80
+    3
56,783
```

6. **a.** Nine hundred eighty-seven
  b. Three thousand, five hundred twelve
  c. Seven thousand, six hundred five
  d. Nine thousand, eighty-seven
  e. One thousand, seventy-eight
  f. Twelve thousand, eight hundred eighty-three
  g. Twenty-five thousand
  h. Fifty-six thousand, seven hundred eighty-three

7. **a.** 432   **b.** 234
  c. Two hundred forty-three, three hundred twenty-four, four hundred thirty-two, two hundred thirty-four, four hundred twenty-three, three hundred forty-two.

8. **a.** 853   **b.** 358

9. **a.**
```
 4,000
   900
    30
+    5
 4,935
```
b.
```
 9,000
    10
+    7
 9,017
```
c.
```
10,000
 6,000
   300
    80
+    7
16,387
```

d.
```
 8,000
   200
+    3
 8,203
```
e.
```
60,000
 1,000
   800
+   90
61,890
```
f.
```
20,000
 4,000
   600
    20
+    9
24,629
```

10. **a.** Four thousand, nine hundred thirty-five
  b. Nine thousand, seventeen
  c. Sixteen thousand, three hundred eighty-seven
  d. Eight thousand, two hundred three
  e. Sixty-one thousand, eight hundred ninety
  f. Twenty-four thousand, six hundred twenty-nine

Review 2, page 13

2. **a.** 31   **b.** 278   **c.** 295.19   **d.** $2,985.24

3. $531.93 + $3.25 + $51.77 + $50.00 + $28.56 + $167.32 = $832.83

4. $267.91 + $248.09 + $264.33 + $275.26 = $1,055.59   total of Lee's paychecks
    $235.55 + $287.64 + $253.68 + $277.83 = $1,054.70   total of Alan's paychecks
    $1,055.59 + $1,054.70 = $2,110.29   total of combined paychecks

5. $2,600.00 + $467.29 + $251.72 + $9,207.78 + $1,508.09 + $2,078.21 + $2,145.00 = $18,258.09

6. $684.24 + $187.23 + $32.35 + $27.00 + $45.32 = $976.14

Section 3.   Columnar Cash Payments Records

Exercise 1, page 15

1.
```
 6 +  4 +  5 = 15
 3 +  6 +  7 = 16
 8 +  5 +  2 = 15
17 + 15 + 14 = 46
```

4.
```
 7 +  9 +  3 +  1 = 20
 5 +  5 +  6 +  8 = 24
 3 +  8 +  2 +  5 = 18
 4 +  4 +  2 +  7 = 17
19 + 26 + 13 + 21 = 79
```

2.
```
34 + 56 =  90
21 + 39 =  60
16 + 85 = 101
71 + 180 = 251
```

5.
```
  93 + 122 =   215
 237 + 154 =   391
 593 +  47 =   640
 134 +  89 =   223
1,057 + 412 = 1,469
```

3.
```
 24 +  33 +  53 = 110
 51 +  27 +  22 = 100
 33 +  96 +  56 = 185
108 + 156 + 131 = 395
```

6.
```
123 +  39 + 221 =   383
140 +  66 +  84 =   290
155 +  31 + 219 =   405
 79 +  51 + 106 =   236
497 + 187 + 630 = 1,314
```

Exercise 2, page 15

1.

Food		Clothing		Auto		Savings		Other		Total Payments
$15.76	+	$25.99	+	$15.23	+	$10.00	+	$ 3.25	=	$ 70.23
14.27	+			12.77	+			5.09	=	32.13
22.88	+	23.79	+	12.87	+	10.00	+	17.49	=	87.03
12.67	+			15.67	+			12.34	=	40.68
6.45	+			3.78	+			5.56	=	15.79
$72.03	+	$49.78	+	$60.32	+	$20.00	+	$43.73	=	$245.86

2.

Rent		Payroll		Office Expenses		Other Expenses		Total Payments
$975.00	+	$7,311.92	+	$345.61	+	$241.08	+	$ 8,873.61
		617.25	+	207.67	+	97.12	+	922.04
		617.25	+	89.56	+	178.31	+	885.12
		617.25	+	306.45	+	81.02	+	1,004.72
$975.00	+	$9,163.67	+	$949.29	+	$597.53	+	$11,685.49

Review 3, page 16

2. a. $15 + 4 = 19$ e. $35 - 20 = 15$ i. $14 + 15 = 7 + 22$
    b. $4 + 16 = 20$ f. $20 - 5 = 15$ j. $23 - 7 = 8 + 8$
    c. $0 + 4 = 4$ g. $22 - 0 = 22$
    d. $6 + 23 = 29$ h. $25 - 7 = 18$

3. $\$470.89 + \$592.93 + \$604.31 + \$556.82 + \$498.67 = \$2{,}723.62$ cash receipts

4. $\$478.00 + \$27.00 + \$145.23 + \$245.98 + \$25.98 + \$45.29 = \$967.48$ total spent

5. $\$250.50 + \$412.75 + \$324.25 = \$987.50$ total collected

6. $\$45.78 + \$135.98 + \$67.12 + \$12.76 + \$27.45 + \$15.77 + \$207.87 = \$512.73$ total spent

Section 4.   Check Register Records

Exercise 1, page 24

1.	Bills	$122.00		3.	Bills	$3,220.00
	Coins	3.30			Coins	201.82
	Checks	218.49			Checks	124.68
		+ 1.45				132.08
	Total deposit	$345.24				1.29
2.	Bills	$576.00			+	5.79
	Coins	16.45			Total deposit	$3,685.66
	Checks	28.75				
		+ 2.07				
	Total deposit	$623.27				

Exercise 2, page 25

1.	March	1	Balance	$501.32
		3	Check	− 34.66
		3	Balance	$466.66
		9	Check	− 98.62
		9	Balance	$368.04
		21	Deposit	+ 298.43
		21	Balance	$666.47
		25	Check	− 108.45
		25	Balance	$558.02
		30	Interest	+ 23.78
		30	Balance	$581.80

2. **a.** $278.98
        + 125.00

        $403.98
        − 230.12

        $173.86
        −   1.50

        $172.36
        − 20.72

        $151.64

b. $ 67.54
        + 35.71

        $103.25
        −   3.67

        $ 99.58
        − 43.81

        $ 55.77
        −   9.33

        $ 46.44
        − 15.10

        $ 31.34

c. $807.22
        + 97.12

        $904.34
        + 50.00

        $954.34
        − 145.90

        $808.44
        −   6.08

        $802.36
        − 62.44

        $739.92
        − 35.19

        $704.73

d. $262.43
        + 43.99

        $306.42
        + 55.00

        $361.42
        −   3.77

        $357.65
        − 87.29

        $270.36
        − 38.12

        $232.24
        −   0.78

        $231.46

3.

Beginning balance	$482.63
Deposit on Tuesday	+ 78.55
Total	$561.18
Checks written	− 131.28
New balance	$429.90

4.

Beginning balance	$4,070.65
Deposit	+ 1,006.54
Total	$5,077.19
Checks written	− 2,087.41
New balance	$2,989.78

Exercise 3, page 27

1. $845.19 − $74.89 − $245.64 − $35.77 = $488.89

2. $307.92 + $568.33 − $200.00 = $676.25

3. $690.06 + $328.66 − $56.89 − $78.99 − $27.79 = $855.05

4. $103.45 + $125.09 − $56.08 − $23.12 − $24.99 = $124.35

Exercise 4, page 28

1. 29 − 7 = 22

2. 25 − 13 = 12

3. 42 − 12 = 30

4. 105 − 75 = 30

5. 220 − 80 = 140

6. 475 − 125 = 350

7.   256.82
        −137.93
        118.89

8.   964.64
        − 0.55
        964.09

9. $1,370.52
        − 583.64
        $ 786.88

10. $5,008.37
         − 3,905.88
         $1,102.49

11. $21,803.27
         − 12,652.52
         $ 9,150.75

12. $73,835.89
         − 44,769.93
         $29,065.96

Exercise 5, page 28

1. 39,539

2. 77,254

3. $22,075.06

4. $27,422.44

5. $50,956.65

6. $16,483.19

7. $4,481.71

8. $17,409.79

Exercise 6, page 28

1. 14.2   lbs. gross weight
   − 1.8   lbs. box
   12.4   lbs. net weight

2. $137.98   gross bill
   − 2.76   discount
   $135.22   net payment

3. $2.00   gross price
   − 0.73   cost
   $1.27   net amount profit

4. a. 8:00 a.m. − 5:00 p.m. = 9   hrs. gross
   b. 2 × 15 min. + 1 hr.   = $1\frac{1}{2}$ hrs. non-work
   $7\frac{1}{2}$ hrs. net

5. $416.29   gross pay
   − 98.67   deductions
   $317.62   net pay

6. $287,806.22   gross sales
   − 11,512.24   returns
   $276,293.98   net sales

Exercise 7, page 29

1. a. $45.00   cutting lawns
   + 35.75   yard work
   $80.75   total earnings

   b. $80.75   total earnings
   + 14.78   cash on hand
   $95.53   available to spend

   c. $95.53   available to spend
   − 27.67   balance at end of week
   $67.86   spent during week

2. a. 245 + 150 + 250 = 645   additional boxes
   b. 645   additional boxes
   + 300   boxes on hand
   945   boxes available

   c. 945   boxes available
   − 12   boxes left
   933   boxes sold

3. a. $269.34 + $276.58 + $216.17 + $108.02 = $870.11   oil bought
   b. $ 870.11   oil bought
   + 178.56   oil on hand
   $1,048.67   oil available

   c. $1,048.67   oil available
   − 108.37   oil left
   $ 940.30   cost of oil used

4. a. 432 + 1,152 + 1,008 = 2,592   baseballs bought
   b. 2,592   baseballs bought
   + 120   baseballs on hand
   2,712   baseballs available

   c. 2,712   baseballs available
   − 137   baseballs left
   2,575   baseballs used

Review 4, page 30

2. a. 29 − 16 = 13
   b. 125 − 75 = 50
   c. 250 − 125 = 125

   d. 23,978.65
   −14,087.96
   9,890.69

   e. $78,308.23
   − 25,611.90
   $52,696.33

3. $2,078.25 + $1,467.40 + $2,076.50 + $1,208.20 = $6,830.35

4. $767.24 + $689.34 + $14.56 + $239.78 + $6.89 + $34.56 = $1,752.37

5. 18,295   lbs. gross weight
   − 15,207   lbs. truck weight
   3,088   lbs. net weight of contents

6.

Beginning balance	$380.48
Deposit	+ 108.56
Total	$489.04
Checks written	− 135.70
Final balance	$353.34

7.

Bills	$ 657.00
Coins	66.72
Checks	14.88
	307.61
	+ 149.01
Total deposit	$1,195.22

Section 5. Proving the Check Register Balance

Exercise 1, page 35

1.

Check register balance	$873.09	Bank statement balance	$1,378.49
Deduct:		Deduct:	
Service charge	− 5.75	Outstanding checks:	
	$867.34	#806 $326.11	
Add:		#808 97.56	
Interest earned	+ 5.45	#809 82.03	− 505.70
Correct check register balance	$872.79	Available bank balance	$872.79

2.

Check register balance	$277.91	Bank statement balance	$400.78
Deduct:		Deduct:	
Service charge	− 3.75	Outstanding checks:	
	$274.16	#51 $73.09	
Add:		#52 46.28	
Interest earned	+ 1.65	#54 5.60	− 124.97
Correct check register balance	$275.81	Available bank balance	$275.81

3.

Check register balance	$803.12	Bank statement balance	$978.44
Deduct:		Deduct:	
Service charge	− 5.70	Outstanding checks:	
	$797.42	#88 $167.41	
		#90 9.48	− 176.89
Add:			
Interest earned	+ 4.13		
Correct check register balance	$801.55	Available bank balance	$801.55

4.

Check register balance	$231.19	Bank statement balance	$270.56
Deduct:		Deduct:	
Service charge	− 3.10	Outstanding checks:	
	$228.09	#21 $ 5.79	
Add:		#23 15.46	
Interest earned	+ 1.15	#25 20.07	− 41.32
Correct check register balance	$229.24	Available bank balance	$229.24

5. Check register balance $598.01   Bank statement balance $678.12
     Deduct: Deduct:
       Service charge   − 4.12   Outstanding checks:
                       $593.89   #23 $21.57
     Add: #25   40.87
       Interest earned   + 2.81   #26   18.98   − 81.42
     Correct check register balance $596.70   Available bank balance $596.70

6. Check register balance $133.79   Bank statement balance $244.60
     Deduct: Deduct:
       Service charge   − 2.60   Outstanding checks:
                       $131.19   #63 $ 9.56
                                               #64   3.78
     Add: #65   63.14
       Interest earned   + 0.86   #66   36.07   − 112.55
     Correct check register balance $132.05   Available bank balance $132.05

Exercise 2, page 36

1. Check register balance $703.44   Bank statement balance $907.46
     Deduct: Deduct:
       Service charge   − 2.75   Outstanding checks:
            #451 $101.33
            #452   89.56
            #455   12.72
            #456   3.16   − 206.77
     Correct check register balance $700.69   Available bank balance $700.69

2. Check register balance $603.49   Bank statement balance $870.15
     Deduct: Deduct:
       Service charge   − 4.75   Outstanding checks:
            #451 $101.33
            #452   89.56
            #455   12.72
            #456   67.80   − 271.41
     Correct check register balance $598.74   Available bank balance $598.74

Review 5, page 37

2.

a.	b.	c.
4 + 5 + 8 = 17	34 + 12 + 89 = 135	45 + 11 + 54 + 23 = 133
7 + 3 + 2 = 12	59 + 51 + 37 = 147	63 + 17 + 78 + 22 = 180
9 + 2 + 1 = 12	28 + 17 + 32 = 77	64 + 97 + 36 + 13 = 210
20 + 10 + 11 = 41	121 + 80 + 158 = 359	172 + 125 + 168 + 58 = 523

3. Bills $281.00
    Coins   17.23
    Checks   2.75
                 15.75
                 25.00
         + 10.00
    Total deposit $351.73

4. $189.76 - $3.79 = $185.97   net amount of bill

5. $106.76 + $175.00 - $92.78 = $188.98   money left

6.

Check register balance	$248.65	Bank statement balance	$366.13
Deduct:		Deduct:	
Service charge	− 2.75	Outstanding checks:	
		#302 $ 12.35	
		#304 107.88	− 120.23
Correct check register balance	$245.90	Available bank balance	$245.90

‡Section 6. Special Reconciliation Problems

‡Exercise 1, page 39

1.

Bank statement balance	$381.36
Deduct:	
Outstanding checks:	
$45.71	
9.45	
24.90	− 80.06
	$301.30
Add:	
Late deposit	+ 85.00
Available bank balance	$386.30

2.

Bank statement balance	$ 906.88
Deduct:	
Outstanding checks:	
$89.16	
65.12	
1.78	− 156.06
	$ 750.82
Add:	
Late deposit	+ 305.00
Available bank balance	$1,055.82

3.

Bank statement balance	$580.04
Deduct:	
Outstanding checks:	
$20.01	
9.41	
51.78	
3.35	− 84.55
	$495.49
Add:	
Late deposit	+ 176.00
Available bank balance	$671.49

‡Exercise 2, page 39

1. Check register balance $829.76
   Deduct:
Service charge	$ 5.67	
Check not recorded	55.78	
Check #23 correct amount	28.98	− 90.43
		$739.33

   Add:
Deposit not recorded	$135.00	
Check #23 incorrect amount	28.89	+ 163.89
Correct check register balance		$903.22

2. Check register balance $280.66
   Deduct:
Service charge	$2.25	
Check not recorded	5.78	
Check #903 correct amount	7.56	− 15.59
		$265.07

   Add:
Interest earned	$1.14	
Check #903 incorrect amount	6.75	+ 7.89
Correct check register balance		$272.96

3. Check register balance $429.86
   Deduct:
Service charge	$ 4.10	
Check #75 correct amount	19.99	− 24.09
		$405.77

   Add:
Deposit not recorded	$110.00	
Check #75 incorrect amount	19.19	+ 129.19
Correct check register balance		$534.96

4. Check register balance $750.03
   Deduct:
Service charge	$ 5.01	
Check not recorded	63.36	
Deposit recorded twice	86.00	− 154.37
		$595.66

   Add:
Interest earned		+ 2.78
Correct check register balance		$598.44

5. Check register balance $107.87
   Deduct:
Service charge	$ 0.76	
Check #307 correct amount	35.29	− 36.05
		$ 71.82

   Add:
Interest earned	$ 0.85	
Check #307 incorrect amount	32.95	+ 33.80
Correct check register balance		$105.62

6. Check register balance $812.45
   Deduct:
     Check #201 correct amount   −   92.49
                                                               $719.96

   Add:
     Deposit not recorded $135.90
     Check #201 incorrect amount   29.49   + 165.39
   Correct check register balance $885.35

7. Check register balance $506.71
   Deduct:
     Check #322 correct amount   − 108.58
                                                                $398.13

   Add:
     Check entered twice $124.58
     Deposit not recorded   86.08
     Check #322 incorrect amount   158.08   + 368.74
   Correct check register balance $766.87

‡Exercise 3, page 40

1. Check register balance $200.89   Bank statement balance $278.99
   Deduct: Deduct:
     Service charge   −   2.67   Outstanding checks:
                       $198.22   #407 $92.48
   Add: #410   28.12
     Interest earned   +   1.25   #154   17.42   − 138.02
                                                     $140.97
                                           Add:
                                           Late deposit   +   58.50
   Correct check register balance $199.47   Available bank balance $199.47

2. Check register balance $92.45   Bank statement balance $167.23
   Deduct: Deduct:
     Service charge $ 1.45   Outstanding checks:
     Deposit recorded   #85 $ 3.89
       twice   10.75   − 12.20   #90   83.09   −   86.98
   Correct check register balance $80.25   Available bank balance $80.25

3. Check register balance $700.61   Bank statement balance $856.90
   Deduct: Deduct:
     Payroll Savings   − 75.00   Outstanding checks:
                                                           #834 $ 48.33
                                                           #837   21.19
                                                           #838   161.77   − 231.29
   Correct check register balance $625.61   Available bank balance $625.61

4. Check register balance ..... $375.61 Bank statement balance $498.34
Deduct: Deduct:
  Service charge $2.75   Outstanding checks:
  Check #467   #477 $64.00
    correct amount 1.98   −   4.73   #478   57.88   − 121.88
                               $370.88
Add:
  Interest earned $3.69
  Check #467   1.89   +   5.58
Correct check register balance $376.46   Available bank balance $376.46

5. Check register balance ..... $231.78 Bank statement balance $357.48
Deduct: Deduct:
  Service charge   −   2.45   Outstanding checks:
                      $229.33 $16.84
Add: 5.78
  Interest earned $ 1.75   9.60
  Deposit not   34.18   − 66.40
    recorded   60.00   + 61.75
Correct check register balance $291.08 $291.08

6. Check register balance ..... $539.78 Bank statement balance $687.67
Deduct: Deduct:
  Service charge $4.67   Outstanding checks:
  Deposit recorded $89.34
    twice   8.00   − 12.67   12.07
                      $527.11   1.45
Add: 53.92   − 156.78
  Interest earned   +   3.78
Correct check register balance $530.89   Available bank balance $530.89

7. Check register balance ..... $428.73 Bank statement balance $540.06
Deduct: Deduct:
  Service charge   −   2.20   Outstanding checks:
                      $426.53 $ 36.12
Add: 20.50
  Interest earned   +   3.15   123.00
                                   5.76   − 185.38
                                    $354.68
                              Add:
                                Late deposit   + 75.00
Correct check register balance $429.68   Available bank balance $429.68

8. Check register balance ..... $174.32 Bank statement balance $294.56
Deduct: Deduct:
  Service charge   −   2.25   Outstanding checks:
                      $172.07 $10.06
Add: 3.19
  Deposit not   8.10   − 21.35
    recorded $100.00
  Interest earned   1.14   + 101.14
Correct check register balance $273.21   Available bank balance $273.21

9.

Check register balance		$807.58	Bank statement balance	$989.56
Deduct:			Deduct:	
Service charge	$6.25		Outstanding checks:	
Check not			$ 9.95	
recorded	8.73	− 14.98	80.13	
		$792.60	101.76	− 191.84
Add:				
Interest earned		+ 5.12		
Correct check register balance		$797.72	Available bank balance	$797.72

Review 6, page 41

1.
$$34,890$$
$$- 5,384$$
$$29,506$$

2.
$$345.28$$
$$- 296.73$$
$$48.55$$

3.
$$12,345.89$$
$$- 8,627.92$$
$$3,717.97$$

4.
$$\$45,792.84$$
$$- 31,835.95$$
$$\$13,956.89$$

5.
$$16 + 21 + 32 + 8 = 77$$
$$28 + 92 + 45 + 3 = 168$$
$$41 + 88 + 71 + 6 = 206$$
$$87 + 93 + 22 + 65 = 267$$
$$172 + 294 + 170 + 82 = 718$$

6.
$$23 + 49 + 26 + 13 = 111$$
$$15 + 83 + 72 + 66 = 236$$
$$55 + 34 + 49 + 21 = 159$$
$$10 + 19 + 44 + 33 = 106$$
$$103 + 185 + 191 + 133 = 612$$

7.

Check register balance		$598.27	Bank statement balance	$674.21
Deduct:			Deduct:	
Service charge		− 4.73	Outstanding checks:	
		$593.54	#713	$20.88	
Add:			#718	32.10	
Interest earned		+ 3.76	#714	23.93	− 76.91
Correct check register balance		$597.30	Available bank balance	$597.30

8. $240.67 + $148.89 + $57.12 + $9.15 + $86.45 + $125.89 = $668.17 total spent

9.

Beginning Balance	$507.87
Deposit	+ 165.23
Total	$673.10
Checks written	− 434.51
Final Balance	$238.59

‡10.

Check register balance		$542.67	Bank statement balance	$451.61
Deduct:			Deduct:	
Service charge		− 4.75	Outstanding checks:	
		$537.92	#876	$ 7.43	
Add:			#879	30.56	
Interest earned		+ 3.65	#881	75.93	− 113.92
				$337.69
			Add:	
			Late deposit	+ 203.88
Correct check register balance		$541.57	Available bank balance	$541.57

UNIT 2 • GROSS AND AVERAGE PAY

Section 7. Finding Gross Pay

Exercise 1, page 44

1. 16 × $5 = $80   gross pay

2. **a.** 7 + 8 + 8 + 6 + 5 = 34   hours worked
    b. 34 × $9 = $306   gross pay

3. **a.** 8 × 5 = 40   hours worked
    b. 40 × $7 = $280   gross pay

4. 2 × (40 × $7) = $560   total gross pay for 2 weeks

5. 40 × $11 = $440   gross pay from full-time job
    15 × $6 = $90   gross pay from part-time job
    $440 + $90 = $530   total gross pay

6. **a.** 40 × $8 = $ 320
    b. 32 × $8 =   256
    c. 37 × $7 =   259
    d. 40 × $9 =   360
    e. 35 × $7 =   245
    　　　　Total $1,440

Exercise 2, page 45

1. 5 × $76 = $380   gross pay

2. 7 × $52 = $364   gross pay

3. 12 × $1,400 = $16,800   gross pay per year

4. 2 × $389 = $778   gross pay for 2 weeks

5. 4 × $375 = $1,500   would earn in 4 weeks
    52 × $375 = $19,500   would earn in a year

6. **a.** 52 × $300 = $15,600   yearly salary
    b. 52 × $420 = $21,840   yearly salary
    c. 52 × $495 = $25,740   yearly salary

Exercise 3, page 46

1. 27 + 33 + 29 + 27 + 31 = 147   total pieces assembled
    147 × $2.75 = $404.25   gross pay

2. **a.** 54 + 55 + 59 + 62 + 60 = 290   total pieces
    　　　290 × $1.60 = $464   gross pay
    b. 24 + 28 + 30 + 31 + 27 = 140   total pieces
    　　　140 × $2.80 = $392   gross pay
    c. 63 + 69 + 59 + 62 + 50 = 303   total pieces
    　　　303 × $1.55 = $469.65   gross pay
    d. 68 + 65 + 72 + 74 + 75 = 354   total pieces
    　　　354 × $1.18 = $417.72   gross pay

3. **a.** $65 \times \$0.95 = \$61.75$ Hart's pay
    b. $72 \times \$0.95 = \$68.40$ Hassed's pay
    c. $(75 \times \$0.95) + (5 \times \$1.05) = \$76.50$ Cook's pay
    d. $(75 \times \$0.95) + (9 \times \$1.05) = \$80.70$ Nowak's pay
    e. $(75 \times \$0.95) + (25 \times \$1.05) + (8 \times \$1.20) = \$107.10$ Jenke's pay
    f. $(75 \times \$0.95) + (25 \times \$1.05) + (2 \times \$1.20) = \$99.90$ Wong's pay
    g. $68 \times \$0.95 = \$64.60$ Dubois' pay
    h. $(75 \times \$0.95) + (14 \times \$1.05) = \$85.95$ Flynn's pay
    i. $(75 \times \$0.95) + (25 \times \$1.05) + (12 \times \$1.20) = \$111.90$ McCrow's pay

4. $65 - 11 = 54$ usable pieces
    $(50 \times \$1.60) + (4 \times \$1.76) = \$87.04$ gross pay

Review 7, page 47

2. **a.** $27 + 8 = 19 + 16$ **b.** $61 - 30 = 17 + 14$

3. $8 + 4 + 7 + 6 + 8 = 33$ hours worked
    $33 \times \$9 = \$297$ gross pay

4. **a.** $12 \times \$1,510 = \$18,120$ gross pay
    b. $52 \times \$380 = \$19,760$ gross pay
    c. $37 \times \$12 = \$444$ gross pay

5. $220 - 14 = 206$ usable pieces
    $206 \times \$2.08 = \$428.48$ gross pay

6. $\$35.67 + \$41.60 = \$77.27$ total available
    $\$5.20 + \$14.56 + \$7.98 + \$3.56 = \$31.30$ total spent
    $\$77.27 - \$31.30 = \$45.97$ cash left

Section 8.   Multiplication

Exercise 3, page 51

1. $35 \times 43 = 1,505$ 4. $41 \times 432 = 17,712$

2. $26 \times 57 = 1,482$ 5. $357 \times 964 = 344,148$

3. $47 \times 81 = 3,807$ 6. $598 \times 352 = 210,496$

Review 8, page 54

2. $\begin{array}{rcrcrcr} 54 &+& 27 &+& 34 &=& 115 \\ 13 &+& 75 &+& 9 &=& 97 \\ \underline{83} &+& \underline{11} &+& \underline{17} &=& \underline{111} \\ 150 &+& 113 &+& 60 &=& 323 \end{array}$

    4. $1.35 \times 62 = 83.7$

    5. $24 - 15 + 7 = 16$

3. $87 - 9 = 78$

    6. $2 \times 2 \times 0 = 0$

7. **a.** 5.3; 0.4; 736.7; 6
    b. 278.48; 37.72; 0.43
    c. $4.58; $0.40; 19¢
    d. 6,000; 45,000; 180,000

8. **a.** $17 \times 1 = 17$ **c.** $2 \times 23 = 46$ **e.** $89 \times 0 = 0$
    b. $7 \times 9 = 63$ **d.** $56 = 8 \times 7$ **f.** $5 \times 15 = 75$

9. $12 + (24 \times 1) = 36$ ounces, weight of carton and boxes
$276 - 36 = 240$ ounces, net weight of crackers

10.

Check register balance	$410.00	Bank statement balance		$588.96
Deduct:		Deduct:		
Service charge	− 5.00	Outstanding checks:		
	$405.00	#523	$105.40	
Add:		#542	75.36	− 180.76
Interest earned	+ 3.20			
Correct check register balance	$408.20	Available bank balance		$408.20

Section 9.   Multiplication Shortcuts

Exercise 5, page 56

1.	249.6	3.	14.72	5.	$4.76	7.	$6,708.52
2.	313.9	4.	$164.43	6.	$7,267.80	8.	$12,364.44

Exercise 7, page 57

	a.	b.	c.
1.	7.4	1,020	$8.40
2.	28	2,880	$15
3.	38	4,050	$60
4.	426	1,280	$250
5.	258	3,050	$68,000

Exercise 8, page 58

	a.	b.	c.
1.	45,000	$1,480	$224
2.	18,400	$125	$1,050
3.	13,500	$644	$138

Exercise 10, page 59

1.	$0.96	4.	$7.50	7.	$66	10.	$26
2.	$7.14	5.	$1.26	8.	$0.72	11.	$51.10
3.	$4	6.	$8.10	9.	$39	12.	$46.50

Review 9, page 59

2. a. $0.01 \times 489 = $4.89
    b. $0.10 \times 45.2 = $4.52
    c. $0.20 \times 52 = $10.40
    d. $300 \times 16 = $4,800
    e. $2,189 \times 100 = 218,900$
    f. $10 \times 34.8 = 348$
    g. $1,000 \times 4.708 = 4,708$
    h. $4,900 \times 8.2 = 40,180$

3. a. 3.8×489 2,000   1,858.2
    b. 505×12.3 6,000   6,211.5
    c. 7.2×312 2,100   2,246.4
    d. 281×4.1 1,200   1,152.1

4. a. $0.028; $1.361; 76.6¢
    b. 4.6; 3.01; 65.49
    c. 18,000; 42,000; 11,000
    d. 1,800; 32,100; 40,100

5. Bills $ 379.00
 Coins   13.41
 Checks   53.47
         83.00
       + 541.27
 Total Deposit $1,070.15

6. $8 + 7 + 3 + 5 + 8 = 31$ hours worked
 $31 \times \$13 = \$403$ total earnings for week

Section 10. Finding Average Pay

Exercise 1, page 60

1. $\$210 \div 35 = \$6$ average pay per hour

2. $\$73 + \$90 + \$103 + \$108 + \$67 + \$81 = \$522$ total pay for 6 days
 $\$522 \div 6 = \$87$ average daily pay

3. $\$1,300 + \$1,415 + \$1,177 + \$1,260 = \$5,152$ total salaries
 $\$5,152 \div 4 = \$1,288$ average salary per month

4. a. $\$17,200 + \$18,500 + \$20,400 = \$56,100$ total earned for 3 years
 b. $\$56,100 \div 3 = \$18,700$ average earnings per year

5. a. $\$34,944 \div 12 = \$2,912$ average monthly pay
 b. $\$34,944 \div 52 = \$672$ average weekly pay

6. a. $\$435 \div 5 = \$87$ average daily pay, full-time work
 b. $\$84 \div 12 = \$7$ average hourly pay, part-time work

7. a. $44 + 38 + 41 = 123$ hours worked
 b. $\$396 + \$342 + \$369 = \$1,107$ total earnings
 c. $\$1,107 \div 123 = \$9$ average hourly earnings
 d. $\$1,107 \div 3 = \$369$ average weekly earnings

Exercise 2, page 62

1. $(5 \times \$9) + (2 \times \$7) + \$13 = \$72$ total amount per hour
 $\$72 \div 8 = \$9$ average amount per hour employees are paid

2. $(4 \times \$820) + (5 \times \$754) + (6 \times \$1,100) = \$13,650$ total bonus paid
 $\$13,650 \div 15 = \$910$ average bonus paid

3. $(2 \times \$63) + \$68 + (2 \times \$73) = \$340$ total pay for 5 days
 $\$340 \div 5 = \$68$ average daily pay

4. a. $(3 \times \$1,600) + (3 \times \$1,760) + (6 \times \$1,936) = \$21,696$ tot. yrly. pay
 b. $\$21,696 \div 12 = \$1,808$ average monthly pay

5. a. $(8 \times 2) + (9 \times 2) + 11 = 45$ total hours worked for week
  $45 \div 5 = 9$ average hours worked per day
 b. $9 \times \$11 = \$99$ average daily pay

Exercise 3, page 63

1. $5 \times \$77 = \$385$
 $\$68 + \$80 + \$75 + \$79 = \$302$ pay for 4 days
 $\$385 - \$302 = \$83$ amount to be earned on fifth day

2. $4 \times \$86 = \$344$ pay for 4 days
$\$422 - \$344 = \$78$ pay for fifth day

3. $7 \times \$82 = \$574$ total daily pay of 7 employees
$\$680 - \$574 = \$106$ can pay new employee

4. $8 \times 14 = 112$ total computers sold in 8 months
$200 - 112 = 88$
$\frac{88}{4} = 22$ average number that must be sold

Review 10, page 63

2. a. $260 \times 140 = 36{,}400$ d. $\$72.408 = \$72.41$
   b. $2{,}550 \times \$0.01 = \$25.50$ e. $7.4291 = 7.4$
   c. $8.3 \times 1{,}000 = 8{,}300$

3. a. $36 \times 1 = 36$ c. $28 \times 3 = 7 \times 12$ e. $10 \times 62 = 100 \times 6.2$
   b. $2 \times 2.4 = 4.8$ d. $0 \times 53 = 0 \times 34$ f. $14 \times 6 = 3 \times 28$

4. $77 + 78 + 88 + 90 + 85 + 91 + 88 = 597$
$597 \div 7 = 85.2$, or 85 average mark

5. $5 \times \$14 = \$\ 70$
   $8 \times \$22 = \ \ \ 176$
  $11 \times \$36 = \ \ \underline{396}$
             $\$642$

$50 + 80 + 110 = 240$ disks
$\$642 \div 240 = \$2.675$, or $\$2.68$ average price

6. $5 \times 53 = 265$ total bowls
$52 + 57 + 55 + 50 = 214$ total for 4 days
$265 - 214 = 51$ bowls to be made on fifth day

Section 11.   Division

Exercise 2, page 67

	F F P		P F F		F F P
1.	$5 \times 6 = 30$	**4.**	$N \div 9 = 2$	**7.**	$8 \times N = 104$
	F F P		F F P		P F F
2.	$8 \times 9 = 72$	**5.**	$9 \times 6 = N$	**8.**	$N \div 4 = 14$
	P F F		P F F		P F F
3.	$42 \div 7 = 6$	**6.**	$56 \div N = 8$	**9.**	$N = 12 \times 8$

Exercise 3, page 67

	P F F		F P F		P F F
1.	$35 = 5 \times 7$	**5.**	$10 = 50 \div 5$	**9.**	$84 = 7 \times 12$
	F F P		F F P		F P F
2.	$12 \times 8 = 96$	**6.**	$19 \times 27 = 513$	**10.**	$7 = 735 \div 105$
	P F F		F P F		F P F
3.	$51 \div 17 = 3$	**7.**	$23 = 391 \div 17$	**11.**	$13 = 169 \div 13$

	F	P	F			F	F	P			F	F	P
4.	*11*	= 352 ÷ 32			**8.**	15	×	*13* = 195		**12.**	25	×	*25* = 625

Exercise 4, page 68

1. 45.72 ÷ 6 = 7.62   **4.** 7.24 ÷ 8 = 0.905   **7.** 91.08 ÷ 22 = 4.14

2. 5.88 ÷ 8 = 0.735   **5.** 1,347.1 ÷ 5 = 269.42   **8.** 18.025 ÷ 35 = 0.515

3. 304.2 ÷ 9 = 33.8   **6.** 8.533 ÷ 7 = 1.219   **9.** 0.192 ÷ 24 = 0.008

Exercise 5, page 68

1. 1,640 ÷ 8.2 = 200   **5.** 100 ÷ 0.025 = 4,000   **9.** 0.125 ÷ 0.25 = 0.5

2. 16.4 ÷ 0.082 = 200   **6.** 4.32 ÷ 0.144 = 30   **10.** 0.125 ÷ 0.05 = 2.5

3. 0.82 ÷ 0.82 = 1   **7.** 0.65 ÷ 32.5 = 0.02   **11.** 0.015 ÷ 0.25 = 0.06

4. 0.36 ÷ 0.0072 = 50   **8.** 0.18 ÷ 4.5 = 0.04   **12.** 0.5 ÷ 0.125 = 4

Exercise 6, page 69

1. 15.7142 = 15.714   **4.** 1.6109 = 1.611   **7.** \$0.377 = \$0.38

2. 8.5990 = 8.599   **5.** \$0.034 = \$0.03   **8.** \$0.161 = \$0.16

3. 342.9878 = 342.988   **6.** \$0.128 = \$0.13

Exercise 7, page 69

1. \$851 ÷ 165 = \$5.16   average amount spent by customers

2. 1,830 ÷ 23 = 79.6   average points scored per game

3. 5,234 ÷ 850 = 6.2   average days absent

Exercise 8, page 70

1. $2{,}497 \div 4 = 624\frac{1}{4}$ **5.** $5{,}859 \div 5 = 1{,}171\frac{4}{5}$ **9.** $1{,}237 \div 3 = 412\frac{1}{3}$

2. $4{,}072 \div 9 = 452\frac{4}{9}$ **6.** $3{,}213 \div 5 = 642\frac{3}{5}$ **10.** $3{,}255 \div 8 = 406\frac{7}{8}$

3. $2{,}195 \div 6 = 365\frac{5}{6}$ **7.** $2{,}219 \div 9 = 246\frac{5}{9}$ **11.** $377 \div 12 = 31\frac{5}{12}$

4. $1{,}458 \div 7 = 208\frac{2}{7}$ **8.** $3{,}525 \div 7 = 503\frac{4}{7}$ **12.** $659 \div 16 = 41\frac{3}{16}$

Review 11, page 70

		F	F	P			P	F	F
2.	**a.**	20	× *16*	= 320		**c.**	*527*	÷ 31	= 17

		P	F	F			F	F	P
	b.	*437*	÷ 19	= 23		**d.**	*13*	× 64	= 832

3. **a.** \$6.20 × 1,600 = \$9,920   **c.** 834 ÷ 0.1 = 8,340
    b. 360 × \$0.58 = \$208.80   **d.** 92.5 ÷ 0.01 = 9,250

4. **a.** 69.08 ÷ 22 = 3.1   **c.** 0.288 ÷ 0.0072 = 40
    b. 0.8096 ÷ 8 = 0.1   **d.** 2,160 ÷ 7.2 = 300

5.

Balance	$359.03
Deposits	110.78
+	35.00
Balance	$504.81
Checks	56.00
	12.75
−	98.33
Balance	$337.73

6. $(5 \times 121) + (2 \times 135) = 875$ total papers delivered in week
$875 \div 7 = 125$ average papers delivered per day

Section 12.   Division Shortcuts

Exercise 2, page 72

1. $2,112 ÷ 32 = $66   **5.** $2,842 ÷ 49 = $58   **9.** 72.09 ÷ 8.1 = 8.9

2. $3,268 ÷ 43 = $76   **6.** $5,916 ÷ 58 = $102   **10.** 99.11 ÷ 1.87 = 53

3. 258.94 ÷ 2,354 = 0.11   **7.** $26.16 ÷ 2.18 = $12

4. 51.6 ÷ 2.15 = 24   **8.** 3.605 ÷ 10.3 = 0.35

Exercise 3, page 73

1. 72 ÷ 0.18 = 400   **4.** 189 ÷ 0.35 = 540   **7.** 416 ÷ 0.64 = 650

2. 22 ÷ 0.04 = 550   **5.** 119 ÷ 0.68 = 175   **8.** 330 ÷ 0.88 = 375

3. 54 ÷ 0.75 = 72   **6.** 423 ÷ 0.18 = 2,350

Exercise 4, page 73

1. $420   **3.** $29   **5.** $0.52   **7.** 0.5   **9.** 4.894   **11.** 0.002

2. 750   **4.** 0.68   **6.** $0.80   **8.** 0.07   **10.** $0.03   **12.** 0.0704

Exercise 5, page 74

1. 2.825 = 2.83   **4.** 0.055 = 0.06   **7.** 0.36666 = 0.3667

2. 0.088 = 0.09   **5.** 0.10466 = 0.1047   **8.** 2.51315 = 2.5132

3. 0.097 = 0.1   **6.** 0.25609 = 0.2561

Review 12, page 74

1. **a.** 3,800 × 120 = 456,000   **f.** 45 + 16 + 23 + 34 = 118
   b. 709 × 0.001 = 0.709   **g.** $23.78 − $19.87 = $3.91
   c. 314 × 200 = 62,800   **h.** 408.10284 = 408.1
   d. 23.7 ÷ 0.001 = 23,700   **i.** 4,492 = 4,000
   e. $456 ÷ 100 = $4.56

	P	F	F		F	F	P		F	P	F
2. **a.**	252	÷ 14	= 18	**b.**	35	× 7	= 245	**c.**	25	= 450 ÷	18

3. **a.** 387 ÷ 42 = 9.2   **b.** 1,815 ÷ 61 = 29.8   **c.** 31,960 ÷ 77 = 415.1

4. $(10 \times \$1,536) + (20 \times \$909) + (30 \times \$476) = \$47,820$ total spent on desks
    $\$47,820 \div 60 = \$797$ average desk price

5. $\$1,620 \times 12 = \underline{\$19,440}$ Glenda's yearly income
    $\$\ \ \ 370 \times 52 = \underline{\$19,240}$ Dominic's yearly income
    $\$38,680$ Total income

‡6. Check register balance $205.81   Bank statement balance $670.42
    Deduct: Deduct:
      Service charge $ 5.60   Outstanding checks:
      Check not $412.00
        recorded   96.82   − 102.42   218.43   − 630.43
                                       $103.39 $ 39.99
    Add: Add:
      Interest earned   +   2.41   Late deposit   + 65.81
    Correct check register balance $105.80   Available bank balance $105.80

UNIT 3 • REGULAR AND OVERTIME PAY

Section 13. Regular-Time and Overtime Pay

Exercise 2, page 78

1. a. 37 regular-time hours   2. $38\frac{3}{4}$ regular-time hours
    b. 2 overtime hours $6\frac{1}{2}$ overtime hours

Exercise 3, page 80

1. $38 \times \$10 = \$380$ regular-time pay
    $3 \times \$15 = \$45$ overtime pay
    $\$380 + \$45 = \$425$ gross pay for week

2. $40 \times \$6.80 = \$272$ regular-time pay
    $6\frac{1}{2} \times \$10.20 = \$66.30$ overtime pay
    $\$272 + \$66.30 = \$338.30$ gross pay for week

3. a. 40   regular-time hours
    b. $47 - 40 = 7$ overtime hours
    c. $40 \times \$7 = \$280$ regular-time pay
    d. $7 \times \$10.50 = \$73.50$ overtime pay
    e. $\$280 + \$73.50 = \$353.50$ gross pay

4. a. Art: 37 regular-time hours; 2 overtime hours
    b. $37 \times \$8 = \$296$ regular-time pay
        $2 \times \$12 = \$24$ overtime pay
        $\$296 + \$24 = \$320$ Art's gross pay for week
    c. Kurt: 35 regular-time hours; 4 overtime hours
    d. $35 \times \$8 = \$280$ regular-time pay
        $4 \times \$12 = \$48$ overtime pay
        $\$280 + \$48 = \$328$ Kurt's gross pay for week

5. a. $39 \times \$6.40 = \$249.60$ regular-time pay
        $2 \times \$9.60 = \$19.20$ overtime pay
        $\$249.60 + \$19.20 = \$268.80$ Ruth's gross pay for week

b. $37 \times \$6.60 = \$244.20$ regular-time pay
$5 \times \$9.90 = \$49.50$ overtime pay
$\$244.20 + \$49.50 = \$293.70$ Tod's gross pay for week

Review 13, page 81

2. **a.** $72 \div 12 = 6$
b. $320 \times 50 = 16,000$
c. $4,729 \div 0.01 = 472,900$
d. $\$6,000 \times 30 = \$180,000$
e. $\$8,000 \div 20 = \$400$

3. $100 \times \$0.60 = \$60$ pay for first day
$105 \times \$0.60 = \$63$ pay for second day
$(110 \times \$0.60) + (5 \times \$0.75) = \$69.75$ pay for third day
$(110 \times \$0.60) + (15 \times \$0.75) = \$77.25$ pay for fourth day
$(110 \times \$0.60) + (10 \times \$0.75) = \$73.50$ pay for fifth day
$\$60 + \$63 + \$69.75 + \$77.25 + \$73.50 = \$343.50$ gross pay for week

4. $145 + 182 + 177 + 165 + 171 = 840$ covers produced in week
$840 - 17 = 823$ covers passing inspection
$823 \times \$0.32 = \$263.36$ gross pay for week

5. $40 \times \$11 = \$440$ regular-time pay
$4 \times \$16.50 = \$66$ overtime pay
$\$440 + \$66 = \$506$ gross pay for week

6. $52 \times \$480 = \$24,960$ per year
$\$24,960 \div 12 = \$2,080$ per month

7. $(10 \times \$30) + (25 \times \$40) + (15 \times \$50) = \$2,050$ total sales
$\$2,050 \div 50 = \$41$ average selling price

Section 14. Fractions

Exercise 2, page 82

1. **a.** $\frac{12}{2}$ **c.** $\frac{4}{2}$ **e.** $\frac{2}{9}$ **g.** $\frac{6}{7}$
b. $\frac{5}{5}$ **d.** $\frac{24}{4}$ **f.** $\frac{18}{9}$ **h.** $\frac{50}{50}$

2. **a.** $1 \div 7$ **c.** $83 \div 75$ **e.** $12 \div 12$
b. $36 \div 72$ **d.** $9 \div 3$ **f.** $360 \div 30$

Exercise 4, page 83

1. **a.** $\frac{2}{4}, \frac{3}{6}, \frac{4}{8}, \frac{5}{10}$ **c.** $\frac{10}{8}, \frac{15}{12}, \frac{20}{16}, \frac{25}{20}$ **e.** $\frac{10}{2}, \frac{15}{3}, \frac{20}{4}, \frac{25}{5}$
b. $\frac{6}{8}, \frac{9}{12}, \frac{12}{16}, \frac{15}{20}$ **d.** $\frac{2}{2}, \frac{3}{3}, \frac{4}{4}, \frac{5}{5}$ **f.** $\frac{6}{16}, \frac{9}{24}, \frac{12}{32}, \frac{15}{40}$

2. **a.** $\frac{3}{4}$ **b.** $\frac{3}{5}$ **c.** $\frac{2}{3}$ **d.** $\frac{4}{2}$

Exercise 7, page 84

1. $\frac{\overset{1}{\cancel{8}}}{\cancel{8}} \times \frac{\overset{1}{\cancel{4}}}{\underset{1}{\cancel{8}}} = \frac{1}{2}$ **3.** $\frac{\overset{1}{\cancel{3}}}{\underset{2}{\cancel{8}}} \times \frac{\overset{3}{\cancel{12}}}{\cancel{15}} = \frac{3}{10}$ **5.** $\frac{\overset{1}{\cancel{2}}}{3} \times \frac{5}{\underset{4}{\cancel{8}}} = \frac{5}{12}$ **7.** $\frac{\overset{1}{\cancel{3}}}{8} \times \frac{5}{\underset{4}{\cancel{12}}} = \frac{5}{32}$

2. $\frac{\overset{1}{\cancel{5}}}{\underset{1}{\cancel{7}}} \times \frac{\overset{2}{\cancel{14}}}{\underset{5}{\cancel{25}}} = \frac{2}{5}$ **4.** $\frac{\overset{1}{\cancel{3}}}{4} \times \frac{5}{\underset{3}{\cancel{9}}} = \frac{5}{12}$ **6.** $\frac{\overset{1}{\cancel{9}}}{\underset{2}{\cancel{10}}} \times \frac{\overset{3}{\cancel{15}}}{\underset{2}{\cancel{18}}} = \frac{3}{4}$ **8.** $\frac{5}{6} \times \frac{7}{8} = \frac{35}{48}$

Exercise 9, page 85

1. $\frac{7}{3} = 2\frac{1}{3}$ **3.** $\frac{10}{4} = 2\frac{1}{2}$ **5.** $\frac{20}{16} = 1\frac{1}{4}$ **7.** $\frac{5}{5} = 1$ **9.** $\frac{27}{8} = 3\frac{3}{8}$

2. $\frac{12}{3} = 4$ **4.** $\frac{13}{6} = 2\frac{1}{6}$ **6.** $\frac{16}{12} = 1\frac{1}{3}$ **8.** $\frac{33}{7} = 4\frac{5}{7}$ **10.** $\frac{32}{10} = 3\frac{1}{5}$

Exercise 10, page 85

1. $\frac{2}{8} = \frac{1}{4}$ boys as fractional part of pep team

2. $\frac{1}{4} \times \frac{2}{3} = \frac{1}{6}$ part of test on which answers correctly guessed

3. $\frac{1}{2} \times \frac{2}{5} = \frac{1}{5}$ part used for fire station

4. $72 - 18 = 54$ number of universities
$\frac{54}{72} = \frac{3}{4}$ universities as part of all schools

5. $160 + 180 = 340$ total members using track
$\frac{180}{340} = \frac{9}{17}$ part of total members using track that are female

Review 14, page 85

2. **a.** $\frac{1}{2} \times \frac{5}{6} = \frac{5}{12}$ **b.** $\frac{\overset{1}{\cancel{3}}}{\cancel{4}} \times \frac{\overset{1}{\cancel{2}}}{\cancel{15}} = \frac{1}{10}$ **c.** $\frac{1}{\cancel{3}} \times \frac{\overset{1}{\cancel{3}}}{7} = \frac{1}{7}$

3. **a.** $\frac{9}{2} = 4\frac{1}{2}$ **b.** $\frac{17}{4} = 4\frac{1}{4}$ **c.** $\frac{22}{5} = 4\frac{2}{5}$

4. $38\frac{1}{4} \times \$12 = \$459$ regular-time pay
$8 \times \$18 \quad = \quad \underline{144}$ overtime pay
$\qquad\qquad\qquad \$603$ gross pay

5. **a.** $12 \times \$2,000 = \$24,000$ estimated yearly earnings
b. $12 \times \$1,860 = \$22,320$ per year
c. $\$22,320 \div 52 = \$492.23$ per week

6. $11 \times \$40,100 = \$441,100$ sales for 11 months
$12 \times \$39,500 = \$474,000$ desired total for year
$\$474,000 - \$441,100 = \$32,900$ must sell in next month

Section 15. More Fractions

Exercise 1, page 87

1. **a.** $\frac{1}{\cancel{2}} \times \frac{\overset{18}{\cancel{36}}}{1} = 18$ **d.** $\frac{1}{\cancel{3}} \times \frac{\overset{18}{\cancel{54}}}{1} = \$18$ **g.** $\frac{1}{\cancel{6}} \times \frac{\overset{9}{\cancel{54}}}{1} = \$9$

b. $\frac{2}{\cancel{5}} \times \frac{\overset{8}{\cancel{40}}}{1} = 16$ **e.** $\frac{5}{\cancel{6}} \times \frac{\overset{7}{\cancel{42}}}{1} = 35$ **h.** $\frac{3}{\cancel{8}} \times \frac{\overset{5}{\cancel{20}}}{1} = \frac{\$15}{2} = \$7.50$

c. $\frac{2}{\cancel{3}} \times \frac{\overset{8}{\cancel{24}}}{1} = 16$ **f.** $\frac{3}{\cancel{8}} \times \frac{\overset{4}{\cancel{32}}}{1} = \$12$

2. $\frac{1}{\cancel{4}} \times \frac{\overset{2.20}{\cancel{\$8.80}}}{1} = \$2.20$ pay for $\frac{1}{4}$ hour

3. $\frac{3}{\cancel{4}} \times \frac{\overset{90}{\cancel{\$360}}}{1} = \$270$ pay for week

4. $\frac{5}{\cancel{6}} \times \frac{\overset{80.12}{\cancel{\$480.72}}}{1} = \$400.60$ weekly pay

Exercise 4, page 88

1. $\frac{4}{8}, \frac{6}{8}$
2. $\frac{5}{10}, \frac{2}{10}, \frac{6}{10}$
3. $\frac{3}{12}, \frac{4}{12}, \frac{2}{12}$

4. $\frac{8}{16}, \frac{12}{16}, \frac{6}{16}$
5. $\frac{8}{24}, \frac{18}{24}, \frac{15}{24}$
6. $\frac{15}{18}, \frac{3}{18}, \frac{12}{18}$

Exercise 6, page 89

1. a. $\frac{1}{3} + \frac{5}{8} = \frac{23}{24}$ c. $\frac{2}{3} + \frac{1}{2} = 1\frac{1}{6}$ e. $\frac{5}{8} + \frac{7}{16} = 1\frac{1}{16}$ g. $\frac{5}{8} + \frac{3}{4} = 1\frac{3}{8}$
   b. $\frac{1}{4} + \frac{3}{8} = \frac{5}{8}$ d. $\frac{5}{8} + \frac{1}{16} = \frac{11}{16}$ f. $\frac{1}{6} + \frac{2}{3} = \frac{5}{6}$ h. $\frac{2}{3} + \frac{5}{6} = 1\frac{1}{2}$

2. a. $\frac{3}{4} - \frac{1}{8} = \frac{5}{8}$ c. $\frac{3}{4} - \frac{1}{16} = \frac{11}{16}$ e. $\frac{3}{4} - \frac{7}{12} = \frac{1}{6}$ g. $\frac{7}{8} - \frac{1}{2} = \frac{3}{8}$
   b. $\frac{3}{8} - \frac{1}{16} = \frac{5}{16}$ d. $\frac{2}{3} - \frac{1}{6} = \frac{1}{2}$ f. $\frac{1}{2} - \frac{1}{4} = \frac{1}{4}$ h. $\frac{3}{4} - \frac{3}{8} = \frac{3}{8}$

3. $\frac{1}{10} + \frac{1}{4} = \frac{7}{20}$ part of 2 weeks' pay from new customers

4. $\frac{3}{4} - \frac{3}{8} = \frac{3}{8}$ yard, difference in length

5. $\frac{16}{16} - (\frac{1}{16} + \frac{3}{8}) = \frac{9}{16}$ driven on paved road

Exercise 8, page 90

1. $5 \div \frac{2}{3} = 7\frac{1}{2}$
2. $36 \div \frac{4}{5} = 45$
3. $24 \div \frac{3}{8} = 64$
4. $2 \div \frac{7}{9} = 2\frac{4}{7}$

5. $\frac{3}{8} \div \frac{5}{6} = \frac{9}{20}$
6. $\frac{2}{3} \div \frac{4}{5} = \frac{5}{6}$
7. $\frac{8}{15} \div 12 = \frac{2}{45}$

8. $\frac{7}{8} \div 10 = \frac{7}{80}$
9. $2 \div \frac{8}{9} = 2\frac{1}{4}$
10. $\frac{2}{3} \div \frac{1}{2} = 1\frac{1}{3}$

Review 15, page 91

2. a. $\$10 \times \frac{1}{4} = \$2.50$ c. $\frac{1}{3} + \frac{1}{6} = \frac{1}{2}$ e. $\frac{7}{8} - \frac{1}{4} = \frac{5}{8}$
   b. $\$9 \div \frac{3}{7} = \$21$ d. $\frac{4}{5} \times \frac{15}{2} = 6$ f. $\frac{2}{9} + \frac{7}{9} = 1$

3. a. $360 \div 60 = 6$ estimated quotient
   b. $6,000 \times 20 = 120,000$ estimated product
   c. $\$126,500$
   d. 0.999

4. $(10 \times \$45,600) + \$48,230 + \$56,170 = \$560,400$ total receipts
   $\$560,400 \div 12 = \$46,700$ average weekly receipts

5. $10,800 \times \frac{5}{8} = 6,750$ votes Sarah got

6. $240 \times \frac{5}{8} = 150$ cartons sold
   $240 - (150 + 5) = 85$ cartons left

7. $0.65 + $0.09 = $0.74   pay rate for extra pieces
94 × $0.65 = $61.10   pay for Monday
(100 × $0.65) + (28 × $0.74) = $85.72   pay for Tuesday
(100 × $0.65) + (17 × $0.74) = $77.58   pay for Wednesday
(100 × $0.65) + (6 × $0.74) = $69.44   pay for Thursday
(100 × $0.65) + (18 × $0.74) = $78.32   pay for Friday
$61.10 + $85.72 + $77.58 + $69.44 + $78.32 = $372.16   gross pay for week

Section 16. Ratio and Proportion

Exercise 2, page 94

1. **a.** $\frac{5}{12} \times \$12,600 = \$5,250$ amount to spend on food
b. $\frac{7}{12} \times \$12,600 = \$7,350$ amount to spend on housing

2. $\frac{3}{5} \times \$9,500 = \$5,700$ Wes will invest
$\frac{2}{5} \times \$9,500 = \$3,800$ Tony will invest

3. $\frac{1}{6} \times 72 = 12$ boxes small envelopes
$\frac{5}{6} \times 72 = 60$ boxes large envelopes

4. $\frac{15}{16} \times \$24,000 = \$22,500$ amount earned from regular pay
$\frac{1}{16} \times \$24,000 = \$1,500$ amount earned from overtime pay

5. $1,300 : $26,600 = 1 to 20

6. **a.** $420,000 : $600,000 = 7 to 10
b. $600,000 : $180,000 = 10 to 3
c. $180,000 : $420,000 = 3 to 7

‡Exercise 3, page 95

1. $\frac{12}{32} = \frac{\$3.45}{N}$; $12 \times N = \$110.40$; $N = \$9.20$ tips from customers

2. $\frac{6}{52} = \frac{\$63}{N}$; $6 \times N = \$3,276$; $N = \$546$ amount spent for gas and oil

3. $\frac{5}{12} = \frac{\$9,205}{N}$; $5 \times N = \$110,460$; $N = \$22,092$ amount earned in 12 months

4. $\frac{8}{50} = \frac{38}{N}$; $8 \times N = 1,900$; $N = 237\frac{1}{2}$ lbs. weight of paper

5. $\frac{6}{N} = \frac{10}{250}$; $10 \times N = 1,500$; $N = 150$ lbs. meat needed

6. $\frac{\$150}{\$450} = \frac{\$115}{N}$; $150 \times N = \$51,750$; $N = \$345$ sale price of printer

7. **a.** $\left(\frac{\$20}{5}\right) \times 9 = \$36$ estimated cost
b. $\frac{\$19.80}{N} = \frac{5}{9}$; $5 \times N = \$178.20$; $N = \$35.64$ cost of 9 yards silk cloth

8. $\frac{235}{N} = \frac{5}{7}$; $5 \times N = 1,645$; $N = 329$ miles driven in 7 hours

Review 16, page 96

2. **a.** $1,400 × 400 = $560,000
b. 9,300 ÷ 100 = 93
c. $2 \times \frac{3}{8} = \frac{3}{4}$
d. $\$295 \times \frac{3}{5} = \$177$
e. $\$540 \div \frac{3}{4} = \$720$

    f. $\frac{18}{35} + \frac{12}{35} = \frac{6}{7}$

    g. $\frac{5}{6} - \frac{1}{8} = \frac{17}{24}$

    h. $\frac{17}{6} = 2\frac{5}{6}$

    i. $\frac{2}{3} = \frac{6}{9}$

3.   **a.** $52,000; $54,558

    b. $500; $525

4.   **a.** 8 to 3

    b. 3 to 8

    c. 3 to 11

    d. 8 to 11

5.   **a.** 52 × $312 = $16,224   salary per year

    b. $16,224 ÷ 12 = $1,352   salary per month

6.   (40 × $18) + (50 × $12) + ($14 × $13) = $1,502   total selling price of ties

    $1,502 ÷ 104 = $14.44   average selling price

‡**7.** $\frac{120}{N} = \frac{15}{40}$; 15 × N = 4,800; N = 320   baseball caps

Section 17. Figuring Overtime Pay

Exercise 1, page 97

1. $1\frac{1}{2}$ × $11 = $16.50   time-and-a-half rate

    6 × $16.50 = $99   overtime pay

2.   **a.** (2 × $7) × 8 = $112   estimated pay

    b. 2 × $6.95 = $13.90   overtime rate

       8 × $13.90 = $111.20   actual overtime pay

3. $1\frac{1}{2}$ × $7.72 = $11.58   time-and-a-half rate

    2 × $7.72 = $15.44   double-time rate

    (4 × $11.58) + (3 × $15.44) = $92.64   overtime pay

4.   **a.** 47 − 40 = 7   overtime hours

    b. $1\frac{1}{2}$ × $9.95 = $14.925   overtime rate

    c. 7 × $14.925 = $104.475 = $104.48   overtime pay

5.   **a.** 40 × $13 = $520   regular pay

    b. $1\frac{1}{2}$ × $13 = $19.50   overtime rate

       5 × $19.50 = $97.50   overtime pay

    c. $520 + $97.50 = $617.50   gross pay

6. $38\frac{1}{2}$ × $12 = $462   regular pay

    $1\frac{1}{2}$ × $12 = $18   time-and-a-half rate

    $3\frac{1}{2}$ × $18 = $63   time-and-a-half pay

    2 × $12 = $24   double-time rate

    4 × $24 = $96   double-time pay

    $462 + $63 + $96 = $621   gross pay

Exercise 2, page 99

1.

	Regular Time	Time and a Half
Monday	6	0
Tuesday	8	0
Wednesday	8	2
Thursday	8	1
Friday	+ 8	+3
	38	6

a. 38 regular time hours worked
b. 6 overtime hours worked
c. $38 \times \$5 = \$190$ regular-time pay
d. $1\frac{1}{2} \times \$5 = \$7.50$ overtime rate
   $6 \times \$7.50 = \$45$ overtime pay
e. $\$190 + \$45 = \$235$ gross pay

2.

	Regular Time	Time and a Half
Monday	8	0
Tuesday	8	2
Wednesday	8	0
Thursday	8	0
Friday	+ 8	+0
	40	2

a. 40 regular-time hours worked
b. 2 overtime hours worked
c. $40 \times \$9 = \$360$ regular-time pay
d. $1\frac{1}{2} \times \$9 = \$13.50$ overtime rate
   $2 \times \$13.50 = \$27$ overtime pay
e. $\$360 + \$27 = \$387$ gross pay

3.

	Regular Time	Time and a Half
Monday	8	0
Tuesday	6	0
Wednesday	8	3
Thursday	8	2
Friday	+ 8	+0
	38	5

a. $38 \times \$10.30 = \$391.40$ regular-time pay
b. $1\frac{1}{2} \times \$10.30 = \$15.45$ overtime rate
   $5 \times \$15.45 = \$77.25$ overtime pay
c. $\$391.40 + \$77.25 = \$468.65$ gross pay

4. $5 \times 9 = 45$ total hours worked
$1\frac{1}{2} \times \$14 = \$21$ overtime rate
$40 \times \$14 = \$560$ regular-time earnings
$5 \times \$21 = \$105$ overtime earnings
$\$560 + \$105 = \$665$ gross earnings

5.

	Regular Time	Time and a Half
Monday	8	1
Tuesday	4	0
Wednesday	8	0
Thursday	8	2
Friday	+ 8	+2
	36	5

$1\frac{1}{2} \times \$10.67 = \$16.005$ overtime rate
$36 \times \$10.67 = \$384.12$ regular-time pay
$5 \times \$16.005 = \$80.025 = \$80.03$ overtime pay
$\$384.12 + \$80.03 = \$464.15$ gross pay

6. $(7\frac{1}{2} \times 4) + 10 = 40$ total hours worked
$40 - 37\frac{1}{2} = 2\frac{1}{2}$ overtime hours worked
$1\frac{1}{2} \times \$11.70 = \$17.55$ overtime rate
$37\frac{1}{2} \times \$11.70 = \$438.75$ regular-time pay
$2\frac{1}{2} \times \$17.55 = \$43.875 = \$43.88$ overtime pay
$\$438.75 + \$43.88 = \$482.63$ gross pay

7.

	Regular Time	Time and a Half	Double Time
Monday	8	1	0
Tuesday	8	2	0
Wednesday	8	0	0
Thursday	8	0	0
Friday	8	1	0
Saturday	+ 0	+0	+7
	40	4	7

$1\frac{1}{2} \times \$8.15 = \$12.225$ time-and-a-half rate
$2 \times \$8.15 = \$16.30$ double-time rate
$40 \times \$8.15 = \$326$ regular-time pay
$4 \times \$12.225 = \$48.90$ time-and-a-half pay
$7 \times \$16.30 = \$114.10$ double-time pay
$\$326 + \$48.90 + \$114.10 = \$489$ gross pay

8.

	Regular Time	Time and a Half	Double Time
Monday	8	1	0
Tuesday	8	1	0
Wednesday	8	1	0
Thursday	8	1	0
Friday	8	1	0
Saturday	+ 0	+0	+8
	40	5	8

$1\frac{1}{2} \times \$8.20 = \$12.30$ time-and-a-half rate
$2 \times \$8.20 = \$16.40$ double-time rate
$40 \times \$8.20 = \$328$ regular-time pay
$5 \times \$12.30 = \$61.50$ time-and-a-half pay
$8 \times \$16.40 = \$131.20$ double-time pay
$\$328 + \$61.50 + \$131.20 = \$520.70$ gross pay

Review 17, page 100

2. **a.** $\$16 \times \frac{3}{4} = \$12$ **c.** $\frac{12}{35} \times \frac{7}{2} = 1\frac{1}{5}$ **e.** $\frac{2}{5} + \frac{2}{3} = 1\frac{1}{15}$
  b. $38 \div \frac{1}{4} = 152$ **d.** $\frac{3}{8} + \frac{11}{8} = 1\frac{3}{4}$ **f.** $\frac{3}{4} - \frac{1}{8} = \frac{5}{8}$

3. **a.** $3 \times 13 = 82 - 43$ **c.** $64 \div 8 = 1\frac{1}{3} + 6\frac{2}{3}$
  b. $0 \div 3 = 0$ **d.** $16 \times 1 = 1 \times 16$

4. **a.** $1{,}023 \times 96 = 100{,}000$; $98{,}208$
  b. $1{,}248 \div 78 = 15$; 16
  c. $32.1 \div 0.75 = 40$; 42.8
  d. $0.92 \times 7.1 = 7$; 6.532

5. **a.** $\$9.50$; $\$2.89$; $\$57.60$
  b. $\$0.24$; $\$0.90$; $\$5.40$
  c. $5{,}200$; $\$170$; $\$300$
  d. $\$1.80$; $\$3.67$; 700

6.

	Regular Time	Time and a Half	Double Time
Monday	8	2	0
Tuesday	8	0	0
Wednesday	8	1	0
Thursday	6	0	0
Friday	8	0	0
Saturday	0	0	5
	38	3	5

$1\frac{1}{2} \times \$11.40 = \$17.10$ time-and-a-half rate
$2 \times \$11.40 = \$22.80$ double-time rate
$38 \times \$11.40 = \$433.20$ regular-time pay
$3 \times \$17.10 = \$51.30$ time-and-a-half pay
$5 \times \$22.80 = \$114$ double-time pay
$\$433.20 + \$51.30 + \$114 = \$598.50$ gross pay

7. **a.** 80 to 100; 4 to 5
  b. 20 to 100; 1 to 5
  c. 20 to 80; 1 to 4
  d. 80 to 20; 4 to 1

8. $(20 \times \$16) + (14 \times \$12) + (18 \times \$9) = \$650$ selling price of albums
$20 + 14 + 18 = 52$ total albums sold
$\$650 \div 52 = \$12.50$ average price of albums

‡9. $\frac{24}{20} = \frac{6}{N}$; $24 \times N = 120$; $N = 5$ filing cabinets

Section 18. Mixed Numbers

Exercise 1, page 102

1. **a.** $16 \times 3\frac{1}{2} = 56$ **d.** $18\frac{3}{8} \times 24 = 441$ **g.** $16 \times 3\frac{5}{8} = 58$
  b. $24 \times 4\frac{3}{4} = 114$ **e.** $27\frac{2}{5} \times 35 = 959$ **h.** $27 \times 4\frac{2}{3} = 126$
  c. $45 \times 6\frac{3}{5} = 297$ **f.** $17\frac{5}{6} \times 72 = 1{,}284$ **i.** $60 \times 6\frac{4}{5} = 408$

2. $4\frac{1}{4} \times \$1.60 = \$6.80$

3. $3\frac{1}{2} \times 26 = 91$ gallons

Exercise 2, page 103

1. $4\frac{3}{4}$
   $+3\frac{1}{4}$
   ———
   8

2. $5\frac{2}{3}$
   $+\ 9\frac{1}{4}$
   ———
   $14\frac{11}{12}$

3. $7\frac{7}{8}$
   $+\ 2\frac{1}{2}$
   ———
   $10\frac{3}{8}$

4. $5\frac{1}{3}$
   $+\ 7\frac{5}{6}$
   ———
   $13\frac{1}{6}$

5. $6\frac{3}{4}$
   $3\frac{1}{2}$
   $+\ 2\frac{5}{8}$
   ———
   $12\frac{7}{8}$

6. $8\frac{7}{10}$
   $14\frac{2}{5}$
   $+\ 9\frac{1}{4}$
   ———
   $32\frac{7}{20}$

Exercise 3, page 104

1. $8\frac{7}{8}$
   $-4\frac{3}{4}$
   ———
   $4\frac{1}{8}$

2. $12\frac{5}{6}$
   $-\ 7\frac{2}{3}$
   ———
   $5\frac{1}{6}$

3. $7\frac{2}{5}$
   $-4\frac{1}{4}$
   ———
   $3\frac{3}{20}$

4. $9\frac{1}{6}$
   $-7\frac{2}{3}$
   ———
   $1\frac{1}{2}$

5. $8\frac{1}{3}$
   $-2\frac{5}{8}$
   ———
   $5\frac{17}{24}$

6. $21\frac{1}{5}$
   $-16\frac{1}{2}$
   ———
   $4\frac{7}{10}$

Exercise 5, page 105

1. $3\frac{1}{4} \times 2\frac{1}{2} = 8\frac{1}{8}$

2. $2\frac{1}{4} \times 4\frac{1}{5} = 9\frac{9}{20}$

3. $3\frac{1}{5} \times 2\frac{1}{8} = 6\frac{4}{5}$

4. $4\frac{1}{8} \times 3\frac{1}{2} = 14\frac{7}{16}$

5. $1\frac{1}{5} \times 2\frac{5}{8} = 3\frac{3}{20}$

6. $2\frac{3}{4} \times 1\frac{2}{3} = 4\frac{7}{12}$

Exercise 6, page 105

1. $3\frac{1}{8} \div 5 = \frac{5}{8}$

2. $4\frac{4}{5} \div 6 = \frac{4}{5}$

3. $5\frac{5}{6} \div 7 = \frac{5}{6}$

4. $8 \div 1\frac{1}{4} = 6\frac{2}{5}$

5. $6 \div 4\frac{4}{5} = 1\frac{1}{4}$

6. $2\frac{3}{4} \div 2\frac{1}{2} = 1\frac{1}{10}$

7. $4\frac{2}{5} \div 2\frac{3}{4} = 1\frac{3}{5}$

8. $16\frac{1}{2} \div 3\frac{2}{3} = 4\frac{1}{2}$

9. $87\frac{1}{2} \div 3\frac{1}{2} = 25$

Review 18, page 105

1. a. $\frac{2}{7} + \frac{4}{7} + \frac{6}{7} = 1\frac{5}{7}$ c. $\$78.40 \times \frac{3}{4} = \$58.80$ e. $6\frac{3}{4} \div 3\frac{3}{8} = 2$
   b. $\frac{4}{5} - \frac{2}{7} = \frac{18}{35}$ d. $1\frac{1}{4} + 3\frac{5}{6} = 5\frac{1}{12}$ f. $2\frac{1}{2} \times 4\frac{1}{4} = 10\frac{5}{8}$

2. a. 48 to 4   b. 4 to 48   c. 48 to 52   d. 4 to 52

3. $\frac{3}{5} \times \$90 = \$54$ Eric's share of expense
   $\frac{2}{5} \times \$90 = \$36$ Ron's share of expense

4. a. $7\frac{3}{4}$ regular hours worked
   b. $8 \times 9 = \$72$ estimated gross pay
   c. $7\frac{3}{4} \times \$8.94 = \$69.29$ gross pay for Monday

5. $(68 + 74 + 70 + 75 + 78) - 11 = 354$ pieces accepted
   $\$0.98 \times 354 = \$346.92$ gross pay

6.

Check register balance	$534.04	Bank statement balance	$945.63
Deduct:		Deduct:	
Service charge	− 4.25	Outstanding checks:	
	$529.79	#346 $210.00	
		#352 202.24	− 412.24
Add:			
Interest earned	+ 3.60		
Correct check register balance	$533.39	Available bank balance	$533.39

Section 19.   Fractional Relationships

Exercise 2, page 107

1. $\frac{5}{6} \times \$360.42 = \$300.35$ regular-time pay

2. $\frac{1}{10} \times \$22,910 = \$2,291$ overtime pay

3. $\frac{4}{5} \times \$26,780 = \$21,424$ earnings this year

4. $\frac{7}{8} \times 15,816 = 13,839$ alarms sold last year

Exercise 4, page 108

1. $(\frac{3}{10} \times \$24,300) + \$24,300 = \$31,590$ Norma's yearly pay

2. $(\frac{1}{8} \times \$1,712) + \$1,712 = \$1,926$ Gene's March earnings

3. $(\frac{4}{7} \times \$246,750) + \$246,750 = \$387,750$ total sales last year

4. $\$13.20 - (\$13.20 \times \frac{1}{5}) = \$10.56$ hourly pay of new job

5. $\$1,800,000 - (\frac{1}{12} \times \$1,800,000) = \$1,650,000$ labor cost after cut

6. $\$486 - (\$486 \times \frac{1}{9}) = \$432$ new average pay per week

Exercise 6, page 109

1. $\frac{\$1,500}{\$24,000} = \frac{1}{16}$ increase   2. $\frac{\$0.90}{\$8.10} = \frac{1}{9}$ increase   3. $\frac{\$300}{\$360} = \frac{5}{6}$ of last week's pay

4. a. $\frac{\$720}{\$600} = \frac{6}{5}$ b. $\frac{\$600}{\$720} = \frac{5}{6}$

5. a. $\frac{\$14}{\$12} = \frac{7}{6}$ b. $\frac{\$12}{\$14} = \frac{6}{7}$

Exercise 8, page 110

1. $\$1,600 - \$1,400 = \$200$
   $\frac{\$200}{\$1,400} = \frac{1}{7}$

2. $\$20,130 - \$18,300 = \$1,830$
   $\frac{\$1,830}{\$18,300} = \frac{1}{10}$

3. $\$2,025 - \$1,800 = \$225$
   $\frac{\$225}{\$2,025} = \frac{1}{9}$

4. $\$7,140 - \$5,712 = \$1,428$
   $\frac{\$1,428}{\$7,140} = \frac{1}{5}$

5. a. $\$19,500 - \$18,000 = \$1,500$
   $\frac{\$1,500}{\$18,000} = \frac{1}{12}$

   b. $\frac{\$1,500}{\$19,500} = \frac{1}{13}$

Review 19, page 111

1. a. $\frac{1}{8} \times 72 = 9$ c. $\frac{3}{7} \times 49 = 21$ e. $35 - (\frac{1}{7} \times 35) = 30$

   b. $\frac{2}{5} \times 40 = 16$ d. $24 + (\frac{1}{6} \times 24) = 28$ f. $\frac{8}{72} = \frac{1}{9}$

2. $\frac{5}{6} \times \$1,230 = \$1,025$ Herb's pay per month

3. $(\frac{2}{7} \times 742) + 742 = 954$ programs sold this year

4. $\frac{\$26,800}{\$134,000} = \frac{1}{5}$ paid for weekend work

5. $\$14,850 - \$13,200 = \$1,650$
$\frac{\$1,650}{\$14,850} = \frac{1}{9}$ less spent for temporary help

6. **a.** $\$0.75 + \$1.10 + \$0.90 + \$0.62 = \$3.37$ total pay raise
$\$3.37 \div 4 = \$0.842$, or $\$0.84$ average pay raise per worker
b. $40 \times \$0.80 = \$32$ estimated pay increase

‡7.

Check register balance		$565.80	Bank statement balance		$701.32
Deduct:			Deduct:		
Service charge	$ 3.10		Outstanding checks:		
Check #829			#834	$118.00	
not recorded	35.00	− 38.10	#842	17.22	+ 135.22
		$527.70			
Add:					
Interest earned	$ 2.40				
Deposit not					
recorded	36.00	+ 38.40			
Correct check register balance		$566.10	Available bank balance		$566.10

‡Section 20.   More Fractional Relationships

‡Exercise 2, page 112

1. $\$2,800 \div \frac{2}{15} = \$21,000$ total pay for year

2. $\$0.43 \div \frac{1}{20} = \$8.60$ old pay

3. $\$250 \div \frac{1}{5} = \$1,250$ cost of computer

4. $8 \div \frac{2}{25} = 100$ employees

5. $\$42 \div \frac{6}{7} = \$49$ paid for full day

6. $\$200,000 \div \frac{4}{5} = \$250,000$ total weekly wages

7. $\$6,800 \div \frac{1}{4} = \$27,200$ earnings for full year

8. $2 \div \frac{2}{17} = 17$ workers in company

9. $6,000 \div \frac{5}{8} = 9,600$ votes cast in this year's election

‡Exercise 4, page 114

1. $\$19,500 \div \frac{13}{12} = \$18,000$ salary year before

2. $\$380 \div \frac{10}{9} = \$342$ pay the week before

3. $\$4,200 \div \frac{7}{9} = \$5,400$ collected last year

4. $\$71,500 \div \frac{13}{15} = \$82,500$ sales for March last year

5. $\$1,750 \div \frac{7}{6} = \$1,500$ Waidley's average monthly pay

6. $\$936 \div \frac{5}{8} = \$1,497.60$ January 1 checking account balance

‡Exercise 6, page 115

1. $\$4.80 \div \frac{3}{4} = \$6.40$

2. $\$14.70 \div \frac{2}{3} = \$22.05$

3. $\$5.60 \div \frac{5}{7} = \$7.84$

4. $\$5.20 \div \frac{8}{5} = \$3.25$

5. $\$8.80 \div \frac{11}{8} = \$6.40$

6. $\$1.80 \div \frac{9}{5} = \$1$

7. $\$32.48 \div \frac{7}{8} = \$37.12$

8. $\$4.20 \div \frac{7}{10} = \$6$

9. $\$1.92 + (\frac{5}{6} \times \$1.92) = \$3.52$

10. $\frac{5}{8} \times \$4.80 = \$3$

11. $\$9.72 - (\frac{1}{3} \times \$9.72) = \$6.48$

12. $\$3.36 \div \frac{7}{8} = \$3.84$

13. $\$8.40 + (\frac{1}{4} \times \$8.40) = \$10.50$

14. $\$4.20 \div \frac{3}{5} = \$7$

‡Exercise 7, page 115

1. $\$480 \times \frac{1}{8} = \$60$ overtime pay

2. $\$42 + (\frac{1}{5} \times \$42) = \$50.40$ amount of new water bill

3. $\frac{\$16}{\$64} = \frac{1}{4}$ labor charge

4. $72 - 60 = 12$ difference; $\frac{12}{72} = \frac{1}{6}$ smaller

5. $\$8.40 \div \frac{3}{4} = \$11.20$ hourly earnings in two years

6. $\$11.55 \div \frac{11}{12} = \$12.60$ Patrick's hourly pay

Review 20, page 116

1.
   a. $67 + 14 + 36 + 29 = 146$
   b. $86 + 45 - 51 = 80$
   c. $51 \times \frac{5}{6} = 42\frac{1}{2}$
   d. $7\frac{3}{4} \times 4\frac{2}{3} = 36\frac{1}{6}$
   e. $14 \div \frac{5}{6} = 16\frac{4}{5}$
   f. $4\frac{2}{5} \div 5\frac{1}{2} = \frac{4}{5}$
   g. $2 \div 7 = 0.286$
   h. $\frac{2}{7} \times \$49 = \$14$
   i. $\$30 - (\frac{2}{3} \times \$30) = \$10$
   j. $\frac{7}{8} \times \$0.56 = \$0.49$
   k. $\$28 \div \frac{7}{4} = \$16$
   l. $17 \div \frac{1}{8} = 136$

2. $12 \times \$863 = \$10,356$ yearly salary
   $\$10,356 \div 52 = \$199.15$ weekly salary

3.
   $100 \times \$0.47 = \$47.00$
   $50 \times \$0.60 = 30.00$
   $23 \times \$0.75 = \underline{17.25}$
   $\$94.25$ gross pay

4. $\frac{5}{6} \times \$2,474,274 = \$2,061,895$ this year's sales

‡5. $\$240 \div \frac{6}{5} = \$200$

‡6. $\$400 \div \frac{2}{3} = \$600$

‡7. $\$6.30 \div \frac{1}{9} = \$56.70$ original price

‡8. $2,600,000 \div \frac{5}{6} = 3,120,000$ hangers made last year

‡**9.**

Check register balance		$468.95	Bank statement balance		$780.40

Deduct:

Service charge	$5.20		Deduct:		
Check not			Outstanding checks:		
recorded	8.14	− 13.34	#412	$ 68.15	
		$455.61	#415	156.88	− 225.03

Add:

Interest earned	$ 2.76	
Deposit not		
recorded	97.00	+ 99.76
Correct check register balance		$555.37

Available bank balance $555.37

‡**10.** $\frac{\$35}{N} = \frac{3\frac{1}{2}}{8}$, $3\frac{1}{2} \times N = \$280$; $N = \$80$

UNIT 4 • NET PAY, FRINGE BENEFITS, AND COMMISSION

Section 21. Deductions and Take-Home Pay

Exercise 2, page 119

1.	$36.34	**3.**	$19.08	**5.**	$57.32	**7.**	$22.15
2.	$42.56	**4.**	$38.05	**6.**	$13.77	**8.**	$66.08

Exercise 4, page 120

1. **a.** $45   withholding tax   **b.** $33.35   FICA tax
   c. $45 + $33.35 + $35.20 + $35.80 = $149.35   total deductions
   d. $436 − $149.35 = $286.65   net pay

2. **a.** 40 × $9.40 = $376   regular-time pay
   b. 4 × $14.10 = $56.40   overtime pay
   c. $376 + $56.40 = $432.40   gross pay
   d. $51.00   withholding tax
   e. $33.08   FICA tax
   f. $51.00 + $33.08 + $30 + $46.89 = $160.97   total deductions
      $432.40 − $160.97 = $271.43   net pay

3.

		Allow-ances	Gross Wage	Deductions			Total	Net Wages
				Income Tax	FICA	Other		
a.	Dean	1	$ 431.31	$ 51.00	$ 33.00	$ 56.81	$140.81	$ 290.50
b.	Dent	0	335.74	41.00	25.68	38.93	105.61	230.13
c.	Dern	4	436.42	34.00	33.39	65.39	132.78	303.64
d.	Dest	2	333.07	30.00	25.48	49.23	104.71	228.36
e.	Totals		$1,536.54	$156.00	$117.55	$210.36	$483.91	$1,052.63

Review 21, page 121

2. **a.** $25.60 × $\frac{1}{8}$ = $3.20   **c.** $\frac{2}{5} \times \$44.50 = \$17.80$
   b. $3\frac{1}{8} \div \frac{5}{8} = 5$ **d.** $\frac{5}{4} \times 40 = 50$

3. $0.0765 \times \$276 = \$21.11$ FICA tax
    $\$276 - (\$27.00 + \$11.39 + \$21.11) = \$216.50$ net pay

4. $627 \times \$0.38 = \$238.26$ gross pay
    $0.0765 \times \$238.26 = \$18.23$ FICA tax
    $\$238.26 - (\$21.00 + \$25.00 + \$18.23) = \$174.03$ net pay

5. $\$38.52 \div \frac{3}{2} = \$25.68$ overtime pay last week

Section 22. Decimals

Exercise 1, page 123

1. $\frac{21}{100} = 0.21$ 4. $\frac{5}{1,000} = 0.005$ 7. $\frac{11}{1,000} = 0.011$

2. $\frac{592}{1,000} = 0.592$ 5. $\frac{74}{100} = 0.74$ 8. $\frac{107}{10,000} = 0.0107$

3. $\frac{8}{10} = 0.8$ 6. $\frac{3}{10,000} = 0.0003$

Exercise 2, page 124

1. a. $\frac{4}{7} = 0.571$ d. $\frac{8}{11} = 0.727$ g. $\frac{7}{9} = 0.778$
    b. $\frac{5}{9} = 0.556$ e. $\frac{3}{14} = 0.214$ h. $\frac{6}{13} = 0.462$
    c. $\frac{11}{12} = 0.917$ f. $\frac{5}{6} = 0.833$ i. $\frac{4}{15} = 0.267$

2. a. $\frac{6}{21} = 0.29$ d. $\frac{1}{11} = 0.09$ g. $\frac{5}{17} = 0.29$
    b. $\frac{4}{17} = 0.24$ e. $\frac{2}{15} = 0.13$ h. $\frac{5}{7} = 0.71$
    c. $\frac{8}{13} = 0.62$ f. $\frac{3}{16} = 0.19$ i. $\frac{2}{7} = 0.29$

Exercise 3, page 124

1. $\frac{7}{11} = 0.63\frac{7}{11}$ 4. $\frac{2}{13} = 0.15\frac{5}{13}$ 7. $\frac{5}{11} = 0.45\frac{5}{11}$

2. $\frac{5}{14} = 0.35\frac{5}{7}$ 5. $\frac{13}{14} = 0.92\frac{6}{7}$ 8. $\frac{1}{12} = 0.08\frac{1}{3}$

3. $\frac{7}{16} = 0.43\frac{3}{4}$ 6. $\frac{6}{13} = 0.46\frac{2}{13}$ 9. $\frac{7}{17} = 0.41\frac{3}{17}$

Exercise 4, page 125

	1.	2.	3.
a.	$98.2 \times 0.1 = 9.82$	$906 \times 0.001 = 0.906$	$99 \times 0.01 = 0.99$
b.	$14.7 \times 0.01 = 0.147$	$221 \times 0.1 = 22.1$	$70 \times 0.001 = 0.07$
c.	$1.8 \times 0.1 = 0.18$	$59 \times 0.01 = 0.59$	$\$107 \times 0.01 = \$1.07$
d.	$8 \times 0.01 = 0.08$	$3.1 \times 0.001 = 0.0031$	$\$57.40 \times 0.1 = \$5.74$
e.	$845 \times 0.001 = 0.845$	$0.46 \times 0.1 = 0.046$	$\$400 \times 0.001 = \$0.40$

Exercise 5, page 125

	1.	2.	3.	4.
a.	$0.56 = \frac{14}{25}$	$0.98 = \frac{49}{50}$	$0.026 = \frac{13}{500}$	$0.064 = \frac{8}{125}$
b.	$0.45 = \frac{9}{20}$	$0.025 = \frac{1}{40}$	$0.675 = \frac{27}{40}$	$0.075 = \frac{3}{40}$
c.	$0.045 = \frac{9}{200}$	$0.2475 = \frac{99}{400}$	$0.12 = \frac{3}{25}$	$0.375 = \frac{3}{8}$
d.	$0.0375 = \frac{3}{80}$	$0.86 = \frac{43}{50}$	$0.625 = \frac{5}{8}$	$0.85 = \frac{17}{20}$

Exercise 6, page 126

	1.	2.	3.
a.	$6.28 \div 0.1 = 62.8$	$7.23 \div 0.01 = 723$	$2.2 \div 0.01 = 220$
b.	$0.085 \div 0.01 = 8.5$	$33 \div 0.01 = 3,300$	$\$0.18 \div 0.01 = \$18$
c.	$0.0065 \div 0.001 = 6.5$	$476 \div 0.1 = 4,760$	$\$3.00 \div 0.1 = \$30$
d.	$0.208 \div 0.01 = 20.8$	$84 \div 0.1 = 840$	$\$5.31 \div 0.001 = \$5,310$
e.	$0.189 \div 0.001 = 189$	$0.2 \div 0.01 = 20$	$\$7.34 \div 0.001 = \$7,340$
f.	$5.3 \div 0.1 = 53$	$2.76 \div 0.001 = 2,760$	$\$28.78 \div 0.01 = \$2,878$

Review 22, page 126

2.
a. $\frac{5}{7} = 0.714$
   d. $\frac{5}{8} + \frac{3}{4} = 1\frac{3}{8}$
   g. $\$8.24 \div 0.1 = \$82.40$

b. $\frac{2}{11} = 0.18\frac{2}{11}$
   e. $0.065 = \frac{13}{200}$
   ‡h. $21 \div \frac{3}{4} = 28$

c. $3\frac{3}{5} \div 4\frac{2}{3} = \frac{27}{35}$
   f. $23.7 \times 0.001 = 0.0237$

3.
a. $(300 \times \$0.72) + (128 \times \$0.89) = \$329.92$ gross pay
b. $0.0765 \times \$329.92 = \$25.24$ social security tax
c. $\$329.92 - (\$34 + \$11.67 + \$25.24) = \$259.01$ net pay

4. $5 \times 80 = 400$ items for week
$400 - (73 + 84 + 79 + 82) = 82$ items Nathan produced Friday

5. $\frac{3}{8} \times \$180,512 = \$67,692$ Novak's share of profits

‡6. $\$49,000 \div \frac{7}{8} = \$56,000$ earned last year

Section 23. Fringe Benefits and Job Expenses

Exercise 1, page 128

1.
a. $\$1,226 + \$1,534 + \$1,993 + \$2,936 + \$690 = \$8,379$ total value of fringe benefits
b. $\$18,512 + \$8,379 = \$26,891$ total job benefits

2.
a. $40 \times \$12 = \$480$ estimated weekly wage
b. $40 \times \$12.45 = \$498$ exact weekly wage
c. $\$30 + \$15.65 + \$14 + \$5 = \$64.65$ fringe benefits
d. $\$498 + \$64.65 = \$562.65$ total job benefits

3.
a. $40 \times \$9 = \$360$ estimated weekly wage
b. $40 \times \$8.72 = \$348.80$ exact weekly wage
$52 \times \$348.80 = \$18,137.60$ exact annual wage
c. $0.37 \times \$18,137.60 = \$6,710.91$ estimated fringe benefits
d. $\$18,137.60 + \$6,710.91 = \$24,848.51$ total job benefits

4.
a. $\$1,000 \times 12 = \$12,000$ estimated annual wage
b. $\$1,128 \times 12 = \$13,536$ exact annual pay
c. $0.23 \times \$13,536 = \$3,113.28$ estimated fringe benefits
d. $\$13,536 + \$3,113.28 = \$16,649.28$ total job benefits

Exercise 2, page 129

1.
a. $\$276 + \$398 + \$260 + \$96 + \$74 = \$1,104$ yearly job expenses
b. $\$17,220 - \$1,104 = \$16,116$ net job benefits

2. a. $1,374 + $384 = $1,758   total job benefits
   b. $38 + $22 + $24 + $42 = $126   job expenses
   c. $1,758 − $126 = $1,632   net job benefits

3. a. 52 × $420 = $21,840   annual wage
   b. $21,840 × 0.35 = $7,644   annual fringe benefits
   c. $21,840 + $7,644 = $29,484   annual job benefits
   d. $345 + $326 + $745 + $535 = $1,951   annual job expenses
   e. $29,484 − $1,951 = $27,533   annual net job benefits

4. $15,685 + (0.28 × $15,685) = $20,076.80   total job benefits
   (0.06 × $15,685) + $408 + $120 + $20 = $1,489.10   job expenses
   $20,076.80 − $1,489.10 = $18,587.70   net job benefits

Exercise 3, page 130

1. a. $23,650 + (0.19 × $23,650) = $28,143.50   total job benefits
   $28,143.50 − $1,354.00 = $26,789.50   net benefits of current job
   b. $22,490 + (0.26 × $22,490) = $28,337.40   total job benefits
   $28,337.40 − $1,080.00 = $27,257.40   net benefits of other job
   c. $27,257.40 − $26,789.50 = $467.90   greater net benefits from second job

2. a. 52 × (40 × $6.75) = $14,040   yearly wage at Yuler Co.
   (0.09 × $14,040) + $890 + $450 = $2,603.60   fringe benefits at Yuler
   $14,040.00 + $2,603.60 = $16,643.60   total benefits at Yuler
   $385 + $75 + $320 = $780   total expenses at Yuler Co.
   $16,643.60 − $780 = $15,863.60   net job benefits at Yuler Co.
   b. 52 × (40 × $7.20) = $14,976   yearly wage at Zane, Inc.
   (0.07 × $14,976) + $925 + $280 = $2,253.32   fringe benefits at Zane
   $14,976 + $2,253.32 = $17,229.32   total benefits at Zane
   $456 + $75 + $312 = $843   job expenses at Zane, Inc.
   $17,229.32 − $843 = $16,386.32   net job benefits at Zane, Inc.
   c. $16,386.32 − $15,863.60 = $522.72   greater net benefits at Zane, Inc.

3. 52 × (40 × $5.25) = $10,920   yearly wages at Southwest Auto
   0.27 × $10,920 = $2,948.40   fringe benefits at Southwest
   $10,920 + $2,948.40 = $13,868.40   total benefits at Southwest
   $13,868.40 − $568.00 = $13,300.40   net job benefits at Southwest
   52 × (40 × $6.10) = $12,688   yearly wages at Office Solution
   0.17 × $12,688 = $2,156.96   fringe benefits at Office Solution
   $12,688 + $2,156.96 = $14,844.96   total benefits at Office Solution
   $14,844.96 − $785 = $14,059.96   net job benefits at Office Solution
   $14,059.96 − $13,300.40 = $759.56   greater net benefits at Office Solution, Inc.

4. 52 × $360 = $18,720   yearly wage at TRI Co.
   0.19 × $18,720 = $3,556.80   fringe benefits at TRI Co.
   $18,720 + $3,556.80 = $22,276.80   total job benefits at TRI Co.
   $22,276.80 − $956 = $21,320.80   net job benefits at TRI Co.
   12 × $1,505 = $18,060   yearly wage at Ellis, Inc.
   0.24 × $18,060 = $4,334.40   fringe benefits at Ellis, Inc.
   $18,060 + $4,334.40 = $22,394.40   total job benefits at Ellis, Inc.
   $22,394.40 − $237 = $22,157.40   net job benefits at Ellis, Inc.
   $22,157.40 − $21,320.80 = $836.60   job benefits better at Ellis, Inc.

Review 23, page 131

2. **a.** $\frac{3}{7} - \frac{2}{5} = \frac{1}{35}$ **f.** $450 \times 180 = 81{,}000$

b. $3\frac{4}{9} + 8\frac{2}{3} = 12\frac{1}{9}$ **g.** $8 \div 64 = \frac{1}{8}$

c. $8\frac{7}{8} - 3\frac{1}{6} = 5\frac{17}{24}$ **h.** $(12 - 9) \div 9 = \frac{1}{3}$

d. $36 - (\frac{1}{3} \times 36) = 24$ **i.** $\frac{3}{11} = 0.27$

e. $45 + (\frac{2}{5} \times 45) = 63$ **j.** $\frac{5}{14} = 0.35\frac{5}{7}$

3. **a.** $\$21{,}800 + (0.18 \times \$21{,}800) = \$25{,}724$ total job benefits per year

b. $\$1{,}230 + \$185 + \$420 = \$1{,}835$ total expenses per year
$\$25{,}724 - \$1{,}835 = \$23{,}889$ net job benefits per year

4. $40 \times \$8.20 = \$328$ weekly wage
$\$40 + (0.0765 \times \$328) + \$12.00 = \$77.09$ total deductions
$\$328 - \$77.09 = \$250.91$ net pay for week

5. $4 \times 87 = 348$
    $3 \times 90 = 270$
    $3 \times 82 = 246$
    $\underline{4 \times 98 = 392}$
  14   1,256
$1{,}256 \div 14 = 89.7$ average mark earned

‡6. Check register balance $951.21
Deduct:
  Service charge $ 1.34
  Check #211 not recorded   17.82
  Amount recorded for check
   #238 too small $\underline{0.09}$ $\underline{- 19.25}$
                       $931.96

Add:
  Interest earned $\underline{+ 5.67}$
Correct check register balance $\underline{\underline{\$937.63}}$

Section 24. Percents

Exercise 1, page 133

1. 87 to 100 $= \frac{87}{100} = 0.87 = 87\%$ **5.** 500 to 100 $= \frac{500}{100} = 5.00 = 500\%$

2. 31 to 100 $= \frac{31}{100} = 0.31 = 31\%$ **6.** 375 to 100 $= \frac{375}{100} = 3.75 = 375\%$

3. 100 to 100 $= \frac{100}{100} = 1.00 = 100\%$ **7.** 3 to 100 $= \frac{3}{100} = 0.03 = 3\%$

4. 110 to 100 $= \frac{110}{100} = 1.10 = 110\%$ **8.** 19 to 100 $= \frac{19}{100} = 0.19 = 19\%$

Exercise 3, page 134

1. $\frac{1}{2} = 50\%$ **3.** $\frac{5}{10} = 50\%$ **5.** $\frac{3}{25} = 12\%$ **7.** $\frac{4}{10} = 40\%$ **9.** $\frac{15}{50} = 30\%$

2. $\frac{3}{10} = 30\%$ **4.** $\frac{3}{5} = 60\%$ **6.** $\frac{8}{50} = 16\%$ **8.** $\frac{12}{25} = 48\%$ **10.** $\frac{1}{1} = 100\%$

Exercise 4, page 135

1. **a.** $\frac{3}{16} = 18\frac{3}{4}\%$ **c.** $\frac{15}{16} = 93\frac{3}{4}\%$

b. $\frac{2}{15} = 13\frac{1}{3}\%$ **d.** $\frac{5}{32} = 15\frac{5}{8}\%$

2. **a.** $\frac{1}{14} = 7.1\%$ **c.** $\frac{15}{18} = 83.3\%$

    b. $\frac{4}{15} = 26.7\%$ **d.** $\frac{5}{32} = 15.6\%$

Exercise 5, page 135

1. $78\% = 0.78$ **6.** $0.8\% = 0.008$ **11.** $15\frac{3}{4}\% = 0.15\frac{3}{4}$

2. $2\% = 0.02$ **7.** $625\% = 6.25$ **12.** $1,000\% = 10$

3. $6.1\% = 0.061$ **8.** $0.4\% = 0.004$ **13.** $23\frac{1}{2}\% = 0.23\frac{1}{2}$

4. $100\% = 1$ **9.** $1\frac{1}{2}\% = 0.01\frac{1}{2}$ **14.** $\frac{1}{5}\% = 0.00\frac{1}{5}$

5. $16.3\% = 0.163$ **10.** $\frac{1}{4}\% = 0.00\frac{1}{4}$ **15.** $9.8\% = 0.098$

Exercise 6, page 136

1. $12\% = \frac{3}{25}$ **4.** $17\% = \frac{17}{100}$ **7.** $90\% = \frac{9}{10}$ **10.** $175\% = 1\frac{3}{4}$

2. $14\% = \frac{7}{50}$ **5.** $44\% = \frac{11}{25}$ **8.** $70\% = \frac{7}{10}$ **11.** $125\% = 1\frac{1}{4}$

3. $3\% = \frac{3}{100}$ **6.** $5\% = \frac{1}{20}$ **9.** $60\% = \frac{3}{5}$ **12.** $250\% = 2\frac{1}{2}$

‡Exercise 7, page 136

1. $0.3\% = \frac{3}{1,000}$ **3.** $0.7\% = \frac{7}{1,000}$ **5.** $37\frac{1}{2}\% = \frac{3}{8}$

2. $1.3\% = \frac{13}{1,000}$ **4.** $0.5\% = \frac{1}{200}$ **6.** $1.5\% = \frac{3}{200}$

Review 24, page 136

1. **a.** $\frac{3}{20}$, 0.15, 15%   **c.** 0.375, 0.674, 0.004, 0.0025

    b. 275%, 37%, 80%   **d.** $\frac{1}{4}$, $2\frac{1}{2}$, $\frac{1}{10}$

2. $40 \times \$9.50 = \$380$ weekly pay

$0.24 \times \$380 = \$91.20$ fringe benefits

$\$380 + \$91.20 = \$471.20$ total job benefits

$\$24.75 + (\$380 \times 0.08) + \$5.24 = \$60.39$ weekly expenses

$\$471.20 - \$60.39 = \$410.81$ net weekly job benefits

3.

	Regular Time	Time and a Half	Double Time
Monday	8	0	0
Tuesday	8	0	0
Wednesday	7	0	0
Thursday	8	3	0
Friday	8	0	0
Saturday	0	0	5
	39	3	5

    a. $39 \times \$7.80 = \$304.20$ regular-time pay

    b. $3 \times \$11.70 = \$35.10$ time-and-a-half pay

        $5 \times \$15.60 = \$78$ double-time pay

        $\$35.10 + \$78 = \$113.10$ overtime pay

    c. $\$304.20 + \$113.10 = \$417.30$ gross pay

        $\$42 + (0.0765 \times \$417.30) = \$73.92$ total deductions

        $\$417.30 - \$73.92 = \$343.38$ net pay

4.   ($255 + $2,072.47) − $67.82 = $2,259.65   in cash drawer

5.

Check register balance	$1,780.23	Bank statement balance	$2,029.23
Deduct:		Deduct:	
Service Charge	− 3.23	Outstanding checks:	
	$1,777.00	#525 $156.88	
Add:		#528 89.12	
Interest earned	+ 6.23		− 246.00
Correct check register balance	$1,783.23	Available bank balance	$1,783.23

‡6. $\frac{6}{168} = \frac{N}{420}$; $168 \times N = 2,520$; $N = \frac{2,520}{168}$; $N = 15$ boxes

Section 25.   More Percents

Exercise 1, page 138

	1.		2.		3.	
a.	2% of $600	$12	5% of $120	$6	70% of $31	$21.70
b.	8% of $300	$24	1% of $480	$4.80	55% of $50	$27.50
c.	9% of $200	$18	100% of $68	$68	20% of $43	$8.60
d.	6% of $110	$6.60	300% of $3.10	$9.30	80% of $75	$60
e.	4% of $120	$4.80	500% of $109	$545	105% of $600	$630
f.	15% of $40	$6	60% of $90	$54	1% of $1,856	$18.56

Exercise 3, page 139

1.	25%	5.	8%	9.	400%	13.	50%
2.	35%	6.	$12\frac{1}{2}$%	10.	$33\frac{1}{3}$%	14.	25%
3.	$4\frac{1}{2}$%	7.	20%	11.	25%	15.	$6\frac{2}{3}$%
4.	$6\frac{1}{4}$%	8.	500%	12.	$33\frac{1}{3}$%	16.	$16\frac{2}{3}$%

Exercise 5, page 141

	1.	2.
a.	$400	$150.40
b.	$4,640	$72
c.	$870	$150
d.	$44.01	$110
e.	$92	$61.25
f.	$853.30	$795
g.	$61.08	$180
h.	$157	$30.75
i.	$3,015	$294

Exercise 6, page 141

1.	0.4	4.	$0.07	7.	0.9	10.	$19	13.	$150
2.	$0.29	5.	$36.70	8.	$0.20	11.	$805	14.	430
3.	$0.19	6.	$4.75	9.	284	12.	$6.70	15.	$75

Exercise 8, page 142

	1.	2.	3.
a.	$800	$0.16	$0.27
b.	$800	$0.90	$3
c.	$8	$1	$0.12
d.	$1,200	$3	$0.36
e.	$1,200	$6	$0.36

Exercise 9, page 143

	1.	2.	3.	4.
a.	0.005	0.0075	0.00375	$0.0033\frac{1}{3}$
b.	0.002	0.00125	0.004	0.00625

Exercise 10, page 143

	1.	2.	3.	4.	5.
a.	$\frac{3}{4}\%$	$8\frac{1}{2}\%$	$\frac{1}{3}\%$	$\frac{3}{8}\%$	$8\frac{3}{4}\%$
b.	$6\frac{1}{4}\%$	$\frac{1}{2}\%$	$\frac{1}{8}\%$	$\frac{1}{3}\%$	$\frac{7}{8}\%$
c.	$\frac{1}{4}\%$	$\frac{1}{5}\%$	$\frac{2}{5}\%$	$\frac{2}{3}\%$	$\frac{2}{3}\%$

Review 25, page 143

2.
   a. $\frac{1}{5}\% \times \$745 = \$1.49$
   b. $0.01 \times \$9.33 = \$0.09$
   c. $\$350 \div \$500 = 70\%$
   d. $\frac{3}{8} \times \$896 = \$336$
   e. $87\frac{1}{2}\% = 0.875, \frac{7}{8}$
   ‡f. $\$561 \div \frac{3}{4} = \$748$
   ‡g. $\$30 \div \frac{4}{5} = \$37.50$

3.

	Regular Time	Overtime
Monday	8	1
Tuesday	8	0
Wednesday	$6\frac{1}{2}$	0
Thursday	8	1
Friday	+ 8	+ $\frac{1}{2}$
	$38\frac{1}{2}$	$2\frac{1}{2}$

   $38\frac{1}{2} \times \$12.46 = \$479.71$ regular-time pay
   $2\frac{1}{2} \times \$18.69 = \$46.73$ overtime pay
   $\$479.71 + \$46.73 = \$526.44$ gross earnings

4. $(137 + 101 + 186 + 156 + 134) - 57 = 657$ items
   $657 \times \$0.72 = \$473.04$ gross earnings

5. $\frac{4}{9} \times 1,278 = 568$ gallons of orange

Section 26.   Percent Relationships

Exercise 3, page 148

1. $\$20,832 - \$18,600 = \$2,232$ increase
   $\frac{\$2,232}{\$18,600} = 0.12 = 12\%$ increase

2. $75.24 - $66 = 9.24 increase
$\frac{$9.24}{$66} = 0.14 = 14\%$ increase

3. **a.** $75 - $50 = 25 estimated decrease
$\frac{$25}{$75} = 33\frac{1}{3}\%$ estimated decrease
b. $75 - $51 = 24 actual decrease
$\frac{$24}{$75} = 0.32 = 32\%$ actual decrease

4. $205.77 - $180.50 = 25.27 increase
$\frac{$25.27}{$180.50} = 0.14 = 14\%$ increase

5. $1,255 - $1,225 = 30 increase
$\frac{$30}{$1,225} = 0.0244 = 2.4\%$ increase

Review 26, page 148

1. **a.** $45 + (0.24 \times $45) = 55.80
    b. $7 - (0.16 \times $7) = 5.88
    c. $600 - $504 = 96
         $96 \div $600 = 16\%$
    d. $230 - $200 = 30
         $30 \div $200 = 15\%$
    e. $\frac{3}{4}\% = 0.0075$
    f. $\frac{1}{5}\% \times $380 = 0.76

2. $292,068 - $256,200 = $35,868$ increase
$35,868 \div $256,200 = 14\%$ increase

3. $172 - (0.24 \times $172) = 130.72 new job expenses

4. $9.10 - $8.75 = 0.35
$0.35 \div $8.75 = 4\%$ greater

5.

Check register balance	$717.08	Bank statement balance		$763.14
Deduct:		Deduct:		
Service Charge	− 1.65	Outstanding checks:		
	$715.43	#877	$19.78	
Add:		#879	10.00	
Interest earned	+ 3.00	#880	14.93	− 44.71
Correct check register balance	$718.43	Available bank balance		$718.43

6. $($175.00 + $1,864.26) - $58.38 = $1,980.88$ in register

‡**7.** $210 \div \frac{5}{6} = 252 pay for last week

Section 27.   More Percent Relationships

‡Exercise 2, page 151

1. $120 \div 0.25 = 480

2. $36 \div 0.09 = 400

3. $95.70 \div 0.29 = 330

4. $10.78 \div 0.7 = 15.40

5. $0.53 \times $521 = 276.13

6. $2.73 \div 0.21 = 13

7. $0.38 \times $356 = 135.28

8. $24.70 \div 0.65 = 38

9. $81 \div 0.45 = 180

10. $11.20 \div 0.35 = 32

11. $0.40 \times $722 = 288.80

12. $264 \div 0.3 = 880

‡Exercise 4, page 153

1. $2,200 ÷ 1.25 = $1,760

2. $123 ÷ 1.5 = $82

3. $600 ÷ $\frac{4}{3}$ = $450

4. $24.91 ÷ 1.06 = $23.50

5. $369 ÷ 1.64 = $225

6. $47.46 ÷ 1.05 = $45.20

7. $160 ÷ 1.25 = $128

8. $885 ÷ 1.18 = $750

9. $675 ÷ 1.20 = $562.50

10. $2,400 ÷ 1.28 = $1,875

‡Exercise 5, page 153

1. $8,400 ÷ 0.80 = $10,500

2. $312 ÷ 0.96 = $325

3. $33.60 ÷ 0.7 = $48

4. $11.22 ÷ 0.85 = $13.20

5. $638 ÷ 0.55 = $1,160

6. $10.80 ÷ $\frac{5}{6}$ = $12.96

7. $12.30 ÷ $\frac{2}{3}$ = $18.45

8. $3.36 ÷ $\frac{7}{8}$ = $3.84

9. $1,664 ÷ 0.65 = $2,560

Review 27, page 154

1. a. $0.003\frac{1}{3} × $195 = 0.65
    b. $0.087 = 8.7\%$
    c. $8.75 + ($8.75 × 0.36) = $11.90
    d. $1\frac{3}{4}\% = 0.0175$
    e. ($135 − $120) ÷ $120 = $12\frac{1}{2}\%$
    ‡f. $6.72 ÷ 0.7 = $9.60
    ‡g. $64.24 ÷ 1.10 = $58.40
    ‡h. $63 ÷ 0.90 = $70

2. (729 − 675) ÷ 675 = 8% increase

3. 1.06 × $24,650 = $26,129 wages this year

4. (8 × $755) + $771 + $780 + $725 = $8,316 total wages
   $8,316 ÷ 11 = $756 average weekly wages

5. Bills $1,191.00
   Coin   76.94
   Total deposit $1,267.94

6. a. 600 × $1 = $600 estimated gross pay
    b. (500 × $0.95) + (97 × $0.99) = $571.03 gross pay
       0.0765 × $571.03 = $43.68 FICA taxes
       $571.03 − ($43.68 + $61) = $466.35 net pay

7. 0.19 × $425 = $80.75 fringe benefits
   $425 + $80.75 = $505.75 total job benefits
   $34.05 + $7.36 + $25.90 = $67.31 weekly job expenses
   $505.75 − $67.31 = $438.44 net job benefits

‡8. $165 ÷ 0.11 = $1,500 monthly salary

‡9.

Check register balance		$955.30	Bank statement balance			$971.63
Deduct:			Deduct:			
Service charge	$1.10		Outstanding checks:			
Check not recorded	21.36	− 22.46	#345	$31.16		
		$932.84	#346	14.73		
Add:			#348	24.90	− 70.79	
Interest earned		+ 3.00				$900.84
			Add:			
			Deposit not recorded		+ 35.00	
Correct check register balance		$935.84	Available bank balance			$935.84

Section 28.   Commission

Exercise 1, page 156

1.
  a.   78 × $2 = $156   commission
  b.   32 × $0.55 = $17.60   commission
  c.   49 × $1.20 = $58.80   commission

2. $6 × 100 = $600   estimated commission
   $5.75 × 103 = $592.25   commission

3.
  a.   0.04 × $35,986 = $1,439.44
  b.   0.06 × $12,435 = $746.10
  c. $\frac{1}{8}$ × $5,750 = $718.75

4.   0.08 × $31,500 = $2,520

Exercise 2, page 156

1.   0.05 × $5,780 = $289   commission
   $325 + $289 = $614   total earnings

2.   0.06 × $4,120 = $247.20   commission
   $200 + $247.20 = $447.20   weekly earnings

3.   0.075 × ($21,400 − $4,000) = $1,305   commission
   $1,200 + $1,305 = $2,505   total earnings

4.   0.005 × ($43,870 − $11,500) = $161.85   commission
   $400 + $161.85 = $561.85   total earnings

Exercise 3, page 157

1.
  a.   0.10 × $5,000 = $500
      0.15 × $4,000 = $600
      $500 + $600 = $1,100   total commission

  b.   0.03 × $400 = $12
      0.05 × $400 = $20
      $12 + $20 = $32   total commission

  c.   0.06 × $900 = $54
      0.09 × $1,700 = $153
      $54 + $153 = $207   total commission

d. $0.05 \times \$3,500 = \$175$
   $0.07 \times \$4,870 = \$340.90$
   $\$175.00 + \$340.90 = \$515.90$ total commission

2. $0.04 \times \$15,000 = \$600$
   $0.06 \times \$12,000 = \$720$
   $\$600 + \$720 = \$1,320$ June commission
   $0.04 \times \$15,000 = \$600$
   $0.06 \times \$17,000 = \$1,020$
   $\$600 + \$1,020 = \$1,620$ July commission
   $\$1,320 + \$1,620 = \$2,940$ total commission

3. $50 \times \$1.50 = \$75$
   $100 \times \$1.75 = \$175$
   $75 \times \$2.00 = \$150$
   $\$75 + \$175 + \$150 = \$400$ commission

Exercise 4, page 158

1. **a.** $\$448 \div \$6,400 = 0.07 = 7\%$
   b. $\$18.75 \div \$625 = 0.03 = 3\%$
   c. $\$72 \div \$480 = 0.15 = 15\%$
   d. $\$350 \div \$2,800 = 0.125 = 12.5\% = 12\frac{1}{2}\%$
   e. $\$33 \div \$600 = 0.055 = 5.5\% = 5\frac{1}{2}\%$
   f. $\$189 \div \$5,400 = 0.035 = 3.5\% = 3\frac{1}{2}\%$

2. $\$3.60 \div \$24 = 0.15 = 15\%$ commission

3. **a.** $\$3,000 - \$900 = \$2,100$ commission
   b. $\$2,100 \div \$35,000 = 0.06 = 6\%$ rate of commission

4. $\$520 \div (\$16,000 - \$3,000) = 0.04 = 4\%$ rate of commission

‡Exercise 5, page 159

1. $\$2,100 \div 0.06 = \$35,000$ amount of goods must sell

2. $\$2,400 \div 0.08 = \$30,000$ amount of goods must sell

3. $\$600 - \$350 = \$250$
   $\$250 \div 0.05 = \$5,000$ sales needed

4. $\$1,600 - \$700 = \$900$
   $\$900 \div 0.06 = \$15,000$ sales needed

5. $\$800 - \$400 = \$400$
   $\$400 \div 0.04 = \$10,000$ sales needed

Review 28, page 160

2. **a.** $\$108 \div \$360 = 30\%$
   b. $\$27 + (0.17 \times \$27) = \$31.59$
   c. $(\$175 - \$168) \div \$175 = 4\%$
   d. $64\% = \frac{16}{25}$
   e. $\frac{2}{13} = 15.4\%$
   f. $0.00\frac{1}{4} \times \$36,000 = \$90$
   g. $0.37\frac{1}{2} \times \$4,800 = \$1,800$
   h. $0.01 \times \$92,078 = \$920.78$
   ‡**i.** $60 \div 0.15 = 400$

3. $(0.10 \times \$19,800) + (0.03 \times \$4,800) = \$2,124$ commission for week

4. $0.03 \times (\$8,089 - \$5,000) = \$92.67$ commission
   $\$425 + \$92.67 = \$517.67$ gross income

5. $2,578 − $850 = $1,728   commission
$1,728 ÷ $43,200 = 4%   rate of commission

6. (214,537 − 175,850) ÷ 175,850 = 22%   increase

7. 1.15 × 80 = 92   this week's score

‡8. $217,455 ÷ 1.09 = $199,500

9. $750 ÷ 0.08 = $9,375   salesperson must sell

Section 29.   Agent's Commission

Exercise 1, page 163

1. **a.** 0.06 × $45,000 = $2,700   commisson
$2,700 + $187 = $2,887   total deductions
$45,000 − $2,887 = $42,113   net proceeds
b. 0.30 × $2,070 = $621   commission
$2,070 − $621 = $1,449   net proceeds
c. 0.07 × $85,900 = $6,013   commission
$85,900 − $6,013 = $79,887   net proceeds
d. 0.20 × $450 = $90   commission
$90 + $15.75 = $105.75   total deductions
$450 − $105.75 = $344.25   net proceeds
e. 0.06 × $143,750 = $8,625   commission
$8,625 + $207.88 = $8,832.88   total deductions
$143,750 − $8,832.88 = $134,917.12   net proceeds

2. 0.06 × $121,900 = $7,314   commission
$121,900 − $7,314 = $114,586   net proceeds

3. 0.07 × $150,000 = $10,500   commission
$10,500 + $675 = $11,175   total deductions
$150,000 − $11,175 = $138,825   net proceeds

4. 0.05 × $65,800 = $3,290   commission
$3,290 + $320 = $3,610   total deductions
$65,800 − $3,610 = $62,190   net proceeds

5. **a.** 0.80 × $8,000 = $6,400   estimated amount collected
b. 0.78 × $7,700 = $6,006   amount collected
0.375 × $6,006 = $2,252.25   agents' charges
$6,006 − $2,252.25 = $3,753.75   net proceeds

‡Exercise 2, page 164

1. $1,680 ÷ 0.70 = $2,400   amount collected

2. $62,040 ÷ 0.94 = $66,000   sale price

3. $453.60 ÷ 0.72 = $630   amount collected

4. $70,500 ÷ 0.94 = $75,000   sale price

5. $28,000 ÷ 0.94 = $29,787.23, or $29,800   sale price

Review 29, page 165

2. **a.** ($550 − $451) ÷ $550 = 18%   **d.** $6\frac{1}{4}\%$ = .0625
   b. $30 ÷ $24 = 125%   **e.** 0.782 = 78.2%
   c. ($165 − $120) ÷ $120 = $37\frac{1}{2}\%$ **f.** $\frac{6}{7}$ = 85.7%

3. 0.06 × $436,500 = $26,190   commission
   $26,190 + $1,038 = $27,228   total deductions
   $436,500 − $27,228 = $409,272   net proceeds

4. 0.85 × $4,250 = $3,612.50   amount collected
   0.32 × $3,612.50 = $1,156   commission

5. 0.03 × ($7,459 − $5,000) = $73.77   commission
   $210 + $73.77 = $283.77   gross earnings

6. $32,700 − (12 × $1,000) = $20,700   commission
   $20,700 ÷ $230,000 = 9%   rate of commission

7. $426 ÷ $\frac{3}{4}$ = $568   earned last week

‡8. $8,910 ÷ 0.06 = $148,500   selling price

‡9. $75,000 ÷ 0.95 = $78,947.37
   $79,000   lowest selling price to receive proceeds desired

‡10. $3,600 ÷ 0.96 = $3,750   April commission

UNIT 5 ● METRIC MEASUREMENT

Section 30. Length

Exercise 3, page 170

	1.	2.
a.	3 m = 300 cm	340 cm = 3.4 m
b.	6 m = 6 000 mm	41 mm = 0.041 m
c.	7 cm = 70 mm	176 mm = 17.6 cm
d.	4 km = 4 000 m	6.2 m = 6 200 mm
e.	700 m = 0.7 km	0.9 km = 900 m

Exercise 4, page 170

1. **a.** 3 km + 2 km + 1 km = 6 km
   b. 2.8 m + 4.6 m + 1.5 m = 8.9 m
   c. 5 km + 7 km + 0.4 km = 12.4 km
   d. 7 m + 0.5 m + 0.2 m = 7.7 m
   e. 40 cm + 55 cm + 15.7 cm = 110.7 cm

2. **a.** 78 km − 12.6 km = 65.4 km   **c.** 128 m − 4.3 m = 123.7 m
   b. 8.3 m − 4.7 m = 3.6 m   **d.** 30 cm − 12.4 cm = 17.6 cm

3. **a.** 15 m × 3 = 45 m   **d.** 21.4 m × 6 = 128.4 m
   b. 60 km × 7 = 420 km   **e.** 80 km × 0.5 = 40 km
   c. 4.3 cm × 3 = 12.9 cm   **f.** 200 mm × 5 = 1 m

4. **a.** 20 m ÷ 5 = 4 m   **c.** 570 mm ÷ 3 = 190 mm
       b. 72 cm ÷ 4 = 18 cm   **d.** 2 100 km ÷ 7 = 300 km

Exercise 5, page 170

1. 4 m + 2.5 m + 3.7 m + 2.1 m = 12.3 m of cable needed

2. 680 cm − 170 cm = 510 cm of chain left

3. 53 km − 46.4 km = 6.6 km must run on seventh day

4. 6 500 m ÷ 500 m = 13 rolls of fencing needed

5. **a.** 280 km + 244 km + 64 km = 588 km driven in three days
       b. 600 ÷ 3 = 200 km estimated average km driven each day
       c. 588 ÷ 3 = 196 km averaged per day

6.   10 × 2.08 m =   20.8 m
           24 × 0.55 m =   13.2 m
          115 × 2 m = $\underline{+230\quad}$ m
                        264   m   total length needed

Review 30, page 171

2. **a.** ($252 − $168) ÷ $252 = $\frac{1}{3}$
       b. 70 cm + 95 cm + 24 cm = 189 cm
       c. $340 + ($\frac{1}{5}$ × $340) = $408
       d. $3\frac{3}{4} \div 2\frac{1}{2} = 1\frac{1}{2}$

3. **a.**   7 × 4 m =   28 m
              4 × 2.75 m =   11 m
               6 × 1.5 m = $\underline{+\ 9\ m}$
                              48 m   wire needed
       b. 48 m × $0.24 = $11.52   cost of wire

4.   8 m × $0.84 = $ 6.72
             12 m × $1.40 =   16.80
          $\underline{+\ 5}$ m × $1.12 = $\underline{+\ 5.60}$
             25              $29.12

       $29.12 ÷ 25 = $1.16   average selling price

5. 40 × $8.50 = $340   gross pay
       $43 + (0.0765 × $340) + $32 = $101.01
       $340 − $101.01 = $238.99   net pay

‡**6.** $615 ÷ 0.05 = $12,300   amount of sales needed

Section 31. Area

Exercise 3, page 174

1. **a.** 7 km² + 5 km² = 12 km²   **d.** 1 ha + 6 ha = 7 ha
       b. 8 ha + 16 ha = 24 ha   **e.** 9 m² + 0.7 m² = 9.7 m²
       c. 12 cm² + 1 cm² = 13 cm²

2. **a.** $25 \text{ km}^2 - 7 \text{ km}^2 = 18 \text{ km}^2$ **d.** $1 \text{ ha} - 0.6 \text{ ha} = 0.4 \text{ ha}$
b. $50 \text{ cm}^2 - 1 \text{ cm}^2 = 49 \text{ cm}^2$ **e.** $4 \text{ km}^2 - 1 \text{ km}^2 = 3 \text{ km}^2$
c. $8 \text{ km}^2 - 2 \text{ km}^2 = 6 \text{ km}^2$

3. **a.** $35 \text{ m} \times 4 \text{ m} = 140 \text{ m}^2$ **d.** $12 \text{ mm}^2 \times 3 = 0.36 \text{ cm}^2$
b. $0.4 \times 58 \text{ cm}^2 = 23.2 \text{ cm}^2$ **e.** $3 \text{ km}^2 \times 0.5 = 150 \text{ ha}$
c. $100 \text{ m} \times 100 \text{ m} = 1 \text{ ha}$

4. **a.** $64 \text{ m}^2 \div 8 = 8 \text{ m}^2$ **d.** $2\,100 \text{ ha} \div 7 = 300 \text{ ha}$
b. $0.75 \text{ m}^2 \div 3 = 0.25 \text{ m}^2$ **e.** $5 \text{ cm}^2 \div 4 = 1.25 \text{ cm}^2$
c. $30\,000 \text{ mm}^2 \div 6 = 5\,000 \text{ mm}^2$

Exercise 4, page 174

1. $8 \text{ ha} + 120 \text{ ha} + 56 \text{ ha} + 1\,340 \text{ ha} = 1\,524 \text{ ha}$ of land bought

2. $4 \text{ m} \times 4.5 \text{ m} = 18 \text{ m}^2$ of carpeting needed

3. **a.** $7 \text{ m} \times 20 \text{ m} = 140 \text{ m}^2$ area of front lawn
b. $980 \text{ m}^2 \div 140 \text{ m}^2 = 7$ times lawn can be fertilized

4. **a.** $66 \text{ m}^2 \div 1.2 \text{ m}^2 = 55$ coat linings can be sewed
b. $100 \times 1.2 \text{ m}^2 = 120 \text{ m}^2$ of cloth needed for 100 linings

5. $70 \text{ cm} \times 80 \text{ cm} = 5\,600 \text{ cm}^2$ of paper needed

6. **a.** $30 \text{ cm} \times 30 \text{ cm} = 900 \text{ cm}^2$ estimated area covered by one tile
b. $40 \times 900 \text{ cm}^2 = 36\,000 \text{ cm}^2$ estimated area covered by a box of tiles
c. $40 \times (30.5 \text{ cm} \times 30.5 \text{ cm}) = 3.721 \text{ m}^2$

7. **a.** $(20 \text{ cm} \times 120 \text{ cm}) + (30 \text{ cm} \times 120 \text{ cm}) = 6\,000 \text{ cm}^2$
b. $2.88 \text{ m}^2 - 0.6 \text{ m}^2 = 2.28 \text{ m}^2$ of wood left

Review 31, page 175

2. **a.** $0.16 = \frac{4}{25}$
b. $0.628 = 62.8\%$
c. $\$76 \div \$190 = 40\%$
d. $(400 \text{ km} - 350 \text{ km}) \div 400 \text{ km} = \frac{1}{8}$
e. $312 \text{ cm} - (312 \text{ cm} \times 0.25) = 234 \text{ cm}$

3. $1.3 \text{ m} \times 14 \text{ m} = 18.2 \text{ m}^2$

4. $2.2 \text{ m} + 2.2 \text{ m} + 8.1 \text{ m} + 8.1 \text{ m} = 20.6 \text{ m}$ of fencing needed
$28 \text{ m} - 20.6 \text{ m} = 7.4 \text{ m}$ of fencing left over

5. **a.** $0.07 \times \$32,000 = \$2,240$ commission
b. $\$32,000 - \$2,240 = \$29,760$ net proceeds

6. $(\$27,540 - \$25,500) \div \$25,500 = 8\%$ increase

‡7. $\$230,000 \div 0.91 = \$252,747.25$, or $\$252,748$ selling price of building

Section 32. Capacity and Weight

Exercise 3, page 177

1. 37 L + 14 L = 51 L

2. 34.68 L + 79.15 L = 113.83 L

3. 400 mL + 26.1 mL = 426.1 mL

4. 14 L + 0.344 = 14.344 L

5. 786 L − 554 L = 232 L

6. 45.29 kL − 35.31 kL = 9.98 kL

7. 72.45 L − 0.05 L = 72.4 L

8. 250 L × 30 = 7 500 L

9. 4.8 L × 5 = 24 L

10. 20 L × 1.9 = 38 L

11. 0.5 × 682 mL = 341 mL

12. 64 L ÷ 8 = 8L

13. 180 kL ÷ 9 = 20 kL

14. 1 620 mL ÷ 5 = 324 mL

Exercise 4, page 177

1. 18 L ÷ 12 = 1.5 L   juice per member

2. 6 × 0.94 = 5.64 L   of juice can be made from 6 cans

3. a. 56 L + 63.5 L + 47.3 L + 59.1 L = 225.9 L   of gasoline bought
    b. 225.9 ÷ 4 = 56.5 L   average liters bought per stop

4. (0.9 × 130 kL) − (20.5 kL + 24 kL + 21.75 kL) = 50.75 kL   fuel left

5. a. 52 × 2.5 L = 130 L   of juice used in year
    b. 130 × $0.37 = $48.10   saved in one year

6. 30,000 ÷ 48 = 625   cases to be shipped

Exercise 6, page 179

	1.	2.
a.	1 kg = 1 000 g	1 000 mg = 1 g
b.	1 g = 0.001 kg	400 kg = 0.4 t
c.	1 g = 1 000 mg	75 mg = 0.075 g
d.	1 mg = 0.001 g	0.7 kg + 0.6 kg = 1.3 kg
e.	1 t = 1 000 kg	0.65 g − 0.25 g = 0.4 g
f.	1 kg = 0.001 t	2 000 mg − 500 mg = 1 500 mg
g.	900 mg = 0.9 g	12 kg × 9 = 108 kg
h.	250 g = 0.25 kg	0.6 kg × 7 = 4.2 kg
i.	0.75 kg = 750 g	560 kg ÷ 28 = 20 kg

Exercise 7, page 179

1. 6.2 kg + 5 kg + 4.5 kg + 1.7 kg = 17.4 kg   weight of items

2. (350 t + 52 t) − (24 t + 28 t + 17 t + 21 t + 23 t) = 289 t   on hand

3. a. 800 × 2 kg = 1 600 kg   estimated weight of shipment
    b. 800 × 1.8 kg = 1 440 kg   actual weight of shipment

4. 31,200 g ÷ 240 = 130 g   weight of 1 steno pad

5. 460 g × $\frac{1}{2}$ = 230 g   weight of crackers left

6. a. 1 300 kg − 1 196 kg = 104 kg   weight reduction
    b. 104 kg ÷ 1 300 = 8%   weight reduction

7.   4 200 g ÷ 210 = 20   loads of wash

8.   1 136 g ÷ 8 = 142 g   weight of 1 bar of generic soap
405 g ÷ 3 = 135 g   weight of 1 bar of Prose soap

Review 32, page 180

2.   **a.**   23.8 L + 14 L = 37.8 L
b.   7 g + 15 g = 22 g
c.   40 cm + 82 cm + 14.5 cm = 136.5 cm
d.   38 L − 0.04 mL = 37.96 L
e.   9 kg − 3.5 kg = 5.5 kg
f.   24.6 m − 0.45 m = 24.15 m
g.   25.6 t × $8.40 = $215.04
h.   832 L ÷ 14 = 59 L

3.   **a.**   1.5 m + 3 m + 0.4 m + 2.6 m + 1.9 m = 9.4 m   of pipe needed
b.   9.4 × $4.80 = $45.12   cost of pipe

4.   (5 m × 6 m) + (7.5 m × 12 m) = 120 m^2 total area of both sheds

5.   **a.**   340 L + 180 L + 248 L + 427 L + 205 L = 1 400 L   of gasoline used
b.   3 560 L − 1 400 L = 2 160 L   of gasoline left in tank

6.   **a.**   180 kg + 50 kg + 24 kg = 254 kg   total weight of purchase
b.   (180 kg × $1.28) + (50 kg × $0.33) + (24 kg × $3.96) = $341.94   total amount paid

‡**7.** $7\frac{1}{2} \div \frac{5}{4} = 6$ hours overtime worked last week

UNIT 6 • BUDGETING AND BUYING

Section 33.   Planning a Budget

Exercise 1, page 182

1.   **a.** $\frac{\$4,953.60}{\$5,160.00} = \frac{24}{25}$ receipts are of payments
b. $\frac{\$825.60}{\$5,160.00} = \frac{4}{25}$ receipts are of food payments

2.   **a.** $1,985.86 ÷ $5,823.64 = 34%   payments are of housing
b. $563.10 ÷ $5,823.64 = 10%   payments are of transportation
c. $775 ÷ $5,823.64 = 13%   payments are of savings

3. $338,723 ÷ $475,800 = 71%   salary and wage expense is of total expense

4.   **a.** $60,000 ÷ $1,000,000 = 6%   estimate advertising is of total sales
b. $57,370 ÷ $945,860 = 6.1%   advertising is of total sales

Exercise 2, page 184

1. $9,700 ÷ $66,800 = 15%   food budget
$4,680 ÷ $66,800 = 7%   clothing budget
$18,200 ÷ $66,800 = 27%   housing budget
$8,200 ÷ $66,800 = 12%   transportation budget
$16,900 ÷ $66,800 = 25%   other budget
$9,120 ÷ $66,800 = 14%   savings budget

2. $0.15 \times \$69,500 = \$10,425$ food budget
$0.07 \times \$69,500 = \$4,865$ clothing budget
$0.27 \times \$69,500 = \$18,765$ housing budget
$0.12 \times \$69,500 = \$8,340$ transportation budget
$0.25 \times \$69,500 = \$17,375$ other budget
$0.14 \times \$69,500 = \$9,730$ savings budget

3. $0.27 \times \$18,000 = \$4,860$ food budget
$0.12 \times \$18,000 = \$2,160$ clothing budget
$0.31 \times \$18,000 = \$5,580$ housing budget
$0.15 \times \$18,000 = \$2,700$ transportation budget
$0.11 \times \$18,000 = \$1,980$ personal budget
$0.04 \times \$18,000 = \$720$ savings budget

4. $\$7,450 \div \$32,800 = 22.7\%$ food budget
$\$1,300 \div \$32,800 = 4\%$ clothing budget
$\$8,750 \div \$32,800 = 26.7\%$ housing budget
$\$1,500 \div \$32,800 = 4.6\%$ health budget
$\$4,450 \div \$32,800 = 13.6\%$ transportation budget
$\$2,700 \div \$32,800 = 8.2\%$ entertainment budget
$\$3,300 \div \$32,800 = 10.1\%$ education budget
$\$1,600 \div \$32,800 = 4.9\%$ savings budget
$\$1,750 \div \$32,800 = 5.3\%$ other budget

5. $0.021 \times \$5,500,000 = \$115,500$ advertising budget
$0.0775 \times \$5,500,000 = \$426,250$ power budget

6. $\$8,650 \div \$100,000 = 8.65\%$
$\$62,000 \div \$500,000 = 12.4\%$
$12.4\% - 8.65\% = 3.75\% = 3.8\%$

Review 33, page 185

2. **a.** $2\frac{3}{4} + 6\frac{1}{2} + 3\frac{2}{3} = 12\frac{11}{12}$ **d.** $\$108 - (\frac{3}{8} \times \$108) = \$67.50$
b. $3\frac{3}{5} \div \frac{2}{3} = 5\frac{2}{5}$ **e.** $1.5 \text{ L} - 0.08 \text{ L} = 1.42 \text{ L}$
c. $\frac{5}{3} \times \$648 = \$1,080$

3. $\$650,000 \div \$975,000 = 66\frac{2}{3}\%$ spent on salaries and wages

4. $1.10 \times \$22,000 = \$24,200$ expected income
$0.24 \times \$24,200 = \$5,808$ food budget
$0.12 \times \$24,200 = \$2,904$ clothing budget
$0.30 \times \$24,200 = \$7,260$ housing budget
$0.17 \times \$24,200 = \$4,114$ transportation budget
$0.13 \times \$24,200 = \$3,146$ personal budget
$0.04 \times \$24,200 = \$968$ savings budget

5. $\$215.75 \div 37\frac{1}{2} = \$5.75$ hourly rate

6. $0.0765 \times \$436 = \$33.35$ FICA tax

7. $12 \times \$25,000 = \$300,000$ desired sales
$11 \times \$24,870 = \$273,570$ present sales
$\$300,000 - \$273,570 = \$26,430$ needed sales next month

Section 34.   Checking Sales Slips

Exercise 2, page 188

1. 5 × $3 = $15 estimated; 5 × $2.89 = $14.45 exact

2. 4 × $0.60 = $2.40 estimated; 4 × $0.57 = $2.28 exact

3. 7 × $0.30 = $2.10 estimated; 7 × $0.32 = $2.24 exact

4. 2 × $7 = $14 estimated; 1.95 × $6.89 = $13.44 exact

Exercise 4, page 188

1.

Quantity	Item	Unit Price	Amount
4 m	fabric	2 for $6.19	$12.38
3.5 m	lining	$2.78	9.73
7 spools	thread	$0.59	4.13
9 pkg.	tape	$0.49	4.41
1	zipper	$2.99	2.99
3 pkg.	buttons	$0.88	2.64
		Total sales	$36.28

2.

Quantity	Item	Unit Price	Amount
3 lb.	butter	$1.89	$ 5.67
3 lb.	franks	$1.98	5.94
15 lb.	flour	5 for $0.39	1.17
8 jars	pickles	2 for $3.69	14.76
4	oranges	$0.49	1.96
3 cans	sweet potatoes	3 for $1.69	1.69
		Total sales	$31.19

3.

Quantity	Item	Unit Price	Amount
3 bags	charcoal	$2.88	$ 8.64
1 btl.	shampoo	$2.95	2.95
8	cards	$1.25	10.00
3 cans	plant food	3 for $3.99	3.99
12	apples	3 for $0.89	3.56
16 skeins	yarn	2 for $0.87	6.96
		Total sales	$36.10

Exercise 6, page 189

1.   a. 0.08 × $50 = $4   estimated sales tax
    b. 0.08 × $49.39 = $3.95   exact sales tax
    c. $49.39 + $3.95 = $53.34   total of sales slip

2. $94.89 + (0.05 × $94.89) = $99.63   total of sales slip

3.

	Sales Tax Rate	Subtotal	Sales Tax	Total
a.	3%	$ 85	$ 2.55	$ 87.55
b.	6%	740	44.40	784.40
c.	4%	7	0.28	7.28
d.	7%	9.98	0.70	10.68
e.	2%	149.95	3.00	152.95
f.	5%	0.75	0.04	0.79

4. 5% + 2% = 7%   total tax
0.07 × $78 = $5.46   amount of tax

5. 0.08 × $795 = $63.60   tax in their city
0.05 × $795 = $39.75   tax in nearby city
$63.60 − $39.75 = $23.85   less in nearby city

Exercise 7, page 190

1.

Quantity	Description	Unit Price	Amount
3 pair	socks	$2.95	$ 8.85
4	shirts	2 for $35.99	71.98
6	ties	3 for $39.99	79.98
2 pair	slacks	$59.88	119.76
	Subtotal	—	$280.57
	Sales Tax	5%	$14.03
	Total	—	$294.60

2.

Quantity	Description	Unit Price	Amount
1 doz.	printer ribbons	$13.89	$ 13.89
5 pkg.	mailing labels	$12.58	62.90
12 reams	letterhead paper	2 for $129.99	779.94
6	print wheels	$4.75	28.50
15 boxes	paper clips	$0.69	10.35
	Subtotal	—	$895.58
	Sales tax	7%	$62.69
	Total	—	$958.27

Exercise 8, page 191

	Amount Received	Amount of Sale	Change						
			1¢	5¢	10¢	25¢	50¢	$1	$5
1.	$ 5.00	$3.26	4		2		1	1	
2.	1.00	0.56	4	1	1	1			
3.	1.00	0.29	1		2		1		
4.	5.00	3.09	1	1	1	1	1	1	
5.	10.00	3.49	1				1	1	1
6.	1.00	0.47	3				1		
7.	5.00	1.89	1		1			3	
8.	10.00	3.15			1	1	1	1	1

Review 34, page 191

2. **a.** $12\frac{2}{3} \times 6\frac{1}{2} = 82\frac{1}{3}$ **c.** $56 \div 224 = 25\%$

  b. $7\frac{1}{5} \div 2\frac{1}{4} = 3\frac{1}{5}$ **d.** 2.6 L − 0.125 L = 2.475 L

3. 6 ÷ 3 = 2; $0.99 × 2 = $1.98   canned peas
  6 ÷ 3 = 2; $1.19 × 2 = $2.38   celery
  $1.98 + $4.99 + $2.38 = $9.35   subtotal

4. 0.07 × $28.79 = $2.02   taxes
  $28.79 + $2.02 = $30.81   total of sales slip

5. 0.75 × $3,250,000 = $2,437,500   spent on wages and salaries
  0.05 × $3,250,000 = $162,500   spent on advertising

6. 2.4 m × 3.5 m = 8.4 m²   area
  8.4 m² + (0.10 × 8.4 m²) = 9.24 m²   carpet needed

Section 35. Figuring Extensions

Exercise 1, page 194

1. $\frac{3}{4} \times \$24.96 = \$18.72$ fencing
  $\frac{1}{5} \times \$45.90 = \$9.18$ culvert
  $4.89 + $9.18 + $18.72 = $32.79   total cost
  (2 × $20) − $32.79 = $7.21   change

2. $\frac{1}{2} \times \$8.49 = \$4.25$ note pads
  $\frac{5}{8} \times \$10.82 = \$6.76$ ribbon
  $\frac{1}{3} \times \$7.99 = \$2.66$ folders
  $4.25 + $6.76 + $2.66 = $13.67   total cost

3. **a.** $\frac{27}{36} = \frac{3}{4}$ yard
  b. $\frac{3}{4} \times \$2.98 = \$2.24$ cost of cloth
    $2.24 + (0.05 × $2.24) = $2.35   total cost

4. $\frac{7}{8} \times \$3.99 = \$3.49$ cold meat
   $\frac{1}{2} \times \$2.49 = \$1.25$ bacon
   $\frac{3}{8} \times \$1.49 = \$0.56$ cauliflower
   $\frac{2}{3} \times \$3.99 = \$2.66$ onions
   $\$3.49 + \$1.25 + \$0.56 + \$2.66 = \$7.96$ subtotal
   $\$7.96 + (0.03 \times \$7.96) = \$8.20$ total purchase

5. $\frac{3}{4} \times \$63.75 = \$47.81$ tile
   $\frac{1}{2} \times \$19.88 = \$9.94$ covers
   $\frac{1}{3} \times \$1.69 = \$0.56$ fasteners
   $\frac{3}{4} \times \$6.95 = \$5.21$ seed
   $\$47.81 + \$9.94 + \$0.56 + \$5.21 = \$63.52$ subtotal
   $\$63.52 + (0.08 \times \$63.52) = \$68.60$ total price

Exercise 2, page 195

1. $2\frac{2}{3} \times \$1.99 = \$5.31$ cotton
   $3\frac{1}{4} \times \$5.89 = \$19.14$ wool
   $3\frac{1}{2} \times \$2.88 = \$10.08$ muslin
   $4\frac{5}{8} \times \$0.75 = \$3.47$ lace
   $\$5.31 + \$19.14 + \$10.08 + \$3.47 = \$38$ total cost

2. $3\frac{3}{4} \times \$1.29 = \$4.84$ potatoes
   $5\frac{1}{8} \times \$0.59 = \$3.02$ apples
   $1\frac{7}{8} \times \$0.99 = \$1.86$ grapes
   $2\frac{1}{3} \times \$2.98 = \$6.95$ pecans
   $\$4.84 + \$3.02 + \$1.86 + \$6.95 = \$16.67$ cost of items
   $\$20 - \$16.67 = \$3.33$ change

3. $550 \times \$0.18\frac{3}{4} = \$103.13$ wire
   $146 \div 3 = 48\frac{2}{3}; 48\frac{2}{3} \times \$0.24 = \$11.68$ furring strips
   $165 \times \$0.73\frac{1}{2} = \$121.28$ tiles
   $276 \div 3 = 92; 92 \times \$0.28\frac{3}{8} = \$26.11$ molding
   $\$103.13 + \$11.68 + \$121.28 + \$26.11 = \$262.20$ total cost

4. $75 \times \$0.79 = \$59.25$
   $80 \times \$0.84 = \$67.20$
   $115 \times \$0.77 = \$88.55$
   $80 \times \$0.81 = \$64.80$
   $\$59.25 + \$67.20 + \$88.55 + \$64.80 = \$279.80$ total separate purchases
   $350 \times \$0.685 = \$239.75$ single purchase
   $\$279.80 - \$239.75 = \$40.05$ would have saved

Exercise 3, page 196

1. $4.5 \times \$90 = \$450$ estimated; $4.5 \times \$89.78 = \$404.01$ exact

2. $2 \times \$40 = \$80$ estimated; $2.19 \times \$36 = \$78.84$ exact

3. $2 \times \$80 = \$160$ estimated; $1.89 \times \$83.50 = \$157.82$ exact

4. $8 \times \$600 = \$4,800$ estimated; $8.207 \times \$571.99 = \$4,694.32$ exact

5. $5 \times \$6 = \$30$ estimated; $5.35 \times \$6 = \$32.10$ exact

6. $2 \times \$300 = \$600$ estimated; $1.55 \times \$265 = \$410.75$ exact

7. $0.2 \times \$900 = \$180$ estimated; $0.245 \times \$852 = \$208.74$ exact

8. $8 \times \$12 = \$96$ estimated; $7.89 \times \$12 = \$94.68$ exact

9. $0.5 \times \$48 = \$24$ estimated; $0.649 \times \$48 = \$31.15$ exact

10. $12 \times \$10 = \$120$ estimated; $12.45 \times \$9.88 = \$123.01$ exact

11. $0.5 \times \$8 = \$4$ estimated, $0.6 \times \$7.75 = \$4.65$ exact

Review 35, page 196

2. **a.** $8\,250 \text{ kg} \div 1\,000 = 8.25 \text{ t}$
$8.25 \times \$2.50 = \$20.63$
b. $(3\frac{1}{4} \times 2,000) \div 100 = 65 \text{ cwt}$
$65 \times \$2.89 = \$187.85$
c. $8,150 \div 1,000 = 8.15 \text{ M}$
$8.15 \times \$0.30 = \$2.45$
d. $10.6 \text{ m} - 0.925 \text{ m} = 9.675 \text{ m}$
e. $6 \div 7 = 0.86$

3. $\$32.77 + \$10 = \$42.77$ cash on hand
$\$2.89 + \$5.15 + \$0.78 + \$12.99 = \$21.81$ spent
$\$42.77 - \$21.81 = \$20.96$ should have at end of day

4. $1\frac{1}{4} \times \$1.89 = \$2.36$ pencils
$\frac{2}{3} \times \$6.10 = \$4.07$ correction tape
$1\frac{1}{3} \times \$12.73 = \$16.97$ envelopes
$\$2.36 + \$4.07 + \$16.97 = \$23.40$ total bill

5. $(4,500 \div 2,000) \times \$58.78 = \$132.26$ gravel
$1\frac{1}{4} \times \$157.88 = \$197.35$ blocks
$(350 \div 100) \times \$12.25 = \$42.88$ rods
$(3,500 \div 2,000) \times \$8.56 = \$14.98$ sand
$\$132.26 + \$197.35 + \$42.88 + \$14.98 = \$387.47$
$\$387.47 + (0.08 \times \$387.47) = \$418.47$ total bill

Section 36.   Shortcuts to Figuring Extensions

Exercise 5, page 199

1. $\frac{1}{8} \times 4,880 = \$610$ soybean oil
$\frac{1}{3} \times 2,760 = \$920$ bananas
$\frac{5}{8} \times 600 = \$375$ grapes
$\frac{7}{8} \times 1,600 = \$1,400$ tomatoes
$\$610 + \$920 + \$375 + \$1,400 = \$3,305$ total

2. $\frac{3}{8} \times 84 = \$31.50$ cards
$\frac{2}{3} \times 105 = \$70$ pencils
$\frac{3}{5} \times 240 = \$144$ correction fluid
$\frac{3}{4} \times 360 = \$270$ erasers
$\frac{4}{5} \times 150 = \$120$ note pads
$\$31.50 + \$70 + \$144 + \$270 + \$120 = \$635.50$ total

3. $\frac{1}{2} \times 350 = \$175$ fasteners
    $\frac{1}{4} \times 275 = \$68.75$ tape
    $\frac{1}{8} \times 720 = \$90$ bolts
    $\frac{3}{4} \times 54 = \$40.50$ tacks
    $\frac{2}{5} \times 175 = \$70$ glue
    $\frac{1}{5} \times 275 = \$55$ brads
    $\$175 + \$68.75 + \$90 + \$40.50 + \$70 + \$55 = \$499.25$ total

4. $\frac{4}{5} \times 250 = \$200$ candle holders
    $\frac{7}{8} \times 1,250 = \$1,093.75$ tree lights
    $\frac{2}{3} \times 180 = \$120$ lighters
    $\frac{3}{4} \times 300 = \$225$ mugs
    $\$200 + \$1,093.75 + \$120 + \$225 = \$1,638.75$ total

Review 36, page 199

1. a. $\frac{1}{8} \times 160 = \$20$ e. $0.03 \times \$2,078 = \$62.34$
    b. $\frac{7}{8} \times 320 = \$280$ f. $\$24 \div \$75 = 32\%$
    c. $\frac{2}{3} \times 48 = \$32$ g. $\$15.50 - (0.02 \times \$15.50) = \$15.19$
    d. $(4,500 \div 100) \times \$4 = \$180$

2. $\frac{1}{8} \times 1,320 = \$165$ pens
    $\frac{5}{8} \times 1,480 = \$925$ pencils
    $\frac{7}{8} \times 1,240 = \$1,085$ tape
    $\frac{4}{5} \times 1,720 = \$1,376$ cards
    $\$165 + \$925 + \$1,085 + \$1,376 = \$3,551$ total
    $\$3,551 + (0.05 \times \$3,551) = \$3,728.55$ total with tax

3. $0.65 \times \$4,750,000 = \$3,087,500$ salaries
    $0.09 \times \$4,750,000 = \$427,500$ rent
    $0.06 \times \$4,750,000 = \$285,000$ advertising
    $0.08 \times \$4,750,000 = \$380,000$ power
    $0.12 \times \$4,750,000 = \$570,000$ other

4. $\$23,800 - \$8,400 = \$15,400$ commission
    $\$15,400 \div \$308,000 = 5\%$ rate of commission

5. a. $5\,L + 8\,L + 9\,L + 8\,L = 30\,L$ estimate
    b. $5.25\,L + 7.5\,L + 9.25\,L + 8\,L = 30\,L$ exact
    c. $30\,L \div 1\,000 = 0.03\,kL$

Section 37.   Figuring Unit Prices

Exercise 3, page 201

1. a. $\$0.25 \div \frac{7}{16} = \$0.57$ c. $\$1.39 \div \frac{11}{16} = \$2.02$
    b. $\$3.19 \div \frac{7}{8} = \$3.65$ d. $\$1.59 \div \frac{3}{8} = \$4.24$

2. a. $\$0.88 \div \frac{1}{6} = \$5.28$ c. $\$11.67 \div \frac{7}{12} = \$20.01$
    b. $\$2.37 \div \frac{1}{4} = \$9.48$ d. $\$4.29 \div \frac{5}{12} = \$10.30$

3. $\$0.33 \div \frac{9}{25} = \$0.92$ price of plates per 100

4. $1.61 ÷ 7 = $0.23   price per oz. of 7 oz. can
$3.29 ÷ 14 = $0.235   price per oz. of 14 oz. can
$0.235 − $0.23 = $0.005 = $\frac{1}{2}$¢ less for 7 oz. jar

Exercise 4, page 202

1. 250 g = 0.25 kg
$1.89 ÷ 0.25 = $7.56   price per kg

2. 240 cm = 2.4 m
$0.62 × 2.4 = $1.49   price of board

3. 750 mL = 0.75 L
$1.58 ÷ 0.75 = $2.11   price per L

4. 30 cm = 0.3 m
$0.99 ÷ 0.3 = $3.30   price per m

Exercise 5, page 203

1. $296 ÷ $\frac{37}{2}$ = $16   price per square yard

2. $2.19 ÷ $\frac{21}{8}$ = $0.83   price per pound

3. $2.19 ÷ $\frac{5}{4}$ = $1.75   price per pound

4. $0.59 ÷ $\frac{7}{4}$ = $0.34   price per pound

5. $1.29 ÷ $\frac{3}{2}$ = $0.86   price per pound

6. $1.09 ÷ $\frac{9}{8}$ = $0.97   price per pound

Review 37, page 203

1. **a.** 45 ÷ 225 = 20%   **c.** $\frac{2}{15}$ = 13.3%
   b. 32 ÷ $\frac{3}{4}$ = $42\frac{2}{3}$ **d.** 400 ÷ 1,000 = 40%

2. **a.** 0.5 × $1.89 = $0.95   **c.** 0.946 L × $3.79 = $3.59
   b. $6.99 ÷ $\frac{2}{3}$ = $4.66

3. **a.** $8.59 ÷ 3 = $2.87   **b.** $9.79 ÷ 4 = $2.45   **c.** $48.99 ÷ 50 = $0.98

4. 5 × ($7\frac{1}{2}$ × $5.67) = $212.63   total earnings

5. **a.** 4 × 2 888 cm² = 11 552 cm²   space for four files
   b. 11 552 cm² = 1.155 2 m²

‡6. Check register balance $405.58
   Deduct:
     Service charge $3.25
     Amount on check stub too small   2.70   −   5.95
                                                        $399.63
   Add:
     Deposit not recorded   +   16.37
   Correct check register balance $416.00

Section 38.   Buying Wisely

Exercise 1, page 205

1. $(5 \times \$7.99) - \$35.95 = \$4$ saved

2. $(\$399.99 + \$199.99) - \$509.99 = \$89.99$ savings

3. $(3 \times \$219.99) - \$629.85 = \$30.12$ savings on three mats
   $\$30.12 \div 3 = \$10.04$ savings per mat

4. $20 \ m^2 \times \$58.89 = \$1{,}177.80$ regular price
   $20 \ m^2 \times \$48.89 = \$977.80$ sale price
   $\$1{,}177.80 - \$977.80 = \$200$ savings

Exercise 2, page 205

1. $\$298.99 - \$259.75 = \$39.24$ saved on air conditioner
   $\$49.95 - \$37.99 = \$11.96$ saved on fan
   $\$39.24 + \$11.96 = \$51.20$ total saved

2. $(6 \times \$24) - (2 \times \$65.85) = \$12.30$ saved

3. **a.** $0.05 \times \$300 = \$15$ estimated discount
   b. $0.05 \times \$295.99 = \$14.80$ exact discount
   $\$295.99 - \$14.80 = \$281.19$ paid

4. $\$39.99 + (2 \times \$29.98) = \$99.95$ purchase price
   $0.05 \times \$99.95 = \$5$ saved by paying cash

5. **a.** $20 \times \$0.29 = \$5.80$ purchase price
   $0.15 \times \$5.80 = \$0.87$ saved
   b. $\$5.80 - \$0.87 = \$4.93$ paid

Exercise 3, page 205

1. **a.** $\$2.49 \div \frac{5}{4} = \$1.99$ Brand A
   $\$2.79 \div \frac{3}{2} = \$1.86$ Brand B
   $\$1.99 - \$1.86 = \$0.13$ difference
   b. Brand B

2. $\$0.79 \div \frac{7}{4} = \$0.45$
   $\$0.59 \div \frac{5}{4} = \$0.47$
   $\$0.47 - \$0.45 = \$0.02$ less per pound

3. $(\$2.59 \div \frac{3}{2}) - (\$3.49 \div \frac{9}{4}) = \$0.18$ less per pound

4. **a.** $\$4.99 \div \frac{21}{8} = \$1.90$
   $\$6.49 \div \frac{13}{4} = \$2$
   $\$6.59 \div \frac{15}{4} = \$1.76$ least expensive
   b. $\$2 - \$1.76 = \$0.24$ difference

5. **a.** $\$12 \div 3 = \$4$ per case from Store A
   $\$36.96 \div 6 = \$6.16$ per case from Store B
   b. $(12 \times \$6.16) - (12 \times \$4) = \$25.92$ saved

6. $\$5.40 \div 6 = \$0.90$ per quart for 6-qt. package
   $\$20.88 \div 24 = \$0.87$ per quart for case
   $\$0.90 - \$0.87 = \$0.03$ savings per quart

7. $0.78 ÷ 2 L = $0.39   per liter of Freshful
   350 mL = 0.35 L; 0.35 L × 6 = 2.1 L
   $1.49 ÷ 2.1 L = $0.71   per liter of Weller
   $0.71 − $0.39 = $0.32   cheaper for Freshful

Exercise 4, page 206

1. $15 + (4.5 × $2.50) = $26.25   total charged

2. 2.5 × $25 = $62.50   floor sander
   2.5 × $20 = $50   floor edger
   11 × $1.20 = $13.20   sandpaper
   5 × $0.95 = $4.75   edger sandpaper
   $62.50 + $50 + $13.20 + $4.75 = $130.45   total cost

3. a. $48 + (0.05 × $48) = $50.40   cost of tiller
      $50.40 + (4 × $1.15) = $55   total cost of tiller
   b. $288.75 ÷ $50.40 = $5\frac{1}{4}$ years

4. $189 ÷ $27 = 7   days

5. a. $34.75 × 6 = $208.50   daily rate; weekly rate is cheaper
   b. $208.50 − $174.50 = $34   saved
   c. $1,657.75 ÷ $174.50 = 9.5 = $9\frac{1}{2}$ weeks

Review 38, page 207

1. a. ($42 − $24) ÷ $24 = $\frac{3}{4}$ d. 170 m² × 0.25 = 42.5 m²
   b. $0.00\frac{1}{3}$ × $2.28 = $0.0076   e. 28 cwt × $3.50 = $98
   c. $3\frac{3}{5}$ = 3.6   f. 3.978 M × $4.75 = $18.90

2. $12 + $6.75 = $18.75
   $17 + $2.75 = $19.75
   $19.75 − $18.75 = $1   savings

3. Check register balance $307.65   Bank statement balance $372.57
   Deduct: Deduct:
     Service charge   − 4.23   Outstanding checks:
                       $303.42 $17.87
   Add: 2.97
     Interest earned   + 1.79   45.33
                                           1.19   − 67.36
   Correct check register balance $305.21   Available bank balance $305.21

4. 40 × $8.50 = $340   regular pay
   8 × (1.5 × $8.50) = $102   overtime pay
   $340 × $102 = $442   gross pay

5. $22,750 + (0.28 × $22,750) = $29,120   gross job benefits
   (0.07 × $22,750) + $345 + $275 + $75 = $2,287.50   expense
   $29,120 − $2,287.50 = $26,832.50   net job benefits

6. $8,748 ÷ $145,800 = 6%   rate of commission

7. $0.06 \times \$32,500 = \$34,450$ expected income
   $0.24 \times \$34,450 = \$8,268$ food
   $0.06 \times \$34,450 = \$2,067$ clothing
   $0.30 \times \$34,450 = \$10,335$ housing
   $0.18 \times \$34,450 = \$6,201$ cars
   $0.14 \times \$34,450 = \$4,823$ other
   $0.08 \times \$34,450 = \$2,756$ savings

8. $0.06 \times \$8,788 = \$527.28$ sales tax

‡9. $1,920 \div 6 = 320$ miles per week
    $52 \times 320 = 16,640$ miles in a year

Section 39.   Checking Energy Costs

Exercise 1, page 211

1. a. $925 - 278 = 647$ KWH used

500 KWH	@ $0.0762	$ 38.10
147 KWH	@ $0.0986	+ 14.49
Cost of KWH		$ 52.59
Fuel adjustment	@ $0.00435	+ 2.81
Total energy charge		$ 55.40
Tax	@ 0.05	+ 2.77
Total bill		$ 58.17

   b. $1,940 - 730 = 1,210$ KWH used

500 KWH	@ $0.0762	$ 38.10
300 KWH	@ $0.0986	29.58
410 KWH	@ $0.1251	+ 51.29
Cost of KWH		$118.97
Fuel adjustment	@ $0.00435	+ 5.26
Total energy charge		$124.23
Tax	@ 0.05	+ 6.21
Total bill		$130.44

   c. $1,175 - 624 = 551$ KWH used

500 KWH	@ $0.0762	$ 38.10
51 KWH	@ $0.0986	+ 5.03
Cost of KWH		$ 43.13
Fuel adjustment	@ $0.00435	+ 2.40
Total energy charge		$ 45.53
Tax	@ 0.05	+ 2.28
Total bill		$ 47.81

   d. $6,845 - 5,308 = 1,537$ KWH used

500 KWH	@ $0.0762	$ 38.10
300 KWH	@ $0.0986	29.58
737 KWH	@ $0.1251	+ 92.20
Cost of KWH		$159.88
Fuel adjustment	@ $0.00435	+ 6.69
Total energy charge		$166.57
Tax	@ 0.05	+ 8.33
Total bill		$174.90

2. 8,124 − 7,280 = 844 KWH used

500 KWH	@ $0.0875	$ 43.75
344 KWH	@ $0.1292	+ 44.44
Cost of KWH		$ 88.19
Fuel adjustment	@ $0.0029	+ 2.45
Total energy charge		$ 85.74
Tax	@ 0.06	+ 5.14
Total bill		$ 90.88

3. 1,230 KWH used

1,000 KWH	@ $0.0705	$ 70.50
230 KWH	@ $0.0612	+ 14.08
Cost of KWH		$ 84.58
Fuel adjustment	@ $0.0143	+ 17.59
Total energy charge		$102.17
Tax	@ 0.03	+ 3.07
Total bill		$105.24

Exercise 2, page 213

1. a. 380 − 260 = 120   hundreds of cubic feet
120 × 1.486 = 178   therms used

First 90 whole therms (90 × $0.2278)	$20.50
Next 88 whole therms (88 × $0.1568)	+ 13.80
Charge for gas	$34.30
Sales tax at 5%	+ 1.72
Total bill	$36.02

b. 784 − 697 = 87   hundreds of cubic feet
87 × 1.578 = 137   therms

First 90 whole therms (90 × $0.2278)	$20.50
Next 47 whole therms (47 × $0.1568)	+ 7.37
Charge for gas	$27.87
Sales tax at 5%	+ 1.39
Total bill	$29.26

c. 189 − 78 = 111   hundreds of cubic feet
111 × 1.108 = 123   therms

First 90 whole therms (90 × $0.2278)	$20.50
Next 33 whole therms (33 × $0.1568)	+ 5.17
Charge for gas	$25.67
Sales tax at 5%	+ 1.28
Total bill	$26.95

d. 573 − 489 = 84   hundreds of cubic feet
84 × 1.499 = 126   therms

First 90 whole therms (90 × $0.2278)	$20.50
Next 36 whole therms (36 × $0.1568)	+ 5.64
Charge for gas	$26.14
Sales tax at 5%	+ 1.31
Total bill	$27.45

   e. 205 − 132 = 73   hundreds of cubic feet
        72 × 1.228 = 89.6 = 90   therms

Charge for gas (90 × $0.2278)	$20.50
Sales tax at 5%	+ 1.03
Total bill	$21.53

2. 896 − 784 = 112   hundreds of cubic feet
    112 × 1.377 = 154   therms

First 50 therms (50 × $0.2772)	$13.86
Next 50 therms (50 × $0.1798)	8.99
Next 54 therms (54 × $0.1365)	+ 7.37
Charge for gas	$30.22
Sales tax at 5%	+ 1.51
Total bill	$31.73

3. 496 − 357 = 139   hundred cubic feet
    139 × 1.023 = 142   therms

First 70 therms (70 × $0.2036)	$14.25
Next 72 therms (72 × $0.2686)	+ 19.34
Charge for gas	$33.59
Facilities tax	21.97
Sales tax at 3%	+ 1.67
Total bill	$57.23

Review 39, page 214

1. **a.** $1\frac{4}{5} = 1.8$ **d.** $0.23 × 9.256 = $2.13
     b. ($320 − $200) ÷ $320 = $\frac{3}{8}$ **e.** 32 kg ÷ 20 kg = 160%
     c. $98.25 − ($\frac{2}{3}$ × $98.25) = $32.75   **f.** $\frac{7}{8}$% = 0.00875

2. 6,987 − 6,361 = 626   KWH used

100 KWH	@ $0.127	$12.70
100 KWH	@ $0.105	10.50
426 KWH	@ $0.089	+ 37.91
Cost of KWH		$61.11
Fuel adjustment	@ $0.00132	+ 0.83
Total energy charge		$61.94
Tax	@ 0.04	+ 2.48
Total bill		$64.42

3. 2 × ($12.99 + $2.89) = $31.76 Vito's price without rebate
    $31.76 − $10.00 = $21.76 Vito's final price
    $21.76 − $19.99 = $1.77 lower price at Bell's

4. 1.25 × $0.45 = $0.56 apples
    0.5 × $1.19 = $0.60 cream cheese
    $\frac{2}{3}$ × $1.09 = $0.73 carrots
    $0.56 + $0.60 + $0.73 = $1.89 total sale
    $1.89 + (0.05 × $1.89) = $1.98 total bill

Section 40.   Reducing Energy Costs

Exercise 1, page 215

1. $0.09 × 3,500 = $315   saved

2.   ($175 − $140) ÷ $175 = 20%   savings

3.   **a.**   (77° − 72°) × 0.03 = 15%   saved
     b. $212 × 0.15 = $31.80   saved
     c.   2,100 × 0.15 = 315   KWH

4.   **a.**   (140 − 91) ÷ 140 = 35%   reduction
     b. $0.50 × 50 = $25   estimated savings
     c. $0.48 × 49 = $23.52   actual savings

Exercise 2, page 216

1.   (10 × $216) − $59 = $2,101   net savings

2.   0.07 × $900 = $63   savings per year
     (15 × $63) − $12 = $933   net savings

3.   0.15 × $960 = $144   savings per year
     (10 × $144) − $240 = $1,200   net savings

4.   0.09 × $860 = $77.40   savings per year
     (15 × $77.40) − $135 = $1,026   net savings

Exercise 3, page 217

1. $2,800 ÷ $350 = 8   years

2.   0.03 × $870 = $26.10   estimated saving per year
     $750 ÷ $26.10 = 28.7 = 29   years

3.   0.12 × $1,150 = $138   savings per year
     $250 ÷ $138 = 1.8   years

4.   **a.**   0.015 × $1,210 = $18.15   savings each year
     b. $27.50 ÷ $18.15 = 1.5   years

Exercise 4, page 217

1.   **a.**   5 × (10 × 100) = 5,000   watt-hours
     5,000 ÷ 1,000 = 5   KWH
     b.   5 × $0.09 = $0.45   cost to use each day

2.   **a.**   5 × (10 × 60) = 3,000   watt-hours
     5,000 − 3,000 = 2,000   watt-hours
     2,000 ÷ 1,000 = 2   KWH saved each day
     b.   2 × $0.09 = $0.18   saved each day
     365 × $0.18 = $65.70   saved in a year

3.   **a.**   746 ÷ 1,000 = 0.746   KWH
     30 × (3 × 0.746) = 67.14 = 67   KWH used in June
     b.   67 × $0.08 = $5.36   cost to use

    c. $0.746 \div 2 = 0.373$　KWH

          $30 \times (3 \times 0.373) = 33.57 = 34$　KWH saved

    d. $34 \times \$0.08 = \$2.72$　saved

4. $1{,}200$ watts $= 1.2$　KWH

    $5 \times (1.2 \times \$0.075) = \$0.45$　cost of Alaskan

    750 watts $= 0.75$　KWH

    $5 \times (0.75 \times \$0.075) = \$0.28$　cost of Bonner

    $\$0.45 - \$0.28 = \$0.17$　saved

5. **a.** $\$0.08 \times (1{,}100 \div 1{,}000) = \$0.09$　toaster

    b. $\$0.08 \times (5{,}000 \div 1{,}000) = \$0.40$　clothes dryer

    c. $\$0.08 \times (1{,}450 \div 1{,}000) = \$0.12$　microwave

    d. $\$0.08 \times (1{,}000 \div 1{,}000) = \$0.08$　hair dryer

Review 40, page 218

2. **a.** $8\frac{5}{8} = 8.625$

    b. $(\$320 - \$200) \div \$200 = \frac{3}{5}$

    c. $(4{,}000 \div 2{,}000) \times \$10 = \$20$　estimate

          $(4{,}100 \div 2{,}000) \times \$9.89 = \$20.27$　exact

    d. $45 \times \$0.10 = \$4.50$

    e. $3\frac{1}{2} \times 6\frac{2}{3} = 23\frac{1}{3}$

    ‡**f.** $\$2.28 \div \frac{3}{4} = \$3.04$

    ‡**g.** $\$382.50 \div 0.85 = \$450$

3. **a.** $60 \times (12{,}200 \div 1{,}000) = 732$　KWH

    b. $732 \times \$0.11 = \$80.52$　cost for 1 year

4. $(0.18 \times \$800) - \$110 = \$34$　net savings for year

5. $21{,}968 - 21{,}308 = 660$　KWH used

    20 KWH $= \$15.95$

    $150 \times \$0.11 = \$16.50$

    $490 \times \$0.09 = \$44.10$

    $\$15.95 + \$16.50 + \$44.10 = \$76.55$　energy charges

    $\$76.55 + (0.03 \times \$76.55) = \$78.85$　total bill

6.

	Regular Time	Overtime
Monday	8	
Tuesday	$7\frac{1}{2}$	
Wednesday	8	$1\frac{1}{4}$
Thursday	8	2
Friday	$+\ 8$	$+\ \frac{3}{4}$
	$39\frac{1}{2}$	4

    $\$6.50 \times 1.5 = \$9.75$　overtime rate

    $39.5 \times \$6.50 = \$256.75$　regular pay

    $4 \times \$9.75 = \$39$　overtime pay

    $\$256.75 + \$39 = \$295.75$　gross pay

7. $\$337.50 \times 52 = \$17{,}750$　per year

    $\$17{,}750 \div 12 = \$1{,}462.50$　per month

8. $\$135{,}600 - (0.06 \times \$135{,}600) = \$127{,}464$　proceeds

Section 41.   Checking and Reducing Water Costs

Exercise 1, page 222

1. **a.** Basic quarterly charge .... $ \ \ 4.75
         2,170 cu. ft. @ $0.987 per C .... + \ \ 21.42
         Total bill .... $ 26.17

    b. Basic quarterly charge .... $ \ \ 4.75
         First 5,000 cu. ft. @ $0.987 per C 49.35
         Next 930 cu. ft. @ $0.863 per C .... + \ \ \ 8.03
         Total bill .... $ 62.13

    c. Basic quarterly charge .... $ \ \ 4.75
         First 5,000 cu. ft. @ $0.987 per C 49.35
         Next 10,000 cu. ft. @ $0.863 per C 86.30
         Next 2,640 cu. ft. @ $0.724 per C .... + \ \ 19.11
         Total bill $159.51

    d. Basic quarterly charge .... $ \ \ 4.75
         First 5,000 cu. ft. @ $0.987 per C 49.35
         Next 10,000 cu. ft. @ $0.863 per C 86.30
         Next 15,000 cu. ft. @ $0.724 per C 108.60
         Next 2,590 cu. ft. @ $0.563 per C .... + \ \ 14.58
         Total bill $263.58

2. **a.** 12,220 − 8,920 = 3,300 cu. ft. used
         Basic quarterly charge .... $ \ \ 4.75
         3,300 cu. ft. @ $0.987 per C .... + \ \ 32.57
         Total bill .... $ 37.32

    b. 27,740 − 16,000 = 11,740 cu. ft. used
         Basic quarterly charge .... $ \ \ 4.75
         First 5,000 cu. ft. @ $0.987 per C 49.35
         Next 6,740 cu. ft. @ $0.863 per C .... + \ \ 58.17
         Total bill $112.27

    c. 98,370 − 81,090 = 17,280 cu. ft. used
         Basic quarterly charge .... $ \ \ 4.75
         First 5,000 cu. ft. @ $0.987 per C 49.35
         Next 10,000 cu. ft. @ $0.863 per C 86.30
         Next 2,280 cu. ft. @ $0.724 per C .... + \ \ 16.51
         Total bill $156.91

3. 48,170 − 35,180 = 12,990 cu. ft. used
    Basic quarterly charge .... $ \ \ 4.75
    First 5,000 cu. ft. @ $0.987 per C 49.35
    Next 7,990 cu. ft. @ $0.863 per C .... + \ \ 68.95
    Total bill $123.05

4. 96,700 − 72,110 = 24,590 cu. ft. used
    Basic quarterly charge .... $ \ \ 4.75
    First 5,000 cu. ft. @ $0.987 per C 49.35
    Next 10,000 cu. ft. @ $0.863 per C 86.30
    Next 9,590 cu. ft. @ $0.724 per C .... + \ \ 69.43
    Total bill $209.83

Exercise 2, page 222

1. a. $52 \times (2 \times 60) = 6{,}240$ gallons per year
    b. $(6{,}240 \div 1{,}000) \times \$0.87 = \$5.43$ cost per year

2. a. $52 \times (2 \times 27) = 2{,}808$ gallons per year
        $6{,}240 - 2{,}808 = 3{,}432$ gallons saved
    b. $(3{,}432 \div 1{,}000) \times \$0.87 = \$2.99$ saved

3. a. $4 \times 10 = 40$ gallons per day
    b. $365 \times 40 = 14{,}600$ gallons per year
        $(14{,}600 \div 1{,}000) \times \$1{,}182 = \$17.26$ cost per year

4. a. $14{,}600 \times (5 \div 10) = 7{,}300$ gallons saved per year
    b. $(7{,}300 \div 1{,}000) \times \$1.182 = \$8.63$ saved

5. a. $20 \times 30 = 600$ gallons estimated
    b. $18 \times 31 = 558$ gallons wasted
    c. $(558 \div 1{,}000) \times \$0.98 = \$0.55$ cost of wasted water

Review 41, page 224

1. a. $\$1{,}200 \times 0.0415 = \$49.80$
    b. $(\$240 - \$210) \div \$240 = 12\frac{1}{2}\%$
    c. $7\frac{1}{8} = 7.125$
    d. $\$20 \times 4 = \$80$
    e. $(23{,}450 \div 2{,}000) \times \$16 = \$187.60$
    f. $248 \times \$0.375 = \$93$
    g. $(50 \text{ m}^2 - 40 \text{ m}^2) \div 40 \text{ m}^2 = 25\%$
    ‡h. $\$48 \div \frac{5}{6} = \$57.60$

2. $53{,}400 - 42{,}180 = 11{,}220$ cu. ft.

Basic quarterly charge	\$ 4.75
First 5,000 cu. ft. @ \$0.987 per C	49.35
Next 6,220 cu. ft. @ \$0.863 per C	+ 53.68
Total bill	\$107.78

3. $(30 \times 16) - (30 \times 7) = 270$ gallons saved
    $(270 \div 1{,}000) \times \$0.835 = \$2.25$ saved

4.
$231 \times \$0.86$	\$198.66
Fuel adjustment @ \$0.0041	+ 0.95
Total energy charge	\$199.61
Sales tax at 5%	+ 9.98
Total bill	\$209.59

5. $0.60 \times \$3{,}567{,}200 = \$2{,}140{,}320$ salaries and wages
    $0.05 \times \$3{,}567{,}200 = \$178{,}360$ advertising
    $0.10 \times \$3{,}567{,}200 = \$356{,}720$ power and utilities

6. $\$4{,}432 \div \$55{,}400 = 8\%$ rate of commission

7. $1.15 \times \$514{,}678{,}120 = \$591{,}879{,}838$ estimated this year

8. $36.25 \times \$8.50 = \$308.13$ gross pay
    $\$37.00 + \$6.16 + \$12.50 + (0.0765 \times \$308.13) = \$79.23$ deductions
    $\$308.13 - \$79.23 = \$228.90$ net pay

9. $3 \times 5 = 15$ feet
    $\frac{1}{3} \times 15 = 5$ white lights
    $\frac{2}{3} \times 15 = 10$ blue lights

Section 42.   Checking and Reducing Telephone Costs

Exercise 1, page 226

1.

	Charges	U.S. Tax at 3%	State Tax at 5%
Local service	$10.38	$0.31	$0.52
Touch-tone	0.73	0.02	0.04
Push button	2.57	0.08	0.13
Call forwarding	2.50	0.08	0.13
Access charges	2.00	0.06	0.10
Local calls	22.45	0.67	1.12
Totals	$40.63	$1.22	$2.04

$40.63 + $1.22 + $2.04 = $43.89   total bill for month

2.

	Charges	U.S. Tax 3%	State Tax 5%
Local service	$10.38	$0.31	$0.52
Rotary phones (2 @ $1.05)	2.10	0.06	0.11
Access charge	2.00	0.06	0.10
Local calls	17.49	0.52	0.87
Totals	$31.97	$0.95	$1.60

$31.97 + $0.95 + $1.60 = $34.52   total bill

3.

	Charges	U.S. Tax 3%	State Tax 5%
Local service	$10.38	$0.31	$0.52
Touch-tone	0.73	0.02	0.04
Push-button (2 @ $2.57)	5.14	0.15	0.26
Call waiting	3.00	0.09	0.15
Call forwarding	2.50	0.08	0.13
Access charge	2.00	0.06	0.10
Local calls	37.55	1.13	1.88
Totals	$61.30	$1.84	$3.08

$61.30 + $1.84 + $3.08 = $66.22   total bill

4. ($1.05 \times 3) \times (12 \times 5) = $189   rental for 5 years
    $189 - ($18 \times 3) = $135   saved by buying

5. ($2.57 \times 2) \times 12 = $61.68   rental for 1 year
    ($30 \times 2) \div $61.68 = 0.97 = 1   year

Exercise 2, page 228

1. **a.** $0.2760 + (5 \times 0.2398) = $1.48   cost of call
    b. $0.1600 + (5 \times $0.1487) = $0.90   evening cost
        $1.48 - $0.90 = $0.58   savings
    c. $0.1160 + (5 \times $0.1127) = $0.68   Saturday cost
        $1.48 - $0.68 = $0.80   savings

2. a. $0.2810 + (26 \times $0.2797) = $7.55 cost of call
    b. $0.1310 + (26 \times $0.1300) = $3.51 cost of call
    c. Same rates as b: $3.51

3. a. $0.2690 + (14 \times $0.2098) = $3.21 cost of call
    b. $0.1560 + (14 \times $0.1301) = $1.98 cost of call
    c. Same rates as b: $1.98

4. a. $0.2810 + (4 \times $0.2797) = $1.40 cost of call on weekday
        $0.1640 + (4 \times $0.1620) = $0.81 cost of call in evening
        ($1.40 − $0.81) ÷ $1.40 = 42% saved
    b. $0.1310 + (4 \times $0.1300) = $0.65 cost of call at night
        ($1.40 − $0.65) ÷ $1.40 = 54% saved

Review 42, page 229

2. a. 13,240 ÷ 150,000 = 0.0883   c. $9\frac{2}{5} = 9.4$
    b. ($630 − $540) ÷ $630 = $\frac{1}{7}$ d. $3.60 ÷ 0.625 = $5.76

3.

	Charges	U.S. Tax 3%	State Tax 4%
Local charges	$12.50	$0.38	$0.50
Access charges	2.00	0.06	0.08
Local calls	44.23	1.33	1.77
Totals	$58.73	$1.77	$2.35

$58.73 + $1.77 + $2.35 = $62.85

4. 18,450 − 12,880 = 5,570
    First 500 cu. ft. $ 6.34
    Next 5,070 cu. ft. @ $0.79 per C   40.05
    Total bill $46.39

5. a. 40 × $9 = $360 regular pay
        8 × (1.5 × $9) = $108 Saturday pay
        8 × (2 × $9) = $144 Sunday pay
        $360 + $108 + $144 = $612 gross earnings
    b. 0.08 × $600 = $48 estimated FICA tax
        0.0765 × $612 = $46.82 exact FICA tax

UNIT 7 • BORROWING MONEY

Section 43. Interest-Bearing Notes

Exercise 1, page 233

1. a. $500 × 0.10 × 2 = $100 interest
        $500 + $100 = $600 amount due at maturity
    b. $300 × 0.12 × 3 = $108 interest
        $300 + $108 = $408 amount due at maturity

    c. $\$200 \times 0.09 \times 1\frac{1}{2} = \$27$ interest
        $\$200 + \$27 = \$227$ amount due at maturity

    d. $\$900 \times 0.08 \times \frac{1}{4} = \$18$ interest
        $\$900 + \$18 = \$918$ amount due at maturity

    e. $\$250 \times 0.14 \times \frac{1}{4} = \$8.75$ interest
        $\$250 + \$8.75 = \$258.75$ amount due at maturity

    f. $\$450 \times 0.13 \times \frac{5}{6} = \$48.75$ interest
        $\$450 + \$48.75 = \$498.75$ amount due at maturity

    g. $\$720 \times 0.085 \times 2\frac{1}{4} = \$137.70$ interest
        $\$720 + \$137.70 = \$857.70$ amount due at maturity

2.   **a.** $\$20,000 \times 0.10 \times 3 = \$6,000$ estimated interest
    b. $\$20,500 \times 0.11 \times 3 = \$6,765$ exact interest
    c. $\$20,500 + \$6,765 = \$27,265$ total amount due

3. $\$3,600 \times 0.09 \times \frac{3}{4} = \$243$ interest
    $\$3,600 + \$243 = \$3,843$ had to be paid

4. $\$6,200 \times 0.105 \times \frac{2}{3} = \$434$ interest
    $\$6,200 + \$434 = \$6,634$ to be paid on due date

5. $\$4,800 \times 0.1325 \times 1.5 = \$954$ interest
    $\$4,800 + \$954 = \$5,754$ total amount

6. $\$2,000 \times 0.1525 \times \frac{1}{4} = \$76.25$ interest
    $\$2,000 + \$76.25 = \$2,076.25$ must be paid when note is due

7.   **a.** $\$15,000 \times 0.15 \times 1.5 = \$3,375$ interest
    b. $\$15,000 + \$3,375 = \$18,375$ total amount due

Review 43, page 234

2.   **a.** $\$350.70 \times 0.07 = \$24.55$ **d.** $\$9 \div \$7.50 = 120\%$
    b. $2.4 = 240\%$ **e.** $6\frac{1}{4}\% = 0.0625$
    c. $\$70 \div \$280 = 25\%$ **f.** $2.6 \text{ L} \times 0.25 = 0.65 \text{ L}$

3. $\$4,400 \times 0.06 \times \frac{3}{4} = \$198$ interest

4.   **a.** $\$5,000 \times 0.15 \times 3 = \$2,250$ interest
    b. $\$5,000 + \$2,250 = \$7,250$ total amount due

5. $\$157,800 - (\$157,800 \times 0.05) - \$325 = \$149,585$ net proceeds

6. $(\$9.50 \times 40) + (\$9.50 \times 1.5 \times 4\frac{1}{4}) = \$440.56$ gross pay
    $\$440.56 - (\$440.56 \times 0.0765) - \$47 = \$359.86$ net pay

7. $0.425 \text{ km}^2 = 42.5$ hectares
    $(35 + 42.5 + 0.46 + 12.7)$ ha $\times \$207 = \$18,766.62$ total cost

8. $(6 \text{ L} + 30 \text{ L} + 45 \text{ L} + 60 \text{ L}) - 8 \text{ L} = 133 \text{ L}$ used

9. $\$22,000 \times 6 = \$132,000$ total for $\$22,000$ average sales per month
    $\$132,000 - (\$23,890 + \$21,060 + \$18,400 + \$19,780 + \$20,700) = \$28,170$
    sales for 6th month

‡10. $\$4,500 \div 0.08 = \$56,250$ worth of goods to be sold

‡**11.**

Cleo Orr
Reconciliation Statement
May 31, 19 --

Check register balance	$1,214.15	Bank statement balance		$1,342.66
		Deduct:		
		Outstanding checks:		
		#86	$15.88	
Add:		#88	38.45	
Deposit	+ 49.00	#89	25.18	− 79.51
Correct check register balance	$1,263.15	Available bank balance		$1,263.15

Section 44. Exact and Banker's Interest

Exercise 2, page 236

1. $800 \times 0.10 \times \frac{1}{2} = $40

2. $600 \times 0.12 \times \frac{1}{4} = $18

3. $960 \times 0.08 \times \frac{1}{3} = $25.60

4. $400 \times 0.15 \times \frac{3}{4} = $45

5. $1,500 \times 0.16 \times \frac{5}{12} = $100

6. $2,400 \times 0.07 \times \frac{1}{6} = $28

7. $6,900 \times 0.05 \times \frac{2}{3} = $230

8. $3,500 \times 0.09 \times \frac{1}{12} = $26.25

9. $3,000 \times 0.12 \times \frac{5}{6} = $300

10. $4,000 \times 0.075 \times \frac{1}{2} = $150

Exercise 3, page 237

1.
  a. $650 \times 0.06 \times \frac{2}{5} = $15.60
  b. $2,200 \times 0.12 \times \frac{10}{73} = $36.16
  c. $560 \times 0.10 \times \frac{22}{73} = $16.88
  d. $840 \times 0.15 \times \frac{60}{73} = $103.56
  e. $1,450 \times 0.07 \times \frac{20}{73} = $27.81
  f. $500 \times 0.08 \times \frac{18}{73} = $9.86

2. $1,800 \times 0.09 \times \frac{54}{73} = $119.84   exact interest on loan

3.
  a. $5,000 \times 0.12 \times \frac{1}{2} = $300   estimated interest
  b. $5,000 \times 0.12 \times \frac{36}{73} = $295.89   exact interest
  c. $5,000 + $295.89 = $5,295.89   total paid back

Exercise 4, page 237

1.
  a. $600 \times 0.06 \times \frac{1}{6} = $6
  b. $360 \times 0.09 \times \frac{1}{12} = $2.70
  c. $200 \times 0.12 \times \frac{1}{3} = $8
  d. $400 \times 0.08 \times \frac{1}{2} = $16
  e. $960 \times 0.15 \times \frac{3}{4} = $108
  f. $1,800 \times 0.15 \times \frac{1}{10} = $27
  g. $1,200 \times 0.08 \times \frac{2}{3} = $64
  h. $2,400 \times 0.09 \times \frac{1}{8} = $27
  i. $1,500 \times 0.12 \times \frac{1}{4} = $45
  j. $2,000 \times 0.075 \times \frac{1}{3} = $50

2. $\$900 \times 0.14 \times \frac{1}{6} = \$21$ banker's interest

3. $\$3,840 \times 0.12 \times \frac{1}{3} = \$153.60$ interest paid

4. **a.** $\$1,825 \times 0.12 \times \frac{1}{2} = \$109.50$ interest paid
b. $\$1,825 + \$109.50 = \$1,934.50$ total amount paid

5. $\$580 \times 0.125 \times \frac{1}{4} = \$18.13$ interest paid

6. **a.** $\$8,000 \times 0.15 \times \frac{27}{73} = \$443.84$ exact interest with Lender A
b. $\$8,000 \times 0.15 \times \frac{3}{8} = \$450$ banker's interest with Lender B
c. $\$450 - \$443.84 = \$6.16$ difference

Exercise 5, page 238

1. $(12 \times \$4) \div \$400 = 12\%$

2. $(6 \times \$7.50) \div \$500 = 9\%$

3. $(4 \times \$10.50) \div \$300 = 14\%$

4. $(3 \times \$18) \div \$600 = 9\%$

5. $(2 \times \$140) \div \$2,800 = 10\%$

6. $(6 \times \$7.25) \div \$435 = 10\%$

7. $(2 \times \$78) \div \$1,300 = 12\%$

8. $(4 \times \$20) \div \$1,000 = 8\%$

9. $(\frac{3}{2} \times \$80) \div \$800 = 15\%$

10. $(\frac{6}{5} \times \$150) \div \$2,000 = 9\%$

11. $(\frac{2}{3} \times \$600) \div \$4,000 = 10\%$

12. $(\frac{4}{5} \times \$600) \div \$600 = 8\%$

Exercise 6, page 239

1. $(2 \times \$132) \div \$2,400 = 11\%$ rate of interest

2. $(12 \times \$19.50) \div \$2,600 = 9\%$ rate of interest

3. $(\frac{2}{3} \times \$945) \div \$6,000 = 10\frac{1}{2}\%$ rate of interest

4. $(\frac{4}{7} \times \$315) \div \$1,500 = 12\%$ rate of interest

Review 44, page 239

2. **a.** $5.25 = 525\%$
b. $\$80 \div \$50 = 160\%$
c. $9\frac{7}{8}\% = .09875$
d. $320 \text{ g} \div 1\,000 \text{ g} = 32\%$
e. $\$90 \div 0.075 = \$1,200$
f. $100\% - 5\% = 95\%$, or 0.95
Amount $= \$10.64 \div 0.95 = \$11.20$

3. $\$75 + \$25 - (\$1.25 + \$5 + \$25 + \$3.75) = \$65$ left at end of day

4. $(6 \times \$27) \div \$1,800 = 9\%$ rate of interest

5. $\$4,800 \times 0.14 \times 1\frac{1}{2} = \$1,008$ exact interest

6. $\$28,000 \times 6 = \$168,000$ sales for 6 months
$\$168,000 - (\$27,508 + \$29,686 + \$29,130 + \$27,980 + \$28,649) = \$25,047$
sales for next month

7. $\frac{3}{5} \times \$9,300 = \$5,580$ Betty's share of costs

8. $\$10,920 \div 52 = \$210$ per week

9. $(5 \times 7\frac{1}{2}) - 1\frac{1}{2} = 36$ hours
    $36 \times \$6.50 = \$234$ gross earnings

10. $\$650 - \$200 = \$450$ commission
    $\$450 \div \$15,000 = 3\%$ rate of commission

11. $\$580 \times 0.75 = \$435$ collected
    $\$435 \times 0.35 = \$152.25$ commission
    $\$435 - \$152.25 = \$282.75$ net proceeds

12. $(3 \times 16 \text{ L}) - 7 \text{ L} = 41 \text{ L}$ of berries left

13. $\$6,600 \div 0.30 = \$22,000$ amount collected

Section 45. Interest Tables

Exercise 1, page 242

1. $\begin{array}{r} \$0.2740 \\ \times \quad 8 \\ \hline \$2.1920 \end{array}$ interest on $100 for 10 days at 10%
    principal divided by $100
    or $2.19 interest

2. $\begin{array}{r} \$0.4932 \\ \times \quad 4 \\ \hline \$1.9728 \end{array}$ interest on $100 for 15 days at 12%
    principal divided by $100
    or $1.97 interest

3. $\begin{array}{r} \$0.4603 \\ \times \quad 5 \\ \hline \$2.3015 \end{array}$ interest on $100 for 21 days at 8%
    principal divided by $100
    or $2.30 interest

4. $\begin{array}{r} \$0.2110 \\ \times \quad 1 \\ \hline \$0.2110 \end{array}$ interest on $100 for 7 days at 11%
    principal divided by $100
    or $0.21 interest

5. $\begin{array}{r} \$0.3123 \\ \times \quad 3 \\ \hline \$0.9369 \end{array}$ interest on $100 for 12 days at $9\frac{1}{2}\%$
    principal divided by $100
    or $0.94 interest

6. $\begin{array}{r} \$ 0.7397 \\ \times \quad 1.5 \\ \hline \$1.10955 \end{array}$ interest on $100 for 30 days at 9%
    principal divided by $100
    or $1.11 interest

7. $\begin{array}{r} \$0.1644 \\ \times \quad 4.5 \\ \hline \$0.7398 \end{array}$ interest on $100 for 5 days at 12%
    principal divided by $100
    or $0.74 interest

8. $\begin{array}{r} \$0.2877 \\ \times \quad 12 \\ \hline \$3.4524 \end{array}$ interest on $100 for 10 days at $10\frac{1}{2}\%$
    principal divided by $100
    or $3.45 interest

9. $0.6164   interest on $100 for 25 days at 9%
    ×   32.5   principal divided by $100
    $20.033   or $20.03 interest

10. $ 0.6575   interest on $100 for 20 days at 12%
    ×   .75   principal divided by $100
    $0.493125   or $0.49 interest

Exercise 2, page 243

1. **a.** $0.7808   interest on $100 for 30 days at $9\frac{1}{2}$%
    +0.3904   interest on $100 for 15 days at $9\frac{1}{2}$%
    $1.1712   interest on $100 for 45 days at $9\frac{1}{2}$%
    ×   3   principal divided by $100
    $3.5136   or $3.51 interest

    b. $0.9863   interest on $100 for 30 days at 12%
    +0.9863   interest on $100 for 30 days at 12%
    $1.9726   interest on $100 for 60 days
    ×   5   principal divided by $100
    $9.8630   or $9.86 interest

    c. $ 0.6575   interest on $100 for 30 days at 8%
    + 0.5479   interest on $100 for 25 days at 8%
    $ 1.2054   interest on $100 for 55 days at 8%
    ×   9   principal divided by $100
    $10.8486   or $10.85 interest

    d. $ 0.8219   interest on $100 for 30 days at 10%
       0.8219   interest on $100 for 30 days at 10%
    + 0.5479   interest on $100 for 20 days at 10%
    $ 2.1917   interest on $100 for 80 days at 10%
    ×   50   principal divided by $100
    $109.5850   or $109.59 interest

    e. $ 0.7397   interest on $100 for 30 days at 9%
      0.7397   interest on $100 for 30 days at 9%
      0.7397   interest on $100 for 30 days at 9%
    + 0.7397   interest on $100 for 30 days at 9%
    $ 2.9588   interest on $100 for 120 days at 9%
    ×   7.5   principal divided by $100
    $22.1910   or $22.19 interest

    f. $0.2740   interest on $100 for 10 days at 10%
    +0.2466   interest on $100 for 10 days at 9%
    $0.5206   interest on $100 for 10 days at 19%
    ×   4   principal divided by $100
    $2.0824   or $2.08 interest

    g. $0.4384   interest on $100 for 20 days at 8%
    +0.4384   interest on $100 for 20 days at 8%
    $0.8768   interest on $100 for 20 days at 16%
    ×   2   principal divided by $100
    $1.7536   or $1.75 interest

h. $ 0.9863   interest on $100 for 30 days at 12%
    + 0.8219   interest on $100 for 30 days at 10%

    $ 1.8082   interest on $100 for 30 days at 22%
    ×   18   principal divided by $100

    $32.5476   or $32.55 interest

i. $ 0.8219   interest on $100 for 30 days at 10%
    + 0.8219   interest on $100 for 30 days at 10%

    $ 1.6438   interest on $100 for 30 days at 20%
    ×   25   principal divided by $100

    $41.0950   or $41.10 interest

j. $0.4384   interest on $100 for 16 days at 10%
    +0.3507   interest on $100 for 16 days at 8%

    $0.7891   interest on $100 for 16 days at 18%
    ×   9   principal divided by $100

    $7.1019   or $7.10 interest

2. Interest on $100 for 30 days at 12% from table = $0.9863
$0.9863 × 2 × 7 = $13.808, or $13.81   interest
$700 + $13.81 = $713.81   amount owed

3. **a.** $750 × $\frac{20}{360}$ × $\frac{17}{100}$ = $4.722, or $4.72   interest
b. Interest on $500 for 20 days at $8\frac{1}{2}$% from table = $0.4658
$0.4658 × 2 × 5 = $4.658, or $4.66   interest

Review 45, page 244

1. **a.** 4.8 = 480%
b. $510 ÷ $340 = 150%
c. $8\frac{1}{8}$% = 0.08125
d. 23.9% = 0.239
e. (378 ÷ 100) × $3.50 = $13.23

    f. 180 kL ÷ $\frac{3}{8}$ = 480 kL
g. $7.20 ÷ 0.25 = $28.80
h. $50.88 ÷ 0.96 = $53
i. $2.10 ÷ $\frac{7}{5}$ = $1.50

2. ($121.50 ÷ $1\frac{1}{2}$) ÷ $900 = 9%

3. $ 0.7397   interest on $100 for 30 days at 9%
    0.7397   interest on $100 for 30 days at 9%
    0.7397   interest on $100 for 30 days at 9%
  + 0.7397   interest on $100 for 30 days at 9%

    $ 2.9588   interest on $100 for 120 days at 9%
    ×   8   principal divided by $100

    $23.6704   or $23.67 interest

    $800 + $23.67 = $823.67   amount due at maturity

4. **a.** $910 × 12 = $10,920   annual salary
b. $19,920 − $10,920 = $9,000   annual commission
c. $9,000 ÷ $112,500 = 8%   rate of commission

5. **a.** (18 ÷ 3) × $0.90 = $5.40   estimated total cost of soup
b. (18 ÷ 3) × $0.89 = $5.34   exact cost of soup

6. 3 × $17.80 = $53.40   cost of shirts bought 1 at a time
$53.40 − $49.95 = $3.45   saved

Section 46. Due Dates and Times of Notes

Exercise 2, page 246

1. $\frac{4}{4}$ 4. $\frac{6}{30}$ 7. $\frac{11}{14}$ 10. $\frac{3}{3}$

2. $\frac{3}{30}$ 5. $\frac{3}{16}$ 8. $\frac{3}{18}$ 11. $\frac{10}{7}$

3. $\frac{2}{15}$ 6. $\frac{6}{28}$ 9. $\frac{11}{20}$ 12. $\frac{9}{2}$

Exercise 3, page 248

1.
   a. 66 days   e. 120 days
   b. 78 days   f. 71 days
   c. 108 days   g. 86 days
   d. 35 days   h. 10 days

2.
   a. 90 days
   b. $5,000 \times 0.14 \times \frac{18}{73} = \$172.60$ exact interest
   c. $5,000 + \$172.60 = \$5,172.60$ total amount due

3. $8,000 \times 0.08 \times \frac{1}{5} = \$128$ exact interest
   $8,000 + \$128 = \$8,128$ total amount owed

Exercise 4, page 249

1.
   a.
   $$\begin{array}{rl} 164 & \text{June 13} \\ -\ 40 & \text{February 9} \\ \hline 124 & \text{days} \end{array}$$

   e.
   $$\begin{array}{rl} 365 & \text{December 31} \\ -274 & \text{October 1} \\ \hline 91 & \text{days} \\ +\ 14 & \text{January 14} \\ \hline 105 & \text{days} \end{array}$$

   b.
   $$\begin{array}{rl} 365 & \text{December 31} \\ -294 & \text{October 21} \\ \hline 71 & \text{days} \end{array}$$

   f.
   $$\begin{array}{rl} 365 & \text{December 31} \\ -267 & \text{September 24} \\ \hline 98 & \text{days} \\ +\ 50 & \text{February 19} \\ \hline 148 & \text{days} \end{array}$$

   c.
   $$\begin{array}{rl} 210 & \text{July 29} \\ -\ 62 & \text{March 3} \\ \hline 148 & \text{days} \end{array}$$

   g.
   $$\begin{array}{rl} 293 & \text{October 20} \\ -239 & \text{August 27} \\ \hline 54 & \text{days} \end{array}$$

   d.
   $$\begin{array}{rl} 365 & \text{December 31} \\ -319 & \text{November 15} \\ \hline 46 & \text{days} \\ +\ 36 & \text{February 5} \\ \hline 82 & \text{days} \end{array}$$

   h.
   $$\begin{array}{rl} 365 & \text{December 31} \\ -362 & \text{December 28} \\ \hline 3 & \text{days} \\ +\ 61 & \text{March 2} \\ \hline 64 & \text{days} \end{array}$$

2.
   $$\begin{array}{rl} 125 & \text{May 5} \\ -\ 40 & \text{February 9} \\ \hline 85 & \text{days} \end{array}$$

   $600 \times 0.12 \times \frac{17}{73} = \$16.77$ interest
   $600 + \$16.77 = \$616.77$ amount paid

3.   365 December 31
     −277 October 4
      88 days
     +   8 January 8
      96 days

$2,500 × 0.15 × $\frac{96}{365}$ = $98.63   interest
$2,500 + $98.63 = $2,598.63   amount paid

Review 46, page 250

1. a. 3.75 = 375%   f. May 18
    b. $\frac{4}{5}$ = 80%   g.   185 July 4
    c. $30 ÷ $250 = 12%   −134 May 14
    d. 0.0125 × $84 = $1.05   51 days
    e. November 30

2.   264 September 21
      −195 July 14
       69 days

    $3,200 × 0.11 × $\frac{69}{365}$ = $66.54   interest
    $3,200 + $66.54 = $3,266.54   amount paid

3. ($129 × 4) ÷ $4,300 = 12%

4. a. (23,000 − 21,000) = 2,000   estimated difference
        2,000 ÷ 20,000 = 10%   estimated percent of increase
    b. (23,205 − 21,000) ÷ 21,000 = 10.5%   increase

5. July 3 due date
    $500 × 0.09 × $\frac{1}{6}$ = $7.50   banker's interest
    $500 + $7.50 = $507.50   amount due

6. 14 oz ÷ 16 oz = 0.875   pound
    $0.77 ÷ 0.875 = $0.88   per pound for Vigor

    $1\frac{1}{8}$ = 1.125   pounds
    $1.08 ÷ 1.125 = $0.96   per pound for Wakup
    $0.96 − $0.88 = $0.08   less

7. (25 m × 50 m) − 100 m² = 1 150 m²
    1 150 m² ÷ 350 m² = 3.29 or 4 bags

8.
Ken Van
Reconciliation Statement
July 1, 19 --

Check register balance	$333.25	Bank statement balance	$456.70
Deduct:		Deduct:	
Service charge	− 1.75	Outstanding checks	
	$331.50	#678 $56.00	
		#682 23.00	
		#683 44.75	− 123.75
Add:			
Interest earned	+ 1.45		
Correct check register balance	$332.95	Available bank balance	$332.95

Section 47. Discounted Notes

Exercise 1, page 251

1. **a.** $\$2,000 \times 0.09 \times \frac{1}{6} = \$30$ discount
       $\$2,000 - \$30 = \$1,970$ proceeds due July 14
    b. $\$5,900 \times 0.15 \times \frac{1}{4} = \$221.25$ discount
       $\$5,900 - \$221.25 = \$5,678.75$ proceeds due December 3
    c. $\$9,000 \times 0.10 \times \frac{1}{3} = \$300$ discount
       $\$9,000 - \$300 = \$8,700$ proceeds due June 22
    d. $\$12,000 \times 0.12 \times \frac{1}{2} = \$720$ discount
       $\$12,000 - \$720 = \$11,280$ proceeds due September 6
    e. $\$500 \times 0.08 \times \frac{1}{12} = \$3.33$ discount
       $\$500 - \$3.33 = \$496.67$ proceeds due January 15

2. **a.** $\$500 \times 0.13 \times \frac{1}{4} = \$16.25$ discount
       $\$500 - \$16.25 = \$483.75$ proceeds
    b. July 6   due date
    c. $\$500$ amount due at maturity

3. **a.** $\$900 \times 0.18 \times \frac{1}{6} = \$27$ discount
       $\$900 - \$27 = \$873$ proceeds
    b. August 5   due date
    c. $\$900$ amount due at maturity

4. **a.** $\$1,000 \times 0.10 \times \frac{1}{4} = \$25$ estimated bank discount
    b. $\$995 \times 0.10 \times \frac{1}{4} = \$24.88$ discount
       $\$995 - \$24.88 = \$970.12$ proceeds
    c. October 22   due date

Exercise 2, page 252

1. **a.** $\$2,400 \times 0.12 \times \frac{1}{6} = \$48$ discount
       $\$2,400 - \$48 = \$2,352$ proceeds
    b. $(\$48 \times 6) \div \$2,352 = 12.2\%$ real rate of interest

2. **a.** $\$10,000 \times 0.15 \times \frac{1}{4} = \$375$ discount
    b. $\$10,000 - \$375 = \$9,625$ proceeds
    c. $(\$375 \times 4) \div \$9,625 = 15.6\%$ real rate of interest

3. **a.** $\$4,500 \times 0.11 \times \frac{1}{3} = \$165$ discount
    b. $\$4,500 - \$165 = \$4,335$ proceeds
    c. $(\$165 \times 3) \div \$4,335 = 11.4\%$ real rate of interest

4. **a.** $\$4,200 \times 0.13 \times \frac{1}{2} = \$273$ discount
    b. $\$4,200 - \$273 = \$3,927$ proceeds
    c. $\$4,200$
    d. $(\$273 \times 2) \div \$3,927 = 13.9\%$ real rate of interest

Review 47, page 253

2. **a.** $4 = 400\%$
    b. $0.045 \times \$328 = \$14.76$
    c. $\$4.80 \div \$14.40 = 33\frac{1}{3}\%$
    d. $\$2,250 \div \$750 = 300\%$
    e. $8\frac{1}{4}\% = 0.0825$
    f. $4\,108 \text{ mL} = 4.108 \text{ L}$

3. **a.** February 8   due date
    b. $1,800 \times 0.12 \times \frac{1}{3} = 72 total interest paid
    c. $1,800 + $72 = $1,872$ amount due at maturity

4. $1,350 \times 0.09 \times 1\frac{1}{2} = 182.25 total amount of interest

5. ($32.40 \times 4) \div $1,440 = 9\%$ rate of interest

6. $15,150 - $12,500 = $2,650$ sales in excess of $12,500
    $950 + ($15,150 \times 0.04) + ($2,650 \times 0.01) = $1,582.50$ total earnings

7. 7.50×2.75 m $= 20.63 cost of fabric

8. **a.** $325 \times 0.12 \times \frac{1}{4} = 9.75 discount
    $325 - $9.75 = 315.25 proceeds
    b. June 25   due date
    c. $325   amount paid at maturity

9. **a.** $3,000 \times 0.08 \times \frac{1}{3} = 80 discount
    $3,000 - $80 = $2,920$ proceeds
    b. ($80 \times 3) \div $2,920 = 8.2\%$ real rate of interest

‡10. $4,504 \div 0.04 = $112,600$ selling price of house and lot

Section 48.   Installment Loans

Exercise 1, page 255

1. **a.**

End of Month	Unpaid Balance	Finance Charge 1% of Unpaid Balance	Payment on Principal	Total Payment
1	$500.00	$ 5.00	$100	$105.00
2	400.00	4.00	100	104.00
3	300.00	3.00	100	103.00
4	200.00	2.00	100	102.00
5	100.00	1.00	100	101.00
Totals		$15.00	$500	$515.00

b.

End of Month	Unpaid Balance	Finance Charge 1.5% of Unpaid Balance	Payment on Principal	Total Payment
1	$100.00	$1.50	$ 10	$ 11.50
2	90.00	1.35	10	11.35
3	80.00	1.20	10	11.20
4	70.00	1.05	10	11.05
5	60.00	0.90	10	10.90
6	50.00	0.75	10	10.75
7	40.00	0.60	10	10.60
8	30.00	0.45	10	10.45
9	20.00	0.30	10	10.30
10	10.00	0.15	10	10.15
Totals		$8.25	$100	$108.25

c.

End of Month	Unpaid Balance	Finance Charge $\frac{3}{4}\%$ of Unpaid Balance	Payment on Principal	Total Payment
1	$480	$ 3.60	$ 80	$ 83.60
2	400	3.00	80	83.00
3	320	2.40	80	82.40
4	240	1.80	80	81.80
5	160	1.20	80	81.20
6	80	0.60	80	80.60
Totals		$12.60	$480	$492.60

d.

End of Month	Unpaid Balance	Finance Charge 1.5% of Unpaid Balance	Payment on Principal	Total Payment
1	$800	$12.00	$ 80	$ 92.00
2	720	10.80	80	90.80
3	640	9.60	80	89.60
4	560	8.40	80	88.40
5	480	7.20	80	87.20
6	400	6.00	80	86.00
7	320	4.80	80	84.80
8	240	3.60	80	83.60
9	160	2.40	80	82.40
10	80	1.20	80	81.20
Totals		$66.00	$800	$866.00

e.

End of Month	Unpaid Balance	Finance Charge $\frac{4}{5}\%$ of Unpaid Balance	Payment on Principal	Total Payment
1	$350	$ 2.80	$ 50	$ 52.80
2	300	2.40	50	52.40
3	250	2.00	50	52.00
4	200	1.60	50	51.60
5	150	1.20	50	51.20
6	100	0.80	50	50.80
7	50	0.40	50	50.40
Totals		$11.20	$350	$361.20

2. $720 \div 6 = \$120$ monthly payment
$120 + (\$720 \times 0.0125) = \$129.00$
$120 + (\$600 \times 0.0125) = \ \ 127.50$
$120 + (\$480 \times 0.0125) = \ \ 126.00$
$120 + (\$360 \times 0.0125) = \ \ 124.50$
$120 + (\$240 \times 0.0125) = \ \ 123.00$
$120 + (\$120 \times 0.0125) = \ \ \underline{121.50}$
$751.50 total payments
$751.50 - \$720 = \$31.50$ total finance charge

3. **a.** $100 + ($600 \times 0.0175) = 110.50
        $100 + ($500 \times 0.0175) = 108.75$
        $100 + ($400 \times 0.0175) = 107.00$
        $100 + ($300 \times 0.0175) = 105.25$
        $100 + ($200 \times 0.0175) = 103.50$
        $100 + ($100 \times 0.0175) = \underline{101.75}$
                                     636.75 total payments
        $636.75 - $600.00 = 36.75 total finance charge
    b. $636.75   total amount paid to finance company

Exercise 2, page 256

1. **a.** $12 \times $59.00 = 708 total paid
        $708 - $600 = 108 finance charge
    b. $24 \times $118.00 = $2,832$ total paid
        $2,832 - $2,000 = 832 finance charge
    c. $24 \times $28.75 = 690 total paid
        $690 - $500 = 190 finance charge
    d. $18 \times $56 = $1,008$ total paid
        $1,008 - $800 = 208 finance charge
    e. $6 \times $90.80 = 544.80 total paid
        $544.80 - $500 = 44.80 finance charge

2. $9 \times $96.44 = 867.96 total paid
    $867.96 - $750 = 117.96 finance charge

3. $24 \times $141.66 = $3,399.84$ total paid
    $3,399.84 - $2,500 = 899.84 finance charge

4. **a.** $12 \times $100 = $1,200$ estimated amount paid
    b. $12 \times $98.50 = $1,182$ total amount paid
    c. $1,182 - $1,000 = 182 finance charge

5. **a.** $24 \times $88.75 = $2,130$ total amount paid
    b. $2,130 - $1,500 = 630 finance charge

6. **a.** $6 \times $83.60 = 501.60 total amount paid
    b. $501.60 - $480 = 21.60 finance charge

Review 48, page 257

2. **a.** $1.35 \times $95 = 128.25 **d.** 74
    b. $0.125 \times $18.80 = 2.35 **e.** $65.34 \div 1.35 = 48.40
    c. $95\frac{1}{2}\% = 0.955$

3. $6 \times $72.40 = 434.40 total amount paid
    $434.40 - $400 = 34.40 finance charge

4. $154,500 + ($154,500 \times 0.20) = $185,400$ expected sales

5. $(7\frac{1}{2}$ hours per day $\times 5) - 2\frac{1}{2}$ hours $= 35$ total hours
    $35 \times $8.75 = 306.25 gross earnings

6. $5,000 \times 0.15 \times \frac{1}{4} = 187.50 discount
    $5,000 - $187.50 = $4,812.50$ proceeds

7. $3,000 \times 0.11 \times \frac{1}{2} = 165 interest
    $3,000 - $165 = $2,835$ proceeds
    $($165 \times 2) \div $2,835 = 11.6\%$ real rate of interest

‡8. $1,200 ÷ 0.06 = $20,000   worth of goods must be sold

‡9. $110,000 ÷ 0.94 = $117,021.27, or $118,000   minimum price

Section 49. More Installment Loans

Exercise 1, page 259

1. $840 + ($840 × 0.12 × 1) = $940.80   total payments
    $940.80 ÷ 12 = $78.40   monthly payment

2. $600 + ($600 × 0.14 × $\frac{5}{6}$) = $670   total payments
    $670 ÷ 10 = $67   monthly payment

3. $300 + ($300 × 0.08 × $\frac{1}{2}$) = $312   total payments
    $312 ÷ 6 = $52   monthly payment

4. $900 + ($900 × 0.09 × $\frac{3}{4}$) = $960.75   total payments
    $960.75 ÷ 9 = $106.75   monthly payment

5. a. $1,200 × 0.12 × 1 = $144   finance charge
    b. $1,200 + $144 = $1,344   total payments
    c. $1,344 ÷ 12 = $112   monthly payment

Exercise 2, page 259

1. a. ($3,240 × 0.12 × 1.5) + $16.20 = $599.40   total finance charge
    b. ($3,240 + $599.40) ÷ 18 = $213.30   monthly payment

2. a. ($700 × 0.10 × 1) + $7.00 = $77   total finance charge
    b. ($700 × $77) ÷ 12 = $64.75   monthly payment

3. a. ($3,000 × 0.10 × $\frac{1}{2}$) + $24 = $174   estimated total finance charge
    b. ($3,000 × 0.11 × $\frac{1}{2}$) + $24 = $189   total finance charge
    c. ($3,000 + $189) ÷ 6 = $531.50   monthly payment

Exercise 3, page 261

1. a. $\frac{\$78.00 \times 100}{\$800} = \$9.75$ c. $\frac{\$66.00 \times 100}{\$500} = \$13.20$ e. $\frac{\$50.00 \times 100}{\$400} = \$12.50$
    b. $\frac{\$41.00 \times 100}{\$250} = \$16.40$ d. $\frac{\$106.10 \times 100}{\$910} = \$11.66$ f. $\frac{\$89.60 \times 100}{\$760} = \$11.79$

2. a. 15 × $268.73 = $4,030.95   total amount paid
        $4,030.95 − $3,500 = $530.95   finance charge
    b. $3,500   amount financed
    c. $\frac{\$530.95 \times 100}{\$3,500} = \$15.17$ finance charge per $100

3. a. 12 × $220.50 = $2,646   total amount paid
        $2,646 − $2,400 = $246   finance charge
    b. $2,400   amount financed
    c. $\frac{\$246 \times 100}{\$2,400} = \$10.25$ finance charge per $100

Exercise 4, page 262

1. a. $13\frac{1}{2}$%   c. 29%   e. 15%   g. 13%   i. 13%
    b. 15%   d. 28%   f. $28\frac{1}{4}$%   h. $13\frac{1}{4}$%   j. 27%

2. a. $(12 \times \$116) - \$1,300 = \$92$ finance charge
  b. $\frac{\$92 \times 100}{\$1,300} = \$7.08$ finance charge per $100
  c. $12\frac{3}{4}\%$ annual percentage rate

3. a. $(9 \times \$47) - \$400 = \$23$ finance charge
  b. $\frac{\$23 \times 100}{\$400} = \$5.75$ finance charge per $100
  c. $13\frac{1}{2}\%$ annual percentage rate

4. $(15 \times \$116.40) - \$1,600 = \$146$ finance charge
  $\frac{\$146 \times 100}{\$1,600} = \$9.13$ finance charge per $100
  $13\frac{1}{4}\%$ annual percentage rate

Review 49, page 262

2. a. $2.65 \times \$80 = \$212$ **d.** $\$1,410 \times 0.18 \times \frac{1}{12} = \$21.15$
  b. $0.125 \times \$32 = \$4$ **e.** $0.375 \times 380 \text{ kg} = 142.5 \text{ kg}$
  c. $45\frac{1}{4}\% = 0.4525$

3. $(12 \times \$63.50) - \$700 = \$62$ finance charge

4. a. $\frac{\$32 \times 100}{\$400} = \$8$ finance charge per $100
  b. $14\frac{1}{2}\%$ annual percentage rate

5. a. August 24
  b. $\$700 \times 0.14 \times \frac{1}{5} = \$19.60$ interest
  $\$700 + \$19.60 = \$719.60$ amount due at maturity

Section 50. Installment Buying

Exercise 1, page 265

1. $\$67.50 \times 24 = \$1,620$ total payments
  a. $\$1,620 + \$150 = \$1,770$ installment price
  b. $\$1,770 - \$1,500 = \$270$ finance charge

2. $\$115 \times 20 = \$2,300$ total payments
  a. $\$2,300 + \$500 = \$2,800$ installment price
  b. $\$2,800 - \$2,500 = \$300$ finance charge

3. $\$26.50 \times 9 = \$238.50$ total payments
  a. $\$238.50 + \$25 = \$263.50$ installment price
  b. $\$263.50 - \$250 = \$13.50$ finance charge

4. $\$118.25 \times 20 = \$2,365$ total payments
  a. $\$2,365 + \$250 = \$2,615$ installment price
  b. $\$2,615 - \$2,400 = \$215$ finance charge

5. $\$26.50 \times 12 = \$318$ total payments
  a. $\$318 + \$50 = \$368$ installment price
  b. $\$368 - \$350 = \$18$ finance charge

6. a. $\$100 \times 18 = \$1,800$ estimated total payments
  b. $(\$1,800 + \$180) - \$1,800 = \$180$ estimated finance charge
  c. $\$100.80 \times 18 = \$1,814.40$ total payments
  $\$1,814.40 + \$180 = \$1,994.40$ installment price
  $\$1,994.40 - \$1,800 = \$194.40$ finance charge

Exercise 2, page 266

1. **a.** ($455 − $50) ÷ $33.75 = 12   months
    b. ($611 − $50) ÷ 20 = $28.05   a month
    c. ($250 − $75) ÷ $8.75 = 20   weeks
    d. ($1,500 − $200) ÷ 20 = $65   a month

2. ($1,690 − $250) ÷ $120 = 12   months

3. ($2,300 − $500) ÷ 18 = $100   a month

Exercise 3, page 266

1. **a.** ($200 × 30) + $1,000 = $7,000   installment price
    $7,000 − $5,800 = $1,200   finance charge
    $1,200 ÷ $5,800 = 20.7%   installment price greater than cash price
    b. ($18.15 × 36) + $60 = $713.40   installment price
    $713.40 − $600 = $113.40   finance charge
    $113.40 ÷ $600 = 18.9%   installment price greater than cash price
    c. ($29.70 × 12) + $36 = $392.40   installment price
    $392.40 − $360 = $32.40   finance charge
    $32.40 ÷ $360 = 9%   installment price greater than cash price
    d. ($42.50 × 10) + $50 = $475   installment price
    $475 − $425 = $50   finance charge
    $50 ÷ $425 = 11.8%   installment price greater than cash price
    e. ($39 × 6) + $25 = $259   installment price
    $259 − $250 = $9   finance charge
    $9 ÷ $250 = 3.6%   installment price greater than cash price

2. ($5.76 × 5) + $3 = $31.80   installment price
    $31.80 − $30 = $1.80   finance charge
    $1.80 ÷ $30 = 6%   installment price greater than cash price

3. ($11.50 × 12) + $30 = $168   installment price
    $168 − $150 = $18   finance charge
    $18 ÷ $150 = 12%   installment price greater than cash price

Exercise 4, page 268

1. **a.** ($48.50 × 30) = $1,455   installment price
    $1,455 − $1,200 = $255   finance charge
    $\frac{\$255 \times 100}{\$1,200}$ = $21.25   finance charge per $100
    15.5%   annual percentage rate
    b. ($12.25 × 36) = $441   installment price
    $441 − $350 = $91   finance charge
    $\frac{\$91 \times 100}{\$350}$ = $26   finance charge per $100
    15.75%   annual percentage rate
    c. ($126 × 12) + $100 = $1,612   installment price
    $1,612 − $1,500 = $112   finance charge
    $1,500 − $100 = $1,400   amount financed
    $\frac{\$112 \times 100}{\$1,400}$ = $8   finance charge per $100
    14.5%   annual percentage rate
    d. ($75.60 × 6) + $48 = $501.60   installment price
    $501.60 − $480 = $21.60   finance charge
    $480 − $48 = $432   amount financed
    $\frac{\$21.60 \times 100}{\$432}$ = $5   finance charge per $100
    17%   annual percentage rate

    e. ($44.80 × 18) + $80 = $886.40   installment price
$886.40 − $800 = $86.40   finance charge
$800 − $80 = $720   amount financed
$\frac{\$86.40 \times 100}{\$720} = \$12$ finance charge per $100
14.75%   annual percentage rate

2. ($80 × 30) + $500 = $2,900   installment price
$2,900 − $2,500 = $400   finance charge
$2,500 − $500 = $2,000   amount financed
$\frac{\$400 \times 100}{\$2,000} = \$20$ finance charge per $100
14.75%   annual percentage rate

3. ($12.25 × 6) + $5 = $78.50   installment price
$78.50 − $75 = $3.50   finance charge
$75 − $5 = $70   amount financed
$\frac{\$3.50 \times 100}{\$70} = \$5$ finance charge per $100
17%   annual percentage rate

4. ($30.77 × 12) + $55 = $424.24   installment price
$424.24 − $395 = $29.24   finance charge
$395 − $55 = $340   amount financed
$\frac{\$29.24 \times 100}{\$340} = \$8.60$ finance charge per $100
15.5%   annual percentage rate

Review 50, page 268

2. **a.** $350\frac{1}{2}\% = 3.505$ **d.** $360.05 \times 4.3 = 1,548.215$
      b. $(\$4.90 − \$4.20) \div \$4.20 = 16\frac{2}{3}\%$ **e.** 8 000 m + 625 m = 8 625 m
      c. $\$88 + (\frac{5}{8} \times \$88) = \$143$

3. ($9.80 × 12) + $12 = $129.60   installment price
($129.60 − $120) ÷ $120 = 8%   installment price exceeds cash price

4. ($790 − $90) ÷ $50 = 14   months

5. $501.60 − $420 = $81.60   finance charge
$\frac{\$81.60 \times 100}{\$420} = \$19.43$ finance charge per $100
14.25%   annual percentage rate

Eve Day
Reconciliation Statement
May 31, 19--

6.

Check register balance	$339.11	Bank statement balance		$394.62
Deduct:		Deduct:		
Service charge	− 1.74	Outstanding checks:		
		#24	$41.32	
		#25	3.18	
		#27	12.75	− 57.25
Correct check register balance	$337.37	Available bank balance		$337.37

7. $\frac{3}{5} \times 45 = 27$ pounds peanuts
$\frac{2}{5} \times 45 = 18$ pounds cashews

Section 51.   Credit Cards

Exercise 1, page 270

1. **a.** $32,800,000 × 0.04 = $1,312,000   paid to credit card company
    b. $32,800,000 − $1,312,000 = $31,488,000   net receipts

2. $2,700,500 × 0.05 = $135,025   paid to National
    $2,700,500 − $135,025 = $2,565,475   received by Bolin

3. $385,000 × 0.05 = $19,250   paid to AmeriCard
    $268,000 × 0.03 = $8,040   paid to UniCard
    $19,250 + $8,040 = $27,290   paid to credit card companies
    ($385,000 + $268,000) − $27,290 = $625,710   net receipts

4. **a.** $500,000 × 0.06 = $30,000   paid to General card company
    $980,000 − $30,000 = $950,000   net sales receipts
    b. $950,000 − $740,000 = $210,000   increase using card

Exercise 2, page 271

1. $275 − ($275 × 0.04) = $264   by paying cash

2. **a.** $480 + ($480 × 0.04) = $499.20   credit card price
    b. $499.20 − $480 = $19.20   saved by paying cash

3. **a.** $800 × 0.03 = $24   estimated cash discount
    b. $785 − $24 = $761   estimated cash price
    c. $785 − ($785 × 0.03) = $761.45   cash price
    d. $785 − $761.45 = $23.55   saved by paying cash

4. **a.** $3,500 + ($3,500 × 0.035) = $3,622.50   credit card price
    b. $3,622.50 − $3,500 = $122.50   saved by paying cash

Exercise 3, page 272

1. $460 × 0.015 = $6.90   finance charge

2. $25 + (90 × $0.07) = $31.30   cost of card last year

3. $20 + ($275 × 0.0165) = $24.54   total of monthly statement

4. $25 + ($40 × 0.18) = $32.20   yearly membership fees and finance charges
    for Ivy
    $15 + ($40 × 0.20) = $23   yearly membership fees and finance charges
    for Belinda
    $32.20 − $23 = $9.20   more paid by Ivy

Exercise 4, page 273

1. $300 × 0.000628 × 20 = $3.77   finance charge

2. $700 × 0.000453 × 35 = $11.10   finance charge

3. $500 × 0.000512 × 45 = $11.52   finance charge

4. $200 × 0.000722 × 60 = $8.66   finance charge

Review 51, page 273

2. **a.** $8\frac{1}{2} + 1\frac{3}{8} = 9\frac{7}{8}$
   b. 4 500 cm ÷ 2.4 cm = 1 875 cm
   c. August 3

3. $47,800 − ($47,800 × 0.035) = $46,127   net amount received from Premier

4. $22 + ($450 × 0.013) = $27.85   membership fee and finance charge
   $450 + $27.85 = $477.85   total of May statement

5. $25.40 × 18 = $472.20   total payment
   $472.20 − $360 = $97.20   finance charge

6. ($450 − $100) ÷ $14 = 25   months

UNIT 8 • SAVING MONEY

Section 52. Passbook Savings Accounts

Exercise 1, page 276

1.

Date	Withdrawal	Deposit	Interest	Balance
19 --				
Apr. 2		600.00		600.00
17		400.00		1,000.00
May 7	200.00			800.00
June 21	300.00			500.00
July 1			6.82	506.82

2.

Date	Withdrawal	Deposit	Interest	Balance
19 --				
Jan. 2		700.00		700.00
Apr. 1			9.35	709.35
25		400.00		1,109.35
May 4	170.00			939.35
July 2			10.46	949.81

3.

Date	Withdrawal	Deposit	Interest	Balance
19 --				
Jan. 2		984.31		984.31
Apr. 1			14.29	998.60
9	250.00			748.60
May 30	97.00			651.60
July 1			9.86	661.46
Oct. 1			10.01	671.47

Exercise 2, page 277

1. **a.** $300 × 0.05 × $\frac{1}{4}$ = $3.75   **d.** $628.29 × 0.07 × $\frac{1}{4}$ = $11
   b. $750 × 0.06 × $\frac{1}{4}$ = $11.25   **e.** $217.66 × 0.065 × $\frac{1}{4}$ = $3.54
   c. $400 × 0.055 × $\frac{1}{4}$ = $5.50   **f.** $1,400 × 0.0575 × $\frac{1}{4}$ = $20.13

2. **a.** $700 \times 0.05 \times \frac{1}{2} = \$17.50$ **d.** $727 \times 0.055 \times \frac{1}{2} = \$19.99$

    b. $900 \times 0.065 \times \frac{1}{2} = \$29.25$ **e.** $302.95 \times 0.07 \times \frac{1}{2} = \$10.60$

    c. $600 \times 0.0525 \times \frac{1}{2} = \$15.75$ **f.** $612.74 \times 0.0575 \times \frac{1}{2} = \$17.62$

Exercise 3, page 279

1. **a.**

Date	Withdrawal	Deposit	Interest	Balance
19 --				
Jan. 2		840.00		840.00
Apr. 1			12.60	852.60
July 1			12.79	865.39
Oct. 1			12.98	878.37

    b. $12.60 + \$12.79 + \$12.98 = \$38.37$ interest

2.

Date	Withdrawal	Deposit	Interest	Balance
19 --				
Apr. 1		700.00		700.00
July 1			11.38	711.38
Oct. 1			11.56	722.94
Jan. 2			11.75	734.69

3. $1,400 \times 0.05 = \$70$ estimated interest

Date	Withdrawal	Deposit	Interest	Balance
19 --				
July 1		1,400.00		1,400.00
Oct. 1			17.50	1,417.50
19 --				
Jan. 2			17.72	1,435.22
Apr. 1			17.94	1,453.16
July 1			18.16	1,471.32

$17.50 + \$17.72 + \$17.94 + \$18.16 = \$71.32$ actual interest

4.

Date	Withdrawal	Deposit	Interest	Balance
19 --				
Jan. 2		510.00		510.00
July 1			17.85	527.85
19 --				
Jan. 2			18.47	546.32

$17.85 + \$18.47 = \$36.32$ interest

5.

	Date	Withdrawal	Deposit	Interest	Balance
	19 --				
	Jan. 2		900.00		900.00
a.	July 1			27.00	927.00
	19 --				
b.	Jan. 2			27.81	954.81

Exercise 4, page 279

1.

Date	Withdrawal	Deposit	Interest	Balance
19 --				
Apr. 1		400.00		400.00
July 1			6.00	406.00
July 1		300.00		706.00
Oct. 1			10.59	716.59

2.

Date	Withdrawal	Deposit	Interest	Balance
19 --				
Jan. 2		600.00		600.00
Apr. 1			9.75	609.75
Apr. 1		700.00		1,309.75
July 1			21.28	1,331.03

3.

Date	Withdrawal	Deposit	Interest	Balance
19 --				
Apr. 1		800.00		800.00
July 1			14.00	814.00
July 1	270.00			544.00
Oct. 1			9.52	553.52

4.

Date	Withdrawal	Deposit	Interest	Balance
19 --				
Oct. 1		400.00		400.00
19 --				
Jan. 2			5.00	405.00
Jan. 2	60.00			345.00
Apr. 1			4.31	349.31

Exercise 5, page 281

1.

Date	Withdrawal	Deposit	Interest	Balance
19 --				
July 1				682.00
Aug. 17	170.00			512.00
Sep. 12		200.00		712.00
Oct. 1			6.40	718.40

2.

Date	Withdrawal	Deposit	Interest	Balance
19 --				
Apr. 1		900.00		900.00
May 6	210.00			690.00
June 17	60.00			630.00
July 1			9.45	639.45

3.

Date	Withdrawal	Deposit	Interest	Balance
19 --				
July 1				270.00
Nov. 5		140.00		410.00
Dec. 9	220.00			190.00
Jan. 2			5.23	195.23

4.

Date	Withdrawal	Deposit	Interest	Balance
19 --				
Jan. 2				605.00
Jan. 17		115.00		720.00
Feb. 28	180.00			540.00
Apr. 1			9.45	549.45
Apr. 12		70.00		619.45
June 9	90.00			529.45
June 25		40.00		569.45
July 1			9.27	578.72

   a. $9.45 + $9.27 = $18.72   total interest
   b. $578.72

Review 52, page 281

2. **a.** ($120 − $30) ÷ $120 = 75%
     b. $145.20 + ($\frac{1}{3}$ × $145.20) = $193.60
     c. $83\frac{1}{4}$% = 0.8325
     d. $600 × 0.07 × $\frac{1}{3}$ = $14
   ‡**e.** 7.5% = $\frac{3}{40}$

3.

Date	Withdrawal	Deposit	Interest	Balance
19 --				
Jan. 2		760.00		760.00
Apr. 1			9.50	769.50
July 1			9.62	779.12

4. $14,034 − $2,800 = $11,234   balance to be paid
    $11,234 + $1,582 = $12,816   total payments
    $12,816 ÷ 36 = $356   amount of each monthly payment

5. (12 × $40.67) − $420 = $68.04   finance charge
    ($68.04 × 100) ÷ $420 = $16.20   finance charge per $100

6.

Date	Withdrawal	Deposit	Interest	Balance
19 --				
Apr. 1		680.00		680.00
May 15	190.00			490.00
July 1			8.58	498.58

Section 53. Compound Interest

Exercise 1, page 285

1. 1,000 × $1.215506 = $1,215.51   compound amount
    $1,215.51 − $1,000 = $215.51   compound interest

2. 700 × $2.580426 = $1,806.30   compound amount
    $1,806.30 − $700 = $1,106.30   compound interest

3. 800 × $1.073544 = $858.84   compound amount
    $858.84 − $800 = $58.84   compound interest

4. 600 × $1.025313 = $615.19   compound amount
    $615.19 − $600 = $15.19   compound interest

5. $400 \times \$1.713824 = \$685.53$ compound amount
$\$685.53 - \$400 = \$285.53$ compound interest

6. $900 \times \$1.020199 = \$918.18$ compound amount
$\$918.18 - \$900 = \$18.18$ compound interest

Exercise 2, page 285

1. $1,000 \times \$1.195618 = \$1,195.62$ compound amount
$\$1,195.62 - \$1,000 = \$195.62$ compound interest

2. $600 \times \$1.171659 = \$703$ compound amount
$\$703 - \$600 = \$103$ compound interest

3. $2,500 \times \$1.093443 = \$2,733.61$ compound amount
$\$2,733.61 - \$2,500 = \$233.61$ compound interest

4. $800 \times \$1.790848 = \$1,432.68$ compound amount
$\$1,432.68 - \$800 = \$632.68$ compound interest

Exercise 3, page 286

1. $1,000 \times \$1.082432 = \$1,082.43$ compound amount
$\$1,082.43 - \$1,000 = \$82.43$ interest earned
$\$82.43 \div \$1,000 = 0.08243$, or 8.24%   effective rate of interest

2. $800 \times \$1.061364 = \$849.09$ compound amount
$\$849.09 - \$800 = \$49.09$ interest earned
$\$49.09 \div \$800 = 0.06136$, or 6.14%   effective rate of interest

3. $1,400 \times \$1.1025 = \$1,543.50$ compound amount
$\$1,543.50 - \$1,400 = \$143.50$ interest earned
$\$143.50 \div \$1,400 = 0.1025$, or 10.25%   effective rate of interest

4. $1,810 \times \$1.1449 = \$2,072.27$ compound amount
$\$2,072.27 - \$1,810 = \$262.27$ interest earned
$\$262.27 \div \$1,810 = 0.1449$, or 14.49%   effective rate of interest

5. $0.082 \times \$2,000 \times 1 = \$164$ interest earned at Coles Savings Bank
$\$164 \div \$2,000 = 0.082$, or 8.2%   effective rate of interest paid by Coles
$2,000 \times 1.084482 = \$2,168.96$ compound amount
$\$2,168.96 - \$2,000 = \$168.96$ interest earned at Drew Savings Bank
$\$168.96 \div \$2,000 = 0.08448$, or 8.45%   effective rate of interest paid by Drew
Higher effective rate paid by Drew; 8.45%

Review 53, page 286

1. **a.** $\frac{2}{5} \times \$170 = \$68$
   b. $0.015 \times \$3,200 = \$48$
   c. $\$490 \div \$560 = 87\frac{1}{2}\%$
   d. $\$32.80 + (0.6 \times \$32.80) = \$52.48$
   e. $(\$1.50 - \$1.20) \div \$1.20 = 25\%$
   f. $3.6 \text{ L} \times \$1.28 = \$4.61$

2. May 10 to July 29 = 80 days
    $\$600 \times 0.14 \times \frac{2}{9} = \$18.67$ interest
    $\$600 + \$18.67 = \$618.67$ amount paid

3. $(\$245,000 \times 0.07) + \$8,400 = \$25,550$ selling expenses
    $\$245,000 - \$25,550 = \$219,450$ net proceeds to company

4.

Date	Withdrawal	Deposit	Interest	Balance
19 --				
July 1		4,000.00		4,000.00
Oct. 1			70.00	4,070.00
19 --				
Jan. 2			71.23	4,141.23

5. $0.05 \times (\$8,300 - \$4,000) = \$215$ commission
    $0.02 \times (\$8,300 - \$7,000) = \$26$ commission
    $\$900 + \$215 + \$26 = \$1,141$ total of salary and commission

6. a. $6 \times \$200 = \$1,200$ installment price
        $\$1,200 - \$1,000 = \$200$ finance charge
        $(\$200 \times 100) \div \$1,000 = \$20$ estimated finance charge per $100
    b. $6 \times \$198 = \$1,188$ installment price
        $\$1,188 - \$1,000 = \$188$ finance charge
        $(\$188 \times 100) \div \$1,000 = \$18.80$ finance charge per $100

‡7. $\$325 - \$210 = \$115$ earned from commission
    $\$115 \div (\$4,800 - \$2,500) = 5\%$ rate of commission

Section 54. Special Savings Plans

Exercise 1, page 288

1. $\$708 - \$490.91 = \$217.09$ more interest

2. a. $\$3,000 \times 0.095 \times \frac{1}{4} = \$71.25$ interest on the certificate
    b. $\$71.25 - \$41.25 = \$30$ more interest

3. $\$2,000 \times 0.12 \times \frac{1}{2} = \$120$ interest earned first 6 months
    $\$2,000 + \$120 = \$2,120$ amount to be invested second 6 months
    $\$2,120 \times 0.12 \times \frac{1}{2} = \$127.20$ interest earned second 6 months
    $\$120.00 + \$127.20 = \$247.20$ total interest earned

4. a. $\$12,000 \times 0.052 \times \frac{1}{4} = \$156$ interest first quarter
        $\$12,000 + \$156 = \$12,156$
        $\$12,156 \times 0.052 \times \frac{1}{4} = \$158.03$ interest second quarter
        $\$156 + \$158.03 = \$314.03$ interest for 6 months
    b. $\$522 - \$314.03 = \$207.97$ more interest

5. a. $\$18,000 \times 0.05 \times \frac{1}{4} = \$225$ interest first quarter
        $\$18,000 + \$225 = \$18,225$
        $\$18,225 \times 0.05 \times \frac{1}{4} = \$227.81$ interest second quarter
        $\$225 + \$227.81 = \$452.81$ interest for 6 months
    b. $\$1,125 - \$452.81 = \$672.19$ more interest

6. $\$4,000 \times 0.1225 = \$490$ interest earned from time deposit account
    $\$490 - \$235.02 = \$254.98$ more interest

7. $0.0875 \times \$7,000 = \$612.50$ interest on time deposit
$\$7,000 \times 0.055 \times \frac{1}{4} = \$96.25$ interest first quarter
$\$7,096.25 \times 0.055 \times \frac{1}{4} = \$97.57$ interest second quarter
$\$7,193.82 \times 0.055 \times \frac{1}{4} = \$98.92$ interest third quarter
$\$7,292.74 \times 0.055 \times \frac{1}{4} = \$100.28$ interest fourth quarter
$\$96.25 + \$97.57 + \$98.92 + \$100.28 = \$393.02$ compound interest on passbook savings
$\$612.50 - \$393.02 = \$219.48$ more interest

Exercise 2, page 289

1. **a.** $\$2,000 \times 0.07 \times \frac{1}{4} = \$35$ penalty
   b. $\$5,000 \times 0.07 \times \frac{1}{4} = \$87.50$ penalty

2. **a.** $\$900 \times 0.14 \times \frac{1}{2} = \$63$ penalty
   b. $\$3,000 \times 0.14 \times \frac{1}{2} = \$210$ penalty

3. **a.** $\$24,000 \times 0.09 \times \frac{1}{6} = \$360$ penalty
   b. $\$540 - \$360 = \$180$ net interest

4. $\$12,000 \times 0.11 \times \frac{3}{4} = \$990$ penalty
   $\$1,210 - \$990 = \$220$ net interest

5. **a.** $\$17,000 \times 0.1 = \$1,700$ estimated penalty
   b. $\$17,000 \times 0.095 = \$1,615$ penalty
   c. $\$1,615 - \$942 = \$673$ penalty greater

6. $\$4,000 \times 0.07 \times \frac{1}{2} = \$140$ penalty
   $\$4,000 - (\$140 - \$23.33) = \$3,883.33$ amount received

Exercise 3, page 290

1. **a.** $\$3,000 \times 0.081 \times \frac{1}{4} = \$60.75$ interest first three months
   b. $\$3,000 \times 0.079 \times \frac{1}{4} = \$59.25$ interest next three months

2. $\$8,400 \times 0.0757 \times \frac{1}{4} = \$158.97$ interest for quarter

3. $\$2,100 \times 0.0525 \times \frac{1}{4} = \$27.56$ interest for first quarter

Review 54, page 291

2. **a.** $(\$480 - \$320) \div \$320 = 50\%$ **d.** $5 \text{ g} \div 2 = 2.5 \text{ g}$
   b. $(\$1.20 - \$0.90) \div \$1.20 = 25\%$ **e.** $7 \text{ m} \times 5 \text{ m} = 35 \text{ m}^2$
   c. $\$7,200 \times 0.08 \times \frac{1}{3} = \$192$

3. $\$6,000 \times 0.08 = \$480$ interest on time deposit
   $\$6,000 \times 0.05 \times \frac{1}{2} = \$150$ interest for first 6 months
   $\$6,000 + \$150 = \$6,150$
   $\$6,150 \times 0.05 \times \frac{1}{2} = \$153.75$ interest for next 6 months
   $\$150 + \$153.75 = \$303.75$ compound interest on passbook savings
   $\$480 - \$303.75 = \$176.25$ more would be earned

4. $\$7,500 \times 0.1 \times \frac{1}{12} = \$62.50$ penalty
   $\$437 - \$62.50 = \$374.50$ net interest

UNIT 9 • INVESTING MONEY

Section 55.   Buying Bonds

Exercise 2, page 296

	a.	b.	c.
1.	$3 \times \$920 = \$2,760$	$7 \times \$890 = \$6,230$	$9 \times \$1,070 = \$9,630$
2.	$6 \times \$980 = \$5,880$	$5 \times \$950 = \$4,750$	$8 \times \$1,040 = \$8,320$
3.	$2 \times \$985 = \$1,970$	$6 \times \$922.50 = \$5,535$	$4 \times \$913.75 = \$3,655$
4.	$4 \times \$560 = \$2,240$	$8 \times \$450 = \$3,600$	$12 \times \$393.75 = \$4,725$

Exercise 3, page 297

1. **a.** $8 \times (0.85 \times \$1,000) = \$6,800$ market price of 8 bonds
$(8 \times \$8) + \$6,800 = \$6,864$ total investment

b. $5 \times (0.92 \times \$1,000) = \$4,600$ market price of 5 bonds
$(5 \times \$8) + \$4,600 = \$4,640$ total investment

c. $4 \times (1.03 \times \$1,000) = \$4,120$ market price of 4 bonds
$(4 \times \$8) + \$4,120 = \$4,152$ total investment

d. $12 \times (1.13 \times \$1,000) = \$13,560$ market price of 12 bonds
$(12 \times \$8) + \$13,560 = \$13,656$ total investment

e. $6 \times (0.895 \times \$1,000) = \$5,370$ market price of 6 bonds
$(6 \times \$8) + \$5,370 = \$5,418$ total investment

f. $9 \times (1.0525 \times \$1,000) = \$9,472.50$ market price of 9 bonds
$(9 \times \$8) + \$9,472.50 = \$9,544.50$ total investment

g. $10 \times (0.93625 \times \$1,000) = \$9,362.50$ market price of 10 bonds
$(10 \times \$8) + \$9,362.50 = \$9,442.50$ total investment

h. $16 \times (1.1275 \times \$1,000) = \$18,040$ market price of 16 bonds
$(16 \times \$8) + \$18,040 = \$18,168$ total investment

i. $7 \times (0.995 \times \$1,000) = \$6,965$ market price of 7 bonds
$(7 \times \$8) + \$6,965 = \$7,021$ total investment

2. $(14 \times \$1,035) = \$14,490$ market price of 14 bonds
$\$14,490 + \$105 = \$14,595$ total investment

3. $8 \times \$730 = \$5,840$ market price of 8 bonds
$\$5,840 + \$56 = \$5,896$ total investment

4. $4 \times (0.875 \times \$1,000) = \$3,500$ market price of 4 bonds
$\$3,500 + (4 \times \$10) = \$3,540$ total investment

5. $6 \times (0.93 \times \$500) = \$2,790$ market price of 6 bonds
$\$2,790 + (6 \times \$9) = \$2,844$ total investment

6. **a.** $12 \times \$1,000 = \$12,000$ estimated investment in 12 bonds

b. $\begin{array}{l} 5\,(0.89875 \times \$1,000) = \$\ \ 4,493.75 \\ \underline{7\,(0.90125 \times \$1,000) = \ \ \ 6,308.75} \\ 12 \qquad\qquad\qquad\qquad\quad \$10,802.50 \ \ \text{actual investment in 12 bonds} \end{array}$

7. $2 \times (0.96 \times \$1,000) = \$1,920$ market price of 2 bonds
$14 \times (1.23 \times \$500) = \$8,610$ market price of 14 bonds
$\$1,920 + \$8,610 + \$125 = \$10,655$ total investment in 16 bonds

Exercise 4, page 299

1. $11\frac{5}{8}\%$ annual rate of interest

2. 2005, year bonds due

3. $0.925 \times \$1,000 = \$925$ closing price of bond

4. 18, number of bonds sold for day

5. $(101 - 1\frac{1}{4}) = 99\frac{3}{4}$ last price of day before
   $0.9975 \times \$1,000 = \$997.50$ last price of day before, in dollars

Exercise 5, page 300

1. $\$50 \div 2 = \$25$ purchase price of $50 bond
   $\$75 \div 2 = \$37.50$ purchase price of $75 bond

2. $8 \times (\$500 \div 2) = \$2,000$ purchase price of eight $500 bonds

3. $3 \times \$32.94 = \$98.82$ total received

4. $\$200 \div \$50 = 4$ equivalent number of $50 units
   $4 \times \$28.14 = \$112.56$ amount received

5. a. $(3 \times \$500) \div 2 = \$750$ paid for bonds
   b. $3 \times (\$500 \div \$50) = 30$ equivalent number of $50 units
      $30 \times \$30.30 = \$909$ redemption value
   c. $\$909 - \$750 = \$159$ interest earned

6. $10 \times (\$50 \div 2) = \$250$ purchase price of 10 bonds
   $(10 \times \$45.42) - \$250 = \$204.20$ total interest earned

Review 55, page 301

2. $6 \times (1.07 \times \$1,000) = \$6,420$ market price of 6 bonds
   $\$6,420 + (6 \times \$7.50) = \$6,465$ total investment in bonds

3. July 30, due date
   $\$5,100 \times 0.08 \times \frac{5}{24} = \$85$ interest
   $\$5,100 + \$85 = \$5,185$ amount due at maturity

4.

Date	Withdrawal	Deposit	Interest	Balance
19 --				
Jan. 2		740.00		740.00
July 1			18.50	758.50
Jan. 2			18.96	777.46

Section 56.   Bond Income

Exercise 1, page 302

1. a. $0.09 \times \$1,000 = \$90$ interest on 1 bond
      $4 \times \$90 = \$360$ annual income
   b. $0.14 \times \$1,000 = \$140$ interest on 1 bond
      $16 \times \$140 = \$2,240$ annual income
   c. $0.06 \times \$1,000 = \$60$ interest on 1 bond
      $7 \times \$60 = \$420$ annual income

    d. $0.12 \times \$500 = \$60$ interest on 1 bond
          $12 \times \$60 = \$720$ annual income
    e. $0.07 \times \$500 = \$35$ interest on 1 bond
          $8 \times \$35 = \$280$ annual income
    f. $0.115 \times \$1,000 = \$115$ interest on 1 bond
          $10 \times \$115 = \$1,150$ annual income
    g. $0.0725 \times \$1,000 = \$72.50$ interest on 1 bond
          $16 \times \$72.50 = \$1,160$ annual income
    h. $0.1475 \times \$1,000 = \$147.50$ interest on 1 bond
          $3 \times \$147.50 = \$442.50$ annual income
    i. $0.055 \times \$1,000 = \$55$ interest on 1 bond
          $9 \times \$55 = \$495$ annual income
    j. $0.09375 \times \$1,000 = \$93.75$ interest on 1 bond
          $20 \times \$93.75 = \$1,875$ annual income

2. $0.08125 \times \$1,000 = \$81.25$ interest on 1 bond
    $4 \times \$81.25 = \$325$ annual income

3. $0.0775 \times \$1,000 = \$77.50$ interest on 1 bond
    $23 \times \$77.50 = \$1,782.50$ annual income

4. $0.09 \times \$500 \times \frac{1}{2} = \$22.50$ each interest payment

5. $0.07 \times \$1,000 \times 8 = \$560$ estimated annual interest
    $0.06875 \times \$1,000 \times 8 = \$550$ actual annual interest

Exercise 2, page 303

1. $5 \times (0.87 \times \$1,000) = \$4,350$ price of bonds
    $5 \times \$10 = \$50$ commission
    $\$4,350 + \$50 = \$4,400$ total investment
    $5 \times (0.08 \times \$1,000) = \$400$ annual income

2. $10 \times (0.925 \times \$1,000) = \$9,250$ price of bonds
    $10 \times \$7.50 = \$75$ commission
    $\$9,250 + \$75 = \$9,325$ total investment
    $10 \times (0.12 \times \$1,000) = \$1,200$ annual income

3. $30 \times (1.0525 \times \$1,000) = \$31,575$ price of bonds
    $30 \times \$5 = \$150$ commission
    $\$31,575 + \$150 = \$31,725$ total investment
    $30 \times (0.105 \times \$1,000) = \$3,150$ annual income

4. $45 \times (0.96 \times \$1,000) = \$43,200$ price of bonds
    $45 \times \$5 = \$225$ commission
    $\$43,200 + \$225 = \$43,425$ total investment
    $45 \times (0.076 \times \$1,000) = \$3,420$ annual income

5. $16 \times (1.05 \times \$500) = \$8,400$ price of bonds
    $16 \times \$7.50 = \$120$ commission
    $\$8,400 + \$120 = \$8,520$ total investment
    $16 \times (0.14 \times \$500) = \$1,120$ annual income

6. $4 \times (0.72 \times \$500) = \$1,440$ price of bonds
    $4 \times \$10 = \$40$ commission
    $\$1,440 + \$40 = \$1,480$ total investment
    $4 \times (0.0675 \times \$500) = \$135$ annual income

Exercise 3, page 304

1. **a.** $0.91 \times \$1,000 = \$910$ market price
$\$910 + \$5 = \$915$ amount invested
$0.16 \times \$1,000 = \$160$ annual income
$\$160 \div \$915 = 17.5\%$ rate of income
  b. $0.87 \times \$1,000 = \$870$ market price
$\$870 + \$10 = \$880$ amount invested
$0.07 \times \$1,000 = \$70$ annual income
$\$70 \div \$880 = 8.0\%$ rate of income
  c. $1.09 \times \$1,000 = \$1,090$ market price
$\$1,090 + \$10 = \$1,100$ amount invested
$0.12 \times \$1,000 = \$120$ annual income
$\$120 \div \$1,100 = 10.9\%$ rate of income
  d. $0.74 \times \$1,000 = \$740$ market price
$\$740 + \$10 = \$750$ amount invested
$0.085 \times \$1,000 = \$85$ annual income
$\$85 \div \$750 = 11.3\%$ rate of income
  e. $1.12 \times \$1,000 = \$1,120$ market price
$\$1,120 + \$5 = \$1,125$ amount invested
$0.115 \times \$1,000 = \$115$ annual income
$\$115 \div \$1,125 = 10.2\%$ rate of income
  f. $0.95 \times \$500 = \$475$ market price
$\$475 + \$5 = \$480$ amount invested
$0.0525 \times \$500 = \$26.25$ annual income
$\$26.25 \div \$480 = 5.5\%$ rate of income
  g. $0.62 \times \$500 = \$310$ market price
$\$310 + \$5 = \$315$ amount invested
$0.078 \times \$500 = \$39$ annual income
$\$39 \div \$315 = 12.4\%$ rate of income

2. $0.685 \times \$1,000 = \$685$ market price
$\$685 + \$5 = \$690$ amount invested
$0.08 \times \$1,000 = \$80$ annual income
$\$80 \div \$690 = 11.6\%$ rate of income

3. $1.24 \times \$1,000 = \$1,240$ market price
$0.18 \times \$1,000 = \$180$ annual income
$\$180 \div \$1,240 = 14.5\%$ rate of income

4. $1.04 \times \$1,000 = \$1,040$ amount invested
$0.045 \times \$1,000 = \$45$ annual income
$\$45 \div \$1,040 = 4.3\%$ rate of income

5. $1.08 \times \$1,000 = \$1,080$ amount invested
$0.12 \times \$1,000 = \$120$ annual income
$\$120 \div \$1,080 = 11.1\%$ rate of income

6. $0.98 \times \$1,000 = \$980$ amount invested
$0.09 \times \$1,000 = \$90$ annual income
$\$90 \div \$980 = 9.2\%$ rate of income

7. $7 \times (1.5 \times \$1,000) = \$10,500$ market price
$\$10,500 + (7 \times \$10) = \$10,570$ amount invested
$7 \times (0.13 \times \$1,000) = \$910$ annual income
  a. $\$910 \times \frac{1}{2} = \$455$ semiannual interest
  b. $\$910 \div \$10,570 = 8.6\%$ rate of income

†Exercise 4, page 304

1. **a.** $0.06 \times \$1,000 = \$60$ annual income   **b.** $\$720 \div \$60 = 12$ bonds

2. $0.8 \times \$1,000 = \$800$ investment in 1 bond
   $0.07 \times \$1,000 = \$70$ annual income from 1 bond
   $\$2,800 \div \$70 = 40$ bonds
   $40 \times \$800 = \$32,000$ must be invested

3. $1.07 \times \$1,000 = \$1,070$ investment in one bond
   $0.095 \times \$1,000 = \$95$ annual income from one bond
   $\$1,520 \div \$95 = 16$ bonds
   $16 \times \$1,070 = \$17,120$ must be invested

4. **a.** $0.05 \times \$1,000 = \$50$ annual income one bond
   $\$750 \div \$50 = 15$ bonds
   b. $0.42 \times \$1,000 = \$420$ market price of one bond
   $15 \times \$420 = \$6,300$ total investment

5. **a.** $0.84 \times \$1,000 = \$840$ investment in mining company bond
   $0.09 \times \$1,000 = \$90$ annual income from bond
   $\$90 \div \$840 = 10.7\%$ yield from mining company bond
   $0.68 \times \$1,000 = \$680$ investment in oil company bond
   $0.07 \times \$1,000 = \$70$ annual income from bond
   $\$70 \div \$680 = 10.3\%$ yield from oil company bond
   Mining company bonds pay the higher yield
   b. 10.7%   yield paid by mining company bonds

Review 56, page 305

1. **a.** $\$15,000 \times 0.3482 = \$5,223$ **d.** $\$1,108 \times 0.14 \times \frac{12}{73} = \$25.50$
   b. $\$54 - (0.35 \times \$54) = \$35.10$ **e.** $\$349,500$
   c. $(\$32.00 - \$11.84) \div \$32 = 63\%$ **f.** $20 \times 100 = 2,000$

2. $15 \times (0.075 \times \$1,000) = \$1,125$ annual income

3. $20 \times (1.055 \times \$500) = \$10,550$ market price of bonds
   $20 \times \$5 = \$100$ commission
   $\$10,550 + \$100 = \$10,650$ total investment
   $20 \times (0.14 \times \$500) = \$1,400$ annual income
   $\$1,400 \div \$10,650 = 13.1\%$ rate of income

4. $7 \times (0.9125 \times \$1,000) = \$6,387.50$ market price of seven bonds
   $4 \times (1.0575 \times \$500) = \$2,115$ market price of four bonds
   $11 \times \$7.50 = \$82.50$ commission
   $\$6,387.50 + \$2,115.00 + \$82.50 = \$8,585$ total investment

5.

Date	Withdrawal	Deposit	Interest	Balance
19 --				
Apr. 1		600.00		600.00
July 1			7.50	607.50
July 5	200.00			407.50
Oct. 1			5.09	412.59

6.

	Regular Time	Overtime
Monday	8	0
Tuesday	8	3
Wednesday	8	2
Thursday	8	1
Friday	7	0
	39	6

$1\frac{1}{2} \times \$6 = \$9$ overtime rate
$39 \times \$6 = \$234$ regular time pay
$6 \times \$9 = \underline{54}$ overtime pay
$\$288$ gross earnings

7. $0.0765 \times \$24{,}000 = \$1{,}836$ FICA tax deducted

Section 57.   Buying Stock

Exercise 1, page 309

1. Market price, $100 \times \$28$ $2,800.00
     Broker's commission   + 67.60
     Total cost $2,867.60

2. Market price, $200 \times \$20.625$ $4,125.00
     Broker's commission   + 86.81
     Total cost $4,211.81

3. Market price, $100 \times \$15.25$ $1,525.00
     Broker's commission   + 50.33
     Total cost $1,575.33

4. Market price, $50 \times \$64.375$ $3,218.75
     Broker's commission   + 73.67
     Total cost $3,292.42

5. Market price, $20 \times \$109.875$ $2,197.50
     Broker's commission   + 58.86
     Total cost $2,256.36

6. Market price, $80 \times \$30.50$ $2,440.00
     Broker's commission   + 62.38
     Total cost $2,502.38

7. Market price, $400 \times \$4$ $1,600.00
     Broker's commission   + 46.80
     Total cost $1,646.80

8. Market price, $140 \times \$36.625$ $5,127.50
     Broker's commission   + 101.09
     Total cost $5,228.59

9. Market price, $30 \times \$45.25$ $1,357.50
     Broker's commission   + 41.22
     Total cost $1,398.72

10. Market price, 150 × $55.25 $8,287.50
     Broker's commission   +   140.60
     Total cost $8,428.10

11. Market price, 20 × $62 $1,240.00
     Broker's commission   +   50.00
     Total cost $1,290.00

12. 0.4 × $80 = $32   less cost by using discount broker

Exercise 2, page 310

1. a. Selway Foods   **3. a.** 130,000   shares   **5. a.** Selway Foods
    b. Amliss Corp.   **b.** 41,300   shares   **b.** Kell Products

2. a. Amliss Corp., $2   **4. a.** Borco
    b. Harter Co., $0.40   **b.** Harter

Review 57, page 311

2. a. $2,800 × 4.09 = $11,452
    b. 45 × $4\frac{2}{5}$ = 198
    c. 32.8 ÷ 1,600 = 0.0205
    d. ($16.80 − $11.20) ÷ $16.80 = $33\frac{1}{3}$%

3. Market price, 42 × $48.50 $2,037.00
    Broker's commission   +   63.56
    Total investment $2,100.56

4. 25 × (0.12 × $500) = $1,500   annual income from 25 bonds
    $1,500 ÷ $12,125 = 12.4%   yield on investment

5. $18,000 + ($18,000 × 0.15 × 3) = $26,100   total amount repaid

6. a. $30 + ($30 × 0.025) = $30.75   cost of purchase
    b. $30.75 − $30 = $0.75   saved by paying cash

7. 520 × $0.0762   = $39.62   basic cost of electricity
    520 × $0.00034 =   0.18   fuel adjustment
              $39.80   total cost of 520 KWH

Section 58.   Stock Income

Exercise 1, page 313

1. 0.06 × $100 = $6   dividend on 1 share
    100 × $6 = $600   total annual dividend

2. 0.09 × $100 = $9   dividend on 1 share
    80 × $9 = $720   total annual dividend

3. 0.05 × $50 = $2.50   dividend on 1 share
    35 × $2.50 = $87.50   total annual dividend

4. 0.075 × $50 = $3.75   dividend on 1 share
    82 × $3.75 = $307.50   total annual dividend

5. $50 \times \$0.65 = \$32.50$ dividend for 1 quarter
    $4 \times \$32.50 = \$130$ total annual dividend

6. $160 \times \$1.70 = \$272$ dividend for 1 quarter
    $4 \times \$272 = \$1,088$ total annual dividend

7. $200 \times \$0.48 = \$96$ dividend for 1 quarter
    $4 \times \$96 = \$384$ total annual dividend

Exercise 2, page 313

1. a. $0.08 \times \$100 = \$8$ annual dividend
        $\$8 \div \$130 = 6.2\%$ rate of income
    b. $0.05 \times \$100 = \$5$ annual dividend
        $\$5 \div \$60 = 8.3\%$ rate of income
    c. $0.04 \times \$50 = \$2$ annual dividend
        $\$2 \div \$34 = 5.9\%$ rate of income
    d. $4 \times \$0.57 = \$2.28$ annual dividend
        $\$2.28 \div \$90 = 2.5\%$ rate of income
    e. $4 \times \$1.30 = \$5.20$ annual dividend
        $\$5.20 \div \$56 = 9.3\%$ rate of income
    f. $4 \times \$0.17 = \$0.68$ annual dividend
        $\$0.68 \div \$12 = 5.7\%$ rate of income

2. $4 \times \$0.315 = \$1.26$ annual dividend
    $\$1.26 \div \$18 = 7\%$ rate of income

3. $160 \times \$1.51 = \$241.60$ dividend on 1 share
    $4 \times \$241.60 = \$966.40$ total annual dividend
    $\$966.40 \div \$6,840 = 14.1\%$ rate of income

4. a. $50 \times (0.06 \times \$50) = \$150$ total dividend
    b. $(50 \times \$47.375) + \$62.43 = \$2,431.18$ cost of stock
        $\$150 \div \$2,431.18 = 6.2\%$ rate of income

5. a. $0.027 \times \$100 = \$2.70$ annual dividend
        $\$2.70 \div \$28 = 9.6\%$ rate of income for Regal Paint Company
        $4 \times \$0.18 = \$0.72$ annual dividend
        $\$0.72 \div \$8.25 = 8.7\%$ rate of income for Esteem Footwear Company
        Regal Paint Company stock earns the higher rate of income
    b. $9.6\% - 8.7\% = 0.9\%$ higher

Review 58, page 314

1. a. $7.004 \times 0.035 = 0.24514$
    b. $1,800 \div 10.7 = 168.2$
    c. $\$798.72 \div \$12,800 = 6.24\%$
    d. $\frac{2}{3} \times \$9.51 = \$6.34$
    e. $84 + (0.225 \times 84) = 102.9$

2. $4 \times (250 \times \$0.37) = \$370$ income for 1 year

3. $120 \times (0.07 \times \$150) = \$1,260$ annual dividend income

4. $0.092 \times \$50 = \$4.60$ annual dividend
    $\$4.60 \div \$117 = 3.9\%$ rate of income

5. $15 \times (1.08 \times \$500) = \$8,100$ total investment
$15 \times (0.054 \times \$500) = \$405$ annual income
$\$405 \div \$8,100 = 5\%$ yield

6. $(36 \times \$31) - \$900 = \$216$ finance charge

7. July 5, maturity date
$\$3,500 + (\$3,500 \times 0.12 \times \frac{1}{3}) = \$3,640$ amount due

‡8. $0.07 \times \$1,000 = \$70$ annual income from 1 bond
$\$1,610 \div \$70 = 23$ bonds

Section 59.   Selling Stock

Exercise 1, page 315

1. $(100 \times \$34) - \$61.34 = \$3,338.66$ net proceeds

2. $(50 \times \$12.25) - \$48.22 = \$564.28$ net proceeds

3. $(230 \times \$81) - \$145.57 = \$18,484.43$ net proceeds

4. $(80 \times \$28.125) - \$52.68 = \$2,197.32$ net proceeds

5. $(300 \times \$17) - \$75.31 = \$5,024.69$ net proceeds

6. $(200 \times \$45) - \$182.50 = \$8,817.50$ net proceeds from Neal stock
$(300 \times \$17) - \$124.30 = \$4,975.70$ net proceeds from Wicker stock
$\$8,817.50 + \$4,975.70 = \$13,793.20$ total net proceeds

7. a. $(100 \times \$20) - \$50 = \$1,950$ estimated net proceeds
b. $(100 \times \$19.875) - \$50.11 = \$1,937.39$ net proceeds

Exercise 2, page 316

1. a. $(100 \times \$42) - \$88.04 = \$4,111.96$ net proceeds
$\$4,111.96 - \$3,935.56 = \$176.40$ profit
b. $(80 \times \$8.50) - \$50.73 = \$629.27$ net proceeds
$\$629.27 - \$558.42 = \$70.85$ profit
c. $(400 \times \$17) - \$97.39 = \$6,702.61$ net proceeds
$\$7,003.67 - \$6,702.61 = \$301.06$ loss
d. $(75 \times \$28.25) - \$57.58 = \$2,061.17$ net proceeds
$\$2,840.31 - \$2,061.17 = \$779.14$ loss
e. $(110 \times \$37) - \$86.47 = \$3,983.53$ net proceeds
$\$3,983.53 - \$3,200.75 = \$782.78$ profit
f. $(90 \times \$51.125) - \$92.25 = \$4,601.25$ net proceeds
$\$4,618.66 - \$4,601.25 = \$17.41$ loss

2. $(60 \times \$51) - \$94 = \$2,966$ net proceeds
$\$2,985 - \$2,966 = \$19$ loss

Exercise 3, page 316

1. $3 \times 2 \times \$3.10 = \$18.60$ dividends from 1 share
$40 \times \$18.60 = \$744$ total dividends
$(\$4,211 - \$3,757) + \$744 = \$1,198$ total gain

2. 6 × $0.27 = $1.62   dividends from 1 share
    75 × $1.62 = $121.50   total dividends
    ($1,194 + $121.50) − $1,298 = $17.50   net gain

3. 3 × $0.90 = $2.70   dividends from one share of Wexor stock
    62 × $2.70 = $167.40   total dividends from Wexor stock
    ($345 + $167.40) − $490 = $22.40   net gain from both stocks

‡Exercise 4, page 316

1. $360 ÷ $4 = 90   shares

2. a. $1,000 ÷ $2.50 = 400   shares
    b. (400 × $56) + (4 × $82) = $22,728   total investment

3. 0.12 × $10 = $1.20   dividend from 1 share
    $960 ÷ $1.20 = 800   shares must be bought
    800 × $20 = $16,000   must be invested

4. a. $308 ÷ $1.40 = 220   shares
    b. 220 × $34 = $7,480   total investment

Review 59, page 317

2. a. $37,000 × 2.38 = $88,060
    b. 5,724 ÷ 12,000 = 0.477
    c. 6,350 ÷ 50,000 = 12.7%
    d. 22 m × 40 m = 880 m²
    e. 5 600 m = 5.6 km

3. $88.20 − (0.2 × $88.20) = $70.56   commission
    (100 × $32.50) − $70.56 = $3,179.44   net proceeds

4. 2 × $0.48 = $0.96   dividends from 1 share
    150 × $0.96 = $144   total dividends
    ($3,890 + $144) − $3,200 = $834   total gain

5. 2 × $3.60 = $7.20   annual dividend
    $7.20 ÷ $90 = 8%   rate of income

Section 60.   Mutual Funds

Exercise 1, page 320

1. a. 40 × $9.27 = $370.80   total investment
    b. 132 × $6.37 = $840.84   total investment
    c. 80 × $10.96 = $876.80   total investment
    d. 260 × $19.17 = $4,984.20   total investment

2.   50 × $13.56 = $ 678.00
      120 × $13.84 =   1,660.80
       90 × $14.05 =   1,264.50
                      $3,603.30   total investment

3. 100 × $16.82 = $1,682   investment in Foster A-2
    100 × $ 8.03 =   803   investment in Foster Growth
                   $2,485   total investment

Exercise 2, page 320

1. $2,500 ÷ $16.20 = 154.3209, or 154.321   shares

2. $5,000 ÷ $17.34 = 288.3506, or 288.351   shares

3. $8,000 ÷ $6.73 = 1,188.7072, or 1,118.707   shares

4. a. $500 ÷ $25 = 20   shares, estimate
    b. $500 ÷ $24.75 = 20.202   shares
    c. 804.726 + 20.202 = 824.928   total shares owned

Exercise 3, page 321

1. a. $6.42 − $6.29 = $0.13   commission
        $0.13 ÷ $6.42 = 0.0202, or 2.0%   rate of commission
    b. $13.44 − $12.78 = $0.66   commission
        $0.66 ÷ $13.44 = 0.0491, or 4.9%   rate of commission
    c. $19.40 − $17.75 = $1.65   commission
        $1.65 ÷ $19.40 = 0.085, or 8.5%   rate of commission
    d. $8.98 − $8.58 = $0.40   commission
        $0.40 ÷ $8.98 = 0.0445, or 4.5%   rate of commission

2. $6.24 − $6.08 = $0.16   commission
   $0.16 ÷ $6.24 = 0.0256, or 2.6%   rate of commission

3. $14.80 − $14.06 = $0.74   commission
   $0.74 ÷ $14.80 = 0.05, or 5%   rate of commission

4. a. $0.80 ÷ $10 = 0.08, or 8%   estimated rate of commission
    b. $0.78 ÷ $10.04 = 0.0776, or 7.8%   rate of commission

Exercise 4, page 322

1. 810.4 × $8.84 = $7,163.94   proceeds

2. a. 320 × $11.87 = $3,798.40   proceeds
    b. $3,798.40 − $3,198 = $600.40   profit

3. 500.271 × $22.86 = $11,436.20   proceeds
   $12,520 − $11,436.20 = $1,083.80   loss

4. a. $4,000 ÷ $8 = 500   estimated number of shares purchased
    b. $4,000 ÷ $8.10 = 493.827   actual number of shares purchased
    c. 493.827 × $8.11 = $4,004.94   proceeds
    d. $4,004.94 − $4,000 = $4.94   profit

Review 60, page 322

2. 300 × $15.62 = $4,686   investment

3. $8,000 ÷ $31.20 = 256.410   shares can be bought

4. a. $18.23 − $17.44 = $0.79   commission
    b. $0.79 ÷ $18.23 = 0.0433, or 4.3%   rate of commission

5. 350 × $21.75 = $7,612.50   proceeds
   $7,612.50 − $7,192.50 = $420   profit

6. $8 \times (\$500 \times 0.95) = \$3,800$ price of bonds
$8 \times \$7.50 = \$60$ commission
$\$3,800 + \$60 = \$3,860$ total investment

7. $0.85 \times \$1,000 = \$850$ market price of bond
$0.067 \times \$1,000 = \$67$ annual interest from bond
$\$67 \div \$850 = 0.0788$, or 7.9%   yield

Section 61. Buying Real Estate

Exercise 1, page 325

1. **a.** $12 \times \$590 = \$7,080$ annual rental income
$\$1,720 + \$470 + \$500 + \$2,100 + \$1,300 + \$50 = \$6,140$ annual expenses
$\$7,080 - \$6,140 = \$940$ annual net income
   b. $12 \times \$310 = \$3,720$ annual rental income
$\$950 + \$360 + \$380 + \$1,100 + \$560 + \$40 = \$3,390$ annual expenses
$\$3,720 - \$3,390 = \$330$ annual net income
   c. $12 \times \$840 = \$10,080$ annual rental income
$\$2,800 + \$210 + \$590 + \$3,000 + \$2,050 + \$90 = \$8,740$ annual expenses
$\$10,080 - \$8,740 = \$1,340$ annual net income
   d. $12 \times \$540 = \$6,480$ annual rental income
$\$1,630 + \$840 + \$360 + \$1,870 + \$1,200 + \$75 = \$5,975$ annual expenses
$\$6,480 - \$5,975 = \$505$ annual net income

2. $12 \times \$950 = \$11,400$ annual rental income
$\$4,800 + (0.03 \times \$58,000) + \$3,750 = \$10,290$ annual expenses
$\$11,400 - \$10,290 = \$1,110$ annual net income

3. $8 \times (\$460 \times 12) = \$44,160$ annual rental income
$\$20,400 + (0.02 \times \$130,000) + \$14,900 = \$37,900$ annual expenses
$\$44,160 - \$37,900 = \$6,260$ annual net income

Exercise 2, page 326

1. **a.** $12 \times \$500 = \$6,000$ annual rental income
$\$2,400 + \$1,900 = \$4,300$ annual expenses
$\$6,000 - \$4,300 = \$1,700$ annual net income
$\$1,700 \div \$21,000 = 0.0809$, or 8.1%   rate of income
   b. $12 \times \$780 = \$9,360$ annual rental income
$\$1,600 + \$3,300 = \$4,900$ annual expenses
$\$9,360 - \$4,900 = \$4,460$ annual net income
$\$4,460 \div \$38,000 = 0.1173$, or 11.7%   rate of income
   c. $12 \times \$1,800 = \$21,600$ annual rental income
$\$9,600 + \$9,300 = \$18,900$ annual expenses
$\$21,600 - \$18,900 = \$2,700$ annual net income
$\$2,700 \div \$46,000 = 0.0586$, or 5.9%   rate of income
   d. $12 \times \$390 = \$4,680$ annual rental income
$\$2,200 + \$1,450 = \$3,650$ annual expenses
$\$4,680 - \$3,650 = \$1,030$ annual net income
$\$1,030 \div \$12,000 = 0.0858$, or 8.6%   rate of income

    e. $12 \times \$640 = \$7,680$ annual rental income
        $\$2,200 + \$2,150 = \$4,350$ annual expenses
        $\$7,680 - \$4,350 = \$3,330$ annual net income
        $\$3,330 \div \$31,000 = 0.1074$, or 10.7%   rate of income

2. $(12 \times \$560) + (12 \times \$580) = \$13,680$ annual rental income
    $\$8,200 + \$4,400 = \$12,600$ annual expenses
    $\$13,680 - \$12,600 = \$1,080$ annual net income
    $\$1,080 \div \$11,000 = 0.0981$, or 9.8%   rate of income

3. **a.** $12 \times \$920 = \$11,040$ annual rental income
        $\$3,900 + \$1,200 = \$5,100$ annual expenses
        $\$11,040 - \$5,100 = \$5,940$ annual net income
        $\$5,940 \div \$78,000 = 0.0761$, or 7.6%   rate of income
    b. $(12 \times \$1,050) - \$5,100 = \$7,500$ annual net income
        $\$7,500 \div \$78,000 = 0.0961$, or 9.6%   rate of income

4. $6 \times (12 \times \$290) = \$20,880$ annual rental income
    $\$9,800 + (0.04 \times \$55,000) + \$6,300 = \$18,300$ annual expenses
    $\$20,880 - \$18,300 = \$2,580$ annual net income
    $\$2,580 \div \$20,000 = 0.129$, or 13%   rate of income

5. $12 \times \$490 = \$5,880$ annual rental income
    $\$990 + \$270 + \$2,400 + \$900 + (0.02 \times \$24,000) = \$5,040$ annual expenses
    $\$5,880 - \$5,040 = \$840$ annual net income
    $\$840 \div \$7,000 = 0.12$, or 12%   rate of income

Review 61, page 327

1. **a.** $\$4.20 + (0.60 \times \$4.20) = \$6.72$ **d.** $13\frac{1}{2} \div 2\frac{1}{4} = 6$
    b. $\$6.30 - (\frac{1}{5} \times \$6.30) = \$5.04$ **e.** $\$150,000 \div \$50,000 = 300\%$
    c. $37\frac{1}{2}\% = \frac{3}{8}$ **f.** $958.8006 = 958.801$

2. $12 \times \$800 = \$9,600$ annual rental income
    $\$2,780 + \$1,400 + \$800 + \$3,650 = \$8,630$ annual expenses
    $\$9,600 - \$8,630 = \$970$ annual net income

3. $12 \times \$900 = \$10,800$ annual rental income
    $\$5,100 + \$1,570 + \$940 + \$800 + \$1,800 = \$10,210$ annual expenses
    $\$10,800 - \$10,210 = \$590$ annual net income
    $\$590 \div \$22,000 = 0.0268$, or 2.7%   rate of income

4. $(199.521 \times \$11.83) - \$2,500 = \$139.67$ loss

Section 62.   Real Estate Income

Exercise 1, page 329

1. **a.** $(0.14 \times \$20,000) + \$3,500 = \$6,300$ desired annual rental income
        $\$6,300 \div 12 = \$525$ monthly rental charge
    b. $(0.07 \times \$8,000) + \$2,560 = \$3,120$ desired annual rental income
        $\$3,120 \div 12 = \$260$ monthly rental charge
    c. $(0.12 \times \$45,000) + \$9,120 = \$14,520$ desired annual rental income
        $\$14,520 \div 12 = \$1,210$ monthly rental charge
    d. $(0.09 \times \$36,000) + \$8,400 = \$11,640$ desired annual rental income
        $\$11,640 \div 12 = \$970$ monthly rental charge

2. a. $(0.15 \times \$12,000) + \$540 = \$2,340$ annual rental income
    b. $\$2,400 \div 12 = \$200$ estimated monthly rental charge
    c. $\$2,340 \div 12 = \$195$ actual monthly rental charge

3. a. $(0.08 \times \$12,000) + \$4,320 = \$5,280$ annual rental income
        $\$5,280 \div 12 = \$440$ monthly rental charge
    b. $0.05 \times \$4,320 = \$216$ increase in expenses, second year
        $(\$5,280 + \$216) \div 12 = \$458$ monthly rental charge, second year

‡Exercise 2, page 330

1. $\$6,720 \div 0.14 = \$48,000$ can invest

2. $\$8,740 - \$3,280 = \$5,460$ annual net income
    $\$5,460 \div 0.08 = \$68,250$ can invest

3. $(12 \times \$640) - \$3,080 = \$4,600$ annual net income
    $\$4,600 \div 0.115 = \$40,000$ can invest

4. $(12 \times \$1,140) - \$4,560 = \$9,120$ annual net income
    $\$9,120 \div 0.095 = \$96,000$ can invest

Exercise 3, page 330

1. $\$68,000 + \$2,200 = \$70,200$ capital investment

2. a. $\$28,000 + \$12,000 = \$40,000$ capital investment
    b. $\$2,600 + (0.07 \times \$40,000) = \$5,400$ annual net income
        $\$5,400 \div 12 = \$450$ monthly rental charge

3. $\$26,000 + \$32,000 = \$58,000$ capital investment
    $(4 \times 12 \times \$280) - \$8,700 = \$4,740$ annual net income
    $\$4,740 \div \$58,000 = 0.0817$, or 8.2%   rate of income

‡4. $(2 \times 12 \times \$380) - \$5,100 = \$4,020$ annual net income
     $\$4,020 \div 0.12 = \$33,500$ can invest

Review 62, page 331

2. $\$3,900 + (0.075 \times \$60,000) = \$8,400$ annual rental income
    $\$8,400 \div 12 = \$700$ monthly rental charge

3. $\$56,000 + \$22,000 = \$78,000$ capital investment

4. $\$2,400 \times 0.08 \times \frac{1}{6} = \$32$ penalty

UNIT 10 • HOME AND TRANSPORTATION EXPENSES

Section 63.   Buying a Home

Exercise 1, page 334

1. a. $0.2 \times \$90,000 = \$18,000$ cash needed for down payment
    b. $\$90,000 - \$18,000 = \$72,000$ will need to borrow
    c. $0.03 \times \$90,000 = \$2,700$ closing costs

2. a. $0.25 \times \$59,000 = \$14,750$ down payment
 b. $\$180 + \$125 + \$190 + \$50 + \$393 + \$242 = \$1,180$ closing costs
 c. $\$1,180 \div \$59,000 = 2\%$ closing costs were of purchase price

3. a. $0.15 \times \$53,500 = \$8,025$ down payment
 $\$40 + \$420 + \$115 + \$210 + \$401 + \$312 = \$1,498$ closing costs
 $\$8,025 + \$1,498 = \$9,523$ amount of cash must have on August 1
 b. $\$1,498 \div \$53,500 = 2.8\%$ closing costs are of purchase price

Exercise 2, page 336

1. a. $\$539.84$ monthly payment
 b. $(12 \times 20) \times \$539.84 = \$129,561.60$ total amount paid
 $\$129,561.60 - \$60,000 = \$69,561.60$ total interest cost

2. a. $\$451.14$ monthly payment
 b. $(12 \times 25) \times \$451.14 = \$135,342$ total amount paid
 $\$135,342 - \$40,000 = \$95,342$ total interest cost

3. a. $\$714.25$ monthly payment
 b. $(12 \times 30) \times \$714.25 = \$257,130$ total amount paid
 $\$257,130 - \$75,000 = \$182,130$ total interest cost

4. a. $\$507.53$ monthly payment
 b. $(12 \times 25) \times \$507.53 = \$152,259$ total amount paid
 $\$152,259 - \$45,000 = \$107,259$ total interest cost

Exercise 3, page 337

1. $12 \times \$539.75 = \$6,477.00$ payment under old mortgage
 $12 \times \$464.32 = \underline{\quad 5,571.84}$ payment under new mortgage
 $\$\ \ \ 905.16$ less paid under new mortgage

2. $12 \times \$813.58 = \$9,762.96$ payment under new mortgage
 $12 \times \$734.87 = \underline{\quad 8,818.44}$ payment under old mortgage
 $\$\ \ \ 944.52$ more paid under new mortgage

3. a. $12 \times (\$800 - \$600) = \$2,400$ less paid under new mortgage
 $\$2,400 - (\$1,000 + \$1,000) = \$400$ estimated first year net payments
 b. $12 \times \$796.69 = \ \ \$9,560.28$ payment under old mortgage
 $12 \times \$602.41 = \underline{\quad 7,228.92}$ payment under new mortgage
 $\$2,331.36$ less paid under new mortgage
 $\$990 + \$1,005 = \underline{\quad 1,995.00}$ closing and prepayment
 $\$\ \ \ 336.36$ net payments first year

4. a. $3 \times 12 \times \$614.41 = \$22,118.76$ payments under old mortgage
 b. $3 \times 12 \times \$471.35 = \underline{\quad 16,968.60}$ payments under new mortgage
 c. $\$\ 5,150.16$ difference
 $\underline{\quad 1,630.00}$ closing costs
 $\$\ 3,520.16$ net amount paid less in three years

Review 63, page 338

2. a. $\$84 \div \$24 = 350\%$
 b. $1.4 \times \$85 = \$119$
 c. March 15 to August 7 = 145 days
 d. $\$420 \times 0.12 \times \frac{1}{5} = \$10.08$

3. **a.** $0.25 \times \$85,000 = \$21,250$ down payment
    b. $\$799 + \$340 + \$280 + \$150 + \$80 = \$1,649$ closing costs
    c. $\$1,649 \div \$85,000 = 0.0194$, or 1.9%   closing costs were of purchase price

4. $4 \times 12 \times \$420 = \$20,160$ gross income
    $\$20,160 - \$17,280 = \$2,880$ net income
    $\$2,880 \div \$24,000 = 12\%$ rate of income on cash investment

5. $4 \times \$0.56 = \$2.24$ annual dividend per share
    $4 \times 40 \times \$2.24 = \$358.40$ total dividends for 4 years
    $\$1,850 - \$1,690 = \$160$ loss on sale of stock
    $\$358.40 - \$160 = \$198.40$ net gain

Section 64.   Owning a Home

Exercise 1, page 340

1. $0.02 \times \$75,300 = \$1,506$ depreciation

2. $0.032 \times \$52,700 = \$1,686.40$ depreciation

3. $0.025 \times \$74,900 = \$1,872.50$ depreciation

4. $(10 \times 0.018) \times \$55,200 = \$9,936$ depreciation for 10 years

5. $(3 \times 0.05) \times \$32,000 = \$4,800$ depreciation for 3 years

Exercise 2, page 341

1. $0.113 \times \$17,600 = \$1,988.80$ income lost

2. $0.055 \times \$8,400 = \$462$ interest lost

3. **a.** $0.09 \times \$9,000 = \$810$ estimated interest lost
    b. $0.0891 \times \$8,987 = \$800.74$ actual interest lost

Exercise 3, page 341

1. $\$7,128 + \$1,800 + \$515 + \$1,680 + \$1,237 + \$1,472 = \$13,832$ total expenses
    $\$13,832 - \$3,112 = \$10,720$ net cost

2. $\$10,180 + \$3,690 + \$833 + \$3,800 + \$900 + \$2,375 = \$21,778$ total expenses
    $\$21,778 - \$5,700 = \$16,078$ net cost

3. $0.2 \times \$55,000 = \$11,000$ down payment
    $0.12 \times \$11,000 = \$1,320$ lost interest income
    $\$4,914 + \$1,208 + \$260 + (0.02 \times \$55,000) + \$1,050 + \$1,320 = \$9,852$ total expenses
    $\$9,852 - \$1,280 = \$8,572$ net cost

4. $0.25 \times \$64,800 = \$16,200$ down payment
$0.085 \times \$16,200 = \$1,377$ lost interest income
$\$6,005 + \$850 + \$395 + (0.025 \times \$64,800) + \$1,400 + \$1,377 = \$11,647$
total expenses
$\$11,647 - \$1,847 = \$9,800$ net cost

Exercise 4, page 343

1. $12 \times \$475 = \$5,700$ yearly rental
$\$7,250 - \$5,700 = \$1,550$ saved by renting

2. **a.** $12 \times \$640 = \$7,680$ rent for year
   b. $(0.07 \times \$10,400) + \$9,300 = \$10,028$ total expenses
$\$10,028 - \$1,428 = \$8,600$ net cost of owning
   c. $\$8,600 - \$7,680 = \$920$ less to rent

3. **a.** $12 \times \$850 = \$10,200$ rent for year
   b. $\$4,800 + \$1,400 + \$1,980 + \$900 + \$410 + \$1,100 = \$10,590$ total
expenses
$\$10,590 - \$1,736 = \$8,854$ net cost of owning
   c. $\$10,200 - \$8,854 = \$1,346$ less to buy

4. **a.** $0.15 \times \$44,000 = \$6,600$ down payment
$0.075 \times \$6,600 = \$495$ lost income
   b. $\$570 + \$1,400 + \$290 + \$4,516 + \$1,120 + \$495 = \$8,391$ total
expenses
$\$8,391 - \$1,026 = \$7,365$ net cost
   c. $12 \times \$510 = \$6,120$ annual rental
$\$7,365 - \$6,120 = \$1,245$ less to rent

5. **a.** $\$1,870 + \$2,800 + \$2,360 + \$570 + \$1,900 + (0.092 \times \$50,000) =$
$\$14,100$
$\$14,100 - \$1,290 = \$12,810$ net cost
   b. $12 \times \$850 = \$10,200$
$\$12,810 - \$10,200 = \$2,610$ could have saved

Review 64, page 344

1. **a.** $2\frac{3}{4} + 5\frac{1}{2} + 7\frac{5}{6} = 16\frac{1}{12}$
   b. $28.940 - 17.736 = 11.204$
   c. $6\frac{1}{4} \times 8\frac{1}{2} = 53\frac{1}{8}$
   d. $24 \div \frac{2}{3} = 36$
   e. $5.65 \times 0.58 = 3.277$
   f. $0.00\frac{1}{2} \times \$56,000 = \$280$
   g. $50 \times 80 = 4,000$
   h. $\$5,089,764 = \$5,090,000$

2. $12 \times \$640 = \$7,680$ annual rental
$0.125 \times \$12,000 = \$1,500$ lost interest
$\$5,300 + \$380 + \$1,700 + \$770 + \$1,460 + \$1,500 = \$11,110$ total
expenses
$\$11,110 - \$1,876 = \$9,234$ net cost
$\$9,234 - \$7,680 = \$1,554$ saved by renting

3. $12 \times \$900 = \$10,800$ rental income
$\$4,320 + \$1,800 + \$650 + \$1,740 + \$400 = \$8,910$ total expenses
$\$10,800 - \$8,910 = \$1,890$ net income
$\$1,890 \div \$18,000 = 0.105$, or 11%   rate of income on investment

4.

Check register balance	$286.34	Bank statement balance		$830.28
Deduct:		Deduct:		
Service charge	− 2.60	Outstanding checks:		
	$283.74	#67	$172.13	
Add:		#70	292.54	
Interest earned	+ 0.72	#72	81.15	− 545.82
Correct check register balance	$284.46	Available bank balance		$284.46

5. $238.50 ÷ 37.5 = $6.36   hourly rate of pay

6.

$$\$1,350 \qquad\qquad = \$1,350 \quad \text{total earnings for March}$$
$$\$1,350 + (0.04 \times \$1,400) = 1,406 \quad \text{total earnings for April}$$
$$\$1,350 + (0.04 \times \$4,800) = \underline{1,542} \quad \text{total earnings for May}$$
$$\$4,298 \quad \text{total earnings for 3 months}$$

7. $47.94 + (6 × $54.16) = $372.90   installment price
$372.90 − $330 = $42.90   difference
$42.90 ÷ $330 = 13%   installment price more than cash price

8. $0.07 \times \$600 \times \frac{1}{2} = \$21$ semiannual interest
$600 + $21 = $621   new balance
$0.07 \times \$621 \times \frac{1}{2} = \$21.74$ semiannual interest
$621.00 + $21.74 = $642.74   balance after 1 year

Section 65.   Depreciating a Car or Truck

Exercise 1, page 346

1.
  a. $14,500 − $3,100 = $11,400   total depreciation
  b. $7,050 − $3,850 = $3,200   total depreciation
  c. $28,900 − $9,600 = $19,300   total depreciation
  d. $10,220 − $1,850 = $8,370   total depreciation

2. $14,740 − $6,790 = $7,950   total depreciation

3. $8,100 − $2,400 = $5,700   total depreciation

4. $7,300 − $700 = $6,600   total depreciation

Exercise 2, page 347

1.
  a. ($9,500 − $6,200) ÷ 3 = $1,100
  b. ($18,500 − $3,800) ÷ 7 = $2,100
  c. ($13,525 − $8,775) ÷ 2 = $2,375
  d. ($8,100 − $2,025) ÷ 5 = $1,215

2. ($20,250 − $5,100) ÷ 5 = $3,030   average annual depreciation

3. ($12,417 − $3,710) ÷ 4 = $2,176.75, or $2,177   average annual depreciation

4.
  a. ($17,000 − $3,000) ÷ 7 = $2,000   estimate of average annual depreciation
  b. ($17,072 − $2,890) ÷ 7 = $2,026   average annual depreciation

5.
  a. ($8,850 − $3,825) ÷ 3 = $1,675   annual depreciation if trade-in is taken
  b. ($8,850 − $4,500) ÷ 3 = $1,450   annual depreciation if car is sold

Exercise 3, page 348

1. **a.** ($14,500 − $5,600) ÷ 4 = $2,225   average annual depreciation
   $2,225 ÷ $14,500 = 15%   rate of depreciation
   b. ($8,100 − $4,200) ÷ 3 = $1,300   annual annual depreciation
   $1,300 ÷ $8,100 = 16%   rate of depreciation
   c. ($9,450 − $1,800) ÷ 6 = $1,275   average annual depreciation
   $1,275 ÷ $9,450 = 13%   rate of depreciation
   d. ($12,680 − $7,700) ÷ 2 = $2,490   average annual depreciation
   $2,490 ÷ $12,680 = 20%   rate of depreciation

2. ($10,400 − $4,300) ÷ 4 = $1,525   average annual depreciation
   $1,525 ÷ $10,400 = 15%   rate of depreciation

3. ($9,210 − $4,800) ÷ 3 = $1,470   average annual depreciation
   $1,470 ÷ $9,210 = 16%   rate of depreciation

4. ($15,300 − $8,000) ÷ 2 = $3,650   average annual depreciation
   $3,650 ÷ $15,300 = 24%   rate of depreciation

5. ($8,675 − $725) ÷ $7\frac{1}{2}$ = $1,060   average annual depreciation
   $1,060 ÷ $8,675 = 12%   rate of depreciation

6. ($13,060 − $2,900) ÷ 4 = $2,540   average annual depreciation
   $2,540 ÷ $13,060 = 19%   rate of depreciation

7. ($17,380 − $5,200) ÷ 6 = $2,030   average annual depreciation
   $2,030 ÷ $17,380 = 12%   rate of depreciation

Review 65, page 349

2. **a.** $63,000 × 0.105 = $6,615
   b. (960 − 192) ÷ 960 = 80%
   c. $500 × 0.15 × $\frac{1}{3}$ = $25
   d. 48 ÷ $\frac{2}{3}$ = 72

3. ($28,000 − $12,880) ÷ 6 = $2,520   average annual depreciation

4. ($19,000 − $2,280) ÷ 8 = $2,090   average annual depreciation
   $2,090 ÷ $19,000 = 11%   rate of depreciation

5. $5,000 ÷ 9.08 = 550.661   shares

6. September 17 to November 29 = 73   days
   $5,400 × 0.14 × $\frac{1}{5}$ = $151.20   interest
   $5,400 + $151.20 = $5,551.20   amount of payment

7. $500 × 0.92 = $460   market price of bond
   $500 × 0.06 = $30   annual interest
   $30 ÷ $460 = 0.0652, or 6.5%   yield

Section 66.   Cost of Operating a Car or Truck

Exercise 1, page 351

1. **a.** (0.07 × $9,600) + (0.16 × $9,600) + $1,600 = $3,808   total operating cost
   b. (0.12 × $15,400) + (0.2 × $15,400) + $1,940 = $6,868   total operating cost

c. $(0.1 \times \$12{,}800) + (0.15 \times \$12{,}800) + \$2{,}100 = \$5{,}300$ total operating cost

d. $(0.09 \times \$11{,}900) + (0.21 \times \$11{,}900) + \$1{,}570 = \$5{,}140$ total operating cost

2. $\$755 + \$125 + \$562 + \$42 + (0.07 \times \$13{,}500) + (0.17 \times \$13{,}500) = \$4{,}724$ operating cost

3. $\$46 + \$640 + \$670 + (0.11 \times \$9{,}800) + \$30 + (0.23 \times \$9{,}800) = \$4{,}718$ operating cost

4. $\$4{,}120 + \$843 + \$160 + \$710 + \$1{,}734 + \$583 + \$170 = \$8{,}320$ total expenses for year
$\$8{,}320 \div 52 = \$160$ average weekly cost

Exercise 2, page 351

1. $(2{,}400 \div 100) \times \$1.05 = \$25.20$ cost of license plates
$(1\,080 \text{ kg} \div 100) \times \$2.33 = \$25.16$ cost of license plates

2. $448 \div 14 = 32$ miles per gallon
$756 \text{ km} \div 54 \text{ L} = 14$ kilometers per liter

3. $316 \div 32 = 9.8$, or 10 miles per gallon
$508 \text{ km} \div 121 \text{ L} = 4.19$, or 4 kilometers per liter

4. **a.** $552 \div 24 = 23$ miles per gallon
$882 \text{ km} \div 90 \text{ L} = 9.8$, or 10 kilometers per liter
   b. $24 \times \$1.21 = \$29.04$ cost of gas
$90 \text{ L} \times \$0.323 = \$29.07$ cost of gas
   c. $\$29.04 \div 552 = \$0.0526$, or $\$0.053$ per mile
$\$29.07 \div 882 \text{ km} = \$0.0329$, or $\$0.033$ per kilometer

5. **a.** $\$811.50 + \$419 + \$630 + \$1{,}350 + \$125 + \$46 + \$271.80 = \$3{,}653.30$
   b. $\$3{,}653.30 \div 14{,}600 = \$0.25$ average cost per mile
$\$3{,}653.30 \div 23\,500 \text{ km} = \$0.155$, or $\$0.16$ average cost per kilometer
   c. $14{,}600 \div 770 = 18.9$, or 19 miles per gallon
$23\,500 \text{ km} \div 2{,}918 = 8$ km per gallon

6. $(24{,}318 \div 18) \times \$1.28 = \$1{,}729.28$, or $\$1{,}729$ spent for gas last year
$(39\,116 \text{ km} \div 7.7) \times \$0.34 = \$1{,}727.20$, or $\$1{,}727$ spent for gas last year

Exercise 3, page 353

1. $12 \times \$221 = \$2{,}652$ cost of lease

2. **a.** $(4 \times 12 \times \$170) + (4 \times \$1{,}600) = \$14{,}560$ 4-year operating cost of truck
   b. $4 \times 14{,}000 = 56{,}000$ total miles driven in 4 years
$\$14{,}560 \div 56{,}000 = \$0.26$ cost per mile

3. $(14{,}000 + 17{,}000 + 16{,}000 + 15{,}000) - 60{,}000 = 2{,}000$ excess miles driven
$(4 \times 12 \times \$122) + \$4{,}434 + (\$0.06 \times 2{,}000) = \$10{,}410$ total cost of operating

4. **a.** $6,350 + (0.6 \times \$15,250) + \$3,600 = \$19,100$ total cost of owning
and operating
   b. $(4 \times 12 \times \$236) + \$6,350 = \$17,678$ cost of leasing
   c. $\$19,100 - \$17,678 = \$1,422$; cheaper to lease

5. **a.** $12 \times \$190 = \$2,280$ leasing cost of 4-door sedan
$12 \times \$328.70 = \$3,944.40$ leasing cost of van
$\$3,944.40 - \$2,280 = \$1,664.40$ van will cost more
   b. $(\$328.70 - \$190) \div \$190 = 73\%$ more to lease van

6. $18,700 - 15,000 = 3,700$ excess miles driven
$(12 \times \$122) + (\$0.06 \times 3,700) = \$1,686$ first-year leasing cost

Exercise 4, page 354

1. $600 \times \$1.15 = \$690$ cost of gasoline near work
$600 \times \$1.07 = \$642$ cost of gasoline near home
$\$690 - \$642 = \$48$ saved by buying near home

2. $(24,000 \div 32) \times \$1.25 = \$937.50$ cost of gas for compact car
$(24,000 \div 15) \times \$1.25 = 2,000$ cost of gas for sports car
$\$2,000 - \$937.50 = \$1,062.50$ saved by buying compact car

3. $\$12,700 - \$3,556 = \$9,144$ total depreciation
$\$9,144 \div \$12,700 = 72\%$ total percent depreciation of 2-door car
$\$15,800 - \$5,530 = \$10,270$ total depreciation
$\$10,270 \div \$15,800 = 65\%$ total percent depreciation of 4-door car
Two-door car, 72%

4. **a.** $0.75 \times \$14,000 = \$10,500$ resale value at end of 1 year
   b. $0.60 \times \$14,000 = \$8,400$ resale value at end of 2 years
   c. $(\$14,000 - \$8,400) \div 2 = \$2,800$ average annual depreciation

5. $78 + 91 + 55 + 140 + 118 = 482$ total miles driven in week
$(\$0.21 \times 482) + \$12.50 = \$113.72$ amount Matt will get

Review 66, page 354

1. **a.** $(\$72 - \$48) \div \$72 = \frac{1}{3}$ **d.** $\$20,000 \times 1.05 = \$21,000$
   b. $17.8 \text{ m} \times 8 \text{ m} = 142.4 \text{ m}^2$ **e.** $\$856 - (\$856 \times 0.62\frac{1}{2}) = \$321$
   c. $34.8 \div 0.04 = 870$

2. $\$436 + \$670 + \$28 + \$42 + (0.05 \times \$9,200) + (0.18 \times \$9,200) = \$3,292$
operating cost
$\$3,292 \div 12,000 = \$0.27$ operating cost per mile

3. $(2 \times 16,500) - (2 \times 15,000) = 3,000$ excess miles
$(2 \times 12 \times \$238) + (\$0.07 \times 3,000) = \$5,922$ amount paid for leasing

4. $(\$11,900 - \$1,400) \div 7 = \$1,500$ average annual depreciation

5. $20 \times 12 = 240$ number of payments
$(240 \times \$495.49) - \$45,000 = \$73,917.60$ interest paid

6. $4 \times \$0.45 = \$1.80$ annual dividend
$\$1.80 \div \$60 = 3\%$ rate of income

UNIT 11 ● TAXES

Section 67. Property Taxes

Exercise 1, page 359

1. a. $80,000 ÷ $100 = 800   units of $100
       800 × $5.20 = $4,160   amount of tax
    b. $48,500 ÷ $100 = 485   units of $100
       485 × $7.10 = $3,443.50   amount of tax
    c. $15,000 ÷ $1,000 = 15   units of $1,000
       15 × $34 = $510   amount of tax
    d. $20,800 ÷ $1,000 = 20.8   units of $1,000
       20.8 × $28 = $582.40   amount of tax
    e. $18,000 ÷ $100 = 180   units of $100
       180 × $3.085 = $555.30   amount of tax
    f. $40,500 ÷ $1,000 = 40.5   units of $1,000
       40.5 × $25.764 = $1,043.44   amount of tax

2. $60,500 ÷ $100 = 605   units of $100
    605 × $3.775 = $2,283.88   amount of tax

3. $25,900 ÷ $1,000 = 25.9   units of $1,000
    25.9 × $38.20 = $989.38   amount of tax

4. $17,500 ÷ $100 = 175   units of $100
    175 × $4.155 = $727.13   amount of tax

5. $250,000 × 0.60 = $150,000   assessed value
    $150,000 ÷ $1,000 = 150   units of $1,000
    150 × $45.089 = $6,763.35   amount of tax

6. a. $150,000 × 0.50 = $75,000   estimated assessed value
       $75,000 ÷ $1,000 = 75   units of $1,000
       75 × $20 = $1,500   estimated amount of tax
    b. $151,000 × 0.50 = $75,500   assessed value
       $75,500 ÷ $1,000 = 75.5   units of $1,000
       75.5 × $19 = $1,434.50   amount of tax

Exercise 2, page 360

1.	Assessed Value	Tax Rate Per $1	Tax Due
a.	$80,000	35 mills	$0.035 × $80,000 = $2,800
b.	48,500	82.1 mills	0.0821 × $48,500 = $3,981.85
c.	15,000	77.3 mills	0.0773 × $15,000 = $1,159.50
d.	20,800	9 cents	0.09 × $20,800 = $1,872
e.	18,000	2.7 cents	0.027 × $18,000 = $486
f.	40,500	4.54 cents	0.0454 × $40,500 = $1,838.70

2. 48 mills ÷ 1,000 = $0.048   mills to dollars
    $0.048 × $35,200 = $1,689.60   amount of tax

3. 3.5 cents ÷ 100 = $0.035   cents to dollars
    $0.035 × $20,750 = $726.25   amount of tax

4. $125,000 × 0.25 = $31,250   assessed value
   72.5 ÷ 1,000 = $0.0725   mills to dollars
   $0.0725 × $31,250 = $2,265.63   tax bill

5. $70,800 × 0.35 = $24,780   assessed value of 1 house
   $140,300 × 0.35 = $49,105   assessed value of second house
   28.5 ÷ 1,000 = 0.0285   mills to dollars
   ($0.0285 × $24,780) + (0.0285 × $49,105) = $2,105.72   total tax

Review 67, page 361

2. a. $28,000 × 0.08076 = $2,261.28
   b. ($440 − $264) ÷ $440 = $\frac{2}{5}$
   c. $480 ÷ $192 = 250%
   d. 250 mL = 0.25 L
      0.25 L ÷ 4 L = 6.25% or $6\frac{1}{4}$%

3. $25,400 ÷ $1,000 = 25.4   units of $1,000
   25.4 × $56.731 = $1,440.97   tax bill

4. $20 + (52 × $2.50) = $150   total cost at Ashcroft's
   $25 + (12 × $10) = $145   total cost at Leneen's
   $150 − $145 = $5   amount saved

5. 0.92125 × $1,000 = $921.25   market price per bond
   ($921.25 × 9) + (9 × $6) = $8,345.25   total investment

6. $1,000 × 0.095 = $95   annual income
   $95 ÷ $760 = 12.5% or $12\frac{1}{2}$%   yield

7. ($880 × 12) × 20 = $211,200   total paid in 20 years
   $211,200 − $80,000 = $131,200   interest

8. a. $150 + ($59.99 × 24) = $1,589.76   installment price
      $1,589.76 − $1,500 = $89.76   finance charge
   b. $1,500 − $150 = $1,350   amount financed

‡9. $1,000 × 0.08 = $80   income per bond
    $10,000 ÷ $80 = 125   bonds

Section 68.   Property Tax Rates

Exercise 1, page 362

1. a. $507,000 ÷ $8,000,000 = 0.06338
   b. $483,200 ÷ $6,000,000 = 0.08053
   c. $158,500 ÷ $2,700,000 = 0.0587
   d. $889,600 ÷ $9,800,000 = 0.09078
   e. $100,500 ÷ $1,750,000 = 0.05743
   f. $125,800 ÷ $5,390,000 = 0.02334
   g. $22,750 ÷ $725,000 = 0.03138
   h. $282,500 ÷ $7,400,000 = 0.03818
   i. $1,279,000 ÷ $15,320,000 = 0.08349
   j. $2,528,600 ÷ $24,130,000 = 0.10479

2. a. $878,000 − $97,500 = $780,000   raised by property tax
$780,000 ÷ $36,000,000 = 0.022   tax rate

   b. $382,700 − $68,400 = $314,300   raised by property tax
$314,300 ÷ $22,750,000 = 0.014   tax rate

   c. $396,300 − $45,600 = $350,700   raised by property tax
$350,700 ÷ $7,900,000 = 0.044   tax rate

3. $583,400 ÷ $24,780,000 = 0.024   tax rate

4. $278,000 ÷ $6,800,000 = 0.041   tax rate

5. a. $2,000,000 − $800,000 = $1,200,000   estimated property tax to be raised

   b. $2,210,000 − $835,000 = $1,375,000   property tax to be raised

   c. $1,375,000 ÷ $40,000,000 = 0.0344   tax rate

6. $4,000,000 − $2,900,000 = $1,100,000   property tax to be raised
$1,100,000 ÷ $89,500,000 = 0.0123   tax rate

Exercise 2, page 363

1. 0.0145 × $82,000 = $1,189   amount of school tax

2. 0.04218 × $15,600 = $658.01   tax on property

3. (0.0375 × $9,900) + (0.0375 × $27,300) = $1,395   total tax

4. a. $2,000,000 ÷ $200,000,000 = 0.01   estimated tax rate

   b. $2,100,000 ÷ $198,000,000 = 0.0106   tax rate

   c. 0.0106 × $24,000 = $254.40   tax on property

5. a. $6,750,000 − $650,000 = $6,100,000   amount to be raised by property tax

   b. $6,100,000 ÷ $80,000,000 = 0.076   tax rate

   c. 0.076 × $40,000 = $3,040   tax on property

Exercise 3, page 364

1.

	Decimal Rate	Rate in Dollars per $100	Rate in Dollars per $1,000	Rate in Cents per $1	Rate in Mills per $1
a.	0.03478	3.478	34.78	3.478	34.78
b.	0.01208	1.208	12.08	1.208	12.08
c.	0.10675	10.675	106.75	10.675	106.75
d.	0.08462	8.462	84.62	8.462	84.62
e.	0.01782	1.782	17.82	1.782	17.82

2. $680,000 ÷ $32,000,000 = 0.02125   decimal rate
0.02125 × $1,000 = $21.25   tax rate per $1,000

3. $636,000 ÷ $240,000,000 = 0.00265   decimal rate
0.00265 × $100 = $0.265   tax rate per $100

4. a. $4,800,000 ÷ $64,000,000 = 0.075   decimal rate
0.075 × 100 = 7.5   cents per $1

   b. 0.075 × 1,000 = 75   mills per $1

    c. 0.075 × $100 = 7.50   dollars per $100
    d. 0.075 × $1,000 = 75   dollars per $1,000

5. $2,310 ÷ $55,000 = 0.042   decimal rate
    0.042 × $1,000 = $42   per $1,000

6. **a.** $9,500,000 − $3,000,000 = $6,500,000   needed in property tax
      $6,500,000 ÷ $125,000,000 = 0.052   decimal rate
      0.052 × $100 = $5.20   per $100
    b. 0.052 × $1,000 = $52   per $1,000

Review 68, page 365

1. **a.** 2,800 ÷ 175,000 = 0.016
    b. 2.50 × $60 = $150
    c. July 6 to October 19 = 105   days
    d. $6,400 × 0.06 × $\frac{1}{3}$ = $128

2. $720,000 − $128,000 = $592,000   property tax to be raised
    $592,000 ÷ $21,000,000 = 0.02819   tax rate

3. **a.** 0.01182 × $1,000 = $11.82   rate per $1,000
    b. 0.01182 × 1,000 = 11.82   mills per $1

4. $16,800 ÷ $1,000 = 16.8   units per $1,000
    16.8 × $82.19 = $1,380.79   tax

5. $400 × 12 = $4,800   annual rent
    $13,000 × 0.12 = $1,560   interest that could be earned on down payment
    $1,560 + $6,240 = $7,800   annual cost of buying home
    $7,800 − $4,800 = $3,000   saved annually by renting

Section 69. Sales and Excise Taxes

Exercise 2, page 366

1. **a.** (10 × $0.05) + $0.04 = $0.54   sales tax
    b. $10.79 + $0.54 = $11.33   total price

2. (24 × $0.05) + $0.05 = $1.25   sales tax

3. $99.95 + $10.79 = $110.74   total sales
    (110 × $0.05) + $0.04 = $5.54   sales tax

Exercise 3, page 367

1. $45 × 0.06 = $2.70   sales tax on goods
    $30 × 3 = $90   cost of services
    $90 + $45 + $2.70 = $137.70   total cost

2. $2.79 + $1.29 = $4.08   total of taxable items
    $4.08 × 0.03 = $0.12   sales tax
    $1 + (2 × $0.87) + (5 × $0.88) + $4.08 + $0.12 = $11.34   total bill

3.

	Total of Taxable Items	Total of Nontaxable Items	Sales Tax	Total Bill
a.	$145.70	$103.00	$ 7.29	$255.99
b.	39.39	128.89	1.97	170.25
c.	8.34	201.12	0.42	209.88
d.	378.50	100.08	18.93	497.51
e.	44.67	34.87	2.23	81.77

Exercise 4, page 368

1. $0.08 \times \$210 = \$16.80$ excise tax
$\$210 + \$16.80 = \$226.80$ total cost of ticket

2. $\$15.75 + (0.03 \times \$15.75) + (0.06 \times \$15.75) = \$17.17$ total cost of regular service
$\$22.57 + (0.03 \times \$22.57) + (0.06 \times \$22.57) = \$24.60$ total cost of long distance
$\$17.17 + \$24.60 = \$41.77$ total bill

3. $\$18.62 + (\$0.001 \times 19) + (0.06 \times \$18.62) = \$19.76$ total bill

4.

	Item	Cost	Sales Tax	Excise Tax	Total Cost
a.	Videotape	$ 6.89	6%	0%	$ 7.30
b.	15 gal. gas	13.35	4%	$0.001 per gallon	13.90
c.	Airline ticket	274.59	0%	8%	296.56
d.	Tackle box	19.99	5%	10%	22.99
e.	Telephone service	24.92	7%	3%	27.41
f.	Baseball glove	29.89	5%	11%	34.67

‡Exercise 5, page 368

1. **a.** $\$88,620 \div 1.05 = \$84,400$ store's sales without tax
b. $\$88,620 - (\$88,620 \div 1.05) = \$4,220$ sales tax

2. **a.** $\$378 \div 1.08 = \$350$ airline service
b. $\$378 - \$350 = \$28$ excise tax

Review 69, page 369

1. **a.** $0.0146 = \$14.60$
b. $(\$540 - \$450) \div \$540 = \frac{1}{6}$
c. $\$380 \times 0.005 = \$1.90$
d. $5 \text{ m} = 500$ cm
$500 \text{ cm} \times 3 = 1\,500$ cm
e. $\$150 \div \frac{1}{3} = \$450$

2. $\$45.87 + \$13.22 + (\$13.22 \times 0.05) = \$59.75$ total bill

3. $\$18.56 + (\$18.56 \times 0.06) + (\$18.56 \times 0.03) = \$20.23$ total bill

4. $(56 + 100) - 65 = 91$ gallons

5. March 17 to May 29 = 73   days
$2,000 × 0.12 × $\frac{1}{5}$ = $48   interest
$2,000 + $48 = $2,048   amount of payment

6. **a.** $100,000 × 0.06 = $6,000   estimated commission
   b. $96,200 × 0.06 = $5,772   commission
       $96,200 − $5,772 = $90,428   net proceeds

7. **a.** $1,419.12 ÷ $21,600 = 0.0657 × $1,000 = $65.70   per $1,000
   b.   0.0657 × $100 = $6.57   per $100

Section 70.   Social Security Taxes and Benefits

Exercise 1, page 370

1. **a.**   0.0765 × $206 = $15.76   **d.**   0.0765 × $422.50 = $32.32
   b.   0.0765 × $399.70 = $30.58   **e.**   0.0765 × $380.80 = $29.13
   c.   0.0765 × $516.20 = $39.49   **f.**   0.0765 × $295.07 = $22.57

2. 0.0765 × $38,746 = $2,964.07   FICA tax

3. 0.153 × $42,370 = $6,482.61   self-employment tax

4. **a.** $45,000   salary subject to FICA tax
   b. $58,800 − $45,000 = $13,800   salary not subject to FICA tax
   c. $50,000 × 0.08 = $4,000   estimated FICA tax
   d.   0.0765 × $45,000 = $3,442.50   must be paid

5. **a.** $61,500 ÷ 12 = $5,125   monthly salary
       0.0765 × $5,125 = $392.06   deductible in January
   b. $392.06   deducted in August
   c.   10 × $5,125 = $51,250; Exceeds $45,000
       $0.00   FICA tax

Exercise 2, page 371

1. **a.** $505 at age 65
   b. $505 − ($505 × 0.20) = $404   at age 62

2. $633 × $6\frac{2}{3}$% = $633 × $\frac{20}{300}$ = $42.20   less
   $633 − $42.20 = $590.80   benefits at age 64

3. **a.** $441 × $13\frac{1}{3}$% = $441 × $\frac{40}{300}$ = $58.80   less
       $441 − $58.80 = $382.20   benefits at age 63
   b. $441 at age 65

4. $697 × 0.20 = $139.40   more in monthly benefits at age 65

5. **a.**   12 × $569 = $6,828   total yearly benefits at age 65
   b. $569 − ($569 × 0.20) = $455.20   monthly benefit
       12 × $455.20 = $5,462.40   yearly benefit at age 62
   c. $6,828 − $5,462.40 = $1,365.60   more at age 65

6. **a.** $811.70 × $6\frac{2}{3}$% = $811.70 × $\frac{20}{300}$ = $54.11   less
       $811.70 − $54.11 = $757.59   monthly benefit at age 64
   b. $811.70 − $757.59 = $54.11   more if she retires at age 65

Review 70, page 372

2.
  a. $3,800 \times 0.0025 = \$9.50$
  b. $(\$700 - \$420) \div \$420 = \frac{2}{3}$
  c. $\$4,800 \times 0.09 \times \frac{1}{12} = \$36$
  d. $67 \div 1,000 = 0.067$ tax rate
      0.067 mills $\times \$1,000 = \$67$
  e. $\$14 \div \frac{4}{3} = \$10.50$

3. $\$633 - (\$633 \times 0.20) = \$506.40$ monthly benefits at age 62

4. $0.0765 \times \$45,000 = \$3,442.50$ FICA tax employer paid

5. $0.153 \times \$45,000 = \$6,885$ self-employment tax

6. $\$4,104,670 - \$376,800 = \$3,767,870$ to be raised by property tax
    $\$3,767,870 \div \$93,600,000 = 0.040$ decimal tax rate

7. $(\$790 - \$100) \div 30 = \$23$ monthly payment

8. June 8   due date
    $\$1,200 + (\$1,200 \times 0.12 \times \frac{1}{4}) = \$1,236$ amount due

9. $\$0.65 \times 20 = \$13$ quarterly dividend
    $(\$13 \times 4) \times 3 = \$156$ total dividends in 3 years
    $(\$1,660 - \$1,580) + \$156 = \$236$ total gain

‡10. $\$148.40 \div 1.06 = \$140$ selling price of camera

Section 71.   Federal Income Taxes

Exercise 1, page 374

1. $\$18,648 - \$1,380 = \$17,268$ adjusted gross income

2.
  a. $\$13,820 + \$5,495 + \$341 = \$19,656$ gross income
  b. $\$2,000 + \$19 = \$2,019$ adjustments to income
  c. $\$19,656 - \$2,019 = \$17,637$ adjusted gross income

3. $\$45,635.90 + \$1,926.12 + \$4,101.73 + \$2,180 = \$53,843.75$ gross income
    $\$53,843.75 - \$5,108.33 = \$48,735.42$ adjusted gross income

4. $\$27,850 + \$26,378 + \$750 + \$1,610 + \$787.35 = \$57,375.35$ gross income
    $\$4,330 + \$78 = \$4,408$ adjustments to income
    $\$57,375.35 - \$4,408 = \$52,967.35$ adjusted gross income

Exercise 2, page 375

1.
$15,354	adjusted gross income
− 5,650	itemized deductions
$ 9,704	
− 2,000	exemption
$ 7,704	taxable income

2. $32,007   adjusted gross income
     − 4,700   itemized deductions
     $27,307
     − 6,000   exemptions (3 × $2,000)
     $21,307   taxable income

3. a. $45,000   estimated adjusted gross income
     − 7,000   estimated deductions
     $38,000
     − 8,000   exemptions (4 × $2,000)
     $30,000   estimated taxable income

b. $45,208   adjusted gross income
     − 7,107   itemized deductions
     $38,101
     − 8,000   exemptions (4 × $2,000)
     $30,101   taxable income

Exercise 5, page 377

1. $8,450 − $8,278 = $172   tax refund

2. $17,448 − $16,118 = $1,330   tax owed

3. a. $1,957 = actual tax (from table)
   b. $2,140.75 − $1,957 = $183.75   tax refund

4. $3,221 = actual tax (from table)
   $3,221 − $3,205.46 = $15.54   tax owed

Review 71, page 377

2. a. ($35 − $28) ÷ $28 = $\frac{1}{4}$
   b. $270 ÷ $90 = 300%
   c. 0.005 × $250 = $1.25
   d. $500 × 0.06 × $\frac{1}{10}$ = $3
   e. (480 m − 360 m) ÷ 480 m = 25%

3. $3,995   actual tax
   $4,110 − $3,995 = $115   tax refund

4. $32,908   adjusted gross income
     − 4,808   itemized deductions
     $28,100
     − 6,000   exemptions (3 × $2,000)
     $22,100   taxable income

5. $64,000 × 0.50 = $32,000   assessed value
   $32,000 ÷ 1,000 = 32   units per $1,000
   $38.20 × 32 = $1,222.40   property tax

Section 72.   More Federal Income Taxes

Exercise 1, page 379

1. $250   earned income is higher
    $500   standard deduction

2. $1,950   earned income is higher
    $1,950   standard deduction

3. $200   unearned income is higher
    $500   standard deduction

4. $1,200   unearned income is higher
    $500   standard deduction

5. $4,875   earned income is higher
    $3,000   standard deduction

Exercise 2, page 380

1. a. $2,406   wages
        +   148   interest

        $2,554   adjusted gross income
        − 2,406   less deductions

        $ 148   taxable income
    b. $336 − $15 = $321   refund

2. a. $3,256   wages
        +   174   interest

        $3,430   adjusted gross income
        − 3,000   less deductions

        430   taxable income
    b. $420 − $48 = $372   refund

3. $2,855   gross earnings
    2,855   less deductions

    $ 0.00   taxable income
    $384 − $0.00 = $384   refund

4. $3,288 + $78 + $16 = $3,382   gross earnings
    $3,382 − $3,000 = $382   taxable income
    $410 − $43 = $367   refund

5. a. $1,600 + $330 = $1,930   gross earnings
        $1,930 − $1,930 = $0.00
    b. $220 − $0 = $220   refund

6. $15   tax on taxable income of $148
    $277 − $15 = $262   refund

Review 72, page 380

1. a. ($270 − $189) ÷ $270 = 30%
    b. $4,800 × 0.00125 = $6
    c. 625 grams = 0.625 kg
        0.625 kg ÷ 5 kg = $12\frac{1}{2}$%

‡**d.** $50 × 2.50 = $125
‡**e.** $100\% - 33\frac{1}{3}\% = 67\frac{2}{3}\%$, or $\frac{2}{3}$
$300 ÷ \frac{2}{3} = $450

2. $3,312 + $38 = $3,350   gross earnings
$3,350 - $3,000 (deduction) = $350   taxable income
$456 - $40 (tax from table) = $416   refund

3. $3,241

4.   **a.** $20 + (2 × $5) + $30 = $60   estimated total cost
0.05 × $60 = $3   estimated sales tax
$60 + $3 = $63   estimated bill
   b. $19.79 + (2 × $4.95) + $28.99 = $58.68   total cost
0.05 × $58.68 = $2.93   sales tax
$58.68 + $2.93 = $61.61   exact bill

5. $60 + (10 × $42) = $480   installment price
$480 - $450 = $30   would be saved

6. $866,250 ÷ $16,500,000 = 0.0525   decimal rate
0.0525 × $1,000 = $52.50   per $1,000

Section 73.   State and City Income Taxes

Exercise 1, page 383

1. $550 + 0.05 × ($15,798 - $15,000) = $589.90   state income tax

2. $2,400 + 0.09 × ($35,470 - $35,000) = $2,442.30   state income tax

3. $2,900 + 0.10 × ($41,548 - $40,000) = $3,054.80   state income tax

4. $250 + 0.04 × ($12,892 - $10,000) = $365.68   state income tax

5.   **a.** $57,722 - $13,230 = $44,492   taxable income
   b. $2,900 + 0.10 × ($44,492 - $40,000) = $3,349.20   state income tax

6.   **a.** $12,400 - ($3,000 + $2,000) = $7,400   taxable income
   b. $100 + 0.03 × ($7,400 - $5,000) = $172   state income tax
   c. $420 - $172 = $248   refund

Exercise 2, page 383

1. $18,345 × 0.025 = $458.63   city income tax

2. $23,616 × 0.005 = $118.08   city income tax

3.   **a.** $16,900 × 0.01 = $169   city income tax
   b. $550 + 0.05 × ($16,900 - $15,000) = $645   state income tax
   c. $169 + $645 = $814   total city and state income taxes

4. $22,896 × 0.02 = $457.92   city tax
$1,200 + 0.06 × ($22,896 - $20,000) = $1,373.76   state income tax
$457.92 + $1,373.76 = $1,831.68   total city and state income tax

5. $42,834 × 0.0225 = $963.77   city income tax
$2,900 + 0.10 × ($42,834 - $40,000) = $3,183.40   state income tax
$963.77 + $3,183.40 + $8,231 = $12,378.17   total city, state, and federal
income taxes

Review 73, page 384

1. a. $15.3 \times 2.4 = 36.72$
    b. $32.4 \div 2.4 = 13.5$
    c. $4\frac{2}{5} + 6\frac{1}{2} = 10\frac{9}{10}$
    d. $17\frac{1}{4} - 6\frac{1}{3} = 10\frac{11}{12}$
    e. $8\frac{1}{2} \times 5\frac{1}{3} = 45\frac{1}{3}$
    f. $5\frac{1}{3} \div 1\frac{1}{3} = 4$

2. $\$43,780 \times 0.035 = \$1,532.30$ state income tax
    $\$43,780 \times 0.0125 = \$547.25$ city income tax
    $\$1,532.30 + \$547.25 = \$2,079.55$ total city and state income taxes

3. $5 \times \$84 = \$420$ desired earnings
    $140 + 136 + 148 + 144 = 568$ pieces completed
    $568 \times \$0.60 = \$340.80$ earned in four days
    $\$420 - \$340.80 = \$79.20$ needed to be earned on Friday
    $\$79.20 \div \$0.60 = 132$ pieces must be completed on Friday

4. $\$256.80 + \$287.77 + \$297.89 = \$842.46$ gross wages
    $0.0765 \times \$842.46 = \$64.45$ FICA tax withheld from wages

5. $\$42,800 + \$1,280 + \$789 = \$44,869$ gross income
    $\$44,869 - (\$6,240 + \$2,890) = \$35,739$ adjusted gross income

6. $0.05 \times \$15,000 = \$750$ commission ($15,000 or less)
    $0.07 \times (\$25,750 - \$15,000) = \$752.50$ (over $15,000)
    $\$750 + \$752.50 = \$1,502.50$ total commission

7. a. $\$20 \times 24 = \$480$ estimated total payments
        $\$480 - \$400 = \$80$ estimated finance charge
    b. $\$19.50 \times 24 = \$468$ total payments
        $\$468 - \$400 = \$68$ finance charge
    c. $\$400$ amount financed
    d. $(\$68 \times 100) \div 400 = \$17$ finance charge per $100

‡8. $\$3,600 \div 0.09 = \$40,000$ par value needed
    $\$40,000 \times 0.97 = \$38,800$ money to be invested

UNIT 12   •   INSURANCE

Section 74. Life Insurance Premiums

Exercise 1, page 388

1. a. $(\$10,000 \div \$1,000) \times \$8.37 = \$83.70$
    b. $(\$80,000 \div \$1,000) \times \$1.28 = \$102.40$
    c. $(\$12,000 \div \$1,000) \times \$38.89 = \$466.68$
    d. $(\$40,000 \div \$1,000) \times \$1.41 = \$56.40$
    e. $(\$7,600 \div \$1,000) \times \$31.42 = \$238.79$
    f. $(\$14,000 \div \$1,000) \times \$17.62 = \$246.68$

2. $(\$20,000 \div \$1,000) \times \$44.72 = \$894.40$ cost of policy at age 45
    $(\$20,000 \div \$1,000) \times \$27.77 = \$555.40$ cost of policy at age 25
    $\$894.40 - \$555.40 = \$339$ difference

3. ($7,000 ÷ $1,000) × $28.29 = $198.03   cost of 20-payment life policy
   ($7,000 ÷ $1,000) × $8.94 = $62.58   cost of whole life policy
   $198.03 − $62.58 = $135.45   difference

4. ($45,000 ÷ $1,000) × $1.45 = $65.25   cost of 1-year term
   ($45,000 ÷ $1,000) × $10.16 = $457.20   cost of whole life policy
   $457.20 − $65.25 = $391.95   difference

5. ($9,000 ÷ $1,000) × $25.54 = $229.86   premium for one year
   20 × $229.86 = $4,597.20   total premium

6. ($30,000 ÷ $1,000) × $30.75 = $922.50   premium for 20-payment life
   20 × $922.50 = $18,450   total premium for 20 years
   ($30,000 ÷ $1,000) × $34.15 = $1,024.50   premium for 20-payment life
   20 × $1,024.50 = $20,490   total premium for 20 years
   $20,490 − $18,450 = $2,040   difference

7. **a.** $600 ÷ $6.22 = 96.46   units or 96 whole units
       96 × $1,000 = $96,000   of whole life insurance
   b. $600 ÷ $1.22 = 491.80   or 491 whole units
       491 × $1,000 = $491,000   of 1-year term

8. ($50,000 ÷ $1,000) × $2.45 = $122.50   premium on a 1-year term
   0.20 × $122.50 = $24.50   more than a nonsmoker

9. ($20.02 − $12.58) ÷ $12.58 = 59%

Review 74, page 389

2. **a.** 0.02 × $36,000 = $720   tax
   b. $15.10 + (0.3 × $15.10) = $19.63
   c. 96 − (0.625 × 96) = 36
   d. 16.8 m + 0.239 m + 1.4 m = 18.439 m

3. **a.** ($20,000 ÷ $1,000) × $16 = $320   estimated male premium
       ($20,000 ÷ $1,000) × $14 = $280   estimated female premium
       $320 − $280 = $40   estimated difference
   b. ($20,000 ÷ $1,000) × $16.30 = $326   premium for male
       ($20,000 ÷ $1,000) × $14.34 = $286.80   premium for female
       $326 − $286.80 = $39.20   actual difference

4. 2.3 mills = $0.0023
   70,000 × $0.0023 = $161   property tax

5. $2,500 − $2,500 = $0   taxable income

Section 75. Life Insurance Benefits

Exercise 1, page 391

1. ($50,000 ÷ $1,000) × $17.80 = $890   cash value

2. ($25,000 ÷ $1,000) × $76.09 = $1,902.25   could borrow

3. ($6,000 ÷ $1,000) × $1,599 = $9,594   paid-up whole life

4. 8 years, 274 days

5. **a.** $30 \times \$200 = \$6,000$ estimated cash value
  b. $(\$33,000 \div \$1,000) \times \$170.72 = \$5,633.76$ actual cash value
  c. $(\$33,000 \div \$1,000) \times \$716 = \$23,628$ paid-up whole life
  d. 21 years, 80 days
  e. $33,000 extended term

Exercise 2, page 391

1. $(\$8,000 \div \$1,000) \times \$12.80 = \$102.40$ annual premium
  $\$102.40 - \$18.90 = \$83.50$ should send to insurance company

2. $(\$15,000 \div \$1,000) \times \$32.64 = \$489.60$ annual premium
  $\$489.60 - \$62.46 = \$427.14$ should send to company

3. $(\$40,000 \div \$1,000) \times \$21 = \$840$ annual premium
  $(20 \times \$840) - \$621.68 = \$16,178.32$ net cost of policy

4. $(\$25,000 \div \$1,000) \times \$17.20 = \$430$ annual premium
  $10 \times \$430 = \$4,300$ total premiums paid
  $(\$25,000 \div \$1,000) \times \$97 = \$2,425$ cash value
  $\$4,300 - (\$2,425 + \$318.55) = \$1,556.45$ net cost of policy

5. $\$993 \times 0.0425 = \$42.20$ interest for one year

Review 75, page 392

2. **a.** $248\frac{2}{5}\% = 2.484$
  b. $\$8,000 \times 0.14 \times \frac{1}{2} = \$560$
  c. $\$384 + (\frac{1}{8} \times \$384) = \$432$

3. $(\$35,000 \div \$1,000) \times \$14.76 = \$516.60$ annual premium
  $5 \times \$516.60 = \$2,583$ total premiums paid
  $(\$35,000 \div \$1,000) \times \$35 = \$1,225$ cash value
  $\$2,583 - (\$1,225 + \$62) = \$1,296$ net cost

4. **a.** $(\$60,000 \div \$1,000) \times \$175 = \$10,500$ maximum amount that can be borrowed
  b. $0.08 \times \$10,500 = \$840$ interest

‡**5.**

Check register balance		$764.20
Deduct:		
Service charge		4.80
		$759.40
Add:		
Amount in register too large	$72.00	
Interest earned	1.21	
Deposit not recorded	78.34	151.55
Correct check register balance		$910.95

Section 76. Health and Accident Insurance

Exercise 1, page 394

1. **a.** $\$1,740 + \$1,175 = \$2,915$ insurance company paid
  b. $(\$1,900 + \$1,250) - \$2,915 = \$235$ Lela had to pay

2. a. $(9 \times \$140) + \$738 = \$1,998$ insurance company paid
    b. $9 \times (\$210 - \$140) = \$630$ Gerald had to pay

3. a. $\$3,045 + \$590 + \$260 + \$520 + \$950 = \$5,365$ total bill
    b. $(15 \times \$190) + \$545 + \$900 + \$260 + \$520 = \$5,075$ insurance company paid
    c. $\$5,365 - \$5,075 = \$290$ Despana had to pay

4. a. $9 \times \$100 = \$900$ estimated amount of disability
    b. $(0.70 \times \$148) \times 9 = \$932.40$ insurance company paid

Exercise 2, page 395

1. a. $\$36,000 - \$800 = \$35,200$ balance
        $0.90 \times \$35,200 = \$31,680$ paid by insurance company
    b. $(0.10 \times \$35,200) + \$800 = \$4,320$ you will pay

2. a. $\$260 - (6 \times \$10) = \$200$ balance
        $0.80 \times \$200 = \$160$ insurance company's share
    b. $(0.20 \times \$200) + \$60 = \$100$ Molly's share

3. a. $\$75 + \$65 + \$90 + \$12 = \$242$ total bill
        $\$242 - \$25 = \$217$ balance
        $0.70 \times \$217 = \$151.90$ paid by insurance company
    b. $(0.30 \times \$217) + \$25 = \$90.10$ paid by Daniel

4. $\$24,490 - \$750 = \$23,740$ balance
    $0.85 \times \$23,740 = \$20,179$ paid by major medical
    $17 \times \$65 = \$1,105$ disability income
    $(\$24,490 - \$20,179) - \$1,105 = \$3,206$ amount owed

5. $0.90 \times (\$34,460 - \$250) = \$30,789$ amount hospital bill paid
    $0.70 \times (30 \times \$75) = \$1,575$ amount of therapist bill paid
    $\$8,700 + \$30,789 + \$1,575 = \$41,064$ amount paid by insurance company

6. a. $\$530 - \$70 = \$460$ total covered expenses
        $\$0$ paid for Adele's expenses
    b. $0.90 \times (\$950 - \$500) = \$405$ paid for Jim's expenses

Review 76, page 396

2. a. $(\$6.65 - \$5.32) \div \$5.32 = 25\%$
    b. $36.2 + (\frac{3}{4} \times 36.2) = 63.35$
    c. $(\$288 - \$192) \div \$288 = 33\frac{1}{3}\%$
    d. $\$55,600 - (0.08 \times \$55,600) = \$51,152$

3. $\$85 + \$160 = \$245$ total claim
    $0.90 \times (\$245 - \$85) = \$144$ insurance company paid
    $\$245 - \$144 = \$101$ still owed by Steve

4. $8 \times \$350 = \$2,800$ total premiums
    $(\$25,000 \div \$1,000) \times \$62 = \$1,550$ cash value
    $\$2,800 - (\$1,550 + \$187.40) = \$1,062.60$ net cost of policy

Section 77. Property Insurance

Exercise 1, page 397

1. a. ($51,000 ÷ $100) × $0.38 = $194
    b. ($25,000 ÷ $100) × $0.68 = $170
    c. ($109,000 ÷ $100) × $0.35 = $382
    d. ($62,000 ÷ $100) × $0.41 = $254
    e. ($33,500 ÷ $100) × $0.39 = $131
    f. ($135,200 ÷ $100) × $0.32 = $433

2. ($45,000 ÷ $100) × $0.87 = $392   annual premium

3. a. ($56,000 ÷ $100) × $0.75 = $420   Hobarth's annual premium
    b. ($56,000 ÷ $100) × $0.68 = $381   Dexter's annual premium
    c. $420 − $381 = $39   difference

4. a. ($90,000 ÷ $100) × $0.20 = $180   estimated
    b. ($89,500 ÷ $100) × $0.19 = $170   actual cost of increase

5. ($60,000 ÷ $100) × $0.50 = $300   annual premium
    $300 − ($300 × 0.02) = $294   discounted annual premium

6. ($12,500 ÷ $100) × $1.20 = $150   extra premium cost
    $902 + $150 = $1,052   total premium

Exercise 2, page 399

1. $94   annual premium
    0.10 × $10,000 = $1,000   off-premises coverage
    0.20 × $10,000 = $2,000   living expense coverage

2. $114   annual premium
    0.10 × $16,000 = $1,600   off-premises coverage
    0.20 × $16,000 = $3,200   living expense coverage

3. $70   annual premium
    0.10 × $5,000 = $500   off-premises coverage
    0.20 × $5,000 = $1,000   living expense coverage

4. $94   annual premium
    0.10 × $12,000 = $1,200   off-premises coverage
    0.20 × $12,000 = $2,400   living expense coverage

5. $121   annual premium
    0.10 × $14,000 = $1,400   off-premises coverage
    0.20 × $14,000 = $2,800   living expense coverage

6. $61   annual premium

Exercise 3, page 399

1. $1,200 − $100 = $1,100   collected by Anita from insurance company

2. ($900 + $2,800) − $250 = $3,450   paid by insurance company

3. $487 − $414 = $73   saved

4. $218 − ($218 × 0.35) = $142   new premium

5. a. $300 − ($300 × 0.20) = $240   estimated premium
    b. $284 − ($284 × 0.18) = $233   actual premium

6. $1,200 − (0.22 × $1,200) = $936   annual premium

7. $85 ÷ $340 = 25%   reduction

8. $238 ÷ $680 = 35%   reduction

Exercise 4, page 401

1. ($20,000 ÷ $100) × $0.62 = $124   annual premium
    0.75 × $124 = $93   amount insurance company kept
    $124 − $93 = $31   refund

2. ($4,000 ÷ $100) × $2.45 = $98   annual premium
    0.50 × $98 = $49   amount insurance company kept
    $98 − $49 = $49   refund

3. $60 × 2 = $120   annual premium
    0.25 × 120 = $30   for 15 days' insurance

4. a. $\frac{146}{365}$ × $275 = $110   cost of insurance
    b. $275 − $110 = $165   refund

5. $\frac{219}{365}$ × $85 = $51   cost of insurance
    $85 − $51 = $34   returned to Phil

Review 77, page 401

2. a. 261 ÷ 58,000 = 0.0045
    b. ($104 − $13) ÷ $104 = 0.875 or $\frac{7}{8}$
    c. $76.35 − (0.6 × $76.35) = $30.54
    d. 12.25 = $12\frac{1}{4}$
    e. $2,000 × 0.14 × $\frac{8}{365}$ = $6.14

3. ($34,700 ÷ $100) × $0.47 = $163   annual premium

4. $1,800 − $750 = $1,050   insurance company will pay

5. $\frac{73}{365}$ × $430 = $86   cost of insurance
    $430 − $86 = $344   refund

6. ($24,000 ÷ $1,000) × $10.45 = $250.80   annual premium

7. 0.60 × $76,000 = $45,600   assessed value
    ($45,600 ÷ $1,000) × $34.70 = $1,582.32   amount of tax bill

Section 78. Collecting on Property Insurance

Exercise 2, page 403

1.

	Company	Percentage	Share
a.	American	$\frac{1}{3}$ × $60,000	$ 20,000
	General	$\frac{2}{3}$ × $60,000	40,000
b.	American	$\frac{1}{1}$ × $20,000	20,000

Company	Percentage	Share
c. American	$\frac{1}{2} \times \$42,000$	21,000
General	$\frac{1}{2} \times \$42,000$	21,000
d. American	$\frac{1}{10} \times \$96,000$	9,600
General	$\frac{9}{10} \times \$96,000$	86,400
e. American	$\frac{2}{5} \times \$540,000$	216,000
General	$\frac{3}{5} \times \$540,000$	324,000
f. American	$\frac{1}{8} \times \$320,000$	40,000
General	$\frac{7}{8} \times \$320,000$	280,000

2. $\$3,000,000 + \$9,000,000 = \$12,000,000$ total insurance
$\$3,000,000 \div \$12,000,000 = \frac{1}{4}$ of loss borne by Lane
$\$9,000,000 \div \$12,000,000 = \frac{3}{4}$ of loss borne by Alb
$\frac{1}{4} \times \$180,000 = \$45,000$ to be paid by Lane
$\frac{3}{4} \times \$180,000 = \$135,000$ to be paid by Alb

3. $\$1,800,000 + \$4,200,000 + \$6,000,000 = \$12,000,000$ total insurance
$\$1,800,000 \div \$12,000,000 = \frac{3}{20}$ of loss borne by Trent
$\$4,200,000 \div \$12,000,000 = \frac{7}{20}$ of loss borne by Morgan
$\$6,000,000 \div \$12,000,000 = \frac{1}{2}$ of loss borne by States
$\frac{3}{20} \times \$1,000,000 = \$150,000$ to be paid by Trent
$\frac{7}{20} \times \$1,000,000 = \$350,000$ to be paid by Morgan
$\frac{1}{2} \times \$1,000,000 = \$500,000$ to be paid by States

4. $\$300,000 + \$400,000 + \$200,000 = \$900,000$ total insurance
$\$300,000 \div \$900,000 = \frac{1}{3}$ of loss borne by Company A
$\$400,000 \div \$900,000 = \frac{4}{9}$ of loss borne by Company B
$\$200,000 \div \$900,000 = \frac{2}{9}$ of loss borne by Company C
$\frac{1}{3} \times \$72,000 = \$24,000$ should be paid by Company A
$\frac{4}{9} \times \$72,000 = \$32,000$ should be paid by Company B
$\frac{2}{9} \times \$72,000 = \$16,000$ should be paid by Company C

5. $\$5,000,000 + \$8,000,000 + \$7,000,000 = \$20,000,000$ total insurance
$\$5,000,000 \div \$20,000,000 = \frac{1}{4}$ of loss borne by Elgin
$\$8,000,000 \div \$20,000,000 = \frac{2}{5}$ of loss borne by Grand
$\$7,000,000 \div \$20,000,000 = \frac{7}{20}$ of loss borne by Marlin
$\frac{1}{4} \times \$600,000 = \$150,000$ to be paid by Elgin
$\frac{2}{5} \times \$600,000 = \$240,000$ to be paid by Grand
$\frac{7}{20} \times \$600,000 = \$210,000$ to be paid by Marlin

Exercise 3, page 404

1. **a.** $0.80 \times \$90,000 = \$72,000$, 80% of value
$\frac{\$63,000}{\$72,000} = \frac{7}{8} \times \$5,600 = \$4,900$ paid
b. $0.80 \times \$75,000 = \$60,000$, 80% of value
$\frac{\$45,000}{\$60,000} = \frac{3}{4} \times \$8,000 = \$6,000$ paid
c. $0.80 \times \$60,000 = \$48,000$, 80% of value
$\frac{\$40,000}{\$48,000} = \frac{5}{6} \times \$13,200 = \$11,000$ paid
d. $0.80 \times \$62,500 = \$50,000$, 80% of value
$\frac{\$45,000}{\$50,000} = \frac{9}{10} \times \$7,000 = \$6,300$ paid

e. $0.90 \times \$70,000 = \$63,000$, 90% of value
$\frac{\$49,000}{\$63,000} = \frac{7}{9} \times \$22,500 = \$17,500$ paid

f. $0.80 \times \$40,000 = \$32,000$, 80% of value
$\frac{\$32,000}{\$32,000} = 1 \times \$4,620 = \$4,620$ paid

g. $0.80 \times \$70,000 = \$56,000$, 80% of value
$\$27,000$ paid

h. $0.90 \times \$105,000 = \$94,500$, 90% of value
$\$35,000$ paid

2. $0.80 \times \$80,000 = \$64,000$, 80% of value
$\frac{\$48,000}{\$64,000} = \frac{3}{4} \times \$7,600 = \$5,700$ paid

3. $0.80 \times \$240,000 = \$192,000$, 80% of value
$\frac{\$128,000}{\$192,000} = \frac{2}{3} \times \$3,870 = \$2,580$ paid

4. $0.90 \times \$200,000 = \$180,000$, 90% of value
$\frac{\$144,000}{\$180,000} = \frac{4}{5} \times \$16,000 = \$12,800$ paid

Exercise 4, page 405

1. $0.80 \times \$17,500 = \$14,000$, 80% of replacement cost
$\frac{\$7,000}{\$14,000} = \frac{1}{2} \times \$3,250 = \$1,625$ paid

2. $0.80 \times \$70,000 = \$56,000$, 80% of replacement cost
$\frac{\$48,000}{\$56,000} = \frac{6}{7} \times \$21,000 = \$18,000$ paid

3. $0.80 \times \$42,000 = \$33,600$, 80% of replacement cost
$\frac{\$22,400}{\$33,600} = \frac{2}{3} \times \$12,000 = \$8,000$ paid

Review 78, page 406

2. **a.** $(\$77 - \$56) \div \$56 = \frac{3}{8}$ **d.** $0.084 \times \$800 \times \frac{1}{4} = \$16.80$
b. $\$68.70 - (0.40 \times \$68.70) = \$41.22$ **e.** $\$0.54 \div \$1.20 = 45\%$
c. August 15 to October 30 = 76 days

3. $\$540,000 + \$120,000 = \$660,000$ total insurance
$\$540,000 \div \$660,000 = \frac{9}{11}$ of loss borne by Federated
$\$120,000 \div \$660,000 = \frac{2}{11}$ of loss borne by National
$\frac{9}{11} \times \$44,000 = \$36,000$ to be paid by Federated
$\frac{2}{11} \times \$44,000 = \$8,000$ to be paid by National

4. $0.90 \times \$90,000 = \$81,000$, 90% of replacement cost
$\frac{\$45,000}{\$81,000} = \frac{5}{9} \times \$10,800 = \$6,000$ paid

5. $(\$160 - \$136) \div \$160 = 15\%$ reduction

6. $0.055 \times \$60 = \$3.30$ annual dividend
$\$3.30 \div \$42 = 7.9\%$ rate of income

7. $\$80 + (12 \times \$19.75) = \$317$ offer of Store A
$\$25 + (26 \times \$10.50) = \$298$ offer of Store B
$\$317 - \$298 = \$19$ saved by taking Store A's offer

8. $(64 \text{ L} + 195 \text{ L}) - 21 \text{ L} = 238 \text{ L}$

Section 79. Automobile Insurance

Exercise 1, page 409

1. $90 + $12 + $612 + $101 = $815   cost of standard coverage

2. **a.** $118 + $16 + $796 + $132 = $1,062   annual premium
    b. $1,062 − ($118 + $16 + $436 + $98) = $394   saved with largest deductibles

3. $126 + $12 + $428 + $101 = $667   total premium

4. $82 + $10 + $550 + $92 = $734   pleasure car
    $162 + $20 + $796 + $132 = $1,110   business car
    $734 + $1,110 = $1,844   total premium
    $1,844 − ($1,844 × 0.10) = $1,659.60   net premium for 1 year

5. ($90 + $12 + $336 + $76) × 0.70 = $359.80   annual premium at 70% of usual rate

6. ($90 + $12 + $612 + $101) × 2.2 = $1,793   annual premium
    $1,793 ÷ 2 = $896.50   premium for one-half year

7. **a.** ($82 + $10 + $550 + $92) × 4 = $2,936   annual premium
    b. ($82 + $10) × 4 = $368   annual premium with reduced coverage

Review 79, page 410

2. **a.** $34.89 + 133.9 + 4.275 + 1.47 = 174.535$
    b. $9\frac{1}{2} \div \frac{1}{4} = 38$
    c. $23,896.73 = $24,000

3. $108 + $14 + $428 + $76 = $626   driving to work premium
    $ 98 + $12 + $386 + $68 = $564   pleasure driving premium
    $ 62   difference

4. ($9,502 − $2,850) ÷ 4 = $1,663   average annual depreciation

5. 0.023 × $17,200 = $395.60   state tax
    0.005 × $17,200 = $86   city tax
    $395.60 + $86.00 = $481.60   total tax

UNIT 13 • FINDING AND DISTRIBUTING BUSINESS INCOME AND LOSS

Section 80.   The Balance Sheet

Exercise 1, page 413

1. **a.** $2,100 + $51,700 + $7,800 + $930 = $62,530   assets
    b. $3,175 + $1,850 = $5,025   liabilities
    c. $62,530 − $5,025 = $57,505   capital

2. $3,850 + $42,000 + $520 + $9,200 + $8,400 + $60,000 = $123,970   assets
$8,600 + $23,800 = $32,400   liabilities
$123,970 + $32,400 = $91,570   capital

3. $1,400 + $1,600 + $23,500 + $3,700 + $2,100 + $25,500 = $57,800   assets
$7,500 + $3,300 + $9,100 = $19,900   liabilities
$57,800 − $19,900 = $37,900   capital

4. $2,620 + $2,875 + $29,250 = $34,745   assets
$580 + $2,700 + $17,200 + $1,200 = $21,680   liabilities
$34,745 − $21,680 = $13,065   capital

Exercise 2, page 414

1.

Clyde Slade
Balance Sheet, December 31, 19 --

Assets		Liabilities	
Cash	$ 2,744	On-Time Distributors	$ 6,230
Parts Inventory	40,316	Do-All Suppliers	+ 2,970
Shop Supplies	1,650	Total Liabilities	$ 9,200
Shop Equipment	+ 18,500		
		Capital	
		Clyde Slade, Capital	− 54,010
Total Assets	$63,210	Total Liabilities and Capital	$63,210

2.

Jill Grover
Balance Sheet, December 31, 19 --

Assets		Liabilities	
Cash	$ 3,842	Dren Company	$ 44,655
Accounts Receivable	4,915	Total Liabilities	$ 44,655
Merchandise Inventory	97,150		
Store Equipment	21,470		
Delivery Equipment	14,752		
Supplies	+ 1,732	**Capital**	
		Jill Grover, Capital	+ 99,206
Total Assets	$143,861	Total Liabilities and Capital	$143,861

3.

Bezard Brothers'
Balance Sheet, March 31, 19 --

Assets		Liabilities	
Cash	$ 15,450	Roform Supply	$ 5,960
Accounts Receivable	4,550	Meldex, Inc.	2,670
Merchandise Inventory	79,990	Cole Industries	+ 1,010
Store Equipment	5,430	Total Liabilities	$ 9,640
Delivery Equipment	20,450		
Supplies	+ 450	**Capital**	
		Bezard Brothers', Capital	+ 116,680
Total Assets	$126,320	Total Liabilities and Capital	$126,320

4.

Saturn Jewelry Suppliers
Balance Sheet, June 30, 19--

Assets		Liabilities	
Cash	$ 17,643.10	Lern County Bank	$325,000.00
Accounts Receivable	32,524.65	New Creations, Inc.	+ 140,000.00
Merchandise Inventory	234,631.50	Total Liabilities	$465,000.00
Supplies	13,398.00		
Equipment	129,463.00		
Building	+ 154,770.00	Capital	
		Saturn Jewelry Suppliers, Capital	+ 117,430.25
Total Assets	$582,430.25	Total Liabilities and Capital	$582,430.25

Review 80, page 414

2.
  a. $4,678 × 0.01 = $46.78
  b. July 7 to September 22 = 77 days
  c. $760 × 0.15 × $1\frac{1}{2}$ = $171
  d. 8 m × 12.4 m = 99.2 m^2
  e. 7.5 mills = $7.50

3. ($1,000 + $7,000 + $60,000 + $12,000) − $10,000 = $70,000   estimated capital
($1,015 + $7,125 + $59,800 + $12,008) − $10,040 = $69,908   capital

4. ($41,000 ÷ $100) × $3.23 = $1,324.30   tax

5. $\frac{3}{5}$ × $840 = $504   Greta's share
$\frac{2}{5}$ × $840 = $336   Marge's share

6. 0.03 × $7,000 = $ 210
0.04 × $10,000 =   400
0.05 × $8,600 =   430
$1,040   state tax owed

Section 81.   Finding Profit and Loss

Exercise 1, page 416

1. $152,296 − $6,450 = $145,846   net sales

2. $40,310.00 − $1,230.40 = $39,079.60   net sales

3. **a.** $590,000 − $10,000 = $580,000   estimated net sales
  b. $589,900.04 − $9,975.23 = $579,924.81   net sales

Exercise 2, page 416

1. $61,538 − $33,740 = $27,798   gross profit

2. $39,720 − $20,348 = $19,372   gross profit

3. ($38,432 − $2,812) − $21,792 = $13,828   gross profit

Exercise 3, page 417

1. Merchandise Inventory, May 1 $ 49,400
    Purchases   + 32,100

    Merchandise Available for Sale $ 81,500
    Merchandise Inventory, May 31   − 58,294

    Cost of Merchandise Sold $ 23,206

2. Merchandise Inventory, September 1 $ 42,790
    Purchases   + 18,400

    Merchandise Available for Sale $ 61,190
    Merchandise Inventory, September 30 − 34,782

    Cost of Merchandise Sold $ 26,408

3. Merchandise Inventory, January 1 $ 75,070
    Purchases   + 201,500

    Merchandise Available for Sale $276,570
    Merchandise Inventory, December 31 − 50,730

    Cost of Merchandise Sold $225,840

4. Merchandise Inventory, July 1 $ 89,935
    Purchases   + 184,725

    Merchandise Available for Sale $274,660
    Merchandise Inventory, June 30   − 70,172

    Cost of Merchandise Sold $204,488

Exercise 4, page 418

1. a. $21,700 − $4,008 = $17,692   net sales
        $17,692 − $12,050 = $5,642   gross profit
    b. $40,180 − $3,694 = $36,486   net sales
        $36,486 − $24,630 = $11,856   gross profit
    c. $58,170 − $1,132 = $57,038   net sales
        $57,038 − $48,100 = $8,938   gross profit
    d. $90,438 − $6,342 = $84,096   net sales
        $84,096 − $60,942 = $23,154   gross profit

2. a. $33,480 − $1,402 = $32,078   net sales
    b. ($52,500 + $12,950) − $51,673 = $13,777   cost of merchandise sold
    c. $32,078 − $13,777 = $18,301   gross profit

3. ($32,475 + $82,890) − $30,750 = $84,615   cost of merchandise sold
    $135,720 − $84,615 = $51,105   gross profit

Exercise 5, page 419

1. a. $6,430 − $4,010 = $2,420   gross profit
        $2,420 − $1,630 = $790   net income
    b. $21,235 − $10,105 = $11,130   gross profit
        $11,130 − $8,920 = $2,210   net income
    c. $35,950 − $26,900 = $9,050   gross profit
        $10,490 − $9,050 = $1,440   net loss
    d. $7,800 − $5,200 = $2,600   gross profit
        $4,007 − $2,600 = $1,407   net loss

    e. $50,785 − $30,945 = $19,840   gross profit
          $19,840 − $18,231 = $1,609   net income
    f. $70,385 − $52,174 = $18,211   gross profit
          $23,984 − $18,211 = $5,773   net loss

2. $22,500 − $13,600 = $8,900   gross profit
     $8,900 − $7,230 = $1,670   net income

3. ($32,000 + $66,000) − $30,000 = $68,000   cost of merchandise sold
     $140,000 − $68,000 = $72,000   gross profit
     $72,000 − $42,000 = $30,000   net income

4. $101,000 − $2,500 = $98,500   net sales
     ($27,500 + $65,000) − $21,700 = $70,800   cost of merchandise sold
     $98,500 − $70,800 = $27,700   gross profit
     $33,500 − $27,700 = $5,800   net loss

Review 81, page 420

2. **a.** $0.04 \times \$1,050 = \$42$
     b. $0.642 \times \$33 = \$21.186$, or $21.19
     c. $\$18.56 \div 0.005 = \$3,172$
     d. $\frac{5}{8} + \frac{1}{4} + \frac{1}{8} = 1$

3. **a.** $200,000 − $135,000 − $40,000 = $25,000   estimated net income
     b. $199,910 − $135,107 = $64,803   gross profit
         $64,803 − $39,950 = $24,853   net income

4. $(0.08 \times \$1,000) \div \$920 = 0.0869$, or 8.7%   yield

Section 82. The Income Statement

Exercise 2, page 422

1. **a.** $42,000 ÷ $70,000 = 60%   cost of merchandise was of net sales
     b. $28,000 ÷ $70,000 = 40%   gross profit was of net sales

2. **a.** $440,000 − $286,000 = $154,000   gross profit on sales
         $154,000 − $105,600 = $48,400   net income
     b. $286,000 ÷ $440,000 = 65%   cost of merchandise is of net sales
         $154,000 ÷ $440,000 = 35%   gross profit is of net sales
         $105,600 ÷ $440,000 = 24%   operating expenses are of net sales
         $48,400 ÷ $440,000 = 11%   net income is of net sales

3. **a.** $180,000 − $99,000 = $81,000   gross profit on sales
         $81,000 − $61,200 = $19,800   net income
     b.

Net sales	$180,000	100%
Cost of merchandise sold	− 99,000	− 55%
Gross profit	$ 81,000	45%
Operating expenses	− 61,200	− 34%
Net income	$ 19,800	11%

4. $55,200 − $42,780 = $12,420   net income
    $12,420 ÷ $138,000 = 9%   net income was of net sales

Exercise 3, page 423

1. a. ($48,200 + $29,800) ÷ 2 = $39,000   average inventory
   b. $31,200 ÷ $39,000 = 0.8   monthly rate
   c. 12 × 0.8 = 9.6   annual rate

2. a. ($44,000 + $94,100 + $62,300) ÷ 3 = $66,800   average inventory
   b. $300,600 ÷ $66,800 = 4.5   turnover rate for 6 months
   c. 2 × 4.5 = 9   turnover rate for a year

3. ($39,450 + $55,800 + $49,950) ÷ 3 = $48,400   average inventory
   $121,000 ÷ $48,400 = 2.5   turnover rate for 3 months
   4 × 2.5 = 10   annual turnover rate

4. ($84,000 + $74,800 + $111,600 + $82,400) ÷ 4 = $88,200   average inventory
   $617,400 ÷ $88,200 = 7   merchandise turnover rate for year

Review 82, page 424

2. a. 89.2% = 0.892, or 0.89
   b. 1.5 × $42 = $63
   c. ($560.00 − $481.60) ÷ $560 = 14%

3. a. $120,000 ÷ $240,000 = 50%   estimated gross profit was of net sales
      $118,090 ÷ $241,000 = 49%   gross profit was of net sales
   b. $118,090 − $59,045 = $59,045   net income
      $60,000 ÷ $240,000 = 25%   estimated net income was of net sales
      $59,045 ÷ $241,000 = 24.5%   net income was of net sales

4. ($108,400 + $87,100 + $155,500) ÷ 3 = $117,000   average inventory
   $292,500 ÷ $117,000 = 2.5   turnover rate for quarter
   4 × 2.5 = 10   annual merchandise turnover rate

5. 12 × ($3,042 − $3,000) = $504   annual interest
   $504 ÷ $3,000 = 16.8%   interest rate

6. 4 × $0.42 = $1.68   annual income from one share
   340 × $1.68 = $571.20   total annual income

7. a. 840 ÷ 12 = 70 L   gas used
   b. 70 × $0.35 = $24.50   spent for gas

Section 83.   Distributing Partnership Income

Exercise 1, page 426

1. a. $6,000 + $18,000 = $24,000   total investment

   $\frac{\$6,000}{\$24,000}$ or $\frac{1}{4}$ × $8,400 = $2,100   X's share

   $\frac{\$18,000}{\$24,000}$ or $\frac{3}{4}$ × $8,400 = $6,300   Y's share

   b. $27,000 + $45,000 = $72,000   total investment

   $\frac{\$27,000}{\$72,000}$ or $\frac{3}{8}$ × $5,600 = $2,100   X's share

   $\frac{\$45,000}{\$72,000}$ or $\frac{5}{8}$ × $5,600 = $3,500   Y's share

c. $18,000 + $36,000 = $54,000   total investment

$\frac{\$18,000}{\$54,000}$ or $\frac{1}{3}$ × $2,925 = $975   X's share

$\frac{\$36,000}{\$54,000}$ or $\frac{2}{3}$ × $2,925 = $1,950   Y's share

d. $16,000 + $40,000 = $56,000   total investment

$\frac{\$16,000}{\$56,000}$ or $\frac{2}{7}$ × $8,540 = $2,440   X's share

$\frac{\$40,000}{\$56,000}$ or $\frac{5}{7}$ × $8,540 = $6,100   Y's share

e. $18,000 + $27,000 + $36,000 = $81,000   total investment

$\frac{\$18,000}{\$81,000}$ or $\frac{2}{9}$ × $12,618 = $2,804   X's share

$\frac{\$27,000}{\$81,000}$ or $\frac{1}{3}$ × $12,618 = $4,206   Y's share

$\frac{\$36,000}{\$81,000}$ or $\frac{4}{9}$ × $12,618 = $5,608   Z's share

f. $8,000 + $16,000 + $24,000 = $48,000   total investment

$\frac{\$8,000}{\$48,000}$ or $\frac{1}{6}$ × $17,220 = $2,870   X's share

$\frac{\$16,000}{\$48,000}$ or $\frac{1}{3}$ × $17,220 = $5,740   Y's share

$\frac{\$24,000}{\$48,000}$ or $\frac{1}{2}$ × $17,220 = $8,610   Z's share

g. $7,000 + $21,000 + $42,000 = $70,000   total investment

$\frac{\$7,000}{\$70,000}$ or $\frac{1}{10}$ × $36,720 = $3,672   X's share

$\frac{\$21,000}{\$70,000}$ or $\frac{3}{10}$ × $36,720 = $11,016   Y's share

$\frac{\$42,000}{\$70,000}$ or $\frac{3}{5}$ × $36,720 = $22,032   Z's share

2. $5,000 + $15,000 = $20,000   total investment

a. $\frac{\$5,000}{\$20,000}$ or $\frac{1}{4}$ × $12,000 = $3,000   Ed's estimated share

$\frac{\$15,000}{\$20,000}$ or $\frac{3}{4}$ × $12,000 = $9,000   Lou's estimated share

b. $\frac{\$5,000}{\$20,000}$ or $\frac{1}{4}$ × $12,016 = $3,004   Ed's share

$\frac{\$15,000}{\$20,000}$ or $\frac{3}{4}$ × $12,016 = $9,012   Lou's share

3. $25,000 + $30,000 = $55,000   total investment

$\frac{\$25,000}{\$55,000}$ or $\frac{5}{11}$ × $8,965 = $4,075   Dujovny's share of loss

$\frac{\$30,000}{\$55,000}$ or $\frac{6}{11}$ × $8,965 = $4,890   Ching's share of loss

4. $480,800 − $312,800 = $168,000   gross profit
$168,000 − $96,960 = $71,040   net income
$12,000 + $36,000 + $48,000 = $96,000   total investment

$\frac{\$12,000}{\$96,000}$ or $\frac{1}{8}$ × $71,040 = $8,880   Baird's share

$\frac{\$36,000}{\$96,000}$ or $\frac{3}{8}$ × $71,040 = $26,640   Ehardt's share

$\frac{\$48,000}{\$96,000}$ or $\frac{1}{2}$ × $71,040 = $35,520   Polley's share

Review 83, page 427

2. **a.** $0.007 = 0.7\%$
  b. $28\% = \frac{7}{25}$

   c. May 9

   d. 36 L ÷ 1.6 = 22.5 L

3. $124,000 − $77,900 = $46,100   net income
$36,000 + $48,000 + $60,000 = $144,000   total investment

$\frac{\$36,000}{\$144,000}$ or $\frac{1}{4}$ × $46,100 = $11,525   Bower's share

4. (4 × $5.79) − $20.40 = $2.76   saved by buying 4 boxes at a time

5. 0.15 × $1,200 = $180   annual saving
$2,800 ÷ $180 = 15.5, or 16   years

Section 84. More About Distributing Partnership Income

Exercise 1, page 428

1. **a.** 0.08 × $50,000 = $4,000   A's interest
0.08 × $30,000 = $2,400   B's interest
$23,000 − ($4,000 + $2,400) = $16,600
$16,600 ÷ 2 = $8,300   each partner's share of remainder
$4,000 + $8,300 = $12,300   A's share
$2,400 + $8,300 = $10,700   B's share

   b. 0.12 × $22,000 = $2,640   A's interest
0.12 × $37,000 = $4,440   B's interest
0.12 × $46,000 = $5,520   C's interest
$38,100 − ($2,640 + $4,440 + $5,520) = $25,500
$25,500 ÷ 3 = $8,500   each partner's share of remainder
$2,640 + $8,500 = $11,140   A's share
$4,440 + $8,500 = $12,940   B's share
$5,520 + $8,500 = $14,020   C's share

   c. 0.15 × $82,000 = $12,300   A's interest
0.15 × $58,000 = $8,700   B's interest
0.15 × $69,000 = $10,350   C's interest
$59,010 − ($12,300 + $8,700 + $10,350) = $27,660
$27,660 ÷ 3 = $9,220   each partner's share of remainder
$12,300 + $9,220 = $21,520   A's share
$8,700 + $9,220 = $17,920   B's share
$10,350 + $9,220 = $19,570   C's share

2. 0.065 × $20,000 = $1,300   Dean's interest
0.065 × $30,000 = $1,950   Coliett's interest
$21,780 − ($1,300 + $1,950) = $18,530
$18,530 ÷ 2 = $9,265   each partner's share of remainder
$1,300 + $9,265 = $10,565   Dean's share
$1,950 + $9,265 = $11,215   Coliett's share

3. 0.09 × $50,000 = $4,500   Healy's interest
0.09 × $75,000 = $6,750   Myers' interest
$68,428 − ($4,500 + $6,750) = $57,178
$57,178 ÷ 2 = $28,589   each partner's share of remainder
$4,500 + $28,589 = $33,089   Healy's share
$6,750 + $28,589 = $35,339   Myers' share

4. $82,370 − $68,139 = $14,231   net income
$0.07 \times \$9,400 = \$658$ Dunn's interest
$0.07 \times \$14,000 = \$980$ Rice's interest
$0.07 \times \$18,500 = \$1,295$ Hardaway's interest
$14,231 − ($658 + $980 + $1,295) = $11,298
$11,298 ÷ 3 = $3,766   each partner's share of remainder
$658 + $3,766 = $4,424   Dunn's share
$980 + $3,766 = $4,746   Rice's share
$1,295 + $3,766 = $5,061   Hardaway's share

5. $0.1 \times \$864,000 = \$86,400$ net income
$0.13 \times \$150,000 = \$19,500$ Jones' interest
$0.13 \times \$90,000 = \$11,700$ Crump's interest
$0.13 \times \$30,000 = \$3,900$ Young's interest
$86,400 − ($19,500 + $11,700 + $3,900) = $51,300
$51,300 ÷ 3 = $17,100   each partner's share of remainder
$19,500 + $17,100 = $36,600   Jones' share
$11,700 + $17,100 = $28,800   Crump's share
$3,900 + $17,100 = $21,000   Young's share

Exercise 2, page 429

1. $\frac{3}{5} \times \$80,375 = \$48,225$ Obiawu's share
$\frac{2}{5} \times \$80,375 = \$32,150$ Saeed's share

2. $0.4 \times \$82,500 = \$33,000$ Daniels' share
$0.6 \times \$82,500 = \$49,500$ Multon's share

3. $524,528 − ($392,500 + $97,028) = $35,000   net income
$0.56 \times \$35,000 = \$19,600$ Cade's share
$0.44 \times \$35,000 = \$15,400$ Purdon's share

4. $\frac{7}{11} \times \$147,400 = \$93,800$ Pace's share
$\frac{4}{11} \times \$147,400 = \$53,600$ Gibson's share

Review 84, page 430

1. a. $7.8 = 780\%$
   b. $\frac{3}{200} = 1.5\%$
   c. $0.01 \times 4.7 = 0.047$
   d. $18 ÷ 0.25 = 72$
   e. 5 m + 34 m = 39 m

2. $0.18 \times \$46,000 = \$8,280$ Driscoe's interest
$0.18 \times \$87,000 = \$15,660$ Levin's interest
$32,400 − ($8,280 + $15,660) = $8,460
$8,460 ÷ 2 = $4,230   each partner's share of remainder
$8,280 + $4,230 = $12,510   Driscoe's share
$15,660 + $4,230 = $19,890   Levin's share

3. $0.34 \times \$121,000 = \$41,140$ Lee's share
$0.28 \times \$121,000 = \$33,880$ Maxwell's share
$0.38 \times \$121,000 = \$45,980$ Tyler's share

4. $0.153 \times \$3,400 = \$520.20$ amount of FICA tax

5. **a.** $9,460 − $3,400 = $6,060   total depreciation
$6,060 ÷ 5 = $1,212   average annual depreciation
b. $1,212 ÷ $9,460 = 0.1281, or 12.8%   rate of depreciation

6. $6,000 × 0.09 × $\frac{1}{2}$ = $270   amount of interest forfeited

Section 85.   Distributing Corporate Income

Exercise 1, page 432

1. $108,000 ÷ $900,000 = 12%   rate of dividend should be declared

2. $36,800 ÷ $460,000 = 8%   rate of dividend was paid

3. $210,000 ÷ $1,500,000 = 14%   rate of dividend

4. $122,400 ÷ 51,000 = $2.40   rate of dividend per share

5. **a.** $4,800 ÷ 8,000 = 60¢   estimated rate of dividend
b. $4,720 ÷ 8,000 = 59¢   actual rate of dividend

6. **a.** 30,000 × $100 = $3,000,000   capital stock
0.75 × $280,000 = $210,000   dividend
$210,000 ÷ $3,000,000 = 7%   dividend rate as a percent
b. $210,000 ÷ 30,000 = $7   dividend amount in dollars

7. 0.06 × $120,000 = $7,200   dividend payment on preferred stock
$50,400 − $7,200 = $43,200
$43,200 ÷ $480,000 = 9%   largest percent of dividend that can be paid

8. 0.12 × $800,000 = $96,000   dividend payment on preferred stock
$384,000 − $96,000 = $288,000
$288,000 ÷ $4,000,000 = 7.2%   largest percent of dividend that can be paid

Exercise 2, page 433

1. $55,675 − $41,875 = $13,800   kept in retained earnings account

2. 0.05 × $780,000 = $39,000   dividend paid to shareholders
$61,568 − $39,000 = $22,568   kept in retained earnings account

3. 25,000 × $100 = $2,500,000   capital stock
0.0675 × $2,500,000 = $168,750   dividend paid to shareholders
$228,400 − $168,750 = $59,650   kept in retained earnings

4. 4 × ($0.08 × 175,000) = $56,000   dividend paid to shareholders
$325,000 − $56,000 = $269,000   kept in retained earnings account

5. 0.06 × (5,000 × $100) = $30,000   dividend on preferred stock
70,000 × $0.40 = $28,000   dividend on common stock
$132,720 − ($30,000 + $28,000) = $74,720   kept in retained earnings account

Exercise 3, page 434

1. 0.06 × (20 × $25) = $30   dividend on capital stock
0.08 × $1,250 = $100   patronage dividend
$30 + $100 = $130   total dividend

2. $0.05 \times (30 \times \$60) = \$90$ dividend on capital stock
$0.08 \times \$1,650 = \$132$ patronage dividend
$\$90 + \$132 = \$222$ total dividend

3. $0.09 \times (80 \times \$15) = \$108$ dividend on capital stock
$0.02 \times \$5,470 = \$109.40$ patronage dividend
$\$108.00 + \$109.40 = \$217.40$ total dividend

4. $0.045 \times (140 \times \$30) = \$189$ dividend on capital stock
$0.06 \times \$2,518 = \$151.08$ patronage dividend
$\$189.00 + \$151.08 = \$340.08$ total dividend

Review 85, page 434

2.   **a.** $\$108,000$
   b. $\frac{1}{3} \times \$588 = \$196$
   c. $\$800 \div 0.8 = \$1,000$

3. $0.045 \times \$1,500,000 = \$67,500$ dividend paid
$\$206,974 - \$67,500 = \$139,474$ put in retained earnings

4. $5,250 \times \$100 = \$525,000$ capital stock
$\$84,000 \div \$525,000 = 16\%$ rate of dividend

5. $\$947,227 \div \$19,520,000 = 0.048525$
$0.048525 \times \$100 = \$4.853$ tax rate per $100

6. $\$1.35 \times (\$14,000 \div \$100) = \$189$ cost of additional insurance
$\$189 + \$756 = \$945$ total premium

Section 86.   Bankruptcy

Exercise 1, page 436

1.   **a.** $\$13,600 \div \$34,000 = 40\%$
   b. $\$5,580 \div \$18,600 = 30\%$
   c. $\$17,115 \div \$48,900 = 35\%$
   d. $\$124,800 \div \$192,000 = 65\%$

2.   **a.** $\$24,320 \div \$38,000 = 64¢$
   b. $\$19,320 \div \$55,200 = 35¢$
   c. $\$41,160 \div \$98,000 = 42¢$
   d. $\$2,896 \div \$18,100 = 16¢$

3. $\$34,040 \div \$92,000 = 37\%$ of claims

4. $\$5,715.50 \div \$12,425 = 46¢$ per dollar creditors will get

5.   **a.** $0.50 \times \$7,000 = \$3,500$ estimated amount creditor will get
   b. $0.49 \times \$6,994 = \$3,427.06$ actual amount creditor will get

6. $0.326 \times \$1,280 = \$417.28$ creditor will get

7.   **a.** $\$69,600 - \$17,800 = \$51,800$ available for all creditors
   b. $\$51,800 \div \$148,000 = 35\%$ of each creditor's claim
   c. $0.35 \times \$9,200 = \$3,220$ amount Eastern Supply got

Review 86, page 437

1. **a.** $14.7 \times 23.75 = 349.125$
    b. $8.6 \div 0.04 = 215$
    c. $0.084 \div 0.006 = 14$
    d. $\$7,000 \times 0.0628 \times \frac{1}{4} = \$109.90$
    e. $\$14,600,000$
    f. $\$0.793$
    g. $5 \times 30 = 150$
    h. $\$10,000 \div 20 = \$500$

2. $\$57,000 \div \$150,800 = \$0.38$ per dollar creditors will get

3. $\$11,190 \div \$74,600 = 0.15$
    $0.15 \times \$5,250 = \$787.50$ will be paid on claim

4. $0.9 \times \$60,000 = \$54,000$ required insurance
    $\frac{\$42,000}{\$54,000} \times \$900 = \$700$ amount insurance company will pay

5. **a.** $(12 \times 30) \times \$623.50 = \$224,460$ total payments
    b. $\$224,460 - \$65,000 = \$159,460$ total interest

6. $\$0.07 \times (21,000 - 16,000) = \$350$ charge for excess miles
    $\$350 + (12 \times \$129) = \$1,898$ yearly cost of leasing

7. $23 \times (0.000615 \times \$500) = \$7.07$ finance charge

8. $150 \times \$12.80 = \$\ 1,920$
    $240 \times \$16.40 = \ \ \ \ 3,936$
    $\underline{320} \times \$23.70 = \ \ \underline{\ \ 7,584}$
    $710 \ \ \ \ \ \ \ \ \ \ \ \ \ \ \ \ \$13,440$

    $\$13,440 \div 710 = \$18.93$ average price per chair

9. $1.5 \times \$9.80 = \$14.70$ time-and-a-half rate
    $7\frac{1}{2} \times \$14.70 = \$110.25$ total overtime pay

UNIT 14 • PURCHASING FOR A BUSINESS

Section 87. Purchasing Merchandise

Exercise 1, page 441

1. **a.** August 26   **d.** June 23
    b. April 4   **e.** January 11
    c. February 12   **f.** February 21

2. Videotapes $ 42.00 ✓
    Cassette tapes   22.40 ✓
    Storage boxes   280.50 $285.00
    Tape cases   15.00 ✓
    Tape recorders   + 472.50 ✓
                        _____
                       $832.40 $836.90

3. Ice cube trays $ 55.50
    Food storage boxes   108.00
    Trash bags   319.70
    Plastic gloves   72.50
    Measuring cups   +   14.58
                         _____
           c. $570.28
    d. August 16 + 45 days = September 30

Exercise 2, page 442

1.

Items	Purchases	Purchases Returns	Net Purchases
Shutters	$ 4,418	$135	$ 4,283
Cabinets	12,876	562	12,314
Towel racks	1,317	35	1,282
Picture frames	2,089	172	1,917
Totals	$20,700	$904	$19,796

2.

Month	Purchases	Purchases Returns	Net Purchases
January	$ 14,618	$ 316	$ 14,302
February	17,830	387	17,443
March	38,512	571	37,941
April	46,984	1,309	45,675
May	53,011	1,470	51,541
June	38,737	698	38,039
Totals	$209,692	$4,751	$204,941

Review 87, page 444

2. a. $48 \times 4\frac{1}{3} = 208$
    b. $0.12 \times \$4,500 \times \frac{1}{4} = \$135$
    c. $45.9 \div 1,000 = 0.0459$ tax rate
        $0.0459 \times \$100 = \$4.59$ rate on $100

3. Combs $ 302.40 $25.20
    Toothpaste   529.20 ✓
    Key chains   216.00 ✓
    Batteries   +   98.00 $980.00
                    _____
                   $1,145.60 $1,750.40

4. **a.** ($70,000 + $50,000 + $80,000) − $3,000 = $197,000   estimated
    purchases
    b. $67,982 + $51,910 + $78,295 = $198,187   total purchases
    $198,187 − $2,863 = $195,324   net purchases

5. 0.06 × $1,000 = $60   income on bond
    $60 ÷ (0.75 × $1,000) = 8%   rate of income

Section 88. Trade Discounts

Exercise 1, page 446

1. **a.** 0.4 × $360 = $144   trade discount
    $360 − $144 = $216   invoice price
    b. 0.30 × $80 = $24   trade discount
    $80 − $24 = $56   invoice price
    c. 0.25 × $280 = $70   trade discount
    $280 − $70 = $210   invoice price
    d. 0.35 × $38 = $13.30   trade discount
    $38.00 − $13.30 = $24.70   invoice price
    e. $0.33\frac{1}{3} × $276 = $92   trade discount
    $276 − $92 = $184   invoice price
    f. 0.15 × $56 = $8.40   trade discount
    $56.00 − $8.40 = $47.60   invoice price
    g. 0.45 × $14 = $6.30   trade discount
    $14.00 − $6.30 = $7.70   invoice price

2. 30 × $54 = $1,620   list price
    0.28 × $1,620 = $453.60   trade discount
    $1,620 − $453.60 = $1,166.40   invoice price

3. **a.** 0.3 × $650 = $195   trade discount from Rinz
    $650 − $195 = $455   invoice price from Rinz
    0.40 × $800 = $320   trade discount from Okemar
    $800 − $320 = $480   invoice price from Okemar
    Rinz Company offers the lower price
    b. $480 − $455 = $25   lower

4. **a.** 0.3 × $570 = $171   trade discount from Avetel
    $570 − $171 = $399   invoice price from Avetel
    0.42 × $700 = $294   trade discount from Hexell
    $700 − $294 = $406   invoice price from Hexell
    Avetel, Inc. has the lower price
    b. $406 − $399 = $7   lower

5. **a.** 200 × $12 = $2,400
    0.05 × $2,400 = $120   estimated quantity discount
    b. 200 × $11.90 = $2,380   list price
    0.05 × $2,380 = $119   actual quantity discount
    c. $2,380 − $119 = $2,261   invoice price

6. 240 × $0.80 = $192   list price of July purchase
    0.04 × $192 = $7.68   quantity discount for July
    300 × $0.80 = $240   list price for August purchase
    0.07 × $240 = $16.80   quantity discount for August
    $7.68 + $16.80 = $24.48   saved by taking the 2 discounts

Exercise 2, page 447

1. **a.** $40 − $28 = $12   trade discount
   $12 ÷ $40 = 30%   rate of trade discount
   b. $140 − $105 = $35   trade discount
   $35 ÷ $140 = 25%   rate of trade discount
   c. $70 − $40.60 = $29.40   trade discount
   $29.40 ÷ $70 = 42%   rate of trade discount
   d. $380 − $247 = $133   trade discount
   $133 ÷ $380 = 35%   rate of trade discount
   e. $630 − $420 = $210   trade discount
   $210 ÷ $630 = $33\frac{1}{3}$%   rate of trade discount
   f. $90 − $49.50 = $40.50   trade discount
   $40.50 ÷ $90 = 45%   rate of trade discount

2. $96 − $64 = $32   trade discount
   $32 ÷ $96 = $33\frac{1}{3}$%   rate of trade discount

3. $450 − $270 = $180   trade discount
   $180 ÷ $450 = 40%   rate of trade discount

‡4. **a.** $760 + $40 = $800   total value of goods received
   b. $40 ÷ $800 = 5%   value free goods are of whole shipment

‡5. (15 + 1) × $48 = $768   total value of goods
   $48 ÷ $768 = 6.25%   rate of trade discount

‡6. 1 ÷ 20 = 5%   rate of trade discount

Review 88, page 448

2. **a.** 0.375 × $440 = $165   **d.** 700 × 3 = 2,100
   b. $\frac{4}{7}$ = 0.571, or 0.57   **e.** 600 ÷ 20 = 30
   c. $9\frac{1}{4} − 3\frac{4}{5} = 5\frac{9}{20}$

3. 40 × $48 = $1,920   list price
   0.35 × $1,920 = $672   trade discount
   $1,920 − $672 = $1,248   invoice price

4. $360 − $237.60 = $122.40   trade discount
   $122.40 ÷ $360 = 34%   rate of trade discount

5. **a.** $200,000 − $120,000 = $80,000   gross profit on sales
   b. $80,000 − $55,000 = $25,000   net income
   c. $25,000 ÷ $200,000 = 12.5%   percent net income was of sales

6. 50,000 × $100 = $5,000,000   capital value of stock
   0.023 × $5,000,000 = $115,000   dividend
   $285,600 − $115,000 = $170,600   amount kept in retained earnings

7. 0.14 × $12,800 = $1,792   annual depreciation
   4 × $1,792 = $7,168   total depreciation in four years
   $12,800 − $7,168 = $5,632   value of truck at end of fourth year

8. $45,700 + $34,820 = $80,520   total inventories
   $80,520 ÷ 2 = $40,260   average inventory
   $74,481 ÷ $40,260 = 1.85   monthly rate
   12 × 1.85 = 22.2   annual turnover rate

Section 89.   Series Discounts

Exercise 1, page 450

1. a. $90 - $18 = $72; $72 - $7.20 = $64.80   invoice price
        $90 - $64.80 = $25.20   trade discount
    b. $36 - $9 = $27; $27 - $2.70 = $24.30   invoice price
        $36 - $24.30 = $11.70   trade discount
    c. $48 - $12 = $36; $36 - $7.20 = $28.80   invoice price
        $48 - $28.80 = $19.20   trade discount
    d. $51 - $17 = $34; $34 - $6.80 = $27.20   invoice price
        $51 - $27.20 = $23.80   trade discount
    e. $130 - $13 = $117; $117 - $11.70 = $105.30   invoice price
        $130 - $105.30 = $24.70   trade discount
    f. $125 - $25 = $100; $100 - $10 = $90; $90 - $9 = $81   invoice price
        $125 - $81 = $44   trade discount
    g. $240 - $48 = $192; $192 - $38.40 = $153.60; $153.60 - $15.36 =
        $138.24   invoice price
        $240 - $138.24 = $101.76   trade discount
    h. $170 - $42.50 = $127.50; $127.50 - $25.50 = $102; $102 - $5.10 =
        $96.90   invoice price
        $170 - $96.90 = $73.10   trade discount
    i. $145 - $43.50 = $101.50; $101.500 - $15.225 = $86.275; $86.275 -
        $8.628 = $77.65   invoice price
        $145 - $77.65 - $67.35   trade discount
    j. $115 - $11.50 = $103.50; $103.50 - $10.35 = $93.15; $93.150 -
        $27.945 = $65.21   invoice price
        $115 - $65.21 = $49.79   trade discount

2. $280 - $70 = $210; $210 - $31.50 = $178.50   invoice price

3. 6 × $130 = $780   list price
    $780 - $234 = $546; $546 - $109.20 = $436.80; $436.80 - $43.68 =
    $393.12   invoice price

4. $185 - $37 = $148; $148 - $18.50 = $129.50; $129.500 - $6.475 =
    $123.03   invoice price

5. 15 × $107 = $1,605   list price
    $1,605 - $321 = $1,284; $1,284 - $192.60 = $1,091.40; $1,091.40 -
    $54.57 = $1,036.83   invoice price

6. $1,500 - $375 = $1,125; $1,125 - $225 = $900; $900 - $90 = $810
    invoice price of Morland Brothers
    $1,500 - $450 = $1,050; $1,050 - $210 = $840; $840 - $42 = $798
    invoice price of Wick Wholesale
    $810 - $798 = $12   saved by taking better offer of Wick Wholesale

Exercise 2, page 451

1. a.

100%	100%	b.	100%	100%	c.	100%	100%
− 10%	− 81%		− 25%	− 60%		− 20%	− 70%
90%	19%		75%	40%		80%	30%
− 9%			− 15%			− 10%	
81%			60%			70%	

d. | 100% | 100% |
|---|---|
| − 10% | − 60% |
| 90% | 40% |
| − 30% | |
| 60% | |

e. | 100% | 100% |
|---|---|
| − 25% | − 57% |
| 75% | 43% |
| − 15% | |
| 60% | |
| − 3% | |
| 57% | |

f. | 100% | 100% |
|---|---|
| − 30% | − 49% |
| 70% | 51% |
| − 14% | |
| 56% | |
| − 7% | |
| 49% | |

g. | 100% | 100% |
|---|---|
| − 20% | − 48% |
| 80% | 52% |
| − 8% | |
| 72% | |
| − 24% | |
| 48% | |

h. | 100% | 100% |
|---|---|
| − 20% | − 56% |
| 80% | 44% |
| − 16% | |
| 64% | |
| − 8% | |
| 56% | |

2. **a.**

100%	100%	
− 30%	− 56.7%	
70%	43.3%	single discount
− 7%		for Plan A
63%		
− 6.3%		
56.7%		

b.

100%	100%	
− 20%	− 64.8%	
80%	35.2%	single discount
− 8%		for Plan B
72%		
− 7.2%		
64.8%		

c.

100%	100%	
− 20%	− 72.2%	
80%	27.8%	single discount
− 4%		for Plan C
76%		
− 3.8%		
72.2%		

3. **a.** $0.278 \times \$300 = \$83.40$ discount amount
$\$300 − \$83.40 = \$216.60$ invoice price

b. $0.433 \times \$140 = \$60.62$ discount amount
$\$140 − \$60.62 = \$79.38$ invoice price

c. $0.352 \times \$90 = \$31.68$ discount amount
$\$90 − \$31.68 = \$58.32$ invoice price

d. $0.278 \times \$160 = \$44.48$ discount amount
$\$160 − \$44.48 = \$115.52$ invoice price

e. $0.352 \times \$70 = \$24.64$ discount amount
$\$70 − \$24.64 = \$45.36$ invoice price

Exercise 3, page 452

1. $0.76 \times \$4.95 = \$3.76$ invoice price

2. $0.63 \times \$16.50 = \$10.40$ invoice price

3. $0.72 \times \$28 = \$20.16$ invoice price

4. $0.67688 \times \$8.20 = \$5.55$ invoice price

5. $0.72675 \times \$12.40 = \$9.01$ invoice price

‡Exercise 4, page 452

1. a. $0.9 \times 0.95 = 0.855$, or 85.5%
     $100\% - 85.5\% = 14.5\%$
   b. $0.7 \times 0.95 = 0.665$, or 66.5%
     $100\% - 66.5\% = 33.5\%$
   c. $0.85 \times 0.9 = 0.765$, or 76.5%
     $100\% - 76.5\% = 23.5\%$
   d. $0.9 \times 0.95 \times 0.95 = 0.81225$, or 81.225%
     $100\% - 81.225\% = 18.775\%$
   e. $0.75 \times 0.9 \times 0.9 = 0.6075$, or 60.75
     $100\% - 60.75\% = 39.25\%$
   f. $0.7 \times 0.9 \times 0.9 = 0.567$, or 56.7%
     $100\% - 56.7\% = 43.3\%$
   g. $0.8 \times 0.95 \times 0.95 = 0.722$, or 72.2%
     $100\% - 72.2\% = 27.8\%$
   h. $0.7 \times 0.8 \times 0.9 = 0.504$, or 50.4%
     $100\% - 50.4\% = 49.6\%$
   i. $0.7 \times 0.85 \times 0.9 = 0.5355$, or 53.55%
     $100\% - 53.55\% = 46.45\%$
   j. $0.9 \times 0.85 \times 0.75 = 0.57375$, or 57.375%
     $100\% - 57.375\% = 42.625\%$

2. a. $100\% - 14.5\% = 85.5\%$
   b. $100\% - 33.5\% = 66.5\%$
   c. $100\% - 23.5\% = 76.5\%$
   d. $100\% - 18.775\% = 81.225\%$
   e. $100\% - 39.25\% = 60.75\%$
   f. $100\% - 43.3\% = 56.7\%$
   g. $100\% - 27.8\% = 72.2\%$
   h. $100\% - 49.6\% = 50.4\%$
   i. $100\% - 46.45\% = 53.55\%$
   j. $100\% - 42.625\% = 57.375\%$

Review 89, page 453

2. a. $76 \div 2\frac{1}{2} = 30\frac{2}{5}$
   b. $78 \times \$1.60 = \$124.80$
   c. $\$154 \div \$1.10 = 140$
   d. $\$280 \times 0.09 \times \frac{1}{3} = \$8.40$

3. $\begin{array}{ll} 100\% & 100\% \\ -\quad 25\% & -\ 63.75\% \end{array}$

       $\begin{array}{ll} \underline{75\%} & 36.25\% \quad \text{equivalent single rate discount} \\ -\ 11.25\% \\ \overline{63.75\%} \end{array}$

4. $\$1,400 - \$490 = \$910;\ \$910 - \$91 = \$819$ invoice price of L & T
    Electronics
    $\$1,200 - \$240 = \$960;\ \$960 - \$48 = \$912;\ \$912 - \$45.60 = \$866.40$
    invoice price of Inex
    $\$866.40 - \$819 = \$47.40$ amount saved by taking the lower offer

5. $\$125 - \$80 = \$45$ trade discount
    $\$45 \div \$125 = 36\%$ rate of trade discount

6. $\frac{4}{9} \times \$54,000 = \$24,000$ Loretta's share of net profit

7. a. $\$1 \times (\$200,000 \div \$1,000) = \$200$ estimated annual premium
    b. $\$1.07 \times (\$200,000 \div \$1,000) = \$214$ actual annual premium

Section 90.   Cash Discounts

Exercise 2, page 455

1. 10 days
    $\$758 - (0.02 \times \$758) = \$742.84$ needed to pay invoice

2. 10 days
    $\$485 - (0.03 \times \$485) = \$470.45$ needed to pay invoice

3. 15 days
    $\$920 - (0.02 \times \$920) = \$901.60$ needed to pay invoice

4. 30 days
    $\$386 - (0.01 \times \$386) = \$382.14$ needed to pay invoice

5. 20 days
    $\$369 - (0.02 \times \$369) = \$361.62$ needed to pay invoice

6. 39 days
    $\$861$ needed to pay invoice

7. 7 days
    $\$724 - (0.03 \times \$724) = \$702.28$ needed to pay invoice

8. 15 days
    $\$580 - (0.04 \times \$580) = \$556.80$ needed to pay invoice

9. 21 days
    $\$455$ needed to pay invoice

Exercise 3, page 455

1. a. $\$800 - \$200 = \$600$ invoice price
        $\$600 - (0.03 \times \$600) = \$582$ cash price
    b. $\$600 - \$150 = \$450;\ \$450 - \$45 = \$405$ invoice price
        $\$405 - (0.02 \times \$405) = \$396.90$ cash price

    c. $750 - $150 = $600; $600 - $90 = 510 invoice price
         $510 - (0.01 \times $510) = 504.90 cash price
    d. $500 - $100 = $400; $400 - $80 = 320 invoice price
         $320 - (0.03 \times $320) = 310.40 cash price
    e. $420 - $84 = $336; $336.00 - $33.60 = $302.40; $302.40 - $15.12 =$
         287.28 invoice price
         $287.28 - (0.05 \times $287.28) = 272.92 cash price

2. $970 - $291 = $679; $679.00 - $67.90 = 611.10 invoice price
    $611.10 - (0.02 \times $611.10) = 598.88 cash price

Review 90, page 456

2. **a.** $48 \times $1.25 = 60
     b. $14.7 \times 0.89 = 13.083$
     c. $2.50 - $1 = 1.50
        $\frac{$1.50}{$2.50} = \frac{3}{5}$

3. December 6

4. $3,600 - $720 = $2,880; $2,880 - $288 = $2,592$ invoice price
    $2,592 - (0.02 \times $2,592) = $2,540.16$ amount of cash paid

5.
    100%   100%
   − 10%   − 85.5%   single discount equivalent
     90%   14.5%
   − 4.5%
    85.5%

Section 91. More About Cash Discounts

Exercise 1, page 457

1. $780 \times 0.12 \times \frac{1}{8} = 11.70 interest
    $20.00 - $11.70 = 8.30 saved

2. $3,675 \times 0.08 \times \frac{1}{12} = 24.50 interest
    $75.00 - $24.50 = 50.50 saved

3. $0.04 \times $9,000 = 360 discount
    $9,000 - $360 = $8,640$ amount borrowed
    $8,640 \times 0.15 \times \frac{1}{18} = 72 interest
    $360 - $72 = 288 saved

4. $0.03 \times $23,000 = 690 discount
    $23,000 - $690 = $22,310$ amount borrowed
    $22,310 \times 0.16 \times \frac{1}{6} = 594.93 interest
    $690.00 - $594.93 = 95.07 saved

5. $0.04 \times $2,400 = 96 discount
    $2,400 - $96 = $2,304$ amount borrowed
    $2,304 \times 0.13 \times \frac{1}{12} = 24.96 interest
    $96.00 - $24.96 = 71.04 saved

6. $0.03 \times $56,000 = $1,680$ discount
    $56,000 - $1,680 = $54,320$ amount borrowed
    $54,320 \times 0.18 \times \frac{1}{8} = $1,222.20$ interest
    $1,680.00 - $1,222.20 = 457.80

Exercise 2, page 458

1. a. $900 − $873 = $27   cash discount
        $27 ÷ $900 = 3%   rate of discount
    b. $750 − $735 = $15   cash discount
        $15 ÷ $750 = 2%   rate of discount
    c. $800 − $768 = $32   cash discount
        $32 ÷ $800 = 4%   rate of discount
    d. $1,240 − $1,178 = $62   cash discount
        $62 ÷ $1,240 = 5%   rate of discount
    e. $582 + $18 = $600   invoice price
        $18 ÷ $600 = 3%   rate of discount
    f. $4,116 + $84 = $4,200   invoice price
        $84 ÷ $4,200 = 2%   rate of discount
    g. $1,782 + $18 = $1,800   invoice price
        $18 ÷ $1,800 = 1%   rate of discount

2. a. $6,000 − $5,760 = $240   cash discount
    b. $240 ÷ $6,000 = 4%   cash discount as percent of invoice price

3. $680 − $659.60 = $20.40   cash discount
    $20.40 ÷ $680 = 3%   rate of discount

4. $855 + $45 = $900   invoice price
    $45 ÷ $900 = 5%   rate of discount

‡Exercise 3, page 458

1. $11 ÷ 0.02 = $550   invoice price

2. $38 ÷ 0.04 = $950   invoice price

3. $25.86 ÷ 0.03 = $862   invoice price

4. 100% − 2% = 98%
    $2,548 ÷ 0.98 = $2,600   invoice price

5. 100% − 2% = 98%
    $407.68 ÷ 0.98 = $416   invoice price

6. 100% − 5% = 95%
    $2,945 ÷ 0.95 = $3,100   amount of invoice

Review 91, page 459

1. a. $1.8 \times \$15.50 = \$27.90$
    b. $\$1,800 \times 0.13 \times \frac{1}{3} = \$78$
    c. $\$9.80 − \$7.00 = \$2.80$
        $\frac{\$2.80}{\$7.00} = \frac{2}{5}$
    d. $\$0.1784 = \$0.178$
    e. $0.0045 = 0.45\%$

2. $2,890 − $2,774.40 = $115.60   discount
    $115.60 ÷ $2,890 = 4%   rate of discount

3. $0.02 \times \$16,400 = \$328$ discount
$\$16,400 - \$328 = \$16,072$ amount borrowed
$\$16,072 \times 0.12 \times \frac{1}{12} = \$160.72$ interest
$\$328 - \$160.72 = \$167.28$ saved

4.
100%	100%
− 35%	− 61.75%
65%	38.25% single discount equivalent
− 3.25%	
61.75%	

5. $\$4,800 - \$640 = \$4,160$ total depreciation
$\$4,160 \div 4 = \$1,040$ average annual depreciation

6. 540 m $\times$ 240 m = 129 600 m^2 area of field
129 600 m^2 − 1 800 m^2 = 127 800 m^2 available for planting

UNIT 15 • SELLING FOR A BUSINESS

Section 92.   Cash Sales Records

Exercise 1, page 463

1.
Cash Proof Form
Date: July 3, 19--

Change fund	$ 100.00
Register total of cash received	2,793.68
Total	2,893.68
Register total of cash paid out	29.50
Cash that should be in drawer	2,864.18
Cash actually in drawer	2,863.38
Cash short	$ 0.80
Cash over	

2.
Change fund	$ 75.00	
Register total of cash received	3,812.34	$3,887.34
Register total of cash paid out	$ 213.88	
Cash removed for personal use	50.00	− 263.88
Remainder to be accounted for		$3,623.46
Cash on hand in money drawer		− 3,624.75
Cash over		$ 1.29

3.
Change fund	$ 100.00	
Register total of cash received	3,307.43	$3,407.43
Register total of cash paid out		− 418.75
Remainder to be accounted for		$2,988.68
Cash on hand in money drawer		$2,988.68

4. 27 × $2.45 = $ 66.15
23 × $2.55 = $ 58.65
34 × $2.60 = $ 88.40
12 × $2.70 = $ 32.40
28 × $2.80 = $ 78.40
11 × $2.85 = $ 31.35
21 × $2.90 = $ 60.90
22 × $2.95 = $ 64.90
 3 × $3.05 = $ 9.15
44 × $3.10 = $ 136.40
49 × $3.15 = $ 154.35
36 × $3.20 = $ 115.20
74 × $3.25 = $ 240.50
28 × $3.50 = $ 98.00
55 × $3.75 = $ 206.25
————————
$1,441.00

$1,441 + $100 = $1,541   amount Ron should have
$1,541 − $1,540.90 = $0.10   short

Exercise 2, page 464

1. a.

Department	Cash Sales	Cash Refunds for Returns	Net Cash Sales
Prescription Drugs	$1,798.22	$ —	$1,798.22
Nonprescription Drugs	2,666.23	27.89	2,638.34
Cosmetics	902.56	78.12	824.44
Hygiene Items	613.55	43.49	570.06
Totals	$5,980.56	$149.50	$5,831.06

b. $5,980.56 Cash sales
−   149.50 Cash refunds for returns
————————
$5,831.06 Total

2. a.

Salesperson	Cash Sales	Cash Refunds	Net Cash Sales
Allen	$ 308.25	$ 22.87	$ 285.38
Brett	478.29	68.45	409.84
Cruz	511.98	15.77	496.21
Deng	278.41	12.39	266.02
Eaton	645.90	34.85	611.05
Farrell	198.34	5.89	192.45
Totals	$2,421.17	$160.22	$2,260.95

b. $2,421.17 Cash sales
−   160.22 Cash refunds
————————
$2,260.95 Net cash sales

Review 92, page 465

2. a. $9\frac{2}{3} + 12\frac{3}{4} + 15\frac{5}{6} = 38\frac{1}{4}$
b. $28\frac{1}{3} \div 1\frac{5}{9} = 15$
c. $3,500 × 0.12 × $\frac{50}{365}$ = 57.53
d. 2 107 L ÷ 1,000 = 2.107 kL

     e. $2,500 × 0.20 = $500
     f. $2,489 × 0.21 = $522.69
     g. 22.75 ÷ 6.5 = 3.5
     h. 45.6784 × 1,000 = 45,678.4

3. ($100 + $4,107.56) − $163.88 = $4,043.68
$4,044.55 − $4,043.68 = $0.87   over

4. ($1,280 − $768) ÷ $1,280 = 40%

5. April 4

6. $100,000 × 0.80 = $80,000   minimum amount
$$\frac{\$60,000}{\$80,000} = \frac{3}{4}$$
$\frac{3}{4}$ × $12,800 = $9,600

Section 93.   Charge Sales Records

Exercise 1, page 469

1.

Date	Explanation	Charges	Credits	Balance
19 --				
Aug. 1				$2,353.90
8	Invoice No. 3369	$1,685.49		4,039.39
16	Credit Memo No. 388		$ 45.66	3,993.73
20	Payment		2,353.90	1,639.83
26	Invoice No. 3672	2,275.00		3,914.83
Sept. 9	Payment		1,639.83	2,275.00
12	Invoice No. 4180	1,216.00		3,491.00
15	Credit Memo No. 412		120.00	3,371.00
25	Payment		2,275.00	1,096.00

2.

Date	Explanation	Charges	Credits	Balance
19 --				
June 1				$4,116.53
3	Payment		$4,116.53	—
5	Invoice No. 9708	$3,642.39		3,642.39
17	Credit Memo No. 398		488.12	3,154.27
18	Invoice No. 9934	1,785.84		4,940.11
25	Payment		3,154.27	1,785.84
26	Credit Memo No. 416		21.72	1,764.12

3.

Date	Explanation	Charges	Credits	Balance
19 --				
Feb. 1				$ 653.23
2	Credit Memo No. 278		$ 29.15	624.08
5	Invoice No. 7451	$438.27		1,062.35
8	Payment		624.08	438.27
17	Credit Memo No. 302		8.52	429.75
Mar. 2	Invoice No. 8459	904.72		1,334.47
6	Payment		429.75	904.72
16	Credit Memo No. 296		12.83	891.89

Review 93, page 470

2. **a.** $44\frac{1}{2} \times 6\frac{1}{4} = 278\frac{1}{8}$

b. ($108 − $75.60) ÷ $108 = 30%
$32.40 ÷ $108 = 0.30 = 30%

No.
Days

c.

	No. Days		**d.**	
June 15–30	15			$ 1.30
July	31			× 30
Aug.	31			$39.00
Sept.	30			
Oct. 15	+ 15			
	122			

e. $1,000 × 0.10 = $100   **f.** $1,008 × 0.09875 = $99.54
‡g. $8.40 ÷ $\frac{3}{4}$ = $11.20

3.

Account balance $5,893.11
Invoice   + 1,007.49
                    $6,900.60
Credit memo   −   23.78
                    $6,876.82
Payment   − 5,000.00
                    $1,876.82

4. **a.** $1,700 × 0.03 = $51   cash
$1,700 − $51 = $1,649   discount

b. $1,649 × 0.09 = $148.41
$148.41 × $\frac{50}{360}$ = $20.61   interest
$51 − $20.61 = $30.39   saved

Section 94.   Figuring Discounts and Prices

Exercise 1, page 472

1. **a.** $590 − $472 = $118   amount of discount
$118 ÷ $590 = 0.20 = 20%   rate of discount

b. $147.90 − $98.60 = $49.30   amount of discount
$49.30 ÷ $147.90 = 0.333 = $33\frac{1}{3}$%   rate of discount

   c. $199 − $179.10 = $19.90   amount of discount
       $19.90 ÷ $199 = 0.10 = 10%   rate of discount
   d. $485.80 − $412.93 = $72.87   amount of discount
       $72.87 ÷ $485.80 = 0.15 = 15%   rate of discount

2. $199.99 − $159.99 = $40   amount of discount
    $40 ÷ $199.99 = 0.20 = 20%   rate of discount

3. $127.50 − $99.45 = $28.05   amount of discount
    $28.05 ÷ $127.50 = 0.22 = 22%   rate of discount

4. $35 + $19 + $59 = $113   total of individual prices
    $113 − $73.45 = $39.55   discount for buying set
    $39.55 ÷ $113 = 0.35 = 35%   rate of discount

5. $3.87 ÷ $129 = 0.03 = 3%   rate of discount

6. $89.95 − $75.95 = $14   amount of discount
    $14 ÷ $89.95 = 0.1556 = 15.6%   rate of discount

Exercise 2, page 472

1. (5 × $7.50) − $33 = $4.50   saved
    $4.50 ÷ $37.50 = 0.12 = 12%   saved

2. 4 × $59.75 = $239   regular cost of trees
    $239 − $179.25 = $59.75   saved
    $59.75 ÷ $239 = 0.25 = 25%   rate of discount

3. a. 2 × $36 = $72   regular price of 2-year subscription
       $72 − $63 = $9   saved
       $9 ÷ $72 = 0.125 = $12\frac{1}{2}$%   rate of discount
   b. 3 × $36 = $108   regular price of 3-year subscription
       $108 − $91.80 = $16.20   saved
       $16.20 ÷ $108 = 0.15 = 15%   rate of discount

4. 2 × $2.99 = $5.98   regular cost of 2 wrenches
    $5.98 − ($2.99 + $0.01) = $2.98   saved
    $2.98 ÷ $5.98 = 0.498 = 50%   rate of discount

5. 2 × $9.95 = $19.90   cost of two 5,000 sq. ft. bags
    $19.90 − $16.95 = $2.95   saved
    $2.95 ÷ $19.90 = 0.1482 = 14.8%   rate of discount

Exercise 3, page 473

1. a. 10% × $259.90 = $25.99   discount
       $259.90 − $25.99 = $233.91   selling price
   b. 20% × $22.95 = $4.59   discount
       $22.95 − $4.59 = $18.36   selling price
   c. 12.5% × $170 = $21.25   discount
       $170 − $21.25 = $148.75   selling price
   d. 25% × $289 = $72.25   discount
       $289 − $72.25 = $216.75   selling price
   e. 37.5% × $370 = $138.75   discount
       $370 − $138.75 = $231.25   selling price
   f. 40% × $1,599.95 = $639.98   discount
       $1,599.95 − $639.98 = $959.97   selling price

2. $15.95 × 0.15 = $2.39   discount
$15.95 − $2.39 = $13.56   amount customer pays

3. $75 × 0.24 = $18   discount
$75 − $18 = $57   discount price

4. $49.99 × 0.20 = $10   discount
$49.99 − $10.00 = $39.99   sale price

5. a. $60 × 0.40 = $24   estimated discount
b. $57.95 × 0.40 = $23.18
$57.95 − $23.18 = $34.77   reduced price

‡Exercise 4, page 474

1. 100% − 30% = 70%

2. a. 100% − 16% = 84%   of the marked price
b. $37.80 ÷ 0.84 = $45   marked price

3. a. 100% − 25% = 75%   of the marked price
b. $693.75 ÷ 0.75 = $925   marked price

4. $108.50 ÷ 87.5% = $124   marked price

5. $270 ÷ 75% = $360   marked price

6. $119.60 ÷ 65% = $184   catalog price

Review 94, page 475

2. a. $34\frac{3}{8} × 26 = 893\frac{3}{4}$
b. September 3
c. 1.25 × $2.80 = $3.50

3. ($350 − $245) ÷ $350 = 30%   rate of markdown

4. $100 + $3,678.34 − $125.44 = $3,652.90   should have
$3,652.90 − $3,652.12 = $0.78   short

5. $9,397.66 + $4,798.56 − $89.98 − $8,000 = $6,106.24   balance

6. $976.50 − ($277.50 + $28.32) = $670.68   net on sale

7. $1,400 − $1,358 = $42   amount of discount
$42 ÷ $1,400 = 3%   rate of discount

8.
```
   100%          100%
 −  20%        −  54%
   ────          ────
    80%           46%   single discount equivalent to series
 −  20%
   ────
    60%
 −   6%
   ────
    54%
```

‡9. $893.75 ÷ 65% = $1,375   invoice price

Section 95.   Finding Profit on Unit Sales

Exercise 1, page 477

1. 15 × $999 = $14,985
     5 × $945 =   4,725
     5 × $925 =   4,625
                  $24,335   selling price

    $14,750 + $275 = $15,025   total cost
    $24,335 − $15,025 = $9,310   gross profit

2. 375 × $12.95 = $4,856.25
    150 × $10.95 =   1,642.50
     75 × $ 8.95 =   671.25
                    $7,170.00   selling price

    (50 × $75) + $35 = $3,785   total cost
    $7,170 − $3,785 = $3,385   gross profit

3. 3 × 12 = 36; 36 × $7.95 = $286.20   selling price
    $78 × 3 = $234; $234 × 0.35 = $81.90   discount amount
    ($234 − $81.90) + $22.40 = $174.50   total cost
    $286.20 − $174.50 = $111.70   gross profit

4. (90 × $1.48) + (35 × $1.25) = $176.95   selling price
    (125 × $0.88) + $4.68 = $114.68   total cost
    $176.95 − $114.68 = $62.27   gross profit

5. 50 × $67.88 = $3,394   selling price
    (50 × $45) + $23 = $2,273   total cost
    $3,394 − $2,273 = $1,121   gross profit

Exercise 2, page 478

1. $49 − $29 = $20   gross profit
    $20 − (0.26 × $49) = $7.26   net income

2. $375 − $195 = $180   gross profit
    $180 − (0.28 × $375) = $75   net income

3. $22,090 − $14,750 = $7,340   gross profit
    $7,394 − $7,340 = $54   net loss

4. 30 × $70 = $2,100
    $2,100 − $210 = $1,890; $1,890 − $189 = $1,701   cost
    15 × $135 = $2,025
    10 × $120 =   1,200
     5 × $ 75 =   375
                  $3,600   net sales

    $3,600 − $1,701 = $1,899   gross profit
    $1,899 − (0.35 × $3,600) = $639   net income

5. $8 − $1.60 = $6.40; $6.40 − $0.64 = $5.76
    $5.76 + $0.50 = $6.26   cost
    $12 − $6.26 = $5.74   gross profit
    $5.74 − (0.25 × $12) = $2.74   net income per can opener

Exercise 3, page 479

1. $175 − $98 = $77   markup
   $77 ÷ $175 = 44%   rate of markup

2. $55 − $35.20 = $19.80   gross profit
   $19.80 ÷ $55 = 36%   rate of gross profit

3. a. $47.50 − $30.40 = $17.10   gross profit
      $17.10 ÷ $47.50 = 36%   rate of gross profit
   b. less
   c. $37\frac{1}{2}$% − 36% = $1\frac{1}{2}$%   less

4. (144 ÷ 2) × $1.60 = $115.20   selling price
   $115.20 − $74.88 = $40.32   gross profit
   $40.32 ÷ $115.20 = 35%   rate of gross profit

5. $750 − (0.20 × $750) − $348 = $252   gross profit
   $252 ÷ $600 = 42%   rate of gross profit

Exercise 4, page 479

1. $18.00 − (12 × $0.69) = $9.72   gross profit
   0.38 × $18 = $6.84   operating expenses
   $9.72 − $6.84 = $2.88   net income
   $2.88 ÷ $18 = 16%   rate of net income

2. $4.50 − $2.79 = $1.71   gross profit
   0.26 × $4.50 = $1.17   operating expenses
   $1.71 − $1.17 = $0.54   net income
   $0.54 ÷ $4.50 = 12%   rate of net income

3. $3,900 − $2,964 = $936   gross profit
   $936 − $585 = $351   net income
   $351 ÷ $3,900 = 9%   rate of net income

4. $10,400 − $6,760 = $3,640   gross profit
   0.40 × $10,400 = $4,160   operating expenses
   $4,160 − $3,640 = $520   net loss
   $520 ÷ $10,400 = 5%   rate of net loss

5. $145 − $87 = $58   gross profit
   0.30 × $145 = $43.50   operating expenses
   $58.00 − $43.50 = $14.50   net income
   $14.50 ÷ $145 = 10%   rate of net income

Review 95, page 480

2. a. $16\frac{1}{2}$ ÷ $2\frac{3}{4}$ = 6
   b. ($4.86 − $3.60) ÷ $3.60 = 35%
   c. $3,500 × 0.12 × $\frac{1}{6}$ = $70
   ‡d. $4\frac{1}{2}$ × 8 = 36

3. a. (80 × $14) + (20 × $12) + (20 × $8) = $1,520   selling price
      $1,520 − $872 = $648   gross profit
   b. $648 ÷ 120 = $5.40   average gross profit per drier

4. **a.** $0.88 − $0.66 = $0.22   gross profit
        $0.22 ÷ $0.88 = 25%   rate of gross profit
    b. $0.22 − $0.13 = $0.09   net income
        $0.09 ÷ $0.88 = 10.2%   rate of net income

5. $770 − $731.50 = $38.50   amount of discount
    $38.50 ÷ $770 = 5%   rate of cash discount

6. **a.** $500 − $300 = $200   amount of discount
        $200 ÷ $500 = 40%   rate of discount
    b. $475 − $308.75 = $166.25   amount of discount
        $166.25 ÷ $475 = 35%   rate of discount

Section 96. Pricing Goods — Sales Price Basis

Exercise 1, page 481

1. $25 − (0.35 × $25) = $16.25   maximum price that can be paid

2. 12 × $27.98 = $335.76   per dozen
    $335.76 − (0.34 × $335.76) = $221.60   most owner can pay

3. $49.50 − (0.44 × $49.50) = $27.72   most wholesaler can pay

4. **a.** $30 − (0.40 × $30) = $18   estimated cost per pair to store
    b. $29.50 − (0.38 × $29.50) = $18.29   cost per pair to store

‡Exercise 2, page 482

1. **a.** $93.06 ÷ 0.55 = $169.20   selling price
    b. $72 ÷ 0.60 = $120   selling price
    c. $63.18 ÷ 0.65 = $97.20   selling price
    d. $8.20 ÷ 0.625 = $13.12   selling price

2. $29 ÷ 0.58 = $50   selling price

3. $28.44 ÷ 0.60 = $47.40   selling price per bracelet

4. $5,850 ÷ 200 = $29.25   cost per box
    $29.25 ÷ 0.65 = $45   selling price per box

5. $480 − $120 = $360; $360 − $36 = $324   cost per dozen
    $324 ÷ 12 = $27   cost per tree
    $27 ÷ 0.70 = $38.57

6. $1,248.50 ÷ 0.55 = $2,270

‡Exercise 3, page 483

1. **a.** $60.45 ÷ 0.62 = $97.50
    b. $125.19 ÷ 0.65 = $192.60
    c. $2.67 ÷ 0.60 = $4.45
    d. $103.60 ÷ 0.56 = $185
    e. $1,075.20 ÷ 0.56 = $1,920

2. $111 ÷ 0.60 = $185   selling price

3. $38.35 ÷ 0.65 = $59   selling price

4. $195 ÷ 0.60 = $325   selling price

5. $984.75 ÷ 0.65 = $1,515   selling price

Review 96, page 484

1. a. $440 × 0.0325 = $14.30
   b. 150 m^2 ÷ 120 m^2 = 125%
   c. 74.375
   d. $(21\frac{7}{8} - 12\frac{1}{2}) ÷ 12\frac{1}{2} = \frac{3}{4}$

2. $59.95 − ($59.95 × 0.35) = $38.97

3. a. 300 × 50 = $15,000
   b. $288 × 52 = $14,976 ÷ 12 = $1,248   per month

4. $2,800,000 + $1,200,000 = $4,000,000   total insurance
   $2,800,000 ÷ $4,000,000 = $\frac{7}{10}$ of loss borne by Zale
   $1,200,000 ÷ $4,000,000 = $\frac{3}{10}$ of loss borne by Filers
   $\frac{7}{10}$ × $12,400 = $8,680   to be paid by Zale
   $\frac{3}{10}$ × $12,400 = $3,720   to be paid by Filers

5.

Check register balance		$425.60	Bank statement balance		$489.47
Deduct:			Deduct:		
Service charge	−	5.22	Outstanding checks:		
		$420.38	#35	$28.34	
			#37	2.87	
Add:			#38	32.12	
Earned interest	+	1.78	#40	3.98	− 67.31
Correct check register balance		$422.16	Available bank balance		$422.16

‡6. $698.75 ÷ 0.65 = $1,075   selling price

‡7. $147 ÷ 0.60 = $245

Section 97.   Pricing Goods—Cost Price Basis

Exercise 1, page 486

1. a. $25 − $15 = $10   markup
      $10 ÷ $15 = $66\frac{2}{3}$%   rate of markup based on cost
   b. $525 − $315 = $210   markup
      $210 ÷ $315 = $66\frac{2}{3}$%   rate of markup based on cost
   c. $101.97 − $77.25 = $24.72   markup
      $24.72 ÷ $77.25 = 32%   rate of markup based on cost
   d. $155.10 − $112.80 = $42.30   markup
      $42.30 ÷ $112.80 = $37\frac{1}{2}$%   rate of markup based on cost

2. $1.74 − $1.20 = $0.54   markup
   $0.54 ÷ $1.20 = 45%   rate of markup based on cost

Exercise 2, page 486

1. a. $90 − $72 = $18   markup
      $18 ÷ $72 = 25%   rate of markup based on cost
      $18 ÷ $90 = 20%   rate of markup based on selling price

b. $225 − $150 = $75   markup
$75 ÷ $150 = 50%   rate of markup based on cost
$75 ÷ $225 = $33\frac{1}{3}$%   rate of markup based on selling price
c. $864 − $720 = $144   markup
$144 ÷ $720 = 20%   rate of markup based on cost
$144 ÷ $864 = $16\frac{2}{3}$%   rate of markup based on selling price
d. $147.00 − $110.25 = $36.75   markup
$36.75 ÷ $110.25 = $33\frac{1}{3}$%   rate of markup based on cost
$36.75 ÷ $147.00 = 25%   rate of markup based on selling price

2. **a.** $250 − $150 = $100   markup
$100 ÷ $150 = $66\frac{2}{3}$%   rate of markup based on cost
   b. $100 ÷ $250 = 40%   rate of markup based on selling price

3. $360 − $120 = $240; $240 − $24 = $216
$360 − $216 = $144   markup
$144 ÷ $216 = $66\frac{2}{3}$%   rate of markup based on cost

Exercise 3, page 487

1. $0.48 × ($157.50 + $17.25) = $83.88   markup
$174.75 + $83.88 = $258.63   lowest price

2. $348 − $87 = $261; $261 − $26.10 = $234.90   invoice price
$234.90 + $25.00 = $259.90   total cost
$0.40 × $259.90 = $103.96   markup
$259.90 + $103.96 = $363.86   selling price

3. $230.00 − $86.25 = $143.75; $143.75 − $28.75 = $115   invoice price
$115 + $38 = $153   total cost
$0.50 × $153 = $76.50   markup
$153 + $76.50 = $229.50   selling price

4. $15.50 × 60 = $930   invoice price
(12 × 60) − 24 = 696   number of salable baskets
$0.40 × $930 = $372   markup
$930 + $372 = $1,302   sales price of 60 crates
$1,302 ÷ 696 = $1.87   selling price

Review 97, page 488

1. **a.** April 20
   b. $8 × 2.155 = $17.24
   c. $700 × 0.16 × $\frac{1}{4}$ = $28

2. $54.40 − $34.00 = $20.40   markup
$20.40 ÷ $34 = 60%   profit based on cost

3. $0.55 × ($59 + $10) = $37.95   gross profit
$69 + $37.95 = $106.95   marked price

4. **a.** $6 × 50 = $300   estimated cost before discounts
   b. $5.95 × 50 = $297.50
   $297.50 − $59.50 = $238; $238 − $11.90 = $226.10   total cost
   $226.10 − ($226.10 × 0.02) = $221.58

5. a. $1,290 × 20 = $25,800
$25,800 − $9,030 = $16,770; $16,770 − $1,677 = $15,093   cost of local dealer
($1,210 × 20) − $9,680 = $14,520
$14,520 + $165.88 = $14,685.88   cost of out-of-town dealer
Out-of-town dealer has better offer
b. $15,093 − $14,685.88 = $407.12   savings

6.

$$
\begin{array}{r}
100\% \\
-\ 20\% \\
\hline
80\% \\
-\ 12\% \quad (15\% \text{ of } 80\%) \\
\hline
68\% \\
-\ 6.8\% \quad (10\% \text{ of } 68\%) \\
\hline
61.2\%
\end{array}
\qquad
\begin{array}{r}
100\% \\
-\ 61.2\% \\
\hline
38.8\%
\end{array}
$$

‡7. $61.48 ÷ 0.58 = $106

‡Section 98. Special Pricing Problems

‡Exercise 1, page 489

1. a. 50% ÷ 50% = 100.0%
b. 30% ÷ 70% = 42.9%
c. 15% ÷ 85% = 17.6%
d. 45% ÷ 55% = 81.8%
e. 40% ÷ 60% = 66.7%
f. 36% ÷ 64% = 56.3%

2. 55% ÷ 45% = 122.2%

3. 27% ÷ 73% = 37%

4. $37\frac{1}{2}\% ÷ 62\frac{1}{2}\% = 60\%$

‡Exercise 2, page 490

1. a. $53.80 ÷ 1.45 = $37.10
b. $3.85 ÷ 1.55 = $2.48
c. $134.60 ÷ 1.60 = $84.13
d. $80.00 ÷ 1.70 = $47.06
e. $258.90 ÷ 1.52 = $170.33
f. $15.70 ÷ 1.63 = $9.63

2. $59.98 ÷ 1.60 = $37.49   highest price

3. $125 ÷ 1.58 = $79.11   purchase price

4. $178.50 ÷ 1.70 = $105   cost

5. $16.89 × 12 = $202.68   selling price per dozen
$202.68 ÷ 1.50 = $135.12   most stores should pay per dozen cans

Review 98, page 490

1. a. $21\frac{3}{4} − 6\frac{4}{5} = 14\frac{19}{20}$
b. $2,000 × 0.10 × $\frac{1}{2}$ = $100

c. $1,850 \times 0.11 \times \frac{1}{2} = \$101.75$
d. September 1
e. $15.75 \div 1.125 = \$14$

‡2. $0.34 \div 0.66 = 51.5\%$ gain on cost

‡3. $39 \div 1.40 = \$27.86$ highest price

‡4. $124 - (\$124 \times 0.25) = \$93$ dealer's cost
$93 \div 0.62 = \$150$ selling price

‡5. $355.99 \div 0.97 = \$367$

‡6. $48.75 \div 0.03 = \$1,625$ amount of invoice

‡7. $0.04 \times \$100 = \$4$ annual dividend per share
$4,800 \div \$4 = 1,200$ shares must be bought

‡8. $115,200 - \$110,400 = \$4,800$ annual net income
$4,800 \div 0.08 = \$60,000$ amount that can be invested

UNIT 16 • MANUFACTURING AND OFFICE COSTS

Section 99. Factory Costs

Exercise 1, page 494

1. $316,780 + \$376,300 + \$175,390 = \$868,470$ total factory cost

2. $264,963 + \$378,208 + \$78,672 = \$721,843$ total factory cost

3. $108,342 + \$7,278 + \$23,207 + \$7,725 + \$12,465 + \$3,674 = \$162,691$
total factory overhead

4. **a.** $56,388.80 + \$25,825 + \$31,103.76 + \$15,281.50 + \$16,950.40 +$
$6,204.86 = \$151,754.32$ total factory overhead
   b. $478,392.70 + \$610,729.20 + \$151,754.32 = \$1,240,876.22$ total factory cost

5. $1,282.29 + \$1,975.26 + \$1,234.31 = \$4,491.86$ total factory cost
$4,491.86 \div 150 = \$29.95$ average cost per radio

6. **a.** $400,000 + \$1,000,000 + \$300,000 = \$1,700,000$ estimated factory cost
   b. $391,444 + \$1,027,044 + \$303,759 = \$1,722,247$ total factory cost
   $1,722,247 \div 12,000 = \$143.52$ average cost per unit

Exercise 2, page 495

1. $3,000 + 1,800 + 2,000 + 1,200 = 8,000$ sq. ft. total floor space
Printers: $\frac{3,000}{8,000}$ or $\frac{3}{8} \times \$18,000 = \$6,750$
Copiers: $\frac{2,000}{8,000}$ or $\frac{1}{4} \times \$18,000 = \$4,500$
Assembly: $\frac{1,800}{8,000}$ or $\frac{9}{40} \times \$18,000 = \$4,050$
Finishing: $\frac{1,200}{8,000}$ or $\frac{3}{20} \times \$18,000 = \$2,700$

2. $108 + 36 + 12 + 84 = 240$ workers
Department A: $\frac{108}{240}$ or $\frac{9}{20} \times \$400,000 = \$180,000$
Department B: $\frac{36}{240}$ or $\frac{3}{20} \times \$400,000 = \$60,000$
Department C: $\frac{12}{240}$ or $\frac{1}{20} \times \$400,000 = \$20,000$
Department D: $\frac{84}{240}$ or $\frac{7}{20} \times \$400,000 = \$140,000$

3. $3,000 + 4,500 + 7,500 = 15,000$ horsepower hours
Department X: $\frac{3,000}{15,000}$ or $\frac{1}{5} \times \$4,500 = \$900$
Department Y: $\frac{4,500}{15,000}$ or $\frac{3}{10} \times \$4,500 = \$1,350$
Department Z: $\frac{7,500}{15,000}$ or $\frac{1}{2} \times \$4,500 = \$2,250$

4. $\$36,125 + \$21,675 + \$86,700 = \$144,500$ total value of equipment
Department G: $\frac{\$36,125}{\$144,500}$ or $\frac{1}{4} \times \$2,890 = \$722.50$
Department K: $\frac{\$21,675}{\$144,500}$ or $\frac{3}{20} \times \$2,890 = \$433.50$
Department R: $\frac{\$86,700}{\$144,500}$ or $\frac{3}{5} \times \$2,890 = \$1,734$

Review 99, page 496

2. **a.** $\$81.20 \div 1.40 = \$58$
b. $10 \div \frac{2}{5} = 25$
c. $60\% = \frac{3}{5}$
d. $2.75 \text{ m} + 4 \text{ m} + 7.20 \text{ m} = 13.95 \text{ m}$

3. $\$3,589.12 + \$6,128.43 + \$721.31 = \$10,438.86$ total factory cost
$\$10,438.86 \div 300 = \$34.796$ or $\$34.80$ average cost per cover

4. $5,600 + 2,400 + 4,800 + 3,200 = 16,000$ sq. ft.   total floor space
Department A: $\frac{5,600}{16,000}$ or $\frac{7}{20} \times \$180,000 = \$63,000$
Department B: $\frac{2,400}{16,000}$ or $\frac{3}{20} \times \$180,000 = \$27,000$
Department C: $\frac{4,800}{16,000}$ or $\frac{3}{10} \times \$180,000 = \$54,000$
Department D: $\frac{3,200}{16,000}$ or $\frac{1}{5} \times \$180,000 = \$36,000$

5. $(0.20 \times \$12,900) + (0.12 \times \$12,900) + \$1,860 = \$5,988$ total expenses
$\$5,988 \div 15,000 = 39.92$ or $39.9\cent$ operating cost per mile

6.
$$\begin{array}{ll} 100\% & 100\% \\ -\ 20\% & -\ 66.5\% \\ \hline 80\% & 33.5\%, \text{ or } 33\tfrac{1}{2}\% \\ -\ 10\% & \\ \hline 70\% & \\ -\ 3.5\% & \\ \hline 66.5\% & \end{array}$$

Section 100.   Finding the Break-Even Point

Exercise 1, page 497

1. $\$88.75 - (\$19.50 + \$25.90 + \$8.15) = \$35.20$ gross profit

2. $\$47.25 - (\$12.19 + \$17.71 + \$5.48) = \$11.87$ gross profit
$\$11.87 - (0.12 \times \$47.25) = \$6.20$ net income

3. $\$39 - (\$6.74 + \$15.25 + \$3.36) = \$13.65$ gross profit
$\$13.65 - (0.15 \times \$39) = \$7.80$ net income
$\$7.80 \div \$39 = 20\%$ rate of net income

4. a. $2,000 + $3,000 + $1,000 = $6,000

   b. 5,000 × $1.50 = $7,500   sales
      $7,500 − ($1,849 + $3,062 + $825) = $1,764   gross profit
      $1,764 − (0.12 × $7,500) = $864   net income

5. a. 1,000 × $7.60 = $7,600   sales
      $1,750 + $2,800 = $4,550   material and labor cost
      $4,550 + (0.25 × $4,550) = $5,687.50   total factory cost
      $7,600 − $5,687.50 = $1,912.50   gross profit
      $1,912.50 − (0.15 × $7,600) = $772.50   net income

   b. $772.50 ÷ $7,600 = 0.1016 or 10.2%   rate of net income

Exercise 2, page 499

1. $105,000 + $195,000 = $300,000   break-even point

2. a. $800,000 + $200,000 = $1,000,000   break-even point
   b. $1,000,000 ÷ $20 = 50,000   toy trucks must be sold

3. $360,000 + $140,000 = $500,000   break-even point
   $500,000 ÷ $62.50 = 8,000   chairs must be sold

4. a. $29,500 ÷ $5 = 5,900   bowls must be sold
   b. 10,000 × $5 = $50,000   selling price
      $50,000 − $29,500 = $20,500   net income
   c. 4,000 × $5 = $20,000   sale price
      $29,500 − $20,000 = $9,500   net loss

5. a. (3,000 × $3) + (3,000 × $5) = $24,000   total production cost
   b. $24,000 ÷ $10 = 2,400   games must be sold
   c. (3,000 × $10) − $24,000 = $6,000   net income

6. (20,000 × $4.25) − $60,000 = $25,000   variable costs to break even

Exercise 3, page 499

1. a. $270,000   break-even point
   b. $270,000 ÷ 30,000 = $9   unit price

2. $60,000 ÷ 5,000 = $12   minimum selling price

3. ($7,500,000 + $9,800,000) ÷ 50,000 = $346   minimum selling price

4. ($250,000 + $125,000) ÷ 20,000 = $18.75   price each book must be sold

5. a. $288,000 ÷ 30,000 = $9.60   break-even price per reel
   b. 0.25 × $288,000 = $72,000   desired net profit
      ($288,000 + $72,000) ÷ 30,000 = $12   selling price per reel

Review 100, page 500

2. a. $82 \times 21\frac{1}{2} = 1,763$
   b. $4.85 × 1,000 = $4,850
   c. May 7

3. $11,970 + $12,560 + $5,910 = $30,440   total factory cost
   0.40 × $30,440 = $12,176   selling and administrative expenses
   400 × $121.50 = $48,600   total sales
   $48,600 − ($30,440 + $12,176) = $5,984   net income
   $5,984 ÷ $48,600 = 0.123 or 12%   net income was of net sales

4. ($3,600,000 + $10,800,000) ÷ $900 = 16,000   computers must be sold

5. $245,000 ÷ $1,750,000 = 0.14
0.14 × $2,890 = $404.60   Painting Dept. should be charged

6. $14,000 + $12,000 + $18,000 + $31,000 = $75,000   total creditors' claims
Amani: $\frac{18,000}{75,000}$ or $\frac{6}{25}$ × $24,000 = $5,760

7. $12,000 − $8,900 = $3,100   trade-in value
$7,500 − $3,100 = $4,400   depreciation
$4,400 ÷ 4 = $1,100   average annual depreciation

8. 12 × $7 = $84   selling price
$84 − $56 = $28   markup
$28 ÷ $84 = $33\frac{1}{3}$%   markup on selling price

9. $3,400 × 0.12 × $\frac{1}{3}$ = $136   discount
$3,400 − $136 = $3,264   proceeds

Section 101.   Depreciation Costs

Exercise 1, page 502

1. **a.**   0.07 × $1,500 = $105   depreciation first year
$1,500 − $105 = $1,395   book value end of first year
0.07 × $1,395 = $97.65   depreciation second year
$1,395 − $97.65 = $1,297.35   book value end of second year
0.07 × $1,297.35 = $90.81   depreciation third year
$1,297.35 − $90.81 = $1,206.54   book value end of third year

b.   0.08 × $8,500 = $680   depreciation first year
$8,500 − $680 = $7,820   book value end of first year
0.08 × $7,820 = $625.60   depreciation second year
$7,820 − $625.60 = $7,194.40   book value end of second year
0.08 × $7,194.40 = $575.55   depreciation third year
$7,194.40 − $575.55 = $6,618.85   book value end of third year

c.   0.09 × $4,000 = $360   depreciation first year
$4,000 − $360 = $3,640   book value end of first year
0.09 × $3,640 = $327.60   depreciation second year
$3,640 − $327.60 = $3,312.40   book value end of second year
0.09 × $3,312.40 = $298.12   depreciation third year
$3,312.40 − $298.12 = $3,014.28   book value end of third year

d.   0.12 × $3,800 = $456   depreciation first year
$3,800 − $456 = $3,344   book value end of first year
0.12 × $3,344 = $401.28   depreciation second year
$3,344 − $401.28 = $2,942.72   book value end of second year
0.12 × $2,942.72 = $353.13   depreciation third year
$2,942.72 − $353.13 = $2,589.59   book value end of third year

e.   0.14 × $7,000 = $980   depreciation first year
$7,000 − $980 = $6,020   book value end of first year
0.14 × $6,020 = $842.80   depreciation second year
$6,020 − $842.80 = $5,177.20   book value end of second year
0.14 × $5,177.20 = $724.81   depreciation third year
$5,177.20 − $724.81 = $4,452.39   book value end of third year

f. $0.15 \times \$6,500 = \$975$ depreciation first year
$\$6,500 - \$975 = \$5,525$ book value end of first year
$0.15 \times \$5,525 = \$828.75$ depreciation second year
$\$5,525 - \$828.75 = \$4,696.25$ book value end of second year
$0.15 \times \$4,696.25 = \$704.44$ depreciation third year
$\$4,696.25 - \$704.44 = \$3,991.81$ book value end of third year

2. $0.10 \times \$20,000 = \$2,000$ depreciation first year
$\$20,000 - \$2,000 = \$18,000$ book value end of first year
$0.10 \times \$18,000 = \$1,800$ depreciation second year
$\$18,000 - \$1,800 = \$16,200$ book value end of second year
$0.10 \times \$16,200 = \$1,620$ depreciation third year
$\$16,200 - \$1,620 = \$14,580$ book value end of third year
$0.10 \times \$14,580 = \$1,458$ depreciation fourth year
$\$14,580 - \$1,458 = \$13,122$ book value end of fourth year

3. $0.08 \times \$5,000 = \$400$ depreciation first year
$\$5,000 - \$400 = \$4,600$ book value end of first year
$0.08 \times \$4,600 = \$368$ depreciation second year
$\$4,600 - \$368 = \$4,232$ book value end of second year
$0.08 \times \$4,232 = \$338.56$ depreciation third year
$\$4,232 - \$338.56 = \$3,893.44$ book value end of third year
$0.08 \times \$3,893.44 = \$311.48$ depreciation fourth year
$\$3,893.44 - \$311.48 = \$3,581.96$ book value end of fourth year
$0.08 \times \$3,581.96 = \$286.56$ depreciation fifth year
$\$3,581.96 - \$286.56 = \$3,295.40$ book value end of fifth year
$0.08 \times \$3,295.40 = \$263.63$ depreciation sixth year
$\$3,295.40 - \$263.63 = \$3,031.77$ book value end of sixth year

4.   **a.** $\$1,000$
b. $0.20 \times \$4,800 = \$960$ depreciation first year
$\$4,800 - \$960 = \$3,840$ book value end of first year
$0.20 \times \$3,840 = \$768$ depreciation second year
$\$3,840 - \$768 = \$3,072$ book value end of second year
$0.20 \times \$3,072 = \$614.40$ depreciation third year
$\$3,072 - \$614.40 = \$2,457.60$ book value end of third year
$0.20 \times \$2,457.60 = \$491.52$ depreciation fourth year
$\$2,457.60 - \$491.52 = \$1,966.08$ book value end of fourth year

Exercise 2, page 503

1. $\$31,700 - \$6,500 = \$25,200$ total depreciation
$1 + 2 + 3 + 4 + 5 + 6 = 21$ sum-of-the-years-digits
$\frac{6}{21} \times \$25,200 = \$7,200$ depreciation end of first year
$\$31,700 - \$7,200 = \$24,500$ book value end of first year
$\frac{5}{21} \times \$25,200 = \$6,000$ depreciation end of second year
$\$24,500 - \$6,000 = \$18,500$ book value end of second year

2. $\$40,000 - \$5,000 = \$35,000$ total depreciation
$1 + 2 + 3 + 4 + 5 + 6 + 7 + 8 + 9 = 45$ sum-of-the-years-digits
$\frac{1}{5} \times \$35,000 = \$7,000$ depreciation first year
$\$40,000 - \$7,000 = \$33,000$ book value end of first year
$\frac{8}{45} \times \$35,000 = \$6,222.22$ depreciation second year
$\$33,000 - \$6,222.22 = \$26,777.78$ book value end of second year
$\frac{7}{45} \times \$35,000 = \$5,444.44$ depreciation third year
$\$26,777.78 - \$5,444.44 = \$21,333.34$ book value end of third year

3. $66,500 − $13,500 = $53,000   total depreciation
    $1 + 2 + 3 + 4 + 5 + 6 + 7 + 8 + 9 + 10 = 55$ sum-of-the-years-digits
    $\frac{2}{11} \times \$53,000 = \$9,636.36$ depreciation first year
    $\frac{9}{55} \times \$53,000 = \$8,672.73$ depreciation second year
    $\frac{8}{55} \times \$53,000 = \$7,709.09$ depreciation third year

4. **a.** $420,000 − $0 = $420,000   total depreciation
    $1 + 2 + 3 + 4 + 5 + 6 + 7 + 8 + 9 + 10 + 11 + 12 + 13 + 14 +$
    $15 = 120$ sum-of-the-years-digits
    $\frac{1}{8} \times \$420,000 = \$52,500$ depreciation first year
    $420,000 − $52,500 = $367,500   book value end of first year
    $\frac{7}{60} \times \$420,000 = \$49,000$ depreciation second year
    $367,500 − $49,000 = $318,500   book value end of second year
    $\frac{13}{120} \times \$420,000 = \$45,500$ depreciation third year
    $318,500 − $45,500 = $273,000   book value end of third year
    b. $52,500 + $49,000 + $45,500 = $147,000   total depreciation at end of
    3 years

‡Exercise 3, page 505

1. **a.** 0.20 × $4,200 = $840   depreciation first year
        0.32 × $4,200 = $1,344   depreciation second year
        0.192 × $4,200 = $806.40   depreciation third year
        0.115 × $4,200 = $483.00   depreciation fourth year
        0.115 × $4,200 = $483.00   depreciation fifth year
    b. $0.00   book value end of machine's life

2. **a.** 0.20 × $45,000 = $9,000   depreciation end of first year
    b. $45,000 − $9,000 = $36,000   book value end of first year

3. **a.** $100,000   total amount of depreciation for life of asset
    b. 0.20 × $100,000 = $20,000   depreciation first year
        $100,000 − $20,000 = $80,000   book value end of first year

Review 101, page 505

2. **a.** $4\frac{1}{2} \times 3\frac{1}{2} = 15\frac{3}{4}$
    b. $\$600 \times 0.14 \times \frac{1}{2} = \$42$
    c. $\frac{3}{8} = 0.38$
    d. $534.12 \div 100 = 5.3412$

3. 0.20 × $12,500 = $2,500   depreciation first year
    $12,500 − $2,500 = $10,000   book value end of first year
    0.20 × $10,000 = $2,000   depreciation second year
    $10,000 − $2,000 = $8,000   book value end of second year
    0.20 × $8,000 = $1,600   depreciation third year
    $8,000 − $1,600 = $6,400   book value end of third year

4. $12,000 − $2,500 = $9,500   total depreciation
    1 + 2 + 3 + 4 + 5 = 15   sum-of-the-years-digits
    $\frac{1}{3}$ × $9,500 = $3,166.67   depreciation first year
    $12,000 − $3,166.67 = $8,833.33   book value end of first year
    $\frac{4}{15}$ × $9,500 = $2,533.33   depreciation second year
    $8,833.33 − $2,533.33 = $6,300   book value end of second year

‡5. a. 0.20 × $350,000 = $70,000   depreciation first year
        0.32 × $350,000 = $112,000   depreciation second year
        0.192 × $350,000 = $67,200   depreciation third year
        $70,000 + $112,000 + $67,200 = $249,200   total depreciation after
        3 years
    b. $350,000 − $249,200 = $100,800   book value end of three years

6. $34,000 + $56,000 = $90,000   break-even point
    $90,000 ÷ $20 = 4,500   hoses must be sold

7. 3 + 2 = 5
    $\frac{3}{5}$ = 60%

8. $23,890 + $21,060 + $18,400 + $19,780 + $20,700 = $103,830   sales for
    5 months
    $22,000 × 6 = $132,000   total sales for 6 months
    $132,000 − $103,830 = $28,170   sales for 6th month

Section 102.   Office Costs

Exercise 1, page 507

1. a. $42 ÷ 10 = $4.20   cost per ream
    b. $5.75 − $4.20 = $1.55   saved per ream

2. $259.75 + $99.50 + (2 × $187.50) + $119.95 + $59.45 + $17.50 +
    $2,595 + $59 + $89.85 + $29.95 = $3,704.95

3. a. $5.50 × 2,000 = $11,000   straight wages for year
    b. $11,000 + (0.18 × $11,000) = $12,980   total wages and fringe bene-
        fits for year

4. a. (5,000 × $0.33) − (5,000 × $0.30) = $150   wasted
    b. $150 ÷ $4 = 37.5   hours

5. $4.50 × 120 = $540   cost of cheaper pens
    120 − (0.20 × 120) = 96   number of better pens needed
    $5.25 × 96 = $504   cost of better pens
    $540 − $504 = $36   saved

6. a. 25 × 30 = 750   sheets
        (750 ÷ 500) × $6.20 = $9.30   cost of paper for 25 copies
    b. 20 × 30 = 600   sheets
        (600 ÷ 500) × $6.20 = $7.44   cost of paper for 20 copies
        $9.30 − $7.44 = $1.86   could have been saved by running only
        needed copies

7. $15 \times (\$52 \div 8) = \$97.50$ daily cost of nonworking activities

Exercise 2, page 508

1. **a.** $(\$42,000 + \$4,800) \div 4,500 = \$10.40$ yearly cost per sq. ft.
   b. $64 \times \$10.40 = \$665.60$ cost of work station per year

2. **a.** $\$50,560 \div 3,200 = \$15.80$ annual cost per sq. ft.
   b. $150 \times \$15.80 = \$2,370$ annual cost of manager's work station

3. **a.** 3   aisles will be eliminated
   b. $3 \times 3 \times 58 = 522$ sq. ft.
   c. $2 \times 10 = 20$ added work stations
      $6 \times 10 = 60$ existing work stations
      $20 \div 60 = 33\frac{1}{3}\%$ increase in number of work stations
   d. $\$12,420 \div 60 = \$207$ annual rent per work station with old arrangement
   e. $\$12,420 \div (60 + 20) = \$155.25$ annual rent per work station with new arrangement

Exercise 3, page 509

1. **a.** $\$46,000$ $(\$40,000 + \$1,000 + \$1,000 + \$4,000)$
   b. $(\$38,325 + \$1,100 + \$1,340 + \$4,320) \div 3 = \$15,028.33$ annual average cost per work station

2. **a.** $576 \div (8 \times 60) = 1.2$ lines per minute
   b. $(\$5.40 \div 60) \div 1.2 = \$0.07\frac{1}{2}$ labor cost per line

3. **a.** $180 \times 7\frac{1}{2} = 1,350$ invoices
   b. $\$4.50 \div 180 = 2\frac{1}{2}\cent$ to file each invoice

4.
$$\begin{array}{rll}
1,950 \times \ \ \$5.80 = & \$11,310 & \text{wages per year} \\
0.25 \times \$11,310 = & 2,827.50 & \text{fringe benefits} \\
60 \times \ \ \$16.50 = & 990 & \text{space} \\
12 \times \ \ \ \ \ \ \$50 = & 600 & \text{data terminal rental} \\
& 275 & \text{supplies} \\
& \underline{1,200} & \text{depreciation of other equipment} \\
& \$17,202.50 & \text{yearly cost of 1 station}
\end{array}$$

$5 \times \$17,202.50 = \$86,012.50$ yearly cost of 5 stations

5. $\$278 + \$288 + \$174 + \$22 + \$28 + \$94 = \$884$ total cost
   $\$884 \div 100 = \$8.84$ average cost per letter

6. 30×13.5 cents $= \$4.05$ average cost per page

7. $12,500 + 11,600 + 10,300 = 34,400$ total number of lines
   $\$1,651.20 \div 34,400 = 4.8$ cents cost of each line

8. **a.** $\$138,000 + \$8,590 + \$890 + \$13,600 + \$17,098 = \$178,178$ total cost of work stations
      $\$178,178 \div 11 = \$16,198$ average cost of each work station
   b. $\$16,198 \div 250 = \$64.79$ cost of station per day
   c. $\$64.79 \div 130 = \$0.50$ cost of completing each order

Review 102, page 510

1.   **a.** $16\frac{1}{8} \times 24 = 387$
    b. $0.048 \div 0.008 = 6$
    c. $4.078 = 407.8\%$
    d.   90
    e. $\$400 \times 0.15 \times \frac{1}{4} = \$15$

2. $\begin{aligned} 5 \times \$4.50 &= \$\ 22.50 \\ 25 \times \$4.25 &= 106.25 \\ 25 \times \$2.45 &= 61.25 \\ 25 \times \$0.03 &= \underline{\quad 0.75} \\ &\ \ \$190.75 \quad \text{total cost} \end{aligned}$

$\$190.75 \div 25 = \$7.63$ cost of materials per report

3. $(3,515 \div 95) \times \$5.25 = \$194.25$ labor cost for file clerk

4. $\$50 + (12 \times \$27.25) = \$377$ total cost on installment plan
$\$377 - \$350 = \$27$ more if purchased using installment plan

5. $400 + 1,500 + 600 = 2,500$ total sq. ft. of floor space

Jewelry: $\frac{400}{2,500}$ or $\frac{4}{25} \times \$1,200 = \$192$

Household: $\frac{1,500}{2,500}$ or $\frac{3}{5} \times \$1,200 = \$720$

Paint: $\frac{600}{2,500}$ or $\frac{6}{25} \times \$1,200 = \$288$

6. $\$1.80 \times 4 = \$7.20$ annual dividend
$\$7.20 \div \$90 = 8\%$ rate of income on investment

7. $\frac{\$60,000}{\$80,000} = \frac{3}{4} \times \$12,800 = \$9,600$ amount paid by company

8. $\$72,000 \times 0.45 = \$32,400$ assessed value of property
$\$52,122 \times (\$32,400 \div 1,000) = \$1,688.75$ tax on property

Section 103. Payroll Costs

Exercise 1, page 512

1.

Miriam, Inc.—For the Week Ended June 8, 19--

Employee	No. of Allow-ances	Total Hours Reg.	Total Hours Over-time	Rate per hour	Total Earn-ings	Deductions Fed. Inc. Tax	Deductions FICA Tax	Deductions Other	Deductions Total	Net Pay
A. Sanchez	2	40	2	$9.50	$408.50	$42.00	$31.25	$10.94	$ 84.19	$324.31
B. Tanaka	0	39	0	5.40	210.60	29.00	16.11	8.20	53.31	157.29
C. Unger	1	40	0	4.70	188.00	19.00	14.38	5.00	38.38	149.62
				TOTALS	$807.10	$90.00	$61.74	$24.14	$175.88	$631.22

2.

Wickham Corporation — For the Week Ended May 18, 19 - -

Employee	No. of Allow-ances	Total Hours Reg.	Total Hours Over-time	Rate per hour	Total Earn-ings	Deductions Fed. Inc. Tax	Deductions FICA Tax	Deductions Hosp. Ins.	Total	Net Pay
D. Barlow	0	40	0	$3.75	$150.00	$20.00	$11.48	$00.00	$ 31.48	$118.52
E. Boski	0	39	0	5.60	218.40	29.00	16.71	00.00	45.71	172.69
F. Buell	1	40	2	4.80	206.40	22.00	15.79	8.90	46.69	159.71
				TOTALS	$574.80	$71.00	$43.98	$ 8.90	$123.88	$450.92

3.

Coastal Line Company — For Period Ended October 2, 19 - -

Employee	No. of Allow-ances	Total Hours Reg.	Total Hours Over-time	Rate per hour	Total Earn-ings	Deduction Fed. Inc. Tax	Deduction FICA Tax	Deduction State Inc. Tax	Other	Total	Net Pay
G. Carr	3	$37\frac{1}{2}$	0	$ 7.36	$ 276.00	$ 17.00	$21.11	$ 8.28	$15.50	$ 61.89	$214.11
H. Levin	4	40	6	9.95	487.55	42.00	37.30	14.63	21.80	115.73	371.82
I. Napoli	2	40	0	10.05	402.00	42.00	30.75	12.06	12.35	97.16	304.84
				TOTALS	$1,165.55	$101.00	$89.16	$34.97	$49.65	$274.78	$890.77

Exercise 2, page 513

1.

Week Ended	Gross Pay	With-holding Tax	Deductions FICA Tax	Deductions State Income Tax	Deductions Health Insurance	Total	Net Pay	Total Accumulated Earnings
1/4	$ 334.60	$ 36.00	$ 25.60	$ 5.02	$ 8.18	$ 74.80	$ 259.80	$ 334.60
1/11	334.60	36.00	25.60	5.02	8.18	74.80	259.80	669.20
1/18	334.60	36.00	25.60	5.02	8.18	74.80	259.80	1,003.80
1/25	334.60	36.00	25.60	5.02	8.18	74.80	259.80	1,338.40
2/1	334.60	36.00	25.60	5.02	8.18	74.80	259.80	1,673.00
2/8	334.60	36.00	25.60	5.02	8.18	74.80	259.80	2,007.60
2/15	334.60	36.00	25.60	5.02	8.18	74.80	259.80	2,342.20
2/22	334.60	36.00	25.60	5.02	8.18	74.80	259.80	2,676.80
3/1	334.60	36.00	25.60	5.02	8.18	74.80	259.80	3,011.40
3/8	334.60	36.00	25.60	5.02	8.18	74.80	259.80	3,346.00
3/15	334.60	36.00	25.60	5.02	8.18	74.80	259.80	3,680.60
3/22	334.60	36.00	25.60	5.02	8.18	74.80	259.80	4,015.20
3/29	334.60	36.00	25.60	5.02	8.18	74.80	259.80	4,349.80
Totals First Quarter	$4,349.80	$468.00	$332.80	$65.26	$106.34	$972.40	$3,377.40	$4,349.80

2.

Employee Earnings Record, Alicia Edwards

Week Ended	Gross Pay	With-holding Tax	Deductions				Net Pay	Total Accumulated Earnings
			FICA Tax	State Income Tax	Health Insurance	Total		
1/3	$ 435.00	$ 51.00	$ 33.28	$ 17.40	$ 7.15	$ 108.83	$ 326.17	$ 435.00
1/10	435.00	51.00	33.28	17.40	7.15	108.83	326.17	870.00
1/17	435.00	51.00	33.28	17.40	7.15	108.83	326.17	1,305.00
1/24	435.00	51.00	33.28	17.40	7.15	108.83	326.17	1,740.00
1/31	435.00	51.00	33.28	17.40	7.15	108.83	326.17	2,175.00
2/7	435.00	51.00	33.28	17.40	7.15	108.83	326.17	2,610.00
2/14	435.00	51.00	33.28	17.40	7.15	108.83	326.17	3,045.00
2/21	435.00	51.00	33.28	17.40	7.15	108.83	326.17	3,480.00
2/28	435.00	51.00	33.28	17.40	7.15	108.83	326.17	3,915.00
3/7	435.00	51.00	33.28	17.40	7.15	108.83	326.17	4,350.00
3/14	435.00	51.00	33.28	17.40	7.15	108.83	326.17	4,785.00
3/21	435.00	51.00	33.28	17.40	7.15	108.83	326.17	5,220.00
3/28	435.00	51.00	33.28	17.40	7.15	108.83	326.17	5,655.00
Totals First Quarter	$5,655.00	$663.00	$432.64	$226.20	$92.95	$1,414.79	$4,240.21	$5,655.00

Exercise 3, page 515

1. a. $0.0765 \times \$103,789.45 = \$7,939.89$ FICA tax owed by company
   b. $\$7,939.89 \times 2 = \$15,879.78$ total FICA owed to government

2. $30 \times \$7,000 = \$210,000$ wages (at least) of 30 workers
   $0.062 \times \$210,000 = \$13,020$ FUTA tax

3. a. $8,000 (Estimate: $200,000 \times 0.04 = \$8,000$)
   b. $\$210,000 \times 0.037 = \$7,770$ State Unemployment Taxes
   c. $\$13,020 - (0.90 \times \$7,770) = \$6,027$

4. a. $0.0765 \times \$520,000 = \$39,780$ Bryant's share of FICA taxes
   b. $0.037 \times 20 \times \$7,000 = \$5,180$ state unemployment tax liability
   c. $(0.062 \times 20 \times \$7,000) - (0.90 \times \$5,180) = \$4,018$ FUTA tax liability
   d. $\$39,780 + \$5,180 + \$4,018 = \$48,978$ total payroll taxes

Review 103, page 516

2. a. $1.2078 \times 10 = 12.078$
   $1.2078 \times 100 = 120.78$
   $1.2078 \times 1,000 = 1,207.8$
   b. $36.8 \div 10 = 3.68$
   $36.8 \div 100 = 0.368$
   $36.8 \div 1,000 = 0.0368$
   ‡c. $\$50.44 \div 0.08 = \$630.50$

3. $(0.0765 \times \$178,500) + (0.0765 \times \$178,500) = \$27,310.50$ FICA tax for both employees and firm

4. $(\$24,000 \div \$100) \times \$4.633 = \$1,111.92$ tax to be paid on property

5. $0.90 \times \$72,000 = \$64,800$ amount of insurance
   $(\$64,800 \div \$100) \times \$0.65 = \$421.20$ annual premium

6. $\$420,300 + \$135,000 = \$555,300$ merchandise available for sale
   $\$555,300 - \$400,600 = \$154,700$ cost of merchandise sold

7. $0.05 \times \$3,000 = \$150$ commission on 1st $3,000
   $\$450 - \$150 = \$300$ left to earn
   $\$300 \div 0.06 = \$5,000$ have to sell over $3,000
   $\$3,000 + \$5,000 = \$8,000$ salesperson will have to sell

Section 104.   Shipping Costs

Exercise 1, page 518

1. **a.** Argos Castings, Inc.
   b. $379.85   total cost

2. **a.** Buyer
   b. $(60 \times \$16) + (120 \times \$5.95) + (120 \times \$25.80) = \$4,770$ list price
   $0.02 \times \$4,770 = \$95.40$ discount
   $\$4,770 - \$95.40 = \$4,674.60$ invoice price
   $\$4,674.60 + \$85.80 = \$4,760.40$ total cost

3. **a.** $26 \times \$39 = \$1,014$ list price
   $\$1,014 - (0.25 \times \$1,014) = \$760.50; \$760.50 - (\$760.50 \times 0.20) =$
   $\$608.40$ invoice price
   $\$608.40 + \$35 = \$643.40$ total cost
   b. $\$643.40 \div 26 = \$24.75$ average total cost per backstop

4. **a.** $\$6,000 - (0.25 \times \$6,000) = \$4,500; \$4,500 - (0.20 \times \$4,500) = \$3,600$
   invoice price
   $\$3,600 + \$10.96 = \$3,610.96$ total cost
   b. $\$3,610.96 \div 1,000 = \$3.61$ average total cost of each box

5. **a.** Manufacturer A:
   $\$70 - (0.05 \times \$70) = \$66.50$ invoice price
   $\$66.50 + \$5.15 = \$71.65$ total cost of suit
   Manufacturer B:
   $\$80 - (0.10 \times \$80) = \$72; \$72 - (0.10 \times \$72) = \$64.80$ invoice price
   $\$64.80 + \$4.75 = \$69.55$ total cost of suit
   Manufacturer C:
   $\$80 - (0.15 \times \$80) = \$68; \$68 - (0.05 \times \$68) = \$64.60$ invoice price
   $\$64.60 + \$6.25 = \$70.85$ total cost of suit
   Manufacturer D:
   $\$90 - (0.20 \times \$90) = \$72; \$72 - (0.05 \times \$72) = \$68.40$ invoice price
   $\$68.40 + \$2.25 = \$70.65$ total cost of suit
   b. Manufacturer B

Exercise 3, page 520

1. $5.87 + $3.15 = $9.02   cost of shipping

2. $1.85 + $1.90 = $3.75   cost of shipment

3. (4 × $2.21) + (4 × $1.90) = $16.44   total shipping cost

Exercise 4, page 521

1. (120 × $0.21) + $2.50 = $27.70   cost of shipping

2. (2 × 30 × $0.25) + (2 × $2) = $19   express cost
    2 × ($500 ÷ $100) × $0.35 = $3.50   cost of insurance
    $19 + $3.50 = $22.50   cost of shipment

3. ($62.40 − $7.80) ÷ $7.80 = 700%

4. ($300 ÷ $100) × $0.40 = $1.20   cost of insurance
    $45 + $15.60 + $1.20 = $61.80   total shipping cost

5. a. (10 × 100) + (10 × 20) = 1,200 lb   estimated weight
    b. 1,200 ÷ 100 × $20 = $240   estimated shipping charge
    c. (12 × 95) + (9 × 21) = 1,329   pounds total weight
        1,329 ÷ 100 = 13.29; 14 × $23.88 = $334.32   shipping charge

Review 104, page 522

2. a. $28 \times 4\frac{1}{4} = 119$ c. 140 days
    b. 1.40 × $34 = $47.60   d. $0.09\frac{1}{4} = \frac{37}{400}$

3. Malta:
    $1,000 − (0.20 × $1,000) = $800; $800 − (0.10 × $800) = $720;
    $720 − (0.05 × $720) = $684   total cost
    Vesta:
    $1,000 − (0.25 × $1,000) = $750; $750 − (0.20 × $750) = $600   invoice
    price
    $600 + $42.75 = $642.75   total cost
    $684 − $642.75 = $41.25   saved

4. (8 × $4) + (8 × $1.50) = $44   total cost

5. $260,000 − $5,200 = $254,800   net sales
    ($84,326 + $158,500) − $74,746 = $168,080   cost of goods sold
    $254,800 − $168,080 = $86,720   gross profit
    $86,720 − $68,800 = $17,920   net income

6. $2,800 − (0.20 × $2,800) = $2,240   book value first year
    $2,240 − (0.20 × $2,240) = $1,792   book value second year
    $1,792 − (0.20 × $1,792) = $1,433.60   book value third year
    $1,433.60 − (0.20 × $1,433.60) = $1,146.88   book value fourth year

Section 105. Computer Costs

Exercise 1, page 524

1. **a.** $780 + $600 + $180 + $75 + $300 + $1,200 = $3,135   cost of each
    system
    b. 20 × $3,135 = $62,700   total cost of 20 systems

2. $867,000 + $30,000 + $3,500 + $5,000 + $6,300 = $911,800   total cost to
    buy and install system

3. $48,500 + $5,400 + (2 × $13,600) + (10 × $450) + $900 = $86,500   total
    cost to buy and install system

4. $1,200 + $300 + (2 × $350) + (15 × $40) = $2,800   leasing cost per month
    12 × $2,800 = $33,600   total yearly cost of leasing system

5. **a.** 12 × (10 × $600) = $72,000   estimated annual cost
    b. 12 × (10 × $575) = $69,000   actual annual cost

Exercise 2, page 525

1. $75 + $895 + $495 + $375 = $1,840   total cost of software

2. **a.** $50 + $495 + $420 + $375 = $1,340   cost of software per system
    25 × $1,340 = $33,500   total cost of software

3. 3 × 640 × $15 = $28,800   cost of labor

4. $14 × 900 = $12,600   total cost
    $12,600 ÷ 3,000 = $4.20   average labor cost per line

5. **a.** 2,400 ÷ (2 × 25) = 48   days
    b. 2 × 48 × $72 = $6,912   labor costs

Exercise 3, page 526

1. $14.76 ÷ 10 = $1.476   cost per disk
    $1.476 ÷ 360 = $0.0041   cost per kilobyte

2. **a.** $25.20 ÷ 10 = $2.52   cost per disk
    $2.52 ÷ 720 = $0.0035   cost per KB
    b. $36 ÷ 10 = $3.60   cost per disk
    $3.60 ÷ 1,200 = $0.003   cost per KB

3. $320 ÷ 80 = $4   storage cost per MB for pack

4. $14 ÷ 140 = $0.10   cost per MB

Review 105, page 527

2. **a.** $6\frac{1}{8} - 3\frac{3}{4} = 2\frac{3}{8}$
    b. 2.05 × 0.004 = 0.0082
    c. 78   days
    d. 75 m^2 ÷ 60 m^2 = 125%

3. $25,800 + $4,800 + $2,600 + $5,480 + (15 × $425) + $500 + $750 = $46,305   total cost of system

4. 5,000 ÷ 20 = 250   days required
$480 ÷ 5 = $96   paid each day
250 × $96 = $24,000   cost

5. 12 × $700 = $8,400   rent for year
$5,400 + $355 + $695 + $1,200 = $7,650   expenses for year
$8,400 − $7,650 = $750   net income
$750 ÷ $15,000 = 5%   yield on investment

6. $50,000 × $0.0145 = $725   tax on property

UNIT 17 • BUSINESS STATISTICS AND GRAPHS

Section 106.   Measures of Central Tendency

Exercise 1, page 530

1. **a.** 11 + 12 + 12 + 17 + 18 + 20 + 22 = 112   total
112 ÷ 7 = 16   mean
17 = median
12 = mode
22 − 11 = 11   range
b. 2 + 2 + 7 + 7 + 9 + 13 + 15 + 17 = 72   total
72 ÷ 8 = 9   mean
(7 + 9) ÷ 2 = 8   median
2, 7 = mode
17 − 2 = 15   range
c. 16 + 18 + 19 + 25 + 25 + 29 = 132   total
132 ÷ 6 = 22   mean
(19 + 25) ÷ 2 = 22   median
25 = mode
29 − 16 = 13   range
d. 2 + 3 + 7 + 8 + 10 + 10 + 17 + 17 + 19 + 20 + 21 + 23 + 25 = 182   total
182 ÷ 13 = 14   mean
17 = median
10, 17 = mode
25 − 2 = 23   range
e. 5 + 6 + 6 + 12 + 17 + 18 + 19 + 21 + 22 + 23 + 28 + 30 + 37 + 43 = 287   total
287 ÷ 14 = 20.5   mean
(19 + 21) ÷ 2 = 20   median
6 = mode
43 − 5 = 38   range

2. 18,000 + 23,400 + 45,600 + 16,300 = 103,300   total
103,300 ÷ 4 = 25,825   mean

3. $4.00, $4.00, $4.00, $4.10, $4.20, $4.25, $4.25, $4.40, $4.45
   $4.20 = median
   $4.00 = mode

4. **a.** $320 + $350 + $400 + $405 + $410 + $410 + $410 + $420 + $420 +
   $425 + $425 + $430 + $435 + $440 + $450 + $450 + $455 =
   $7,055 total
   $7,055 ÷ 17 = $415   mean
   $420 = median
   $410 = mode
   b. $455 − $320 = $135   range

Exercise 2, page 531

1. | Number | Frequency | | |
   |---|---|---|---|
   | 20 | 2 | 20 × 2 = | 40 |
   | 22 | 3 | 22 × 3 = | 66 |
   | 24 | 2 | 24 × 2 = | 48 |
   | 25 | 2 | 25 × 2 = | 50 |
   | 26 | 1 | 26 × 1 = | 26 |
   | | 10 | | 230   Total |

   230 ÷ 10 = 23   mean
   (22 + 24) ÷ 2 = 23   median
   22 = mode
   26 − 20 = 6   range

2. | Number | Frequency | | |
   |---|---|---|---|
   | 17 | 1 | 17 × 1 = | 17 |
   | 19 | 2 | 19 × 2 = | 38 |
   | 20 | 1 | 20 × 1 = | 20 |
   | 21 | 1 | 21 × 1 = | 21 |
   | 24 | 1 | 24 × 1 = | 24 |
   | 26 | 1 | 26 × 1 = | 26 |
   | 28 | 3 | 28 × 3 = | 84 |
   | | 10 | | 230   Total |

   230 ÷ 10 = 23   mean
   (21 + 24) ÷ 2 = 22.5   median
   28 = mode
   28 − 17 = 11   range

3. | Number | Frequency | | |
   |---|---|---|---|
   | 9 | 1 | 9 × 1 = | 9 |
   | 10 | 2 | 10 × 2 = | 20 |
   | 11 | 2 | 11 × 2 = | 22 |
   | 12 | 2 | 12 × 2 = | 24 |
   | 14 | 3 | 14 × 3 = | 42 |
   | 15 | 1 | 15 × 1 = | 15 |
   | 16 | 2 | 16 × 2 = | 32 |
   | 17 | 2 | 17 × 2 = | 34 |
   | 18 | 1 | 18 × 1 = | 18 |
   | | 16 | | 216   Total |

216 ÷ 16 = 13.5   mean
(14 + 14) ÷ 2 = 14   median
14 = mode
18 − 9 = 9   range

4.   Number   Frequency

12	1	12 × 1 = 12
14	7	14 × 7 = 98
16	1	16 × 1 = 16
17	1	17 × 1 = 17
18	2	18 × 2 = 36
19	3	19 × 3 = 57
20	3	20 × 3 = 60
21	2	21 × 2 = 42
22	1	22 × 1 = 22
27	2	27 × 2 = 54
	23	414 Total

414 ÷ 23 = 18   mean
18 = median
14 = mode
27 − 12 = 15   range

5.   Number   Frequency

$0.0154	20,000	20,000 × $0.0154 = $308
0.0160	15,000	15,000 × $0.016 = 240
0.0180	+ 5,000	5,000 × $0.018 = 90
	40,000	$638

$638 ÷ 40,000 = $0.01595   mean
($0.0154 + $0.0160) ÷ 2 = $0.0157   median
$0.0154 = mode

Review 106, page 532

2.   **a.** $24 × 10 = $240
   b. $5,000,000 ÷ 25 = $200,000
   c.   0.1896 = 0.19

3.   180 + 206 + 210 + 214 + 225 + 225 = 1,260   total
1,260 ÷ 6 = 210   mean
(210 + 214) ÷ 2 = 212   median
225 = mode

4.   **a.**   1,250 + 1,469 + 781 + 960 + 1,351 + 1,076 = 6,887   total
6,887 ÷ 6 = 1,147.8, or 1,148   mean
   b.   1,469 − 781 = 688   range

5.   100% − 45% = 55%   cost
0.55 × $150 = $82.50   highest price to be paid

6.   **a.**   ($1.20 + $2.00) × 7,000 = $22,400   production cost
   b. $22,400 ÷ $5 = 4,480   cans, break even point
   c.   (7,000 × $5) − $22,400 = $12,600   net income

Section 107.   Probability

Exercise 2, page 535

1. $\frac{1}{5} \times 6,000 = 1,200$ approximate times event would happen

2. **a.** $\frac{1}{4}$ probability of picking a 4 card
    b. $\frac{1}{4} \times 2,400 = 600$ approximate times 3 card would be picked

3. 6 different ways

4. **a.** $\frac{1}{6}$ probability of tossing a 3
    b. 0   probability of tossing a 7
    c. $\frac{6}{6}$ or 1   probability of tossing a numeral less than 7
    d. $\frac{4}{6}$ or $\frac{2}{3}$ probability of tossing a numeral greater than 2
    e. $\frac{3}{6}$ or $\frac{1}{2}$ probability of tossing a numeral less than 4
    f. $\frac{5}{6}$ probability of tossing a numeral that is not a 6

5. **a.** $\frac{1}{6} \times 7,200 = 1,200$ approximate times a 4 would be tossed
    b. $0 \times 7,200 = 0$ times a 7 would be tossed
    c. $\frac{1}{2} \times 7,200 = 3,600$ approximate times a numeral less than 4 would be tossed
    d. $\frac{5}{6} \times 7,200 = 6,000$ approximate times a numeral greater than 1 would be tossed

Exercise 3, page 536

1. $\frac{12}{400} \times 1,200 = 36$ defective chips

2. **a.** $\frac{292}{365} = \frac{4}{5}$
    b. $\frac{4}{5} \times 30 = 24$ days

3. **a.** $97,000 \div 100,000 = 0.97$ probability of living to be 20
    b. $(100,000 - 97,000) \div 100,000 = 0.03$ probability of not living to be 20

4. **a.** $90,000 \div 98,000 = 0.92$ probability for a 10-year-old to live to be 50
    b. $82,000 \div 98,000 = 0.84$ probability for a 10-year-old to live to be 60
    c. $65,000 \div 98,000 = 0.66$ probability for a 10-year-old to live to be 70
    d. $39,000 \div 98,000 = 0.40$ probability for a 10-year-old to live to be 80

Review 107, page 537

2. **a.** $\frac{1}{3} \times 2,016 = 672$
    b. $0.042 \times 5,000 = 210$
    c. $\$45.78 + \$332.98 - \$189.00 + \$23.81 - \$1.56 = \$212.01$
    d. $\frac{62}{7} = 8\frac{6}{7}$
    e. $\$48 + (0.20 \times \$48) = \$57.60$

3. **a.** $82,000 \div 97,000 = 0.85$ probability of a 20-year old living to age 60
    b. $0.85 \times 40 = 34$ will reach age 60

4. $15 + 22 + 19 + 34 + 40 + 5 + 12 = 147$ total
    $147 \div 7 = 21$ mean days between service calls

5. **a.** $\$160 - \$120 = \$40$ discount
    b. $\$40 \div \$160 = 25\%$ rate of discount

Section 108.   Bar and Line Graphs

Exercise 2, page 539

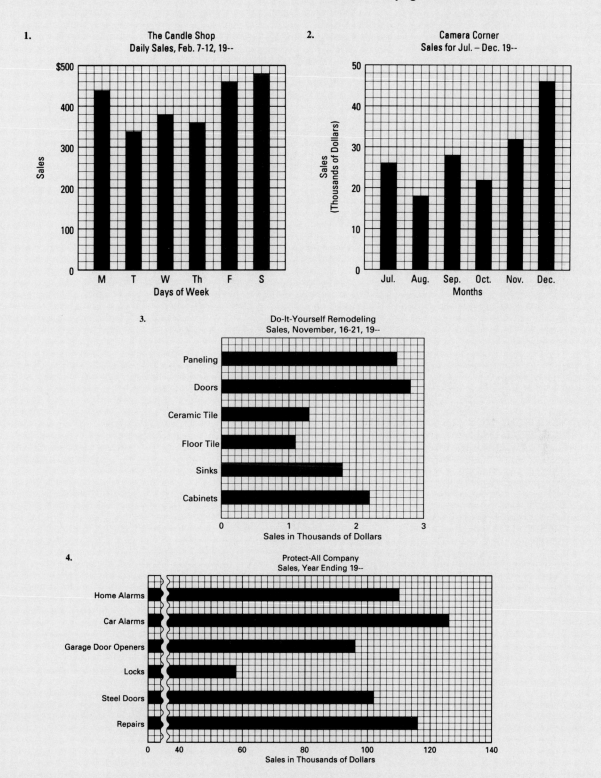

1.

The Candle Shop
Daily Sales, Feb. 7-12, 19--

2.

Camera Corner
Sales for Jul. – Dec. 19--

3.

Do-It-Yourself Remodeling
Sales, November, 16-21, 19--

4.

Protect-All Company
Sales, Year Ending 19--

Exercise 4, page 542

1.

The Poster Shop
Sales for May 22-28, 19--

2.

Merlund Cable Company
6-Month Summary of Service Calls

3.

Paper Place
Monthly Sales, Jan.-June
19-- and 19--

Review 108, page 543

2. a. ($56 − $48) ÷ $48 = $\frac{1}{6}$
   b. ($310 − $266.60) ÷ $310 = 0.14, or 14%
   c. 23.80 L + 1.85 L + 0.39 L = 26.04 L
   d. 104 m² ÷ 13 m = 8 m

3. (8 × 2) × $200 = $3,200

4. a.

$ 810,000	beginning inventory
+ 285,000	purchases during month
$1,095,000	merchandise available for sale
− 862,000	ending inventory
$ 233,000	cost of merchandise sold

   b. $412,000 − $233,000 = $179,000 gross profit

5. 0.8 × $60,000 = $48,000 required insurance
   $\frac{\$40,000}{\$48,000} = \frac{5}{6}; \frac{5}{6} \times \$8,100 = \$6,750$ insurance company pays

Section 109. Rectangle and Circle Graphs

Exercise 1, page 545

1. a. $400,000 total sales
   b. $400,000 − $240,000 = $160,000 gross profit
   c. $160,000 ÷ $400,000 = 40%
   d. $40,000 ÷ $400,000 = 10%

2. a. 60%   **b.** 30%   **c.** 10¢

3. Graph follows this page

4. Graph follows this page

Exercise 2, page 546

1.

Hardware	50%	180°	(Graph follows this page)
Training	15%	54°	
Software	30%	108°	
Repair	5%	18°	

2.

Newspaper	$3,600	30%	108°	(Graph follows)
Radio	2,400	20%	72°	
Yearbook ads	600	5%	18°	
Circulars	3,000	25%	90°	
Mailings	1,800	15%	54°	
Baseball t-shirts	600	5%	18°	

3.

Raw materials	$ 5,000	10%	36°	(Graph follows)
Direct labor	12,500	25%	90°	
Overhead	15,000	30%	108°	
Delivery and testing	7,500	15%	54°	
Training	10,000	20%	72°	

3.

Melron Furniture
Sales Dollar Last Year

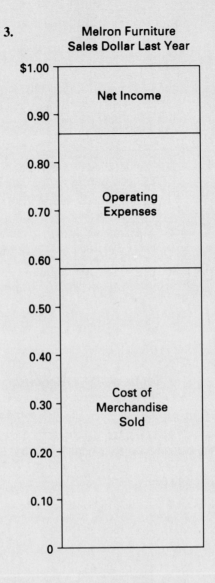

4.

XAC Company
Percent of Sales Dollar

1.

Redi-Solutions Computer Company
Departmental Sales Last Year

Software 30%
(108°)

Training 15%
(54°)

Repairs 5%
(18°)

Hardware 50%
(180°)

2.

Teal Company
Advertising Expenditures

Newspaper 30%
(108°)

Radio (20%)
(72°)

Baseball T-Shirts
5%   (18°)

Yearbook Ads 5%
(18°)

Mailings 15%
(54°)

Circulars 25%
(90°)

3.

Robolink Company
Cost Estimate

Direct Labor 25%
(90°)

Raw Materials 10%
(36°)

Overhead 30%
(108°)

Training 20%
(72°)

Delivery and
Testing 15%
(54°)

Review 109, page 547

2. **a.** $78 \div 2\frac{1}{2} = 31\frac{1}{5}$
  b. $(\$618 - \$515) \div \$618 = \frac{1}{6}$
  c. $0.10 \times \$7,500 \times \frac{1}{3} = \$250$
  d. August 19 to November 8 = 81   days
  e. 23.8 mills $\div$ 1,000 = 0.0238   decimal tax rate
    $0.0238 \times \$1,000 = \$23.80$

3. $\$16,380 \div 12 = \$1,365$ equivalent monthly salary
  $\$16,380 \div 52 = \$315$ equivalent weekly salary

4. $4 \times (0.03 \times \$100) = \$12$ annual income on one share
  $150 \times \$12 = \$1,800$ annual income from stock

5. $12 \times \$600 = \$7,200$ annual gross income
  $\$4,300 + \$1,260 + \$910 = \$6,470$ annual expenses
  $\$7,200 - \$6,470 = \$730$ annual net income
  $\$730 \div \$12,000 = 0.0608$, or 6.1%   rate of income

6. $\$4,720 - \$112 = \$4,608$ net sales
  $\$250 + (0.02 \times \$4,608) = \$342.16$ earned last week

7.

Check register balance	$852.07	Bank statement balance		$682.56
Deduct:		Deduct:		
Loan payment	− 260.00	Outstanding checks:		
		#259	$56.71	
		#261	33.78	− 90.49
Correct register balance	$592.07	Available bank balance		$592.07

Section 110.   Economic Statistics

Exercise 1, page 548

1. 7.7%   inflation rate for 1978

2. 1986   year with lowest inflation rate
  1.9%   inflation rate

3. 1980   year with highest inflation rate
  13.5%   inflation rate

4. 1979 and 1980; consecutive years with greatest total inflation
  11.3% + 13.5% = 24.8%   total inflation for two years

5. **a.** 7.7% + 11.3% + 13.5% + 10.4% = 42.9%   total rate of inflation
  b. 42.9% ÷ 4 = 10.72, or 10.7%   average rate of inflation

Exercise 2, page 549

1. **a.** $0.677   1974 purchasing power of dollar
  b. $1.000 − $0.677 = $0.323   amount of purchasing power drop

2. **a.** $1.000 − $0.751 = $0.249
  b. $1.000 − $0.405 = $0.595
  c. $1.000 − $0.289 = $0.711

3. 1973 and 1974   2 years with greatest amount of change
  $0.751 − $0.677 = $0.074   amount of greatest drop

4. 1979 value of $0.460 is less than one-half 1967 base

5. 1985–1986   2-year period with least amount of change
$0.310 − $0.304 = $0.006   amount of change

Exercise 3, page 550

1. a. 331.1   CPI for all items in 1986
   b. 331.1 − 100.0 = 231.1, or 231.1%   increase in CPI

2. Apparel and Upkeep = category with smallest price increase

3. Medical Care (446.8) and Housing (362.1)

4. a. 157.8 − 100.0 = 57.8, or 57.8%   housing prices increased
   b. 362.1 − 100.0 = 262.1, or 262.1%   housing prices increased

5. a. 331.1% × $10,000 = $33,110   annual wage Yvonne should have been earning
   b. 331.1% × $4 = $13.24   hourly wage Tom should have been earning

Exercise 4, page 551

1. Single Black Men = persons with highest rate of unemployment
20.5%   rate

2. 9.7% − 8.8% = 0.9%   higher unemployment rate for men

3. 4.3% × 1,000 = 43   number of married women expected to be unemployed

4. Married, spouse present (2.8%)

Review 110, page 552

2.   116.9   Transportation
      −115.3   Food and Beverages
         1.6   difference

3. a. $245,000   **b.** $250,000

4. Number Group: 5, 5, 7, 8, 8, 9, 9, 10, 14, 15, 16
Median is 9

5. $\frac{3}{6} = \frac{1}{2}$ probability that car will be blue

Appendix B.   Supplementary Problems

Sections 1–6, Unit 1

1. $ 5,893.23   Register #1
      6,709.44   Register #2
      1,078.98   Register #3
   + 9,101.45   Register #4
   $22,783.10   Total sales

2. $ 54.57   gasoline
      14.79   oil
      15.78   wiper blade
   + 25.00   city sticker
   $110.14   spent

3.

5 × $20	=	$100.00
6 × $10	=	60.00
5 × $ 5	=	25.00
61 × $ 1	=	61.00
23 × $ 0.50	=	11.50
9 × $ 0.25	=	2.25
8 × $ 0.10	=	0.80
21 × $ 0.05	=	1.05
19 × $ 0.01	=	0.19
Check	=	309.78
Check	=	7.24
		$578.81 total deposit

4.

$126.89	gross bill
− 2.54	discount
$124.35	net bill

5.

$106.50	gross sales
− 37.50	cost of houses
$ 69.00	
− 24.63	other expenses
$44.37	net sales

6.

138	on hand Feb. 1
+ 250	bought
388	available
− 159	on hand end of Feb.
229	used during Feb.

7.

$145.67	bank balance
+ 50.00	deposit
$195.67	
− 106.15	debit card purchases
$ 89.52	new bank balance

8.

Check register balance	$344.05	Bank statement balance	$504.25
Deduct:		Deduct:	
Service charge	− 1.95	Outstanding checks:	
	$342.10	#21 $24.15	
		#23 38.90	
Add:		#24 46.50	
Interest earned	+ 1.60	#25 51.00	− 160.55
Correct check register balance	$343.70	Available bank balance	$343.70

9.

Check register balance	$412.08	Bank statement balance	$539.12
Deduct:		Deduct:	
Service charge	− 2.66	Outstanding checks:	
	$409.42	#156 $34.41	
Add:		#157 80.33	
Interest earned	+ 3.02	#160 11.94	− 126.68
Correct check register balance	$412.44	Available bank balance	$412.44

‡10.

Check register balance	$1,319.05	Bank statement balance	$1,165.75
Deduct:		Deduct:	
Check not recorded	− 57.10	Outstanding checks:	
		#89 $16.60	
		#91 23.10	
		#93 34.60	− 74.30
			$1,091.45
		Add:	
		Late deposit	+ 170.50
Correct check register balance	$1,261.95	Available bank balance	$1,261.95

‡**11.**

Check register balance		$150.77	Bank statement balance		$307.98
Deduct:			Deduct:		
Service charge		− 1.02	Outstanding checks:		
		$149.75	#101	$ 28.54	
Add:			#102	19.29	
Interest earned	$0.30		#104	101.10	− 148.93
Amount on check					
too large	9.00	+ 9.30			
Correct check register balance		$159.05	Available bank balance		$159.05

‡**12.**

Check register balance		$210.52	Bank statement balance		$349.82
Deduct:			Deduct:		
Service charge		− 2.25	Outstanding checks:		
		$208.27	#45	$50.80	
Add:			#46	$21.15	
Deposit not			#47	18.40	− 90.35
recorded	$50.00				
Interest earned	1.20	+ 51.20			
Correct check register balance		$259.47	Available bank balance		$259.47

Sections 7–12, Unit 2

1. **a.** $40 \times \$8 = \$320$ weekly gross pay
   b. $52 \times \$320 = \$16,640$ yearly gross pay

2. $12 \times \$2,056 = \$24,672$ amount earned in 1 year

3. $40 + 37 + 35 + 41 + 44 = 197$ total chairs produced
   $197 - 5 = 192$ usable chairs
   $192 \times \$2.40 = \$460.80$ gross pay

4. $(60 \times \$0.70) + (15 \times \$0.80) + (11 \times \$0.95) = \$64.45$ gross earnings for day

5.
9 × $1,138 =	$10,242	
1 × 1,228 =	1,228	
1 × 1,875 =	1,875	
1 × 1,290 =	1,290	
1 × 1,329 =	1,329	
13	$15,964	total sales for 13 weeks

   $\$15,964 \div 13 = \$1,228$ average sales per week

6. $5 \times \$255 = \$1,275$ earnings needed for 5 weeks
   $\$246 + \$288 + \$234 + \$276 = \$1,044$ earnings for 4 weeks
   $\$1,275 - \$1,044 = \$231$ fifth week earnings

7. $\$296.40 \div 38 = \$7.80$ hourly rate of pay

8.
2 × $250 =	$ 500	
1 × $320 =	320	
1 × $400 =	400	
4	$1,220	total earnings for 4 weeks

   $\$1,220 \div 4 = \$305$ average earnings per week

Sections 13–20, Unit 3

1. **a.** 10 to 82   **b.** 70 to 2   **c.** 2 to 82

2. $2 \times \$ 8.20 = \$ 16.40$ overtime rate
$37 \times \$ 8.20 = \$303.40$
$6 \times \$16.40 = \underline{98.40}$
$\$401.80$ gross earnings

3. $1\frac{1}{2} \times \$12.70 = \$19.05$ time-and-a-half rate
$(7 + 9 + 9 + 10 + 8) - 40 = 3$ overtime hours worked
$40 \times \$12.70 = \$508.00$
$3 \times \$19.05 = \underline{57.15}$
$\$565.15$ total pay for week

4. $23\frac{1}{2} \times \$12.40 = \$291.40$ cost of worker's time

5. $4\frac{1}{2} \times \$25 = \$112.50$ this week's earnings

6. $32\frac{1}{2} \div 2\frac{1}{2} = 13$ lots

7. $\frac{1}{8} \times \$440 = \$55$ earnings from part-time job

8. $\$280 \div \frac{7}{8} = \$320$ amount usually earned

9. $\frac{5}{8} \times \$96,000 = \$60,000$ Misek's share

10. $\$10.50 - (\frac{1}{7} \times \$10.50) = \$9$ new hourly pay rate

Sections 21–29, Unit 4

1. $\$672.35 \times 0.0765 = \$51.43$ Elroy
$\$829.87 \times 0.0765 = \$63.49$ Costello
$\$497.23 \times 0.0765 = \$38.04$ McMahon

2. $40 \times \$7.50 = \$300$ regular pay
$8 \times \$11.25 = \$90$ overtime pay
$\$300 + \$90 = \$390$ total earnings
$\$45 + \$29.84 + \$12 + \$5 + \$23.88 = \$115.72$ total deductions
$\$390 - \$115.72 = \$274.28$ take-home pay

3. $60 \times \$0.50 = \$30; \ 15 \times \$0.60 = \$9; \ 32 \times \$0.70 = \$22.40$
$\$30 + \$9 + \$22.40 = \$61.40$ gross earnings
$\$61.40 - \$10.60 = \$50.80$ net pay

4. $(0.28 \times \$1,254) + \$1,254 = \$1,605.12$ total old job benefits
$(0.38 \times \$995) + \$995 = \$1,373.10$ total new job benefits
$\$1,605.12 - \$1,373.10 = \$232.02$ difference (old job offers more)

5. $\$23,589 + (0.31 \times \$23,589) = \$30,901.59$ total job benefits
$(0.08 \times \$23,589) + \$269 + \$245 + \$38 = \$2,439.12$ job expenses
$\$30,901.59 - \$2,439.12 = \$28,462.47$ net job benefits

6. $0.05 \times \$10,000 = \$500$
$0.08 \times (\$35,678 - \$10,000) = \$2,054.24$
$\$500 + \$2,054.24 = \$2,554.24$ gross pay

7. $0.10 \times (\$8,459 - \$5,000) = \$345.90$ commission
$\$650 + \$345.90 = \$995.90$ gross earnings

8. $\$34,200 - (12 \times \$1,100) = \$21,000$ commission
$\$21,000 \div \$350,000 = 0.06 = 6\%$ average commission

9. $\$130 - (72 \times \$0.50) = \$94$ commission on Mother's Day Cards
$\$94 \div \$0.40 = 235$ boxes of Mother's Day cards

10. $\$175 + (0.05 \times \$620.40) + (0.08 \times \$238.50) = \$225.10$ gross earnings

11. $0.40 \times (0.06 \times \$140,000) = \$3,360$ agent's share

12. $0.80 \times \$2,350 = \$1,880$ amount collected
$\$1,880 - (0.40 \times \$1,880) = \$1,128$ net proceeds

13. $\$109,782 - \$96,300 = \$13,482$ difference
$\$13,482 \div \$96,300 = 14\%$ builder's price exceeds cost of house already built

14. **a.** $\$2,700 - \$1,200 = \$1,500$ commission
    b. $\$1,500 \div \$30,000 = 5\%$ rate of commission

‡15. $\$4,500 \div 0.06 = \$75,000$ selling price

‡16. $\$3,000 \div 0.40 = \$7,500$ worth of magazines class must sell

‡17. $184 \div 0.92 = 200$ registered last year

‡18. $\$4,200 \div 0.08 = \$52,500$ total income last year

‡19. $\$2,318 \div 1.22 = \$1,900$ monthly pay of current job

Sections 30–32, Unit 5

1. $4.5 + 1.0 = 5.5$ parts   total of parts of water and concentrate
5.5×354 mL $= 1\,947$ mL or 1.95 L   amount of orange juice made

2. 1.97 m $+ 1.85$ m $+ 2.08$ m $+ 1.81$ m $+ 1.94$ m $= 9.65$ m   total height of players
9.65 m $\div 5 = 1.93$ m   average height of players

3. 144×210 g $= 30\,240$ g or 30.24 kg   weight of rubber cement alone
30.24 kg $+ 2.2$ kg $= 32.44$ kg   weight of shipment

4. **a.** 4 m $\times 5.4$ m $= 21.6$ m^2, or 22 m^2 whole square meters of carpeting needed
    b. 22 m$^2 \times \$14 = \$308$ cost of carpeting

5. 18×20 mm $= 360$ mm   space needed for 18 characters
$(2 \times 40$ mm$) + 360$ mm $= 440$ mm or 44 cm   exact width of sign needed

6. 0.9×9 kL $= 8.1$ kL   water in truck at start of day
2 kL $+ 0.8$ kL $+ 1.3$ kL $+ 1.4$ kL $+ 0.9$ kL $= 6.4$ kL   water delivered
8.1 kL $- 6.4$ kL $= 1.7$ kL   water left in truck

7. 25×160 g $= 4\,000$ g or 4 kg   meat needed

8. 30 m × 50 m = 1 500 m²   area of lot
    0.2 × 1 500 m² = 300 m²   area of driveway and sidewalk
    1 500 m² − (300 m² + 210 m²) = 990 m²   area available for planting grass

Sections 33–42, Unit 6

1. 0.22 × $37,500 = $8,250   food
    0.28 × $37,500 = $10,500   housing
    0.18 × $37,500 = $6,750   transportation
    0.10 × $37,500 = $3,750   clothing
    0.15 × $37,500 = $5,625   other
    0.07 × $37,500 = $2,625   savings

2. $59,664 ÷ $745,800 = 8%   delivery as percent of sales

3. $32 × (3,600 ÷ 100) = $1,152   cost

4. $0.72 × (6 ÷ 2) = $2.16   cost

5. $2.99 ÷ 8 = $0.37   unit price

6. $289.89 + (0.055 × $289.89) = $305.83   total cost

7. $27.98 × (34,500 ÷ 2,000) = $482.66   cost

8. $39.99 × (12 ÷ 3) = $159.96   reduced price
    ($15 × 12) − $159.96 = $20.04   savings

9. 24 × $0.375 = $9
    15 × $0.60 = $9
    18 × $0.33\frac{1}{3} = $6
    16 × $0.75 = $12
    $9 + $9 + $6 + $12 = $36   total cost

10. **a.** ($25 × 6) − $100 = $50   cheaper
    b. $989 ÷ $100 = 9.9   weeks

11. 44,885 − 42,789 = 2,096   KWH used

500 KWH	@ $0.1052	$ 52.60
1,596 KWH	@ $0.1247	+ 199.02
Total energy charge		$251.62
Tax @ 0.05		+ 12.58
Total bill		$264.20

12. $12.76 − (0.55 × $12.76) = $5.74   Saturday call

13. $246 ÷ (0.20 × $820) = $1\frac{1}{2}$ years

14. 56 × 1.115 = 62   therms

First 50 whole therms (50 × $0.2011)	$10.06
Next 12 whole therms (12 × $0.1892)	+ 2.27
Charge for gas	$12.33
Facilities charge	15.00
Sales tax at 3%	+ 0.82
Total bill	$28.15

15. $0.895 × (1,200 ÷ 100) = $10.74   water bill for quarter

Sections 43–51, Unit 7

1. August 31 − August 4 = 27 days in August
   30 days in September
   31 days in October
   + 2 days in November
   ‾‾‾‾‾‾‾‾‾‾‾‾‾‾‾‾‾‾‾‾‾
   90 days total

2. a. July 24
   b. $2,000 \times 0.14 \times \frac{1}{5}$ = $56 interest
   $2,000 + $56 = $2,056 owed on due date

3. $6,000 + ($6,000 \times 0.12 \times \frac{1}{4})$ = $6,180 amount Genaro will pay on due date

4. a. February 5
   b. $5,900 − ($5,900 \times 0.15 \times \frac{1}{3})$ = $5,605 proceeds

5. a. $25 + ($12 × 24) = $313 installment price
   $313 − $250 = $63 finance charge
   b. $63 ÷ $250 = 25% rate installment price exceeds cash price

6. a. $350 × 0.10 = $35 down payment
   b. ($350 − $35) ÷ $21 = 15 months

7. a. ($1,500 − $120) ÷ 24 = $57.50 monthly payment
   b. $120 ÷ $1,500 = 8% of installment price is down payment

8. a. $850 × 0.10 = $85 down payment
   b. $85 + ($48.45 × 20) = $1,054 installment price
   c. $1,054 − $850 = $204 finance charge
   d. $\frac{\$204 \times 100}{(\$850 - \$85)}$ = $26.67 finance charge per $100

9. a. $2,500 + ($2,500 × 0.03) = $2,575 credit card price
   b. $2,575 − $2,500 = $75 saved by paying cash

10. $378 + $20 + ($378 × 0.0135) = $403.10 credit card balance

Sections 52–54, Unit 8

1.
Date	Withdrawal	Deposit	Interest	Balance
19--				
Mar 31				501.27
Apr 1			5.81	507.08
Apr 8		141.00		648.08
Apr 17	25.00			623.08
Apr 22		160.00		783.08
Apr 30	55.00			728.08

2. $800 × 0.06 × $\frac{1}{4}$ = $12 October 1 interest
   $800 + $12 = $812
   $812 × 0.06 × $\frac{1}{4}$ = $12.18 January 2 interest
   $812 + $12.18 = $824.18 balance on January 2

3. $1,200 × 0.055 × $\frac{1}{2}$ = $33 interest earned

4.

Date	Withdrawal	Deposit	Interest	Balance
19--				
Oct 1				630.00
Nov 14		300.00		930.00
Dec 19	400.00			530.00
Jan 2			6.63	536.63

$530 \times 0.05 \times \frac{1}{4} = \$6.63$ interest on minimum balance

5. a. $700 \times \$1.020199 = \$714.14$ compound amount
       $\$714.14 - \$700 = \$14.14$ interest
     b. $700 \times \$1.040806 = \$728.56$ compound amount
       $\$728.56 - \$700 = \$28.56$ interest

6. $\$38.21 \div \$400 = 0.09552$, or 9.55%   effective rate of interest

7. $0.09 \times \$8,000 = \$720$ interest on certificate
    $\$8,000 \times 0.06 \times \frac{1}{4} = \$120$ interest first quarter
    $\$8,120 \times 0.06 \times \frac{1}{4} = \$121.80$ interest second quarter
    $\$8,241.80 \times 0.06 \times \frac{1}{4} = \$123.63$ interest third quarter
    $\$8,365.43 \times 0.06 \times \frac{1}{4} = \$125.48$ interest fourth quarter
    $\$120 + \$121.80 + \$123.63 + \$125.48 = \$490.91$ total interest on passbook
    $\$720 - \$490.91 = \$229.09$ more interest

8. $\$3,500 \times 0.14 \times \frac{3}{4} = \$367.50$ penalty

9. $\$5,000 \times 0.0805 \times \frac{1}{4} = \$100.63$ interest first quarter
    $\$5,000 + \$100.63 = \$5,100.63$ account balance at end of first quarter
    $\$5,100.63 \times 0.0827 \times \frac{1}{4} = \$105.46$ interest second quarter

Sections 55–62, Unit 9

1. $12 \times (0.96 \times \$500) = \$5,760$ market price of bonds
    $\$5,760 + (12 \times \$6.50) = \$5,838$ total cost of bonds

2. $16 \times (0.085 \times \$1,000) = \$1,360$ annual interest from bonds
    $\$1,360 \times \frac{1}{2} = \$680$ semiannual interest

3. $1.2 \times \$1,000 = \$1,200$ amount invested
    $0.12 \times \$1,000 = \$120$ annual income
    $\$120 \div \$1,200 = 10\%$ yield

4. $(40 \times \$47.75) + \$42.50 = \$1,952.50$

5. a. $80 \times (4 \times \$0.82) = \$262.40$ annual dividend on common stock
     b. $140 \times (0.068 \times \$100) = \$952$ annual dividend on preferred stock

6. $(70 \times \$51.125) + \$64.25 = \$3,643$ investment in stock
    $70 \times (0.073 \times \$50) = \$255.50$ annual income
    $\$255.50 \div \$3,643 = 7.0\%$ rate of income

7. a. $(150 \times \$33.75) - \$85 = \$4,977.50$ proceeds
       $\$4,977.50 - \$4,672 = \$305.50$ profit
     b. $150 \times (2 \times \$1.30) \times 2 = \$780$ annual income for 2 years
       $\$780 + \$305.50 = \$1,085.50$ total gain

8. $\$4,500 \div \$8.72 = 516.055$ shares bought

9. $15.78 − $14.58 = $1.20   amount of commission
$1.20 ÷ $15.78 = 7.6%   rate of commission

10. (52 × $400) − $15,800 = $5,000   annual net income
$5,000 ÷ $29,000 = 0.1724, or 17.2%   rate of income

11. (0.25 × $24,000) + $900 = $6,900   desired annual net income
$6,900 ÷ 6 = $1,150   monthly rent to be charged

12. $15,000 + $7,000 + $3,200 = $25,200   capital investment

‡13. $8,400 − $3,900 = $4,500   annual net income
$4,500 ÷ 0.15 = $30,000   can invest

Sections 63–66, Unit 10

1. ($80,000 × 0.35) + $250 + $472 + $320 = $29,042   cash needed

2. (12 × 30) × $692.37 = $249,253.20   total payments
$249,253.20 − $71,400 = $177,853.20   interest

3. 12 × ($493.67 − $457.91) = $429.12   more paid in year

4. 12 × ($683 − $571) = $1,344   gross amount paid less
$1,344 − ($670 + $450) = $224   net amount paid less

5. 0.0125 × $78,000 = $975   annual depreciation

6. ($4,592 + $1,673 + $319 + $890 + $780 + $1,400) − $2,300 = $7,354
net cost of owning home

7. a. 12 × $735 = $8,820   annual expense of renting
$6,300 + (0.105 × $10,600) = $7,413   annual expense of owning home
Cheaper to buy
   b. $8,820 − $7,413 = $1,407   amount cheaper

8. a. $12,790 − $9,590 = $3,200   trade in amount
$10,370 − $3,200 = $7,170   total depreciation
$7,170 ÷ 5 = $1,434   average annual depreciation
   b. $1,434 ÷ $10,370 = 0.1382, or 13.8%   rate of depreciation

9. 22,000 − 15,000 = 7,000   excess mileage
(12 × $236) + ($0.08 × 7,000) = $3,392   cost of leasing for 1 year

10. 16,830 ÷ 20.4 = 825   gallons used in year
825 × $1.24 = $1,023   spent for gas

11. ($648 + $937 + $15 + $51 + $293) ÷ 12 = $162   average monthly operating cost

Sections 67–73, Unit 11

1. $25,000 ÷ $1,000 = 25   units per $1,000
$37.89 × 25 = $947.25   property tax

2. $113,000 × 0.50 = $56,500   assessed value
$56,500 ÷ $100 = 565   units per $100
565 × $2.56 = $1,446.40   tax bill

3. $1,789,300 - $47,140 = $1,742,160   amount to be raised
$1,742,160 \div $42,700,000 = 0.0408   decimal rate
$0.0408 \times $100 = $4.08   rate per $100

4. $[0.06 \times (2 \times $12.50)] + (0.06 \times $29.95) = 3.30 tax on goods
$3.30 + (2 \times $12.50) + $29.95 + (2 \times $8.75) = 75.75 total repair bill

5. $18.98 + ($18.98 \times 0.03) + ($18.98 \times 0.05) = 20.50 local service
$23.77 + ($23.77 \times 0.03) + ($23.77 \times 0.05) = 25.67 long distance
$20.50 + $25.67 = $46.17   total bill

‡6. $52 \div 1.04 = $50   price of sweater before tax is added

7. $124,660 \times 0.0765 = $9,536.49   FICA taxes

8. $38,895 \times 0.153 = $5,950.94   self-employment tax

9. $29,200   gross income
   − 4,900   deductions
   ───────
    $24,300
   − 2,000   exemption
   ───────
    $22,300

From table, taxes owed are $3,995
$4,160 − $3,995 = $165   overpaid

10. $2,480   wages
    − 2,480   standard deduction (less than $3,000)
    ───────
    $ 0   taxable income

$276 − $0 = $276   refund

11. $($25,789 \times 0.015) + ($25,789 \times 0.03) = $1,160.51$ total city and state income taxes

Sections 74–79, Unit 12

1. $($150,000 \div $1,000) \times $1.37 = 205.50 annual premium

2. $($25,000 \div $1,000) \times $36.80 \times 20 = $18,400$ total premium paid by smoker
$($25,000 \div $1,000) \times $28.40 \times 20 = $14,200$ total premium paid by non-smoker
$18,400 − $14,200 = $4,200   amount smoker pays more

3. $($15,000 \div $1,000) \times $22.18 = 332.70 annual premium
$332.70 − $49.80 = $282.90   net premium

4. $($30,000 \div $1,000) \times $82.04 = $2,461.20$ cash value of policy

5. $($1,580 + $800) − ($1,125 + $575) = 680 amount Wilbur paid

6. $($1,600 − $500) \times 0.9 = 990 amount insurance company should pay

7. $0.75 \times $60,000 = $45,000   insured value of property
$($45,000 \div $100) \times $0.64 = 288 annual premium

8. $80 − ($80 \times 0.2) = $64   premium with higher deductible

9. $360 − (0.25 \times $360) = $270   amount of refund

10. $2,400,000 + $1,200,000 = $3,600,000   total coverage
$\frac{\$1,200,000}{\$3,600,000} = \frac{1}{3}$ part that Freedom Company pays
$\frac{1}{3} \times \$48,000 = \$16,000$ amount Freedom Company pays

11. $0.8 \times \$55,000 = \$44,000$ required insurance
$\frac{\$35,200}{\$44,000} = \frac{4}{5}$ part insurance company pays
$\frac{4}{5} \times \$3,300 = \$2,640$ amount insurance company pays

12. $0.8 \times \$75,000 = \$60,000$ required insurance
$\frac{\$45,000}{\$60,000} = \frac{3}{4}$ part insurance company pays
$\frac{3}{4} \times \$12,000 = \$9,000$ amount insurer pays

13. $2 \times (\$14 + \$72 + \$257 + \$37) = \$760$ annual premium

Sections 80–86, Unit 13

1. $4,760 + $78,200 + $25,600 + $1,240 = $109,800   total assets
$15,070 + $7,213 = $22,283   total liabilities
$109,800 − $22,283 = $87,517   owner's capital

2. $36,508.72 − ($23,810.14 + $7,834.28) = $4,864.30   net income

3. $28,417 + $67,118 = $95,535   merchandise available for sale
$95,535 − $36,982 = $58,553   cost of merchandise sold

4. $162,000 − ($118,500 + $28,920) = $14,580   net profit
$14,580 ÷ $162,000 = 0.09, or 9%   of net sales

5. $366,600 ÷ $15,600 = 23.5   annual merchandise turnover rate

6. $50,000 + $30,000 = $80,000   total investment
$\frac{\$50,000}{\$80,000} \times \$53,600 = \$33,500$ amount Larkin receives

7. a. $318,000 − ($186,200 + $51,700) = $80,100   net income
   b. $26,000 + $39,000 + $65,000 = $130,000   total investment
   $\frac{\$26,000}{\$130,000} \times \$80,100 = \frac{1}{5} \times \$80,100 = \$16,020$ Crowe's share

   $\frac{\$39,000}{\$130,000} \times \$80,100 = \frac{3}{10} \times \$80,100 = \$24,030$ Juliano's share

   $\frac{\$65,000}{\$130,000} \times \$80,100 = \frac{1}{2} \times \$80,100 = \$40,050$ Stevens' share

8. $(0.05 \times \$32,000) + \$10,130 = \$11,730$ total earnings

9. $300 \times (0.06 \times \$100) = \$1,800$ dividends on preferred stock
$4,000 − $1,800 = $2,200   total available for common stock dividends
$2,200 ÷ 2,000 = $1.10   per share dividend on common stock

10. a. $100,000 \times \$1.18 = \$118,000$ total dividends paid
       $360,000 − $118,000 = $242,000   kept as retained earnings
    b. $220 \times \$1.18 = \$259.60$ dividends received by Flim

11. $0.057 \times (150 \times \$8) = \$68.40$ dividend on stock
$0.03 \times \$4,280 = \$128.40$ dividend on purchases
$68.40 + $128.40 = $196.80   total dividend

12. $0.57 \times \$3,600 = \$2,052$ amount creditors get

13. $12,500 − $3,700 = $8,800   available to pay creditors

14. $28,350 ÷ $90,000 = 31.5¢   on the dollar creditors will be paid

15. 0.21 × $12,800 = $2,688   amount of claim received

Sections 87–91, Unit 14

1. $320 − $64 = $256; $256.00 − $51.20 = $204.80   invoice price

2. $520 − $364 = $156   discount
$156 ÷ $520 = 30%   rate of discount

3. $850 − $323 = $527   invoice price of Anders Wholesale Company
$720 − $144 = $576; $576.00 − $86.40 = $489.60   invoice price of West-
lake Distributing
$527.00 − $489.60 = $37.40   saved by taking Westlake offer

4. 70 × $10.50 = $ 735.00
30 × $ 7.42 =   222.60
  6 × $28.60 =   171.60
                 $1,129.20   amount of invoice

5. $78,210 − $530.87 = $77,679.13   net purchases

6. 0.01 × $12,600 = $126   monthly discount savings
12 × $126 = $1,512   savings in one year

7. 360 × $0.62 = $223.20   list price
0.1 × $223.20 = $22.32   quantity discount

8.   100%   100%
       − 20%   − 68%
        80%   32%   single discount equivalent
       − 12%
        68%

9. 29   days
$712   needed to pay invoice

10. March 22 + 15 days = April 6

11. 0.05 × $7,400 = $370   cash discount
$7,400 − $370 = $7,030   amount borrowed
$7,030 × 0.15 × $\frac{1}{6}$ = $175.75   interest
$370.00 − $175.75 = $194.25   saved

12. $800 − $240 = $560; $560 − $56 = $504   invoice price
$504 − (0.02 × $504) = $493.92   cash price

‡13. $39 ÷ 0.02 = $1,950   invoice price

‡14. (9 + 1) × $2.90 = $29   total value of purchase
$2.90 ÷ $29 = 10%   rate of discount

Sections 92–98, Unit 15

1. Change fund $100.00
   Register total of cash received   614.86 $714.86
   Register total of cash paid out   − 37.50

   Cash that should be in drawer $677.36
   Cash actually in drawer   − 677.46

   Cash over $ 0.10

2. | Date | Explanation | Charges | Credits | Balance |
    |------|-------------|---------|---------|---------|
    | May 1 | Balance | | | $12,308.78 |
    | 3 | Invoice #5763 | $3,588.98 | | 15,897.76 |
    | 8 | Credit Memo #377 | | $ 478.33 | 15,419.43 |
    | 30 | Payment | | 10,000.00 | 5,419.43 |

3. $75 − $60 = $15   discount
   $15 ÷ $75 = 20%   rate of discount

4. $95.88 ÷ 12 = $7.99   cost per diskette holder
   $15.89 − $7.99 = $7.90   gross profit

5. **a.** $42 − $24 = $18   gross profit per pair at $42
   b. $35 − $24 = $11   gross profit per pair at $35
   c. $11 ÷ $35 = 31.4%   rate of markup on selling price

6. $13,176 − $11,595 = $1,581   gross profit
   $2,136 − $1,581 = $555   net loss

7. $35.00 − $22.75 = $12.25   markup based on selling price
   $12.25 ÷ $35 = 35%   rate of markup

8. **a.** $9 ÷ 12 = $0.75   cost per flower
   $1 − $0.75 = $0.25   markup
   $0.25 ÷ $1.00 = 25%   rate of markup on selling price
   b. 50 × $9 = $450   total cost
   (12 × 50) × $1 = $600   selling price
   $600 − $450 = $150   gross profit

9. $336 − $240 = $96   markup
   $96 ÷ $240 = 40%   rate of markup based on cost

10. 350 × $8.50 = $2,975   cost of radios

    160 × $15.98 = $2,556.80
    100 × $12.90 = 1,290.00
    90 × $ 9.75 =   877.50
                   $4,724.30   selling price of radios
    $4,724.30 − $2,975 = $1,749.30   gross profit
    $1,749.30 ÷ $2,975 = 58.8%   rate of gross profit

11. (150 × $10.98) + (150 × $6.98) = $2,694   selling price
    300 × $6.25 = $1,875   cost
    $2,694 − ($1,875 + $680) = $139   net income
    $139 ÷ $1,875 = 7.4%   rate of net income

12. **a.** $2.85 − $1.90 = $0.95   gross profit
    $0.95 ÷ $1.90 = 50%   rate of markup based on cost
    b. $0.95 ÷ $2.85 = $33\frac{1}{3}$%   rate of markup based on selling price

13. $22.80 + $0.80 = $23.60   cost of skateboard
    0.45 × $23.60 = $10.62   gross profit
    $23.60 + $10.62 = $34.22   selling price

14. $486.00 − $388.80 = $97.20   loss
    $97.20 ÷ $486 = 20%   loss based on cost

15. $4,500 − (0.125 × $4,500) + $60 = $3,997.50   total cost
    $3,997.50 + (0.30 × $3,997.50) = $5,196.75   selling price of 6 camcorders
    $5,196.75 ÷ 6 = $866.13   selling price of each camcorder

16. $160 − $128 = $32   gross profit on bicycle costing $128
    $32 ÷ $128 = 25%   gross profit on cost
    0.25 × $144 = $36   desired gross profit on bicycle costing $144
    $144 + $36 = $180   selling price of bicycle costing $144

17. $450 × $3 = $1,350   cost price of staplers
    $1,350 + (0.40 × $1,350) = $1,890   desired total selling price
    $1,890 − (150 × $4.50) = $1,215   selling price of remaining staplers
    $1,215 ÷ (450 − 150) = $4.05   selling price of each remaining stapler

‡18. $63 ÷ 0.70 = $90   selling price

‡19. $900 − (0.20 × $900) = $720; $720 − (0.10 × $720) = $648
    $648 + $16 = $664   cost of computer
    $664 ÷ 0.80 = $830   selling price

‡20. $30 − $7.50 = $22.50; $22.50 − $2.25 = $20.25; $20.25 + $0.75 = $21
    cost
    $21 ÷ 0.60 = $35   selling price

‡21. $40 − $10 = $30; $30 − $3 = $27; $27 + $1.50 = $28.50   cost
    $28.50 ÷ 0.60 = $47.50   selling price

‡22. 0.24 ÷ 0.76 = 31.6%   rate of markup on cost

‡23. 0.26 ÷ 0.74 = 35%   equivalent rate of gross profit

Sections 99–105, Unit 16

1. ($2,978.55 + $4,207.23 + $2,009.43) ÷ 200 = $45.98   average factory cost of each motor

2. 1,500 + 2,400 + 2,500 + 3,600 = 10,000 square feet   total floor space

   Property: $\frac{1,500}{10,000}$ or $\frac{3}{20}$ × $12,000 = $1,800   annual charge

   Casualty: $\frac{2,400}{10,000}$ or $\frac{6}{25}$ × $12,000 = $2,880   annual charge

   Health: $\frac{2,500}{10,000}$ or $\frac{1}{4}$ × $12,000 = $3,000   annual charge

   Automotive: $\frac{3,600}{10,000}$ or $\frac{9}{25}$ × $12,000 = $4,320   annual charge

3. 0.12 × $12.50 = $1.50   selling and administrative expenses
   $1.50 + $3.40 + $4.13 + $1.62 = $10.65   total cost of producing and selling lamp
   $12.50 − $10.65 = $1.85   net income

4. a. $17,400 ÷ $4 = 4,350   calculators need to be sold to break even
    b. 10,000 × $4 = $40,000   selling price
        $40,000 − $17,400 = $22,600   net income
    c. 3,000 × $4 = $12,000   selling price
        $17,400 − $12,000 = $5,400   net loss

5. 0.15 × $52,000 = $7,800   depreciation first year
    $52,000 − $7,800 = $44,200   book value end of first year
    0.15 × $44,200 = $6,630   depreciation second year
    $44,200 − $6,630 = $37,570   book value end of second year

6. $24,500 − $12,500 = $12,000   total depreciation
    1 + 2 + 3 + 4 + 5 = 15   sum-of-the-years-digits
    $\frac{1}{3}$ × $12,000 = $4,000   depreciation, end of first year
    $\frac{4}{15}$ × $12,000 = $3,200   depreciation, end of second year
    $24,500 − ($4,000 + $3,200) = $17,300   book value end of second year

7. 500 × $37 = $18,500   cost per year
    0.10 × $18,500 = $1,850   cost of unneeded or personal use would be saved

8. a. ($6,200 + $960) ÷ 800 = $8.95   yearly cost per sq. ft.
    b. 70 × $8.95 = $626.50   cost of work station per year

9. 20 × 0.062 × $7,000 = $8,680   FUTA tax

10. a. Vilex
    b. $2,840 + $101.37 = $2,941.37   total cost of equipment

11. $0.28 × 52 = $14.56   rate based on weight
    ($200 ÷ $100) × $0.30 = $0.60   insurance costs
    $3 + $14.56 + $0.60 = $18.16   cost of shipment per box
    8 × $18.16 = $145.28   total cost of shipment

12. 5 × 12 × $1,100 = $66,000   annual cost

13. a. $650 + $450 + $120 + $50 + $250 + $1,400 = $2,920   cost of such system
    b. 35 × $2,920 = $102,200   total cost of systems

14. $40 + $275 + $375 + $125 = $815   total cost of software

15. a. $60 + $495 + $420 + $375 = $1,350   cost per system
    b. 12 × $1,350 = $16,200   total cost of software

16. (120 + 140 + 135 + 145) × $12 = $6,480   cost of programming

17. $2,800 ÷ 80 = $35   storage cost per MB

Sections 106–110, Unit 17

1. a. 17 + 18 + 19 + 20 + 20 + 20 + 20 + 21 + 21 + 22 + 23 + 24 + 26 + 28 + 31 = 330
        330 ÷ 15 = 22   mean
    b. 21 = median
    c. 20 = mode

2. 31 − 17 = 14   range

3. a. $\frac{1}{3}$ probability of month containing 30 days
    b. $\frac{5}{12}$ probability of month containing less than 31 days
    c. $\frac{7}{12}$ probability of month containing more than 30 days

4. a. 65,000 ÷ 100,000 = 65% probability of living to 70 at age 0
    b. 65,000 ÷ 98,000 = 66% probability of living to age 70 at age 10

5. $500 × $5\frac{1}{2}$ = $2,750 amount represented on graph

6. a. $28,000 largest sales for a department
    b. $6,000 smallest sales for a department
    c. $24,000 ÷ 6 = $4,000 average daily sales for Tool Department
    d. $10,000 + (0.15 × $10,000) = $11,500 expected sales of Paint Department
    e. $6,000 ÷ 1.20 = $5,000 previous week's sales of Electrical Department
    f. $6,000 + $28,000 + $16,000 + $10,000 + $24,000 = $84,000 total sales

7. $100,000 ÷ $2,000 = 50 number of blocks needed
    50 ÷ 10 = 5 inches needed to draw dollar scale

8. a. 0.3 × $4,200 = $1,260 money earned from bedspread sales
    b. 0.25 × $4,200 = $1,050 money earned from linen sales

9. a. (11.3% + 13.5% + 10.4%) ÷ 3 = 11.7% average rate of inflation
    b. (4.3% + 3.6% + 1.9%) ÷ 3 = 3.3% average rate of inflation

10. 0.058 × 500 = 29 men expected to be unemployed

KEY FOR PRETESTS AND UNIT TESTS

Pretest, Unit 1	Unit 1 Test	Pretest, Unit 2			
1. 3,036	1. $4,141.07	1. a. 2,322		d. $4,130	
2. $3,166.12	2. $2,378.67	b. 50.22		e. $5	
3. 3,947	3. 535	c. $185.20			
4. $1,395.04	4. 5	2. a. $68.42		d. 1.66	
5. $7,020.15; $6,954.43	5. 14	b. $7.69		e. 9.05	
6. a. 6	6. $2,746	c. $0.0015			
b. 3	7. $78.17	3. a. 18		d. 8	
7. a. 24	8. $255.24	b. 8		e. 28	
b. 20	9. $81.89	c. 30		f. 48	
8. $371.25	10. $670.68	4. a. $58.63		c. $0.39	
9. $1,043.23	11. 592	b. $0.62			
10. $509.76	12. $225.68	5. a. 0.9		c. 6.79	
11. 28 ounces	13. $360.90	b. 1.32			
12. a. 275	14. $480.60	6. $340.80 gross pay			
b. 190	‡15. $248.02	7. $16,800 yearly pay			
		8. $44 avg. daily pay			
		9. 7 avg. minutes late			
		10. 84 score on third test			
		11. $46.50 gross pay			

Unit 2 Test

1. $600
2. 16.43
3. 4
4. 75
5. $0.15
6. $311.60
7. $1,658
8. $86
9. $1,640
10. $16,640
11. $79.80
12. $184
13. $7.24
14. 2,900,000
15. $148

Pretest, Unit 3

1. a. $\frac{5}{8}$
   b. $\frac{7}{12}$
   c. $6\frac{8}{15}$
2. a. $\frac{7}{12}$
   b. $\frac{1}{24}$
   c. $4\frac{7}{12}$
3. a. $\frac{2}{5}$ d. 105
   b. $\frac{1}{4}$ e. $30\frac{7}{8}$
   c. 35
4. a. 63   d. $\frac{3}{32}$
   b. $2\frac{1}{3}$ e. 3
   c. 18
5. a. $\frac{6}{10}$ d. $\frac{3}{8}$
   b. $30   e. $2\frac{1}{3}$
   c. $80   f. $\frac{38}{7}$
6. $333.75 gross pay
7. $88 pay for day
8. $\frac{7}{9}$ of earnings spent
9. $36,000 Rose's share of profit

Unit 3 Test

1. $1\frac{11}{12}$
2. $\frac{11}{24}$
3. 24
4. $\frac{3}{8}$
5. $\frac{1}{4}$
6. $362
7. $270
8. $428
9. $15\frac{5}{12}$
10. $260
11. $30
12. $72
13. $\frac{1}{2}$
14. 15 lbs.
15. $\frac{1}{6}$
‡16. $12.80
‡17. $200,000

Pretest, Unit 4

1. a. 0.8%
   b. 300%
   c. $0.14\frac{2}{7}$
   d. 0.11
   e. 678.4
   f. 6,910
   g. $7.20
   h. 0.16
   i. $12\frac{1}{2}\%$
   j. 64
   k. 20%
   l. $\frac{6}{25}$
   m. 2.75
   n. 6%
   o. $\frac{5}{8}$
   p. 2,809,000
‡q. $300
‡r. $22.40
2. a. 41
   b. 57
   c. 21
   d. 4
   e. 48
   f. 14
3. $334.49
4. $319.44
5. $17\frac{1}{4}$
6. $395
7. $380
8. $89,108
9. $32,000
‡10. $1,200

Unit 4 Test

1. 150%
2. 0.43
3. 3.25
4. 0.25%
5. 28
6. $213.71
7. $398.63
8. $6,954
9. $1,571.25
10. $27,000
11. $1,295
12. 6%
13. $28.16
14. 8%
‡15. $4,000
‡16. $428

Unit 5 Test

1. 98 000 mL
2. 14.67 m
3. 600 g
4. 60 t
5. 25%
6. 61 km
7. 4.8 L
8. 5,200 bottles
9. 409 kg
10. 1 650 t
11. 560 m^2
12. 24 m
13. 31.2 km^2
14. 11.3 kg
15. 5 panels

Unit 6 Test

1. $270
2. $2,520
3. $0.48
4. $24.36
5. $525
6. $827.19
7. $10.61
8. $874,835
9. 14
10. $84.68
11. $58.32
12. $4.12
13. 1.2
14. $3.83
15. $39.44

Unit 7 Test

1. $11
2. $210
3. 24%
4. August 25
5. 105 days
6. $1,037.50
7. 16%
8. $128.80
9. $398
10. 7%
11. $570,150
12. $22
13. $6.10
14. $3,456
15. 12.4%

Unit 8 Test

1. $515.11
2. $13.50
3. 0.0525
4. $6\frac{1}{4}\%$
5. $11.25
6. $40
7. $589.21
8. $9.20
9. $101.25
10. $7.50
11. $150
12. $114.55
13. $6.29
14. 5.8%
15. $12.04

Unit 9 Test

1. $500
2. $86.625
3. 8%
4. $533.75
5. $350
6. 400
7. $600
8. 4%
9. $98
10. $39,000
11. $6,000
12. 10%
13. $1,100
14. $8,100
15. $2,132
‡16. $126,250

Unit 10 Test

1. $6,023.89
2. $181,080
3. $9,760
4. $1,710
5. 0.03
6. $1,500
7. $10,880
8. $1,290
9. $80,450
10. $6,044
11. $984
12. 10%
13. $0.25
14. $2,580
15. $9,020

Unit 11 Test

1. $84.51
2. $350
3. $300
4. $8\frac{1}{4}$
5. $13\frac{2}{3}$
6. $1,088.13
7. $1,021.20
8. $2,022.30
9. $17.19
10. $12.40
11. $5,446.80
12. $16,332.75
13. $21,500
14. $148
15. $429.33
16. $96

Unit 12 Test

1. 127.5
2. $132,000
3. $237
4. $\frac{8}{9}$
5. $14,000
6. $390
7. $465.25
8. $190.40
9. $171.60
10. $3,600
11. $6,000
12. $1,030
13. $2,100
14. $1,396
15. $48

Unit 13 Test

1. 15%
2. 1.97
3. $\frac{1}{5}$
4. $2,800
5. $0.40
6. 15%
7. $21,000
8. 12%
9. $41,570
10. $35,600
11. 6
12. 8%
13. $320
14. $812
15. $114,200

Unit 14 Test

1. October 3
2. $1,169.40
3. $127.68
4. $36
5. 2%
6. $377,325
7. $434.74
8. $276.25
9. $20.75
10. 36%
11. $298.35
12. $1,332.80
13. $129.78
14. 28%
15. $0.23
‡16. 4%

Unit 15 Test

1. $1,191.80
2. 76.5%
3. $411.87
4. $33\frac{1}{3}$%
5. $175
6. $1.08 short
7. $1,209.47
8. 18%
9. 8%
10. $31.20
11. $237
12. 25%
13. $332.35
14. $24,875
‡15. $60
‡16. $41.67
‡17. $9.09

Unit 16 Test

1. $30
2. 36%
3. $1.75
4. 0.02
5. $240
6. $1,100; $2,100; $4,100; $700
7. $2.81
8. 4,250
9. $82,835.20
10. $4,045
11. $7.79
12. $0.03
13. $13,020
14. Trantax; $195
15. MemMagic; $0.03

Unit 17 Test

1. $4,000
2. 90 degrees
3. $\frac{3}{4}$
4. 20%
5. 12
6. 16 miles
7. 600
8. 12
9. 15.3%
10. $125
11. 1,134
12. 18 degrees
13. $52,000
14. 50%
15. June
16. 180,000 yards

SOLUTIONS TO SEMESTER TESTS

First Semester Test

Part A

1. D
2. A
3. D
4. C
5. C
6. A
7. C
8. C
9. D
10. A
11. A
12. B
13. C
14. A
15. A

Part B

1. 2,310
2. 3,349
3. 176
4. 30
5. 28.6%
6. $0.21\frac{3}{7}$
7. $1\frac{11}{12}$
8. 24
9. 45
10. 28
11. 18
12. 15
13. 36
14. 12.306
15. 20.5 g
16. 407,200
17. 40%
18. $30
19. 125%
20. 40%
21. $64
22. $273.60
23. $370.50
24. $56.25
25. $144

Part C

1. 210
2. $2,040
3. $444
4. $256.25
5. $75,361.88
6. $138.18
7. $38,008.32
8. $389.02
9. $75.05
10. $2,108
11. $239.54
‡12. $150,000
‡13. $309.10

Part D

1. $2,000
2. $2,000
3. $30.00
4. $2,030
5. $1,500
6. $530
7. $7.95
8. $537.95
9. $5.32
10. $818.84
11. $6.04
12. $824.88
13. $68.82
14. $184.54
15. $253.36
16. $824.88

Second Semester Test

Part A	Part B	Part C	Part D
1. D	1. $958.75	1. $1,088.13	1. $1,487.54
2. A	2. $2,100	2. $169	2. $1,737.54
3. C	3. 0.007	3. $6,000	3. $185.73
4. B	4. 3%	4. $3,840	4. $1,551.81
5. C	5. 18.8%	5. $6,044	5. $1,552.17
6. D	6. $39.78	6. $675	6. $0.36 over
7. C	7. 23	7. $21,000	7. $50,000
8. D	8. $47.78	8. $5,100	8. $53,000
9. B	9. $68,000	9. $812	9. $38,000
10. B	10. $\frac{3}{5}$	10. 8	10. $12,000
11. A	11. $14,000	‡11. $15	11. $4,500
12. B	12. 1.97	‡12. $48,000	12. 76%
13. A	13. $14,560		13. 24%
14. A	14. 7%		14. 15%
15. D	15. 3%		15. 9%
	16. $171.50		16. $17,000
	17. $12		17. Week 3
	18. $61.25		18. $59,000
	19. $4,992		19. 100%
	20. 35.2%		20. 15%
	21. 1,000		
	22. $13.67		
	23. $39		
	24. 35.2%		
	25. 8%		

Applied Business Mathematics

13th Edition

Robert A. Schultheis

Professor of Management Information Systems
and
Professor of Business Education
Southern Illinois University
Edwardsville, Illinois

Raymond M. Kaczmarski

Supervisor of Business Education
Detroit Public Schools
Detroit, Michigan

Roswell E. Fairbank

Professor Emeritus of Business Education
State University of New York at Albany
Albany, New York

M47
PUBLISHED BY
SOUTH-WESTERN PUBLISHING CO.
CINCINNATI, OH   WEST CHICAGO, IL   DALLAS, TX   LIVERMORE, CA

ISBN: 0-538-13472-0

Library of Congress Catalog Card Number: 89-61716

123456789Ki765432109

Printed in the United States of America

Photo Credits: Cover, © Geoffrey Gove; p. 19, Courtesy of International Business Machines Corporation; p. 27, First Interstate Bancorp; p. 155, Peter Correz/TSW-Tony Stone Worldwide; p. 162, © Henley and Savage/TSW-Tony Stone Worldwide; p. 215, PHOTO © BOB KRIST; p. 342, Honeywell Inc.; p. 462, NCR Corporation; p. 506, Photo courtesy of Xerox Corporation; p. 508, Duffy Incorporated, Interior Designers; p. 523, Courtesy of Sperry Corporation; p. 524, Photo courtesy of Hewlett-Packard Company; p. 526, Photo courtesy of Hewlett-Packard Company.

For assistance and cooperation with this textbook project, especially in contributing locations for the unit openers, we would like to acknowledge the following: p. 43, University of Cincinnati, Cashier's office; p. 76, Watson's Clock Shop, Cincinnati, OH; p. 167, Xavier University, Cincinnati, OH; p. 181, Thriftway Food-Drug, Hyde Park Plaza, Cincinnati, OH; p. 275, Xavier University, Logan Hall; p. 333, Queen City Metro, Cincinnati, OH; p. 461, Highland Coffee House, Cincinnati, OH; p. 493, The Cincinnati Gear Co., uniform supplied by Cintas Corporation.

Preface

The thirteenth edition of APPLIED BUSINESS MATHEMATICS reflects the changes that have taken place in business, personal finance, and education. This edition also reflects technology's impact on the way in which mathematical problems are solved.

Users of previous editions of APPLIED BUSINESS MATHEMATICS will notice that substantial changes have been made in both the content and organization of many units. The text has been updated and many new topics introduced, including electronic funds transfer, money market accounts, home-equity loans, income tax preparation for dependents, computer costs, measures of central tendency, and economic statistics.

Several new features have been added to the text and the workbook. New features include:

1. The use of the *calculator* has been integrated into the problem work where it was found appropriate. Through *Calculator Clinics*, students are taught how to use the calculator to solve business mathematics problems. The optional CoverCalc™* puts a solar-powered calculator at your students' fingertips. Designed to slide on the front or back cover of APPLIED BUSINESS MATHEMATICS, CoverCalc makes it easy for you to incorporate the use of calculators in your classroom. All students can be prepared with calculators for doing classwork and homework. Your job will be easier, since you will not have to deal with problems caused by students using different calculators.

2. *Computer spreadsheet* problems have been integrated into the text as well. Through *Computer Clinics*, students are taught how to use spreadsheets to solve business mathematics problems and are involved in "what if" problem solving. Optional spreadsheet template diskettes are available for Lotus® 1-2-3®,* AppleWorks®,* and MicroTools™*

---

*CoverCalc is a trademark of South-Western Publishing Co. All references to Cover-Calc refer to this footnote.

*Lotus®, and 1-2-3® are registered trademarks of Lotus Development Corporation. All references to Lotus® 1-2-3® refer to this footnote.

*AppleWorks® is a registered trademark of Apple Computer, Inc. licensed to CLARIS Corporation. All references to AppleWorks® refer to this footnote.

*MicroTools™ is a trademark of South-Western Publishing Co. All references to Micro-Tools™ refer to this footnote.

3. In Unit 1, students are taught to recognize and analyze *problems that contain more information than is needed* to solve the problems. Such problems are included in almost every section thereafter.

4. In Unit 2, students are taught to *estimate the answers* to problems. Estimation problems are included in almost every section thereafter.

5. Each unit in the workbook has a *vocabulary review* and an *integrated project*. The integrated project is designed to provide a review and synthesis of the unit.

6. A set of *transparency masters* is provided in the teacher's edition of the workbook.

7. The teacher's manual, included in the teacher's edition of the textbook, contains a list of *teaching resources* for each unit of the text.

A new test package is available in printed form or on diskette. The package includes: *pretests* for the first four units, which review the fundamental arithmetical processes; seventeen *unit tests;* and two comprehensive *semester examinations,* one covering the first part of the course and one covering the second.

The thirteenth edition of APPLIED BUSINESS MATHEMATICS and its related materials are designed to be effective for students of widely differing backgrounds and abilities. Short sentences, informal writing style, low syllabic intensity, and familiar vocabulary make the book easy to read. Technical vocabulary is limited to essential terms. New terms are first shown in boldface type and then included in a subsequent vocabulary-building activity at the end of a section. The terms are also included in the vocabulary exercises, found in the workbook, which review each unit.

Illustrations are used purposefully throughout the thirteenth edition to heighten student interest, increase understanding, and expand student knowledge of the business world and business practices. Marginal notes and illustrations focus student attention on key points.

To help students learn, the objectives of each unit are presented on the opener page of each unit. Guide answers are provided for selected problems in the written exercises. These answers let students know whether the problems are being solved correctly, thus increasing the chance of effective practice or homework.

Although the thirteenth edition of APPLIED BUSINESS MATHEMATICS has many new features, the basic and highly successful instructional strategies that characterized previous editions have been retained. Early units include relatively simple small business or personal business problems to develop basic principles and improve skill in fundamental operations. Those units include cash records; gross and average pay; regular and overtime pay; net pay, fringe benefits, and commission; and the metric system.

Basic arithmetic principles and processes are reviewed and practiced in later units dealing with topics such as saving, investing, home and transportation expenses, taxes, insurance, business income and loss, business purchasing, business selling, manufacturing and office costs, and business statistics and graphs.

Generally, each topic is developed using the following five-step learning pattern:

1. A functional approach that introduces each new principle or process in a meaningful or interesting way to students.

2. A simple explanation that provides the essential background information for student understanding of the new principle or process.

3. An example with a model solution.

4. An exercise for immediate practice with problems similar to the example and arranged in order of increasing difficulty.

5. A review of the new type of problem at planned intervals throughout the text to insure retention.

APPLIED BUSINESS MATHEMATICS is organized into 17 units of 110 sections. New principles and new types of problems are introduced in graded sequence, one at a time. This step-by-step development of subject matter, with simple explanations, examples, model solutions, and subsequent review, enables students to progress with a minimum of teacher help.

The thirteenth edition of APPLIED BUSINESS MATHEMATICS has many optional topics and problems. Challenge problems are identified with a double dagger (‡). Challenge problems, supplementary problems, drills in the appendixes, integrated projects, workbook problems, calculator sections, and computer spreadsheet problems all can be used to provide for individual and group differences.

The authors want to thank the many teachers who have offered suggestions and the governmental agencies and businesses that have provided information and problem material for this edition of APPLIED BUSINESS MATHEMATICS.

Robert A. Schultheis
Raymond M. Kaczmarski
Roswell E. Fairbank

EDITORIAL ADVISORS

Jack Baroody
Plattsburg Senior High School
Plattsburg, New York

Stephen J. Cutney
Mount Vernon High School
New York, New York

Stan Merrill
Kokomo High School
Kokomo, Indiana

Emily Perlman
Mathematics Consultant
Houston, Texas

Contents

Money Records

Keeping records of cash that is collected and spent is an important activity. Businesses, families, and individuals keep records of the cash they receive and pay out. To do so, they use cash receipts records, cash payments records, and checkbook records. These records may be kept manually or they may be kept electronically by using calculators and computers.

Keeping cash records and many other personal and business records requires the use of addition and subtraction. So, adding and subtracting quickly and accurately are very important skills for you to learn.

After you finish Unit 1, you will be able to:

- Add vertically and horizontally and prove your addition.
- Subtract vertically and horizontally and prove your subtraction.
- Use addition and subtraction to complete cash receipts records, cash payments records, and checkbook records.
- Complete deposit slips, checks, and check registers.
- Prepare bank reconciliation statements.
- Find gross and net amounts.
- Solve simple number sentences.
- Read, write, say, and recognize decimal system numbers.
- Solve problems that contain more information than you need.
- Read, write, say, and recognize the meanings of the key terms.
- Use a calculator to add and subtract.
- Use a computer spreadsheet to complete a cash payments record.

Many persons, families, organizations, and businesses keep records of the cash they receive and the cash they pay out. Cash records can be a great help when you are planning how to use your money. They are also helpful when you fill out income tax forms.

Laverne and Ramon Mendez receive weekly pay from their full-time jobs. Ramon also receives pay from a part-time job. Laverne and Ramon Mendez keep track of all their cash receipts manually by using a form called a **cash receipts record.** Their cash receipts record for the week of June 6 is shown in Illustration 1–1.

The Mendez Family			
Cash Receipts Record			
Date		**Explanation**	**Amount**
19-- June	6	Ramon's part-time pay for week	$ 85 50
	7	Refund on state income tax	87 20
	8	Refund on returned purchase	29 75
	8	Insurance dividend	44 25
	10	Ramon's full-time pay for week	480 75
	10	Laverne's pay for week	609 75
		Total	$1,337 20

Illustration 1–1. Cash Receipts Record for the Mendez Family

At the end of the week, the Mendezes add the Amount column and find the total of their cash receipts. Their total receipts for the week of June 6 were $1,337.20.

**Exercise 1
Written**

1. VideoRama, a video store, had these cash receipts for a week: Monday, $548.66; Tuesday, $296.78; Wednesday, $361.93; Thursday, $500.24; Friday, $958.12; Saturday, $986.97; Sunday, $732.99. What were the total cash receipts for the week? $4,385.69

2. Alice Buffom uses a computer to keep her cash receipts. Her computer screen shows the following receipts for the week of March 10:

```
                         CASH RECEIPTS

       Date        Explanation                     Amount

     19--
     March 10      Birthday gift from Dad             50.00
          10       Repayment of personal loan from friend  25.00
          11       Returned bottles to store           2.65
          12       Interest on savings               115.15
          13       Refund on canceled insurance policy  37.18
          14       Weekly pay                        382.40

                   Total                             612.38
```

Find Alice's total cash receipts for the week. To find the total, place the edge of a sheet of paper under the last amount. Then add the column, and write the total on the paper.

3. The senior class of Westport High School uses a computer to keep records of their cash receipts. Find the total cash receipts for the class by adding the amount column for the month of October shown on the computer printout.

■ A workbook (M471) contains additional problems that parallel the topics in this text.

```
●  Senior Class Cash Receipts                                ●

●     Date                   Explanation              Amount ●
                                                             ●
●  19--
●  Oct.  4            Senior Class car wash           124.00 ●
●        6            Senior Class bake sale           75.00
●        6            Class dance night               264.75 ●
●       14            Interest on savings              10.34
●       28            Food sales at football games    165.85 ●
●       29            Sales of class hats             389.25
                                                             ●
●                    Total                          1,029.19 ●
```

4. An auto service station had these cash receipts for a week: auto parts, $367.45; repairs, $1,824.76; gasoline, $19,832.89; car wash, $215.00; other sales, $189.88. What were the total cash receipts? $22,429.98

Addition and the Cash Receipts Record. Addition is the process of combining two numbers to get one number. The result is called the **sum**, or **total.** You have used addition to find total cash receipts. Of course, you can use addition in many other ways.

■
```
   42
 +16
   58 sum, or
      total
```

Adding Faster. Addition should be done quickly. You can add faster by mentally combining two or three numbers that total 10, then adding that 10 to the other numbers.

This method is shown in the example in the left margin. When you add from the top down, you think "10, 20, 30, 40, 48." When you check your work by adding from the bottom up, you think "8, 18, 28, 38, 48."

Exercise 2
Oral

Add orally, from the top down, the columns that follow. Use groups of two or three numbers when possible. Check your work by adding the columns from the bottom up.

1.	2.	3.	4.	5.	6.	7.	8.	9.	10.
5	6	9	5	4	5	4	4	6	9
5	4	1	5	6	8	3	8	1	3
6	5	9	6	8	4	6	5	8	8
4	2	1	2	3	3	2	2	1	4
2	1	8	3	7	3	4	5	5	6
8	9	1	5	6	0	9	6	3	4
4	4	5	2	3	5	1	7	6	5
1	6	3	1	2	6	8	3	2	3
+ 5	+ 7	+ 2	+ 7	+ 4	+ 4	+ 2	+ 8	+ 7	+ 7
40	44	39	36	43	38	39	48	39	49

Checking Addition. Addition must be done accurately. Accuracy requires that you check your work. The best way to check a total in addition is by **reverse addition.** To do this you add the column in the opposite direction from the way you added it the first time. Reverse addition usually gives you new combinations, so you avoid making the same mistake twice.

Exercise 3
Written

Copy and add each problem. Check each answer by reverse addition.

1.	2.	3.	4.	5.	6.
$18.79	$ 7.45	$98.45	$55.38	$ 8.32	$16.75
2.11	23.45	10.63	31.02	11.71	90.34
1.92	74.17	2.82	94.46	91.07	1.03
17.28	76.52	30.26	6.74	87.65	82.11
1.55	1.48	81.74	10.23	11.32	20.97
+ 21.05	+ 39.40	+ 26.36	+ 84.17	+ 10.13	+ 15.83
$62.70	$222.47	$250.26	$282.00	$220.20	$227.03

Drills for accuracy and speed are provided on pages 554 to 569. You might start with Drill 1.

Exercise 4
Written

Check each problem by reverse addition.

1. Allnite Qwik Market's seven cash registers showed the following cash receipts for Saturday: cash register #1, $3,497.22; #2, $2,259.86; #3, $4,178.40; #4, $2,863.17; #5, $4,888.33; #6, $3,892.21; #7, $2,003.62. What were the total cash receipts for Saturday? $23,582.81

2. A neighborhood garage sale had these cash receipts for 5 days: $136.97, $256.21, $366.10, $218.06, $89.42. What were the total cash receipts? $1,066.76

3. Isabelle Santiago's home computer screen shows her cash receipts for May. What were her total receipts?

```
    Date        Explanation                        Amount

  19--
  May     4     Weekly pay                         548.04
          4     Interest on savings                 26.86
          7     Expense check                      782.33
         11     Weekly pay                         548.24
         18     Weekly pay                         548.23
         25     Weekly pay                         548.23
         30     Stock dividend                      53.40
                                                 3,055.33
```

4. The Little League in Scoville held 6 car washes to raise money for equipment. The cash receipts from the car washes were:

Week 1	$204.50	Week 4	$ 77.75
2	137.25	5	120.50
3	93.15	6	137.25

What were the total cash receipts from the car washes? $770.40

5. A computer store's cash receipts for a week were:

Computers	$37,027.78	Computer books	$134.56
Computer software	8,107.39	Training	672.00
Printers	4,527.19	Repairs	879.42
Other equipment	2,365.08		

What were the store's total cash receipts for the week? $53,713.42

 # Calculator Clinic

Using the Hand-Held Calculator. Electronic calculators are inexpensive and are used nearly everywhere, including the home, farm, factory, and office. Using most hand-held calculators is easy, and they make your work faster and more accurate.

Nearly every model of hand-held calculator differs slightly from other models. However, most calculators have certain features in common.

On-Off Keys. Many calculators are battery powered. Some calculators have separate keys for turning the battery on and off. Others have a switch that can be moved from the On position to the Off position. Be careful when you turn off your calculator because any numbers you have in it will be erased. If you turn off your calculator before you have finished a problem, you must start over again.

AC Key. Some calculators do not use batteries. Instead they are powered by energy from a light source, including sunlight or light from lamps. These "solar" calculators are always on. However, they should be cleared before they are used by pressing the AC (All Clear) key. The calculator shown in Illustration 1–2 is a solar calculator and has an AC key.

Illustration 1–2. Hand-Held Calculator

Number Keys. The number keys are part of the *keyboard*.

Display. Most calculators have a small window called a *display*. As you press or *enter* numbers on the keyboard, they will appear in the display.

The display will also show you the results of your calculations. Many calculator displays hold only 8 digits and the decimal point, so you cannot solve problems on these calculators if a number to be entered or the solution is larger than 99,999,999.

Clear Key. The Clear key (C), when pressed, will clear your calculator of any numbers or results that are in it. You can also clear your calculator by turning it off and then on again.

Some calculators have no special Clear key. Instead, you clear these calculators by pressing the On key. On these calculators, the On key serves two purposes: (1) to turn the machine on, and (2) to clear it if it's already on.

Clear Entry Key. If you make a mistake while entering an amount, the Clear Entry key (CE) will erase the numbers you have just entered but will not erase amounts you have already recorded.

Some calculators have no special Clear Entry key. The On key on these calculators will clear your entry if you press it once. The On key will clear the machine if you press it twice.

Other calculators have a Clear Entry/Clear key (CE/C). Pressing this key once will clear any entry you have made without clearing the machine. Pressing this key twice will clear the machine. The calculator shown in Illustration 1–2 has a Clear Entry/Clear key.

Decimal Key. You use the decimal key to place decimal points where you need them as you enter numbers.

Plus, Minus, Multiply, and Divide Keys. These keys are used to add, subtract, multiply, and divide. They are called the *operation keys*.

Equals Key. The Equals key will complete the arithmetic problem you are entering and place the answer in the display.

Other Keys. Calculators may have many other keys. For example, the calculator in Illustration 1–2 has keys for figuring percents (%) and markups (MU). Other calculators may have keys for the advanced mathematics used by scientists, engineers, statisticians, and others.

Using the Calculator for Addition. To add $58.60 and $17.90:

a. Clear your calculator by pressing this key twice: [CE/C]

b. Press these keys in order: [5] [8] [·] [6] [0]

c. Press the key marked: [+]

d. Press these keys in order: [1] [7] [·] [9] [0]

e. Press the key marked [=]

(The answer, 76.5, will appear in the display.) | 76.5 |

On most calculators the final zero and the dollar sign ($) will not appear in the display. You will have to remember to write the final zero and the dollar sign when you write your answer on paper ($76.50). On some calculators, the answer, 76.5, will appear without pressing the equals key.

You may want to add more than two numbers; for example, $58.60 + $17.90 + $4.30. To do so, complete the steps above and below.

f. Press the key marked: [+]

g. Press these keys in order: [4] [·] [3] [0]

h. Press the key marked: [=] (The answer, 80.8, will appear in the display and should be written as $80.80.)

Saving Time. You do not need to enter final zeros in amounts if the final zero appears to the *right* of the decimal point. For example, in the practice problem above, you can save time by entering only 58.6, 17.9, and 4.3. You will get the same answer whether you enter the final zeros or not.

Always check your work with reverse addition.

Checking Your Work. To check your work re-add the numbers on the calculator in reverse order (4.30 + 17.90 + 58.60). **Remember, it is just as important to check your addition when you do it with a calculator as when you do it manually.**

Calculator Practice. Apply what you have learned in this calculator clinic first to the problems in Exercise 3, second to the problems in Exercise 1, and then to any other exercises in this section that your teacher may assign.

Section 2
Cash Payments Records

Laverne and Ramon Mendez also keep a record of the cash they spend. That record is called a **cash payments record.** The cash payments record for the Mendez family for the week of June 6 is shown in Illustration 2–1.

The Mendez Family			
Cash Payments Record			
Date		**Explanation**	**Amount**
19-- June	6	Power bill for May	$ 92 41
	7	Home mortgage payment	772 33
	8	Auto payment	165 78
	9	Savings deposit	130 00
	10	Auto repair	85 00
	10	Groceries	135 23
		Total	$1,380 75

Illustration 2–1. Cash Payments Record for the Mendez Family

At the end of each week the Mendezes find the total of their payments by adding the Amount column. Their total payments for the week of June 6 were $1,380.75.

**Exercise 1
Written**

1. The cash payments for Ina Stein for the week of September 14 are shown in the following chart. Find her total cash payments for the week.

Date	Explanation	Amount
19-- Sept. 14	Dinner out	$ 24.88
15	Groceries	65.75
15	Movie rental	6.50
17	Telephone bill	53.81
18	Clothing	145.29
19	Lawn mowing service	15.00
20	Gift	37.59
	Total	$348.82

2. Charlie O'Hara uses a home computer to keep his cash payments records. At the end of the month his computer screen shows these expenses:

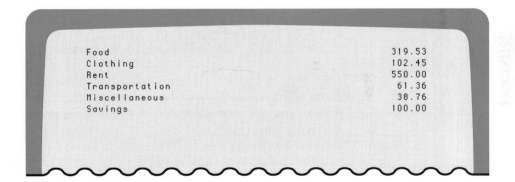

Food	319.53
Clothing	102.45
Rent	550.00
Transportation	61.36
Miscellaneous	38.76
Savings	100.00

Find Charlie's total payments for the month. $1,172.10

3. A small business spent these amounts in one month: salaries and wages, $8,129.33; delivery expenses, $134.89; rent, $1,230.00; supplies, $214.64; postage, $422.13; power, $692.61; telephone, $385.93. What were the total cash payments of the business for the month? $11,209.53

4. The Edgemont Data Processing Managers Association had the following cash payments for the month: national dues, $120.36; postage, $315.78; award plaques, $75.89; printing costs, $702.34; telephone, $27.34. What were the Association's total cash payments for the month? $1,241.71

5. Sonia Perez uses fuel oil to heat her house. From September to June she spent these amounts on fuel oil: $67.63, $101.94, $197.55, $256.29, $177.92, $82.45, $73.12. What were her total cash payments for fuel during that period? $956.90

Numerals. When you keep cash records or other records about numbers, you make marks to represent the numbers. These marks or symbols are called numerals. For example, the marks 2, 54, and 135 are numerals.

■ Numerals are symbols for numbers.

A **numeral** is a symbol or name for a number. A number may be represented by many different numerals or names. For example, the number 10 is usually represented by the numeral 10. This number, however, may be represented also by the numerals 4 + 6, 12 − 2, 2 × 5, 30 ÷ 3, $\frac{20}{2}$, and others. (See Illustration 2−2.)

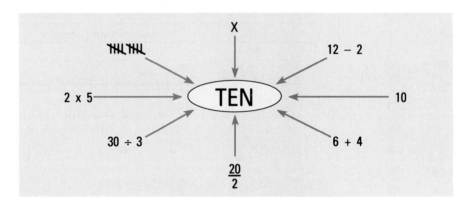

Illustration 2−2. Numerals Naming the Number 10

Number Sentences. To show that two numerals are names for the same number, you may write an equals sign (=) between them. For example, you may write 3 + 7 = 2 × 5. This statement is called **a number sentence.** It says that the number named by 3 + 7 is equal to the number named by 2 × 5.

A number sentence may be either true or false. The sentence 3 + 7 = 2 × 5 is true because 3 + 7 and 2 × 5 are names for the same number, 10. The sentence 3 + 7 = 3 × 5 is false because 3 + 7 is a name for 10 but 3 × 5 is a name for 15.

Exercise 2
Oral

Look at each sentence. Is it true or false?

1. 28 = 11 + 1	F		10. 9 − 4 = 15 − 9	F
2. 23 − 8 = 14	F		11. 12 + 6 = 21 − 3	T
3. 9 + 16 = 19	F		12. 2 + 9 = 23 − 11	F
4. 34 − 6 = 32	F		13. 8 + 3 + 4 = 2 + 7 + 6	T
5. 2 + 7 = 7 + 2	T		14. 3 − 1 + 8 = 5 + 7 − 2	T
6. 8 − 5 = 5 − 2	T		15. 6 + 7 − 9 = 4 + 8 − 8	T
7. 4 + 7 = 15 − 3	F		16. 4 + 5 − 3 = 6 − 2 + 3	F
8. 8 − 2 = 3 + 3	T		17. 9 − 8 + 5 = 2 + 9 − 5	T
9. 6 − 2 = 3 + 1	T		18. 7 + 7 − 6 = 5 − 2 + 6	F

A sentence like $2 + 7 = 3 + N$ has a numeral missing, so it is incomplete. As it stands the sentence is neither true nor false. To make it complete you must replace the N with a numeral that makes the sentence true. The numeral 6 makes the sentence true, so you may write $2 + 7 = 3 + 6$. You now have a complete, true statement. Use this method to make complete and true sentences when solving many problems in this book.

**Exercise 3
Written**

As you copy each sentence, replace the letter N with the numeral that makes the sentence true.

1. $5 + 4 = 4 + N$ 5
2. $8 + 7 = N + 8$ 7
3. $N - 4 = 6 + 9$ 19
4. $18 - 9 = 4 + N$ 5
5. $N + 3 = 9$ 6
6. $4 + 5 = 7 + N$ 2
7. $8 - 3 = N + 3$ 2
8. $8 + N = 7 + 6$ 5
9. $9 - 6 = 7 - N$ 4
10. $3 + N = 15$ 12
11. $N + 6 = 9 - 2$ 1
12. $3 + 9 = N - 2$ 14

Reading and Writing Numbers in the Decimal System. The symbols that represent the numbers from zero through nine are called digits. These ten digits are: 0, 1, 2, 3, 4, 5, 6, 7, 8, 9. Because this system uses ten digits, it is called the decimal system. The word "decimal" comes from a Latin word meaning ten.

■ **Digits = 0, 1,
2, 3, 4, 5, 6, 7, 8, 9.**

Place Value in the Decimal System. Using the ten digits of the decimal system, we can write the symbol for any number. We can do this because the value of a digit depends on its position in the number. We call this the **place value** of the digit.

Illustration 2–3 shows the place value of each digit in the number 55,555.

Ten-thousands	Thousands	Hundreds	Tens	Ones
5	5	5	5	5

Illustration 2–3. Place Value of Each Digit in 55,555

The 5 at the far right has a value of 5 *ones* or 5. You would write the number 5 as *five*.

The next 5 to the left has a value of 5 *tens* or 50, which is ten times 5. You would write the number 55 as *fifty-five*.

The next 5 has a value of 5 *hundreds* or 500, which is ten times 50. You would write the number 555 as *five hundred fifty-five*.

The next 5 has a value of 5 *thousands* or 5,000, which is ten times 500. You would write the number 5,555 as *five thousand, five hundred fifty-five*.

The next 5 has a value of 5 *ten-thousands* or 50,000, which is ten times 5,000. You would write the number 55,555 as *fifty-five thousand, five hundred fifty-five*.

Notice that moving a digit one place to the left multiplies its value by ten.

Exercise 4
Written

1. Look at this number: 34,967
   a. How many ten thousands are there?   3
   b. How many thousands?   4
   c. How many hundreds?   9
   d. How many tens?   6
   e. How many ones?   7
   f. Write the number in words.
      Thirty-four thousand, nine hundred sixty-seven

2. In the number 6,185 what digit is in the
   a. Thousands place? 6   c. Tens place? 8
   b. Hundreds place? 1   d. Ones place? 5

3. In the number 2,571 what is the value of the digit
   a. 2? 2,000   b. 5? 500   c. 7? 70   d. 1? 1

4. In 5,389 what is the value of
   a. The 5? 5,000   b. The 3? 300
   c. The 8? 80   d. The 9? 9
   e. Write the number in words.
      Five thousand, three hundred eighty-nine

5. The value of any number is the sum of the values of the digits in the number. For example, the table in the margin shows that 8,358 is equal to 8,000 + 300 + 50 + 8.

   Make tables like the one on the left to show the value of each digit and the sum of the values of the digits in each of these numbers.
   a. 987   c. 7,605   e. 1,078   g. 25,000
   b. 3,512   d. 9,087   f. 12,883   h. 56,783

   ```
     8,000
       300
        50
         8
   ───────
     8,358
   ```

6. Write each of the sums from Problem 5 in words.

7. The numbers 243, 324, 432, 234, 423, and 342 are all made up of the same digits.
   a. Which number represents the largest number?   432
   b. Which number represents the smallest number?   234
   c. Write each of the 6 numbers in words.

8. a. What is the largest number you can write with the digits 3, 8, and 5, using each digit only once?   853
   b. What is the smallest number?   358

9. To find the number that 6 thousands, 2 hundreds, 9 tens, and 5 ones, you find the sum of the values of the digits, as shown in the margin.

   In the same way, find the number that has:
   a. 4 thousands, 9 hundreds, 3 tens, 5 ones   4,935
   b. 9 thousands, 0 hundreds, 1 tens, 7 ones   9,017
   c. 1 ten-thousands, 6 thousands, 3 hundreds, 8 tens, 7 ones
      16,387
   d. 8 thousands, 2 hundreds, 0 tens, 3 ones   8,203

   ```
     6,000
       200
        90
         5
   ───────
     6,295
   ```

e.   6 ten-thousands, 1 thousands, 8 hundreds, 9 tens, 0 ones
     61,890
f.   24 thousands, 6 hundreds, 2 tens, 9 ones   24,629

10.   Write in words each of the numbers you found in Problem 9.

REVIEW 2

Terms

1.   Write the letters A through H in a column on your paper. Match each term below with the correct statement and write the term next to the proper letter on your paper.

addition   number sentence   reverse addition
cash payments record   numeral   sum or total
cash receipts record   place value

a.   The best check for addition   reverse addition
b.   A name for a number   numeral
c.   The result of addition   sum or total
d.   The process of combining two numbers into one   addition
e.   A written record of cash spent   cash payments record
f.   A written record of cash taken in   cash receipts record
g.   Says that two numerals are equal   number sentence
h.   A digit's position determines its value   place value

Skills

■ Check each problem as you do it.

2.   Add each problem quickly. Combine numbers that total 10 when you can. Check your work by reverse addition.

a.	b.	c.	d.
3	13	67.23	$357.31
8	75	28.58	923.17
7	50	32.10	515.53
2	47	41.32	682.62
4	25	72.17	108.97
+ 7	+ 68	+ 53.79	+ 397.64
31	278	295.19	$2,985.24

Problems

■ Always check by reverse addition.

3.   Eu Hook Ti received these cash amounts during one week: wages, $531.93; returned bottles, $3.25; interest on savings, $51.77; gift from parents, $50; refund on returned purchase, $28.56; tax refund, $167.32. What were his total cash receipts? $832.83 [1]

4.   Lisa Orr's paychecks for June were: $267.91, $248.09, $264.33, and $275.26. Alan Orr's paychecks for June were: $235.55, $287.64, $253.68, and $277.83. What were their total cash receipts? $2,110.29 [1]

5.   The Oli Co. spent these amounts last month: rent, $2,600; electricity, $467.29; natural gas, $251.72; salaries, $9,207.78; supplies, $1,508.09; travel expenses, $2,078.21; computer services, $2,145. How much did the company spend last month? $18,258.09 [2]

6.   A canoe club spent these amounts during June, July, and August: $684.24 for canoe rentals, $187.23 for refreshments, $32.35 for copying, $27 for award certificates, and $45.32 for postage. How much did the club spend? $976.14 [2]

The Mendezes used a cash payments record with a single column. Many people, organizations, and businesses use records with special columns to keep similar payments together. A cash payments record with special columns is shown in Illustration 3–1.

Ralph Kowalski						
Cash Payments Record						
			Types of Payments			
Week	**Housing**	**Food**	**Personal**	**Auto**	**Savings**	**Total Payments**
19-- *Dec.* *1–7*	*$ 500.00*	*$ 124.45*	*$ 45.80*	*$ 23.56*	*$ 25.00*	*$ 718.81*
8–14		*52.12*	*25.84*	*17.87*		*95.83*
15–21	*67.54*	*107.22*	*17.45*	*37.60*	*25.00*	*254.81*
22–28		*37.23*	*12.45*	*33.33*		*83.01*
29–31	*124.78*	*72.34*	*65.12*	*18.98*	*25.00*	*306.22*
Total	*$ 692.32*	*$ 393.36*	*$ 166.66*	*$ 131.34*	*$ 75.00*	*$ 1,458.68*

Illustration 3–1. Cash Payments Record with Special Columns

At the end of each week or partial week and at the end of the month, Ralph put the amounts for each type of payment on one line. He added the amounts across to find the total for the week and put that amount in the Total Payments column. At the end of the month he added down each payment column to find how much he had spent for each type of payment.

Horizontal
= ⟵⟶
Vertical = ↑

Using Horizontal and Vertical Addition in Cash Payments Records. Ralph Kowalski found his weekly totals by adding across each row without rewriting the figures. Adding across in this way is called **horizontal addition.** When you add across you save the time and bother of recopying the figures. Adding up and down, as you usually do, is called **vertical addition.**

Exercise 1
Written

Copy the following problems and find the missing totals. Add across (horizontal addition) to get the total of each line. Add up and down (vertical addition) to get the total of each column. Check your work by adding the column totals horizontally and the line totals vertically. The two totals should be equal.

Example

$$2 + 5 + 3 = 10$$
$$6 + 3 + 5 = 14$$
$$\underline{4 + 9 + 2} = \underline{15}$$
$$12 + 17 + 10 = 39$$

1.

$$6 + 4 + 5 = 15$$
$$3 + 6 + 7 = 16$$
$$\underline{8 + 5 + 2} = \underline{15}$$
$$17 + 15 + 14 = 46$$

2.

$$34 + 56 = 90$$
$$21 + 39 = 60$$
$$\underline{16 + 85} = \underline{101}$$
$$71 + 180 = 251$$

3.

$$24 + 33 + 53 = 110$$
$$51 + 27 + 22 = 100$$
$$\underline{33 + 96 + 56} = \underline{185}$$
$$108 + 156 + 131 = 395$$

4.

$$7 + 9 + 3 + 1 = 20$$
$$5 + 5 + 6 + 8 = 24$$
$$3 + 8 + 2 + 5 = 18$$
$$\underline{4 + 4 + 2 + 7} = \underline{17}$$
$$19 + 26 + 13 + 21 = 79$$

5.

$$93 + 122 = 215$$
$$237 + 154 = 391$$
$$593 + 47 = 640$$
$$\underline{134 + 89} = \underline{223}$$
$$1{,}057 + 412 = 1{,}469$$

6.

$$123 + 39 + 221 = 383$$
$$140 + 66 + 84 = 290$$
$$155 + 31 + 219 = 405$$
$$\underline{79 + 51 + 106} = \underline{236}$$
$$497 + 187 + 630 = 1{,}314$$

Exercise 2
Written

1. Olga Petroff is a college student who lives with her parents. Her cash payments for April are shown in the following chart.

	Types of Payments					
Week	**Food**	**Clothing**	**Auto**	**Savings**	**Other**	**Total Payments**
19-- April 1–7	$15.76	$25.99	$15.23	$10.00	$ 3.25	$70.23
8–14	14.27		12.77		5.09	32.13
15–21	22.88	23.79	12.87	10.00	17.49	87.03
22–28	12.67		15.67		12.34	40.68
29–31	6.45		3.78		5.56	15.79
Totals	$72.03	$49.78	$60.32	$20.00	$43.73	$245.86

Use both horizontal and vertical addition.

Complete Olga's cash payments record for April. Place a sheet of paper under the columns, add them, and write the totals on the paper. Prove your work by adding the five Types of Payments totals horizontally (across). The sum should equal the total of the Total Payments column.

2. Metzger and Associates is a small legal firm. The firm's cash payments for February are shown in the following chart:

			Types of Payments		
Week	Rent	Payroll	Office Expenses	Other Expenses	Total Payments
19-- Feb. 1–7	$975.00	$7,311.92	$345.61	$241.08	$8,873.61
8–14		617.25	207.67	97.12	922.04
15–21		617.25	89.56	178.31	885.12
22–28		617.25	306.45	81.02	1,004.72
Totals	$975.00	$9,163.67	$949.29	$597.53	$11,685.49

Find the totals for each week by adding horizontally (across). Find the total for each type of payment by adding vertically (up and down). Prove your work by adding the four Types-of-Payment column totals horizontally. This sum should equal the total of the Total Payments column.

REVIEW 3

Terms

1. Match the terms with the statements. Then write the terms in a column on your paper, as you did before.

    horizontal addition   vertical addition

    a. Adding across horizontal addition
    b. Adding up and down vertical addition

Skills

2. Find the value of N in each problem.

    a. $15 + N = 19$ 4
    b. $N + 16 = 20$ 4
    c. $0 + N = 4$ 4
    d. $6 + 23 = N$ 29
    e. $N - 20 = 15$ 35

    f. $20 - N = 15$ 5
    g. $22 - N = 22$ 0
    h. $N - 7 = 18$ 25
    i. $14 + N = 7 + 22$ 15
    j. $23 - 7 = 8 + N$ 8

Problems

■ Remember to check every calculation.

3. A roadside vegetable stand had these cash receipts for 5 weeks: $470.89, $592.93, $604.31, $556.82, $498.67. What were the total cash receipts for the 5 weeks? $2,723.62 [1]

4. Olga Svenson spent these amounts on a business trip: airfare, $478; taxis, $27; food, $145.23; hotel room, $245.98; gifts, $25.98; other expenses, $45.29. What total amount did Olga spend on the trip? $967.48 [2]

5. The Service League of Evansville ran a dart game at the town's 3-day homecoming event. The League collected $250.50 on Friday, $412.75 on Saturday, and $324.25 on Sunday. What was the total amount collected by the League? $987.50 [1]

6. Archer, Inc. spent these amounts on office supplies during June: typewriting paper, $45.78; copy paper, $135.98; manila folders, $67.12; paper clips, $12.76; lined pads, $27.45; notepads, $15.77; and letterhead paper, $207.87. What was the total amount Archer spent on office supplies? $512.73 [2]

Calculator Clinic

Using the Memory Keys. Many calculators have a *memory register*. A memory register can be used to store numbers or answers for later use. To learn how to use the memory register for addition, look at how this problem is solved:

Total

1.   14.56 + 12.35 = ____

2.   20.13 + 87.43 = ____

Grand Total   ____

You are to find the totals for each row (1 and 2). You are also to find the grand total (the sum of the totals for Rows 1 and 2). Here is how you can do it quickly:

a.   Press these keys in order: 1 4 · 5 6

b.   Press the addition key: +

c.   Press these keys in order: 1 2 · 3 5

d.   Press = and the sum, [26.91], appears in the

display.

e.   Press the *memory add* key: M+

You have just added the sum, 26.91, to the memory register. On many calculators a little M will appear in the display. This tells you that you have stored something in the memory register.

f.   Clear your calculator by pressing the clear CE/C key twice. This

will clear your calculator but will *not* clear the memory register.

g. Press these keys in order: 2 0 · 1 3

h. Press the key marked: +

i. Press these keys in order: 8 7 · 4 3

j. Press = , and the sum, 107.56, will appear in the display.

k. Press the key marked: M+

You have just added the second sum, 107.56, to the memory register.

l. Press this key: MR/C

MR/C stands for Memory Recall/Clear. This key lets you place what you have in the memory register in the calculator display. Once it is in the display you can use it for other calculations. When you press the Memory Recall key 134.47 will appear in the display. This is the sum of 26.91 + 107.56, the two amounts you added to the memory register.

m. Press the Memory Recall/Clear key again: MR/C

This will clear the memory register. The little M in the display should now be off. Pressing the Memory Recall/Clear key once places the contents of the register in the display. Pressing the Memory Recall/Clear key *twice* clears the memory register. You can also clear the memory register *and* the display of any amounts by pressing the AC, or All Clear, key.

You can use the memory register to solve many types of addition problems in business. For example, you can use the memory register to find the sum of the totals in a cash payments record with special columns.

Calculator Practice. Apply what you have learned in this calculator clinic to the problems in Exercises 1 and 2 in this Section and to any other exercises your teacher may assign.

Computer Clinic

Computer Systems. Computer systems are made up of two basic parts: computer hardware and computer software. *Computer hardware* is the computer equipment and machinery. The computer equipment for a small computer system, such as the *microcomputer* shown in Illustration 3–2, usually includes a keyboard, a screen or monitor, one or more disk drives, and the computer brain, or *central processing unit.*

Illustration 3–2. Computer System

Computer hardware is very dumb. To make computers work detailed instructions called *programs* must be fed into the computer hardware so that it knows what it is supposed to do. These programs are called *computer software.* Computer programs for microcomputers are usually placed on *diskettes.* (See Illustration 3–3.)

Illustration 3–3. Computer Software on a Diskette

Spreadsheet Software. A commonly used computer program is an *electronic spreadsheet.* A spreadsheet program lets you prepare many types of tables and forms easily and quickly. Spreadsheets also can be used to help you make decisions such as whether to lease or buy a car.

Spreadsheets were developed to eliminate the need for you to copy numbers on a notepad or columnar sheet of paper and then use a calculator to get your answers. For example, spreadsheet software can be used to develop the columnar cash payments record that is shown on the computer screen in Illustration 3–4.

```
           A          B         C        D        E        F          G ──────────── Column G
  1                        Bernice Elam
  2                        Cash Payments Record
  3   =================================================================
  4                         Types of Payments
  5                                                          Total
  6   Week         Housing    Food     Auto     Other   Savings  Payments ──────── Row 6
  7   =================================================================
  8   August  1-7   450.00    85.98   175.64    12.56    50.00    774.18
  9           8-14            120.77    14.89    25.44             161.10
 10          15-21    22.61    65.43    28.96    10.90             127.90
 11          22-28            110.19     5.10    35.98             151.27
 12          29-31             19.81    10.16    28.13              58.10
 13   -----------------------------------------------------------------
 14   Totals        472.61   402.18   234.75   113.01    50.00   1272.55
 15   =================================================================
```

Illustration 3–4. Cash Payments Record on a Computer Screen

Notice that the spreadsheet is composed of *rows,* which are numbered, and *columns,* which are lettered. Words and numbers are shown in *cells,* which are where rows and columns meet. For example, the word Housing is found in the cell B6, or the place where Column B and Row 6 meet. Likewise, the number 50.00 is found in F8, or where Column F and Row 8 meet.

To develop her cash payments record, Bernice Elam made a spreadsheet that contained only the information that she would use repeatedly each month and that wouldn't change. This type of spreadsheet is called a *template* and is shown in Illustration 3–5.

The template contained the row and column headings of Bernice's cash payments record. She left blank those cells in which she would enter new data each month. She entered *formulas* in the Total Payments cells on the right. These formulas tell the computer to find the sums of each of the rows. She also entered formulas in the Totals cells at the bottom of the spreadsheet. These formulas tell the computer to find the sums of each of the columns. Since the rows and columns contained no data, the sums of the rows and columns were zero. That is why the Total Payments column and the Totals row have zeros in them.

```
            A           B        C        D        E        F        G
 1                                   Bernice Elam
 2                                Cash Payments Record
 3  ==========================================================================
 4                                  Type of Payments
 5                                                                  Total
 6        Week      Housing    Food     Auto     Other   Savings  Payments
 7  --------------------------------------------------------------------------
 8                                                                   0.00
 9                                                                   0.00
10                                                                   0.00
11                                                                   0.00
12                                                                   0.00
13      ----------------------------------------------------------------------
14  Totals          0.00     0.00     0.00     0.00     0.00      0.00
15  ==========================================================================
```

Illustration 3–5. Template for a Cash Payments Record

In September Bernice will enter the dates in Column A, Rows 8–12. She will then enter each of the payment amounts in the correct Types of Payments column. When she does this the amounts in the Total Payments column and the Totals row will be calculated *automatically* by the computer.

Getting Started. To use a spreadsheet program you must first *load*, or put, the software into the computer. Each type of computer and each spreadsheet program is somewhat different. Load your Spreadsheet Applications Diskette and refer to your operator's manual for start-up procedures.

Filling in the Template. In September Bernice will load the spreadsheet program and then her applications diskette, which contains the template. After loading, the template will be displayed on her computer screen. Using the arrow keys, she will move the cursor to Cell A8 and enter Sept. 1–7. Then she will press the Return or Enter key to place the data into the cell. She could also do this by moving the cursor with the arrow keys.

If Bernice makes a mistake while entering data, she will use the Backspace key to erase the error and then reenter the data. If she wants to change the contents of a cell already filled with data, she will use the arrow keys to move the cursor to that cell and enter what she wants. When she uses the arrow keys again or presses the Return/Enter key, the new data she has entered will replace the old data in that cell.

Using a Spreadsheet for a Cash Payments Record. Follow the steps to complete and interpret a cash payments record for Curtis Jackson.

1. Insert your Spreadsheet Applications Diskette and call up the file "Sec3." After you have done this, your computer screen should look like Illustration 3–6.

```
Sec3                                    Curtis Jackson
                                      Cash Payments Record
     ===================================================================
                                     Type of Payments
                                                                    Total
          Week      Housing    Food      Auto      Other   Savings Payments
        -----------------------------------------------------------------
                                                                      .00
                                                                      .00
                                                                      .00
                                                                      .00
                                                                      .00
        -----------------------------------------------------------------
     Totals            .00       .00       .00       .00       .00     .00
     ===================================================================
```

Illustration 3–6. Spreadsheet Used for a Cash Payments Record

2. Complete the cash payments record for Curtis Jackson by entering these data into the template:

A8	Sept.	1–7	B8	350.00	C8	45.66	D8	205.00	E8	19.23	F8 75.00
A9		8–14	B9	25.78	C9	102.34	D9	91.88	E9	49.82	
A10		15–21	B10	179.98	C10	89.79	D10	23.23	E10	9.20	
A11		22–28			C11	60.41	D11	82.10	E11	67.44	
A12		29–30			C12	4.98	D12	7.45	E12	69.50	

3. Answer the questions about your completed cash payments record.

   a. What type of payment had the largest total for the month?
      Housing
   b. What type of payment had the smallest total for the month?
      Savings
   c. What was the total amount spent during the first week of the month? $694.89
   d. What was the total amount spent during the last two days of the month? $81.93
   e. What was the total amount spent on "Other" payments? $215.19
   f. On what types of payment were no payments made in some weeks of the month? Housing, savings
   g. Was the total amount spent on food expenses for the month larger or smaller than the total amount spent on auto expenses?
      Smaller
   h. Was the total amount spent on food expenses for the month larger or smaller than the total amount spent on housing? Smaller

Section 4
Check Register Records

Many people deposit their cash receipts in a checking account at a bank and make their payments by check. A checking account is safe and easy to use, and the canceled checks provide you with a record of your payments. You will use addition and subtraction often when you keep a checking account.

Checkbook Deposit Slips. When Laverne and Ramon Mendez deposit into their checking account their paychecks for the first week of July, they fill out a **deposit slip** like the one shown in Illustration 4–1.

The Mendezes list the total bills or paper money after Bills and the total coins after Coins. They list each check using the check's **transit number.** This number is the top part of the group of bank numbers on the check shown in Illustration 4–2. They then add the columns and write the sum on the Total Deposit line.

Transit number

Ramon's full-time weekly pay

Laverne's weekly pay

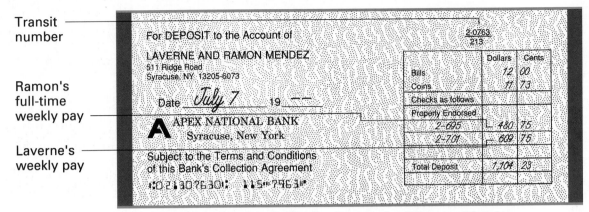

Illustration 4–1. Deposit Slip for Laverne and Ramon Mendez

Exercise 1 Written

■ Check each problem carefully.

For each problem list the total bills, total coins, and each check in a column. Then add to find the total deposit.

1. Edna Schwartz deposited these items in a bank: (bills) 2 twenties, 5 tens, 6 fives, 2 ones; (coins) 12 quarters, 3 dimes; (checks) $218.49, $1.45. $345.24

2. Brad Nolan, treasurer of Eaton's Microcomputer Managers Association, made this deposit: (bills) 12 twenties, 23 tens, 14 fives, 36 ones; (coins) 22 halves, 9 quarters, 32 dimes; (checks) $28.75, $2.07. $623.27

3. The Craft Corner made this deposit: (bills) 72 twenties, 126 tens, 57 fives, 235 ones; (coins) 186 halves, 287 quarters, 312 dimes, 48 nickels, 347 pennies; (checks) $124.68, $132.08, $1.29, $5.79. $3,685.66

Using Check Registers. Both Laverne and Ramon Mendez write orders directing their bank to make payments. These orders are called **checks**. A check completed by Laverne Mendez is shown in Illustration 4–2.

Illustration 4–2. Completed Check

The Mendezes record each deposit and check in their **check register,** shown in Illustration 4–3. The check register is that part of the checkbook in which deposits and checks are recorded. They add each deposit to their last **balance,** which is the amount of money left in their account. They subtract each check from their last balance. In this way they always know how much money they have in their checking account.

Check No.	Date	Check Issued To or Description of Deposit	(−) Check	(+) Deposit	√	Balance
						982 62
1341	7 / 6	TV Time Magazine, Inc.	25 75			956 87
– –	7 / 7	Paycheck		1,104 23		2,061 10

Illustration 4–3. Part of a Check Register

Exercise 2 Written

■ Check your work.

1. The last page of Eve Dent's check register shows the balance in the account on March 1 and the deposits and checks written. Find the correct balance after *each* deposit and *each* check.

Check No.	Date	Check Issued To Or Description of Deposit	(−) Check	(+) Deposit	✔	Balance
						$501 32
478	3/3	Mandy's Clothing Store	34 66			466 66
479	3/9	Evergreen Power Company	98 62			368 04
—	3/21	Paycheck		298 43		666 47
480	3/25	Keller Auto Company	108 45			558 02
—	3/30	Interest on savings		23 78		581 80

2. For each problem find the final balance.

■ Put a zero in front of the decimal point to show that there is no whole dollar amount—$0.78.

	Previous Balance	Deposits	Checks Issued	Final Balance
a.	$278.98	$125	$230.12, $1.50, $20.72	$151.64*
b.	67.54	35.71	$3.67, $43.81, $9.33, $15.10	31.34
c.	807.22	97.12, $50	$145.90, $6.08, $62.44, $35.19	704.73
d.	262.43	43.99, $55	$3.77, $87.29, $38.12, $0.78	231.46

3. The Avalon Canoe Club's checking account balance was $482.63 on Monday. On Tuesday a deposit of $78.55 was made and checks for $35, $40.19, and $56.09 were written. What was the club's new balance? $429.90

_____

*The answer is given for this problem and others in the text. If you do not get the same answer, check the way you did the problem and your calculations.

4. York, Inc.'s checking account balance was $4,070.65. A deposit of $1,006.54 was made and checks for $25.22, $1,980.30, $6.89, and $75 were written. What was the new balance of their account? $2,989.78

EFT =
Electronic Funds Transfer

MICR =
Magnetic Ink Character Recognition

Electronic Funds Transfer. Banks increasingly transfer deposits and checks, or "funds," from person to person and bank to bank electronically, using computers. This process is called **Electronic Funds Transfer,** or **EFT**.

Banks print the account numbers of customers and their banks in **Magnetic Ink Character Recognition,** or **MICR,** form at the bottom of deposit slips and checks. This allows special computer equipment to read the MICR data on the deposit slips and checks and then update bank accounts and transfer funds from account to account electronically.

For example, the MICR numbers written at the bottom of the deposit slip in Illustration 4–1 and the check in Illustration 4–2 are the Mendezes' account number and the number of the Apex National Bank. (See Illustration 4–4.)

The Mendezes' account number written in MICR

The number of the Apex National Bank in MICR

Illustration 4–4. Customer and Bank Numbers Printed in MICR Form

EFT also occurs when you use **automatic teller machines.** Using a special card issued to you by the bank, you can withdraw or deposit money or make transfers from your savings account to your checking account from automatic teller machines at any time of the day. (See Illustration 4–5.)

Your bank may place automatic teller machines on the outside of its building and at shopping malls, grocery stores, airports, and other places convenient to you.

EFT may also be used to pay your monthly bills, such as power and telephone bills. You simply instruct your bank to transfer funds automatically each month from your bank account to the bank accounts of your utility company and telephone company. No checks need be written or mailed. In fact many companies pay their employees by transferring funds directly from their banks to their employees' banks without writing any checks to the employees.

Some people are able to use a special form of EFT called a **debit card.** A debit card allows you to access your bank account through special computer terminals at cooperating stores and businesses. You pay for your purchases without cash by inserting your debit card into the special terminal. The computer system subtracts the amount of each purchase automatically from your bank account and adds the same amount to the store's bank account.

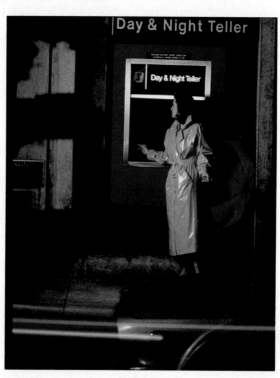

Illustration 4–5.

Automatic Teller Machine.

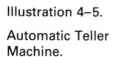

Exercise 3 Written

1. On Tuesday Terry Kowolski used a debit card to pay for the following purchases: groceries, $74.89; clothing, $245.64; and garden plants, $35.77. If Terry's bank balance was $845.19 at the start of the day, what is her new balance? $488.89

2. After work Agnes O'Day used the automatic teller machine to deposit her paycheck for $568.33 and to withdraw $200 in cash for shopping. If her starting bank balance was $307.92, what is her new balance? $676.25

3. On Saturday afternoon Eiko Yoshino deposited a tax refund check for $328.66 in her bank's automatic teller machine at a shopping center. She then used her debit card to make these purchases: sweater, $56.89; wrench set, $78.99; audio tapes, $27.79. If her starting bank balance was $690.06, what is her new balance? $855.05

4. Ed Kosner started the day with a bank balance of $103.45. He used the automatic teller to deposit a check for $125.09 and his debit card to make these purchases: $56.08, $23.12, and $24.99. What will be the balance in his account after these transactions are processed by his bank? $124.35

Subtraction is the reverse of addition.

What Subtraction Means. You have used subtraction to deduct check amounts from check register balances and debit card purchases from bank balances.

Subtraction is the reverse of addition. In subtraction you are given one known number and the total of an addition problem. You find the missing number in the addition problem by subtracting the known number from the total.

```
   62
 − 24
   38 difference
```

For example, in the problem 62 − 24, 62 is the total of the addition problem. The known number is 24. The missing number is the number to which 24 was added to give 62. To find the missing number, you reverse the addition by subtracting 24. The **difference**, 38, is the missing number.

**Exercise 4
Written**

Find the differences.

1. 29 − 7 = 22	7. 256.82	9. $1,370.52	11. $21,803.27
2. 25 − 13 = 12	− 137.93	− 583.64	− 12,652.52
3. 42 − 12 = 30	118.89	$ 786.88	$ 9,150.75
4. 105 − 75 = 30			
5. 220 − 80 = 140	8. 964.64	10. $5,008.37	12. $73,835.89
6. 475 − 125 = 350	− 0.55	− 3,905.88	− 44,769.93
	964.09	$1,102.49	$29,065.96

Checking Subtraction. Every subtraction should be checked as soon as it is finished. The best way to check subtraction is to add the amount subtracted and the difference. The sum should equal the top number.

**Exercise 5
Written**

Find the difference in each problem. Then check each result immediately by adding the amount subtracted and the difference.

1. 45,824	2. 81,006	3. $28,485.34	4. $35,405.56
− 6,285	− 3,752	− 6,410.28	− 7,983.12
39,539	77,254	$22,075.06	$27,422.44
5. $75,804.23	6. $63,090.06	7. $20,220.20	8. $51,318.48
− 24,847.58	− 46,606.87	− 15,738.49	− 33,908.69
$50,956.65	$16,483.19	$ 4,481.71	$17,409.79

Gross and Net. Gross and net are very common business terms. For example, gross profit and net profit, gross weight and net weight, and gross wages and net wages are used often. A **net** amount is the smaller figure that you get when you deduct or subtract something from a larger, gross amount. Looked at another way, a **gross** amount is the total of a net amount plus deductions.

Gross − Deductions = Net

Net + Deductions = Gross

For example, the gross cost of a camera is $375. When you subtract the rebate of $50 you get from the camera's manufacturer, the net cost of the camera is only $325 ($375 − $50 = $325).

**Exercise 6
Written**

Find the net amount in each problem by subtracting the deductions from the gross amount. Check your work by adding the net amount and the deductions.

1. The gross weight of a box and its contents was 14.2 pounds. The weight of the box alone was 1.8 pounds. What was the net weight of the contents?   12.4 pounds

2. Ann Ackerman's gross gas and electric bill for June was $137.98. If she pays early she will get a discount of $2.76. What will be the net amount she has to pay if she pays early? $135.22

3. A little league baseball club sold candy bars at a gross price of $2.00 each. Each bar cost the class 73 cents. What net amount did the club make per candy bar? $1.27

4. A data entry clerk worked at a computer terminal from 8:00 a.m. until 5:00 p.m. The clerk left the terminal for a 15-minute break in the morning, a 15-minute break in the afternoon, and a 1-hour lunch break at noon. What was the
   a. Gross number of hours the clerk worked?   9 hours
   b. Net number of hours the clerk worked? $7\frac{1}{2}$ hours

5. Sol Levine's gross pay for a week was $416.29. A total of $98.67 was deducted from his gross pay. What was Sol's net pay for the week? $317.62

6. A department store had gross sales of $287,806.22 last week. However, customers returned $11,512.24 of their purchases. What were the net sales of the store last week? $276,293.98

Related Problems. You have learned to find the total amount received, the total amount spent, and the amount left, or the balance. There are many personal and business situations in which you will use the same skills.

**Exercise 7
Written**

1. On Monday morning Sergio Pappas had $14.78 in cash. During the week he earned $45.00 for cutting lawns and $35.75 for yard work.
   a. What were Sergio's total earnings for the week? $80.75
   b. What total amount did he have to spend during the week? $95.53
   c. If his balance at the end of the week was $27.67, how much did he spend during the week? $67.86

 Boxes on hand
+ Boxes
   bought
———————
= Total boxes
− Boxes left
———————
= Boxes sold

2. A school band sold boxes of Christmas cards to earn money for a trip. On October 1 they had 300 boxes on hand. During the next three months they bought more boxes as follows: 245, 150, and 250.
   a. How many boxes did they buy during the three-month period? 645
   b. What is the largest number of boxes they could have sold during the period?   945
   c. If they had 12 boxes on hand at the end of the period, how many boxes did they sell?   933

3. On October 1 Oki Kimura had on hand heating oil that cost $178.56. During the winter Oki bought more oil at these costs: $269.34; $276.58; $216.17; and $108.02.

a. How much did Oki spend to buy oil during the winter? $870.11
b. What was the total cost of the oil that Oki could have used for heating during the winter? $1,048.67
c. If Oki had $108.37 worth of oil left at the end of the winter, what was the cost of the heating oil used during the winter? $940.30

4. A baseball team had a total of 120 baseballs on hand at the start of the season. During the season the team purchased 432, 1,152, and 1,008 baseballs.
   a. How many baseballs did the team buy during the season? 2,592
   b. What was the greatest number of baseballs that the team could have used during the season? 2,712
   c. If the team found that they had 137 baseballs on hand at the end of the season, how many baseballs were actually used?
      2,575

REVIEW 4

Terms

1. Match the terms with the statements.

automatic teller machine   Electronic Funds Transfer
balance   gross
check   MICR
check register   net
debit card   subtraction
deposit slip   transit number
difference

a. The reverse of addition   subtraction
b. The missing number in subtraction   difference
c. A record of deposits made and checks written   check register
d. A number used to list checks on deposit slips   transit number
e. Net plus deductions   gross
f. A form used to list money deposited   deposit slip
g. An order to pay money   check
h. Gross less deductions   net
i. The amount of money left in an account   balance
j. Magnetic ink character recognition   MICR
k. Allows you to bank at any time   automatic teller machine
l. Computers process deposits, withdrawals, and transfers
   Electronic Funds Transfer
m. Used to pay for goods without using cash   debit card

Skills

2. Find the differences.

a.	29 − 16	13	d.	23,978.65	e.	$78,308.23
b.	125 − 75	50		− 14,087.96		− 25,611.90
c.	250 − 125	125		9,890.69		$52,696.33

Problems

3. A train station's four turnstiles collected these amounts for one day: $2,078.25, $1,467.40, $2,076.50, $1,208.20. What was the total amount of cash collected? $6,830.35 [1]

4. Alfredo Ramos spent these amounts landscaping his home: patio stones, $767.24; stone bed cover, $689.34; edging, $14.56; shrubs,

$239.78; plastic sheeting, $6.89; and mulch, $34.56. How much did Alfredo spend on the landscaping? $1,752.37 [2]

5. The gross weight of a truck and its contents was 18,295 pounds. The weight of the truck alone was 15,207 pounds. What was the net weight of the contents?   3,088 pounds [4]

6. Lee Malone's check register showed a balance of $380.48. During the day he made a deposit of $108.56 and wrote checks for $4.12, $1.69, $28.27, $100.87, and $0.75. What was Lee's final balance? $353.34 [4]

7. Daniel Clark deposited these items: (bills) 17 twenties, 21 tens, 13 fives, 42 ones; (coins) 65 halves, 43 quarters, 208 dimes, 267 pennies; and (checks) $14.88, $307.61, and $149.01. What was Daniel's total deposit? $1,195.22 [4]

A drill for accuracy and speed in subtraction is given on page 555.

Calculator Clinic

Using the Calculator for Subtraction. Subtracting with the calculator is the same as adding except you must press the – key instead of the + key. For example, to subtract $16.23 from $45.78 on the calculator, follow these steps:

a. Clear your calculator by pressing the CE/C key.

b. Press these keys in order: 4 5 · 7 8

c. Press the key marked: –

d. Press these keys in order: 1 6 · 2 3

e. Press = , and the result, 29.55, will appear in the display.

As in addition, the dollar sign and a final zero, if there is one, may not appear in the display.

   If you want to subtract two or more numbers, as you might if you were doing calculations in your check register, continue steps a through e above. For example, if you had a check register balance of $45.78 and you wished to subtract checks for $16.23 and $8.15 from that balance, you would complete the steps a through e above, then continue with the following:

f. Press the key marked: $-$

g. Press these keys in order: 8 · 1 5

h. Press = , and the result, 21.40, will appear in the display.

To check your work add the final difference, 21.40, to the amounts of both checks. Your total should be the original balance of the register.

$45.78	Old balance		Check:	
− 16.23	First check		$21.40	Final difference
$29.55	First difference		16.23	First check
− 8.15	Second check		+ 8.15	Second check
$21.40	New balance		$45.78	Old balance

Combining Addition and Subtraction. When you keep a check register you must add deposits as well as subtract checks. There are many other personal and business situations in which you will need to know how to add and subtract amounts from an original number.

Here is how to add a deposit of $6.89 and subtract a check for $2.67 from an original balance of $60.58 by using your calculator:

a. Clear your calculator by pressing the CE/C key.

b. Press these keys in order: 6 0 · 5 8

c. Press the key marked: $+$

d. Press these keys in order: 6 · 8 9

e. Press = and enter the result, 67.47, in the Balance column of your check register.

f. Press the key marked: $-$

g. Press these keys in order: 2 · 6 7

h. Press = and enter the answer, 64.80, in the Balance column of your check register.

If you want to subtract more than one check press the minus (−) key before you enter the amount of each check. Press the equals (=) key after you have entered the amount of each check. If you want to add more than one deposit press the plus (+) key before you enter the amount of each deposit and the equals (=) key after each amount is entered.

Calculator Practice. Apply what you have learned in this calculator clinic first to the problems in Exercises 3 and 4 in this section, second to the problems in Exercise 2, and third to any other exercises your teacher may assign.

Proving the Check Register Balance

If you have a checking account your bank will send you a report of your account, usually once each month. The report shows deposits you have made and checks that the bank has paid for you from your account. It also lists any charges made by the bank, any interest earned on your account, and the balance of your account. You use this report to check the accuracy of your checkbook records and the bank's records.

The Bank Statement. The monthly report the bank sends to each depositor is called the **bank statement.** The bank statement that Karl Olson received from the Drury National Bank for the month of September is shown in Illustration 5–1.

DN B DRURY NATIONAL BANK 4309 South Broad Street Philadelphia, PA 19148-3978			Karl Olson 3123 Baltimore Avenue Philadelphia, PA 19104-3481	
Checks	Check Numbers	Deposits	Date	Balance
			Sep 1	608.12
34.67	1072		2	573.45
125.54	1074		9	447.91
8.32	1073		10	439.59
		481.56	12	921.15
311.01	1076		17	610.14
7.90	1075		20	602.24
(1) 61.90	1078	(2)	22	540.34 (3)
		298.44	25	838.78
26.19	1077		27	812.59
450.00	1079	104.55	28	467.14
78.32	1082		30	388.82
(4) 4.50 SC		2.11 IN (5)	30	386.43

CC certified check	EC error corrected	OD overdraft
CM credit memo	IN interest credited	RT returned item
DM debit memo	NC check not counted	SC service charge

Illustration 5–1. Bank Statement for Karl Olson

The bank statement lists (1) nine checks paid by the bank, (2) three deposits received by the bank, (3) a running balance, (4) a service charge of $4.50, and (5) $2.11 in interest earned. A **service charge** is a deduction charged by the bank for handling the checking account. Many banks now pay interest on checking accounts. Interest is money paid for the use of money. You will learn more about interest in Units 7 and 8.

Outstanding Checks. With his bank statement Karl Olson received several canceled checks. A **canceled check** is a check that the bank has paid and then marked so it can't be used again. (See Illustration 5–2.)

Illustration 5–2. Canceled Check

When Karl Olson compared his bank statement with his check register he found that some checks (#1080 and #1081) that he had written had not been returned by the bank. These checks had not yet been received by the bank for payment and so could not be canceled. That is why they were not listed on the bank statement. These checks are called **outstanding checks** because they are still out. They have not yet been paid by the bank.

The Reconciliation Statement. The final balance of Karl Olson's bank statement was $386.43. The balance of his check register for September was $246.89. The difference between these records was caused by the service charge, the outstanding checks, and the interest earned.

Bringing the checkbook balance and the bank balance into agreement with each other is called reconciling the bank balance. The form that shows the calculations is called the **reconciliation statement.**

To bring the two balances into agreement and to make sure that his records and the bank's records were correct, Karl Olson prepared the reconciliation statement shown in Illustration 5–3.

When he looked at his bank statement Karl Olson found the $4.50 service charge that had been subtracted on the bank statement but not in his check register. He then subtracted $4.50 from the checkbook balance on the left side of the reconciliation statement. He also added the interest that his account had earned to the left side of the statement to show the correct checkbook balance, $244.50.

Next he matched the checks listed on the statement with his check register and found that Check #1080 for $48.65 and #1081 for $93.28 were outstanding. He subtracted the sum, $141.93, from the bank balance on the right side of the statement to show the available bank balance, $244.50.

Since the available bank balance, $244.50, was the same as the correct checkbook balance, $244.50, Karl Olson was satisfied that his records and the bank's records were correct. If the balances had not agreed he would have had to find out why.

Checkbook balance or check register balance is what you think you have in your checking account.

Karl Olson
Reconciliation Statement
September 30, 19——

Checkbook balance	$246.89	Bank statement balance		$386.43
Deduct:		Deduct:		
Service charge	4.50	Outstanding checks:		
	$242.39	#1080	$48.65	
Add:		#1081	93.28	141.93
Interest earned	2.11			
Correct checkbook balance	$244.50	Available bank balance		$244.50

Illustration 5–3. Reconciliation Statement for Karl Olson

■ Checkbook balance and check register balance are different words for the checking account balance in a depositor's records.

Of course when Karl Olson finishes his reconciliation statement he must record the service charge and the interest earned in his check register to bring it up to date. His updated check register is shown in Illustration 5–4.

Check No.	Date	Check Issued To or Description of Deposit	(−) Check	(+) Deposit	√	Balance
						246 89
– –	9 / 30	Service charge	4 50			242 39
– –	9 / 30	Interest earned		2 11		244 50

Illustration 5–4. Updated Check Register for Karl Olson

**Exercise 1
Written**

Prepare a reconciliation statement for Problems 1–6. Use your own name in the headings for Problems 3 through 6.

1. Anne Oster's checkbook balance on May 31 was $873.09. Her May 31 bank statement showed a balance of $1,378.49. Checks outstanding were #806 for $326.11, #808 for $97.56, and #809 for $82.03. The bank service charge for May was $5.75 and the interest earned was $5.45. $872.79

2. Ed Acker's bank statement balance on June 30 was $400.78. On that same date his checkbook balance was $277.91. The bank statement showed a service charge of $3.75 and interest earned of $1.65. The outstanding checks were #51 for $73.09, #52 for $46.28, and #54 for $5.60. $275.81

■ Check your
work.

Date	Check-book Balance	Bank State-ment Balance	Service Charge	Inter-est	Outstanding Checks
3. Apr. 30	$803.12	$978.44	$5.70	$4.13	#88, $167.41; #90, $9.48 Balance, $801.55
4. Feb. 28	231.19	270.56	3.10	1.15	#21, $5.79; #23, $15.46; #25, $20.07 $229.24
5. Dec. 31	598.01	678.12	4.12	2.81	#23, $21.57; #25, $40.87; #26, $18.98 $596.70
6. Oct. 31	133.79	244.60	2.60	0.86	#63, $9.56; #64, $3.78; #65, $63.14; #66, $36.07 $132.05

Analyzing Problems For the Information You Need. In the problems you have solved so far you have been given only the information needed to solve the problems, and nothing more. In real life, however, you may be given more information than you need, so you must learn to identify the information that you need and ignore the rest. For example, look at this problem:

Vera Tokheim opened a checking account on July 1. On October 31 her bank statement balance was $1,207.88 and her check register balance was $978.34. Her statement showed twelve checks, two deposits, a service charge of $6.20, and interest earned of $5.78. A comparison of her check register and bank statement showed these outstanding checks: #2078 for $90.21, #2084 for $110.23, and #2085 for $29.52. $977.92

Can you find the information that does *not* help you solve the problem? If you chose these items, you are correct:

1. Opening an account with her bank on July 1

2. Her statement showed twelve checks and two deposits

To solve the problem you only needed information for the

1. Heading of the reconciliation statement: the person's name and the date

2. Check register side of the statement: the check register balance, service charge, and interest earned

3. Bank statement side of the statement: the bank balance and checks outstanding

**Exercise 2
Written**

The following problems contain more information than is needed for their solution. Prepare reconciliation statements for each problem.

1. Elena Morales has had an account with Arcola National Bank for five years. When she got her bank statement on October 31 it showed

a balance of $907.46 and a $2.75 service charge. Along with the statement was an advertisement for savings certificates at 7.5%. Outstanding checks were: #451, $101.33; #452, $89.56; #455, $12.72; #456, $3.16. Her checkbook register showed a balance of $703.44 on October 31. Prepare a reconciliation statement. $700.69

2. On June 30 Al Olm's check register balance was $603.49 and his bank statement balance was $870.15. The bank statement showed a service charge of $4.75. With the bank statement were 2 canceled checks: #453, $35.78 to A-1 Pet Shop and #454, $25 to the Town Fund. Outstanding checks were: #451, $101.33 to Benton Power Co.; #452, $89.56 to Al's TV Repair; #455, $12.72 to Arno Locksmith Co.; #456, $67.80 to Route 54 Garage. Prepare a reconciliation statement. $598.74

REVIEW 5

Terms

1. Match the terms with the statements.

bank statement   outstanding check   service charge
canceled check   reconciliation statement

a. Deduction for handling account   service charge
b. Unpaid check   outstanding check
c. Form used to make balances agree   reconciliation statement
d. Report to depositor   bank statement
e. Paid and marked check   canceled check

Skills

2. Copy each problem and find the totals. Check your work by adding the column totals horizontally and the line totals vertically.

a.	b.	c.
4 + 5 + 8 = 17	34 + 12 + 89 = 135	45 + 11 + 54 + 23 = 133
7 + 3 + 2 = 12	59 + 51 + 37 = 147	63 + 17 + 78 + 22 = 180
9 + 2 + 1 = 12	28 + 17 + 32 = 77	64 + 97 + 36 + 13 = 210
20 + 10 + 11 = 41	121 + 80 + 158 = 359	172 + 125 + 168 + 58 = 523

Problems

3. Hal Young, treasurer of Alton's Senior Club, deposited the following receipts from a bake sale. What was the total deposit?

Bills: 8 twenties; 3 tens; 11 fives; 36 ones
Coins: 7 halves; 45 quarters; 12 dimes; 23 nickels; 13 pennies
Checks: $2.75; $15.75; $25.00; $10.00 $351.73 [4]

■ Remember to check your work.

4. Sean Orr's gross power bill for July was $189.76. By paying early he earned a discount of $3.79. What was the net amount of his bill? $185.97 [4]

5. Dina Maglio started the day with $106.76. During the day she cashed a check for $175 at her bank and spent $92.78 in a store. How much money did she have left at the end of the day? $188.98 [5]

6. On April 30, Eve Kato's check register balance was $248.65 and her bank statement balance was $366.13. The bank statement showed a service charge of $2.75. These checks were outstanding: #302, $12.35; #304, $107.88. Prepare a reconciliation statement. $245.90 [4]

‡Section 6
Special Reconciliation Problems

You have learned to reconcile bank statement and checkbook balances when service charges, interest earned, and outstanding checks occur. Now you will learn how to reconcile bank statement and checkbook balances when deposits and checks are not recorded and other errors are made.

On April 30 Ella LaGarce's bank statement balance was $105.35 and her check register balance was $58.20. When Ella compared the bank statement and canceled checks with her check register, she found that

1. A service charge of $1.75 had been subtracted from the bank statement balance but not from the check register balance

2. Check #98 for $9.50, which she wrote and cashed on April 5, had not been recorded and subtracted in the check register

3. Check #103 for $15 was recorded twice in the check register

4. A deposit of $76 made on April 21 had not been recorded in the check register

5. Interest of $2.48 was earned on the account

6. Check #106 for $7.50 had been recorded in the register as $5.70

7. Check #107 for $42 and #108 for $26 were outstanding

8. A deposit of $101.28 made on April 30 was recorded in the check register but deposited too late to appear on that month's bank statement

Knowing these facts Ella prepared the reconciliation statement shown in Illustration 6–1.

The service charge for $1.75 and check #98 for $9.50 had not been recorded in the register. This left the check register balance higher than it should have been. Ella deducted these amounts from the register balance.

The unrecorded deposit of $76 and interest earned of $2.48 made the register balance lower than it should have been. Ella added these amounts to the register balance.

Since Ella had subtracted check #103 for $15 twice, she needed to add this amount back once. She added this amount to the register balance.

To correct the error in recording check #106 Ella deducted the correct check amount, $7.50. She then added the incorrect amount, $5.70. This had the effect of wiping out the incorrect check amount.

Some people correct errors by finding the difference between the two checks. For example, Ella could subtract $5.70 from $7.50. The difference, $1.80, is the extra amount that would have been subtracted if she had recorded the check correctly. Ella could then subtract $1.80 in the Deduct section of the statement on the checkbook side.

38

Illustration 6–1. Reconciliation Statement for Ella LaGarce

If the $7.50 check had been recorded for $9.30 instead of $5.70 the difference would still have been $1.80. But this extra amount would not have been subtracted. Ella would then have added $1.80 to the Add section of the statement on the check register side.

The outstanding checks left the bank statement balance $68 more than it should have been. The late deposit made the balance $101.28 less. Ella deducted $68 and added $101.28 to the bank statement balance to get the available bank balance of $138.63.

Find the available bank balances in Problems 1–4. Use a form like the right half of the reconciliation statement shown in Illustration 6–1.

‡**Exercise 1**
Written

Date	Bank Statement Balance	Outstanding Checks	Late Deposit Not Recorded on Bank Statement	
1. Dec. 31	$381.36	$45.71; $9.45; $24.90	$ 85	$386.30
2. Mar. 31	906.88	$89.16; $65.12; $1.78	305	$1,055.82
3. Nov. 30	580.04	$20.01; $9.41; $51.78; $3.35	176	$671.49

‡**Exercise 2**
Written

Find the correct check register balances in Problems 1–7. Use a form like the left half of Illustration 6–1.

| Check Register Balance | Not Recorded in Check Register | | | Other Adjustments |
	Service Charge	Check for	Other	
1. $829.76	$5.67	$55.78	Deposit of $135	Check #23 for $28.98 entered in register as $28.89 $903.22
2. 280.66	2.25	5.78	Interest of $1.14	Check #903 for $7.56 entered in register as $6.75 $272.96
3. 429.86	4.10	None	Deposit of $110	Check #75 for $19.99 entered in register as $19.19 $534.96
4. 750.03	5.01	63.36	Interest of $2.78	Deposit of $86 entered twice in register $598.44

5. On March 31 your check register balance is $107.87. Your bank statement shows a service charge of $0.76 and interest earned of $0.85 which were not recorded in the register. You also find that check #307 for $35.29 had been entered in the register as $32.95. $105.62

6. At the end of May Tomas Orroyo's check register balance was $812.45. An examination of his bank statement showed that a deposit of $135.90 had not been entered in the register and that check #201 for $92.49 had been entered in the register as $29.49. $885.35

7. Helga Svaboda's check register balance on July 31 was $506.71. By comparing her bank statement and register, she found that check #342 for $124.58 had been entered in the register twice, a deposit of $86.08 had not been recorded, and check #316, dated July 3, had been recorded as of July 2. She also found that check #322 for $108.58 had been recorded in the register as $158.08. $766.87

‡Exercise 3 Written

■ Be sure to check every calculation.

Prepare reconciliation statements for Problems 1–9. Use Illustration 6–1 as a guide. Use February 28 and your own name in the headings for Problems 5–9.

1. On May 31 Haru Gihei's checkbook balance was $200.89 and her bank statement balance was $278.99. Checks outstanding were: #407, $92.48; #410, $28.12; #154, $17.42. A deposit for $58.50, mailed on May 30, was received by the bank too late to be shown on the statement. The statement showed a service charge of $2.67 and interest earned of $1.25. $199.47

2. On March 31 Melissa Sisson's check register balance was $92.45 and her bank statement balance was $167.23. The statement showed a service charge of $1.45. Check #85 for $3.89 and #90 for $83.09 were outstanding. Melissa also found that she had recorded a deposit of $10.75 twice in the check register. $80.25

3. On September 30 Bud Benson's check register showed a balance of $700.61. His bank statement balance on that date was $856.90. With the statement, there was a slip showing that Bud's account had been charged $75 for his payroll savings plan. Checks outstanding were: #834 for $48.33, #837 for $21.19, #838 for $161.77. $625.61

4. Timothy Knowlton's check register balance on June 30 was $375.61. His June bank statement showed a balance of $498.34 on the same date. When Timothy examined the statement he found a service charge of $2.75, interest earned of $3.69, and that check #467 for $1.98 had been recorded in the check register as $1.89. Checks outstanding were: #477 for $64 and #478 for $57.88. $376.46

Bank State-ment Balance	Check-book Balance	Service Charge	Interest Earned	Outstanding Checks	Other Adjustments
5. $357.48	$231.78	$2.45	$1.75	$16.84; $5.78; $9.60; $34.18	$60 deposit not recorded in check register $291.08
6. 687.67	539.78	4.67	3.78	$89.34; $12.07; $1.45; $53.92	Deposit of $8 recorded twice in register $530.89
7. 540.06	428.73	2.20	3.15	$36.12; $20.50; $123; $5.76	$75 late deposit not on bank statement $429.68
8. 294.56	174.32	2.25	1.14	$10.06; $3.19; $8.10	Deposit of $100 not recorded in register $273.21
9. 989.56	807.58	6.25	5.12	$9.95; $80.13; $101.76	Check for $8.73 not recorded in register $797.72

REVIEW 6

Skills

Find the difference in Problems 1–4. Check your work by adding the amount subtracted and the difference.

1. 34,890
   − 5,384
   29,506

2. 345.28
   − 296.73
   48.55

3. 12,345.89
   − 8,627.92
   3,717.97

4. $45,792.84
   − 31,835.95
   $13,956.89

5. 16 + 21 + 32 + 8 = 77
   28 + 92 + 45 + 3 = 168
   41 + 88 + 71 + 6 = 206
   87 + 93 + 22 + 65 = 267
   172 + 294 + 170 + 82 = 718

6. 23 + 49 + 26 + 13 = 111
   15 + 83 + 72 + 66 = 236
   55 + 34 + 49 + 21 = 159
   10 + 19 + 44 + 33 = 106
   103 + 185 + 191 + 133 = 612

Problems

7. Connie Bergman's check register balance on July 31 was $598.27. Her bank statement showed a balance of $674.21 on July 31. On the statement was a service charge of $4.73 and interest earned of $3.76. Outstanding checks were: #713 for $20.88, #718 for $32.10, and #714 for $23.93. Prepare a reconciliation statement. $597.30 [5]

■ Check your
work.

8. On a business trip Yi Wang spent these amounts: hotels, $240.67; food, $148.89; gasoline, $57.12; tolls, $9.15; entertainment, $86.45; gifts, $125.89. What total amount did she spend? $668.17 [2]

9. Jack Smith's checking account had a balance of $507.87 on Monday. On the same day he deposited $165.23 and wrote checks for $15.67, $75.98, $267.11, and $75.75. What was his final balance? $238.59 [4]

‡10. Vera Gannt's bank statement balance was $451.61 on April 30. Her check register balance was $542.67 on the same date. Checks outstanding were: #876 for $7.43, #879 for $30.56, #881 for $75.93. A deposit of $203.88, mailed on April 30, was not received by the bank in time to be added to the statement. There was a service charge of $4.75 and interest earned of $3.65. Prepare a reconciliation statement. $541.57 [6]

Gross and Average Pay

The amount of pay a person receives for working usually depends on the type of job held, the company worked for, and the amount of time worked. Most people are paid an hourly rate or a salary. To make sure a paycheck is correct, a worker needs to know how to figure gross pay.

An employee also needs to compute average pay for a certain period of time, such as a month or year. Often this information is needed in order to apply for a car or home loan or a credit card.

Finding gross pay requires the use of multiplication. Division must also be used to find average pay.

After you finish Unit 2, you will be able to:

- Place a decimal point in products and quotients.
- Round numbers.
- Estimate products and quotients and check work in multiplication and division.
- Use short cuts in multiplication and division.
- Identify and find unknown factors and products.
- Solve open sentences using multiplication and division.
- Find gross pay for hourly rate, salaried, and piece-rate employees.
- Find simple and weighted averages.
- Solve problems that contain more information than you need.
- Estimate answers to problems.
- Read, write, say, and recognize the meanings of the key terms.
- Use a calculator to multiply and divide.
- Use a computer spreadsheet to figure gross pay.

Most people earn money by working for others. Those who work for others are called **employees**. The person or company an employee works for is called an **employer**.

■ **Total pay is gross pay.**

An employee may be paid by the hour, day, week, month, or year. The total amount of money that an employee is paid is called **gross pay** or *gross wages*.

An employee who is paid by the hour is paid an **hourly rate,** which is a certain amount for each hour worked. An hourly rate employee is usually paid each week. The employee's total pay for the week is called gross pay.

Some employees are paid a **salary**, which is a fixed amount of money for a day, week, month, or year of work. Others, such as salespeople, may earn all or part of their gross pay from a commission on the amount they sell.

Finding Gross Pay for Hourly Rate Employees. The gross pay earned by an employee who is paid by the hour is found by multiplying the pay per hour by the hours worked.

Example

Sandra Almont works as a mechanic and is paid $12 an hour. How much gross pay did she earn last week by working 34 hours?

	Solution	**Explanation**
$ 12	hourly rate of pay	The amount of money that Sandra is paid an hour is multiplied by the total hours worked to find gross pay or gross wages.
× 34	hours worked	
48		
36		
$408	gross pay **Ans.**	

**Exercise 1
Written**

1. Paul Hunt earns $5 an hour at his part-time job. Last week he worked 16 hours. What was his gross pay for the week? $80

2. Kevin O'Leary worked the following schedule this week: Monday, 7 hours; Tuesday, 8 hours; Wednesday, 8 hours; Thursday, 6 hours; Friday, 5 hours. He was paid $9 an hour.
   a. How many hours did Kevin work during the week? 34 hours
   b. What was his gross pay for the week? $306

3. Rachel Solero is paid $7 an hour. Last week she worked 8 hours a day for 5 days.
   a. How many hours did Rachel work last week? 40 hours
   b. What was her gross pay for the week? $280

44

4. Toni Holtz works 40 hours a week and is paid $7 an hour. What is her gross pay for 2 weeks of work? $560

5. Evorn Reed has a full-time job that pays $11 an hour. She is paid $6 an hour at her part-time job. During the past week Evorn worked 40 hours at her full-time job and 15 hours at her part-time job. What total gross pay did she earn last week from both jobs? $530

6. The Breslon company has five employees. The chart below shows the hourly pay of each employee and the hours each employee worked last week. Find last week's gross pay for each employee. Then find the total gross pay earned by all the employees last week.

	Employees	Hourly Pay	Hours Worked	Gross Pay
a.	Ed Alvarez	$8	40	$ 320
b.	Mark Dalton	8	32	256
c.	Vicky Mazur	7	37	259
d.	Tina McDowell	9	40	360
e.	Tom Dane	7	35	245
	Total			$1,440

Finding Gross Pay for Salaried Employees. Salaried employees are paid a fixed amount of money for each time period worked, such as a day, week, or month. To find their gross pay, multiply the pay for a time period by the number of time periods worked.

Example

Tom Chin is paid a salary of $435 a week. How much gross pay will Tom get for 4 weeks of work?

Solution

$ 435   pay for one week
×   4   weeks worked
$1,740   gross pay **Ans.**

Explanation

The weekly salary is multiplied by the number of weeks worked. The result is gross pay for the 4 weeks of work.

Exercise 2 Written

1. Art Hall is a part-time computer operator. When he works he is paid a salary of $76 a day by his employer. What is Art's gross pay for 5 days of work? $380

2. Roy Lampley is a temporary employee. He earns $52 for each full day he works. What is Roy's gross pay if he works 7 full days during a 2-week period? $364

■ 1 year = 12 months

3. The Video-Tek Company pays its security guards a salary of $1,400 a month. What is each guard's gross pay per year? $16,800

4. Mildred Tompkins earns a salary of $389 a week. If Mildred is paid every 2 weeks, what gross pay does she receive each payday? $778

**1 year =
52 weeks**

5. William Stolitz is paid a weekly salary of $375.00.
    a. How much would William earn in 4 weeks of work? $1,500
    b. How much would he earn by working for a year? $19,500

6. Find the yearly salary for each employee.

Employee	Weekly Salary	Yearly Salary
a. Gene Clark	$300	$15,600
b. Bertha Rowland	420	21,840
c. Lloyd Weisberg	495	25,740

Finding Gross Pay for Piece-Rate Employees. Some employees are paid for each item or **piece** they produce. Their wages are paid on a **piece-rate** basis. To figure their gross pay, you must multiply their pay per piece by the number of pieces produced. If employees are paid only for usable pieces produced, they get no pay for the pieces that are rejected.

Example

Susan Gerby works at Pactor Electronics and is paid $1.70 for each timer she produces. Last week Susan produced the following quantities of timers: Monday, 48; Tuesday, 44; Wednesday, 47; Thursday, 50; Friday, 46. What was Susan's gross pay for the week?

Solution

48 + 44 + 47 + 50 + 46 = 235 timers produced
235 × $1.70 = $399.50 gross pay **Ans.**

**Exercise 3
Written**

1. Lu Ying works at the Randor Bike Shop and is paid $2.75 for each bike he assembles. During the five working days of one week he assembled these numbers of bikes: 27, 33, 29, 27, 31. What was Lu's gross pay that week? $404.25

2. For each of these piece-rate employees at Lockler Products, find the total pieces produced and the gross pay for the week.

| | | Number of Pieces | | | | | Total | Rate per | Gross |
Name		M	T	W	Th	F	Pieces	Piece	Pay
a. Block, B.		54	55	59	62	60	290	$1.60	$464
b. Campagna, T.		24	28	30	31	27	140	2.80	392
c. Schweib, V.		63	69	59	62	50	303	1.55	469.65
d. Zullo, Y.		68	65	72	74	75	354	1.18	417.72

3. Employees at the Graf Company are paid on this piece-rate schedule:

First 75 or fewer pieces, $0.95
Next 25 pieces, $1.05
All pieces over 100, $1.20

One day last week 9 Graf Company employees produced the number of pieces shown below. What was each employee's gross pay for the day?

a. Hart   65 $ 61.75   f. Wong   102 $ 99.90
b. Hassed 72 $ 68.40   g. Dubois   68 $ 64.60
c. Cook   80 $ 76.50   h. Flynn   89 $ 85.95
d. Nowak 84 $ 80.70   i. McCrow 112 $111.90
e. Jenke 108 $107.10

4. Melanie Crane is paid $1.60 for each of the first 50 usable clamps she produces in a day, and $1.76 for each usable clamp over 50. What is Melanie's gross pay for a day in which she produces 65 clamps, 11 of which are unusable? $87.04

REVIEW 7

Terms

1. Match the terms with the statements.

employee   gross pay   piece   salary
employer   hourly rate   piece-rate

a. An item produced or made by a worker   piece
b. A person who works for someone else   employee
c. A rate of pay earned by the hour   hourly rate
d. A person or company that employs workers   employer
e. A fixed amount of pay for working a week or a month   salary
f. A wage rate based on amounts produced   piece-rate
g. The total of all pay earned   gross pay

Skills

2. Find the value of N in each number sentence.
    a. $27 + N = 19 + 16$ 8   b. $N - 30 = 17 + 14$ 61

Problems

3. Arlon Hamsa worked these hours last week: Monday, 8 hours; Tuesday, 4 hours; Wednesday, 7 hours; Thursday, 6 hours; Friday, 8 hours. If he was paid $9 an hour, what was Arlon's gross pay last week? $297 [7]

4. Find the gross pay for the time worked by each employee. [7]

	Employee	Pay Rate	Time Worked	Gross Pay
a.	Nick Marsa	$1,510 per month	12 months	$18,120
b.	Carter Woo	$380 per week	52 weeks	$19,760
c.	Karla Wright	$12 per hour	37 hours	$444

5. Cary Hunt is paid $2.08 for every usable machine part she makes. During one week she made 220 parts, 14 of which were unusable. What was Cary's gross pay for the week? $428.48 [7]

6. Fred Lowery started the day with $35.67. He returned a pair of shoes for a cash refund of $41.60. Later in the day he paid cash for items costing $5.20, $14.56, $7.98, and $3.56. How much cash did he have left at the end of the day? $45.97 [4]

Calculator Clinic

Using the Calculator for Multiplication. The calculator will help you figure gross pay for different types of wage payment plans. Here is how you find the gross pay for an hourly rate employee who works 38 hours and is paid $9.25 an hour.

a. Clear your calculator by pressing the $\boxed{\text{CE/C}}$ key.

b. Press these keys in order: $\boxed{3}$ $\boxed{8}$

c. Press the key marked: $\boxed{\times}$

d. Press these keys in order: $\boxed{9}$ $\boxed{\cdot}$ $\boxed{2}$ $\boxed{5}$

e. Press $\boxed{=}$, and the result, 351.5, will appear in the display. Add a dollar sign and an end zero to record the gross pay as $351.50.

Notice that the decimal point was automatically put in the right place. This feature is called the floating decimal point. "Floating" indicates that the decimal point will always appear in the correct place in the answer.

The actual answers to some problems may continue for more digits than the 8-digit capacity of the display. If your calculator can only display eight digits, it will round every answer to the nearest whole eight digits that it can display.

The calculator will also help you figure the yearly wage when the weekly or monthly wage is known. When you want to find a yearly wage, you multiply the wage you know by 12 or 52, depending on whether the known wage is for a month or a week.

To find the gross pay for piece-rate employees, you may have to use the addition and subtraction features of your calculator, as well as multiplication. For example, you will have to add an employee's daily production to find the number of units produced for a week. You will have to use subtraction to deduct the number of pieces produced that are not usable. Then you will find gross pay by multiplying the piece rate by the number of pieces produced.

Calculator Practice. Apply what you have learned in this calculator clinic to the problems in Exercises 1, 2, and 3 in this section.

Computer Clinic

The Wilson Company pays its employees weekly. Follow these steps to complete a weekly payroll record for Department 16 employees.

1. Insert your Spreadsheet Applications Diskette and call up the file "Sec7." After you do, your computer screen should look like Illustration 7–1.

```
Sec7                             Wilson Company
                        Weekly Payroll Record--Department 16
        ------------------------------------------------------------------
                                  Hours Worked           Total Hrs
        Employee    Pay Rate  M    T    W    T    F      Worked  Gross Pay
        ------------------------------------------------------------------
                          0    0    0    0    0    0        0       .00
                          0    0    0    0    0    0        0       .00
                          0    0    0    0    0    0        0       .00
                          0    0    0    0    0    0        0       .00
                          0    0    0    0    0    0        0       .00
                          0    0    0    0    0    0        0       .00
        ------------------------------------------------------------------
        Totals            0    0    0    0    0    0        0       .00
        ------------------------------------------------------------------
```

Illustration 7–1. Weekly Payroll Record

2. Complete the payroll record for the department by entering these data into the template:

A7 BARDO N	B7 6.75	C7 8	D7 8	E7 8	F7 8	G7 8
A8 GRUEN C	B8 7.84	C8 8	D8 8	E8 8	F8 8	G8 4
A9 ILSIN T	B9 7.08	C9 0	D9 7	E9 7	F9 7	G9 4
A10 TRENT M	B10 8.76	C10 8	D10 8	E10 4	F10 7	G10 8
A11 WONG L	B11 9.46	C11 8	D11 8	E11 7	F11 8	G11 7
A12 WOODS K	B12 8.32	C12 7	D12 6	E12 8	F12 0	G12 5

3. Answer these questions about your completed payroll record.
   a. Which employee earned the highest gross pay for the week? Wong
   b. Which employee earned the lowest gross pay for the week? Ilsin
   c. What was the total gross pay earned by the department's workers? $1,611.64
   d. On what day were the total hours worked by the department the greatest? Tuesday

e. The least total hours worked by the department occurred on
    what day? Friday
f. Which employee worked the greatest total number of hours
    during the week? Bardo

Section 8
Multiplication

You have already used multiplication to solve gross pay problems.
Doing multiplication quickly and accurately is an important business skill.

Multiplication is a short way of adding two or more equal numbers. So 3 × 5 is the same as 5 + 5 + 5. You do not have to add the
numbers because you have learned the multiplication table and know
that 3 × 5 = 15.

When you multiply, you use two numbers. Each of the two num-
bers you multiply is called a **factor**. The result is the **product**. Look at
this example.

**Multiplying
is a short way
of adding.**

Example

What is the product of 15 times 26?

	Solution				**Check**	
Factor	26	(Factor)			15	(Factor)
× Factor	× 15	(Factor)			× 26	(Factor)
Product	130				90	
	26				30	
	390	(Product) **Ans.**			390	(Product) **Ans.**

Checking Multiplication. The best way to check multiplication is to
reverse the numbers and multiply again. Look at the example above

to see how the work was checked. Notice that the answers (products) are the same even though the numbers (factors) that are multiplied are reversed.

Exercise 1
Oral

Find the product for each problem. Then mentally reverse the factors and multiply again.

	1.		2.		3.		4.		5.	
a.	2×0	0	3×0	0	4×0	0	5×0	0	6×0	0
b.	2×1	2	3×1	3	4×1	4	5×1	5	6×1	6
c.	2×2	4	3×2	6	4×2	8	5×2	10	6×2	12
d.	2×3	6	3×3	9	4×3	12	5×3	15	6×3	18
e.	2×4	8	3×4	12	4×4	16	5×4	20	6×4	24
f.	2×5	10	3×5	15	4×5	20	5×5	25	6×5	30
g.	2×6	12	3×6	18	4×6	24	5×6	30	6×6	36
h.	2×7	14	3×7	21	4×7	28	5×7	35	6×7	42
i.	2×8	16	3×8	24	4×8	32	5×8	40	6×8	48
j.	2×9	18	3×9	27	4×9	36	5×9	45	6×9	54

	6.		7.		8.		9.		10.	
a.	7×0	0	8×0	0	9×0	0	11×0	0	12×0	0
b.	7×1	7	8×1	8	9×1	9	11×1	11	12×1	12
c.	7×2	14	8×2	16	9×2	18	11×2	22	12×2	24
d.	7×3	21	8×3	24	9×3	27	11×3	33	12×3	36
e.	7×4	28	8×4	32	9×4	36	11×4	44	12×4	48
f.	7×5	35	8×5	40	9×5	45	11×5	55	12×5	60
g.	7×6	42	8×6	48	9×6	54	11×6	66	12×6	72
h.	7×7	49	8×7	56	9×7	63	11×7	77	12×7	84
i.	7×8	56	8×8	64	9×8	72	11×8	88	12×8	96
j.	7×9	63	8×9	72	9×9	81	11×9	99	12×9	108

Exercise 2
Oral

What is the value of N in each of the number sentences below?

1. $5 \times N = 6 \times 5$ 6   5. $N = 1 \times 72$ 72   9. $N = 7 \times 6$ 42
2. $16 \times 4 = 4 \times N$ 16   6. $1 \times 1 = N$ 1   10. $24 \times N = 0$ 0
3. $7 \times 3 = N \times 7$ 3   7. $N = 0 \times 48$ 0   11. $1 \times N = 7$ 7
4. $9 \times 6 = N \times 6$ 9   8. $N \times 45 = 45$ 1   12. $33 \times N = 0$ 0

Exercise 3
Written

Find each product. Check your answers by reversing the factors and multiplying again.

1.	2.	3.	4.	5.	6.
43	57	81	432	964	352
$\times 35$	$\times 26$	$\times 47$	$\times 41$	$\times 357$	$\times 598$
1,505	1,482	3,807	17,712	344,148	210,496

Placing the Decimal Point in the Product. When multiplying decimal numbers, you place the decimal point in the product by counting off from the right of the product as many decimal places as there are in both factors combined.

Example

What gross pay does an employee earn by working 14.5 hours at $7.24 an hour?

Solution	Explanation	Check
$7.24	There are two decimal places in the	14.5
× 14.5	first factor and one decimal place in	× 7.24
3 620	the second factor, for a total of three	580
28 96	places. Count off three places from	2 90
72 4	the right of the product and put the	101 5
104.980	decimal point there.	104.980
	$104.98 **Ans.**	

**Exercise 4
Oral**

Place the decimal point in the products of the problems.

1. 2.4 × 7.1 = 1704   17.04
2. 3.12 × 8.5 = 26520   26.52
3. 1.11 × 345 = 38295   382.95
4. 7.1 × 8.23 = 58433   58.433
5. 42.5 × 68.9 = 292825   2,928.25

6. 9.92 × 0.57 = 56544   5.6544
7. 0.7 × 0.6 = 42   0.42
8. 100 × 8.7 = 8700   870
9. 10 × 0.03 = 30   0.3

Rounding. The results of many problems you do will have to be **rounded**. Numbers are rounded to make them more useful or easier with which to work.

Money amounts are usually rounded to the cent because our money system does not use coins smaller than one cent. The kind of rounding you may do in business will depend on the practice of that business. Some businesses, such as retail stores, treat any part of a cent as a whole cent. Others will drop the part of the cent if the part is less than half a cent.

When you solve the problems in this text, round the final results to the nearest cent unless the directions tell you otherwise.

Rounding Money Amounts. When writing money amounts, 58¢ is the same as $0.58. The digit 8 is in the cents position. Also, 87.5¢ is the same as $0.875. Study the example below to locate the cents and tenth of a cent places.

8 7.5 ¢

$0.8 7 5

cent ⌐   ⌐tenth of a cent

Money figures are usually rounded to the cents position. The following example shows how to round to the nearest cent.

Example

Round 76.25¢ and $8.4182 to the nearest cent.

	Solution		Explanation
76.25¢	$8.4182	1.	Find the place to which you want to round. In this example, it is the cents place, as shown by the underscore.
76.25¢	$8.4182	2.	Look at the first digit to the right of the cents place. If the digit is less than 5 (4, 3, 2, 1, or 0), leave the cents amount as shown. If the digit is 5 or more (5, 6, 7, 8, or 9), add 1 to the cents place.
	+ 1		
76.25¢	$8.4282	3.	Drop all digits to the right of the cents place.
76¢	$8.42 **Ans.**	4.	Write the rounded answer.

Exercise 5
Oral

1. Round each to the nearest
   a. Cent: 3.56¢; 2.97¢; 29.95¢; 50.449¢
           4¢   3¢   30¢   50¢
   b. Cent: $7.2894; $4.9548; $32.2954; $60.9961
           $7.29 $4.95 $32.30 $61
   c. Tenth of a cent: 4.603¢; 42.229¢; 50.399¢; 6.854¢
           4.6¢   42.2¢   50.4¢   6.9¢
   d. Tenth of a cent: $0.0863; $0.0276; $0.2085; $8.5455
           $0.086 $0.028 $0.209 $8.546

2. As the billing clerk for the Delmar Company, you are to figure the costs of several orders. Round these cost figures to the nearest cent.

a.	$345.925	$345.93	g.	$67.999	$68
b.	$203.924	$203.92	h.	$42.434	$42.43
c.	$400.995	$401	i.	$40.006	$40.01
d.	$532.733	$532.73	j.	$840.009	$840.01
e.	$515.577	$515.58	k.	$200.999	$201
f.	$975.616	$975.62	l.	$999.996	$1,000

Rounding Decimals and Other Numbers. Decimals are often rounded to places such as tenths, hundredths, or thousandths. The basic rules for rounding money figures are used in rounding decimals. For example, 3.4918 rounded to the nearest tenth is 3.5; to the nearest hundredth, 3.49; to the nearest thousandth, 3.492.

The rounding principle is used for rounding whole numbers also. For example, 62,299 rounded to the nearest thousand is 62,000; to the nearest hundred, 62,300; and so on.

Whole numbers may be rounded in business reports where the exact number is not needed. For example, if a business had as few as 191 and as many as 212 employees last year, you could say that there were about 200 employees. You have rounded the exact number to the nearest hundred.

1. Round each decimal to the nearest tenth, to the nearest hundredth, and to the nearest thousandth.
    a. 5.2379   5.2; 5.24; 5.238
    b. 8.2741   8.3; 8.27; 8.274
    c. 3.1875   3.2; 3.19; 3.188
    d. 62.8684   62.9; 62.87; 62.868
    e. 92.6597   92.7; 92.66; 92.66
    f. 10.1999   10.2; 10.2; 10.2

2. Round each number to the nearest hundred thousand, to the nearest ten thousand, to the nearest thousand, and to the nearest hundred.
    a. 435,751   400,000 440,000
                   436,000 435,800
    b. 280,837   300,000 280,000
                   281,000 280,800
    c. 179,078   200,000 180,000
                   179,000 179,100
    d. 373,348   400,000 370,000
                   373,000 373,300
    e. 529,655   500,000 530,000
                   530,000 529,700
    f. 934,979   900,000 930,000
                   935,000 935,000

3. A retail store had 2,106 customers on Monday and 1,890 customers on Tuesday. How many total customers did the store have for the two days, rounded to the nearest hundred?   4,000

4. While writing a report you found that a certain state had a population of 2,369,872. What is the state's population rounded to the nearest hundred thousand?   2,400,000

REVIEW 8

1. Match the terms with the statements.

    factor   multiplication   product   rounded

    a. The result of multiplication   product
    b. A short way to add two or more equal numbers   multiplication
    c. Each of the numbers in multiplication   factor
    d. A number with digits dropped from the right   rounded

2. $54 + 27 + 34 =$ 115
    $13 + 75 + 9 =$ 97
    $83 + 11 + 17 =$ 111
    $150 + 113 + 60 =$ 323

3. $87 - 9 = ?$ 78
4. $1.35 \times 62 = ?$ 83.7
5. $24 - 15 + 7 = ?$ 16
6. $2 \times 2 \times 0 = ?$ 0

7. Round each number to the nearest
    a. Tenth: 5.3412; 0.3856; 736.6523; 5.9872   5.3; 0.4; 736.7; 6
    b. Hundredth: 278.4782; 37.7165; 0.4318   278.48; 37.72; 0.43
    c. Cent: $4.582; $0.399; 18.77¢ $4.58; $0.40; 19¢
    d. Thousand: 6,099; 45,437; 179,695   6,000; 45,000; 180,000

8. Find the value of N in each of these number sentences.
    a. $17 \times N = 17$ 1
    b. $7 \times 9 = N$ 63
    c. $N \times 23 = 46$ 2
    d. $N = 8 \times 7$ 56
    e. $89 \times N = 0$ 0
    f. $5 \times 15 = N$ 75

9. A store bought a carton of crackers that weighed a total of 276 ounces. The carton contained 24 boxes of crackers. If the empty carton weighed 12 ounces and each empty box weighed 1 ounce, what was the net weight of the crackers, in ounces?   240 ounces [4]

10. On April 1 Jean Monier's check register balance was $410. The bank statement balance for that date was $588.96. A comparison

of the check register and bank statement showed a service charge of $5, interest earned of $3.20, and these outstanding checks: #523 for $105.40 and #542 for $75.36. Prepare a reconciliation statement. $408.20 [5]

Section 9
Multiplication Shortcuts

When doing multiplication problems you can use estimation to help check the accuracy of your work. Your estimate lets you know if your actual product is reasonably close to being correct. There are also short cuts in multiplication that you can use to solve business problems. These short cuts will save you time.

■ **Estimate to improve the accuracy of your work.**

Estimating the Product. Before you multiply, you should **estimate** the product. To find an estimated product, round both factors to simple numbers that you can multiply easily. Then compare the exact product with the estimated product to see if the exact product is a reasonable answer.

For example, in the problem 28.5 × $1.04 you could round 28.5 to 30 and $1.04 to $1 to make the factors easier to multiply. The estimated product is $30 (30 × $1). If you calculate an exact product of $29.64 (which is close to $30) it is a reasonable answer. On the other hand, if you calculate an exact product of $3.97 or $296.40, your answer would not be reasonable. It might mean that you made an error when you multiplied or counted off the decimal point.

If the exact product is not reasonable, refigure the estimated product to be sure you did it right. If you did it right, then refigure the exact product.

What rounded factors were used to find each estimated product?

Exercise 1
Oral

		Estimate				Estimate	
1.	6.78 × $8.95	$63	7 × $9	6.	27.5 × 7.26	210	30 × 7
2.	5.62 × $7.78	$48	6 × $8	7.	56.7 × 12.3	720	60 × 12
3.	4.01 × $4.22	$16	4 × $4	8.	93 × 27	2,700	90 × 30
4.	96¢ × 3.97	$4	$1 × 4	9.	57¢ × 876	$540	60¢ × 900
5.	9.20 × 12.21	108	9 × 12	10.	1.874 × $0.48	$1	2 × $0.50

Round-Down Method. One of the ways to estimate products is to **round down** both factors to the tens or hundreds. For example, to estimate the product of 23 × 48, round down both factors to the tens position. So, 23 becomes 20 and 48 becomes 40. The estimated product is 800 (20 × 40). When the round-down method is used, the estimate will always be less than the actual product.

When you estimate the product for smaller numbers, round down the factors to the ones place or even to the tenths place. For example, the estimated product of 2.1 × 0.87 may be found by rounding 2.1 to 2 and 0.87 to 0.8. The estimated product is 1.6 (2 × 0.8).

Exercise 2
Oral

Use the round-down method to identify the factors used to estimate the product in each problem.

1. 56 × 72   50 × 70
2. 41 × 59   40 × 50
3. 512 × $67   500 × $60
4. 929 × 22   900 × 20
5. 23.8 × 17¢   20 × 10¢

6. 57.1 × 44.9   50 × 40
7. 4.29 × $5.76   4 × $5
8. 0.87 × 0.56   0.8 × 0.5
9. 1.4 × 3.497   1 × 3
10. 2.45 × 87¢   2 × 80¢

Round-Up Method. Another way to estimate the product is to **round up** both factors to the tens or hundreds. To estimate the product of 37 × 128 by this method, we round 37 to 40 and 128 to 130. The estimated product is 5,200 (40 × 130). Smaller factors may be rounded up to the ones place or to the tenths place to find the estimated product. When the round-up method is used, the estimate will always be more than the actual product.

Exercise 3
Oral

Use the round-up method to identify the factors used to estimate the product in each problem.

1. 49 × 78   50 × 80
2. 31 × 16   40 × 20
3. 410 × 33   410 × 40
4. 788 × 56¢   800 × 60¢
5. $15.80 × 24 $20 × 30

6. 27.3 × 40.7   30 × 41
7. 5.87 × 0.56   6 × 0.6
8. 0.476 × 0.23   0.5 × 0.3
9. $1.80 × 3.8267 $2 × 4
10. 0.097 × 98.5¢ 0.1 × $1

Rule-of-Five Method. The **rule-of-five** method of estimating products will usually give you an estimate that is closer to the exact product than other methods. In this method, you find the place to which you wish to round and look at the digit to the right. If it is 5 or more, round up. If the digit to the right is less than 5, round down. For example, if you round 484 to the hundreds position the answer is 500, and if you round the same number to the tens position the answer is 480.

When you estimate the product for problems in this text, use the rule-of-five method unless you are directed otherwise.

Exercise 4
Oral

Use the rule-of-five method to identify the factors that will be used to estimate the product in each problem.

1. 56 × 78   60 × 80
2. 72 × 91   70 × 90
3. $25 × 850 $30 × 900
4. 0.84 × 0.55¢   0.8 × 0.6¢
5. 473 × 65.5   500 × 70

6. $0.34 × 6.58 $0.30 × 7
7. 1.7 × 2.04   2 × 2
8. 0.852 × 3.456 0.9 × 3.5
9. 0.004 × 0.98   0.004 × 1
10. 7,840 × 50¢   8,000 × 50¢

Exercise 5
Written

For each problem, estimate the product, find the exact product, check the exact product against the estimate, and check the exact product by reverse multiplication.

1.	52 × 4.8	249.6	
2.	7.3 × 43	313.9	
3.	1.6 × 9.2	14.72	
4.	87¢ × 189	$164.43	

5.	$0.85 × 5.6	$4.76
6.	$605.65 × 12	$7,267.80
7.	$737.20 × 9.1	$6,708.52
8.	$650.76 × 19	$12,364.44

■ Move the decimal point to the right ———→ .

Multiplication by 10, 100, or 1,000. To multiply by 10, 100, or 1,000, move the decimal point in the one factor to the right as many places as there are zeros in the other factor (10, 100, or 1,000). Drop the decimal point if the product is a whole number. Attach zeros to the product if you need to. For example:

$$10 \times 9.42 = 94.2 \qquad 10 \times \$9.42 = \$94.20$$

$$100 \times 9.42 = 942 \qquad 100 \times \$9.42 = \$942$$

$$1,000 \times 9.42 = 9,420 \qquad 1,000 \times \$9.42 = \$9,420$$

Exercise 6
Oral

Multiply each number by (a) 10, (b) 100, (c) 1,000.

1.	29	5.	0.568	9.	$9.42	13.	$0.08	17.	4¢
2.	55	6.	0.37	10.	$6.83	14.	$0.04	18.	7¢
3.	68	7.	4.9	11.	$3.88	15.	$0.75	19.	62¢
4.	17	8.	0.08	12.	$0.425	16.	$0.125	20.	43.5¢

■ Move the decimal point to the right ———→ .

Multiplication by a Multiple of 10, 100, or 1,000. To multiply by a number such as 40, 400, or 4,000, first multiply by 4, and then multiply by either 10, 100, or 1,000. A number such as 400 is a multiple of 100, since 4 times 100 equals 400.

For example, to multiply $2.20 by 400:

1. Multiply $2.20 by 4. You now have $8.80.

2. Now multiply by 100 by moving the decimal two places to the right in the first product, $8.80. Now you have $880, which is the product of 400 × $2.20.

Exercise 7
Written

Write the product only for each problem. Multiply the numbers mentally.

	a.		b.		c.	
1.	20 × 0.37	7.4	300 × 3.4	1,020	40 × 21¢	$8.40
2.	70 × 0.4	28	400 × 7.2	2,880	60 × 25¢	$15
3.	40 × 0.95	38	500 × 8.1	4,050	80 × $0.75	$60
4.	60 × 7.1	426	2,000 × 0.64	1,280	200 × $1.25	$250
5.	30 × 8.6	258	5,000 × 0.61	3,050	4,000 × $17	$68,000

Multiplying Numbers That Have End Zeros. Sometimes either one of the factors, or both, have end zeros. Look at the problem in Example A (140 × 2,000). To do this problem, you arrange and multiply only the numbers to the left of the end zeros. Then you attach to the product as many zeros as there are in both factors.

Example

A. 140 × 2,000 = ?   B. 210 × $1.80 = ?

                   Solution   Solution

                14 × 2 = 28 $1.8
        attach zeros = 280000   210
                     = 280,000 **Ans.**   18
                                                                   36
                                                         $3780. or $378 **Ans.**

Example B above shows that end zeros at the *right* of the decimal point have no effect on the value of the number. For example, 1.8, 1.80, and 1.800 all have the same value. When multiplying with numbers such as 1.80 or 1.800, drop the end zeros at the right of the decimal point. The zero in the factor 210 is not dropped because it is to the left of the decimal point. Dropping this zero would change the value of both the factor and the product.

**Exercise 8
Written**

■ Drop end zeros at the right of the decimal point.

Multiply mentally as you were shown above. Write the products only.

	a.		b.		c.	
1.	150 × 300	45,000	200 × $7.40	$1,480	$5.60 × 40	$224
2.	230 × 80	18,400	50 × $2.50	$125	350 × $3	$1,050
3.	270 × 50	13,500	70 × $9.20	$644	$6,900 × 0.02	$138

Multiplication by 1¢ and 10¢. To multiply by 1¢, or by $0.01, move the decimal point in the other factor *two places to the left* and attach a dollar sign. For example:

■ @ = at or times

186 sheets of paper @ $0.01 = $1.86

To multiply by 10¢, or $0.10, move the decimal point in the other factor *one place to the left* and attach a dollar sign. For example:

38 folders @ $0.10 = $3.80

**Exercise 9
Oral**

Find the products.

1.	450 @ $0.01	$4.50	9.	82.6 @ 10¢	$8.26
2.	156 @ $0.10	$15.60	10.	39.2 @ 10¢	$3.92
3.	635 @ $0.01	$6.35	11.	25.5 @ 10¢	$2.55
4.	218 @ $0.10	$21.80	12.	18 @ 1¢	$0.18
5.	719 @ $0.01	$7.19	13.	240 @ $0.10	$24
6.	73 @ 10¢	$7.30	14.	153 @ $0.01	$1.53
7.	245 @ 1¢	$2.45	15.	2,730 @ 1¢	$27.30
8.	1,300 @ 1¢	$13			

Multiplication by a Multiple of 1¢ and 10¢. To multiply by a price such as $0.05 or $0.50, multiply by 5 or 50 and write the product. Then move the decimal point two places to the left in the product and attach a dollar sign. For example, to find the cost of 135 items at $0.50:

1. Multiply 135 by 50 and write the product, 6750.

2. Point off 2 places in 6750 and attach a dollar sign, $67.50.

Exercise 10
Written

Find the cost of each of these mentally. Write the product only.

1.	24 @ $0.04	$0.96		7.	110 @ 60¢	$66
2.	102 @ $0.07	$7.14		8.	0.8 @ 90¢	$0.72
3.	80 @ $0.05	$4		9.	130 @ 30¢	$39
4.	250 @ 3¢	$7.50		10.	65 @ $0.40	$26
5.	21 @ 6¢	$1.26		11.	73 @ $0.70	$51.10
6.	90 @ 9¢	$8.10		12.	93 @ $0.50	$46.50

REVIEW 9

Terms

1. Match the terms with the statements.

   estimate   round down   round up   rule of five

   a. Make factors greater   round up
   b. Usually produces closest estimate   rule of five
   c. Find approximate answer   estimate
   d. Make factors smaller   round down

Skills

2. Multiply.
   a. $0.01 × 489 $4.89
   b. $0.10 × 45.2 $4.52
   c. $0.20 × 52 $10.40
   d. $300 × 16 $4,800
   e. 2,189 × 100   218,900
   f. 10 × 34.8   348
   g. 1,000 × 4.708 4,708
   h. 4,900 × 8.2   40,180

3. Find the estimated and exact products.
   a. 3.8 × 489   2,000; 1,858.2
   b. 505 × 12.3   6,000; 6,211.5
   c. 7.2 × 312   2,100; 2,246.4
   d. 281 × 4.1   1,200; 1,152.1

4. Round to the nearest
   a. Tenth of a cent: $0.0284; $1.3607; 76.55¢ $0.028; $1.361; 76.6¢
   b. Hundredth: 4.6039; 3.00743; 65.48701   4.6; 3.01; 65.49
   c. Thousand: 17,804; 42,186; 10,740   18,000; 42,000; 11,000
   d. Hundred: 1,763; 32,117; 40,081   1,800; 32,100; 40,100

Problems

5. Louise Trent makes this deposit at her bank: (coins) 36 pennies, 24 nickels, 36 dimes, 15 quarters, 9 halves; (bills) 19 ones, 8 fives, 6 tens, 13 twenties; (checks) $53.47, $83, and $541.27. What is the total amount of Louise's deposit? $1,070.15 [4]

6. Sal Furtado is paid $13 an hour. Last week he worked these hours: Monday, 8 hours; Tuesday, 7 hours; Wednesday, 3 hours; Thursday, 5 hours; Friday, 8 hours. What were Sal's total earnings for the week? $403 [7]

The word average is used often in everyday life. You can figure an average score for the tests you take in school. Charts in books show the average height and weight of people. Government reports give information about the average income of families.

■ Average: one number that stands for a group of numbers.

An **average** is a single number used to represent a group of numbers. Two of the most commonly used averages are the simple average and the weighted average.

Finding Simple Averages. A **simple average*** is found by adding several numbers and dividing the sum by the number of items added.

Example

Maxine Hutchins earned these amounts of pay for the 5 days she worked last week: Monday, $82; Tuesday, $91; Wednesday, $96; Thursday, $80; Friday, $86. What was her average pay for the 5 days?

Solution	Explanation
$82 + $91 + $96 + $80 + $86 = $435 total pay	The sum or total of the daily earnings, $435, was found by adding the daily amounts. That sum was then
$435 ÷ 5 = $87 average pay per day **Ans.**	divided by the number of days, 5, to find the average daily pay, $87.

Exercise 1 Written

1. Jack earned $210 for 35 hours of work. What was his average pay per hour? $6

2. Ellen hand carves wooden figures. Her wages depend on the amount of figures she makes. Ellen's daily earnings for work she did from Monday through Saturday were: $73, $90, $103, $108, $67, $81. What was her average daily pay for the days she worked? $87

■ Divide the sum by the number of items.

3. Four employees are paid a monthly salary as follows: Bob, $1,300; Eleanor, $1,415; Howard, $1,177; Martha, $1,260. What average salary per month are these employees paid? $1,288

4. Two years ago you earned $17,200. Last year you earned $18,500. If you earn $20,400 this year
   a. What total amount will you have earned for the 3 years? $56,100
   b. What will be your average earnings per year? $18,700

---

*The simple average is also called the *mean*. More information about the mean will be presented in Section 106.

60

5. A computer programmer has been offered a job that pays $34,944 for working a 52-week year. What average amount does the job pay
   a. Per month? $2,912
   b. Per week? $672

6. Farouk earned $435 by working 5 days a week at his full-time job. He earned $84 for 12 hours work at his part-time job.
   a. What average pay per day did he earn from full-time work? $87
   b. What average amount per hour did he earn from part-time work? $7

7. Three weeks ago you worked 44 hours and earned $396. Two weeks ago you earned $342 by working 38 hours. Last week you worked 41 hours and were paid $369. For the three weeks
   a. How many hours did you work? 123
   b. What were your total earnings? $1,107
   c. What were your average *hourly* earnings? $9
   d. What were your average *weekly* earnings? $369

Figuring Weighted Averages. The **weighted average** method is used when one or more of the items has greater importance or "weight" than the others. Look at the example of a weighted average shown below:

Example

Parker Brile works part time at a roadside stand selling fruits and vegetables. During the first month the stand was open he earned $30. In each of the next 3 months he earned $150 per month. In the last month Parker earned $60. What were his average earnings per month for those five months?

Solution	Explanation

Solution

1 month @ $30   = $ 30
3 months @ $150 =   450
1 month @ $60   =   60
5 total months   = $540 total
                      earnings

$540 ÷ 5 = $108 per month   **Ans.**

■ Divide the sum of the products by the sum of the quantities.

Explanation

Each amount earned is multiplied by the number of months for which it was earned. Those products are then added and the total, $540, is divided by the sum of the months, 5. The quotient, $108, equals Parker's average earnings per month.

You should notice in the example that, using the weighted average method, the $150 earned per month for each of 3 months was counted 3 times. Each of the other amounts was counted only once. Thus, the $150 became 3 times as important or "weighty" as the other amounts.

If the simple average method had been used, the $150 would have been counted only once. The full weight of the $150 for 3 months would not have been shown, and the average would have been only $80 per month ($30 + $150 + $60, or $240 ÷ 3 = $80 simple average).

**Exercise 2
Written**

1. The Wilmark Company has 8 employees. Five of the employees earn $9 an hour, two earn $7 an hour, and 1 earns $13 an hour. What is the average amount per hour that these employees are paid? $9

2. The Hy-Gloss Paint Company gave its employees bonuses. Four employees received a bonus of $820 each; 5 employees received a bonus of $754 each; 6 employees were paid a bonus of $1,100 each. What was the average bonus paid to these employees? $910

3. At her job of repairing fences, LaShaundra worked 8 hours a day on Monday and Tuesday and earned $63 each day. On Wednesday, she earned $68. On Thursday and Friday, she earned $73 a day. What was LaShaundra's average daily pay for the 5 days she worked? $68

4. Midori Saga was offered a new job. For the first 3 months she works, she will be paid a monthly salary of $1,600. Her monthly pay for the next 3 months will be $1,760. For the next 6 months after that, Midori's monthly salary will be raised to $1,936.
   a. How much will Midori earn during a full year? $21,696
   b. What average pay per month will she receive if she works a full year? $1,808

5. During one week Sam Iannaci worked 8 hours a day for 2 days, 9 hours a day for the next two days, and 11 hours the following day. Sam is paid $11 an hour.
   a. What average number of hours did Sam work each day? 9 hours
   b. What was his average daily pay? $99

Illustration 10–1. Everyday Uses of Averages

Finding an Unknown Item in a Series. If one item in a series or group is unknown, you may have to find the unknown item. Averages are used often in finding the value of the unknown, or missing, item.

Example

The weekly pay of four employees in a company averages $433 per employee. The weekly pay amounts of three of the four employees are $400, $410, and $460. What is the weekly pay of the fourth employee?

Solution	Explanation
4 × $433 = $1,732 total pay of 4 employees	The average weekly pay of the 4 employees, $433, is multiplied by the number of employees, 4, to find the total weekly pay of the 4 employees, $1,732. The known weekly pay amounts of the 3 employees are added to find their total pay, $1,270. Then, the total pay of the 3 employees, $1,270, is subtracted from the total pay of the 4 employees, $1,732, to find the unknown amount, $462. The unknown amount, $462, is the pay of the fourth employee.
$400 + $410 + $460 = $1,270 total pay of 3 employees	
$1,732 − $1,270 = $462 weekly pay of fourth employee	

Exercise 3
Written

1. Your daily pay for the first 4 days of the week was $68, $80, $75, and $79. How much do you have to earn on the fifth day to average $77 a day in earnings for the 5-day week? $83

2. Rodger Blair was paid $422 for 5 days of work. For 4 of those days, his average daily pay was $86. Find his pay for the fifth day. $78

3. The owner of Mid-Town Delivery Service plans to spend no more than $680 a day for his employees' wages. The owner now has 7 employees who earn an average of $82 a day. What is the most he can pay a new employee without spending more money than he had planned? $106

4. Alma Thorpe plans to sell 200 computers this year. She earns $100 for every computer she sells. For the first 8 months of this year, she sold an average of 14 computers a month and earned total gross pay of $11,200. How many computers must she sell in each of the remaining 4 months to reach her goal? 22

REVIEW 10

Terms

1. Match the terms with the statements.

    average   simple average   weighted average

    a. Sum of the numbers divided by the number of items
        simple average
    b. Sum of the products divided by sum of the quantities
        weighted average
    c. A single number used to represent a group of numbers
        average

Skills

2. a. Multiply: 260 by 140   36,400
   b. Multiply: 2,550 by $0.01 $25.50
   c. Multiply: 8.3 by 1,000   8,300
   d. Round: $72.408 to the nearest cent $72.41
   e. Round: 7.4291 to the nearest tenth   7.4

3. Find the value of N.
   a. $36 \times N = 36$ 1   d. $0 \times 53 = N \times 34$ 0
   b. $N \times 2.4 = 4.8$ 2   e. $10 \times 62 = N \times 6.2$ 100
   c. $28 \times N = 7 \times 12$ 3   f. $14 \times 6 = 3 \times N$ 28

Problems

4. Beverly's scores on seven tests were 77, 78, 88, 90, 85, 91, and 88. What was her average score on the tests, rounded to the nearest whole number?   85 [10]

5. The owner of a small business bought 5 boxes of computer disks for $14 each, 8 boxes for $22, and 11 boxes for $36 each. There are 10 disks in each box. What average price did the owner pay for each disk, to the nearest cent? $2.68 [10]

6. In four days of work, Arnold produced these numbers of glass bowls: 52, 57, 55, 50. How many glass bowls must he make on the fifth day to average 53 glass bowls per day for 5 days of work?   51 [10]

Calculator Clinic

Using the Calculator for Division. To divide with the calculator, you enter the dividend, press the divide key, enter the divisor, and press the equals key. To find the average of pay amounts, you have to find the total of the pay amounts before dividing by the number of pay amounts you added. Follow these steps to find the simple average of these daily pay amounts of three employees: $56, $71, $68.

a. Use addition to find the total gross pay earned by the three employees. You combine the numbers in this way: 56 + 71 + 68 = 195. The total, 195, is now in your calculator display.

b. Press these keys in order: [÷] [3] [=] and write the answer,

$65, which is the average pay.

Finding Weighted Averages. Some problems require you to find a weighted average. For example, a problem may ask you to find the average pay of a department where 2 employees earn $11 an hour and 4 others earn $8 an hour. To solve this type of problem, you set it up in this way.

$$2 @ \$11 = $$
$$\underline{4} @ \ \ \$8 = \_\_\_$$

Totals

a. First find the total number of employees. Record the result, 6.

b. Use multiplication to find the total pay earned by each group of employees. So, you multiply 2 × $11 and press the M+ key to complete the multiplication and store the product, 22, in the memory register. Then you multiply 4 × $8 and press M+. The product, 32, is added to the amount already in the memory register.

c. Press MR/C to place the total of the memory register, 54, into the display. Divide by the number of employees, 6, to get the average, 9. Your finished problem will look like this:

$$2 @ \$11 = \$22$$
$$\underline{4} @ \ \ \$8 = \ \underline{32}$$

Totals   6 $54 $54 ÷ 6 = 9, average

Calculator Practice. Apply what you have learned in this calculator clinic to the simple average problems in Exercise 1 and the weighted average problems in Exercise 2.

You have used division to figure averages. There are other business problems that you will solve by using division. Being able to divide numbers accurately will be important.

 Division is the opposite of multiplication.

Division is the opposite process of multiplication. For example, if you start with 6 and multiply it by 3, you get 18. If you now divide 18 by 3, you get 6, which is the number you started with. Dividing by 3 "undoes" what you did by multiplying by 3.

When you multiply, you use two factors to get a product. For example, when you multiply the factor 6 by the factor 3, you get the product, 18. Look at the way the factors and product are related:

$$\text{Factor} \times \text{Factor} = \text{Product}$$

or   F × F = P

or   3 × 6 = 18

When you divide, you do the opposite of multiplication. You separate the product into the two factors. So, when you divide the product, 18, by the factor 3, you get the other factor, 6. Look at another way the product and the factors are related:

$$\text{Product} \div \text{Factor} = \text{Factor}$$

or   P ÷ F = F

or   18 ÷ 3 = 6

You can also think of division as a way of finding the unknown factor when you know one factor and the product. In solving 18 ÷ 3, ask yourself what number multiplied by 3 gives 18 as a product. Since the answer is 6, we can say that 18 ÷ 3 = 6.

Ways of Indicating Division. There are several ways to indicate division. For example, to show that 18 divided by 3 is 6, you may use any of these forms:

$$18 \div 3 = 6 \qquad \frac{18}{3} = 6 \qquad 3\overline{)18}^{\,6} \qquad 3\overline{)18} = 6 \qquad 3\overline{)18}\,\,6$$

In each case, 18 is the dividend, 3 is the divisor, and 6 is the quotient. A **dividend** is any number that is to be divided. A **divisor** shows the size or number of groups into which the dividend is to be split. A **quotient** shows how many times the divisor is included in the dividend.

Study the following illustration that shows how the terms used in division and multiplication are related.

$$3\overline{)18}^{\,6} \quad \text{or} \quad \text{Divisor}\overline{)\text{Dividend}}^{\,\text{Quotient}} \quad \text{or} \quad \text{Factor}\overline{)\text{Product}}^{\,\text{Factor}}$$

$$\frac{18}{3} = 6 \quad \text{or} \quad \frac{\text{Dividend}}{\text{Divisor}} = \text{Quotient} \quad \text{or} \quad \frac{\text{Product}}{\text{Factor}} = \text{Factor}$$

Exercise 1
Oral

Find the quotients.

	1.	2.	3.	4.	5.
a.	10 ÷ 5 2	8 ÷ 4 2	42 ÷ 6 7	21 ÷ 7 3	28 ÷ 4 7
b.	27 ÷ 9 3	24 ÷ 4 6	24 ÷ 3 8	30 ÷ 3 10	36 ÷ 12 3
c.	32 ÷ 4 8	18 ÷ 9 2	12 ÷ 4 3	20 ÷ 5 4	24 ÷ 12 2
d.	27 ÷ 3 9	15 ÷ 3 5	16 ÷ 4 4	40 ÷ 4 10	8 ÷ 2 4
e.	21 ÷ 3 7	16 ÷ 8 2	28 ÷ 7 4	28 ÷ 4 7	12 ÷ 12 1
f.	24 ÷ 6 4	14 ÷ 7 2	25 ÷ 5 5	20 ÷ 4 5	10 ÷ 2 5
g.	12 ÷ 6 2	30 ÷ 5 6	30 ÷ 6 5	12 ÷ 3 4	48 ÷ 12 4

Identifying the Factors and the Product. While you work with number sentences in multiplication or division, you will find it helpful to identify mentally the factors and the product. You may also want to write the letter *F* or *P* above each numeral or letter in the number sentence. For example:

$$\begin{array}{ccc} \overset{F}{}\ \overset{F}{}\ \overset{P}{} & \overset{P}{}\ \overset{F}{}\ \overset{F}{} & \overset{P}{}\ \overset{F}{}\ \overset{F}{} & \overset{F}{}\ \overset{P}{}\ \overset{F}{} \\ 3 \times 6 = 18 & 18 = N \times 6 & 18 \div 3 = 6 & 6 = N \div 3 \end{array}$$

Exercise 2
Written

Copy each number sentence. Above each numeral or letter, write F or P to show whether it is a factor or product.

F F P	P F F
1. 5 × 6 = 30	4. $N \div 9 = 2$
F F P	F F P
2. 8 × 9 = 72	5. 9 × 6 = N
P F F	P F F
3. 42 ÷ 7 = 6	6. 56 ÷ N = 8

F   F   P
7. 8 × N = 104
P   F   F
8. $N \div 4 = 14$
P   F   F
9. $N = 12 \times 8$

Finding an Unknown Product or Unknown Factor. In the sentences $3 \times 6 = N$ and $N \div 3 = 6$, the two factors are known; however, the product, N, is unknown. You find the value of the unknown product, N, by multiplying 3×6. The product, 18, is the value of N.

In the sentences $3 \times N = 18$ and $18 \div N = 3$, the product 18, and one factor, 3, are known. The other factor, N, is unknown. To find the value of N, you divide the known product, 18, by the known factor, 3. The quotient, 6, is the value of N, the unknown factor.

Remember, in any division problem, the dividend is a known product, and the divisor is a known factor. The quotient is an unknown factor.

Exercise 3
Written

Copy each problem. Above each numeral or letter, write F or P to show if it is a factor or a product. Then find the value of the unknown number.

P   F   F
1. 35 = 5 × N 7
F   F   P
2. 12 × N = 96   8
P   F   F
3. $N \div 17 = 3$ 51
F   P   F
4. $N = 352 \div 32$ 11
F   P   F
5. 10 = $N \div 5$ 50
F   F   P
6. 19 × N = 513   27

F   P   F
7. 23 = 391 ÷ N 17
F   F   P
8. 15 × N = 195   13
P   F   F
9. 84 = $N \times 12$ 7
F   P   F
10. $N = 735 \div 105$ 7
F   P   F
11. 13 = 169 ÷ N 13
F   F   P
12. 25 × N = 625   25

Placing the Decimal Point in the Quotient When the Divisor Is a Whole Number. Where do you put the decimal point in the quotient if the divisor is a whole number and the dividend has a decimal point in it? You put the decimal point right above the decimal point in the dividend.

Example

Solution	Explanation	Check
4.02 7)28.14	The problem at the left shows the division of 28.14 by 7. The decimal point in the quotient, 4.02, is put right above the decimal point in the dividend, 28.14.	4.02 × 7 28.14 **Ans.**

Checking Division. Division may be checked by going over the work again. It may also be checked by multiplying the quotient by the divisor. The result should equal the dividend.

Study the previous example to see how division can be checked this way. The quotient, 4.02, times the divisor, 7, gives 28.14, which equals the dividend.

Solve and check.

Exercise 4
Written

1.	45.72 ÷ 6	7.62	4.	7.24 ÷ 8	0.905	7.	91.08 ÷ 22	4.14
2.	5.88 ÷ 8	0.735	5.	1,347.1 ÷ 5	269.42	8.	18.025 ÷ 35	0.515
3.	304.2 ÷ 9	33.8	6.	8.533 ÷ 7	1.219	9.	0.192 ÷ 24	0.008

Placing the Decimal Point in the Quotient When the Divisor Has a Decimal. When the divisor has a decimal, change the divisor to a whole number by multiplying both the divisor and the dividend by 10, 100, or 1,000, and so on. Then divide. Look at this example.

Example

Divide 54.6 by 3.25.

Solution	Explanation	Check
16.8 **Ans.** 3.25.)54.60.0	The decimal points in both the dividend and divisor are moved to the right two places by multiplying both numbers by 100. This makes the divisor a whole number.	16.8 × 3.25 54.6

Multiplying both numbers by 100 does not change the value of the quotient. The decimal point in the quotient is put right above the new position of the decimal point in the dividend.

Solve and check.

Exercise 5
Written

1.	1,640 ÷ 8.2	200	7.	0.65 ÷ 32.5	0.02
2.	16.4 ÷ 0.082	200	8.	0.18 ÷ 4.5	0.04
3.	0.82 ÷ 0.82	1	9.	0.125 ÷ 0.25	0.5
4.	0.36 ÷ 0.0072	50	10.	0.125 ÷ 0.05	2.5
5.	100 ÷ 0.025	4,000	11.	0.015 ÷ 0.25	0.06
6.	4.32 ÷ 0.144	30	12.	0.5 ÷ 0.125	4

Divide to one place farther than you want, then round back.

Dividing to a Stated Number of Decimal Places. Problems involving the division of decimals usually require that answers be found to a certain number of decimal places. In such cases, the division must be carried out one place farther. The quotient is then rounded to the number of places stated in the problem.

Study the given example carefully to be sure you understand how the figures were rounded.

Example

Find the average wage per hour, to the nearest cent, for an employee who worked 36 hours and earned $312.42.

Solution	Explanation
$ 8.678 36)$312.42 **Ans. $8.68**	Since the second decimal place is the cents position, the answer must be given correct to two decimal places. The quotient must be carried to three places. Since the last number in the

quotient is an 8, the number to the left must be increased by 1. Rounded to two decimal places, the quotient is $8.68.

You can get an approximate check of the example's answer by multiplying the quotient by the divisor, or $8.68 × 36 = $312.48. Because you multiply a *rounded* quotient by the *exact* divisor, the result will not be the exact dividend. However, the result of your check, $312.48, is close to the original dividend of $312.42, and shows that you have a reasonable answer.

**Exercise 6
Written**

In each problem you are to do the division and find the quotient correct to the number of decimal places asked. Then check the quotient.

To 3 decimal places

1. 34.1 ÷ 2.17   15.714
2. 5.34 ÷ 0.621   8.599
3. 45 ÷ 0.1312   342.988
4. 0.3544 ÷ 0.22   1.611

To the nearest cent

5. $17.54 ÷ 504 $0.03
6. $39.05 ÷ 304 $0.13
7. $88.78 ÷ 235 $0.38
8. $68.27 ÷ 423 $0.16

**Exercise 7
Written**

1. A convenience store sold $851 worth of goods to 165 customers. To the nearest cent, how much did the average customer spend? $5.16

2. A basketball team scored 1,830 points in 23 games. Find the average number of points scored per game, to the nearest tenth of a point.   79.6

3. The 850 students at a local high school were absent a total of 5,234 days last year. To the nearest tenth of a day, what was the average number of days absent per student last year?   6.2

Using a Remainder to Show an Exact Quotient. When you do a problem such as 10 ÷ 5 = 2 or 15 ÷ 2 = 7.5, you get an exact quotient.

However, in a division problem such as $1 \div 3 = 1.333333$, the quotient will never be exact. You could, as you have already done, round the answer to two decimal places and show the quotient as 1.33. However, you know that rounded quotients are not exact quotients.

To show an exact quotient when the division does not result in an exact answer, you do this: (1) carry out the division to the stated place; (2) show the **remainder**, or number left over, as the fractional part of the divisor. You check the problem by multiplying the whole number part of the quotient times the divisor and adding the remainder to the product.

Example

Find an exact quotient to the ones place for $89 \div 14$.

Solution

$$14\overline{)89} \quad = 6\frac{5}{14} \text{ Ans.}$$

$$\begin{array}{r} 6 \\ 14\overline{)89} \\ 84 \\ \hline 5 \end{array} \text{ (Remainder)}$$

Check

$$\begin{array}{r} 6 \times 14 = 84 \\ + 5 \\ \hline 89 \end{array}$$

Exercise 8
Written

Find the exact quotient to the ones place for each problem. Check your division.

1. $2,497 \div 4$ $624\frac{1}{4}$
2. $4,072 \div 9$ $452\frac{4}{9}$
3. $2,195 \div 6$ $365\frac{5}{6}$
4. $1,458 \div 7$ $208\frac{2}{7}$
5. $5,859 \div 5$ $1,171\frac{4}{5}$
6. $3,213 \div 5$ $642\frac{3}{5}$

7. $2,219 \div 9$ $246\frac{5}{9}$
8. $3,525 \div 7$ $503\frac{4}{7}$
9. $1,237 \div 3$ $412\frac{1}{3}$
10. $3,255 \div 8$ $406\frac{7}{8}$
11. $377 \div 12$ $31\frac{5}{12}$
12. $659 \div 16$ $41\frac{3}{16}$

REVIEW 11

Terms

1. Match the terms with the statements.

   dividend   division   divisor   quotient   remainder

   a. Shows how many times the divisor is included in the dividend
      quotient
   b. The reverse of multiplication   division
   c. A number left over in division   remainder
   d. Shows the size or number of groups into which a dividend is to be split   divisor
   e. A number to be divided   dividend

Skills

2. Copy each problem and place an F or P above each numeral or letter to show if it is a factor or a product. Then find the value of the unknown number.

 F   F   P   P   F   F
a. 20 × N = 320   16   c. N ÷ 31 = 17   527
 P   F   F   F   F   P
b. N ÷ 19 = 23   437   d. N × 64 = 832   13

3. a. Multiply $6.20 by 1,600 $9,920
    b. Multiply 360 by 58¢ $208.80
    c. Divide 834 by 0.1   8,340
    d. Divide 92.5 by 0.01   9,250

4. Divide, and round each quotient to the nearest tenth when necessary.
    a. 69.08 ÷ 22   3.1   c. 0.288 ÷ 0.0072   40
    b. 0.8096 ÷ 8   0.1   d. 2,160 ÷ 7.2   300

Problems

5. Glynda Wylo's check register balance was $359.03 on August 15. During the next week she deposited a check for $110.78 and $35 in cash and wrote checks for these amounts: $56, $12.75, and $98.33. What was Glynda's correct check register balance at the end of the week? $337.73 [4]

6. From Monday through Friday, a newspaper carrier delivered 121 papers each day. On Saturday and Sunday the carrier delivered 135 papers each day. What average number of papers were delivered each day over the 7-day period?   125 [10]

Section 12
Division Shortcuts

In many business problems you will divide by whole numbers such as 50, $100, or 4,000. Many of your answers will have to be rounded, especially those involving money. When dividing, you will also estimate answers and use shortcuts to help you get the right answer and save time.

Estimating the Quotient. Either just before or just after dividing, you should estimate the quotient. This estimated quotient is used to check whether the exact quotient is a reasonable answer.

To estimate the quotient, round the divisor to the first digit on the left. Then round the dividend either up or down to a number that can be easily divided by the rounded divisor, and divide.

Example

Find the estimated and exact quotients of 4,590 ÷ 204.

Solutions

Estimated Quotient	**Exact Quotient**

Round the divisor, 204, to 200.

Round the dividend, 4,590, to 4,600, the nearest easy multiple of 2.

4,600 ÷ 200 = 23, estimated quotient

$$\begin{array}{r} 22.5 \quad \textbf{Ans.} \\ 204\overline{)4590} \end{array}$$

(The calculations that are necessary for this division are omitted.)

In the above example, 23 is close to 22.5, so 22.5 is a reasonable answer. If the exact quotient was 225, or about ten times larger than the estimated quotient of 23, the answer would not be reasonable. If this happens in any problem you do, the estimated and exact quotients should be refigured.

Here are more examples of estimating the quotient:

	Rounded Divisor	Rounded Dividend	Estimated Quotient	Exact Quotient
2,337 ÷ 61.5	60	2,400	40	38
7,644 ÷ 42	40	8,000	200	182
4,608 ÷ 36	40	4,800	120	128
4,257 ÷ 25.8	30	4,200	140	165

**Exercise 1
Oral**

Explain how you could get the estimated quotient in each problem.

1,600 ÷ 400 = 4
1. 1,623 ÷ 389 is about 4
800 ÷ 200 = 4
2. 775 ÷ 205 is about 4
1,000 ÷ 100 = 10
3. 1,020 ÷ 105 is about 10
900 ÷ 300 = 3
4. 960 ÷ 279 is about 3
600 ÷ 20 = 30
5. 537 ÷ 18 is about 30

200 ÷ 10 = 20
6. 213.6 ÷ 9.8 is about 20
480 ÷ 80 = 6
7. 482.6 ÷ 78.5 is about 6
$7,200 ÷ 60 = $120
8. $7,120 ÷ 55 is about $120
$8,000 ÷ 40 = $200
9. $7,762.40 ÷ 44 is about $200
$600 ÷ 12 = $50
10. $570.42 ÷ 11.8 is about $50

**Exercise 2
Written**

Estimate and write the estimated quotient of each problem. Also write the rounded divisor and dividend you used. Then figure and write the exact quotient.

$2,100 ÷ 30 = $70
1. $2,112 ÷ 32 $66
$3,200 ÷ 40 = $80
2. $3,268 ÷ 43 $76

200 ÷ 2,000 = 0.1
3. 258.94 ÷ 2,354   0.11
52 ÷ 2 = 26
4. 51.6 ÷ 2.15   24

$3,000 ÷ 50 = $60   4 ÷ 10 = 0.4
5. $2,842 ÷ 49 $58   8. 3.605 ÷ 10.3   0.35
    $6,000 ÷ 60 = $100   72 ÷ 8 = 9
6. $5,916 ÷ 58 $102   9. 72.09 ÷ 8.1   8.9
    $26 ÷ 2 = $13   100 ÷ 2 = 50
7. $26.16 ÷ 2.18 $12   10. 99.11 ÷ 1.87   53

Estimating the Quotient for Divisors Less Than One. When the divisor is a number less than 1, it must be changed to a whole number before it can be rounded to an estimated divisor. To make this change, move the decimal point in the divisor to the right as many places as necessary to arrive at a whole number. Then move the decimal point in the dividend an equal number of places. Now, estimate the quotient as you did before. Study this example.

$$29 ÷ 0.025 = 0.025\overline{)29} = .025.\overline{)29.000.} \text{ Divisor changed to a whole number}$$

$$= 30\overline{)30000} \quad \overset{1000}{} \text{ Estimated quotient}$$

**Exercise 3
Written**

Estimate and write the estimated quotient of each problem. Also write the rounded divisor and dividend you used. Then figure and write the exact quotient.

7,200 ÷ 20 = 360   14,000 ÷ 70 = 200
1. 72 ÷ 0.18   400   5. 119 ÷ 0.68   175
    2,000 ÷ 4 = 500   42,000 ÷ 20 = 2,100
2. 22 ÷ 0.04   550   6. 423 ÷ 0.18   2,350
    5,600 ÷ 80 = 70   42,000 ÷ 60 = 700
3. 54 ÷ 0.75   72   7. 416 ÷ 0.64   650
    20,000 ÷ 40 = 500   36,000 ÷ 90 = 400
4. 189 ÷ 0.35   540   8. 330 ÷ 0.88   375

Division by 10, 100, or 1,000. To divide by 10, 100, or 1,000, move the decimal point in the dividend to the left as many places as there are zeros in the divisor. Study the examples below.

5,700 ÷ 10 = 570   9,300 ÷ 1,000 = 9.3   0.46 ÷ 100 = 0.0046

$398 ÷ 100 = $3.98 $16.40 ÷ 10 = $1.64 $4,580 ÷ 1,000 = $4.58

**Exercise 4
Written**

For each problem, do the division mentally as explained above. Write the quotient only.

1. $4,200 ÷ 10 $420   7. 500 ÷ 1,000   0.5
2. 75,000 ÷ 100   750   8. 7 ÷ 100   0.07
3. $29,000 ÷ 1,000 $29   9. 489.4 ÷ 100   4.894
4. 6.8 ÷ 10   0.68   10. $30 ÷ 1,000 $0.03
5. $5.20 ÷ 10 $0.52   11. 0.02 ÷ 10   0.002
6. $80 ÷ 100 $0.80   12. 7.04 ÷ 100   0.0704

Dividing by Multiples of 10, 100, or 1,000. Sometimes the divisor is a whole number with zeros at the end, but it is not 10, 100, or 1,000. In such cases, you cross out the end zeros in the divisor. You then move the decimal point in the dividend as many places to the left as there were zeros in the divisor. Finally, you divide in the usual way.

Example

What was the average number of gallons of paint used by a painting crew per day, to the nearest tenth of a gallon, if 231.5 gallons of paint were used in 20 days?

Solution	Explanation

231.5 ÷ 20 = ?

$$20\overline{)23.1,5} \quad \begin{array}{c} 11.5\,7 \end{array}$$

11.6 **Ans.**

When you cross out the end zero in the divisor and move the decimal point one place to the left in the dividend, you divide both the divisor and the dividend by 10. This does not change the value of the quotient. You would get the same answer if you did not divide both the divisor and the dividend by 10, but doing so makes the work easier.

**Exercise 5
Written**

In each problem you are to: estimate the quotient, do the division and find the quotient correct to the number of decimal places asked, and check the quotient.

To 2 decimal places

1. 113 ÷ 40   2.83
2. 37.2 ÷ 420   0.09
3. 340 ÷ 3,500   0.1
4. 410 ÷ 7,400   0.06

To 4 decimal places

5. 125.6 ÷ 1,200   0.1047
6. 2,100 ÷ 8,200   0.2561
7. 880 ÷ 2,400   0.3667
8. 191,000 ÷ 76,000   2.5132

REVIEW 12

Skills

1. a. Find the product of 3,800 × 120. 456,000
    b. Multiply: 709 by 0.001   0.709
    c. Multiply: 314 by 200   62,800
    d. Divide: 23.7 by 0.001   23,700
    e. Divide: $456 by 100 $4.56
    f. Add: 45 + 16 + 23 + 34   118
    g. Subtract: $23.78 − $19.87 $3.91
    h. Round to the nearest hundredth: 408.10284   408.10
    i. Round to the nearest thousand: 4,492   4,000

2. Copy each problem and place an F or P above each numeral or letter to show if it is a factor or a product. Then find the value of the unknown number.

        P   F   F   F   F   P   F   P   F
    a. $N ÷ 14 = 18$ 252   b. $35 × N = 245$ 7   c. $25 = 450 ÷ N$ 18

3. For each problem, estimate the quotient. Then find the quotient, correct to the nearest tenth.
    a. 387 ÷ 42   9.2   b. 1,815 ÷ 61   29.8   c. 31,960 ÷ 77   415.1

Problems

4. The manager of a large company bought 10 executive desks for $1,536 each, 20 supervisor's desks for $909 each, and 30 operator's desks for $476 each. What was the average price paid for each desk? $797 [10]

5. Glenda Marcione earns $1,620 a month and Dominic Marcione earns $370 a week. What is the total year's income for both? $38,680 [7]

‡6. On November 30 Nancy Wordlaw's bank statement showed a balance of $670.42, a service charge of $5.60, and interest earned of $2.41. Her check register balance on that same date was $205.81. When she compared her statement to her register, she found that a canceled check for $96.82 had not been recorded in the check register and that a deposit of $65.81 had been made too late to be recorded on the bank statement. There were two outstanding checks: #175, $412; #182, $218.43. Prepare a reconciliation statement. $105.80 [6]

Regular and Overtime Pay

To manage your business and personal life, you will need to know the amount of regular and overtime pay you earn. To find this you will figure the amount of time you've worked on a regular time or overtime basis. Then, using regular and overtime pay rates, you will find your gross pay.

When doing these calculations you will use fractions and mixed numbers. The study of fractions will also help you solve other business problems and understand the additional work you will be doing soon with decimals and percents.

After you finish Unit 3, you will be able to:

- Figure regular and overtime hours shown on a time card.
- Figure gross pay for regular-time work and for overtime work.
- Add, subtract, multiply, and divide fractions and mixed numbers.
- Solve problems using ratios and proportions.
- Solve problems using fractions.
- Solve problems that contain more information than you need.
- Estimate answers to problems.
- Read, write, say, and recognize the meanings of the key terms.
- Use a calculator to multiply and divide fractions and to calculate total pay using the memory function.

An employee is paid a certain amount of money for each hour worked. The employee's gross or total pay is called wages, and wages can be figured for a day or a week.

Recording Time Worked. In many jobs an exact record is kept of the times that employees arrive for work and leave from work. This may be done by having employees stamp their **time cards** in a **time clock.** The amount of time worked in a day or week can then be figured from the time card.

Paula Steel's time card for the week ending August 7 is shown in Illustration 13–1. Paula's regular working hours are from 8:00 a.m. to 12:00 noon and from 1:00 p.m. to 5:00 p.m. She is not paid for her lunch hour, which lasts from 12:00 noon to 1:00 p.m. For all time worked during those regular working hours, Paula is paid a **regular-time** rate of $8 an hour. For any time worked over those regular working hours, Paula is paid an overtime rate of $12 an hour.

No. **63**   Pay Period Ending

Employee: **Paula Steel**   August 7, 19—

Hours	Rate	Earnings	Deductions	Allowances
Regular	Regular	Regular	Fed. With. Tax	
38	8.00	304.00	37.00	1
Overtime	Overtime	Overtime	FICA Tax (Soc. Sec.)	Gross (Total) Pay
$2\frac{1}{2}$	12.00	30.00	25.55	334.00
Total		Total	Insurance	Total Deductions
$40\frac{1}{2}$	- - -	334.00	12.00	80.80
			Other	Net Pay
- - -	- - -	- - -	6.25	253.20

Days	In	Out	In	Out	In	Out	Regular Hours	Overtime Hours
1	M 8 05	M 12 10	M 12 55	M 5 02			$7\frac{3}{4}$	
2	T 7 56	T 11 32	T 1 03	T 4 58			$7\frac{1}{2}$	
3	W 8 20	W 12 00	W 1 00	W 4 45			$7\frac{1}{4}$	
4	Th 7 59	Th 11 58	Th 12 59	Th 5 00	Th 6 00	Th 8 30	8	$2\frac{1}{2}$
5	F 8 01	F 12 02	F 12 55	F 4 30			$7\frac{1}{2}$	
6								
7								
	In	Out	In	Out	In	Out	Total Regular	Total Overtime
	Morning		Afternoon		Overtime		38	$2\frac{1}{2}$

Arrived Late   Left Early   Overtime

Illustration 13–1. Time Card for Paula Steel

Overtime. Some companies pay their employees for **overtime**, which is time worked beyond the regular working day or week. Daily overtime is figured on a regular working day, such as an 8-hour day. So, an employee who works 10 hours in one day will be paid for 8 hours regular time and 2 hours overtime.

A regular working week may be 40 hours. In this type of week, an employee who works 45 hours is paid for 40 regular hours and 5 overtime hours.

Figuring Hours Worked from a Time Card. The times when Paula arrived (In) and left (Out) each morning and afternoon are shown by the time clock figures stamped on the lower part of her time card. The total regular-time hours and overtime hours worked each day are figured by the payroll clerk and recorded at the right of the time clock figures. On the upper part of the card, the payroll clerk also records the regular-time hours, overtime hours, and other amounts.

Where Paula works, no credit is given for time of less than $\frac{1}{4}$ hour (15 minutes). No credit is given for arriving early. No credit is given for leaving late unless it is for scheduled overtime work. Paula is penalized in units of $\frac{1}{4}$ hour if she arrives more than 3 minutes late or leaves more than 3 minutes early.

For example, on Monday Paula's arrival at 8:05 a.m. was treated as 8:15 a.m. She left for lunch at 12:10 p.m., which was treated as 12:00 noon. Paula returned from lunch at 12:55 p.m., which was treated as 1:00 p.m. She left for the day at 5:02 p.m., which was treated as 5:00 p.m.

On Tuesday, 7:56 a.m. was treated as 8:00 a.m., 11:32 a.m. was treated as 11:30 a.m., 1:03 p.m. was treated as 1:00 p.m., and 4:58 p.m. was treated as 5:00 p.m. On Wednesday, 8:20 a.m. was treated as 8:30 a.m.

■ Being late to work costs you money.

Exercise 1 Oral

Arnold's regular working hours are from 8:00 a.m. to 12:00 noon and from 1:00 p.m. to 5:00 p.m. Time less than $\frac{1}{4}$ hour is not counted. Three minutes are allowed without penalty for arriving late or leaving early. For how many hours would Arnold be paid in each of these problems?

	In	Out			In	Out	
1.	7:56	12:00	4	6.	12:56	4:10	3
2.	8:00	12:06	4	7.	1:05	4:58	$3\frac{3}{4}$
3.	7:45	12:09	4	8.	1:02	5:02	4
4.	8:07	12:00	$3\frac{3}{4}$	9.	1:20	3:45	$2\frac{1}{4}$
5.	9:25	11:57	$2\frac{1}{2}$	10.	12:45	5:02	4

Exercise 2 Written

1. Alma Pelgreen's regular-time work hours are from 8:00 a.m. to 12:00 noon and from 1:00 p.m. to 5:00 p.m. Overtime is figured daily for time worked beyond 8 hours in a day. Alma can arrive 3 minutes late or leave 3 minutes early without penalty; otherwise, time worked of less than $\frac{1}{4}$ hour is not counted. Alma's time card for a week is shown on the following page.
   a. How many regular-time hours did Alma work?   37
   b. How many overtime hours did she work?   2

Employee: Osami Kinoshita					
Morning		Afternoon		Evening	
In	Out	In	Out	In	Out
≥ 7⁵⁹	≥ 11⁵⁸	≥ 1⁰⁰	≥ 5⁰²		
⊢ 8⁰³	⊢ 12⁰⁵	⊢ 12⁵⁸	⊢ 5⁰⁰	⊢ 5³⁰	⊢ 9⁰⁵
≥ 8¹²	≥ 11⁵⁹	≥ 1⁰³	≥ 4⁵⁵		
⋶ 7⁵⁷	⋶ 12⁰¹	⋶ 12⁵⁹	⋶ 4²⁰		
∟ 8⁰⁰	∟ 12⁰⁰	∟ 1⁰¹	∟ 4⁵⁹	∟ 5⁰⁰	∟ 7⁵⁸

2. Osami Kinoshita's regular work day is from 8:00 a.m. to 12:00 noon and from 1:00 p.m. to 5:00 p.m. Time worked of less than $\frac{1}{4}$ hour is not counted. Three minutes are allowed without penalty for arriving late or leaving early. Overtime is figured daily as time worked beyond 8 hours each day. Based on Osami's time card shown below, find how many regular-time and overtime hours he worked. $38\frac{3}{4}$; $6\frac{1}{2}$

Employee: Alma Pelgreen					
Morning		Afternoon		Evening	
In	Out	In	Out	In	Out
≥ 8⁰⁰	≥ 12⁰¹	≥ 12⁵⁹	≥ 5⁰⁰		
⊢ 7⁵⁸	⊢ 11⁵⁵	⊢ 12⁵²	⊢ 3⁵⁰		
≥ 8⁰²	≥ 12⁰⁰	≥ 1⁰¹	≥ 4⁵⁸	≥ 5⁵⁹	≥ 8⁰²
⋶ 8²⁷	⋶ 11⁵⁸	⋶ 12⁵⁴	⋶ 5⁰²		
∟ 7⁵⁹	∟ 11⁵⁰	∟ 1⁰⁵	∟ 4³²		

Figuring Regular-Time and Overtime Wages. For an employee who has worked both regular time and overtime, you figure gross pay by using the following three steps:

1. Find the regular-time pay by multiplying the regular-time hourly rate by the number of regular-time hours worked.

2. Find the overtime pay by multiplying the overtime hourly rate by the number of overtime hours worked.

3. Add the regular-time pay and the overtime pay.

Example

Last week Brian worked 40 regular-time hours at $6 an hour and 4 overtime hours at $9 an hour. What was Brian's gross pay for the week?

Solution

40 × $6 = $240 regular-time pay
4 × $9 =   36 overtime pay
          $276 gross pay   **Ans.**

**Exercise 3
Written**

1. Last week Harold Perkins worked 38 regular-time hours and 3 overtime hours. He is paid $10 an hour for regular-time work and $15 an hour for overtime work. What was Harold's gross pay for the week? $425

2. Marta Gruen's average pay is $277.50 a week. Last week Marta worked 40 hours at the regular-time rate of $6.80 an hour and $6\frac{1}{2}$ hours at the overtime rate of $10.20 an hour. What was Marta's gross pay for the week? $338.30

3. Ralph Humes is paid overtime for all time worked past 40 hours in a week. His regular-time pay rate is $7 an hour, and his overtime pay rate is $10.50 an hour. Last week Ralph worked 47 hours.
   a. How many regular-time hours did Ralph work last week? 40
   b. How many overtime hours did Ralph work last week? 7
   c. What was Ralph's regular-time pay last week? $280
   d. What was his overtime pay last week? $73.50
   e. What was his gross or total pay last week? $353.50

4. Art Lantzy and Kurt Voss work for Lansco Products. Their time cards for 1 week are shown below. Employees of Lansco Products have regular working hours of 8:00 a.m. to 12:00 noon and 12:30 p.m. to 4:30 p.m. They can arrive 3 minutes late or leave 3 minutes early without penalty. Time worked of less than $\frac{1}{4}$ hour is not counted. Art and Kurt are both paid $8 an hour for regular-time work. An overtime rate of $12 an hour is paid for time worked beyond 8 hours in a day.
   a. How many regular and overtime hours did Art work? 37; 2
   b. What was Art's gross pay for the week? $320
   c. How many regular and overtime hours did Kurt work? 35; 4
   d. What was Kurt's gross pay for the week? $328

Employee: Art Lantzy					
Morning		Afternoon		Evening	
In	Out	In	Out	In	Out
7 58	12 04	12 33	4 29		
8 02	11 50	12 29	4 31		
8 57	11 32	12 30	4 15		
8 30	12 00	1 00	4 32		
8 00	11 59	12 30	4 30	5 00	7 01

Employee: Kurt Voss					
Morning		Afternoon		Evening	
In	Out	In	Out	In	Out
8 25	12 01	12 31	4 30		
7 59	11 58	12 30	4 31	6 00	10 00
8 01	12 00	1 12	4 32		
9 00	11 59	12 30	3 45		
8 03	12 02	12 29	2 30		

5. The time cards for Ruth Hirsch and Tod Groot are shown on the next page. Their working hours are from 8:00 a.m. to 12:00 noon and 1:00 p.m. to 5:00 p.m. If they arrive more than 3 minutes late or leave more than 3 minutes early they are penalized 15 minutes. Ruth earns $6.40 an hour for regular-time work and $9.60 an hour for overtime work. Tod's regular-time rate is $6.60 an hour, and his overtime rate is $9.90 an hour. Ruth and Tod are paid on an 8-hour day basis, with daily overtime figured on time worked beyond 8 hours.

a. What is Ruth's gross pay for the week? $268.80

b. What is Tod's gross pay for the week? $293.70

Employee: Ruth Hirsch					
Morning		Afternoon		Evening	
In	Out	In	Out	In	Out
7⁵⁸	12⁰⁴	12⁵⁵	5⁰²		
8⁰²	11⁵⁰	12⁵⁹	5⁰⁰		
8⁰⁰	11³²	1⁰⁸	4⁵⁸		
8⁰¹	12⁰⁰	1⁰¹	5⁰⁰		
7⁵⁷	11⁵⁹	12⁵⁷	4⁵⁹	5¹⁵	7¹⁷

Employee: Tod Groot					
Morning		Afternoon		Evening	
In	Out	In	Out	In	Out
8¹⁰	12⁰¹	12⁵⁹	4²⁰		
7⁵⁹	11⁵⁸	1⁰⁰	5⁰⁴	6⁰⁰	9⁰⁵
8⁰¹	12⁰⁰	12⁵⁷	5⁰⁰	5⁴⁵	7⁵⁰
9⁰⁰	11⁵⁹	1⁰⁰	5⁰⁹		
8⁰³	12⁰²	1⁰¹	4⁰⁸		

REVIEW 13

Terms

1. Match the terms with the statements.

    overtime   regular time   time clock   time card

    a. A record of an employee's time   time card
    b. A device that stamps the time on a time card   time clock
    c. Time worked beyond the usual end of the work day   overtime
    d. Time worked within the usual work hours   regular time

Skills

2. a. Find the value of N: $N \div 12 = 6$ 72
    b. Multiply: 320×50 16,000
    c. Divide: $4,729 \div 0.01$ 472,900
    d. Estimate the product of $\$5,820 \times 31$. $180,000
    e. Estimate the quotient of $\$8,111 \div 18.7$. $400

Problems

3. Lisabeth Awrey is paid $0.60 for the first 110 plates she produces per day and $0.75 for any plate she produces beyond 110 per day. Last week, she produced these amounts per day: 100 plates, 105 plates, 115 plates, 125 plates, and 120 plates. What was Lisabeth's gross pay for the week? $343.50 [7]

4. Owen Hall is paid $0.32 for each cover he finishes that passes inspection. Last week Owen finished these amounts of covers: Monday, 145; Tuesday, 182; Wednesday, 177; Thursday, 165, Friday, 171. Of the covers he finished, 17 did not pass inspection. What was Owen's gross pay for the week? $263.36 [7]

5. Mel Hamell is paid $11 an hour for regular-time hours and $16.50 for overtime hours. Last week Mel worked 40 regular hours and 4 overtime hours. What was Mel's gross pay for the week? $506 [13]

Yearly pay ÷ 12 = monthly pay

6. Lorraine earns a salary of $480 a week. How much will she earn in a year? in a month? $24,960; $2,080 [7,10]

7. A furniture store sold 50 discontinued model lamps at these prices: 10 at $30, 25 at $40, and the rest at $50. What was the average selling price of the lamps? $41 [10]

In the previous section you used the fractions $\frac{1}{4}$, $\frac{1}{2}$, and $\frac{3}{4}$ in figuring gross pay. In the remaining sections of this unit, you will review working with fractions and then apply them to solving problems.

Fractional Numbers. So far, most of your work in this book has been with whole numbers. **Whole numbers,** such as 0, 1, 2, 12, 50, and so on, are complete or "whole" units. In some of the gross pay problems, though, you used parts of an hour such as $\frac{1}{4}$, $\frac{1}{2}$, or $\frac{3}{4}$. Parts of whole numbers are called **fractional numbers.**

Fractions. A symbol for a fractional number, such as $\frac{1}{4}$, $\frac{1}{2}$, or $\frac{3}{4}$, is a **fractional numeral.** Fractional numerals are also called **fractions,** or *common fractions.* In this text we will call them *fractions.*

Fractions are written with a numeral above and a numeral below a line. The numeral above the line in a fraction is called the **numerator.** The numeral below the line is called the **denominator.** The denominator shows the number of equal parts into which a whole is divided. The numerator shows the number of parts with which you are working. For example, in the fraction $\frac{3}{4}$:

$$\frac{3}{4} = \frac{\textbf{Numerator}}{\textbf{Denominator}} = \frac{\textbf{Shows that 3 parts are being used}}{\textbf{Shows that the whole is divided into 4 parts}}$$

Fractions may name either fractional numbers or whole numbers. For example, fractions such as $\frac{2}{3}$ and $\frac{5}{6}$ name fractional numbers. Fractions such as $\frac{3}{3}$ and $\frac{8}{2}$ name whole numbers. A fraction having the same numeral for the numerator and denominator, such as $\frac{5}{5}$ or $\frac{7}{7}$, names the number one.

A fraction may be read in three ways. For example, the fraction $\frac{3}{4}$ may be read as "three fourths," "three divided by four," or "three over four."

1. Read each of these fractions in three ways.

   a. $\frac{1}{4}$ b. $\frac{1}{2}$ c. $\frac{2}{3}$ d. $\frac{4}{4}$ e. $\frac{3}{8}$ f. $\frac{8}{4}$ g. $\frac{20}{20}$ h. $\frac{5}{12}$

2. Which of the fractional numerals in Problem 1 name whole numbers? Which name fractional numbers?   d, f, g, a, b, c, e, h

1. Write each of these as a fraction.

   a. $12 \div 2$ $\frac{12}{2}$ c. $4 \div 2$ $\frac{4}{2}$ e. $2 \div 9$ $\frac{2}{9}$ g. $6 \div 7$ $\frac{6}{7}$

   b. $5 \div 5$ $\frac{5}{5}$ d. $24 \div 4$ $\frac{24}{4}$ f. $18 \div 9$ $\frac{18}{9}$ h. $50 \div 50$ $\frac{50}{50}$

2. Write each of these with a division sign ($\div$).

   a. $\frac{1}{7}$ $1 \div 7$ c. $\frac{83}{75}$ $83 \div 75$ e. $\frac{12}{12}$ $12 \div 12$

   b. $\frac{36}{72}$ $36 \div 72$ d. $\frac{9}{3}$ $9 \div 3$ f. $\frac{360}{30}$ $360 \div 30$

Multiplying a Fraction by a Fraction. To multiply two or more fractions, you multiply the numerators to get the numerator of the product. Then you multiply the denominators to get the denominator of the product.

$$\frac{2}{3} \times \frac{2}{5} = \frac{2 \times 2}{3 \times 5} = \frac{4}{15}$$

Of and *Times* have the same meaning.

A problem such as $\frac{1}{4}$ of $\frac{7}{8}$ means the same as $\frac{1}{4} \times \frac{7}{8}$. So, to find $\frac{1}{4}$ of $\frac{7}{8}$, you multiply the two fractions ($\frac{1}{4} \times \frac{7}{8} = \frac{7}{32}$).

Find the products.

**Exercise 3
Oral**

1. $\frac{1}{2} \times \frac{1}{3}$ $\frac{1}{6}$ 3. $\frac{1}{4} \times \frac{1}{5}$ $\frac{1}{20}$ 5. $\frac{1}{2}$ of $\frac{5}{8}$ $\frac{5}{16}$ 7. $\frac{2}{5} \times \frac{4}{7}$ $\frac{8}{35}$

2. $\frac{1}{3}$ of $\frac{1}{4}$ $\frac{1}{12}$ 4. $\frac{2}{3}$ of $\frac{1}{1}$ $\frac{2}{3}$ 6. $\frac{1}{3} \times \frac{2}{1}$ $\frac{2}{3}$ 8. $\frac{3}{4} \times \frac{3}{8}$ $\frac{9}{32}$

Finding Equivalent Fractions. In using fractions you may need to change them to equivalent fractions. An **equivalent fraction** is a fraction that names the same number as another fraction. For example, $\frac{1}{3}$, $\frac{2}{6}$, and $\frac{4}{12}$ are equivalent fractions.

You get an equivalent fraction by multiplying or dividing the numerator and denominator of a fraction by the same number. For example:

$$\frac{1}{3} \times \frac{2}{2} = \frac{2}{6} \qquad \frac{1}{3} \times \frac{3}{3} = \frac{3}{9} \qquad \frac{2}{6} \div \frac{2}{2} = \frac{1}{3} \qquad \frac{3}{9} \div \frac{3}{3} = \frac{1}{3}$$

**Exercise 4
Written**

1. For each of these fractions, what equivalent fraction do you get when you multiply both the numerator and the denominator by 2, 3, 4, and 5?

a. $\frac{1}{2}$ $\frac{2}{4}, \frac{3}{6}, \frac{4}{8}, \frac{5}{10}$ d. $\frac{1}{1}$ $\frac{2}{2}, \frac{3}{3}, \frac{4}{4}, \frac{5}{5}$

b. $\frac{3}{4}$ $\frac{6}{8}, \frac{9}{12}, \frac{12}{16}, \frac{15}{20}$ e. $\frac{5}{1}$ $\frac{10}{2}, \frac{15}{3}, \frac{20}{4}, \frac{25}{5}$

c. $\frac{5}{4}$ $\frac{10}{8}, \frac{15}{12}, \frac{20}{16}, \frac{25}{20}$ f. $\frac{3}{8}$ $\frac{6}{16}, \frac{9}{24}, \frac{12}{32}, \frac{15}{40}$

2. What equivalent fraction do you get when you divide both the numerator and the denominator by the number shown?

a. $\frac{6}{8}$ by 2 $\frac{3}{4}$ b. $\frac{12}{20}$ by 4 $\frac{3}{5}$ c. $\frac{14}{21}$ by 7 $\frac{2}{3}$ d. $\frac{32}{16}$ by 8 $\frac{4}{2}$

Simplifying Fractions. In your answers you should simplify fractions by changing them to lowest terms. The **terms** of a fraction are the numerator and the denominator. A fraction is in **lowest terms** when no number except 1 will divide evenly into both terms. For example, in the fraction $\frac{3}{6}$, the 3 and the 6 are the terms, and the fraction $\frac{3}{6}$ is in lowest terms when it is simplified to the equivalent fraction $\frac{1}{2}$.

You simplify a fraction by dividing both the numerator and the denominator by the largest number that will divide both of them exactly.

That number is called the *greatest common divisor*. For example, in simplifying the fraction $\frac{3}{6}$, the largest number that will divide each term without a remainder is 3 ($\frac{3}{6} \div \frac{3}{3} = \frac{1}{2}$).

Simplify each fraction.

**Exercise 5
Oral**

1. $\frac{6}{8}$ $\frac{3}{4}$ 3. $\frac{8}{20}$ $\frac{2}{5}$ 5. $\frac{18}{24}$ $\frac{3}{4}$ 7. $\frac{14}{35}$ $\frac{2}{5}$ 9. $\frac{30}{35}$ $\frac{6}{7}$

2. $\frac{5}{10}$ $\frac{1}{2}$ 4. $\frac{15}{18}$ $\frac{5}{6}$ 6. $\frac{16}{40}$ $\frac{2}{5}$ 8. $\frac{27}{45}$ $\frac{3}{5}$ 10. $\frac{14}{25}$ $\frac{14}{25}$

Simplifying the Product of Fractions. You can simplify the product of two or more fractions by *cancellation*. In cancellation you divide the numerators and denominators by common factors before you multiply. Here are two examples:

A. $\frac{1}{9} \times \frac{3}{4} = \frac{1}{\overset{}{\underset{3}{9}}} \times \frac{\overset{1}{\cancel{3}}}{4} = \frac{1}{12}$

B. $\frac{3}{8} \times \frac{4}{15} = \frac{\overset{1}{\cancel{3}}}{\underset{2}{\cancel{8}}} \times \frac{\overset{1}{\cancel{4}}}{\underset{5}{\cancel{15}}} = \frac{1}{10}$

Find the products.

**Exercise 6
Oral**

1. $\frac{1}{2} \times \frac{2}{3}$ $\frac{1}{3}$ 3. $\frac{3}{8}$ of $\frac{2}{3}$ $\frac{1}{4}$ 5. $\frac{1}{2} \times \frac{6}{7}$ $\frac{3}{7}$ 7. $\frac{1}{9}$ of $\frac{9}{1}$ 1

2. $\frac{3}{5} \times \frac{5}{6}$ $\frac{1}{2}$ 4. $\frac{5}{8}$ of $\frac{8}{9}$ $\frac{5}{9}$ 6. $\frac{3}{5} \times \frac{5}{3}$ 1   8. $\frac{3}{4} \times \frac{2}{5}$ $\frac{3}{10}$

Simplify each product.

**Exercise 7
Written**

1. $\frac{5}{8} \times \frac{4}{5}$ $\frac{1}{2}$ 3. $\frac{3}{8}$ of $\frac{12}{15}$ $\frac{3}{10}$ 5. $\frac{2}{3}$ of $\frac{5}{8}$ $\frac{5}{12}$ 7. $\frac{3}{8} \times \frac{5}{12}$ $\frac{5}{32}$

2. $\frac{5}{7} \times \frac{14}{25}$ $\frac{2}{5}$ 4. $\frac{3}{4}$ of $\frac{5}{9}$ $\frac{5}{12}$ 6. $\frac{9}{10} \times \frac{15}{18}$ $\frac{3}{4}$ 8. $\frac{5}{6}$ of $\frac{7}{8}$ $\frac{35}{48}$

Changing Improper Fractions to Mixed Numbers. A **proper fraction** has a numerator that is smaller than the denominator. For example, $\frac{3}{4}$ and $\frac{5}{9}$ are proper fractions. An **improper fraction** has a numerator that is equal to or greater than the denominator. For example, $\frac{2}{2}$ and $\frac{5}{3}$ are improper fractions.

When you multiply fractions the product may be an improper fraction. For example, $\frac{2}{1} \times \frac{3}{5} = \frac{6}{5}$. You usually change such improper fractions to mixed numbers. A **mixed number,** such as $3\frac{1}{8}$ or $5\frac{2}{3}$, consists of both a whole number and a fraction. You generally change an improper fraction to a mixed number by dividing the numerator by the denominator. For example, $\frac{6}{5} = 6 \div 5 = 1\frac{1}{5}$.

Change each improper fraction to a mixed number or a whole number.

**Exercise 8
Oral**

1. $\frac{3}{2}$ $1\frac{1}{2}$ 3. $\frac{9}{4}$ $2\frac{1}{4}$ 5. $\frac{8}{8}$ 1   7. $\frac{9}{5}$ $1\frac{4}{5}$ 9. $\frac{18}{8}$ $2\frac{1}{4}$

2. $\frac{5}{3}$ $1\frac{2}{3}$ 4. $\frac{3}{3}$ 1   6. $\frac{21}{7}$ 3   8. $\frac{10}{3}$ $3\frac{1}{3}$ 10. $\frac{25}{10}$ $2\frac{1}{2}$

**Exercise 9
Written**

Change each improper fraction to a mixed number or a whole number.

1. $\frac{7}{3}$ $2\frac{1}{3}$ 3. $\frac{10}{4}$ $2\frac{1}{2}$ 5. $\frac{20}{16}$ $1\frac{1}{4}$ 7. $\frac{5}{5}$ 1   9. $\frac{27}{8}$ $3\frac{3}{8}$

2. $\frac{12}{3}$ 4   4. $\frac{13}{6}$ $2\frac{1}{6}$ 6. $\frac{16}{12}$ $1\frac{1}{3}$ 8. $\frac{33}{7}$ $4\frac{5}{7}$ 10. $\frac{32}{10}$ $3\frac{1}{5}$

**Exercise 10
Written**

Solve each problem, stating any fraction in lowest terms.

1. The school pep team has 8 members, including 6 girls and 2 boys. What fractional part of the pep team is boys? $\frac{1}{4}$

2. While recently taking a test, Arnold Briggs found that he wasn't sure of the answers to $\frac{1}{4}$ of the questions. He guessed at the correct answers to these questions. Arnold found out later that $\frac{2}{3}$ of his guesses were correct. For what part of the total test did Arnold correctly guess the right answers? $\frac{1}{6}$

3. In her will, Cora Griffen plans to set aside $\frac{1}{2}$ of all her money to be used to establish a public service fund. Further, $\frac{2}{5}$ of the fund is to be used to renovate the local fire station. What part of Cora's money will be used for the fire station? $\frac{1}{5}$

4. Eleven honor students at a high school received information from 72 colleges and universities. Eighteen of these schools were colleges. What fractional part of all of the schools sending information were universities? $\frac{3}{4}$

5. A health club's registration book showed that 160 male and 180 female members used the running track on a certain day. What part of the total members using the track that day were female? $\frac{9}{17}$

REVIEW 14

Terms

1. Match the terms with the statements.

denominator	fractions	numerator
equivalent fraction	improper fraction	proper fraction
fractional numbers	lowest terms	terms
fractional numeral	mixed number	whole numbers

a. Has a numerator equal to or greater than the denominator
   improper fraction
b. The numerator and denominator of a fraction   terms
c. The numeral below the line in a fraction   denominator
d. Whole units, such as 1, 2, and 6   whole numbers
e. Names the same number as another fraction
   equivalent fraction
f. Has a numerator smaller than the denominator
   proper fraction
g. Parts of whole numbers   fractional numbers
h. When both terms of a fraction are divisible only by 1
   lowest terms
i. The number above the line in a fraction   numerator
j. Another name for fractional numerals   fractions

k. Has both a whole number and a fraction   mixed number
l. A symbol for a fractional number   fractional numeral

Skills

2. As you multiply, cancel when you can to simplify your answers.

a. $\dfrac{1}{2} \times \dfrac{5}{6}$ $\dfrac{5}{12}$

b. $\dfrac{3}{4} \times \dfrac{2}{15}$ $\dfrac{1}{10}$

c. $\dfrac{1}{3} \times \dfrac{3}{7}$ $\dfrac{1}{7}$

3. Change each fraction to a mixed number.

a. $\dfrac{9}{2}$ $4\dfrac{1}{2}$

b. $\dfrac{17}{4}$ $4\dfrac{1}{4}$

c. $\dfrac{22}{5}$ $4\dfrac{2}{5}$

Problems

4. Rolf Lada worked $46\frac{1}{4}$ hours last week. Of that time, $38\frac{1}{4}$ hours were at regular-time pay and 8 hours were at overtime pay. Rolf was paid at the regular rate of $12 per hour and at an overtime rate of $18 per hour. What was Rolf's gross pay for the week? $603 [13]

5. Florence McHale earns $1,860 a month.
    a. What estimated amount does Florence earn in a year?
        $24,000 [7]
    b. What are Florence's actual earnings in a year? $22,320 [7]
    c. What is Florence's pay for a week, to the nearest cent?
        $429.23 [10]

6. For the first 11 months of the year a salesperson's sales averaged $40,100 a month. How much must that salesperson sell in the next month so that the average monthly sales for the year are $39,500?
    $32,900 [10]

Section 15
More Fractions

Multiplying a Whole Number or a Decimal and a Fraction. Suppose you want to find the pay for $\frac{3}{4}$ hours of work at $8 an hour and $\frac{2}{3}$ hours of work at $9.60 an hour. To do this, you multiply the pay rate by the time, as shown in these examples:

Example A: $\dfrac{3}{4} \times \dfrac{\$8}{1} = \dfrac{\$24}{4} = \$6$

Example B: $\dfrac{2}{3} \times \dfrac{\$9.60}{1} = \dfrac{\$19.20}{3} = \$6.40$

In these examples the pay rate is shown as the numerator of a fraction, which has a denominator of 1. The numerators are multiplied, then the denominators are multiplied. The product, which is a fraction, is simplified by dividing the numerator by the denominator.

You could also do the problem by cancellation, as shown in the following examples:

Example A: $\dfrac{3}{\cancel{4}_{1}} \times \dfrac{\overset{2}{\cancel{\$8}}}{1} = \$6$ **Example B:** $\dfrac{2}{\cancel{3}_{1}} \times \dfrac{\overset{3.20}{\cancel{\$9.60}}}{1} = \$6.40$

Exercise 1
Written

1. Find the products. (Use cancellation when you can.)

   a. $\dfrac{1}{2} \times 36$ 18

   b. $\dfrac{2}{5}$ of 40   16

   c. $\dfrac{2}{3} \times 24$ 16

   d. $\dfrac{1}{3}$ of $54 $18

   e. $\dfrac{5}{6} \times \$42$ $35

   f. $\dfrac{3}{8}$ of $32 $12

   g. $\dfrac{1}{6}$ of $54 $9

   h. $\dfrac{3}{8} \times \$20$ $7.50

2. Hilda is paid $8.80 an hour. What is her pay for $\frac{1}{4}$ hour? $2.20

3. Celeste usually earns $360 a week at her job. This week she earned only $\frac{3}{4}$ of her usual earnings. What was Celeste's pay this week?
$270

4. The average weekly pay of workers at the Randolph Company is $480.72. Gordon's weekly pay is only $\frac{5}{6}$ of that amount. What is Gordon's weekly pay? $400.60

Adding and Subtracting Like Fractions. Fractions such as $\frac{2}{7}$ and $\frac{4}{7}$ are called **like fractions** because they have the same, or common, denominator. In adding or subtracting like fractions, you add or subtract the numerators and write the result over the common denominator. For example:

These are like fractions: $\frac{2}{7}$ $\frac{3}{7}$ $\frac{6}{7}$.

$$\dfrac{2}{7} + \dfrac{3}{7} = \dfrac{5}{7} \qquad \dfrac{2}{5} + \dfrac{2}{5} = \dfrac{4}{5} \qquad \dfrac{5}{6} - \dfrac{4}{6} = \dfrac{1}{6} \qquad \dfrac{5}{7} - \dfrac{3}{7} = \dfrac{2}{7}$$

Exercise 2
Oral

1. Find the sums.

   a. $\dfrac{1}{5} + \dfrac{2}{5}$ $\dfrac{3}{5}$ c. $\dfrac{3}{8} + \dfrac{4}{8}$ $\dfrac{7}{8}$ e. $\dfrac{3}{8} + \dfrac{3}{8}$ $\dfrac{3}{4}$ g. $\dfrac{5}{12} + \dfrac{3}{12}$ $\dfrac{2}{3}$

   b. $\dfrac{3}{7} + \dfrac{3}{7}$ $\dfrac{6}{7}$ d. $\dfrac{3}{6} + \dfrac{2}{6}$ $\dfrac{5}{6}$ f. $\dfrac{1}{9} + \dfrac{2}{9}$ $\dfrac{1}{3}$ h. $\dfrac{3}{5} + \dfrac{4}{5}$ $1\dfrac{2}{5}$

2. Find the differences.

   a. $\dfrac{3}{7} - \dfrac{2}{7}$ $\dfrac{1}{7}$ d. $\dfrac{9}{10} - \dfrac{4}{10}$ $\dfrac{1}{2}$ g. $\dfrac{11}{16} - \dfrac{5}{16}$ $\dfrac{3}{8}$

   b. $\dfrac{9}{10} - \dfrac{6}{10}$ $\dfrac{3}{10}$ e. $\dfrac{7}{8} - \dfrac{5}{8}$ $\dfrac{1}{4}$ h. $\dfrac{3}{4} - \dfrac{1}{4}$ $\dfrac{1}{2}$

   c. $\dfrac{5}{6} - \dfrac{1}{6}$ $\dfrac{2}{3}$ f. $\dfrac{7}{12} - \dfrac{4}{12}$ $\dfrac{1}{4}$

Raising a Fraction to Higher Terms. When you have two equivalent fractions, the fraction with the larger numerals in the numerator and denominator is in **higher terms.** For example, $\frac{1}{3}$ and $\frac{2}{6}$ are equivalent fractions, and the fraction $\frac{2}{6}$ is in higher terms.

To raise a fraction to higher terms, you multiply its numerator and denominator by the same number. For example, suppose you want to raise $\frac{5}{6}$ to 12ths. The denominator you want, 12, is 2 times the present denominator, 6, so you multiply both the numerator and the denominator by 2 ($\frac{2}{2} \times \frac{5}{6} = \frac{10}{12}$).

**Exercise 3
Oral**

1. Replace N with a numeral to make the sentences true.

   a. $\frac{1}{3} = \frac{N}{9}$ 3   c. $\frac{3}{4} = \frac{N}{12}$ 9   e. $\frac{3}{5} = \frac{N}{10}$ 6   g. $\frac{7}{8} = \frac{N}{16}$ 14

   b. $\frac{1}{2} = \frac{N}{6}$ 3   d. $\frac{2}{3} = \frac{N}{6}$ 4   f. $\frac{3}{8} = \frac{N}{24}$ 9   h. $\frac{5}{6} = \frac{N}{24}$ 20

2. Raise each fraction to the terms shown.

   a. $\frac{1}{2}, \frac{2}{3}, \frac{3}{4}, \frac{5}{6}$ to 12ths $\frac{6}{12}, \frac{8}{12}, \frac{9}{12}, \frac{10}{12}$

   b. $\frac{1}{2}, \frac{1}{4}, \frac{3}{4}, \frac{7}{8}$ to 16ths $\frac{8}{16}, \frac{4}{16}, \frac{12}{16}, \frac{14}{16}$

**Exercise 4
Written**

Rewrite each fraction in the specified higher terms.

1. $\frac{1}{2}, \frac{3}{4}$ to 8ths $\frac{4}{8}, \frac{6}{8}$ 4. $\frac{1}{2}, \frac{3}{4}, \frac{3}{8}$ to 16ths $\frac{8}{16}, \frac{12}{16}, \frac{6}{16}$

2. $\frac{1}{2}, \frac{1}{5}, \frac{3}{5}$ to 10ths $\frac{5}{10}, \frac{2}{10}, \frac{6}{10}$ 5. $\frac{1}{3}, \frac{3}{4}, \frac{5}{8}$ to 24ths $\frac{8}{24}, \frac{18}{24}, \frac{15}{24}$

3. $\frac{1}{4}, \frac{1}{3}, \frac{1}{6}$ to 12ths $\frac{3}{12}, \frac{4}{12}, \frac{2}{12}$ 6. $\frac{5}{6}, \frac{1}{6}, \frac{2}{3}$ to 18ths $\frac{15}{18}, \frac{3}{18}, \frac{12}{18}$

Adding and Subtracting Unlike Fractions. Fractions that have different denominators, such as $\frac{1}{3}$ and $\frac{1}{6}$, are called **unlike fractions.** To add or subtract unlike fractions, you must make sure they have the same denominators. This can be accomplished if you rewrite the fractions in higher terms.

These are unlike fractions: $\frac{1}{4}$ $\frac{3}{7}$ $\frac{1}{8}$ $\frac{5}{6}$.

$$\frac{1}{2} + \frac{1}{3} = \frac{3}{6} + \frac{2}{6} = \frac{5}{6} \qquad\qquad \frac{7}{8} - \frac{1}{4} = \frac{7}{8} - \frac{2}{8} = \frac{5}{8}$$

For the denominators of the new fractions, you can use any number that can be divided evenly by the original denominators. For example, to add $\frac{1}{3}$ and $\frac{1}{4}$, you can change the denominators to 12ths.

$$\frac{4}{4} \times \frac{1}{3} = \frac{4}{12} \qquad\qquad \frac{3}{3} \times \frac{1}{4} = \frac{3}{12} \qquad\qquad \frac{4}{12} + \frac{3}{12} = \frac{7}{12}$$

The *smallest* number that can be divided evenly by the original denominators is used as the new denominator. This number is called the **least common denominator.** For example, to add $\frac{1}{4}$ and $\frac{1}{5}$ you use 20 as the denominator because 20 is the smallest number evenly divisible by 4 and 5.

$$\frac{5}{5} \times \frac{1}{4} = \frac{5}{20} \qquad\qquad \frac{4}{4} \times \frac{1}{5} = \frac{4}{20} \qquad\qquad \frac{5}{20} + \frac{4}{20} = \frac{9}{20}$$

It is possible that the largest denominator of a group of fractions may be the least common denominator. For example, 6 is the least common denominator of the fractions $\frac{1}{2}$, $\frac{1}{3}$, and $\frac{1}{6}$. But finding the least common denominator is not always this simple; sometimes you may have to multiply the largest denominator by 2, 3, 4, or more to find the least common denominator.

Exercise 5
Oral

1. Find the least common denominator of each group.

   a. $\frac{5}{6}, \frac{1}{3}$ 6   e. $\frac{1}{4}, \frac{3}{5}$ 20   h. $\frac{2}{3}, \frac{1}{2}, \frac{3}{5}$ 30

   b. $\frac{1}{2}, \frac{3}{8}$ 8   f. $\frac{7}{8}, \frac{3}{4}$ 8   i. $\frac{5}{6}, \frac{7}{8}, \frac{1}{3}$ 24

   c. $\frac{1}{6}, \frac{7}{12}$ 12   g. $\frac{1}{2}, \frac{3}{4}, \frac{7}{8}$ 8   j. $\frac{3}{4}, \frac{3}{10}, \frac{1}{2}$ 20

   d. $\frac{2}{5}, \frac{2}{3}$ 15

2. Rewrite each fraction in Problem 1, using the least common denominator of its group.

Exercise 6
Written

1. Find the sums.

   a. $\frac{1}{3} + \frac{5}{8}$ $\frac{23}{24}$ d. $\frac{5}{8} + \frac{1}{16}$ $\frac{11}{16}$ g. $\frac{5}{8} + \frac{3}{4}$ $1\frac{3}{8}$

   b. $\frac{1}{4} + \frac{3}{8}$ $\frac{5}{8}$ e. $\frac{5}{8} + \frac{7}{16}$ $1\frac{1}{16}$ h. $\frac{2}{3} + \frac{5}{6}$ $1\frac{1}{2}$

   c. $\frac{2}{3} + \frac{1}{2}$ $1\frac{1}{6}$ f. $\frac{1}{6} + \frac{2}{3}$ $\frac{5}{6}$

2. Find the differences.

   a. $\frac{3}{4} - \frac{1}{8}$ $\frac{5}{8}$ d. $\frac{2}{3} - \frac{1}{6}$ $\frac{1}{2}$ g. $\frac{7}{8} - \frac{1}{2}$ $\frac{3}{8}$

   b. $\frac{3}{8} - \frac{1}{16}$ $\frac{5}{16}$ e. $\frac{3}{4} - \frac{7}{12}$ $\frac{1}{6}$ h. $\frac{3}{4} - \frac{3}{8}$ $\frac{3}{8}$

   c. $\frac{3}{4} - \frac{1}{16}$ $\frac{11}{16}$ f. $\frac{1}{2} - \frac{1}{4}$ $\frac{1}{4}$

3. Of Jack Hulbert's total sales for the past two weeks, these parts came from sales to new customers: $\frac{1}{10}$ the first week, $\frac{1}{4}$ the second week. For the two weeks, what part of Jack's total sales came from new customers? $\frac{7}{20}$

4. Jessica has two pieces of copper tubing. One piece is $\frac{3}{4}$ of a yard long, the other piece is $\frac{3}{8}$ of a yard long. What is the difference in length between the two pieces of tubing? $\frac{3}{8}$

5. Jack O'Shea, using dirt, gravel, and paved roads, drove 20 miles from his farm to reach the nearest city. For $\frac{1}{16}$ of the trip Jack drove on a dirt road. He drove on a gravel road for $\frac{3}{8}$ of the trip. For what part of the trip did Jack drive on paved roads? $\frac{9}{16}$

Dividing with Fractions. When you divide a number by a fraction, you first *invert* the fraction (turn it upside down). Then you multiply the first number by the inverted fraction.

Example

Divide $7.20 by $\frac{3}{4}$.

Solution

$$\$7.20 \div \frac{3}{4} = ?$$

$$\overset{2.40}{\cancel{\$7.20}} \times \frac{4}{\underset{1}{\cancel{3}}} = \$9.60 \quad \textbf{Ans.}$$

Check: $\frac{3}{4} \times \$9.60 = \$7.20$

Explanation

To divide $7.20 by $\frac{3}{4}$, you turn the fraction upside down (invert it) and multiply $7.20 by $\frac{4}{3}$. The product (answer) is $9.60. To check, multiply the answer, $9.60, by the fraction, $\frac{3}{4}$. That product is the same as the number you started with, $7.20, so your answer is correct.

Actually, when you invert the fraction and multiply you are multiplying by the reciprocal of the fraction. The **reciprocal** of any number is the number that gives a product of 1 when it is multiplied by the original number. For example, $\frac{3}{2}$ is the reciprocal of $\frac{2}{3}$, because $\frac{3}{2} \times \frac{2}{3} = 1$. In the same way, $\frac{1}{5}$ is the reciprocal of $\frac{5}{1}$, because $\frac{1}{5} \times \frac{5}{1} = 1$. So, the easy way to find the reciprocal of any number is to turn it upside down, or invert it.

**Exercise 7
Oral**

1. Find the reciprocals.

   a. $\frac{3}{4}$ $\frac{4}{3}$

   b. $\frac{4}{5}$ $\frac{5}{4}$

   c. $\frac{7}{5}$ $\frac{5}{7}$

   d. 14 $\frac{1}{14}$

   e. $\frac{1}{9}$ $\frac{9}{1}$

   f. $\frac{4}{1}$ $\frac{1}{4}$

2. Find the quotients.

   a. $\frac{3}{5} \div 3$ $\frac{1}{5}$

   b. $\frac{3}{8} \div \frac{5}{8}$ $\frac{3}{5}$

   c. $\frac{1}{2} \div \frac{1}{4}$ 2

   d. $\frac{1}{3} \div \frac{1}{3}$ 1

   e. $\frac{8}{11} \div 4$ $\frac{2}{11}$

**Exercise 8
Written**

Find the quotients.

1. $5 \div \frac{2}{3}$ $7\frac{1}{2}$

2. $36 \div \frac{4}{5}$ 45

3. $24 \div \frac{3}{8}$ 64

4. $2 \div \frac{7}{9}$ $2\frac{4}{7}$

5. $\frac{3}{8} \div \frac{5}{6}$ $\frac{9}{20}$

6. $\frac{2}{3} \div \frac{4}{5}$ $\frac{5}{6}$

7. $\frac{8}{15} \div 12$ $\frac{2}{45}$

8. $\frac{7}{8} \div 10$ $\frac{7}{80}$

9. $2 \div \frac{8}{9}$ $2\frac{1}{4}$

10. $\frac{2}{3} \div \frac{1}{2}$ $1\frac{1}{3}$

REVIEW 15

Terms

1. Match the terms with the statements.

higher terms   like fractions   unlike fractions
least common denominator   reciprocal

   a. Smallest number that can be divided evenly by terms
      least common denominator
   b. Have different denominators   unlike fractions
   c. When an equivalent fraction has larger terms   higher terms
   d. Have the same or common denominator   like fractions
   e. When you multiply any number by this number you get 1
      reciprocal

Skills

2. Replace the N with a fraction or a numeral to make the statement true.

   a. $10 \times N = \$2.50$ $\dfrac{1}{4}$

   b. $\$9 \div \dfrac{3}{7} = N$ $\$21$

   c. $\dfrac{1}{3} + \dfrac{1}{6} = N$ $\dfrac{1}{2}$

   d. $\dfrac{4}{5} \times \dfrac{15}{2} = N$ 6

   e. $\dfrac{7}{8} - \dfrac{1}{4} = N$ $\dfrac{5}{8}$

   f. $\dfrac{2}{9} + \dfrac{7}{9} = N$ 1

3. a. Estimate the quotient: $357 \div 63.1$ 6
   b. Estimate the product: $5{,}800 \times 22$ 120,000
   c. Round $126,491 to the nearest hundred. $126,500
   d. Round 0.9987 to the nearest thousandth.   0.999

Problems

4. The average weekly cash receipts of a bus company for the first 10 weeks of the year were $45,600. The cash receipts for weeks eleven and twelve were $48,230 and $56,170. What were the average weekly cash receipts for all 12 weeks? $46,700 [10]

5. This year Sarah won a local election in which 10,800 votes were cast. In the previous election 12,500 people voted. If Sarah received $\frac{5}{8}$ of the total votes in this year's election, what number of votes did she get?   6,750 [15]

6. A store owner bought 240 cartons of eggs. The owner sold $\frac{5}{8}$ of the eggs and set aside 5 cartons which were not to be sold because of damage. How many cartons of eggs did the owner have left to sell?
   85 [4, 15]

7. Lucille Griswold is paid $0.65 for each unit she produces, up to 100 units. She is paid $0.09 more for each unit she produces over 100 units per day. Last week she produced 94 units on Monday, 128 on Tuesday, 117 on Wednesday, 106 on Thursday, and 118 on Friday. What was Lucille's gross pay for the week? $372.16 [7]

Calculator Clinic

Multiplying Fractions. You can use a calculator to multiply a fraction by a whole number or another fraction. For example, to do a problem such as $\frac{2}{3}$ of $54, you must mentally arrange the problem as $\frac{2}{3}$ of $\frac{\$54}{1}$. You then multiply the numerators and denominators in this way:

a. Press these keys in order: [2] [×] [5] [4] [=]

and [108.   ] appears in the display.

b. Now press these keys in order: [3] [×] [1] [=]

and [3.   ] appears in the display.

In the steps above, you multiplied the numerators and denominators to make a new fraction, which can be written as $\frac{108}{3}$. Now use your calculator to complete the problem.

c. Press these keys in order: [1] [0] [8] [÷] [3] [=]

and [36.   ], the answer, appears in the display.

Dividing Fractions. To do a problem such as $9.60 \div \frac{3}{4}$, you must invert the fraction and rewrite the problem as $9.60 \times \frac{4}{3}$. The problem now becomes one of multiplying fractions, and it is solved by following the steps shown above. If you do the problem correctly, you should get $12.80 as your answer.

Calculator Practice. For practice in multiplying fractions, complete the problems in Exercise 1. Then work the problems in Exercise 8 for practice in dividing fractions. For extra practice, solve the problems given here.

Use a calculator to multiply or divide these problems.

a. $\frac{5}{6} \times 96$ 80

c. $126 \times \frac{5}{12}$ $52.50

e. $45 \div \frac{5}{8}$ 72

b. $\frac{2}{3} \times \frac{9}{2} \times 6$ 18

d. $64 \div \frac{2}{3}$ $96

f. $\frac{3}{4} \div \frac{3}{8}$ 2

Section 16
Ratio and Proportion

A small corner market has 12 loaves of bread, 4 of which are Brand A and 8 of which are Brand B. One way of comparing the numbers of each brand is to say that Brand A is to Brand B as 4 is to 8. That way of comparing two amounts is a **ratio**. You may write the ratio of Brand A to Brand B as the fraction $\frac{4}{8}$, as 4 ÷ 8, or as 4:8.

If you want, you may say that the ratio of Brand B to Brand A is 8 to 4. You may write that ratio as $\frac{8}{4}$, as 8 ÷ 4, or as 8:4.

As with fractions, ratios can be simplified by dividing the terms by their greatest common divisor. For example, the ratio of Brand A to Brand B, $\frac{4}{8}$, can be simplified to $\frac{1}{2}$ by dividing each term by 4. The ratio of Brand B to Brand A, $\frac{8}{4}$, can be simplified to $\frac{2}{1}$ in the same way.

Using ratios, you may also say that for every two Brand B loaves there is one Brand A loaf. Or, for every Brand A loaf there are two Brand B loaves. The ratio of Brand A to Brand B is shown in Illustration 16–1.

Illustration 16–1. Ratio of Brand A to Brand B Is 1:2

If you are comparing weights or measures in a ratio, you must show both terms in the same units. For example, to compare a measure in inches with a measure in feet, you must express both measures in either inches or feet.

Exercise 1
Oral

1. Of 24 cars, 16 are small cars and 8 are large cars. Without simplifying the terms, what is the ratio of
    a. Small cars to large cars?   16 to 8
    b. Large cars to small cars?   8 to 16
    c. Small cars to the total number of cars?   16 to 24
    d. Large cars to the total number of cars?   8 to 24

2. A baseball team played 60 games, winning 45 and losing 15. In lowest terms, what is the ratio of the
    a. Games won to games lost?   3 to 1
    b. Games lost to games played?   1 to 4
    c. Games played to games won?   4 to 3
    d. Games won to games played?   3 to 4

3. Find the ratio of
    a. 25¢ to $1.25   1 to 5
    b. $0.20 to $4   1 to 20
    c. 3 yards to 2 feet   9 to 2
    d. 4 feet to 12 inches   4 to 1
    e. 2 pencils to 1 dozen pencils   1 to 6

Using Ratios. Suppose your gross pay for the year is earned from two jobs, a full-time job and a part-time job, in the ratio of 9 to 1. That ratio tells you that you earn $9 at your full-time job for every $1 you earn at your part-time job. In this ratio there are 10 parts, so the ratio of 9 to 1 can also be written in the form $\frac{9}{10}$ to $\frac{1}{10}$.

The ratio of 9 to 1 does not tell you how much pay you will earn. But, for any amount of earnings, you can use the ratio to find how much pay you would earn from full-time and part-time work. For example, if you were to earn gross pay of $25,000 for the year, $\frac{9}{10}$ or $22,500 would be from full-time work and $\frac{1}{10}$ or $2,500 would be from part-time work. This use of ratios is shown in Illustration 16–2.

Illustration 16–2. Full and Part-Time Earnings as a Ratio

**Exercise 2
Written**

■ Check your
answers by
adding the
amounts.

1. The Quinn family has $12,600 to spend for food and housing. The ratio of their food expenses to their housing expenses is 5 to 7. How much of the $12,600 should they plan to spend for
   a. Food? $5,250
   b. Housing? $7,350

2. Wes and Jared are buying a rare coin for $9,500 and investing money in the ratio of 3 to 2. How much will each man invest?   Wes, $5,700; Jared, $3,800

3. An office buys and uses 1 box of small envelopes to every 5 boxes of large envelopes. Of 72 boxes of envelopes in stock, how many boxes of each type of envelope are there?   12 boxes, small; 60 boxes, large

4. Phoebe Switzer earns income from regular pay and overtime pay in the ratio of 15 to 1. Last year she earned a total of $24,000. What amount did Phoebe earn from regular pay? overtime pay?
   $22,500; $1,500

5. Alva Courville's gross earnings for a year were $26,000. Of that amount she saved $1,300. What was the ratio of Alva's savings to her earnings?   1 to 20

6. Last year a business paid its employees a total of $600,000. Of that amount, $420,000 was paid to hourly rate employees and $180,000 to salaried employees. What was the ratio of
   a. Pay of hourly employees to total pay?   7 to 10
   b. Total pay to pay of salaried employees?   10 to 3
   c. Pay of salaried employees to pay of hourly employees?   3 to 7

In a Proportion,
$\frac{6}{9}$ ⤫ $\frac{8}{12}$
6 × 12 = 72
9 × 8 = 72

‡**Meaning of Proportion.** The ratio $\frac{6}{9}$, in lowest terms, is $\frac{2}{3}$. The ratio $\frac{8}{12}$, when simplified, is also $\frac{2}{3}$. So, $\frac{6}{9}$ and $\frac{8}{12}$ are equal, and you can show that equality as $\frac{6}{9} = \frac{8}{12}$. Such a statement, showing that ratios are equal, is called a **proportion**. You read the proportion this way: 6 is to 9 as 8 is to 12.

When working with a proportion, you multiply the numerator of one fraction by the denominator of the other fraction. The result of this multiplication is a **cross product**. *In all proportions, the cross products are equal.* For example, in the proportion $\frac{6}{9} = \frac{8}{12}$ the cross products are both 72. That is, 6 × 12 = 72 and 9 × 8 = 72.

‡**Finding the Unknown Term in a Proportion.** You can find an unknown term in a proportion by applying the idea that the cross products are equal.

Example

Chester Guzdal worked 8 hours and was paid $64. At the same rate, how much would he earn in 24 hours?

Solution	Explanation
$\frac{8}{24} = \frac{\$64}{N}$ 8 × N = 24 × $64 8N = $1,536 N = $192 **Ans.**	Let *N* stand for the unknown earnings, and show the ratio of hours ($\frac{8}{24}$) equal to the ratio of the earnings ($\frac{\$64}{N}$). Write the cross products as a number sentence (8 × *N*, or 8*N* = 24 × $64, or $1,536). Then find the unknown factor, *N*, by dividing the known product, $1,536, by the known factor, 8.

‡Exercise 3
Written

1. A newspaper carrier received $3.45 in tips from 12 customers. At the same rate, how much would be earned in tips from 32 customers? $9.20

2. In 6 weeks Faye Blum spent $63 for gas and oil for her car. At the same rate, how much would she spend for gas and oil in 52 weeks? $546

3. In 5 months Jose Arroyo earned $9,205 in regular-time and overtime wages. At the same rate, how much would he earn in 12 months? $22,092

4. Eight packages of paper weigh a total of 38 pounds. What is the weight of 50 packages of the same kind of paper? $237\frac{1}{2}$ pounds

5. Amanda Janson is planning a picnic and figures that 6 pounds of meat will serve 10 people. At the same rate, how many pounds of meat will she need for 250 people? 150 pounds

6. At the Delta Computer Center, a computer monitor regularly priced at $150 is on sale for $115. At that same rate of discount, what should be the sale price of a printer regularly priced at $450? $345

7. Silk cloth is on sale at a price of $19.80 for 5 yards. If 9 yards of the cloth are bought at the same rate, what is the
   a. Estimated cost of the cloth? $36
   b. Actual cost of the cloth? $35.64

8. Ray Cates made a 235-mile car trip in 5 hours. How many miles will he travel in 7 hours by driving at the same rate?   329

REVIEW 16

Terms

1. Match the terms with the statements.

   cross product   proportion   ratio

   a. Shows that two ratios are equal   proportion
   b. Results from multiplying the numerator of one fraction by the denominator of the other fraction in a proportion   cross product
   c. A way to compare two numbers   ratio

Skills

2. a. $1,400 \times 400 = ?$ $560,000
   b. $9,300 \div 100 = ?$ 93
   c. $N \times \frac{3}{8} = \frac{3}{4}$ 2
   d. $295 \times \frac{3}{5} = ?$ $177
   e. $540 \div \frac{3}{4} = ?$ $720
   f. $\frac{18}{35} + \frac{12}{35} = ?$ $\frac{6}{7}$
   g. $\frac{5}{6} - \frac{1}{8} = ?$ $\frac{17}{24}$
   h. Change $\frac{17}{6}$ to a mixed number. $2\frac{5}{6}$
   i. Raise $\frac{2}{3}$ to an equivalent fraction with a denominator of 9. $\frac{6}{9}$

3. Find the estimated and exact answers.
   a. $1,299 \times 42$ $52,000; $54,558
   b. $40,950 \div 78$ $500; $525

Problems

4. A computer store sells 8 boxes of $5\frac{1}{4}$ inch diskettes to every 3 boxes of $3\frac{1}{2}$ inch diskettes. Find the ratio of [16]
   a. Sales of $5\frac{1}{4}$ inch diskettes to $3\frac{1}{2}$ inch diskettes   8 to 3
   b. Sales of $3\frac{1}{2}$ inch diskettes to $5\frac{1}{4}$ inch diskettes   3 to 8
   c. Sales of $3\frac{1}{2}$ inch diskettes to total diskette sales   3 to 11
   d. Sales of $5\frac{1}{4}$ inch diskettes to total diskette sales   8 to 11

5. A salary of $312 per week is how much
   a. Per year? $16,224 [7]
   b. Per month? $1,352 [10]

6. A retail store bought a shipment of ties at an average cost of $8.21 each. The store sold 40 silk ties for $18 each, 50 polyester ties for $12 each, and 14 knit ties for $13 each. What was the average selling price per tie, to the nearest cent? $14.44 [10]

‡7. A souvenir shop sells 120 baseball caps to every 15 pennants. At the same rate, how many baseball caps would the shop sell if 40 pennants were sold?   320 [16]

Overtime work pays you more.

Overtime pay is an extra amount of money paid for working more than the usual work hours in a day or a week. Overtime pay is often figured at one and a half times the regular-time rate and is called **time-and-a-half pay.** Sometimes **double-time pay** is given for work beyond time-and-a-half work or for work on weekends and holidays. Double-time pay is two times the regular-time pay rate.

Figuring Overtime Pay. To find time-and-a-half pay, you must first multiply the regular pay rate by $1\frac{1}{2}$ to get the time-and-a-half rate. Then you multiply the time-and-a-half rate by the number of time-and-a-half hours.

$$1\frac{1}{2} \times \textbf{Regular Pay Rate} = \textbf{Time-and-a-Half Rate*}$$

$$\textbf{Time-and-a-Half Hours} \times \textbf{Time-and-a-Half Rate}$$
$$= \textbf{Time-and-a-Half Pay}$$

To find double-time pay, you must first multiply the regular pay rate by 2 to get the double-time rate. You then multiply the double-time rate by the number of double-time hours.

$$2 \times \textbf{Regular Pay Rate} = \textbf{Double-Time Rate}$$

$$\textbf{Double-Time Hours} \times \textbf{Double-Time Rate} = \textbf{Double-Time Pay}$$

Example

Lask week Mary Vaughn worked 6 hours at time-and-a-half pay and 2 hours at double-time pay. Her regular pay rate was $9.60 per hour. What was her total overtime pay for the week?

Solution	Explanation
$1\frac{1}{2} \times \$9.60 = \$14.40$ time-and-a-half rate	The time-and-a-half rate and the double-time rate were figured first. The time-and-a-half pay and the double-time pay were then figured and added to find the total overtime pay.
$2 \times \$9.60 = \$19.20$ double-time rate	
$6 \times \$14.40 = \$\ 86.40$ time-and-a-half pay	
$2 \times \$19.20 = \underline{\ \ \ \ 38.40}$ double-time pay	
$\$124.80$ total overtime pay	
Ans.	

**Exercise 1
Written**

1. Felix Garcia worked 6 hours at time-and-a-half pay last week. His regular pay rate was $11 an hour. What was Felix's total overtime pay for the week? $99

---

*Do not round off a fraction of a cent in an overtime rate. Rather, wait to round off until you find the total overtime pay. For example, if a regular pay rate is $7.07 an hour, the time-and-a-half pay is $10.605 an hour ($1\frac{1}{2} \times \$7.07 = \$10.605$). The pay for 3 hours of time-and-a-half work at $10.605 an hour would be $31.82 ($3 \times \$10.605 = \$31.815$, or $31.82).

2. The Grafix Shop pays double time for work done on weekends. An employee who earns a regular pay rate of $6.95 an hour works 8 hours on Saturday. What is the employee's
   a. Estimated pay for work on Saturday? $112
   b. Actual pay for Saturday work? $111.20

3. During one week Joan McFarland worked 4 hours at time-and-a-half pay and 3 hours at double-time pay. Her regular pay rate was $7.72 an hour. What was Joan's total overtime pay for the week? $92.64

■ Do NOT round off an overtime rate.

4. You are paid $9.95 an hour with time-and-a-half pay for all hours you work over 40 hours a week. Lask week you worked 47 hours.
   a. How many overtime hours did you work? 7
   b. What was your overtime rate? $14.925
   c. What was your overtime pay for the week? $104.48

■ To find gross pay, combine regular and overtime pay.

5. Sheldon Berger worked 40 hours last week at his regular pay rate of $13 an hour. He also worked 5 hours at time-and-a-half pay.
   a. What was Sheldon's regular pay for the week? $520
   b. What was his overtime pay for the week? $97.50
   c. What was his gross pay for the week? $617.50

6. In 1 week Mei-yu Li worked $38\frac{1}{2}$ hours at her regular-time rate, $3\frac{1}{2}$ hours at time and a half, and 4 hours at double time. Her regular hourly pay rate was $12. What was Mei-yu's gross pay that week? $621

Figuring Regular-Time Hours, Overtime Hours, and Gross Pay. To figure gross pay when overtime hours are worked, follow these steps: (1) find the number of hours worked at the regular and overtime rates; (2) figure the overtime pay rate or rates; and (3) figure and combine the regular pay and overtime pay. Here is an example:

Example

Peter Sikora works on the basis of an 8-hour day at $8 an hour. He is paid time and a half for overtime on Monday through Friday and double time for weekend and holiday work. In one week Peter worked these hours: Monday, 8; Tuesday, 9; Wednesday, 11; Thursday, 7; Friday, 9; Saturday, 5. What was Peter's gross pay for the week?

	Solution			**Explanation**
	Regular Time	Time and a Half	Double Time	
Monday	8	0	0	$1\frac{1}{2} \times \$8 = \$12$ time-and-a-half rate
Tuesday	8	1	0	$2 \times \$8 = \$16$ double-time rate
Wednesday	8	3	0	
Thursday	7	0	0	$39 \times \$8\ \ = \$312$ regular-time pay
Friday	8	1	0	$5 \times \$12 = \ \ \ \ 60$ time-and-a-half pay
Saturday	0	0	5	$5 \times \$16 = \ \ \ \ 80$ double-time pay
Totals	39	5	5	$452 gross pay **Ans.**

**Exercise 2
Written**

1. Your job pays $5 an hour with time and a half for all overtime hours worked beyond 8 hours a day. This week you worked these hours: Monday, 6; Tuesday, 8; Wednesday, 10; Thursday, 9; Friday, 11.
   a. How many regular hours did you work?   38
   b. How many overtime hours did you work?   6
   c. What is your regular-time pay for the week? $190
   d. What is your overtime pay for the week? $45
   e. What is your gross pay for the week? $235

■ Figure overtime on a daily or weekly basis as directed.

2. Elnora Kar's regular pay rate is $9 an hour. She is paid time and a half for overtime work beyond 40 hours a week. Last week Elnora worked 8 hours a day on Monday, Wednesday, Thursday, and Friday. She worked 10 hours on Tuesday.
   a. How many regular hours did Elnora work?   40
   b. How many overtime hours did she work?   2
   c. What was Elnora's regular-time pay for the week? $360
   d. What was her overtime pay for the week? $27
   e. What was Elnora's gross pay for the week? $387

3. Jeff Irfan is paid on an 8-hour-day basis, with time and a half for all overtime. Jeff worked these hours in one week: Monday, 8; Tuesday, 6; Wednesday, 11; Thursday, 10; Friday, 8. Jeff is paid $10.30 an hour.
   a. What was Jeff's regular-time pay for the week? $391.40
   b. What was his overtime pay for the week? $77.25
   c. What was Jeff's gross or total pay for the week? $468.65

4. During the week of November 8, Roseann Walker worked 9 hours a day, Monday through Friday. Her regular pay rate was $14 an hour, with time and a half for all work beyond 40 hours a week. What were Roseann's earnings for that week? $665

■ Remember!— Do not round an overtime rate.

5. Tim Bjorum worked these hours during one week: Monday, 9; Tuesday, 4; Wednesday, 8; Thursday, 10; Friday, 10. He was paid $10.67 an hour on the basis of an 8-hour working day, with time and a half for all overtime. What was Tim's gross pay for those five days? $464.15

6. The G. R. Price Tool Company pays Marsha Carmichael a regular hourly rate of $11.70 an hour, with time and a half for all hours worked over 37½ per week. What is Marsha's gross pay for a week in which she worked 7½ hours a day Monday through Thursday, and 10 hours on Friday? $482.63

7. Jason Swada is paid $8.15 an hour for an 8-hour work day, with time and a half for overtime Monday through Friday. Work on weekends and holidays is paid as double time. In one recent week, Jason worked these hours: Monday, 9; Tuesday, 10; Wednesday, 8; Thursday, 8; Friday, 9; Saturday, 7. What was Jason's gross pay for that week? $489

8. Last week you worked 9 hours a day, Monday through Friday, and 8 hours on Saturday. Saturday was a holiday. Your employer paid you time and a half for work beyond 40 hours in the week, Monday

through Friday, and double time for the Saturday work. Your regular pay rate was $8.20 an hour. What was your gross pay for the week? $520.70

REVIEW 17

Terms

1. Match the terms with the statements.

    double-time pay   time-and-a-half pay

    a. Twice the regular pay rate   double-time pay
    b. One and a half times the regular pay rate   time-and-a-half pay

Skills

2. a. $16 \times \dfrac{3}{4} = ?$ $12
               d. $\dfrac{3}{8} + \dfrac{11}{8} = ?$ $1\dfrac{3}{4}$

    b. $38 \div \dfrac{1}{4} = ?$ 152
               e. $\dfrac{2}{5} + \dfrac{2}{3} = ?$ $1\dfrac{1}{15}$

    c. $\dfrac{12}{35} \times \dfrac{7}{2} = ?$ $1\dfrac{1}{5}$
               f. $\dfrac{3}{4} - \dfrac{1}{8} = ?$ $\dfrac{5}{8}$

3. Find the value of N.

    a. $N \times 13 = 82 - 43$ 3
               c. $64 \div N = 1\dfrac{1}{3} + 6\dfrac{2}{3}$ 8

    b. $0 \div 3 = N$ 0
               d. $16 \times 1 = 1 \times N$ 16

4. Find the estimated and exact answers.
    a. $1{,}023 \times 96$ 100,000; 98,208
    b. $1{,}248 \div 78$ 15; 16
    c. $32.1 \div 0.75$ 40; 42.8
    d. 0.92×7.1 7; 6.532

5. a. Multiply each by 0.1: $95; $28.90; $576 $9.50; $2.89; $57.60
    b. Multiply each by 0.01: $24; $89.89; $540 $0.24; $0.90; $5.40
    c. Divide each by 0.01:   52; $1.70; $3   5,200; $170; $300
    d. Divide each by 10: $18; $36.72; 7,000 $1.80; $3.67; 700

Problems

6. Stella Lorida worked these hours last week: Monday, 10; Tuesday, 8; Wednesday, 9; Thursday, 6; Friday, 8; Saturday, 5. Stella is paid $11.40 per hour for regular hours, time and a half for overtime during the week, and double time for weekend hours. If Stella works on an 8-hour-day basis, what was her pay for the week? $598.50 [17]

7. An auto dealer sells two types of vehicles: cars and vans. The dealer now has 80 cars and 20 vans in stock. Find the ratio of
    a. Number of cars to total vehicles   80 to 100; 4 to 5
    b. Number of vans to total vehicles   20 to 100; 1 to 5
    c. Number of vans to cars   20 to 80; 1 to 4
    d. Number of cars to vans   80 to 20; 4 to 1 [16]

8. In one day a record store sold 20 albums at $16; 14 albums at $12; and 18 albums at $9. The store also sold 26 compact disks at $16 each. What was the average price of the albums sold that day? $12.50 [10]

‡9. An office supply store usually sells 24 storage cabinets for every 6 filing cabinets it sells. At the same rate, how many filing cabinets should the store have sold if 20 storage cabinets have already been sold?   5 [16]

 # Calculator Clinic

Calculating Total Pay. The calculation of total pay when overtime is worked requires that you use the memory keys of your calculator. Suppose you have to find the total pay of an employee who works 38 regular-time hours at $8 an hour and 6 overtime hours at time and a half. You do this by following this procedure:

a. Clear your calculator by pressing [AC]

b. Press these keys in order: [3] [8] [×] [8] [=] and

    | 304. | appears in the display.

c. Now press [M+] . You have added the regular time pay, 304, into memory.

d. Next, press these keys in order: [1] [.] [5] [×] [8] [=] and the overtime rate | 12. | appears in the display.

e. Now press these keys in order: [×] [6] [=] [M+] . You have added the overtime pay, 72, into memory. Press [MR/C] once to get the total pay from memory into the display as shown.

    | 376. |

Saving Time. You can place the product into memory without using the equals key. Just press 38, ×, 8, and M+, and the product, 304, is displayed on the screen and placed in memory at the same time. The same steps also work for 12 × 6. Just press 12, ×, 6, and M+, and 72 is displayed and stored at the same time.

Calculator Practice. Apply what you have just learned about using your calculator to the problems in this section. Do Problems 2 through 6 in Exercise 1 and Problems 1 through 5 and 7 and 8 in Exercise 2.

Mixed Numbers

In the previous section you found an overtime rate by multiplying the regular pay rate by a mixed number, $1\frac{1}{2}$. You will soon use mixed numbers to solve business and personal problems in other units. These problems include

1. Finding the amount of interest at a rate of $5\frac{1}{4}\%$.

2. Finding the city income tax due when the rate is $1\frac{1}{2}\%$.

3. Writing a stock price of $86\frac{5}{8}$ in dollar terms.

4. Finding the cost per pound of a $3\frac{1}{2}$ lb. box of soap powder selling for $2.80.

5. Finding the selling price when the markup is $33\frac{1}{3}\%$.

Multiplying a Whole Number and a Mixed Number. To multiply a whole number by a mixed number, you multiply the whole number by each part of the mixed number, then add the results. Look at this example:

Example

Multiply 17 by $6\frac{5}{7}$.

Solution

Step 1: $17 \times \dfrac{5}{7} = \dfrac{85}{7} = 12\dfrac{1}{7}$

Step 2: $17 \times 6 \qquad = 102$

$\qquad\qquad\qquad\qquad 114\dfrac{1}{7}$ **Ans.**

Exercise 1
Written

1. Find the products.

    a. $16 \times 3\frac{1}{2}$ 56

    b. $24 \times 4\frac{3}{4}$ 114

    c. $45 \times 6\frac{3}{5}$ 297

    d. $18\frac{3}{8} \times 24$ 441

    e. $27\frac{2}{5} \times 35$ 959

    f. $17\frac{5}{6} \times 72$ 1284

    g. $16 \times 3\frac{5}{8}$ 58

    h. $27 \times 4\frac{2}{3}$ 126

    i. $60 \times 6\frac{4}{5}$ 408

2. When Phoebe Milton started working 25 years ago, her pay rate was $1.60 an hour. Her hourly pay has increased and is now $4\frac{1}{4}$ times what it used to be. What is Phoebe's current hourly pay rate? $6.80

3. Tom's lawn care service uses an average of $3\frac{1}{2}$ gallons of gasoline each working day. How many gallons of gasoline will Tom use in a month that has 26 working days?   91 gallons

Adding Mixed Numbers. To add mixed numbers you may have to change the fractions to equivalent fractions. Here is an example:

Example

Rhonda Clayton ran $4\frac{3}{4}$ miles on Monday and $3\frac{3}{8}$ miles on Wednesday. What total distance did she run in those two days?

Solution

	8ths
4	6
3	3

$$7 + \frac{9}{8} = 8\frac{1}{8} \text{ miles } \textbf{Ans.}$$

Explanation

The least common denominator of 4 and 8 is 8, so the fractions are shown as 8ths. The numerators of the equivalent fractions are written in a column at the right. The numerators are added and the sum, 9, is written as $\frac{9}{8}$. The whole numbers are added and the sum, 7, is combined with the sum of the fractions for a total length of $8\frac{1}{8}$ miles

**Exercise 2
Written**

Find the sums.

1. $4\frac{3}{4}$ 2. $5\frac{2}{3}$ 3. $7\frac{7}{8}$ 4. $5\frac{1}{3}$ 5. $6\frac{3}{4}$ 6. $8\frac{7}{10}$

$3\frac{1}{4}$ $9\frac{1}{4}$ $2\frac{1}{2}$ $7\frac{5}{6}$ $3\frac{1}{2}$ $14\frac{2}{5}$

8 $14\frac{11}{12}$ $10\frac{3}{8}$ $13\frac{1}{6}$ $2\frac{5}{8}$ $9\frac{1}{4}$

                                                        $12\frac{7}{8}$ $32\frac{7}{20}$

Subtracting Mixed Numbers. You may also have to change the fractions to equivalent fractions to subtract mixed numbers. Look at this example:

Example

The height of a building designed to be $120\frac{1}{4}$ feet high was reduced by $6\frac{7}{8}$ feet to cut costs. What is the building's new height?

Solution

	8ths
119 ~~120~~	10 ~~2~~
6	7

$$113 + \frac{3}{8} = 113\frac{3}{8} \text{ feet } \textbf{Ans.}$$

Explanation

The least common denominator of the fractions is 8. The fractions are shown as 8ths, and the numerators of the equivalent fractions are written in the column at the right. Because 7 eighths cannot be subtracted from 2 eighths, one whole unit (or 8 eighths) is borrowed from the 120, leaving 119 whole units. The 8 eighths are added to the 2 eighths in the column at the right for a total of 10 eighths. Then the 7 eighths are subtracted from the 10 eighths, leaving 3 eighths ($\frac{3}{8}$). The whole numbers are subtracted and the difference, 113, is combined with the $\frac{3}{8}$ to give a total difference of $113\frac{3}{8}$ feet.

**Exercise 3
Written**

Find the differences and check your work.

1. $8\frac{7}{8}$ 2. $12\frac{5}{6}$ 3. $7\frac{2}{5}$ 4. $9\frac{1}{6}$ 5. $8\frac{1}{3}$ 6. $21\frac{1}{5}$

   $4\frac{3}{4}$ $7\frac{2}{3}$ $4\frac{1}{4}$ $7\frac{2}{3}$ $2\frac{5}{8}$ $16\frac{1}{2}$

   $4\frac{1}{8}$ $5\frac{1}{6}$ $3\frac{3}{20}$ $1\frac{1}{2}$ $5\frac{17}{24}$ $4\frac{7}{10}$

Changing Mixed Numbers to Improper Fractions. ınge a mixed number to an improper fraction, you must follow the steps shown in this example:

Example

Change $4\frac{5}{6}$ to an improper fraction.

Solution	Explanation
$4 \times 6 = 24$	1. Multiply the whole number by the denominator of the fraction.
$24 + 5 = 29$	2. Add that product to the numerator of the fraction.
$\frac{29}{6}$ **Ans.**	3. Write the sum over the denominator of the fraction.

**Exercise 4
Oral**

Change each mixed number to an improper fraction.

1. $2\frac{1}{5}$ $\frac{11}{5}$ 3. $5\frac{2}{3}$ $\frac{17}{3}$ 5. $10\frac{3}{8}$ $\frac{83}{8}$ 7. $25\frac{1}{4}$ $\frac{101}{4}$

2. $4\frac{1}{8}$ $\frac{33}{8}$ 4. $12\frac{1}{2}$ $\frac{25}{2}$ 6. $33\frac{1}{3}$ $\frac{100}{3}$ 8. $2\frac{7}{16}$ $\frac{39}{16}$

Multiplying Mixed Numbers by Mixed Numbers. To multiply a mixed number by a mixed number, you must follow the steps in this example:

Example

Multiply $4\frac{1}{2}$ by $6\frac{3}{4}$.

Solution	Explanation
$4\frac{1}{2} \times 6\frac{3}{4} = \frac{9}{2} \times \frac{27}{4} = \frac{243}{8} = 30\frac{3}{8}$ **Ans.**	Change the mixed numbers to improper fractions, then multiply.

**Exercise 5
Written**

Find the products.

1. $3\frac{1}{4} \times 2\frac{1}{2}$ $8\frac{1}{8}$

3. $3\frac{1}{5} \times 2\frac{1}{8}$ $6\frac{4}{5}$

5. $1\frac{1}{5} \times 2\frac{5}{8}$ $3\frac{3}{20}$

2. $2\frac{1}{4} \times 4\frac{1}{5}$ $9\frac{9}{20}$

4. $4\frac{1}{8} \times 3\frac{1}{2}$ $14\frac{7}{16}$

6. $2\frac{3}{4} \times 1\frac{2}{3}$ $4\frac{7}{12}$

Dividing with Mixed Numbers. If you are doing a division problem with a mixed number or numbers, you must first change each mixed number to an improper fraction. Then you must invert the divisor and multiply. For example:

$$37\frac{1}{2} \div 1\frac{1}{2} = \frac{75}{2} \div \frac{3}{2} = \frac{\overset{25}{\cancel{75}}}{\cancel{2}} \times \frac{\overset{1}{\cancel{2}}}{\cancel{3}} = 25$$

Find the quotients.

**Exercise 6
Written**

1. $3\frac{1}{8} \div 5$ $\frac{5}{8}$

4. $8 \div 1\frac{1}{4}$ $6\frac{2}{5}$

7. $4\frac{2}{5} \div 2\frac{3}{4}$ $1\frac{3}{5}$

2. $4\frac{4}{5} \div 6$ $\frac{4}{5}$

5. $6 \div 4\frac{4}{5}$ $1\frac{1}{4}$

8. $16\frac{1}{2} \div 3\frac{2}{3}$ $4\frac{1}{2}$

3. $5\frac{5}{6} \div 7$ $\frac{5}{6}$

6. $2\frac{3}{4} \div 2\frac{1}{2}$ $1\frac{1}{10}$

9. $87\frac{1}{2} \div 3\frac{1}{2}$ 25

REVIEW 18

Skills

1. a. $\frac{2}{7} + \frac{4}{7} + \frac{6}{7} = ?$ $1\frac{5}{7}$

   d. $1\frac{1}{4} + 3\frac{5}{6} = ?$ $5\frac{1}{12}$

   b. $\frac{4}{5} - \frac{2}{7} = ?$ $\frac{18}{35}$

   e. $6\frac{3}{4} \div 3\frac{3}{8} = ?$ 2

   c. $\$78.40 \times \frac{3}{4} = ?$ $\$58.80$

   f. $2\frac{1}{2} \times 4\frac{1}{4} = ?$ $10\frac{5}{8}$

Problems

2. During one year Elsie Wyle worked 48 weeks and was on vacation for 4 weeks. Without simplifying the terms, find the ratio of her
   a. Work weeks to vacation weeks   48 to 4
   b. Vacation weeks to work weeks   4 to 48
   c. Work weeks to total weeks in year   48 to 52
   d. Vacation weeks to total weeks in year   4 to 52 [16]

3. On a recent trip Eric and Ron agreed to share gasoline expenses in the ratio of 3 to 2, with Eric paying the larger share. If they bought $90 worth of gasoline, what amount did each pay?
   Eric, $54; Ron, $36 [16]

4. Delphine Atwell works on an 8-hour-day basis and is paid $8.94 an hour for regular-time work. Her hours of work are from 8:00 a.m. to 11:30 a.m. and from 12:30 p.m. to 5:00 p.m. If Delphine arrives more than 3 minutes late or leaves more than 3 minutes early, she is penalized 15 minutes. The time she worked on Monday is shown here: [13]

In	Out	In	Out
7:55 a.m.	11:28 a.m.	12:35 p.m.	4:59 p.m.

a. How many regular-time hours did she work on Monday? $7\frac{3}{4}$
b. What is her estimated gross pay for Monday? $72
c. What exact gross pay did she earn on Monday? $69.29

5. Elmo Tork is paid 98¢ for each welding tip he produces that is accepted. Last week he produced these amounts of tips: Monday, 68; Tuesday, 74; Wednesday, 70; Thursday, 75; Friday, 78. Although 11 of the tips Elmo made last week were not accepted, 18 items were not accepted the week before. What was Elmo's gross pay last week? $346.92 [7]

6. On September 30 Alicia Alvero's check register balance was $534.04 and her bank statement balance was $945.63. A comparison of her register and the bank statement showed a service charge of $4.25 and earned interest of $3.60 on the statement but not recorded in the register. Check #346 for $210 and #352 for $202.24 were outstanding. Prepare a reconciliation statement. $533.39 [5]

Section 19
Fractional Relationships

In this section you will learn how to solve four common types of problems using fractions. They are:

1. Finding a part of a number.

2. Finding a number that is a part greater or smaller than another.

3. Finding what part a number is of another.

4. Finding what part a number is greater or smaller than another.

Finding a Part of a Number. To find a fractional part of a number, you multiply the number by the fraction.

Example

Bev Keegan's gross pay last week was $376. One eighth ($\frac{1}{8}$) of that amount was overtime pay. How much overtime pay did Bev earn?

Solution	Explanation
$\frac{1}{8} \times \$376 = \$47$ overtime pay **Ans.** $F \times F = P$	One eighth ($\frac{1}{8}$) of $376 means the same as $\frac{1}{8} \times \$376$. To find $\frac{1}{8}$ of $376, you multiply $376 by $\frac{1}{8}$.

You will see other phrases such as "$\frac{1}{4}$ as much as ...," "$\frac{5}{8}$ as great as ...," "$\frac{2}{3}$ as large as ...," and "$\frac{3}{5}$ as many as ...." All of those phrases mean the same as "of," "times," or "×." In each case the fraction is a known factor, the number is the other known factor, and the answer is the unknown product. You find the answer by multiplying the number, a known factor, by the fraction, which is the other known factor (F × F = P).

Exercise 1
Oral

1. $\frac{2}{3}$ of 30 is N 20

2. $\frac{3}{4}$ of 36 is N 27

3. $\frac{3}{5}$ of 35 = N 21

4. $\frac{1}{3}$ × 18 = N 6

5. 42 × $\frac{5}{6}$ = N 35

6. 64 × $\frac{3}{8}$ is N 24

7. $\frac{7}{8}$ as large as 56 = N 49

8. $\frac{4}{5}$ as many as 60 = N 48

9. $\frac{3}{10}$ as much as 50 = N 15

Exercise 2
Written

■ Remember — of, as much as, as large as, and as many as all mean times, or "×".

1. In 1 week Marc Kipple earned $360.42, $\frac{5}{6}$ of which was in regular-time pay. What was Marc's regular-time pay? $300.35

2. Kim Wintell's overtime pay was only $\frac{1}{10}$ as much as her regular pay of $22,910. What was her overtime pay? $2,291

3. Last year Pablo Arellano's gross earnings were $26,780. Pablo was unemployed part of this year, so his earnings were only $\frac{4}{5}$ as great as last year's. What were Pablo's earnings this year? $21,424

4. The Car Security Company sold 15,816 burglar alarms in the year before last. Last year they sold only $\frac{7}{8}$ as many alarms. How many alarms did they sell last year?   13,839

Finding a Number That Is a Part Greater or Smaller Than Another.
Suppose that you are to find a number that is $\frac{1}{4}$ greater than another number, or $\frac{1}{4}$ more than another number. Phrases such as "$\frac{1}{4}$ greater than" or "$\frac{1}{4}$ more than" a number mean that you are to *add* $\frac{1}{4}$ of the number to that number. For example, the hourly pay rate that is $\frac{1}{4}$ more than $8 an hour is $10 an hour.

$$\frac{1}{4} \times \$8 = \$2$$

$$\$8 + \$2 = \$10$$

On the other hand, suppose you are to find a number that is $\frac{1}{4}$ less than another number, or $\frac{1}{4}$ smaller than another number. Terms such as those mean that you are to *subtract* $\frac{1}{4}$ of the number from the number. For example, the pay rate that is $\frac{1}{4}$ less than $12 an hour is $9 an hour.

$$\frac{1}{4} \times \$12 = \$3$$

$$\$12 - \$3 = \$9$$

**Exercise 3
Oral**

Find the unknown numbers.

1. $\frac{1}{5}$ more than 20   24

2. $\frac{1}{6}$ greater than $30 $35

3. $\frac{1}{8}$ more than $16 $18

4. $\frac{1}{5}$ larger than $40 $48

5. $12 plus $\frac{1}{4}$ of itself $15

6. $\frac{1}{6}$ smaller than $30 $25

7. $\frac{1}{3}$ less than $60 $40

8. $\frac{1}{4}$ less than $24 $18

9. $\frac{1}{7}$ smaller than $42 $36

10. $24 minus $\frac{1}{8}$ of itself $21

**Exercise 4
Written**

1. Phil's salary is $24,300 a year, or $2,075 a month. Norma's yearly pay is $\frac{3}{10}$ more than Phil's. What is Norma's yearly pay? $31,590

2. Last March Gene Booth worked overtime and earned $\frac{1}{8}$ more than his usual pay of $1,712 a month. How much did Gene earn last March? $1,926

3. Two years ago a cable company's total sales were $246,750. Last year the cable company increased its sales by $\frac{4}{7}$ over the year before. What were the company's total sales last year? $387,750

■ Check—Are you using the right method?

4. Ella Stearns lost her old job that paid $13.20 an hour. Her new job pays $\frac{1}{5}$ less. How much does her new job pay per hour? $10.56

5. The Reese Company has 70 employees and plans to cut its labor costs by $\frac{1}{12}$. The company's total labor cost is now $1,800,000 a year. What will be the company's labor cost per year after the cut?
$1,650,000

6. Fred's average weekly earnings of $486 dropped by $\frac{1}{9}$ after he stopped working overtime. What was his new average pay per week? $432

Finding What Part a Number Is of Another. To find what fractional part one number is of another number, you show the numbers as a fraction. You write the number that is the part as the numerator of the fraction. As the denominator of the fraction, you write the number that is the whole with which the part is being compared. Then you simplify the fraction.

Example

Kim Logan's total pay for a week was $400. Of that amount, $50 was overtime pay. What fractional part of Kim's total pay was the overtime pay?

Solution

$$\frac{\$50}{\$400} = \frac{1}{8} \quad \textbf{Ans.}$$

$$\text{Check: } \frac{1}{\cancel{8}_1} \times \frac{\cancel{\$400}^{50}}{1} = \$50$$

Explanation

The part, $50, is being compared with the whole, $400. So, $50 is written as the numerator of a fraction, with $400 as the denominator. The fraction is then simplified to $\frac{1}{8}$. As a check, the whole ($400) is multiplied by the fractional part ($\frac{1}{8}$) to be sure that the product equals the part ($50).

■ Use this to make sure your answer is reasonable.

When you are finding what part a number is of another, you should use this rough check on your answer:

1. A number when compared with itself equals 1. For example, 6 compared to $6 = \frac{6}{6} = 1$.

2. When a number is compared with a larger number, the result is less than 1. For example, 4 compared to $7 = \frac{4}{7}$.

3. When a number is compared with a smaller number, the result is greater than 1. For example, 3 compared to 2 is $\frac{3}{2}$, or $1\frac{1}{2}$.

**Exercise 5
Oral**

1. 5 is what part of 12? 9? 8? 6? 4? 3? 2? $\frac{5}{12}, \frac{5}{9}, \frac{5}{8}, \frac{5}{6}, \frac{5}{4}, \frac{5}{3}, \frac{5}{2}$

2. 7 is what part of 15? 13? 11? 9? 6? 5? 3? $\frac{7}{15}, \frac{7}{13}, \frac{7}{11}, \frac{7}{9}, \frac{7}{6}, \frac{7}{5}, \frac{7}{3}$

3. $12 is what part of $36? $24? $16? $7? $5? $9? $\frac{1}{3}, \frac{1}{2}, \frac{3}{4}, \frac{12}{7}, \frac{12}{5}, \frac{4}{3}$

4. What part of $12 is $3? $4? $11? $15? $16? $\frac{1}{4}, \frac{1}{3}, \frac{11}{12}, \frac{5}{4}, \frac{4}{3}$

**Exercise 6
Written**

1. Last year Ruth Delisle's salary was $24,000. This year her salary was increased by $1,500. What fractional part of Ruth's old salary was the increase? $\frac{1}{16}$

2. Leonard Chin got a 90¢ raise in his hourly pay rate. His old rate was $8.10 per hour. What part of the old rate was the increase? $\frac{1}{9}$

3. Trudi Zamek's total pay last week was $360. This week Trudi worked fewer hours, so her pay was only $300. What part of Trudi's last week's pay was this week's pay? $\frac{5}{6}$

■ The part may be larger than the whole with which it is compared.

4. In July, Alan Rojas' earnings were $600. In August his earnings totaled $720.
    a. What part of July's earnings were Alan's August earnings? $\frac{6}{5}$
    b. What part of August's earnings were Alan's July earnings? $\frac{5}{6}$

5. In her first year on her job, Halina Mills earned $12 an hour. In her second year on the job, she earned $14 an hour.
    a. What part of her first year's hourly rate was her second year's hourly rate? $\frac{7}{6}$

b. What part of her second year's hourly rate was her first year's hourly rate? $\frac{6}{7}$

Finding What Part a Number Is Greater or Smaller Than Another.

Suppose that a pay rate has been increased from $7.20 to $9 per hour. You want to find what part the new rate of $9 is greater than the old rate of $7.20. To find what part a number is greater or smaller than another, you use the three steps shown here.

Example

$9 is what part greater than $7.20?

Solution	Explanation
$9.00 − 7.20 $1.80 the part	Step 1: Find the number representing the part by subtracting the smaller number from the larger number. That number will be called the part.
$1.80 the part $7.20 the whole	Step 2: Write the part as the numerator of a fraction. As the denominator of the fraction, write the whole number with which the part is being compared.
$\frac{\$1.80}{\$7.20} = \frac{1}{4}$ **Ans.**	Step 3: Simplify the fraction.

To work this kind of problem, you must use as the denominator the number to which the part is being compared. In some problems the denominator is the larger number; in others the denominator is the smaller number.

Exercise 7
Oral

1. 17 is what part more than 14? 11? 12? 9? $\frac{3}{14}, \frac{6}{11}, \frac{5}{12}, \frac{8}{9}$

2. 20 is what part less than 30? 24? 22? 50? $\frac{1}{3}, \frac{1}{6}, \frac{1}{11}, \frac{3}{5}$

3. What part more than 12 is 13? 19? 14? 16? $\frac{1}{12}, \frac{7}{12}, \frac{1}{6}, \frac{1}{3}$

4. What part smaller than 15 is 14? 11? 12? 9? $\frac{1}{15}, \frac{4}{15}, \frac{1}{5}, \frac{2}{5}$

5. 14 equals 10 increased by what part of itself? $\frac{2}{5}$

6. 18 equals 24 decreased by what part of itself? $\frac{1}{4}$

Exercise 8
Written

1. In her first month on her new job, Annie Campo earned $1,400. In her second month Annie earned $1,600. What part more were her second month's earnings than her first month's earnings? $\frac{1}{7}$

2. In his first year on his new job, Mick Grote earned $18,300. In his second year on that job Mick earned $20,130. What part greater were his earnings in the second year than in the first year? $\frac{1}{10}$

3. In March, Ileana Herrera's regular and overtime pay totaled $2,025. In April, Ileana worked no overtime hours, so her pay dropped to $1,800. What part smaller than her March pay was Ileana's April pay? $\frac{1}{9}$

4. Two years ago a senior citizen's club spent $7,140 on bus trips. Last year the club spent $5,712. What part less was spent on bus trips last year than was spent two years ago? $\frac{1}{5}$

5. Last year the Yamaguchi family's expenses totaled $18,000. This year their expenses totaled $19,500.
   a. What part greater were this year's expenses than last year's? $\frac{1}{12}$
   b. What part less were last year's expenses than this year's? $\frac{1}{13}$

REVIEW 19

Skills

1. a. $\frac{1}{8}$ as large as 72 = ?   9   d. $\frac{1}{6}$ more than 24 = ?   28

   b. $\frac{2}{5}$ as much as 40 = ?   16   e. $\frac{1}{7}$ less than 35 = ?   30

   c. $\frac{3}{7}$ as many as 49 = ?   21   f. 8 is what part of 72? $\frac{1}{9}$

Problems

2. Herb Austin's pay is $\frac{5}{6}$ as large as Elaine Frost's pay. If Elaine's pay is $1,230 a month, what is Herb's pay per month? $1,025 [19]

3. The Soto-Weil Software Company sold $\frac{2}{7}$ more software programs this year than last year. If Soto-Weil sold 742 programs last year, how many programs did the company sell this year?   954 [19]

4. Last month the Merdex Company paid wages of $134,000. Of that amount, $26,800 was paid for work on weekends. What part of the month's wages were paid for weekend work? $\frac{1}{5}$ [19]

5. A company spent $13,200 for temporary help this year. Last year a total of $14,850 was spent for the same services. What part less did the company spend on temporary help this year than it spent last year? $\frac{1}{9}$ [19]

6. Trek Products has four workers in the painting department. Last month the workers received these hourly pay raises: first worker, $0.75; second worker, $1.10; third worker, $0.90; fourth worker, $0.62.
   a. What average pay raise did these four workers get, to the nearest cent? $0.84 [10]
   b. Based on the average pay raise, what estimated pay increase will a worker get for a 40-hour week? $32 [7]

[‡]7. On May 31 Jeremy Berg's check register balance was $565.80 and his bank statement balance was $701.32. When he compared his register and the statement, Jeremy found a service charge of $3.10 and earned interest of $2.40 on the statement but not in the register. Check #834 for $118 and #842 for $17.22 were outstanding. Jeremy had also failed to record Check #829 for $35, and a deposit of $36. Prepare Jeremy's reconciliation statement. $566.10 [6]

More Fractional Relationships

In Section 19 you solved four kinds of problems using fractions. Now you will learn to solve these two other kinds of problems using fractions:

1. Finding the whole when a part is known.

2. Finding the whole when an amount that is a part greater or smaller than the whole is known.

In both of these kinds of problems, you divide a known product by a known factor to find an unknown factor (P ÷ F = F).

‡Finding the Whole When a Part Is Known. The following problem is an example of the way you find the whole when you know a part.

Example

Arno Wright is paid $6.30 for working $\frac{7}{8}$ of an hour. What is Arno's hourly pay?

Solution	Explanation
F × F = P	The problem says that $\frac{7}{8}$ of Arno's hourly pay is equal to $6.30. You know one factor, $\frac{7}{8}$, and the product, $6.30. You need to find the unknown factor which was multiplied by $\frac{7}{8}$ to give $6.30. To find the unknown factor, divide the product, $6.30, by the known factor, $\frac{7}{8}$. To divide by $\frac{7}{8}$, invert the fraction and multiply. After you complete this process, you will have a product of $7.20. To check, multiply the known factor by the factor you found; that product should equal the given product.

$$\frac{7}{8} \times \text{hourly pay} = \$6.30$$

$$P \div F = F$$

$$\$6.30 \div \frac{7}{8} = \text{hourly pay}$$

$$\$6.30 \times \frac{8}{7} = \frac{\$50.40}{7} = \$7.20 \textbf{ Ans.}$$

Check: $\frac{7}{8} \times \$7.20 = \$6.30$

‡Exercise 1 Oral

Find the value of N.

1. $\frac{1}{3}$ of N is 6   18

2. $\frac{1}{5}$ of N is 10   50

3. 9 is $\frac{1}{8}$ of N 72

4. 12 is $\frac{2}{3}$ as much as N 18

5. $\frac{5}{6} \times 60$ is N 50

6. $\frac{1}{4}$ as large as $N = 8$ 32

7. N is $\frac{4}{5}$ as much as 20   16

8. N is $\frac{3}{2}$ of 24   36

‡Exercise 2 Written

1. Your overtime pay last year totaled $2,800, which was $\frac{2}{15}$ of your total pay for the year. What was your total pay for the year? $21,000

2. Lorraine Nosal got a pay increase of 43¢ an hour, which was $\frac{1}{20}$ of her old pay rate. What was her old pay rate? $8.60

$P \div F = F$

3. A school club raised $250 from the sale of computer art. That amount was $\frac{1}{5}$ as much as is needed to buy a new computer for the club. What is the cost of the computer? $1,250

4. A company had 8 sales employees who were $\frac{2}{25}$ of the total number of employees of the company. How many employees did the company have?   100

5. Leonard earned $42 by working $\frac{6}{7}$ of a day. What amount would he be paid for a full day of work? $49

6. Of the total weekly wages paid to all employees of the Seal-Craft Company, $200,000, or $\frac{4}{5}$, was paid to workers in the factory. What were the total weekly wages of the Seal-Craft Company? $250,000

7. Denise Selowitz earned $6,800 by working $\frac{1}{4}$ of a year. At this rate, how much will she earn for a full year of work? $27,200

8. A company has 2 secretaries who represent $\frac{2}{17}$ of all workers in the company. How many workers does the company have?   17

9. In last year's election the winning candidate got 6,300 of the 10,800 votes cast in the election. In this year's election the winning candidate got 6,000 votes, or $\frac{5}{8}$ of the total votes in the election. How many votes were cast in this year's election?   9,600

‡**Finding the Whole When an Amount That Is a Part Greater or Smaller Than the Whole Is Known.** Study these two examples.

Example

Mona Grissom's present pay of $24,200 a year is an increase of $\frac{3}{8}$ over her pay of 5 years ago. What was Mona's annual pay 5 years ago?

Solution

$\frac{8}{8}$ = pay 5 years ago (unknown factor F)

$+ \frac{3}{8}$ = increase in pay

$\frac{11}{8}$ = pay now (known factor F)

F × F = P

$\frac{11}{8}$ × pay 5 years ago = $24,200

P ÷ F = F

$24,200 ÷ $\frac{11}{8}$ = F

$24,200 × $\frac{8}{11}$ = $17,600   **Ans.**

Explanation

The problem says that Mona's pay 5 years ago, plus $\frac{3}{8}$ of that pay, equals Mona's present pay of $24,200. So, let Mona's old pay be $\frac{8}{8}$, add $\frac{3}{8}$ for the increase, and her present pay is $\frac{11}{8}$ of her old pay. You then divide the product (present pay of $24,200) by the known factor ($\frac{11}{8}$) to find the unknown factor (old pay of $17,600). To check, add $\frac{3}{8}$ of the old pay to the old pay of $17,600. That sum, $24,200, equals the present pay.

Check: $17,600 + ($\frac{3}{8}$ × $17,600) = $17,600 + $6,600 = $24,200

Example

Ed Virga's pay of $7.50 an hour is $\frac{1}{6}$ less than Roy Stinson's hourly pay. What is Roy Stinson's hourly pay?

Solution

$\frac{6}{6}$ = Roy's pay
(unknown factor F)

$-\frac{1}{6}$ = less pay

$\frac{5}{6}$ = Ed's pay (known factor F)

$F \times \quad F \quad = P$

$\frac{5}{6}$ + Roy's pay = $7.50 (Ed's Pay)

$7.50 \div \frac{5}{6}$ = F

$7.50 \times \frac{6}{5}$ = $9   **Ans.**

Explanation

The problem says that Roy's pay, less $\frac{1}{6}$ of Roy's pay, equals Ed's pay of $7.50 an hour. So, let Roy's pay be $\frac{6}{6}$, subtract $\frac{1}{6}$ for the part that Ed's pay is less, and Ed's pay equals $\frac{5}{6}$ of Roy's pay. Then divide the product (Ed's pay of $7.50) by the known factor, $\frac{5}{6}$, to find the unknown factor (Roy's pay) of $9. Check the answer by subtracting $\frac{1}{6}$ of Roy's pay, $1.50, from Roy's pay of $9. The difference, $7.50, is the same as Ed's pay, so the answer is correct.

Check: $9 - (\frac{1}{6} \times $9) = $7.50

‡Exercise 3 Oral

Find the unknown numbers.

1. 20 is $\frac{1}{4}$ larger than N 16
2. 30 is $\frac{1}{3}$ less than N 45
3. N increased by $\frac{1}{5}$ = 30   25
4. N decreased by $\frac{1}{6}$ = 30   36
5. N plus $\frac{2}{3}$ of itself = $30 $18

6. 10 is $\frac{2}{3}$ more than N 6
7. 4 is $\frac{3}{4}$ less than N 16
8. $\frac{1}{5}$ less than N is $40 $50
9. $20 is N reduced by $\frac{3}{8}$ $32
10. $75 is N less $\frac{2}{5}$ of itself $125

‡Exercise 4 Written

1. Sue's salary last year was $19,500, which was $\frac{1}{12}$ more than the year before. What was Sue's salary the year before? $18,000

2. Last week Fred Rosier's pay totaled $380, which was $\frac{1}{9}$ more than his pay the week before. What was Fred's pay the week before? $342

3. During their annual fund drive this year, a local club raised $4,200, which was a decrease of $\frac{2}{9}$ from last year's collection. Last year's collection was $\frac{1}{2}$ more than the year before. How much did the club collect last year? $5,400

4. The Video Center's sales in March of this year were $71,500. That amount was a decrease of $\frac{2}{15}$ from the sales of March last year. What were the Center's sales in March of last year? $82,500

5. Tillie Leonard's average pay of $1,750 per month is $\frac{1}{6}$ greater than Russ Waidley's average monthly pay. What is Russ Waidley's average monthly pay? $1,500

6. The Ellikan family's current checking account balance is $936, a decrease of $\frac{3}{8}$ from the balance on January 1 of this year. What was the checking account balance on January 1? $1,497.60

Reviewing Problems in Fractional Relationships.

In Sections 19 and 20 you studied how to do six types of problems in fractional relationships. The next three exercises provide more practice with those types of problems.

‡Exercise 5
Oral

Find the unknown numbers.

1. N is $\frac{2}{3}$ as large as 12   8
2. N is $\frac{1}{4}$ more than 32   40
3. 36 is $\frac{3}{4}$ as large as N 48
4. 20 is $\frac{1}{4}$ larger than N 16
5. $\frac{3}{2}$ of N equals 36   24
6. 60 is $\frac{1}{3}$ less than N 90
7. 48 is $\frac{1}{3}$ larger than N 36
8. $\frac{5}{3}$ of 15 = N 25
9. 24 is $\frac{3}{8}$ of N 64
10. 60 is $\frac{1}{4}$ less than N 80

11. 36 is $\frac{1}{2}$ larger than N 24
12. $\frac{1}{5}$ less than N is 40   50
13. N is $\frac{3}{4}$ larger than 36   63
14. $\frac{1}{4}$ more than N is 60   48
15. N is $\frac{1}{4}$ smaller than 80   60
16. $\frac{5}{3}$ of N equals 30   18
17. 28 is $\frac{3}{7}$ less than N 49
18. $\frac{2}{3}$ of N equals 36   54
19. $12 is what part of $15? $\frac{4}{5}$
20. $40 is what part less than $44? $\frac{1}{11}$

‡Exercise 6
Written

Find the unknown numbers.

1. $4.80 is $\frac{3}{4}$ of N $6.40
2. $14.70 is $\frac{2}{3}$ of N $22.05
3. $\frac{5}{7}$ of N equals $5.60 $7.84
4. $5.20 is $\frac{3}{5}$ more than N $3.25
5. $8.80 is $\frac{3}{8}$ more than N $6.40
6. $\frac{4}{5}$ more than N is $1.80 $1
7. $32.48 is $\frac{1}{8}$ less than N $37.12

8. $\frac{3}{10}$ less than N is $4.20 $6
9. N is $\frac{5}{6}$ more than $1.92 $3.52
10. $\frac{5}{8}$ of $4.80 = N $3
11. N is $\frac{1}{3}$ less than $9.72 $6.48
12. $\frac{7}{8}$ of N equals $3.36 $3.84
13. N is $\frac{1}{4}$ more than $8.40 $10.50
14. $4.20 is $\frac{3}{5}$ of N $7

‡Exercise 7
Written

1. Of Josephine Rabo's gross pay of $480, $\frac{1}{8}$ was for overtime work. How much was Josephine's overtime pay? $60

2. Howard Verlyn received a new water bill that was $\frac{1}{5}$ greater than his last bill for $42. How much was his new water bill? $50.40

3. Leo Tripp paid $64 to have his furnace fixed. The bill for repair included a $48 charge for parts and $16 for labor. What part of the total bill was the labor charge? $\frac{1}{4}$

4. A desk 72 inches long was replaced by a desk 60 inches long. What part smaller is the new desk than the old desk? $\frac{1}{6}$

5. As a new worker Esther is paid $8.40 an hour, which is $\frac{3}{4}$ of the amount she will earn two years from now. What amount per hour will Esther earn two years from now? $11.20

6. Jacob Kreel is paid $11.55 an hour, which is $\frac{1}{12}$ less than Patrick McLean earns per hour. How much does Patrick McLean earn per hour? $12.60

REVIEW 20

Skills

1. Solve the problems.
   a. 67 + 14 + 36 + 29   146
   b. 86 + 45 − 51   80
   c. 51 × $\frac{5}{6}$ $42\frac{1}{2}$
   d. $7\frac{3}{4}$ × $4\frac{2}{3}$ $36\frac{1}{6}$
   e. 14 ÷ $\frac{5}{6}$ $16\frac{4}{5}$
   f. $4\frac{2}{5}$ ÷ $5\frac{1}{2}$ $\frac{4}{5}$
   g. Divide 2 by 7, correct to the nearest thousandth.   0.286
   h. What number is $\frac{2}{7}$ as large as $49? $14
   i. $\frac{2}{3}$ less than $30 $10
   j. $\frac{7}{8}$ of $0.56 $0.49
   k. $28 is $\frac{3}{4}$ greater than N $16
   l. 119 is $\frac{7}{8}$ smaller than N 136

Problems

2. What weekly salary, correct to the nearest cent, is equal to a monthly salary of $863? $199.15 [7, 10]

3. Edgar Lowell is paid $0.47 for each of the first 100 locks he assembles. He is paid $0.60 each for the next 50 locks and $0.75 for every lock over 150. If he assembles 173 locks on Monday, what is his gross pay for the day? $94.25 [7]

■ Check the method you are using and all your calculations.

4. The sales of the Hartwell Company for this year are only $\frac{5}{6}$ as much as last year's sales. If last year's sales were $2,474,274, what are this year's sales? $2,061,895 [19]

‡5. What amount increased by $\frac{1}{5}$ of itself gives $240? $200 [20]

‡6. What amount decreased by $\frac{1}{3}$ of itself equals $400? $600 [20]

‡7. A store raised the price of a tire by $6.30, which was $\frac{1}{9}$ of the original price. What was the original price? $56.70 [20]

‡8. The Adwin Company produced 2,600,000 coat hangers this year, which was a decrease of $\frac{1}{6}$ from the total number of hangers made last year. How many coat hangers were made last year?   3,120,000 [20]

‡9. On October 31 Rena Webster's check register balance was $468.95 and her bank statement balance was $780.40. When she compared her register with her statement, she found a service charge of $5.20 and earned interest of $2.76 on the statement but not in the register. These checks were outstanding: #412 for $68.15 and #415 for $156.88. She also found that she had not recorded a deposit of $97 and a check for $8.14. Prepare a reconciliation statement for Rena. $555.37 [6]

‡10. Elaine Rook was paid $35 for working $3\frac{1}{2}$ hours. At that same rate, how much would she be paid for working 8 hours? $80 [16]

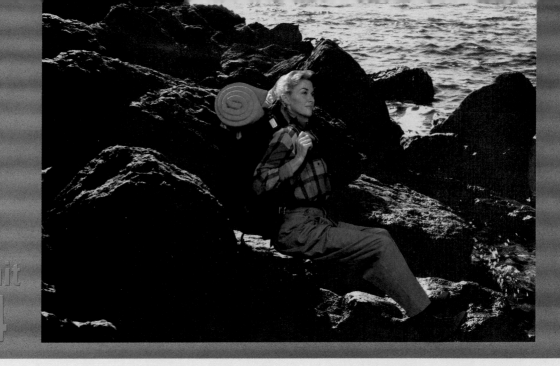

Net Pay, Fringe Benefits, and Commission

Many office employees are paid a weekly or monthly salary, while others are paid an hourly wage. Salespeople, however, often earn income from commissions. In this unit you will learn to figure gross pay from commissions, deductions from gross pay, and net pay.

Most employers provide workers with fringe benefits as well as wages. Sometimes, though, workers spend money on work-related expenses like uniforms and tools. When comparing jobs, you must compare wages as well as fringe benefits and job expenses. In this unit, you will learn to figure fringe benefits and job expenses and to compare jobs.

After you finish Unit 4, you will be able to:

- Add, subtract, multiply, and divide decimals.
- Change decimals, fractions, and percents from one form to another.
- Multiply by common fractional equivalents of 100%.
- Multiply by 0.1, 0.01, 0.001, 1%, 10%, 100%, and 1,000%.
- Divide by 0.1, 0.01, and 0.001.
- Figure net pay, deductions, fringe benefits, and job expenses.
- Compare jobs by finding net job benefits for each.
- Find straight and graduated commissions and net proceeds.
- Find the rate of commission.
- Find sale price needed for a certain amount of net proceeds.
- Find sale price when rate and amount of commission are known.
- Solve problems that contain more information than you need.
- Estimate answers to problems.
- Read, write, say, and recognize the meanings of the key terms.
- Use a calculator to change fractions, decimals, and percents from one form to another.
- Use a calculator to multiply by percents and find rate of commission.
- Use a computer spreadsheet to compute net pay and deductions, to compare jobs, and to find graduated commission.

117

In this section you will learn to calculate some common deductions from a worker's pay and to find the net pay a worker takes home.

Deductions are subtractions from gross pay. An employer must make deductions from an employee's pay for federal and state income taxes and social security taxes. Deductions may also be subtracted for union dues, health and life insurance, government bonds, etc.

After all deductions are subtracted from total or gross wages, an amount remains that is called **net pay,** or **take-home pay.**

Gross Pay − Deductions = Net Pay or Take-home Pay

The gross pay, deductions and net pay for a typical employee are shown in Illustration 21–1.

STATEMENT OF EMPLOYEE EARNINGS AND PAYROLL DEDUCTIONS									
	EARNINGS			DEDUCTIONS					
WEEK ENDED	REGULAR	OVER-TIME	TOTAL	FED. WITH.	FICA	LIFE INS.	HEALTH INS.	OTHER	TOTAL	NET PAY
2 / 4	375.00		375.00	42.00	28.69	12.50	56.45	13.75	153.39	221.61

NO. 4798

Illustration 21–1. Part of a Paycheck Showing Deductions

Finding Withholding Taxes. The federal government and many states and cities require employers to deduct money from employee wages for income taxes. This deduction is called a **withholding tax.**

The amount of withholding tax depends on a worker's wages, marital status, and number of withholding allowances claimed. A **withholding allowance** is used to reduce the amount of tax withheld. Workers may claim one withholding allowance for themselves, one for a husband or a wife, and one for each child or dependent.

To find the amount withheld from a worker's wages, you use an income tax withholding table prepared by the government. Part of a federal income tax withholding table for married employees paid on a weekly basis is shown in Illustration 21–2.

Using the Withholding Table. To find the amount of tax on an employee's wages, read down the Wages Are column at the left until you reach the wage line you want. Then read across to the column headed by the number of withholding allowances claimed by the employee.

For example, if a married employee's weekly wages are $310 and there are 2 withholding allowances, you find the tax on the first line of the table in Column 2. The amount of tax is $27. If the wages are $409 and 4 withholding allowances are claimed, the tax is on the tenth line in Column 4. The tax amount is $29.

MARRIED PERSONS--WEEKLY PAYROLL PERIOD												
And the wages are--		And the number of withholding allowances is--										
At least	But less than	0	1	2	3	4	5	6	7	8	9	10
		The amount of income tax to be withheld shall be--										
310	320	38	33	27	22	16	10	5	0	0	0	0
320	330	40	34	29	23	17	12	6	1	0	0	0
330	340	41	36	30	25	19	13	8	2	0	0	0
340	350	43	37	32	26	20	15	9	4	0	0	0
350	360	44	39	33	28	22	16	11	5	0	0	0
360	370	46	40	35	29	23	18	12	7	1	0	0
370	380	47	42	36	31	25	19	14	8	2	0	0
380	390	49	43	38	32	26	21	15	10	4	0	0
390	400	50	45	39	34	28	22	17	11	5	0	0
400	410	52	46	41	35	29	24	18	13	7	1	0
410	420	53	48	42	37	31	25	20	14	8	3	0
420	430	55	49	44	38	32	27	21	16	10	4	0
430	440	56	51	45	40	34	28	23	17	11	6	0
440	450	58	52	47	41	35	30	24	19	13	7	2
450	460	59	54	48	43	37	31	26	20	14	9	3

Illustration 21–2. Part of an Income Tax Withholding Table

**Exercise 1
Oral**

Use the tax table in Illustration 21–2 to find the withholding tax in each problem.

	Total Wages	Withholding Allowances			Total Wages	Withholding Allowances	
1.	$390.00	1	$45	5.	$328.97	5	$12
2.	399.00	2	39	6.	407.81	3	35
3.	411.00	0	53	7.	457.07	6	26
4.	444.00	4	35	8.	438.88	9	6

Finding the FICA Tax. The tax for social security is part of the Federal Insurance Contributions Act. It is called the **FICA tax** or *social security tax*. The tax rate and the maximum amount of wages on which it is based are changed by Congress from time to time. In this text, a rate of 7.65% on a maximum wage of $45,000 will be used.

To find the amount of tax, change 7.65% to the decimal, 0.0765. Then multiply the employee's wages for the week by the FICA tax rate, or 0.0765. For example, if an employee earned $531.10 a week, or $27,617.20 a year, the FICA tax would be:

$$0.0765 \times \$531.10 = \$40.629, \text{ or } \$40.63$$

**Exercise 2
Written**

Find the FICA tax (0.0765) on each weekly wage.

1.	$475.00	$36.34	4.	$497.45	$38.05	7.	$289.48	$22.15
2.	$556.34	42.56	5.	$749.23	57.32	8.	$863.78	66.08
3.	$249.40	19.08	6.	$180.04	13.77			

Using FICA Tables. In a business that completes payrolls manually, a worker usually uses a table to find the FICA tax. A partial FICA table is shown in Illustration 21–3. In the complete table the FICA tax is shown for pay from $0.07 to $100, and for multiples of $100. To find the tax on pay of more than $100, you must add the tax for $100, or multiple of $100, to the tax for the amount less than $100. For example, for a wage of $531.10, the tax on $500 is $38.25. The tax on $31.10 is $2.38. So, the total FICA tax is $38.25 + $2.38 = $40.63. Notice that the tax you found by using the table is the same as the tax you found by multiplying the wage by the tax rate.

SOCIAL SECURITY EMPLOYEE TAX TABLE- –7.65%

Wages at least	But less than	Tax to be withheld	Wages at least	But less than	Tax to be withheld	Wages at least	But less than	Tax to be withheld	Wages at least	But less than	Tax to be withheld
31.05	31.18	2.38	32.88	33.01	2.52	34.71	34.84	2.66			
31.18	31.31	2.39	33.01	33.14	2.53	34.84	34.97	2.67			
31.31	31.44	2.40	33.14	33.27	2.54	34.97	35.10	2.68			
31.44	31.57	2.41	33.27	33.40	2.55	35.10	35.23	2.69	The FICA tax to be		
31.57	31.70	2.42	33.40	33.53	2.56	35.23	35.36	2.70	withheld on multiples		
31.70	31.84	2.43	33.53	33.67	2.57	35.36	35.50	2.71	of $100 is:		
31.84	31.97	2.44	33.67	33.80	2.58	35.50	35.63	2.72			
									Wage		Tax to be withheld
31.97	32.10	2.45	33.80	33.93	2.59	35.63	35.76	2.73			
32.10	32.23	2.46	33.93	34.06	2.60	35.76	35.89	2.74	100		7.65
32.23	32.36	2.47	34.06	34.19	2.61	35.89	36.02	2.75	200		15.30
32.36	32.49	2.48	34.19	34.32	2.62	36.02	36.15	2.76	300		22.95
32.49	32.62	2.49	34.32	34.45	2.63	36.15	36.28	2.77	400		30.60
32.62	32.75	2.50	34.45	34.58	2.64	36.28	36.41	2.78	500		38.25
32.75	32.88	2.51	34.58	34.71	2.65	36.41	36.54	2.79	600		45.90

Illustration 21–3. Part of a Social Security Tax Table for Weekly Wages

Exercise 3 Oral

Use the table in Illustration 21–3 to find the taxes.

1. $235.78 $18.04   3. $631.05 $48.28   5. $536.53 $41.04   7. $436.24 $33.37
2. $434.99 $33.28   4. $333.53 $25.52   6. $432.75 $33.11   8. $331.43 $25.35

Exercise 4 Written

1. Emi Isobe's gross weekly wage is $436. She has 2 withholding allowances. Each week, her employer deducts $35.20 for payment to the credit union and $35.80 for insurance. For the week, use Illustrations 21–2 and 21–3 to find Emi's
   a. Federal withholding tax $45
   b. FICA tax $33.35
   c. Total deductions $149.35
   d. Net pay $286.65

2. Todd Pratt works a 40-hour week at $9.40 an hour with time and a half for overtime. Last week he worked 44 hours. From his gross pay, $30 was deducted for his savings plan and $46.89 for insurance. He has 1 withholding allowance. For last week, use Illustrations 21–2 and 21–3 to find Todd's
   a. Gross regular pay $376.00
   b. Gross overtime pay $56.40
   c. Gross pay $432.40
   d. Federal withholding tax $51
   e. FICA tax $33.08
   f. Net pay $271.43

■ Remember—
Check your work.

3. Complete the table below. Use the withholding tax table in Illustration 21–2 and the FICA table in Illustration 21–3 to find the taxes. Find the total deductions by adding income tax, FICA tax, and other deductions. Find net wages by subtracting total deductions from gross wages. As a check, you should make sure the sum of the totals of income tax, FICA tax, and other deductions equals the total deductions. The sum of the net wages and the total deductions should equal the gross wages.

Name	Allow-ances	Gross Wages	Income Tax	FICA Tax	Other	Total	Net Wages
			Deductions				
a. Dean	1	$431.31	$51.00	$33.00	$56.81	$140.81	$290.50
b. Dent	0	335.74	41.00	25.68	38.93	105.61	230.13
c. Dern	4	436.42	34.00	33.39	65.39	132.78	303.64
d. Dest	2	333.07	30.00	25.48	49.23	104.71	228.36
e. Totals		$1,536.54	$156.00	$117.55	$210.36	$483.91	$1,052.63

REVIEW 21

Terms

1. Match the terms with the statements.

deductions   net or take-home pay   withholding tax
FICA tax   withholding allowance

a. This reduces the income tax withheld   withholding allowance
b. Amounts subtracted from gross pay   deductions
c. A deduction for federal income tax   withholding tax
d. Gross pay less deductions   net or take-home pay
e. Social security tax   FICA tax

Skills

2. a. $25.60 \times \dfrac{1}{8} = ?$ $3.20   c. $\dfrac{2}{5}$ as large as $44.50 = ?$ $17.80

 b. $3\dfrac{1}{8} \div \dfrac{5}{8} = ?$ 5   d. $\dfrac{1}{4}$ more than 40 = ?   50

Problems

3. Faye Sim is paid $276 a week. Her employer deducts $27 for the federal withholding tax, $11.39 for insurance, and 0.0765 for the FICA tax. What is Faye's net pay for 1 week? $216.50 [21]

4. Lana Hatton is paid $0.38 for each lever she produces. Last week she produced 627 levers. Her employer deducted $21 for the federal withholding tax, $25 for her credit union savings plan, and 0.0765 for the FICA tax. What was Lana's net pay for the week? $174.03 [7,21]

[‡]5. Rick Elving's overtime pay this week was $38.52, which was $\frac{1}{2}$ more than his overtime pay for last week. What was his overtime pay for last week? $25.68 [20]

Computer Clinic

Follow the steps below to complete a weekly payroll sheet for Nashua-Brinkley Corporation.

1. Insert your Spreadsheet Applications Diskette and call up the file "Sec21." After you do your computer screen should look like Illustration 21–4.*

```
Sec21                    Nashua-Brinkley Corporation
                        Payroll Sheet for Jan. 15, 19--
                                  Deductions
          Allow-   Gross   Income   FICA                      Net
No. Name  ances    Wages    Tax      Tax    Other    Total    Pay

 1 Allen    0      0.00     0.00     .00    45.56    45.56    .00
 2 Baker    4      0.00     0.00     .00    23.89    23.89    .00
 3 Cruz     1      0.00     0.00     .00    93.12    93.12    .00
 4 Dolan    3      0.00     0.00     .00    55.23    55.23    .00
 5 Elgin    2      0.00     0.00     .00    37.56    37.56    .00
 6 Faber    0      0.00     0.00     .00    34.87    34.87    .00
 7 Greb     0      0.00     0.00     .00    29.98    29.98    .00
 8 Hirt     2      0.00     0.00     .00    44.34    44.34    .00
 9 Isobe    5      0.00     0.00     .00    37.44    37.44    .00
10 Jain     1      0.00     0.00     .00    64.55    64.55    .00

   Totals            .00      .00    .00   466.54   466.54    .00

   FICA RATE       .0765
```

Illustration 21–4. Spreadsheet Used to Compute a Weekly Payroll

2. Enter these gross wages into cells D7–D16: Allen, $380.67; Baker, $428.88; Cruz, $395.35; Dolan, $438.97; Elgin, $450; Faber, $458.23; Greb, $354.56; Hirt, $349.21; Isobe, $438.39; Jain, $317.44.

3. Enter into cells E7–E16 the withholding, or income, taxes for each employee. Use Illustration 21–2 to find the taxes.

4. Answer the questions about your completed payroll sheet.
   a. Which employee had the largest net pay for the period? Baker
   b. Which employee had the largest amount of deductions? Cruz
   c. What were the total FICA taxes paid by the employees for the week? $306.88
   d. What was the total amount of federal income taxes withheld from wages for the week? $410
   e. What was the total net pay earned by the employees for the week? $2,828.28

5. Move the cursor to cell D20, labeled "FICA Rate." Enter the rate 0.0775. Notice how the FICA Tax, Total Deductions, and Net Pay amounts all have changed. This would happen if the FICA tax rate changed from 7.65% to 7.75%.

---

*Note to students using MicroTools: In this and other computer clinics, your screen may differ slightly from the illustration shown above. The word "Error" or negative numbers may appear in some cells. As you work the problem, the correct numbers will show up on your screen.

You have learned to find the FICA tax by multiplying an employee's wages by the FICA tax rate of 0.0765. The number 0.0765 is called a **decimal**, or decimal fraction.

A decimal is just another way of naming a fractional number when the fraction has a denominator such as 10, 100, or 1,000. For example, one dollar has 100 cents. One cent is one one-hundredth of a dollar, or $1 \div 100 = 0.01$. So, we can write one cent as $\frac{1}{100}$ of a dollar, or $0.01. Both $\frac{1}{100}$ and 0.01 are numerals that name the same fractional number.

You change a fraction with a denominator of 10, 100, or 1,000 to a decimal by dividing the numerator by the denominator. For example:

$$\frac{1}{10} = 1 \div 10 = 0.1 \qquad\qquad \frac{6}{10} = 6 \div 10 = 0.6$$

$$\frac{1}{100} = 1 \div 100 = 0.01 \qquad\qquad \frac{67}{100} = 67 \div 100 = 0.67$$

$$\frac{1}{1,000} = 1 \div 1,000 = 0.001 \qquad\qquad \frac{67}{1,000} = 67 \div 1,000 = 0.067$$

As a shortcut you can divide by denominators of 10 and multiples of 10 by simply moving the decimal point in the numerator to the *left* the same number of places as there are zeros in the denominator. Thus, $235 \div 10 = 23.5$; by 100, 2.35; by 1,000, 0.235.

Write each fraction as a decimal.

**Exercise 1
Written**

1. $\frac{21}{100}$ 0.21
2. $\frac{592}{1,000}$ 0.592
3. $\frac{8}{10}$ 0.8

4. $\frac{5}{1,000}$ 0.005
5. $\frac{74}{100}$ 0.74
6. $\frac{3}{10,000}$ 0.0003

7. $\frac{11}{1,000}$ 0.011
8. $\frac{107}{10,000}$ 0.0107

Changing Fractions to Decimals. Any fraction can be changed to a decimal by dividing the numerator by the denominator. If the division is not exact, divide to one more place than you need and round off.

Example

What is the decimal equivalent of $\frac{5}{8}$, correct to 2 decimal places?

Solution

$$\begin{array}{r} 0.625 = 0.63 \textbf{ Ans.} \\ 8\overline{)5.000} \\ \underline{4\,8} \\ 20 \\ \underline{16} \\ 40 \\ \underline{40} \end{array}$$

Explanation

The numerator, 5, is divided by the denominator, 8. The division is carried to three decimal places, then rounded back to 2 places.

123

**Exercise 2
Written**

1. Find the decimal equivalent of each fraction to three decimal places.

    a. $\frac{4}{7}$ 0.571   d. $\frac{8}{11}$ 0.727   g. $\frac{7}{9}$ 0.778

    b. $\frac{5}{9}$ 0.556   e. $\frac{3}{14}$ 0.214   h. $\frac{6}{13}$ 0.462

    c. $\frac{11}{12}$ 0.917   f. $\frac{5}{6}$ 0.833   i. $\frac{4}{15}$ 0.267

2. Find the decimal equivalent of each fraction to the nearest hundredth.

    a. $\frac{6}{21}$ 0.29   d. $\frac{1}{11}$ 0.09   g. $\frac{5}{17}$ 0.29

    b. $\frac{4}{17}$ 0.24   e. $\frac{2}{15}$ 0.13   h. $\frac{5}{7}$ 0.71

    c. $\frac{8}{13}$ 0.62   f. $\frac{3}{16}$ 0.19   i. $\frac{2}{7}$ 0.29

Sometimes an **exact value** is required. In this case, the quotient is not rounded. Instead, the division is carried to a specified number of places and the remainder is shown as a common fraction.

Example

Change $\frac{1}{7}$ to a decimal of three places of exact value.

Solution

$$
\begin{array}{r}
0.142 \\
7\overline{)1.000} \\
\underline{7} \\
30 \\
\underline{28} \\
20 \\
\underline{14} \\
6
\end{array}
$$

$0.142\frac{6}{7}$ **Ans.**

Explanation

The division is carried to 3 decimal places. Since the **exact value** is required, the quotient is not rounded. Instead, the remainder, 6, is written as a common fraction, $\frac{6}{7}$. The exact decimal equivalent is $0.142\frac{6}{7}$.

**Exercise 3
Written**

Change each fraction to a decimal of two places of exact value.

1. $\frac{7}{11}$ $0.63\frac{7}{11}$ 4. $\frac{2}{13}$ $0.15\frac{5}{13}$ 7. $\frac{5}{11}$ $0.45\frac{5}{11}$

2. $\frac{5}{14}$ $0.35\frac{5}{7}$ 5. $\frac{13}{14}$ $0.92\frac{6}{7}$ 8. $\frac{1}{12}$ $0.08\frac{1}{3}$

3. $\frac{7}{16}$ $0.43\frac{3}{4}$ 6. $\frac{6}{13}$ $0.46\frac{2}{13}$ 9. $\frac{7}{17}$ $0.41\frac{3}{17}$

Other Facts About Decimals. The facts listed here about decimals are important for you to know.

1. The fractions $\frac{7}{10}$, $\frac{70}{100}$, and $\frac{700}{1,000}$ are equivalent fractions. Since $\frac{7}{10} = \frac{70}{100} = \frac{700}{1,000}$, then $0.7 = 0.70 = 0.700$. In other words, we may attach zeros to a decimal without changing the number it represents. For example, $0.75 = 0.750 = 0.7500$.

2. Any whole number can be shown in decimal form by attaching a decimal point and as many zeros as desired. For example, $75 = 75.0 = 75.00 = 75.000$, and so on.

3. Decimals are helpful because they can be used instead of common fractions to make calculations easier. For example, it is easier to add \$5.65 and \$1.75 than $\$5\frac{13}{20}$ and $\$1\frac{3}{4}$.

4. It is often easier to compare fractions if they are shown as decimals. It is easier to see that $\frac{5}{9}$ is a larger number than $\frac{7}{13}$ if $\frac{5}{9}$ is shown as 0.556 and $\frac{7}{13}$ as 0.538.

Multiplication by 0.1, 0.01, or 0.001. To multiply by 0.1, 0.01, and 0.001, move the decimal point in the number to be multiplied to the *left* as many places as there are decimal places in the number by which you are multiplying. Prefix zeros (put them at the beginning) if needed. For example:

$$39.6 \times 0.01 = 0.396 \qquad \$9.70 \times 0.1 = \$0.97$$

$$7 \times 0.001 = 0.007 \qquad \$362 \times 0.01 = \$3.62$$

**Exercise 4
Written**

Multiply each problem mentally. Write the products only.

	1.		2.		3.	
a.	98.2×0.1	9.82	906×0.001	0.906	99×0.01	0.99
b.	14.7×0.01	0.147	221×0.1	22.1	70×0.001	0.07
c.	1.8×0.1	0.18	59×0.01	0.59	$\$107 \times 0.01$	\$1.07
d.	8×0.01	0.08	3.1×0.001	0.0031	$\$57.40 \times 0.1$	\$5.74
e.	845×0.001	0.845	0.46×0.1	0.046	$\$400 \times 0.001$	\$0.40

Changing a Decimal to a Fraction. To change a decimal to an equivalent fraction, drop the decimal point and write the number as the numerator of a fraction. For the denominator, write 1 followed by as many zeros as there are decimal places in the decimal. Then simplify the fraction. For example:

$$0.25 = \frac{25}{100} = \frac{1}{4} \qquad 0.025 = \frac{25}{1,000} = \frac{1}{40}$$

**Exercise 5
Written**

Change each decimal to an equivalent fraction in lowest terms.

	1.		2.		3.		4.	
a.	0.56	$\frac{14}{25}$	0.98	$\frac{49}{50}$	0.026	$\frac{13}{500}$	0.064	$\frac{8}{125}$
b.	0.45	$\frac{9}{20}$	0.025	$\frac{1}{40}$	0.675	$\frac{27}{40}$	0.075	$\frac{3}{40}$

c. 0.045 $\frac{9}{200}$ 0.2475 $\frac{99}{400}$ 0.12 $\frac{3}{25}$ 0.375 $\frac{3}{8}$

d. 0.0375 $\frac{3}{80}$ 0.86 $\frac{43}{50}$ 0.625 $\frac{5}{8}$ 0.85 $\frac{17}{20}$

Division by 0.1, 0.01, or 0.001. When you divide by 0.1, 0.01, or 0.001, move the decimal point in the number to be divided to the *right* as many places as there are decimal places in the number by which you are dividing. Attach zeros if you need to. For example:

2.87	÷	0.01	=	287
339	÷	0.1	=	3,390
0.0416	÷	0.01	=	4.16
$5.20	÷	0.001	=	$5,200

2.87

**Exercise 6
Written**

Divide each problem mentally. Write the quotients only.

	1.		2.		3.	
a.	6.28 ÷ 0.1	62.8	7.23 ÷ 0.01	723	2.2 ÷ 0.01	220
b.	0.085 ÷ 0.01	8.5	33 ÷ 0.01	3,300	$0.18 ÷ 0.01	$18
c.	0.0065 ÷ 0.001	6.5	476 ÷ 0.1	4,760	$3.00 ÷ 0.1	$30
d.	0.208 ÷ 0.01	20.8	84 ÷ 0.1	840	$5.31 ÷ 0.001	$5,310
e.	0.189 ÷ 0.001	189	0.2 ÷ 0.01	20	$7.34 ÷ 0.001	$7,340
f.	5.3 ÷ 0.1	53	2.76 ÷ 0.001	2,760	$28.78 ÷ 0.01	$2,878

REVIEW 22

Terms

1. Match the terms with the statements.

decimal   exact value

a. A quotient that is not rounded   exact value
b. The equivalent of a fraction with a denominator of 10, 100, etc.
    decimal

Skills

2. a. Change $\frac{5}{7}$ to a decimal correct to three places.   0.714
    b. Change $\frac{2}{11}$ to a decimal of two places of exact value. $0.18\frac{2}{11}$
    c. $3\frac{3}{5} ÷ 4\frac{2}{3}$ $\frac{27}{35}$
    d. $\frac{5}{8} + \frac{3}{4}$ $1\frac{3}{8}$
    e. Change 0.065 to a fraction in lowest terms. $\frac{13}{200}$
    f. 23.7 × 0.001   0.0237
    g. $8.24 ÷ 0.1 $82.40
    h. 21 is $\frac{3}{4}$ of   28

Problems

3. Viola LeFarge is paid $0.72 each for the first 300 handles she produces in a week and $0.89 for each handle over 300. Last week she produced 428 handles. Her employer deducted $34 in withholding tax, $11.67 in insurance, and 0.0765 in social security taxes.
    a. What was Viola's gross pay for the week? $329.92
    b. What was her social security tax? $25.24
    c. What was her net pay? $259.01 [7, 21]

4. Nathan Donnely works on a piece-rate basis. He produced these numbers of items last week: Monday, 73; Tuesday, 84; Wednes-

day, 79; Thursday, 82. How many items did Nathan produce Friday so as to average 80 items per day? 82 [7]

5. Novak and Oakes are partners in a lumber yard. They sell $637,109 and $475,224 worth of lumber during the year, respectively. They also share profits in the ratio of 3 to 5, respectively. The profit for the lumber yard for the year is $180,512. What is Novak's share of the profit? $67,692 [16]

‡6. Mary Deist earned $49,000 this year, which is $\frac{1}{8}$ less than she earned last year. How much did she earn last year? $56,000 [20]

Calculator Clinic

Changing Fractions to Decimals. Changing fractions to decimals is easy with a hand-held calculator. All you have to do is divide the numerator of the fraction by the denominator. For example, suppose that you needed to know the decimal equivalent to $\frac{2}{7}$ to two decimal places.

a. Clear your calculator by pressing CE/C twice.

b. Press these keys in order: 2 ÷ 7 =

c. The answer, 0.2857142, will appear in the display.

> 0.2857142

Now all you have to do is round off to the second decimal place to find your final answer, 0.29.

Calculator Practice. Apply what you have learned in this calculator clinic to the problems in Exercise 2 in this section.

Section 23
Fringe Benefits and Job Expenses

Many employers provide more than wages or pay for their workers. They may provide other things of value, called **fringe benefits.** For example, employers may provide free or low-cost health and accident insurance, life insurance, and pensions. They may also provide paid holidays, paid sick leave, paid vacation time, the free use of a car, a

Work With Us!
We offer:
Free health
insurance
Free parking
Paid sick leave
Paid vacations
Paid pension.

credit union, uniforms, parking, discounts for purchases of merchandise, recreational facilities, and education or training.

Finding Total Job Benefits. Fringe benefits are an important part of a job's total value. They are often worth as much as 15% to 40% of the amount paid in wages. So when you are looking at a job, the value of the fringe benefits should be added to the amount of wages to find the **total job benefits.**

Gross Pay + Fringe Benefits = Total Job Benefits

The value of some fringe benefits, such as paid holidays, can be figured very accurately. However, the value of other fringe benefits, such as free recreation facilities, can only be estimated.

Example

Sonia Burgoz is a systems analyst with Tri-State Paper Company. Last year Sonia calculated her total job benefits.

Tuition is a fee charged for instruction.

Solution

Gross pay		$32,400
Fringe benefits:		
Paid pension	$2,592	
Health insurance	1,440	
Paid vacations, holidays	2,278	
Paid course tuition	925	
Free gymnasium (estimated)	360	7,595
Total job benefits		$39,995 **Ans.**

Exercise 1
Written

1. Ray Novotney's gross pay for a year is $18,512. He estimates his yearly fringe benefits to be worth these amounts:

Paid pension	$1,226
Health and life insurance	1,534
Paid vacations, holidays	1,993
Use of company car	2,936
Free parking (estimated)	690

   a. Find the total value of Ray's fringe benefits for the year.
      $8,379
   b. Find his total job benefits for the year. $26,891

2. Jarvis Oertel has been offered a job that pays $12.45 an hour for a 40-hour week. He estimates that his weekly fringe benefits would be: pension, $30; health insurance, $15.65; parking, $14; uniforms, $5.
   a. Find Jarvis' estimated weekly wage. $480
   b. Find Jarvis' exact weekly wage. $498
   c. Find Jarvis' total weekly fringe benefits. $64.65
   d. Find Jarvis' total job benefits per week. $562.65

3. Karin Hedberg is paid $8.72 an hour for a 40-hour week. She estimates that her fringe benefits are 0.37 of her wages.

a. Find her estimated weekly wage. $360
b. Find her exact annual wage. $18,137.60
c. Find the total of her estimated yearly fringe benefits.
   $6,710.91
d. Find her total job benefits for a year. $24,848.51

4. Bob Dees is paid $1,128 per month. He estimates that his fringe benefits amount to 0.23 of his pay.
   a. Find his estimated annual wage. $12,000
   b. Find his exact annual pay. $13,536
   c. Find his estimated fringe benefits for a year. $3,113.28
   d. Find his total job benefits for a year. $16,649.28

Job Expenses. Almost every job has expenses. Some examples of job expenses are union or professional dues, travel and parking, uniforms, licenses, and tools. There may also be funds for birthdays and other events. These expenses can add up to a large part of an employee's salary.

Since job expenses reduce job benefits, you should subtract them from total job benefits to find **net job benefits.**

Total Job Benefits − Job Expenses = Net Job Benefits

■ Almost every job has some expenses, such as:
Pension plan
Parking
Transportation
Uniforms
Tools
Licenses
Union Dues.

Example

Donelda Ogg had total job benefits of $27,320. She found the total of her job expenses and subtracted it from her total job benefits to find her net job benefits.

Solution

Total job benefits		$27,320
Job expenses:		
Travel	$624	
License	35	
Professional dues	175	
Birthday fund	25	859
Net job benefits		$26,461 **Ans.**

**Exercise 2
Written**

1. Kumar Godhwani estimates that his total job benefits are $17,220 per year. He also estimates the following yearly job expenses: uniforms, $276; transportation, $398; parking, $260; dues, $96; other, $74.
   a. Find his yearly job expenses. $1,104
   b. Find his yearly net job benefits. $16,116

2. Jay Orr's job pays $1,374 a month. He estimates that his monthly fringe benefits are worth $384 and his monthly job expenses are tools, $38; dues, $22; travel costs for commuting to work, $24; parking, $42.
   a. Find his total monthly job benefits. $1,758
   b. Find his monthly job expenses. $126
   c. Find his monthly net job benefits. $1,632

3. Mary Ferrillo earns $420 a week. She estimates that her fringe benefits are 0.35 of her wages. She estimates her yearly job expenses to be: licenses, $345; uniforms, $326; travel, $745; dues, $535.
   a. Find her annual wage. $21,840
   b. Find her annual fringe benefits. $7,644
   c. Find her total annual job benefits. $29,484
   d. Find her annual job expenses. $1,951
   e. Find her annual net job benefits. $27,533

4. Rob Boda has worked for 5 years at the same firm. He earns an annual wage of $15,685 and is given a free pension of 0.07 of his total wages. He estimates that his total fringe benefits are 0.28 of his wages. He also estimates that his job expenses are: insurance, 0.06 of his wages; transportation, $408; dues, $120; office birthday fund, $20. Find his annual net job benefits. $18,587.70

Comparing Jobs. When you compare jobs you should consider many features about each job. For example, you should consider how much you like the duties of each job, the chances for raises and promotions, and the chances of layoffs, or job security. Another feature to compare is the net job benefits offered by each job.

**Exercise 3
Written**

1. Ikuko Goro's job pays $23,650 in yearly wages and 0.19 of her wages in yearly fringe benefits. She estimates that yearly job expenses are $1,354. Another job which she is looking at pays $22,490 in yearly wages and has estimated yearly fringe benefits of 0.26, with job expenses of $1,080.
   a. Find the net job benefits of Ikuko's current job. $26,789.50
   b. Find the net job benefits of the other job. $27,257.40
   c. Which job offers the greater net job benefits, and how much greater? The second job; $467.90

■ Check your work.

2. Jack Shank has a job with Yuler Co. which pays $6.75 per hour for a 40-hour week. Jack estimates that the fringe benefits are: pension, 0.09 of wages per year; insurance, $890 per year; free tuition, $450. The job expenses are estimated to be: commuting costs, $385; dues, $75; parking, $320. If he takes a new job with Zane, Inc., he will receive $7.20 an hour for a 40-hour week. He estimates that the fringe benefits for the new job would be: pension, 0.07 of yearly wages; insurance, $925 per year; free parking, $280. The estimated new job expenses would be: commuting costs, $456; dues, $75; uniforms, $312.
   a. Find the net job benefits per year at Yuler Co. $15,863.60
   b. Find the net job benefits per year at Zane, Inc. $16,386.32
   c. Which job has the higher net job benefits, and how much higher are they? Zane, Inc.; $522.72

3. Sherry Downey can work for Southwest Auto Co. for $5.25 an hour for a 40-hour week or take a similar job at Office Solutions, Inc. for $6.10 an hour for a 40-hour week. Fringe benefits at Southwest Auto Co. would be 0.27 of yearly wages. Fringe benefits at Office Solutions, Inc. would be 0.17 of yearly wages. Sherry estimates her

yearly job expenses would be $568 at Southwest Auto Co., and $785 at Office Solutions, Inc. Which job would give Sherry greater net job benefits per year? How much more?
Office Solutions, Inc.; $759.56

4. Georgio Bakalis can work for TRI Co. for $360 per week or Ellis, Inc. for $1,505 per month. Fringe benefits average 0.19 of yearly wages at TRI Co. and 0.24 at Ellis, Inc. Job expenses are estimated to be $956 per year at TRI Co. and $237 per year at Ellis, Inc. Which job would give Georgio more net job benefits? How much more?   Ellis, Inc.; $836.60

REVIEW 23

Terms

1. Match each term below with the statements.

   fringe benefits   net job benefits   total job benefits

   a. Items of value workers get above gross pay   fringe benefits
   b. Fringe benefits plus gross pay   total job benefits
   c. Total job benefits less job expenses   net job benefits

Skills

2. a. $\frac{3}{7} - \frac{2}{5} = ?$ $\frac{1}{35}$
   b. $3\frac{4}{9} + 8\frac{2}{3} = ?$ $12\frac{1}{9}$
   c. $8\frac{7}{8} - 3\frac{1}{6} = ?$ $5\frac{17}{24}$
   d. $\frac{1}{3}$ less than 36 is ?   24
   e. $\frac{2}{5}$ more than 45 is ?   63
   f. $450 \times 180 = ?$ 81,000
   g. 8 is what part of 64? $\frac{1}{8}$
   h. 12 is what part greater than 9? $\frac{1}{3}$
   i. $\frac{3}{11}$ as a decimal to the nearest hundredth is?   0.27
   j. $\frac{5}{14}$ as a decimal of two places of exact value is? $0.35\frac{5}{7}$

Problems

3. You are paid $21,800 a year. You estimate the value of your fringe benefits to be 0.18 of your yearly income and your annual job expenses to be $1,230 for travel, $185 for dues, and $420 for other expenses.
   a. Find your total job benefits per year. $25,724
   b. Find your net job benefits per year. $23,889 [23]

4. Ed O'Donnel is paid $8.20 an hour for a 40-hour week. Each week his employer deducts $40 in withholding taxes, FICA tax at the rate of 7.65%, and $12 for a savings plan. Find Ed's net pay for one week. $250.91 [21]

5. Sally has earned marks of 87 on four tests, 90 on three tests, 82 on three tests, and 98 on four tests. Find the average mark she has earned so far, to the nearest tenth.   89.7 [10]

‡6. Julio's July 31 check register balance was $951.21. His bank statement showed earned interest of $5.67 and a service charge of $1.34. He found that he had not recorded check No. 211 for $17.82 and that check No. 238 for $51.98 had been recorded as $51.89. What was his correct check register balance? $937.63 [6]

Computer Clinic

Your current job pays $4.00 an hour for a 40-hour week. You estimate your yearly fringe benefits at: pension, 0.08 of wages; insurance, $480; free parking, $450. Your estimated yearly job expenses are: commuting costs, $477; dues, $175; tools, $280. Another job offers $4.75 an hour for a 40-hour week and estimated yearly fringe benefits of: pension, 0.06 of wages; insurance, $560; paid vacations, $190. The other job's estimated yearly expenses are: commuting costs, $755; dues, $159; uniforms, $315.

Follow the steps below to use a spreadsheet to find the net job benefits for each job.

1. Insert your Spreadsheet Applications Diskette and call up the file "Sec23." After you do, your computer screen should look like Illustration 23–1.

```
Sec23

JOB BENEFITS:          JOB #1    JOB #2    Job #1
Gross Pay                 .00       .00    Hourly Rate      0.00
Pension                   .00       .00    Pension Rate     0.00
Insurance
Free Parking                               Job #2
Paid Vacations                             Hourly Rate      0.00
    Total Job Benefits    .00       .00    Pension Rate     0.00

JOB EXPENSES:
Commuting Costs
Dues
Tools
Uniforms
    Total Job Expenses    .00       .00

NET JOB BENEFITS          .00       .00
```

Illustration 23–1. Job Benefits Spreadsheet

2. Enter these amounts into the spreadsheet:

E4 4.00   E8 4.75   B6 480   B12 477   B14 280   C8 190   C13 159
E5 0.08   E9 0.06   B7 450   B13 175   C6 560   C12 755   C15 315

3. Answer the questions about your completed spreadsheet.
   a. What are the net job benefits for Job #1? Job #2?
      $8,983.60; $9,993.80
   b. What hourly rate of pay must you receive from Job #1 to make its net job benefits equal to Job #2, when both are rounded to the nearest whole dollar? $4.45
   c. At $4.50 an hour, what would be the net job benefits for Job #1?
      $10,106.80
   d. If the pension rate for Job #2 was 0.08, what would be the pension amount? $790.40

Percent means "per hundred," "by the hundred," or "out of a hundred." A percent shows the comparison or ratio of any number to 100. For example, if 20 video tapes out of 100 in a video store are comedy films, you can say that 20% of the tapes are comedies.

Illustration 24–1. 20% of the Video Tapes Are Comedy Films

You have already learned that a ratio is just another way of showing a fraction. For example, the ratio 20 to 100 (20:100) is the same as $\frac{20}{100}$. So the ratio 20:100, the fraction $\frac{20}{100}$, the decimal 0.20, and the percent 20% are just different numerals that stand for the same number.

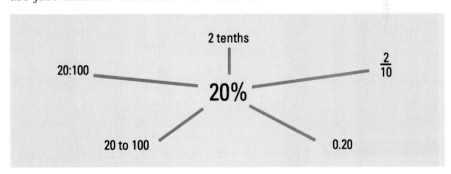

Illustration 24–2. They All Name the Same Number

Exercise 1
Written

Show each ratio as a fraction, a decimal, and a percent. Follow this format: 26 to 100 $= \frac{26}{100} = 0.26 = 26\%$.

1. 87 to 100 $\frac{87}{100} = 0.87 = 87\%$ 5. 500 to 100 $\frac{500}{100} = 5.00 = 500\%$

2. 31 to 100 $\frac{31}{100} = 0.31 = 31\%$ 6. 375 to 100 $\frac{375}{100} = 3.75 = 375\%$

3. 100 to 100 $\frac{100}{100} = 1.00 = 100\%$ 7. 3 to 100 $\frac{3}{100} = 0.03 = 3\%$

4. 110 to 100 $\frac{110}{100} = 1.10 = 110\%$ 8. 19 to 100 $\frac{19}{100} = 0.19 = 19\%$

Changing Decimals or Whole Numbers to Percents. One way to change a decimal or whole number to a percent is first to make the decimal into a fraction with a denominator of 100. Then change the fraction to a percent by dropping the denominator and writing the numerator with a percent sign. For example:

$$0.47 \times \frac{100}{100} = \frac{47}{100} = 47\% \qquad 6 \times \frac{100}{100} = \frac{600}{100} = 600\%$$

$$0.01 \times \frac{100}{100} = \frac{1}{100} = 1\%$$

An easier way to change a decimal or whole number to a percent is to move the decimal point two places to the right and attach a percent sign:

$$0.04 = 4\% \qquad 0.18 = 18\% \qquad 2 = 200\% \qquad 0.009 = 0.9\%$$

Change each decimal or whole number to a percent. Use the easy way.

Exercise 2
Oral

1. 0.58	58%	6. 0.006	0.6%	11. $0.75\frac{3}{4}$	$75\frac{3}{4}\%$
2. 1.0	100%	7. 2.71	271%	12. 4	400%
3. 0.03	3%	8. 0.062	6.2%	13. 0.07	7%
4. 2.6	260%	9. 0.403	40.3%	14. 8.36	836%
5. 0.91	91%	10. $0.28\frac{1}{2}$	$28\frac{1}{2}\%$	15. 0.049	4.9%

Changing Fractions to Percents. As you just found, you can change any fraction with a denominator of 100 to a percent by dropping the 100 and attaching a percent sign. For example:

$$\frac{5}{100} = 5\% \qquad \frac{2}{100} = 2\% \qquad \frac{88}{100} = 88\%$$

Some other fractions can be changed to percents easily even if they do not have denominators of 100. When a fraction has a denominator of 1, 2, 4, 5, 10, 20, 25, and 50, you just change it to an equivalent fraction with a denominator of 100. For example:

$$\frac{1}{2} \times \frac{50}{50} = \frac{50}{100} = 50\% \qquad \frac{1}{5} \times \frac{20}{20} = \frac{20}{100} = 20\%$$

$$\frac{1}{4} \times \frac{25}{25} = \frac{25}{100} = 25\%$$

Exercise 3
Written

Change each fraction to an equivalent fraction with a denominator of 100. Then show the new fraction as a percent.

1. $\frac{1}{2}$	50%	3. $\frac{5}{10}$	50%	5. $\frac{3}{25}$	12%	7. $\frac{4}{10}$	40%	9. $\frac{15}{50}$	30%
2. $\frac{3}{10}$	30%	4. $\frac{3}{5}$	60%	6. $\frac{8}{50}$	16%	8. $\frac{12}{25}$	48%	10. $\frac{1}{1}$	100%

Many fractions do not have denominators of 100 or other denominators that can be easily raised to 100. In those cases, you must change the fractions to decimals and then show the decimals as percents. For example:

$$\frac{2}{9} = 9\overline{)2.00}^{\,0.22\frac{2}{9}} = 0.22\frac{2}{9} = 22\frac{2}{9}\%$$

In the last example, $\frac{2}{9}$ was changed to a two-place decimal of *exact value*. Usually the division is carried to a stated number of places of *approximate value*.

Example

Express $\frac{4}{7}$ as a percent to the nearest *tenth* of a percent.

Solution	Explanation
$$\frac{0.571\frac{3}{7}}{7)4.000}$$	Dividing 4 by 7 to three decimal places gives 0.571 with a remainder of $\frac{3}{7}$. Since $\frac{3}{7}$ is less than $\frac{1}{2}$, the answer is rounded to 0.571. So, $\frac{4}{7} = 0.571 = 57.1\%$, to the nearest *tenth* of a percent.

Exercise 4
Written

1. Change each fraction to a percent. Carry the division to a two-place decimal of exact value.
   a. $\frac{3}{16}$ $18\frac{3}{4}\%$ b. $\frac{2}{15}$ $13\frac{1}{3}\%$ c. $\frac{15}{16}$ $93\frac{3}{4}\%$ d. $\frac{5}{32}$ $15\frac{5}{8}\%$

2. Change each fraction to a percent. Round each answer to the nearest tenth of a percent.
   a. $\frac{1}{14}$ 7.1% b. $\frac{4}{15}$ 26.7% c. $\frac{15}{18}$ 83.3% d. $\frac{5}{32}$ 15.6%

Changing Percents to Decimals. One way to change a percent to a decimal is to make the percent into a fraction with a denominator of 100. Then divide the numerator of the fraction by the denominator. For example:

■ Remember—
Move the decimal point to the left and drop the % sign. (45% = 0.45)

$$25\% = \frac{25}{100} = 100)\overline{25.00}^{\,0.25} = 0.25$$

A much simpler way to change a percent to a decimal is to drop the percent sign and move the decimal point two places to the left. For example:

$$7\% = 0.07 \qquad 37\% = 0.37 \qquad 31\frac{1}{2}\% = 0.31\frac{1}{2}, \text{ or } 0.315$$

$$409\% = 4.09 \qquad 17.8\% = 0.178 \qquad \frac{1}{2}\% = 0.00\frac{1}{2}, \text{ or } 0.005$$

Exercise 5
Written

Change each percent to a decimal or whole number. Use the easy way!

1.	78%	0.78	6.	0.8%	0.008	11.	$15\frac{3}{4}\%$ $0.15\frac{3}{4}$
2.	2%	0.02	7.	625%	6.25	12.	1,000% 10
3.	6.1%	0.061	8.	0.4%	0.004	13.	$23\frac{1}{2}\%$ $0.23\frac{1}{2}$
4.	100%	1	9.	$1\frac{1}{2}\%$	$0.01\frac{1}{2}$	14.	$\frac{1}{5}\%$ $0.00\frac{1}{5}$
5.	16.3%	0.163	10.	$\frac{1}{4}\%$	$0.00\frac{1}{4}$	15.	9.8% 0.098

Changing Percents to Fractions. You can change a percent to a fraction by dropping the percent sign and writing the number as the numerator over the denominator 100. Then simplify the fraction. For example:

$$8\% = \frac{8}{100} = \frac{2}{25} \qquad 140\% = \frac{140}{100} = \frac{7}{5}, \text{ or } 1\frac{2}{5}$$

**Exercise 6
Written**

Change each percent to a fraction or mixed number and simplify.

1. 12% $\frac{3}{25}$ 4. 17% $\frac{17}{100}$ 7. 90% $\frac{9}{10}$ 10. 175% $1\frac{3}{4}$

2. 14% $\frac{7}{50}$ 5. 44% $\frac{11}{25}$ 8. 70% $\frac{7}{10}$ 11. 125% $1\frac{1}{4}$

3. 3% $\frac{3}{100}$ 6. 5% $\frac{1}{20}$ 9. 60% $\frac{3}{5}$ 12. 250% $2\frac{1}{2}$

‡**Changing Percents with Decimals to Fractions.** If the percent has a decimal, you must change the percent to decimal form. Then change the decimal to a fraction. For example: $7.5\% = 0.075 = \frac{75}{1,000} = \frac{3}{40}$.

**‡Exercise 7
Written**

Change each percent to a fraction and simplify.

1. 0.3% $\frac{3}{1,000}$ 3. 0.7% $\frac{7}{1,000}$ 5. $37\frac{1}{2}\%$ $\frac{3}{8}$

2. 1.3% $\frac{13}{1,000}$ 4. 0.5% $\frac{1}{200}$ 6. 1.5% $\frac{3}{200}$

REVIEW 24

Skills

1. a. Show the ratio 15 to 100 as a fraction, decimal, and percent.
     $\frac{3}{20}$, 0.15, 15%
   b. Change to percents: 2.75, 0.37, $\frac{4}{5}$.   275%, 37%, 80%
   c. Change to decimals: $\frac{3}{8}$, 67.4%, 0.4%, $\frac{1}{4}\%$.
     0.375, 0.674, 0.004, 0.0025
   d. Change to fractions or mixed numbers and simplify: 25%,
     250%, 10%. $\frac{1}{4}$, $2\frac{1}{2}$, $\frac{1}{10}$

Problems

2. Ava earns $9.50 an hour for a 40-hour week. Her fringe benefits are worth 0.24 of her pay. She estimates that her weekly job expenses are: transportation, $24.75; pension plan, 0.08 of her pay; dues, $5.24. What are Ava's weekly net job benefits? $410.81 [23]

3. Allen is paid $7.80 an hour for an 8-hour day, time and a half for time past 8 hours per day, and double time on weekends. Last week he worked these hours: Mon., 8; Tues., 8; Wed., 7; Thurs., 11; Fri., 8; Sat., 5. Deductions were: $42 in withholding and 7.65% in FICA.
   a. What was Allen's regular pay for the week? $304.20
   b. What was Allen's overtime pay for the week? $113.10
   c. What was Allen's net pay for the week? $343.38 [17,21]

4. A cash register clerk started with $255 in cash. During the day, the clerk took in $2,072.47 and paid out $67.82. How much cash should remain in the drawer at the end of the day? $2,259.65 [4]

5. On May 31, Noriko's check register balance was $1,780.23 and her bank statement balance was $2,029.23. While comparing the statement with her register, she found a service charge of $3.23, interest earned of $6.23, and two outstanding checks: #525 for $156.88 and #528 for $89.12. Prepare a reconciliation statement for Noriko.
   $1,783.23 [5]

‡6. Six boxes of computer disks cost $168. At the same rate, how many boxes of disks could a company buy for $420?   15 [16]

Calculator Clinic

Changing Fractions to Percents. You can use the division and percent features of your calculator to find the percent equivalent of a fraction. For example, to change $\frac{3}{7}$ to a percent, rounded to the nearest tenth, follow the steps below.

Press these keys in order: [3] [÷] [7] [=]

and 0.4285714 appears in the display.

Now you must change the decimal to a percent by moving the decimal point two places to the right (42.85714). Then round off to the nearest tenth and attach a percent sign (42.9%).

Saving Time. You can get the answer and change it to a percent all at once if you press the percent key instead of the equals key.

Press these keys in order: [3] [÷] [7] [%]

and 42.857142 appears in the display.

All you have to do now is round the answer to the nearest tenth of a percent and attach a percent sign (42.9%). Notice that when you press the percent key the decimal point is automatically placed in the correct position.

Calculator Practice. Apply what you have learned in this calculator clinic to all the problems in Exercise 3 and to Problems 2a–2d in Exercise 4 in this section. For additional practice, complete the exercise below.

Use a calculator to change each fraction to a percent, to the nearest hundredth.

1. $\frac{2}{7}$ 28.6%   3. $\frac{18}{35}$ 51.4%   5. $\frac{156}{476}$ 32.8%

2. $\frac{21}{37}$ 56.8%   4. $\frac{4}{38}$ 10.5%   6. $\frac{49}{128}$ 38.3%

Section 25
More Percents

Finding a Percent of a Number. Suppose you earn $10,000 a year and your fringe benefits are 25% of your wages. Since percent means "hundredths," 25% means 25 hundredths. So, finding 25 percent of $10,000 is the same as multiplying 25 hundredths (0.25) times $10,000.

In other words, when you need to find a percent of a number, you change the percent to a decimal and multiply. For example:

Percent means hundredths.
($25\% = \frac{25}{100}$, or, 0.25)

$$25\% \times \$10,000 = 0.25 \times \$10,000 = \$2,500$$

When you multiply mentally it is usually easier to multiply by the number in the percent and then put the decimal point in the answer. For example, first multiply $25 \times \$10,000$ to find $250,000, then point off two places to get $2,500.

Multiply each problem mentally. Write the answers only.

**Exercise 1
Written**

	1.		2.		3.	
a.	2% of $600	$12	5% of $120	$6.00	70% of $31	$21.70
b.	8% of $300	$24	1% of $480	$4.80	55% of 50	$27.50
c.	9% of $200	$18	100% of $68	$68	20% of $43	$8.60
d.	6% of $110	$6.60	300% of $3.10	$9.30	80% of $75	$60.00
e.	4% of $120	$4.80	500% of $109	$545	105% of $600	$630
f.	15% of $40	$6.00	60% of $90	$54	1% of $1,856	$18.56

Finding What Percent a Number Is of Another. To find what percent a number is of another, divide the one number (the part) by the other number (the whole). Then show the result as a percent.

Example

7 is what percent of 15?

Solution

$$15\overline{)7.00} \quad 0.46\tfrac{2}{3} = 46\tfrac{2}{3}\% \quad \textbf{Ans.}$$

Check:
$46\tfrac{2}{3}\%$ of $15 = 0.46\tfrac{2}{3} \times 15 = 7$

Explanation

7 is the part and 15 is the whole with which the part is to be compared. The fraction $\frac{7}{15}$ shows the relationship of 7 to 15. Dividing 7 by 15 gives $0.46\tfrac{2}{3}$, which is equivalent to $46\tfrac{2}{3}\%$.

Before you divide a fraction, you should simplify it to make the division easier. For example:

$$\frac{36}{81} = \frac{4}{9} = 4 \text{ divided by } 9 = 0.44\frac{4}{9} = 44\frac{4}{9}\%$$

Any Number Is 100% of Itself. You can show that any number is 100% of itself by solving this problem: 26 is what percent of 26? Since the fraction $\frac{26}{26}$ shows the relationship of 26 to 26, then

$$\frac{26}{26} = 26 \text{ divided by } 26 = 1 = 100\%.$$

When you compare one number to another number that is larger, the result is *less* than 100%. When you compare one number to itself, the result is *equal* to 100%. When you compare one number to another number that is smaller, the result is *more* than 100%. For example:

$$24 \text{ compared to } 30 \text{ is } 80\%, \text{ since } \frac{24}{30} = \frac{4}{5} = 80\%;$$

$$24 \text{ compared to } 24 \text{ is } 100\%, \text{ since } \frac{24}{24} = 1 = 100\%;$$

$$24 \text{ compared to } 20 \text{ is } 120\%, \text{ since } \frac{24}{20} = \frac{6}{5} = 120\%.$$

Exercise 2
Oral

Find the unknown percent in each problem.

1. 30 is ?% of 60   50%
2. 12 is ?% of 36 $33\frac{1}{3}\%$
3. $8 is ?% of $32   25%
4. $10 is ?% of $25   40%
5. ?% of 10 is 7   70%
6. ?% of $30 is $6   20%
7. ?% of $24 is $8 $33\frac{1}{3}\%$
8. ?% of $50 is $40   80%

9. 50 is ?% of 25   200%
10. 20 is ?% of 5   400%
11. 20 is ?% of 2   1,000%
12. ?% of 6 is 12   200%
13. ?% of 7 is 28   400%
14. $24 is ?% of $20   120%
15. $31 is ?% of $31   100%
16. $27 is ?% of $36   75%

Exercise 3
Written

Find the unknown percent in each problem

1. 45 is ?% of 180   25%
2. 84 is ?% of 240   35%
3. ?% of $1,200 is $54 $4\frac{1}{2}\%$
4. ?% of $192 is $12 $6\frac{1}{4}\%$
5. $4.80 is ?% of $60   8%
6. ?% of $180 is $22.50 $12\frac{1}{2}\%$
7. $8\frac{1}{4}$ is ?% of $41\frac{1}{4}$ 20%
8. $19 is ?% of $3.80   500%

9. ?% of $8.25 is $33   400%
10. $5\frac{1}{3}$ is ?% of 16 $33\frac{1}{3}\%$
11. 7 is ?% of 28   25%
12. $1.16 is ?% of $3.48 $33\frac{1}{3}\%$
13. ?% of 10.14 is 5.07   50%
14. ?% of $64 is $16   25%
15. $8 is ?% of $120 $6\frac{2}{3}\%$
16. $10\frac{1}{8}$ is ?% of $60\frac{3}{4}$ $16\frac{2}{3}\%$

Fractional Equivalents of Parts of 100%. Some percents are contained in 100% an exact number of times. For example, 25% is contained

■ Base is a number with which another number is compared.

exactly 4 times in 100%. Some other percents like this are 20%, $33\frac{1}{3}\%$ and 50%. These percents are called aliquot parts.

Since 25% is contained exactly four times in 100%, then 25% is $\frac{1}{4}$ of the base number, 100%. We call 100% the **base** because it is the number with which 25% is compared. We call the fraction, $\frac{1}{4}$, a **fractional equivalent** because it shows what part 25% is of the base, 100%.

$$\text{Base} \longrightarrow \left.\frac{25\%}{100\%} = \frac{1}{4}\right] \longleftarrow \text{Fractional equivalent}$$

■ Fractional Equivalent is a fraction showing what part one number is of the base.

Multiplying by Fractional Equivalents of Parts of 100%. When you multiply by a percent that is contained within 100% evenly, you can often multiply mentally using the fractional equivalent. For example, let's say that your fringe benefits are 25% of your wages, which are $12,000. To find the dollar amount of your fringe benefits, you can multiply $12,000 by $\frac{1}{4}$ instead of 0.25.

■ Dividing by 4 is easier than multiplying by 0.25.

$$25\% \text{ of } \$12,000 = \frac{1}{4} \times \$12,000 = \$3,000$$

The same process can also be used for numbers which are multiples of these fractional equivalents. For example, 75% is 3 times 25%, or $\frac{3}{4}$ of 100%; 125% is 5 times 25%, or $1\frac{1}{4}$.

The fractional equivalents of percents which are used often are shown below. You should learn these percents and their fractional equivalents.

$50\% = \frac{1}{2}$	$20\% = \frac{1}{5}$	$12\frac{1}{2}\% = \frac{1}{8}$	$33\frac{1}{3}\% = \frac{1}{3}$
$25\% = \frac{1}{4}$	$40\% = \frac{2}{5}$	$37\frac{1}{2}\% = \frac{3}{8}$	$66\frac{2}{3}\% = \frac{2}{3}$
$75\% = \frac{3}{4}$	$60\% = \frac{3}{5}$	$62\frac{1}{2}\% = \frac{5}{8}$	
	$80\% = \frac{4}{5}$	$87\frac{1}{2}\% = \frac{7}{8}$	

**Exercise 4
Oral**

Use the fractional equivalent of the percent to find

1. 50% of $28; $38 $14, $19
2. 25% of $48; $72 $12, $18
3. 75% of $36; $40 $27, $30
4. $12\frac{1}{2}\%$ of $24; $64 $3, $8
5. 20% of $20; $45 $4, $9
6. $37\frac{1}{2}\%$ of $48; $96 $18, $36
7. 40% of $30; $55 $12, $22
8. 80% of $15; $60 $12, $48

9. 60% of $45; $80 $27, $48
10. $66\frac{2}{3}\%$ of $39; $75 $26, $50
11. $33\frac{1}{3}\%$ of $18; $90 $6, $30
12. $12\frac{1}{2}\%$ of $32; $56 $4, $7
13. $87\frac{1}{2}\%$ of $40; $80 $35, $70
14. $62\frac{1}{2}\%$ of $80; $32 $50, $20
15. $66\frac{2}{3}\%$ of $66; $45 $44, $30
16. $33\frac{1}{3}\%$ of $27; $51 $9, $17

Exercise 5
Written

Multiply in each problem. Use the fractional equivalent of the percent when it is easier.

1.

a.	25% of $1,600	$400
b.	80% of $5,800	$4,640
c.	30% of $2,900	$870
d.	3% of $1,467	$44.01
e.	5% of $1,840	$92
f.	106% of $805	$853.30
g.	20% of $305.40	$61.08
h.	25% of $628	$157
i.	75% of $4,020	$3,015

2.

37.6% of $400	$150.40
$4\frac{1}{2}$% of $1,600	$72
$12\frac{1}{2}$% of $1,200	$150
125% of $88	$110
$166\frac{2}{3}$% of $36.75	$61.25
$62\frac{1}{2}$% of $1,272	$795
$66\frac{2}{3}$% of $270	$180
$187\frac{1}{2}$% of $16.40	$30.75
$33\frac{1}{3}$% of $882	$294

■ Multiply by moving the decimal point.

Finding 1%, 10%, 100%, and 1,000% of a Number. The decimals or whole numbers that are equivalent to 1%, 10%, 100%, and 1,000% are:

$$1\% = 0.01 \qquad 100\% = 1$$

$$10\% = 0.1 \qquad 1,000\% = 10$$

To multiply by 1%, 10%, etc., mentally move the decimal point in the number as if you were multiplying by 0.01, 0.1, 1, or 10. For example:

To Find	Multiply	By Moving the Decimal Point	Answer
1% of 375	0.01 × 375	2 places to left	3.75
10% of 375	0.1 × 375	1 place to left	37.5
100% of 375	1 × 375	no places	375
1,000% of 375	10 × 375	1 place to right	3,750

Exercise 6
Written

Multiply mentally in the problems below. Write the answers only. If the answer has a fraction of a cent, round it to the nearest cent.

1.	1% of 40	0.4	9.	100% of 284	284
2.	1% of $29	$0.29	10.	100% of $19	$19
3.	1% of $18.60	$0.19	11.	100% of $805	$805
4.	1% of $7.48	$0.07	12.	100% of $6.70	$6.70
5.	10% of $367	$36.70	13.	1,000% of $15	$150
6.	10% of $47.45	$4.75	14.	1,000% of 43	430
7.	10% of 9	0.9	15.	1,000% of $7.50	$75
8.	10% of $1.98	$0.20			

■ $\frac{1}{2}$% = half of one percent.

Fractional Parts of 1%. The numeral $\frac{1}{2}$% means $\frac{1}{2}$ of 1%. To find $\frac{1}{2}$% of $2,400, first find 1% of $2,400 and then take $\frac{1}{2}$ of the result. If you want, you can first find $\frac{1}{2}$ of $2,400 and then take 1% of that result. Solve problems using other fractional parts of 1% in the same way.

Example

Find $\frac{1}{2}$% of $2,400

Solution 1	**Solution 2**
1% of $2,400 = $24	$\frac{1}{2}$ of $2,400 is $1,200
$\frac{1}{2}$ of $24 is $12 **Ans.**	1% of $1,200 = $12 **Ans.**

**Exercise 7
Oral**

Solve.

$4 $1 $9 $7 $2.05

1. $\frac{1}{4}$% of $1,600; $400; $3,600; $2,800; $820

$3 $1.20 $4.30 $0.33 $0.21

2. $\frac{1}{2}$% of $600; $240; $860; $66.40; $42.40

$4 $7 $11 $0.60 $1

3. $\frac{1}{8}$% of $3,200; $5,600; $8,800; $480; $800

$3 $0.50 $1 $0.20 $0.17

4. $\frac{1}{10}$% of $3,000; $500; $1,000; $200; $166

**Exercise 8
Written**

Multiply mentally in each problem. Write only the product.

	1.		2.		3.	
a.	25% of $3,200	$800	$\frac{1}{2}$% of $32	$0.16	$\frac{3}{8}$% of $72	$0.27
b.	$\frac{1}{4}$ of $3,200	$800	$\frac{1}{8}$% of $720	$0.90	$\frac{1}{3}$% of $900	$3.22
c.	$\frac{1}{4}$% of $3,200	$8	$\frac{1}{5}$% of $500	$1	$\frac{2}{5}$% of $30	$0.12
d.	50% of $2,400	$1,200	$\frac{3}{4}$% of $400	$3	$\frac{3}{4}$% of $48	$0.36
e.	$\frac{1}{2}$ of $2,400	$1,200	$\frac{2}{3}$% of $900	$6	$\frac{4}{5}$% of $45	$0.36

A fraction of a percent is often shown in decimal form by first dropping the percent sign and moving the decimal point two places to the left. Then the fraction is changed to its decimal equivalent. For example:

$$\frac{3}{4}\% = 0.00\frac{3}{4} = 0.0075 \qquad \frac{1}{4}\% = 0.00\frac{1}{4} = 0.0025$$

When the fraction is one like $\frac{2}{3}$ or $\frac{5}{9}$, the numerator is not exactly divisible by the denominator. So, you just drop the percent sign, move the decimal point two places to the left, and leave the fraction as a fraction. For example:

$$\frac{2}{3}\% = 0.00\frac{2}{3} \qquad \frac{4}{9}\% = 0.00\frac{4}{9}$$

**Exercise 9
Written**

Write each as a decimal.

	1.		2.		3.		4.	
a.	$\frac{1}{2}$ of 1%	0.005	$\frac{3}{4}$%	0.0075	$\frac{3}{8}$ of 1%	0.00375	$\frac{1}{3}$%	$0.003\frac{1}{3}$
b.	$\frac{1}{5}$ of 1%	0.002	$\frac{1}{8}$%	0.00125	$\frac{2}{5}$ of 1%	0.004	$\frac{5}{8}$%	0.00625

**Exercise 10
Written**

Write each numeral as a percent, with the fractional part of 1% written as a fraction

	1.		2.		3.		4.		5.	
a.	0.0075	$\frac{3}{4}$%	0.085	$8\frac{1}{2}$%	$0.00\frac{1}{3}$	$\frac{1}{3}$%	0.00375	$\frac{3}{8}$%	0.0875	$8\frac{3}{4}$%
b.	0.0625	$6\frac{1}{4}$%	0.005	$\frac{1}{2}$%	0.00125	$\frac{1}{8}$%	$0.0033\frac{1}{3}$	$\frac{1}{3}$%	0.00875	$\frac{7}{8}$%
c.	0.0025	$\frac{1}{4}$%	0.002	$\frac{1}{5}$%	0.004	$\frac{2}{5}$%	$0.00\frac{2}{3}$	$\frac{2}{3}$%	$0.0066\frac{2}{3}$	$\frac{2}{3}$%

REVIEW 25

Terms

1. Match the terms with the statements.

base   fractional equivalent   percent

a. Per hundred   percent
b. A number with which another is compared   base
c. Shows what part one number is of another
   fractional equivalent

Skills

2. a. $\frac{1}{5}$% of $745 is ? $1.49

b. 1% of $9.33 is ? $0.09

c. $350 is what percent of $500?   70%

d. $37\frac{1}{2}$% of $896 is ? $336

e. Show $87\frac{1}{2}$%, as a decimal; as a fraction   0.875, $\frac{7}{8}$

‡f. $561 is $\frac{3}{4}$ of ? $748

‡g. $30 equals what amount decreased by $\frac{1}{5}$ of itself? $37.50

Problems

3. Ella Dent works on an 8-hour-day basis at $12.46 an hour with time and a half for overtime. During one week she worked these hours: Monday, 9; Tuesday, 8; Wednesday, $6\frac{1}{2}$; Thursday, 9; Friday, $8\frac{1}{2}$. What were Ella's gross earnings for the week? $526.44 [17]

4. A factory worker is paid 72 cents for each clamp produced that passes inspection. In one week the worker produced these amounts: 137, 101, 186, 156, and 134. A total of 57 clamps did not pass inspection. What were the worker's gross earnings? $473.04 [7]

5. A fruit drink is made with 4 parts of orange to every 5 parts of grapefruit. If a company makes 1,278 gallons of the fruit drink, how many gallons of orange do they use?   568 [16]

Calculator Clinic

Using a Calculator to Find a Percent of a Number. To find a percent of a number, you must change the percent to a decimal and multiply. For example, to find 5% of 45, you change 5% to 0.05 and press these keys in order:

 and `2.25` appears

in the display.

Saving Time. To find a percent of a number quickly, use the multiplication and percent keys. For example, to find 5% of 45, press these keys in order:

 and `2.25` appears in

the display.

Notice that the decimal point was placed in the answer automatically.
   To multiply by a fraction of 1%, you must first change the fraction in the percent to a decimal. For example, to find $\frac{1}{2}$% of 45, change $\frac{1}{2}$% to 0.5%. Then enter .5 × 45%. The answer in your display will be **0.225.**

Using a Calculator to Find What Percent a Number Is of Another. To find what percent one number is of another, use the division and percent keys. For example, to find what percent 1 is of 8, press these keys in order:

 and `0.125` appears in the display.

Now, move the decimal point two places to the right and attach a percent sign.

Saving Time. To do the last problem quickly, use the percent key instead of the equals key.

 and `12.5` appears in the display.

Once again, the decimal point is placed in the answer automatically. All you have to do is attach a percent sign.

Calculator Practice. Apply what you have learned in this calculator clinic to the problems in Exercises 1, 2, 3 (1–8 only), 5 (Column 1 only), and 7 in this section.

144

Percent Relationships

There are six types of problems you will encounter in dealing with percent relationships:

(1) Finding a percent of a number

(2) Finding a number that is a percent greater or smaller than another

(3) Finding what percent a number is of another

(4) Finding what percent one number is greater or smaller than another

‡(5) Finding the whole when a percent of it is known

‡(6) Finding the whole when an amount that is a percent greater or smaller than the whole is known.

These are the same six types of problems in fractional relationships that you studied in Unit 3. You learned how to do (1) and (3) above in Section 25. You will learn how to do (2) and (4) in this section and (5) and (6) in Section 27.

Finding a Number That Is a Percent Greater or Smaller Than Another. When we say "25% greater than 32" and "25% more than 32," we mean 25% *added* to 32, or 32 + 25% of 32. The result is 32 + 8, or 40.

When we say "25% smaller than 32" and "25% less than 32," we mean 25% *subtracted* from 32, or 32 − 25% of 32. The result is 32 − 8, or 24.

Example

32 *increased* by 25% of itself equals what number?

	Solution	
	32 = known number	
25% of 32 =	8 = increase	
	40 = unknown number	**Ans.**

Check: 32 + 25% × 32 = 32 + 8 = 40

Explanation

"32 increased by 25% of itself" means "add 25% of 32 to 32." The unknown number equals the known number, 32, *plus* the amount of the increase, 25% of 32. So, 32 + 25% of 32 = the unknown number.

Example

32 *decreased* by 25% of itself equals what number?

	Solution	
	32 = known number	
25% of 32 =	8 = decrease	
	24 = unknown number	**Ans.**

Check: 32 − 32 × 25% = 32 − 8 = 24

Explanation

"32 decreased by 25% of itself" means "*subtract* 25% of 32 from 32." The unknown number is equal to the known number, 32, *minus* the decrease, 25% of 32. So, 32 − 25% of 32 = the unknown number.

**Exercise 1
Oral**

Solve.

1. 10% more than $500 $550
2. 10% greater than $200 $220
3. 10% as much as $900 $90
4. 10% less than $600 $540
5. 10% smaller than $700 $630
6. 1% larger than $700 $707
7. $500 decreased by 20% $400

8. $80 increased by 10% $88
9. $90 reduced by $33\frac{1}{3}$ $60
10. 30% larger than $50 $65
11. 25% less than $48 $36
12. 2% more than $500 $510
13. 200% more than $20 $60
14. $4 increased by 200% $12

15. A new job pays 20% more per hour than an old job. If the old job paid $8 an hour, what does the new job pay per hour? $9.60

16. Since your employer changed health insurance companies, your health insurance deduction decreased by 10%. If your old health insurance deduction was $60, what is your new deduction? $54

Finding What Percent One Number Is Greater or Smaller Than Another. If one job you are offered pays $40 a day while another pays $32, you may want to know by what percent the one wage is greater than the other wage.

$40 is what percent greater than $32?

To solve the problem, you first subtract the smaller number from the larger number to find the part:

$40 − $32 = $8. $8 is the part.

You then divide the part by the original number that is the whole, or base, and change the result to a percent:

$$\text{\$8 divided by \$32} = \frac{1}{4} = 25\%$$

The original wage, $32, is the amount on which you base the comparison of the two wages. That is why it is called the base.

To find the percent that one number is smaller or less than another, you do the same thing.

Example

24 is what percent smaller, or less, than 30?

Solution

$$30 - 24 = 6$$

$$\frac{6}{30} = \frac{1}{5} = 20\% \quad \textbf{Ans.}$$

Check: $30 - 20\%$ of $30 = 30 - 6 = 24$

Explanation

24 is 6 smaller than 30. So, 6 is the part. "Smaller than 30" means that 30 is the number with which the part, 6, is to be compared. It is the base. The fraction $\frac{6}{30}$ shows the relationship of 6 to 30; $\frac{6}{30} = \frac{1}{5} = 20\%$. So, 20% shows the percent by which 24 is smaller than 30, the base.

Find the unknown percent in each problem.

1. $5 is ? % greater than $4 25%

2. $6 is ? % greater than $5 20%

3. ? % more than $10 is $13 30%

4. $4 is ? % smaller than $5 20%

5. $3 is ? % smaller than $4 25%

6. ? % less than $10 is $7   30%

7. $8 is ? % more than $6 $33\frac{1}{3}$%

8. $8 is ? % less than $10 20%

9. $24 is ? % less than $32 25%

10. ? % more than $16 is $20 25%

11. $35 is ? % more than $30 $16\frac{2}{3}$%

12. ? % less than $25 is $20 20%

13. $44 is ? % more than $40 10%

14. $7 is ? % less than $10   30%

15. $5 is ? % more than $4   25%

16. $6 is ? % more than $5   20%

‡17. $15 is ? % more than $5 200%

‡18. ? % more than $10 is $25 150%

‡19. ? % of $10 is $25   250%

‡20. $12 is ? % more than $6 100%

Percent Increase or Decrease. A practical use for finding what percent one number is greater or smaller than another is to compare amounts for two periods of time. For example, you may want to compare your net job benefits this year with your net job benefits last year. A business may want to compare this year's sales with last year's sales. A shopper may want to compare the price of an item this week with the price of the same item last week.

Sales This Year $600,000

Sales Last Year $450,000

THAT'S A $33\frac{1}{3}$% INCREASE

When you show the increase or decrease as a percent, use the amount for the *earlier* period of time as the base.

Example

A student earned a score of 84% on this week's test and 80% on last week's test. What was the percent increase or decrease in the score?

Solution

84% − 80% = 4% difference

$\frac{4\%}{80\%} = \frac{1}{20} = 5\%$ increase **Ans.**

Check: 80% + 5% of 80% = 80% + 4% = 84%

Explanation

The comparison is based on the test score for last week since that is the earlier week. Since the score this week is larger than last week, the difference is an increase. The difference, 4%, is divided by last week's score, 80%, to find the percent increase.

**Exercise 3
Written**

■ Check your
work.

1. Isabel Muyo's salary is $20,832 this year. Last year her salary was $18,600. What was the percent of increase or decrease? 12% increase

2. In Ed's new job his fringe benefits are $75.24 a week. In his old job the fringe benefits were $66 a week. What was the percent of increase or decrease? 14% increase

3. Since she started carpooling, Carole's job expenses dropped from $75 to $51 per month.
   a. Find the estimated percent of decrease in job expenses.
      $33\frac{1}{3}$% decrease
   b. Find the actual percent of decrease in job expenses.
      32% decrease

4. Garry's net pay on his new job is $205.77. His net pay on his old job was $180.50. What is the percent increase or decrease in his net pay? 14% increase

5. This year Vera's monthly net job benefits total $1,255. Last year her benefits totaled $1,225. By what percent did Vera's job benefits increase or decrease, to the nearest tenth of a percent? 2.4% increase

REVIEW 26

Skills

1. a. $45 increased by 24% of itself is? $55.80
   b. $7.00 decreased by 16% of itself is? $5.88
   c. $600 decreased by what percent of itself equals $504? 16%
   d. $200 increased by what percent of itself equals $230? 15%
   e. Show $\frac{3}{4}$% as a decimal. 0.0075
   f. $\frac{1}{5}$% of $380 is what amount? $0.76

Problems

2. A firm paid its workers a total of $292,068 this week. Last week the firm paid a total of $256,200. By what percent did the total amount paid by the firm increase? 14% [26]

3. If Annice takes a new job closer to her home, her job expenses will drop by 24%. If her job expenses are now $172 a month, what will her job expenses be per month if she takes the new job? $130.72 [26]

4. Owen Company pays its employees an average of $9.10 an hour. The average paid by Baron, Inc., is $8.75 an hour. By what percent is Owen Company's average hourly pay greater than Baron, Inc.'s? 4% [26]

5. On May 31 Elmer's account balances were: bank, $763.14; check register, $717.08. While comparing his check register to the bank statement, Elmer found a service charge of $1.65 and interest earned of $3. Checks outstanding were: #877, $19.78; #879, $10; #880, $14.93. Prepare a reconciliation statement for Elmer. $718.43 [5]

6. A cashier started the day with $175 in change. At the end of the day, the cash register totals showed $1,864.26 taken in and $58.38

paid out. How much cash should remain in the cash register at the end of the day? $1,980.88 [4]

‡7. Doris's net pay this week is $210. This amount is only $\frac{5}{6}$ as much as her pay for last week. What was Doris's pay last week? $252 [20]

Calculator Clinic

Finding a Number That Is a Percent Greater or Smaller Than Another.
To find the number that is 5% greater than 40, you can multiply (40 × 0.05 = 2) and then add (40 + 2 = 42). But, by using the percent key on your calculator, the problem is solved much faster. Follow the steps below.

Press these keys in order: [4] [0] [+] [5] [%]

and the answer, | 42. |, appears in the display.

If the problem is to find the number that is 5% smaller than 40, just press the minus key instead of the plus key. That's all there is to it.

Finding What Percent One Number Is Greater or Smaller than Another. To find what percent 50 is greater than 40, follow these steps:

a. Press these keys in order: [5] [0] [−] [4] [0] [=]

   and | 10. | will appear in the display.

The display shows the difference, or the part. You now need to divide the part by the whole, or 40, to find the percent.

b. Press these keys in order: [÷] [4] [0] [%]

   and the answer, | 25. |, will appear in the display.

Now all you have to do is add a percent sign.

Calculator Practice. Apply what you have learned in this calculator clinic to the problems in Exercise 1, 2, and 3 in this section, and to any other exercises your teacher may assign.

More Percent Relationships

‡**Principles of Percent Relationships.** In this statement, "15 is 20% of 75," 15 is the part and 75 is the whole with which 15 is compared. Since 75 is the number on which the comparison is based, it is called the base. The percent, 20%, is said to be *based* on 75. **Remember—the base, and only the base, may be multiplied by the percent.**

The base is usually the number which comes right after the words that mean multiplication. Such words are "times," "of," "more than," "as large as," and so on.

In each of the following, 75 is the base because it comes right after the words that mean multiplication. So, 75 may be multiplied by the percent.

? is 20% *as large as* 75.	**? is 20% *smaller than* 75.**
20% *of* 75 is ?	**20% *more than* 75 is?**
20% × 75 is?	**? is 20% *greater than* 75.**

In the problems that follow, an *unknown number* is the base, because the space for the unknown number comes right after the words that mean multiplication. In these problems the known number, 75, may *not* be multiplied by the percent because 75 *does not represent the base.*

75 is 20% *as large as* ?	**75 is 20% *smaller than* ?**
20% *of* ? equals 75	**75 is 20% *greater than* ?**
75 is 20% *more than* ?	**75 is 20% *as great as* ?**
75 is 20% *of* ?	**75 is 20% *times* ?**

Problems like these cannot be solved by multiplying the known number by the percent.

Write "yes" after a problem if the known number may be multiplied by the percent. Write "no" if it may not be multiplied.

All of these mean multiply:
times
of
more than
as large as
smaller than
greater than
as great as.

‡**Exercise 1**
Oral

1.	? is 75% of 28	Yes	6.	? is 60% as great as 60	Yes
2.	45 is 50% of ?	No	7.	$180 is 45% as great as ?	No
3.	$80 is 60% of ?	No	8.	$90 is 10% smaller than ?	No
4.	$20 is 25% of ?	No	9.	? is 20% times 55	Yes
5.	45 is 30% times ?	No	10.	10% of ? equals 35	No

‡**Finding the Whole Number When a Percent of It Is Known.** Suppose you know that the fringe benefits of a job are $60 a month and that this is 15% of the monthly salary. Now suppose that you want to find the amount of the monthly salary.

The problem is one of finding the whole (salary) on which the percent is based. It is a problem of finding the unknown factor when the other factor and the product are known. You can solve the problem this way:

Example

$60 is 15% of what monthly salary?

Explanation

The problem tells us that 15% of an unknown number (the monthly salary) is equal to $60. From this we can say that

$$\overset{F}{15\%} \times \overset{F}{\text{the unknown number}} = \overset{P}{\$60}$$

$60 is the product, and 15% is one of the factors of $60. The other factor is the unknown number. This factor can be found by dividing the product, $60, by the known factor, 15%.

Solution

$$15\% \times \text{the unknown number} = \$60$$
$$\text{The unknown number} = \$60 \text{ divided by } 15\%$$
$$= \$60 \text{ divided by } 0.15 = \$400 \quad \textbf{Ans.}$$

Check: $15\% \times \$400 = 0.15 \times \$400 = \$60$

**‡Exercise 2
Written**

Find the unknown number in each problem.

1.	$25\% \times ? = \$120$	$480
2.	$9\% \times ? = \$36$	$400
3.	29% of $?$ is $\$95.70$	$330
4.	$\$10.78$ is 70% of $?$	$15.40
5.	53% of $\$521$	$276.13
6.	$\$2.73$ is 21% of $?$	$13
7.	$?$ is 38% of $\$356$	$135.28
8.	$65\% \times ?$ is $\$24.70$	$38
9.	$\$81 = 45\% \times ?$	$180
10.	$\$11.20$ is 35% of $?$	$32
11.	$?$ is 40% of $\$722$	$288.80
12.	$\$264$ is 30% of $?$	$880

**‡Exercise 3
Oral**

Find the unknown number in each problem.

1.	$\$7$ is 1% of $?$	$700
2.	$\$36$ is 6% of $?$	$600
3.	3% of $?$ is $\$24$	$800
4.	$\$14$ is 2% of $?$	$700
5.	1% of $?$ is $\$2$	$200
6.	$\$4$ is $\frac{1}{2}\%$ of $?$	$800
7.	$\frac{1}{5}\%$ of $?$ is $\$3$	$1,500
8.	$\$9$ is $\frac{3}{4}\%$ of $?$	$1,200
9.	$10\% \times ?$ is $\$78$	$780
10.	$\$40$ is 100% of $?$	$40
11.	$\$40$ is 400% of $?$	$10
12.	$?$ is 25% of $\$120$	$30

13. A worker spends 6% of her salary, or $33.60, each week on health insurance. What is her weekly salary? $560

14. A worker received 15%, or $255, of his total wages in overtime pay last month. What were his total wages for the month? $1,700

‡**Finding the Whole When an Amount That Is a Percent Greater or Smaller Than the Whole Is Known.** When we say "60 is 20% greater than another number," we mean 60 is the result of *adding* 20% of the unknown number to the unknown number.

To find the unknown number, you must find the number on which the percent is based. In other words, you must find the unknown factor when the product and the other factor are known. This means you must divide the product by the known factor.

Example

What number increased by 20% of itself equals 60?

Explanation

The problem tells us that if 20% of an unknown number is added to that number, the sum is 60. Thus, the unknown number + 20% of the unknown number = 60

(1) The unknown number is the base, or whole, and is 100% of itself, or 100% of *the unknown number.*
(2) The increase is 20% of *the unknown number.*
(3) Adding (2) to (1) gives 120% of *the unknown number,* which is equal to 60.

Solution

$$
\begin{aligned}
100\% \times \text{the number} &= \text{the number} \\
+20\% \times \text{the number} &= \underline{\text{the increase}} \\
120\% \times \text{the number} &= 60 \\
\;\;\;\;(F) \qquad\qquad (F) \qquad\qquad\;\; (P)
\end{aligned}
$$

$$
\begin{aligned}
\;\;\;\;\;(F) \qquad\; (P) \quad\;\; (F) \\
\text{The number} = 60 \div 120\% \\
= 60 \div 1.20 = 50 \quad \textbf{Ans.}
\end{aligned}
$$

Check: 50 + 20% of 50 = 50 + 10 = 60

In the same way, when we say "60 is 20% smaller than another number," we mean that 60 is the result of *subtracting* 20% of the unknown number from the unknown number.

Example

What number decreased by 20% of itself equals 60?

Explanation

The problem tells us that if 20% of an unknown number is subtracted from that number, the difference is 60. Thus, the unknown number − 20% of the unknown number = 60

Solution

$$
\begin{aligned}
100\% \times \text{the number} &= \text{the number} \\
-20\% \times \text{the number} &= \underline{\text{the decrease}} \\
80\% \times \text{the number} &= 60 \\
\;\;\;(F) \qquad\qquad (F) \qquad\qquad\;\; (P)
\end{aligned}
$$

$$
\begin{aligned}
\qquad\qquad\quad (F) \qquad\; (P) \quad\;\; (F) \\
\text{the number} = 60 \div 80\% \\
= 60 \div 0.80 = 75 \quad \textbf{Ans.}
\end{aligned}
$$

Check: 75 − 20% of 75 = 75 − 15 = 60

**‡Exercise 4
Written**

Find the unknown number in each problem.

1. ? + 25% of itself = $2,200 $1,760

2. $123 is 50% more than ? $82

3. $600 is $33\frac{1}{3}$% greater than ? $450

4. $24.91 = ? increased by 6% $23.50

5. $369 is 64% greater than ? $225

6. ? + 5% of itself = $47.46 $45.20

7. ? plus 25% of itself gives $160 $128

8. ? increased by 18% of itself equals $885 $750

9. Because he worked overtime, Don Feldman earned $675 last week. This amount was 20% more than his regular pay. What was his regular pay? $562.50

10. Sally was offered a job paying $2,400 a month. This is 28% more than her current job pays. How much does her current job pay a month? $1,875

**‡Exercise 5
Written**

Find the unknown numbers.

1. ? − 20% of itself = $8,400 $10,500

2. ? − 4% of itself = $312 $325

3. ? decreased by 30% of itself equals $33.60 $48

4. $11.22 = ? decreased by 15% $13.20

5. $638 is 45% less than ? $1,160

6. ? minus $16\frac{2}{3}$% of itself gives $10.80 $12.96

7. $12.30 is $33\frac{1}{3}$% smaller than ? $18.45

8. ? less than $12\frac{1}{2}$% of itself equals $3.36 $3.84

9. Due to a layoff, Cyrus earned only $1,664 this month. This was 35% less than he usually earns. What does he usually earn? $2,560

**‡Exercise 6
Oral**

■ Exercise 6 reviews all 6 types of problems in percent relationships.

Review of Percentage Problems. Find the unknown numbers.

1. ? is 60% as much as $30 $18
2. ? is 25% more than $40 $50
3. 20 is ? % of 80   25%
4. $36 is ? % more than $30   20%
5. 50 is ? % less than 60 $16\frac{2}{3}$%
6. 9 is 25% of ?   36
7. $20 is 25% more than ? $16
8. 24 is 25% less than ?   32
9. $48 is $33\frac{1}{3}$% more than ? $36
10. 12 is 20% of ?   60
11. 24 is ? % more than 20   20%
12. ? is 6% of $30 $1.80

13. 20% more than 40   48
14. $30 is ? % of $50   60%
15. $20 is ? % more than $15 $33\frac{1}{3}$%
16. 25% less than $20 $15
17. 12 is $33\frac{1}{3}$% more than ?   9
18. 40% less than $20 $12
19. $24 is 75% as much as $32
20. ? is 30% of $200 $60
21. $10 is ? % less than $50   80%
22. 9 is ? % of 3   300%
23. 150% of ? is $18 $12
24. 10 is ? % of 5   200%

REVIEW 27

Skills

1. a. $\frac{1}{3}$% of $195 is what amount? $0.65
    b. 0.087 equals what percent?   8.7%
    c. $8.75 increased by 36% of itself = ? $11.90
    d. Show $1\frac{3}{4}$% as a decimal.   0.0175
    e. $135 is what percent greater than $120? $12\frac{1}{2}$%
    ‡f. $6.72 is 70% of what amount? $9.60
    ‡g. $64.24 is 10% more than what amount? $58.40
    ‡h. What amount decreased by 10% of itself gives $63? $70

Problems

2. This year Platte High School had 36 teachers and 729 students. Last year it had 33 teachers and 675 students. What is Platte High School's percent increase or decrease in student enrollment from last year?   8% increase [26]

3. Last year Dan Beard's total wages were $24,650. His wages this year are expected to increase 6% over last year. What are his expected wages for this year? $26,129 [26]

4. For 8 weeks, Anne's average wages were $755 a week. For the next 3 weeks, her wages were $771, $780, and $725. Find her average weekly wages for the 11 weeks. $756 [10]

5. On May 10, Xtel, Inc. deposited these items: (bills) 36 twenties, 14 tens, 56 fives, 51 ones; (coins) 15 halves, 79 quarters, 413 dimes, 45 nickels, 614 pennies. What was Xtel, Inc.'s total deposit? $1,267.94 [4]

6. I-chen is paid $0.95 each for the first 500 slats she produces per week and $0.99 for each slat over 500 items per week. Last week she produced 597 slats. Her employer deducted $61 for federal withholding taxes and 7.65% for FICA taxes.
    a. Estimate I-chen's gross pay for the week. $600
    b. What was I-chen's net pay for the week? $466.35 [7, 21]

7. Vince is paid $425 a week in salary. His fringe benefits are 19% of his salary. His weekly job expenses are: pension, $34.05; health insurance, $7.36; parking and transportation, $25.90. What are Vince's weekly net job benefits? $438.44 [23]

‡8. Yvonne's employer pays 11% of her salary, or $165 a month, to her pension plan. What is Yvonne's monthly salary? $1,500 [27]

‡9. On May 31 Frank's account balances were: bank statement, $971.63; check register, $955.30. His statement showed a service charge of $1.10 and interest earned of $3 that had not been recorded in the check register. Checks outstanding were: #345, $31.16; #346, $14.73; #348, $24.90. Of the canceled checks, Frank found that #344 for $21.36 had not been recorded in his register. A deposit of $35, mailed on May 31, had been received by the bank too late to appear on the bank statement. Prepare a reconciliation statement for Frank. $935.84 [6]

Some salespeople earn a commission instead of a fixed salary. The commission may be an amount for each item sold, or it may be a percent of the dollar value of sales. A higher commission may be earned for goods that are hard to sell than for goods that are easy to sell. Both a salary and a commission may be earned.

Illustration 28–1. The Sale of a High-Priced Item Earns a Big Commission

Straight Commission. Salespeople who earn only a commission work on a **straight commission** basis. When the rate of commission is an amount for each item sold, you multiply the number of items by the rate to find the commission.

$$\underset{\textbf{(F)}}{\textbf{\textit{Rate of Commission}}} \times \underset{\textbf{(F)}}{\textbf{\textit{Quantity Sold}}} = \underset{\textbf{(P)}}{\textbf{\textit{Commission}}}$$

Example

Earl Brown sells greeting cards in his spare time. He is paid a straight commission of $0.75 on each box of cards he sells. During March he sold 145 boxes. What was his commission?

Solution

$0.75 × 145 = $108.75 commission   **Ans.**

When the rate of commission is a percent, you multiply the amount of the sales by the rate to find the commission.

$$\underset{\textbf{(F)}}{\textbf{\textit{Rate of Commission}}} \times \underset{\textbf{(F)}}{\textbf{\textit{Sales}}} = \underset{\textbf{(P)}}{\textbf{\textit{Commission}}}$$

Example

Terri Ames is paid a straight commission of 5% on her sales. During September her sales were $32,000. What was her commission?

Solution

0.05 × $32,000 = $1,600 commission **Ans.**

**Exercise 1
Written**

1. Find the commission in each problem.

Item	Quantity	Commission on each	Total Commission
a. Boxes of Candy	78	$2	$156
b. Books	32	$0.55	$17.60
c. Pennants	49	$1.20	$58.80

2. Doralice is paid a straight commission of $5.75 for each item she sells. Last month she sold 103 items. Find her estimated and exact commissions. $600; $592.25

3. Find the commission in each problem.

Total Sales	Rate of Commission	Total Commission
a. $35,986	4%	$1,439.44
b. $12,435	6%	$746.10
c. $5,750	$12\frac{1}{2}\%$	$718.75

Salary and Commission. Salespersons may be paid a salary plus a commission. The commission may be a percent of their total sales, or a percent of their sales above a fixed amount. This fixed amount is called a **quota**.

Example

Mae Barr is paid a salary of $250 a week plus 5% on her sales over $4,000. Last week her sales totaled $7,000. What were her total earnings for the week?

Solution

Sales	= $7,000	Salary	= $250
Quota	= 4,000	Commission (5% of $3,000) =	150
Sales over Quota = $3,000		Total earnings	= $400 **Ans.**

**Exercise 2
Written**

1. Jo Ann White is paid a salary of $325 a week and a commission of 5% on all sales. Her sales last week were $5,780. What were her total earnings for the week? $614

2. Hollis Riggs earns a salary of $200 a week and a commission of 6% on all sales. If Hollis's sales for one week were $4,120, what were his total weekly earnings? $447.20

3. Toni Wild earns a salary of $1,200 a month and a commission of 7.5% on all sales over $4,000. This month her sales were $21,400. What were her total earnings for the month? $2,505

4. Kamil Wise receives a weekly salary of $400 plus $\frac{1}{2}\%$ commission on all sales in excess of $11,500 a week. Last week his sales were $43,870. What were his total earnings for the week? $561.85

Graduated Commission. Some salespersons are paid a **graduated commission.** This means their rate of commission increases as their sales increase (see Illustration 28–2). For example, the rate may be 3% on the first $12,000 of sales; 4% on the next $6,000; and 5% on sales over $18,000. Graduated commissions may also be based on the number of units sold.

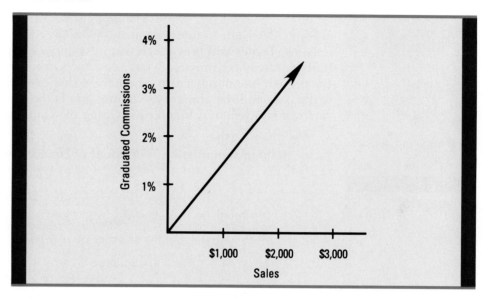

Illustration 28–2. The More You Sell, the Higher Your Rate of Commission

Example

Lori Wells is paid 5% commission on the first $10,000 of monthly sales and 10% on all sales over $10,000. Last month her sales were $34,000. What was her commission?

Solution

$34,000 − $10,000 = $24,000 sales over $10,000
0.05 × $10,000 = $ 500 commission on first $10,000
0.10 × $24,000 = $2,400 commission on sales over $10,000
               $2,900 total commission **Ans.**

**Exercise 3
Written**

1. Find the total commission in each problem.

Sales   Commission

a. $9,000   10% on first $5,000; 15% on sales over $5,000 $1,100
b. $800   3% on first $400; 5% on excess over $400 $32
c. $2,600   6% on first $900; 9% on sales over $900 $207
d. $8,370   5% on first $3,500; 7% on next $6,500 $515.90

2. Armando Lamas sells house siding. He is paid 4% commission on his first $15,000 of monthly sales and 6% commission on all sales over $15,000. In June his sales were $27,000 and in July, his sales totaled $32,000. What were his total commissions for the 2 months? $2,940

3. Rita Gray sells cosmetic kits on a part-time basis. She is paid a weekly commission of $1.50 each on the first 50 kits she sells, $1.75 each on the next 100 kits, and $2 on any kits she sells over 150. Last week she sold 225 kits. What was her commission for the week? $400

Finding the Rate of Commission on Sales. Suppose you know the amount of sales and how much commission was paid on the sales. To find the rate of commission, you follow the same steps you used to find the percent one number is of another. In this case the amount of sales is the base and the amount of commission is the part. The percent, or rate of commission, is found by dividing the commission by the sales.

$$\underset{\textbf{(F)}}{\textbf{Rate of Commission}} = \underset{\textbf{(P)}}{\textbf{Amount of commission}} \div \underset{\textbf{(F)}}{\textbf{Sales}}$$

Example

A salesperson sold a computer for $3,000 and received a $150 commission. What percent commission did the salesperson receive?

Solution

$150 ÷ $3,000 = 0.05 = 5% **Ans.** $\dfrac{\$150}{\$3,000} = \dfrac{1}{20} = 0.05 = 5\%$ **Ans.**

Exercise 4 Written

1. Find the rate of commission in each problem.

| | | Commission | | | | Commission | |
	Sales	Amount	Rate		Sales	Amount	Rate
a.	$6,400	$448	7%	d.	$2,800	$350	$12\frac{1}{2}\%$
b.	$625	$18.75	3%	e.	$600	$33	$5\frac{1}{2}\%$
c.	$480	$72	15%	f.	$5,400	$189	$3\frac{1}{2}\%$

2. An agent who sells subscriptions for a magazine that costs $24 a year makes a commission of $3.60 on each subscription. What percent commission does the agent make? 15%

3. Austin Orr sells motorcycles. He is paid a salary of $900 a month plus a commission on all sales. Each month his employer contributes 8% of his salary to his pension and $56 to his health insurance. Last month his sales were $35,000, and he earned a total salary and commission of $3,000.
    a. How much commission was he paid? $2,100
    b. What rate of commission was he paid? 6%

4. Akemi Soga is paid a commission on all sales over $3,000 a week. Last week she earned a commission of $520 on sales of $16,000. What rate of commission was she paid? 4%

‡**Finding the Amount of Sales When the Amount of Commission and Rate of Commission Are Known.** You may want to find how much a person must sell to earn a certain amount of commission. This is the same type of problem as finding the whole when a percent of the whole is known.

Example

A salesperson is paid a 5% commission. How many dollars' worth of merchandise must the salesperson sell to earn a commission of $840?

Explanation

The rate of commission is always based on the sales. So, "5% commission" means "5% of the sales" or "5% times the sales." The $840 is the amount of the commission. The problem tells us that 5% of the sales is equal to $840.

$$\underset{F}{5\%} \times \underset{F}{sales} = \underset{P}{\$840}$$

$840 is the product, and 5% is one of the factors of $840. The other factor is sales, which is unknown. This factor can be found by dividing the product, $840, by the known factor, 5%.

Solution

5% × sales = $840
sales = $840 divided by 5%
= $840 divided by 0.05 = $16,800 **Ans.**

Check: Rate of Commission × Sales = Commission
5% × $16,800 = 0.05 × $16,800 = $840

Notice that the $840 commission in the example was not multiplied by the rate, 5%, because the rate was based on the sales. Only the sales may be multiplied by the rate of commission, 5%.

$$\underset{F}{\textbf{Rate of Commission}} \times \underset{F}{\textbf{Sales}} = \underset{P}{\textbf{Commission}}$$

$$\textbf{5\%} \qquad \times \quad \textbf{?} \quad = \qquad \textbf{\$840}$$

The rate of commission and the sales are the factors (F), and the commission is the product (P). If the commission and the rate of commission are known, the unknown factor (Sales) is found by dividing the product (Commission) by the known factor (Rate of Commission).

Sales = Commission ÷ Rate of Commission

**Exercise 5
Written**

1. Don Dunn is paid a commission of 6% on all sales. What dollar amount of goods must he sell in one month to earn $2,100 commission? $35,000

2. Lois Hall's commission is 8%. What dollar amount of goods must she sell to earn $2,400? $30,000

3. At a weekly salary of $350 plus 5% commission on all sales, what minimum weekly sales are needed to earn $600 a week? $5,000

4. Raul Diaz earns a salary of $700 a month and a commission of 6% on all sales. What must be the amount of his sales in a month for his total monthly income to be $1,600? $15,000

5. Beth Bolka earns a weekly salary of $400 with a 4% commission on all sales over $8,000 a week. What must be her total weekly sales if she wants a total weekly income of $800? $10,000

REVIEW 28

Terms

1. Match the terms with the statements.

   graduated commission   quota   straight commission

   a. A fixed amount above which a commission is paid   quota
   b. Money earned comes only from commission
       straight commission
   c. The rate increases as sales increase   graduated commission

Skills

2. a. $108 is what percent of $360?   30%
   b. $27 increased by 17% of itself is ? $31.59
   c. $175 decreased by what percent of itself is $168?   4%
   d. Show 64% as a simplified fraction $\frac{16}{25}$
   e. Change $\frac{2}{13}$ to a percent to the nearest tenth of a percent   15.4%
   f. $\frac{1}{4}$% of $36,000 is ? $90
   g. $37\frac{1}{2}$% of $4,800 = ? $1,800
   h. $92,078 × 1% = ? $920.78
   ‡i. 60 is 15% of ?   400

Problems

3. Myrna Blair earns 10% commission on all sales and 3% more commission on sales over $15,000 per week. Her sales this week were $19,800. What was her commission for the week? $2,124 [28]

4. Luke Starr earns $425 a week in salary and 3% commission on all sales over $5,000 a week. Last week his sales were $8,089. What was Luke's gross income for the week? $517.67 [28]

5. Fatima Wyatt's sales last month were $43,200. Her total earnings for the month were $2,578, of which $850 was her monthly salary. What rate of commission was Fatima paid?   4% [28]

6. Zika, Inc., a computer software firm, sold 214,537 copies of a spreadsheet package this year. Last year they sold 175,850 copies. What was the percent of increase or decrease in the sales of the package?   22% increase [26]

7. Leon scored 80 on a test last week. This week his score was 15% more than last week's score. What was Leon's score this week?   92 [26]

‡8. Whalen, Inc., had sales of $217,455 this year. This amount is 9% more than the company's sales were last year. What were the sales for Whalen, Inc., last year? $199,500 [27]

‡9. A salesperson's commission rate is 8% on all sales. To earn $750 commission, how much must the salesperson sell? $9,375 [28]

Calculator Clinic

■ On some calculators you must press [=] before doing Step b.

Finding Salary Plus Commission. You can solve a commission problem on most hand-held calculators by following the steps below. Try it, using this sample problem: Jill is paid $200 a week plus 2% commission on all sales. If she sold $5,600 this week, find her gross income.

a. Press these keys in order: [5] [6] [0] [0] [×] [2] [%] and the total commissions earned, 112. , appears in the display.

b. Press these keys in order: [+] [2] [0] [0] [=] and the gross income, 312. , appears in the display.

If Jill had had a sales quota to meet, you would have started the problem by finding the amount of sales she had over quota. For example, suppose Jill sold $8,600 in the week but was paid a 2% commission on sales over $3,000. Your first step would be to subtract $3,000 from $8,600 by entering: 8600 − 3000 =. The answer, 5600, would show in the display. You would then multiply $5,600 by 2% and add $200, as you did before, to find her total earnings.

Finding Graduated Commission. The memory register can be very useful when you are finding graduated commissions. For example, suppose Jill's sales are $350 and she is paid 1% on her first $100 of sales and 2% on all sales over $100. You can find her total earnings by following the steps below.

a. Find the first commission: [1] [0] [0] [×] [1] [%] .

b. Add the first commission to memory by pressing: [M+] .

c. Compute the next commission: [2] [5] [0] [×] [2] [%] .

d. Add the next commission to memory by pressing: [M+] .

e. Press the [MR/C] key and the total commissions earned, M 6. , appears in the display.

Calculator Practice. Apply what you have learned in this calculator clinic to the problems in Exercises 2 and 3 in this section, and to any other exercises your teacher may assign.

Section 29
Agent's Commission

A person who legally acts for someone else is called an **agent**. An agent is usually paid a commission. The person for whom the agent acts is called the **principal**.

When a principal has a real estate agent sell property, the principal usually pays the agent a percent of the sale price as commission. Sometimes the principal will also pay the agent for unusual expenses caused by the sale of the property. The amount left for the principal, after deducting the agent's commission and expenses, is called the **net proceeds.**

Collection agents collect unpaid bills. They usually are paid a percent of the amount they collect. They may also be repaid for unusual expenses involved in making the collection.

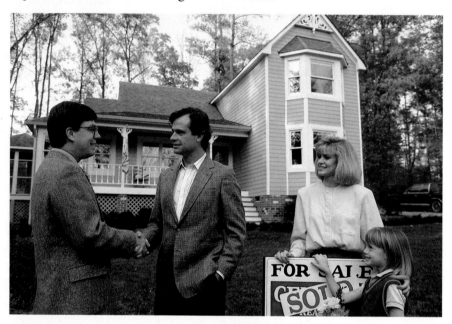

Illustration 29–1. Real Estate and Collection Agents

Finding the Amount of the Agent's Commission. The rate of commission of a real estate agent is based on the sale price of the property sold. For example, a real estate agent sells a house and lot for $80,000 and charges a commission of 6%. The amount of the commission would be:

$$\textbf{Rate of Commission} \times \textbf{Sale Price} = \textbf{Commission}$$
$$\textbf{0.06} \qquad \times \quad \textbf{\$80,000} = \quad \textbf{\$4,800}$$

The commission of a collection agent is figured this way:

$$\textbf{Rate of Commission} \times \textbf{Amount Collected} = \textbf{Commission}$$

Finding the Net Proceeds of the Principal. The net proceeds is the amount of money received by the principal after subtracting the agent's commission and expenses, if any.

Sale Price − (Commission + Expenses) = Net Proceeds

Amount Collected − (Commission + Expenses) = Net Proceeds

Example

Cal Kerr, a collection agent, collected a bill of $1,500 for B-Trix Co. He charged 35% commission and $75 for expenses. What net proceeds did the B-Trix Co. receive?

Solution

Amount collected...................................		$1,500
Deductions:		
Commission (35% × $1,500)	$525	
Expenses	75	− 600
Net proceeds..		$ 900

**Exercise 1
Written**

1. Find the commission, total deductions, and net proceeds in each problem.

Sale Price or Amount Collected	Commission		Agent's Expenses	Total Deduc- tions	Net Proceeds
	Rate	Amount			
a. $ 45,000	6%	$2,700	$187	$2,887	$42,113
b. $ 2,070	30%	$621	None	$621	$1,449
c. $ 85,900	7%	$6,013	None	$6,013	$79,887
d. $ 450	20%	$90	$15.75	$105.75	$344.25
e. $143,750	6%	$8,625	$207.88	$8,832.88	$134,917.12

2. A real estate agent sold a house for Evelyn Reade for $121,900. The agent charged a 6% commission rate. What net proceeds did Evelyn receive? $114,586

3. Eli Cohen, a real estate agent, sold property worth $124,900, for $150,000. Expenses of the sale were $675 and the commission rate was 7%. What was the amount of the net proceeds owed to the principal? $138,825

4. Bi-State Real Estate Agency sold a house for Oscar Lavelle for $65,800. The agency charged 5% for commission and expenses of the sale were $320. What were the net proceeds? $62,190

5. Wright Corporation hired an agent to collect accounts totaling $7,700. The agent collected 78% of the accounts and charged $37\frac{1}{2}\%$ for collecting them.
   a. What estimated amount was collected? $6,400
   b. How much did the Wright Corporation receive? $3,753.75

‡**Finding the Sale Price or Amount Collected When the Amount of the Net Proceeds and the Rate of Commission Are Known.** Sometimes you know the net proceeds and the rate of commission and you want to find the sale price or amount collected. To solve this type of problem, you must identify the number on which the rate is based.

Example

A collection agent gave $700 to a principal after deducting 20% for collecting an account. What was the amount collected?

Explanation

The commission is 20% *of the amount collected.* That means if 20% of the amount collected is subtracted from the amount collected, the difference is $700.

Amount Collected − 20% of Amount Collected = $700

(1) The amount collected is the base, or whole, and is 100% of itself, or 100% *of the amount collected.*
(2) The commission is 20% *of the amount collected.*
(3) So, the net proceeds, $700, represents 80% *of the amount collected,* or 100% − 20% = 80%.

Solution

$$100\% \times \text{amount collected} = \text{amount collected}$$
$$\underline{-20\% \times \text{amount collected} = \text{commission}}$$
$$80\% \times \text{amount collected} = \text{net proceeds (\$700)}$$
$$\text{amount collected} = \$700 \text{ divided by } 80\%$$
$$= \$700 \text{ divided by } 0.80 = \$875 \quad \textbf{Ans.}$$

Check: Amount Collected − Commission = Net Proceeds
$875 − 20% of $875 = $875 − $175 = $700

‡**Exercise 2
Written**

1. An agent sent a principal $1,680 after deducting 30% for collecting an account. What was the amount collected? $2,400

2. Lee Yount sold property through Burger Realty. The company charged 6% commission, and Lee's net proceeds were $62,040. What was the sale price? $66,000

3. A collection agent, who charges 28% commission, collected an account and sent $453.60 to the client. What amount was collected? $630

4. What would the sale price of a house and lot have to be if the owner wanted to make $70,500 on the sale after paying the real estate agent a commission of 6%? $75,000

5. Carry Vosberg wants to sell a lot at a price that will bring her at least $28,000 after deducting the agent's commission of 6%. What is the lowest price, to the nearest hundred dollars, at which she may sell the lot and receive at least $28,000 in net proceeds? $29,800

REVIEW 29

Terms

1. Match the terms with the statements.

   agent   net proceeds   principal

   a. A person for whom an agent acts   principal
   b. The sale price minus commission and expenses   net proceeds
   c. A person who legally acts for another   agent

Skills

2. a. $451 is what percent less than $550? 18%
   b. $30 is what percent of $24? 125%
   c. $165 is what percent greater than $120? $37\frac{1}{2}$%
   d. Show $6\frac{1}{4}$% as a decimal. 0.0625
   e. Show 0.782 as a percent. 78.2%
   f. Show $\frac{6}{7}$ as a percent to the nearest tenth of a percent. 85.7%

Problems

3. A real estate agent sold an apartment house for $436,500. What were the seller's net proceeds from the sale if the commission rate was 6% and the expenses of the sale were $1,038? $409,272 [29]

4. The Ortiz Collection Agency collected 85% of a bill of $4,250 and charged 32% for its services. How much commission did the collection agency receive? $1,156 [29]

5. Rod Jorgenson works as a sales clerk at a department store. He is paid a weekly salary of $210 and a commission of 3% on all sales over $5,000. During one week, his sales totaled $7,459. What were his gross earnings for the week? $283.77 [28]

6. Last year Mary McCarthy was paid a monthly salary of $1,000 and a commission on all sales. What rate of commission was Mary paid on last year's sales of $230,000 if her total earnings for the year, including both salary and commission, were $32,700?   9% [28]

‡7. Bob Bianco earned $426 this week. This amount was $\frac{3}{4}$ as large as the amount he earned last week. How much did Bob earn last week? $568 [20]

‡8. A real estate broker who charges 6% commission received $8,910 for selling a house and lot. What was the selling price of the house and lot? $148,500 [29]

‡9. Lori wants to sell her property at a price that will bring her at least $75,000 after deducting the real estate agent's commission of 5%. What is the lowest price, to the nearest $100, at which she may sell the property and still receive the net proceeds she wants? $79,000 [29]

‡10. A real estate agent's total commission for May was $3,600. This was a 4% decrease from the agent's April commission. What was the agent's April commission? $3,750 [27]

Computer Clinic

Mason-White Corporation uses a Sales-tracking Chart to keep track of the sales made by real estate agents during the month. Follow the steps below to complete the chart for October.

1. Insert your Spreadsheet Applications Diskette and call up the file "Sec29." After you do, your computer screen should look like Illustration 29–2.

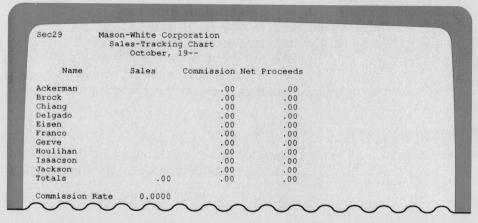

```
Sec29           Mason-White Corporation
                  Sales-Tracking Chart
                     October, 19--

      Name          Sales      Commission Net Proceeds

   Ackerman                        .00          .00
   Brock                           .00          .00
   Chiang                          .00          .00
   Delgado                         .00          .00
   Eisen                           .00          .00
   Franco                          .00          .00
   Gerve                           .00          .00
   Houlihan                        .00          .00
   Isaacson                        .00          .00
   Jackson                         .00          .00
   Totals              .00         .00          .00

   Commission Rate   0.0000
```

Illustration 29–2. Using a Spreadsheet to Track Sales

2. Enter the sales made so far in October into the template:

B7 75000   B9 14000   B11 56000   B13 145000 B15 12000 B19 0.05
B8 289000 B10 789900 B12 473800 B14 90000   B10

3. Answer these questions about your completed chart:
    a. What agent has the most sales so far for the month?   Delgado
    b. What agent has the least sales so far for the month?   Jackson
    c. What is the total amount of commissions so far for the month? $97,235
    d. What would the total commissions be if the rate of commission had to be reduced to 4% to meet competition? $77,788
    e. At a 5% commission rate for the month, what would be the total net proceeds if Jackson sold a property for $190,000? $2,027,965

166

Metric Measurement

The **metric system** of weights and measures is used in most parts of the world. In most countries other than the United States, units such as meters, square meters, liters, and kilograms are used in everyday life. In the United States, the **Customary system** is used more often and includes familiar terms such as feet, miles, square yards, quarts, and pounds.

Metric terms, however, are also used in the United States. Cars are made of parts measured in metric terms. You may buy 35-millimeter film or have a prescription filled for medication that is sold in 250 milligram tablets. Milk may be sold by the liter, and the weight of canned goods is usually given in grams as well as ounces.

In this unit you will use four metric measures: length, area, capacity, and weight. You will find that metrics are easy to learn and to use.

After you finish Unit 5, you will be able to:

- Recall common metric units for length, area, capacity, and weight.
- Write metric amounts correctly.
- Recognize the meanings of the standard metric prefixes as they identify parts and multiples of basic metric units.
- Add, subtract, multiply, and divide metric amounts.
- Convert from one metric unit to another.
- Solve problems that involve metrics.
- Solve problems that contain more information than you need.
- Estimate answers to problems.
- Read, write, say, and recognize the meanings of the key terms.

Have you seen highway signs that give distances in both kilometers and miles? Does your ruler have both a centimeter and an inch scale? Do you know that Olympic athletes run in 100-meter races? If so, you already know some of the ways in which length is given in metric terms. Can you think of other ways?

■ Study these:

deci =
  tenth
centi =
  hundredth
milli =
  thousandth
deka =
  ten
hecto =
  hundred
kilo =
  thousand

Metric Measures of Length. The basic unit of length in the metric system is the meter. The meter is slightly longer than a yard in the Customary system.

To show different lengths, you must use the word *meter* with a prefix. The meter can be divided into smaller parts such as tenths, called *deci*meters; hundredths, called *centi*meters; or thousandths, called *milli*meters. These parts are used to measure lengths of less than a meter.

The meter or its multiples can also be used to measure longer lengths. Multiples of the meter include the *deka*meter, or ten meters; the *hecto*meter, or one hundred meters; and the *kilo*meter, or one thousand meters.

The metric units of length, their symbols, and their values in meters are shown in Illustration 30–1.

	Unit	Symbol	Value in Meters
Parts of a meter	**millimeter**	**mm**	0.001 m (one-thousandth meter)
	centimeter	**cm**	0.01 m (one-hundredth meter)
	decimeter	dm	0.1 m (one-tenth meter)
Basic unit	**meter**	**m**	1 m (one meter)
Multiples of a meter	dekameter	dam	10 m (ten meters)
	hectometer	hm	100 m (one hundred meters)
	kilometer	**km**	1 000 m (one thousand meters)

Note: The terms decimeter, dekameter, and hectometer are not often used.

Illustration 30–1. Metric Units of Length

■ Important rules.

Writing Metric Amounts. The symbol, rather than the unit name, is used for metric values and is written in small letters. The same symbol is used for the singular and the plural of the unit, so you don't add an "s" for plurals. For example, you write 1 kilometer as 1 km and 18 kilometers as 18 km. To break up large numbers, like 1 000 m, you use a space, not a comma.

1. What is the basic unit of length in the metric system? What is its symbol?   meter; m

2. a. Name the parts of a meter.   millimeter; centimeter; decimeter
   b. What are their symbols?   mm; cm; dm

3. What are the names for the multiples of a meter?
   dekameter; hectometer; kilometer

4. What is the metric prefix for 1 000? 100? 10?   kilo; hecto; deka

5. What is the metric prefix for a
   a. Tenth?   deci
   b. Hundredth?   centi
   c. Thousandth?   milli

6. How many meters are there in a kilometer? dekameter? hectometer?
   1 000 m; 10 m; 100 m

7. A meter can be divided into how many millimeters? centimeters? decimeters?   1 000 mm; 100 cm; 10 dm

Changing from One Metric Unit to Another. Suppose you are adding an amount in centimeters to an amount in meters. Since the two metric units are not alike, you must change one of the units to the terms of the other unit.

Because the metric system is a decimal system, each position is either 10 times more than, or one-tenth of, the next unit. This makes it easy to change values to different units. To change values, you multiply or divide by 10 as many times as needed to get to the unit you want. You can also do this by moving the decimal point to the right or to the left.

For example, to change to a *smaller* unit, you move the decimal point to the *right*. Study these examples:

1 meter = 10. decimeters, or 100. centimeters, or 1 000. millimeters

1 kilometer = 10. hectometers, or 100. dekameters, or 1 000. meters

To change to a *larger* unit, you move the decimal point to the *left:*

1 millimeter = 0.1 centimeter, or 0.01 decimeter, or 0.001 meter

1 meter = 0.1 dekameter, or 0.01 hectometer, or 0.001 kilometer

Write the missing metric values.

	1.			2.			3.	
a.	1 m = ? dm	10	1 cm = ? m	0.01	7 km = ? m	7 000
b.	1 m = ? cm	100	1 dm = ? m	0.1	3 m = ? cm	300
c.	1 m = ? mm	1 000	1 mm = ? m	0.001	600 mm = ? m	0.6
d.	1 km = ? m	1 000	1 cm = ? dm	0.1	548 m = ? km	0.548

**Exercise 3
Written**

Write the missing metric values.

1.

a. 3 m = ? cm   300 cm
b. 6 m = ? mm   6 000 mm
c. 7 cm = ? mm   70 mm
d. 4 km = ? m   4 000 m
e. 700 m = ? km   0.7 km

2.

340 cm = ? m   3.4 m
41 mm = ? m   0.041 m
176 mm = ? cm   17.6 cm
6.2 m = ? mm   6 200 mm
0.9 km = ? m   900 m

Examples

3.75 m
+0.60 m
4.35 m

3.7 m
× 2
7.4 m

Adding, Subtracting, Multiplying, and Dividing. You add, subtract, multiply, and divide metric values in the same way as Customary values, but you may have to change some values so that they all have the same terms. For example, to add 3.75 meters and 60 centimeters, you have to change the 60 centimeters to meters (0.60 m) and then add.

To multiply metric values that have decimals, you should do the multiplication first. Then, you must put the decimal point in the answer as many places from the right as there were in the two numbers you multiplied.

**Exercise 4
Written**

1. Find the totals.
    a. 3 km + 2 km + 1 km = ? km   6 km
    b. 2.8 m + 4.6 m + 1.5 m = ? m   8.9 m
    c. 5 km + 7 km + 400 m = ? km   12.4 km
    d. 7 m + 50 cm + 20 cm = ? m   7.7 m
    e. 40 cm + 55 cm + 157 mm = ? cm   110.7 cm

Line up the decimal points when adding or subtracting.

2. Find the differences.
    a. 78 km − 12.6 km = ? km   65.4 km
    b. 8.3 m − 4.7 m = ? m   3.6 m
    c. 128 m − 430 cm = ? m   123.7 m
    d. 30 cm − 124 mm = ? cm   17.6 cm

3. Find the products.
    a. 15 m × 3 = ? m   45 m   d. 21.4 m × 6 = ? m   128.4 m
    b. 60 km × 7 = ? km   420 km   e. 80 km × 0.5 = ? km   40 km
    c. 4.3 cm × 3 = ? cm   12.9 cm   f. 200 mm × 5 = ? m   1 m

4. Find the quotients.
    a. 20 m ÷ 5 = ? m   4 m   c. 570 mm ÷ 3 = ? mm   190 mm
    b. 72 cm ÷ 4 = ? cm   18 cm   d. 2 100 km ÷ 7 = ? km   300 km

**Exercise 5
Written**

1. Ellen Feldman needed these lengths of cable to connect a new computer system in her office: 4 m, 2.5 m, 3.7 m, 2.1 m. What total amount of cable, in meters, did Ellen need?   12.3 m

2. A store sold 170 cm of gold chain from a roll that originally held 680 cm of chain. How much chain was left on the roll?   510 cm

3. Max Rivard has set a goal of running 53 kilometers per week. In 6 days this week he ran 46.4 kilometers. How many kilometers must Max run on the seventh day to reach his goal?   6.6 km

4. Kellie Milon needs 6 500 m of wire fencing. She also needs a total of 250 m of wood fencing. If the kind of wire fencing she needs is in 500 m rolls, how many rolls will she need?   13 rolls

■ Find the
simple average.

5. On a business trip, Enrique Gutierrez drove these distances in
3 days: 280 km, 244 km, 64 km.
a. How many km did he drive in those 3 days?   588 km
b. What estimated average number of km did he drive per day?
200 m
c. What actual average number of km did he drive per day?
196 km

6. Yvette Wyzek is filling an order for copper tubing. The order is for
these pieces and lengths of tubing: 10 pieces, 208 cm long; 24 pieces,
55 cm long; 115 pieces, 2 m long. What total length of tubing, in
meters, does Yvette need to fill the order?   264 m

REVIEW 30

Terms

1. Match the terms with the statements.

centimeter (cm)   kilometer (km)   metric system
Customary system   meter (m)   millimeter (mm)

a. A system of measurement used in most of the world
metric system
b. Basic unit of length or distance in metric system   meter (m)
c. One-hundredth of a meter   centimeter (cm)
d. The system of measure used most often in the United States
Customary system
e. One-thousandth of a meter   millimeter (mm)
f. One thousand meters   kilometer (km)

Skills

2. a. $168 is what part smaller than $252? $\frac{1}{3}$
b. Show the sum in centimeters. 70 cm + 95 cm + 240 mm
189 cm
c. $340 increased by $\frac{1}{5}$ of itself is ? $408
d. Divide $3\frac{3}{4}$ by $2\frac{1}{2}$. $1\frac{1}{2}$

Problems

3. Rae Murphy needs these amounts of electrical wire: seven 4 m
pieces; four 2.75 m pieces; six 1.5 m pieces. [30]
a. How many meters of wire does she need?   48 m
b. At $0.24 per meter, how much will Rae pay for the wire?
$11.52

4. A salesperson in a fabric store sold three types of ribbon in these
amounts: 8 m at $0.84 per m; 12 m at $1.40 per m; 5 m at $1.12 per m.
What was the average selling price of the ribbon per meter, to the
nearest cent? $1.16 [10, 30]

5. Ric Webb was paid $8.50 per hour for 40 hours of work. From his
pay, his employer deducted $43 for withholding taxes, 7.65% for
FICA tax, and $32 for insurance. What was Ric's net pay? $238.99
[13, 21]

‡6. A salesperson is paid a commission of 5% on all sales. To earn a
$615 commission, what amount of sales must the salesperson have?
$12,300 [28]

■ Area = Width × Length

The amount of surface that an item like a desk or table has is called its **area**. To find the area of any flat surface, you multiply its length by its width. Knowing how to figure area is a basic skill used in business.

For example, the owner of a paving company must know how to figure the area of a parking lot to estimate how much to charge for paving the lot. The area of a lot 120 feet long by 60 feet wide is 7,200 square feet. Area is found this way: 60 feet × 120 feet = 7,200 square feet. (See Illustration 31–1.)

Illustration 31–1. Area of a Parking Lot

In the Customary system, area may be figured in square inches, square feet, square yards, or square miles, depending on what is being measured. For example, a tablecloth may cover a certain area shown in square inches. The area covered by a box of floor tile can be measured in square feet. Carpeting is sold by the square yard, while forests may be measured in square miles.

■ The basic unit of area is the square meter (m²).

In the metric system, the basic unit of area is the **square meter.** The square meter is equivalent to approximately 1.2 square yards in the Customary system, or about one square yard.

Parts and Multiples of the Square Meter. In the metric system, square meter is written as m^2. The word "square" is not written, but is named by the number "2" that appears to the right and above the symbol for meter, m.

The parts (smaller units) and multiples (larger units) of the square meter are named by the prefixes you have already studied: milli, centi, deci, deka, hecto, and kilo. Those measures are shown in Illustration 31–2.

The square centimeter and the square meter are the measures of area used most often. When large areas are measured, either the

	Unit	Symbol	Value in Square meters
Parts of a square meter {	square millimeter	mm²	0.000 001 m² (one-millionth square meter)
	square centimeter	cm²	0.000 1 m² (one ten-thousandth square meter)
	square decimeter	dm²	0.01 m² (one-hundredth square meter)
Basic unit ——	**square meter**	**m²**	1 m² (one square meter)
Multiples of a square meter {	square dekameter	dam²	100 m² (one hundred square meters)
	square hectometer, or **hectare**	hm², or **ha**	10 000 m² (ten thousand square meters)
	square kilometer	km²	1 000 000 m² (one million square meters)

Illustration 31–2. Metric Units of Area

hectare (ha) or the square kilometer (km²) is used. **Hectare** is another name for the square hectometer. It is used because it is easier to say and write.

**Exercise 1
Oral**

1. What Customary unit is approximately equal to the square meter?
   square yard

2. How is area found?   multiplying length times width

3. Name the basic metric unit of area and its symbol.
   square meter, m²

4. Of the six prefixes, name the one that stands for the largest quantity; the smallest quantity.   kilo, milli

5. What is a simpler name for the square hectometer?   hectare

6. Write the symbols for the measures of area most often used.
   cm², m²

7. What units of area are used for large measures?   hm² or ha, km²

Changing from One Metric Area Unit to Another. Some metric values have to be changed when doing addition, subtraction, multiplication, or division. Square measures are changed in a different way than metric measures of length.

■ Remember—
Metric units of area are 100 times or one-hundredth of the next unit.

Each square unit is 100 times the next smaller unit, or one-hundredth of the next larger unit. So, to change from a metric unit of area to the next *smaller* unit, you move the decimal point *two* places to the *right* for each area unit. To change to the next *larger* unit of area, you move the decimal *two* places to the *left* for each area unit.

Study these examples to see how the decimal point is moved.

■ For area, move the decimal point two, four, or more places.

Change to a smaller unit of area:	Change to a larger unit of area:
1 cm² = 100. mm²	100 mm² = 1.00 cm²
1 m² = 10 000. cm²	10 000 cm² = 1.0 000 m²

$$1 \text{ ha} = 10\,000. \text{ m}^2 \qquad\qquad 10\,000 \text{ m}^2 = 1.0\,000 \text{ ha}$$

$$1 \text{ km}^2 = 1\,000\,000. \text{ m}^2 \qquad 1\,000\,000 \text{ m}^2 = 1.000\,000 \text{ km}^2$$

Exercise 2
Oral

Move the decimal point this way to change to smaller units ⟶
⟵ larger units.

Write the missing metric numbers.

	1.		2.	
a.	$1 \text{ cm}^2 = ? \text{ mm}^2$	100 mm^2	$4 \text{ ha} = ? \text{ km}^2$	0.04 km^2
b.	$1 \text{ m}^2 = ? \text{ cm}^2$	$10\,000 \text{ cm}^2$	$0.5 \text{ m}^2 = ? \text{ cm}^2$	$5\,000 \text{ cm}^2$
c.	$100 \text{ mm}^2 = ? \text{ cm}^2$	1 cm^2	$7.2 \text{ cm}^2 = ? \text{ mm}^2$	720 mm^2
d.	$1 \text{ ha} = ? \text{ m}^2$	$10\,000 \text{ m}^2$	$1.6 \text{ ha} = ? \text{ m}^2$	$16\,000 \text{ m}^2$
e.	$1 \text{ km}^2 = ? \text{ ha}$	100 ha	$518 \text{ mm}^2 = ? \text{ cm}^2$	5.18 cm^2
f.	$1 \text{ mm}^2 = ? \text{ cm}^2$	0.01 cm^2	$97 \text{ km}^2 = ? \text{ ha}$	$9\,700 \text{ ha}$

Exercise 3
Written

1. Find the sums.
   a. $7 \text{ km}^2 + 5 \text{ km}^2 = ? \text{ km}^2$ 12 km^2
   b. $8 \text{ ha} + 16 \text{ ha} = ? \text{ ha}$ 24 ha
   c. $12 \text{ cm}^2 + 100 \text{ mm}^2 = ? \text{ cm}^2$ 13 cm^2
   d. $10\,000 \text{ m}^2 + 6 \text{ ha} = ? \text{ ha}$ 7 ha
   e. $9 \text{ m}^2 + 7\,000 \text{ cm}^2 = ? \text{ m}^2$ 9.7 m^2

2. Find the differences.
   a. $25 \text{ km}^2 - 7 \text{ km}^2 = ? \text{ km}^2$ 18 km^2
   b. $50 \text{ cm}^2 - 100 \text{ mm}^2 = ? \text{ cm}^2$ 49 cm^2
   c. $8 \text{ km}^2 - 200 \text{ ha} = ? \text{ km}^2$ 6 km^2
   d. $1 \text{ ha} - 6\,000 \text{ m}^2 = ? \text{ ha}$ 0.4 ha
   e. $4 \text{ km}^2 - 1\,000\,000 \text{ m}^2 = ? \text{ km}^2$ 3 km^2

3. Find the products.
   a. $35 \text{ m} \times 4 \text{ m} = ? \text{ m}^2$ 140 m^2
   b. $0.4 \times 58 \text{ cm}^2 = ? \text{ cm}^2$ 23.2 cm^2
   c. $100 \text{ m} \times 100 \text{ m} = ? \text{ ha}$ 1 ha
   d. $12 \text{ mm}^2 \times 3 = ? \text{ cm}^2$ 0.36 cm^2
   e. $3 \text{ km}^2 \times 0.5 = ? \text{ ha}$ 150 ha

4. Find the quotients.
   a. $64 \text{ m}^2 \div 8 = ? \text{ m}^2$ 8 m^2
   b. $0.75 \text{ m}^2 \div 3 = ? \text{ m}^2$ 0.25 m^2
   c. $300 \text{ cm}^2 \div 6 = ? \text{ mm}^2$ $5\,000 \text{ mm}^2$
   d. $21 \text{ km}^2 \div 7 = ? \text{ ha}$ 300 ha
   e. $500 \text{ mm}^2 \div 4 = ? \text{ cm}^2$ 1.25 cm^2

Exercise 4
Written

1. The Crown Home Builders bought these amounts of land: 8 ha, 120 ha, 56 ha, 1 340 ha. How many total hectares of land did the company buy?   1 524 ha

2. Talva Rowan wants to buy carpeting for a room 4 m × 4.5 m. How many square meters of carpeting will she need? 18 m^2

3. Helen Quincy has a front lawn that measures 20 m by 7 m and a backyard lawn that measures 20 m by 14 m. She bought a bag of lawn fertilizer that covers 980 square meters.
   a. What is the area of her front lawn in square meters? 140 m^2
   b. How many times can she fertilize her front lawn using the fertilizer she bought?   7

4. George Nota figures he will use 1.2 m² of cloth to sew the lining for one coat. He is using a bolt that holds 66 m² of cloth.
   a. How many coat linings can he sew with this bolt of cloth?   55
   b. How many m² of cloth will he need to sew 100 linings?   120 m²

5. Zina Flores needs a sheet of paper 80 cm × 70 cm to wrap a package. The roll of paper she is using is 90 cm wide by 400 m long. In cm² terms, how much paper does Zina need to wrap the package? 5 600 cm²

6. A box holds 40 floor tiles. Each tile measures 30.5 cm by 30.5 cm.
   a. What estimated area, in cm², is covered by a tile?   900 cm²
   b. What estimated area, in cm², is covered by a box of tiles? 36 000 cm²
   c. What area, in m², will a box of tiles cover?   3.721 m²

7. Mike cut 2 boards for shelving out of a 2.88 m² sheet of wood. One board was 20 cm by 120 cm; the other was 30 cm by 120 cm.
   a. How much wood, in cm², did he cut for both shelves?   6 000 cm²
   b. How much wood, in m², was left from the large sheet?   2.28 m²

REVIEW 31

Terms

1. Match the terms with the statements.

   area   hectare (ha)   square meter (m²)

   a. Another name for square hectometer   hectare (ha)
   b. Basic unit of area in metric system   square meter (m²)
   c. Width times length   area

Skills

2. a. Show 0.16 as a fraction in lowest terms. $\frac{4}{25}$
   b. Show 0.628 as a percent.   62.8%
   c. $76 is what percent of $190?   40%
   d. 350 km is what part less than 400 km? $\frac{1}{8}$
   e. 312 cm decreased by 25% is how many centimeters?   234 cm

Problems

3. Marcy Duvall's boat dock is 1.3 m wide by 14 m long. What is the area of the dock in square meters?   18.2 m² [31]

4. Ludwik Wadarski is building a fenced exercise area for his dog. Each of the sides will be 2.2 m wide and the long ends will be 8.1 m long. If he buys 28 m of fencing and wastes none of it, how many meters of fencing will he have left over?   7.4 m [30]

5. A real estate agent was paid a 7% commission by the owner of a property for selling it for $32,000. [29]
   a. What was the amount of the agent's commission? $2,240
   b. What net proceeds did the owner get from the sale? $29,760

6. Ned Stellif's sales for June were $27,540. In May his sales were $25,500. What was the percent increase or decrease in Ned's June sales compared to his May sales?   8% increase [26]

‡7. Carla Fielding wants to sell an office building for a net amount of at least $230,000 after deducting the realtor's commission of 9%. What is the lowest price, to the dollar, at which Carla can sell the building and receive the net amount she wants? $252,748 [29]

Items such as fruit juice or cooking oil are sold by capacity. You may buy these items in quarts, gallons, or liters. Goods such as rice, flour, apples, or tomatoes are sold by weight. Their weight may be given in Customary pounds or in metric measures of grams or kilograms.

■ **The basic unit of capacity is the liter (L).**

Metric Measures of Capacity. The basic metric measure of capacity is the **liter**. A liter is slightly larger than a quart. The symbol for the liter is a capital L.

As shown in Illustration 32–1, the prefixes milli, centi, deci, deka, hecto, and kilo are used with the liter to state other metric capacity measures. Notice that different parts and multiples of a liter are either one-tenth of the next larger unit or ten times the next smaller unit.

	Unit	Symbol	Value in Liters
Parts of a liter {	**milliliter**	**mL**	0.001 L (one-thousandth liter)
	centiliter	cL	0.01 L (one-hundredth liter)
	deciliter	dL	0.1 L (one-tenth liter)
Basic unit	**liter**	**L**	1 L (one liter)
Multiples of a liter {	dekaliter	daL	10 L (ten liters)
	hectoliter	hL	100 L (one hundred liters)
	kiloliter	**kL**	1 000 L (one thousand liters)

Illustration 32–1. Metric Units of Capacity

Most small capacity measures are shown in milliliters or as decimal parts of a liter. For example, a measure of 400 mL is equivalent to 0.4 L. Larger measures may be written in liters or kiloliters. For example, 4 000 L is the same as 4 kL.

**Exercise 1
Oral**

1. What is the basic unit of capacity in the metric system? What is its symbol?   liter, L

2. To what Customary measure is the liter approximately equal?   quart

3. Are units of capacity related to each other in the same way as units of length? In the same way as units of area?   yes; no

4. What prefixes name units less than a liter?   milli, centi, deci

5. How much larger than a liter is a dekaliter? How much larger than a liter is a kiloliter?   10 times larger; 1,000 times larger

**Exercise 2
Oral**

Find the missing units of capacity.

	1.		2.		3.	
a.	1 L = ? dL	10 dL	1 dL = ? L	0.1 L	1 000 mL = ? L	1 L
b.	1 L = ? cL	100 cL	1 cL = ? L	0.01 L	1 000 L = ? kL	1 kL
c.	1 L = ? mL	1 000 mL	1 mL = ? L	0.001 L	10 dL = ? L	1 L
d.	1 L = ? daL	0.1 daL	1 hL = ? L	100 L	800 mL = ? L	0.8 L
e.	1 L = ? kL	0.001 kL	1 kL = ? L	1 000 L	320 L = ? kL	0.32 kL

Adding, Subtracting, Multiplying, and Dividing. You add, subtract, multiply, and divide capacity measures in the same way as other numbers. When the measures are in different units, change them to the same unit.

**Exercise 3
Written**

Solve each problem.

1. 37 L + 14 L = ? L   51 L
2. 34.68 L + 79.15 L = ? L   113.83 L
3. 400 mL + 26.1 mL = ? mL   426.1 mL
4. 14 L + 344 mL = ? L   14.344 L
5. 786 L − 554 L = ? L   232 L
6. 45.29 kL − 35.31 kL = ? kL 9.98 kL
7. 72.45 L − 50 mL = ? L   72.4 L

8. 250 L × 30 = ? L   7 500 L
9. 4.8 L × 5 = ? L   24 L
10. 20 L × 1.9 = ? L   38 L
11. 0.5 × 682 mL = ? mL   341 mL
12. 64 L ÷ 8 = ? L   8 L
13. 180 kL ÷ 9 = ? kL   20 kL
14. 1 620 mL ÷ 5 = ? mL   324 mL

**Exercise 4
Written**

1. You are hosting a party for 12 members of the drama club. If you buy 18 liters of juice, how many liters of juice will you have for each member? 1.5 L

2. A 354 mL can of frozen concentrate makes 0.94 L of lemonade. How many liters of lemonade can you make from 6 cans? 5.64 L

3. On a recent car trip, Frances Zaphir stopped and bought these amounts of gasoline: 56 L, 63.5 L, 47.3 L, and 59.1 L.
   a. How many liters of gasoline did she buy in these four stops? 225.9 L
   b. What average number of liters of gasoline did Frances buy per stop, to the nearest tenth liter? 56.5 L

4. A storage tank holds 130 kL of fuel oil when full. On Monday, the tank was 90% full. These amounts of fuel oil were pumped from the tank in the next three days: 20 500 L, 24 000 L, 21 750 L. How many kL of fuel oil were left in the tank at the end of the third day? 50.75 kL

5. Clarence Hanson saves 37¢ a liter by buying orange juice in bulk. He figures that his family uses 2.5 liters of orange juice a week.
   a. How many liters of orange juice does the Hanson family use in a year? 130 L
   b. How much will they save in a year by buying juice in bulk? $48.10

6. Natural Farm Products has 30 kiloliters of catsup ready for shipment. The catsup is in one-liter bottles and is packed in cases that hold 48 bottles. How many cases of catsup will be shipped? 625 cases

Metric Measures of Weight. The basic metric measure of weight is the **kilogram**. The kilogram, or 1 000 grams, is equivalent to 2.2 Customary pounds. A **gram** is equivalent to about 0.04 of a Customary ounce.

■ The basic unit of weight is the kilogram (kg).

Although the basic unit of weight is the kilogram, the prefixes you already know are used with the gram to show the parts and multiples of the gram. These are shown in Illustration 32–2. Notice that each metric unit of weight is one-tenth or ten times the next unit.

You use kilograms, grams, or milligrams to measure small weights. You use kilograms or **metric tons** to measure large weights.

As before, do the addition, subtraction, multiplication, and division of metric weight measures as you would other numbers. You may first have to change all measures to the same unit.

Unit	Symbol	Value in Grams
milligram	**mg**	0.001 g (one-thousandth gram)
centigram	cg	0.01 g (one-hundredth gram)
decigram	dg	0.1 g (one-tenth gram)
gram	**g**	1 g (one gram)
dekagram	dag	10 g (ten grams)
hectogram	hg	100 g (one hundred grams)
kilogram	**kg**	1 000 g (one thousand grams)
metric ton	**t**	1 000 kg (one thousand kilograms)

Basic unit ———

Illustration 32–2. Metric Units of Weight

Exercise 5
Oral

1. What is the basic unit of weight in the metric system? What is its symbol? kilogram; kg

2. What is the metric unit of weight to which prefixes are attached to show parts and multiples of the unit? What is its symbol? gram; g

3. What Customary measure is equivalent to the kilogram? 2.2 lbs.

4. How many grams make a kilogram? 1 000 g

5. What part of a gram is a milligram? 0.001 g

6. How many kilograms are there in a metric ton? 1 000 kg

7. What part of a metric ton is a kilogram? 0.001 t

8. What metric weight measures are generally used with large amounts? with small amounts? kg, t; kg, g, mg

9. How many milligrams make a gram? 1 000 mg

10. Is a gram larger or smaller than a Customary ounce? smaller

Exercise 6
Written

Find the missing units of weight.

1.

a. 1 kg = ? g   1 000 g
b. 1 g = ? kg   0.001 kg
c. 1 g = ? mg   1 000 mg
d. 1 mg = ? g   0.001 g
e. 1 t = ? kg   1 000 kg
f. 1 kg = ? t   0.001 t
g. 900 mg = ? g 0.9 g
h. 250 g = ? kg   0.25 kg
i. 0.75 kg = ? g 750 g

2.

1 000 mg = ? g   1 g
400 kg = ? t   0.4 t
75 mg = ? g   0.075 g
0.7 kg + 0.6 kg = ? kg   1.3 kg
0.65 g − 0.25 g = ? g   0.4 g
2 g − 500 mg = ? mg   1 500 mg
12 kg × 9 = ? kg   108 kg
600 g × 7 = ? kg   4.2 kg
560 kg ÷ 28 = ? kg   20 kg

Exercise 7
Written

1. Millie Sorensen bought these items at the market: a 6.2 kg turkey, a 5 kg bag of potatoes, a 4.5 kg bag of flour, and 1.7 kg apples. These items were placed in one grocery bag. What was the total weight in kilograms of the items that were placed in the bag?   17.4 kg

2. At the beginning of the week, the Wisteg Company had 350 metric tons of coal on hand. During the week the Wisteg Company received a shipment of 52 metric tons of coal. These amounts of coal were used during the week: 24 t, 28 t, 17 t, 21 t, 23 t. How many metric tons of coal should have been on hand at the end of the week?   289 t

3. The Chelsay Company is shipping 800 computer keyboards. The weight of one keyboard and its shipping box is 1.8 kg.
    a. What is the total estimated weight in kilograms of this shipment?
        1 600 kg
    b. What is the actual total weight in kilograms of this shipment?
        1 440 kg

4. A box contains 240 steno pads. The pads alone weigh 31.2 kg and the box weighs 3 kg. How many grams does each steno pad weigh?
    130 g

5. A full box of crackers weighed 0.46 kg. The box is now $\frac{1}{2}$ full. What is the weight in grams of the crackers left?   230 g

6. A certain model of a car used to weigh 1 300 kg. The car has been redesigned so that its total weight is now 1 196 kg.
    a. By how many kilograms was the weight of the car reduced?
        104 kg
    b. What percent of the car's original weight is this reduction?
        8%

7. Clarke LeBlanc bought a box of soap powder that held 4.2 kilograms of soap. He figures that he uses 210 grams of the soap for each load of clothes he washes. How many loads of wash can Clarke do with one box of soap powder?   20

8. A generic hand soap is sold in 8-bar packs. Each pack weighs 1.136 kg. Hand soap made by Prose is sold in 3-bar packs with a total weight of 405 g. What is the average weight in grams of one bar of each brand of soap?   generic, 142 g; Prose, 135 g

REVIEW 32

Terms

1. Match the terms with the statements.

gram (g)   liter (L)   milligram (mg)
kilogram (kg)   metric ton (t)   milliliter (mL)
kiloliter (kL)

   a. One thousand kilograms   metric ton (t)
   b. Basic measure of capacity   liter (L)
   c. One thousand liters   kiloliter (kL)
   d. One-thousandth gram   milligram (mg)
   e. Basic measure of weight   kilogram (kg)
   f. One-thousandth liter   milliliter (mL)
   g. One-thousandth kilogram   gram

Skills

2. a. 23.8 L + 14 L = ? L   37.8 L
    b. 7 000 mg + 15 g = ? g   22 g
    c. 40 cm + 82 cm + 145 mm = ? cm   136.5 cm
    d. 38 L − 40 mL = ? L   37.96 L
    e. 9 kg − 3 500 g = ? kg   5.5 kg
    f. 24.6 m − 450 mm = ? m   24.15 m
    g. 25.6 t @ $8.40 = ? $215.04
    h. 832 L ÷ 14, to the nearest liter = ?   59 L

Problems

3. Fern Wolters needs these lengths of plastic pipe: 1.5 m, 3 m, 0.4 m, 2.6 m, and 1.9 m. The pipe costs $4.80 a meter. [30]
    a. How many meters of plastic pipe does Fern need?   9.4 m
    b. What will be the total cost of the pipe Fern needs? $45.12

4. Paul needs to find the area of two storage sheds on his farm. One shed is 6 m long by 5 m wide. The other shed is 12 m long by 7.5 m wide. What is the total area of the two storage sheds in square meters?   120 m² [31]

5. The Clair Transit Company started the week with 3 560 L of gasoline in its storage tank. During the week it used these amounts of gasoline for its trucks: 340 L, 180 L, 248 L, 427 L, and 205 L. [4, 32]
    a. How many liters of gasoline were used?   1 400 L
    b. How many liters of gasoline were left in the tank?   2 160 L

6. A grocer bought these items from a supplier: 180 kg of apples at $1.28 per kg; 50 kg of bananas at $0.33 per kg; 24 kg of walnuts at $3.96 per kg. [32]
    a. What was the total weight of the purchase?   254 kg
    b. What total amount did the grocer pay for these items? $341.94

‡7. Yang Pai worked $7\frac{1}{2}$ hours of overtime this week. This was $\frac{1}{4}$ more overtime than she worked last week. How many hours of overtime did Yang work last week?   6 hours [20]

Unit 6

Budgeting and Buying

As a consumer, you must be able to plan your spending so that you get the most value for your money. You also need to be able to check the totals on sales slips, electric bills, gas bills, telephone bills, and water bills before you pay them.

As a buyer, you should know how to compare the prices of products and services and the costs of buying versus renting tools and appliances. As a user of energy, water, and telephone services, you should know how to minimize the costs of these services.

After you finish Unit 6, you will be able to:

- Use a cash record summary; solve problems related to planning expenses.
- Figure and check extensions, sales taxes, and totals on sales slips.
- Find the cost of a fraction of a unit.
- Find cost when price or quantity is a mixed number.
- Find cost when price is for a large quantity.
- Use exact fractional equivalents of $1 to figure extensions.
- Figure unit prices.
- Compare cost of buying products in different sizes or quantities.
- Find the cost of home energy, water, and telephone services.
- Figure savings that result from using energy wisely.
- Compare cost of renting versus buying tools and appliances.
- Solve problems that contain more information than you need.
- Estimate answers to problems.
- Read, write, say, and recognize the meanings of the key terms.
- Use a calculator to figure amounts on sales slips.
- Use a computer spreadsheet to complete budgets, compare buying to renting items, find the payback period for energy-saving devices, and find cost of telephone service.

181

In Unit 1 you learned how cash receipts and payments records are kept. Now you will learn how the monthly totals from those records are transferred to a **cash record summary** sheet. At the end of the year, the summary sheet is totaled and used to review **income**, or money received, and payments. Payments included **expenses**, or money paid out, and savings for the year. The summary sheet is also used to plan ahead.

Monthly Cash Record Summary. Part of the monthly cash record summary of Laverne and Ramon Mendez is shown in Illustration 33–1.

Monthly Cash Record Summary								
Month	Receipts	Payments	Food	Cloth-ing	Hous-ing	Transpor-tation	Other	Savings
Jan.	5,160.00	4,953.60	825.60	365.75	1,345.20	616.46	1,040.59	760.00
Feb.	5,989.15	6,089.15	793.55	867.79	1,458.47	857.22	1,356.12	756.00
Nov.	6,123.64	5,823.64	785.62	275.79	1,985.86	563.10	1,438.27	775.00
Dec.	6,084.21	6,484.21	869.34	920.50	1,619.48	777.99	1,546.90	750.00
Total	66,800.00	66,800.00	9,700.00	4,680.00	18,200.00	8,200.00	16,900.00	9,120.00

Illustration 33–1. Cash Record Summary of Laverne and Ramon Mendez

After writing in the December figures, the Mendezes totaled and ruled the summary to show their total receipts and cash payments for the year.

Exercise 1
Written

Use the figures from the Mendez's monthly cash record summary shown in Illustration 33–1 to answer Problems 1 and 2.

1. What fractional part of their January receipts were the Mendez's
   a. January payments? $\frac{24}{25}$
   b. January payments for food? $\frac{4}{25}$

2. To the nearest whole percent, what percent of the Mendez's November payments were their payments for
   a. Housing? 34%
   b. Transportation? 10%
   c. Savings? 13%

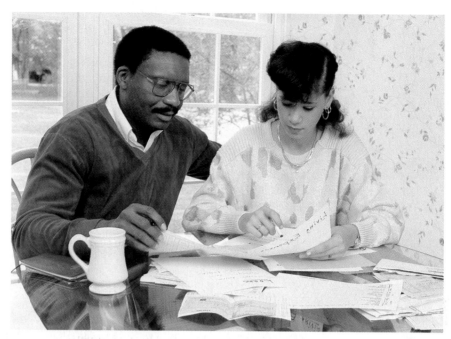

Illustration 33–2. Planning a Budget by Reviewing Expenses and Income

■ **Expenses**
means money
paid out.

3. Last year, Triad Company's expenses totaled $475,800. Of that
    amount, $338,723 was spent for salaries and wages. What percent
    of the total expenses was the salary and wage expense, to the
    nearest whole percent? 71%

4. Myron Security, Inc., had total sales for 1 year of $945,860. Their
    advertising expenses were $57,370.
    a. Estimate the percent advertising expenses were of total sales.
        6%
    b. Find the percent that advertising expenses were of total sales,
        to the nearest tenth of a percent. 6.1%

■ A budget is a
plan for spending
income.

Budgeting Income. A **budget** is a plan for spending income. Preparing
a budget can help you or a business with setting goals and spending
money for things that are really needed or wanted. By budgeting, you
can get more for your money.

Budgeting is easy. You look back to see what income, expenses, and
savings you had. You look ahead to see what income, expenses, and
savings you expect. You also think about what choices you have in your
spending. Then you make up your budget, allowing amounts for each
type of planned expense and for savings.

In budgeting, the amounts allowed for each type of payment are
often shown as a percent of income or of total payments. You can use
those percents to figure future allowances and to compare your
payments with other people's payments.

■ **Income** means
money received.

For example, the percent of income that Laverne and Ramon
Mendez spent for food (15%) is found by dividing their total food
expense for the year, $9,700, by their total income, $66,800. The result
is rounded to the nearest whole percent.

$$\frac{\$9,700}{\$66,800} = 0.145, \quad \text{or} \quad 0.15 = 15\%$$

The percents for other types of payments can be found in the same way.

To plan next year's budget, using the same percents, the Mendezes multiply the income they expect next year by the percent allowed for each type of payment. For example, if the Mendezes expect to receive $68,800 next year, their food allowance would be $10,320.

$$15\% \text{ of } \$68,800 = 0.15 \times \$68,800 = \$10,320$$

**Exercise 2
Written**

1. Illustration 33–1 shows that the Mendez's income for the year was $66,800. The amount of income spent for each type of payment is shown below. You are to figure what percent of their income the Mendezes spent for each type of payment, to the nearest whole percent.

Food	Clothing	Housing	Transportation	Other	Savings
$9,700	$4,680	$18,200	$8,200	$16,900	$9,120
15%	7%	27%	12%	25%	14%

2. The Mendezes (Problem 1 above) expect their income next year to be $69,500. They want to budget that income using the percents found in Problem 1. Copy and complete the form below to show the dollar amounts the Mendezes should allow for each type of payment.

Check—the total should be $69,500.

Food	Clothing	Housing	Transportation	Other	Savings
$10,425	$4,865	$18,765	$8,340	$17,375	$9,730

3. Barry Todd's annual income is $18,000. He has savings of $15,000 and owes $6,500 on his car. He wants to budget his net income using the following percents. What amount should Barry allow for each type of payment?

Food	27% $4,860	Transportation	15% $2,700
Clothing	12% $2,160	Personal	11% $1,980
Housing	31% $5,580	Savings	4% $720

4. Of their $32,800 income, Michi and Rinji Okano allowed these budgeted amounts for payments:

Food	$7,450	22.7%	Entertainment	$2,700	8.2%
Clothing	1,300	4.0%	Education	3,300	10.1%
Housing	8,750	26.7%	Savings	1,600	4.9%
Health	1,500	4.6%	Other	1,750	5.3%
Transportation	4,450	13.6%			

What percent of their income did the Okanos allow for each kind of payment, to the nearest tenth of a percent?

5. Tri-County Medical Center budgets 2.1% of its total receipts for advertising and 7.75% of its receipts for power. For receipts of $5,500,000, what amount would the Center budget for each of those payments? $115,500, advertising; $426,250, power

6. For each $100,000 in sales, Castor, Inc., spends $8,650 for sales expenses. For each $500,000 of sales, Island Fabrics spends $62,000 for sales expenses. To the nearest tenth percent, what percent more does Island Fabrics spend for sales expenses than Castor, Inc.? 3.8%

REVIEW 33

Terms

1. Match the terms with the statements.

   budget   cash record summary   expenses   income

   a. Used to review income, expenses, and savings for year
      cash record summary
   b. Money received   income
   c. A plan for spending income   budget
   d. Money paid out   expenses

Skills

2. a. Add: $2\frac{3}{4} + 6\frac{1}{2} + 3\frac{2}{3}$ $12\frac{11}{12}$

   b. Divide: $3\frac{3}{5}$ by $\frac{2}{3}$ $5\frac{2}{5}$

   c. $648.00 increased by $\frac{2}{3}$ of itself equals what number? $1,080

   d. What amount equals $108 decreased by $\frac{3}{8}$ of itself? $67.50

   e. Show in liters: 1.5 L − 80 mL   1.42 L

Problems

3. Dylor Metals, Inc., had total sales of $975,000 last year and spent $650,000 on salaries and wages. What percent of total sales was the amount they spent on salaries and wages? $66\frac{2}{3}$% [25]

4. Kay's total income last year was $22,000. She expects to earn 10% more this year and wants to budget that income using the percentages below. What amount should Kay allow for each type of payment? [33]

Food	24%	$5,808	Transportation	17%	$4,114
Clothing	12%	$2,904	Personal	13%	$3,146
Housing	30%	$7,260	Savings	4%	$968

5. An office worker is paid $215.75 for a $37\frac{1}{2}$-hour week. What is the office worker's hourly rate of pay to the nearest cent? $5.75 [15]

6. Find the FICA (social security) tax, at 7.65%, on wages of $436. $33.35 [21]

7. For the first 11 months of this year, Dan's sales averaged $24,870 a month. What must be Dan's sales for the next month if he wants his monthly average for the year to be $25,000? $26,430 [10]

Computer Clinic

Janice Miller estimates that she will earn $18,000 in net income during the coming year. Follow the steps below to complete her annual budget.

1. Insert your Spreadsheet Applications Diskette and call up the file "Sec33." After you do, your computer screen should look like Illustration 33–3.

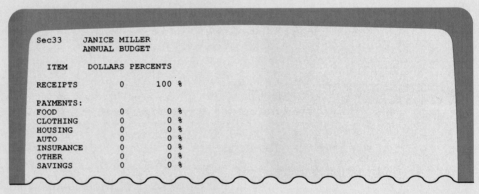

```
Sec33     JANICE MILLER
          ANNUAL BUDGET

  ITEM     DOLLARS PERCENTS

RECEIPTS       0      100 %

PAYMENTS:
FOOD           0        0 %
CLOTHING       0        0 %
HOUSING        0        0 %
AUTO           0        0 %
INSURANCE      0        0 %
OTHER          0        0 %
SAVINGS        0        0 %
```

Illustration 33–3. Using a Spreadsheet for a Budget

2. Enter these data into the template:

B6	18000		C10	7		C12	24		C14	8
C9	16		C11	34		C13	6		C15	5

3. Answer the questions about Janice's completed budget.
    a. How much does Janice plan to spend on food next year? $2,880
    b. What type of payment would be the smallest total dollar amount for the year?   Savings
    c. What type of expense would be the largest total dollar amount for the year?   Housing
    d. How much would Janice spend on housing if her estimated annual income would be $19,000? $6,460
    e. How much would Janice spend on clothing if her estimated annual income would be $16,000? $1,120
    f. If Janice's annual income would be $18,000, how much would she plan to spend on food and housing if the percent used was 18% for food and 32% for housing?
        Food, $3,240; Housing, $5,760

The Sales Slip. Most store employees give customers cash register receipts, or **sales slips,** after a transaction is completed. The customers can then use the receipts or slips to check that all the goods bought were received and that the prices and calculations were correct. Receipts or sales slips can also be used to keep expense records, or as proofs of purchase if the goods are returned.

Most sales slips show these items:

1. The number of units, or quantity, and description of each item sold.

2. The **unit price,** or the price of one item or group of items treated as one. In the sales slip in Illustration 34–1, "1 printer cable" is a unit and the unit price is $25.89. One *dozen* diskette caddies is also a unit, and the unit price is $34.99 for one *dozen*.

STATE ELECTRONICS
16 State St., Bellingham, WA 98225-7981
206-555-8982

SOLD TO: *Jessie Podanski*
STREET: *245 South Brevard St.*
DATE: *March 22* 19--   CITY, STATE, ZIP: *Bellingham, WA 98225-9080*

SOLD BY *R.G.* | CASH | CHARGE ✓ | C.O.D. | DELIVER BY *Taken*

QUANTITY	DESCRIPTION	UNIT PRICE	AMOUNT
10 boxes	Computer diskettes, 5 1/4"	15 98	159 80
1	Printer cable, parallel	25 89	25 89
1 doz.	Diskette caddies	34 99	34 99
2 reams	Printer paper, white	22 99	45 98

EVERYTHING YOU EVER WANTED IN ELECTRONICS!

SUBTOTAL	——— ——	266 66
SALES TAX	5%	13 33
TOTAL	——— ——	279 99

Extensions

Illustration 34–1. Sales Slip

3. The **extension,** which is the product of the unit price and the quantity of each item. The amount, $159.80, is the extension of 10 boxes at $15.98.

4. The **subtotal,** which is the sum of the extensions.

5. The **sales tax.**

6. The total sale, which is the sum of the subtotal and the sales tax.

Figuring Extensions. To find the extension of an item on a sales slip, you multiply the quantity by the unit price.

Quantity × Unit Price = Extension

For example, in the sales slip in Illustration 34–1, the extension of 2 reams at $22.99 is $45.98 (2 × $22.99 = $45.98).

"At" or "@" means the price of a single unit. For example, "1 dozen rolls @ $1.25" means "1 dozen at $1.25 *per dozen*," and "3 lbs. of turkey at 79 cents" means "3 lbs. at 79 cents *per pound*." But a price of "3 lbs. of ground beef, $5.99," means that the price is $5.99 for 3 lbs.

■ "At" or "@" means the price per unit.

**Exercise 1
Oral**

Find the extensions of each of the items.

1. 5 video cassettes @ $4.20 $21
2. 10 patio blocks at 69 cents $6.90
3. 12 qts. of motor oil, $9.89 $9.89
4. 12 cans of apple juice, $2.59 $2.59
5. 3.5 kg meat, $17.99 $17.99
6. 3 L gas at $0.24 $0.72

**Exercise 2
Written**

Find the estimated and exact extensions of each of the items.

1. 5 boxes cards at $2.89 $15; $14.45
2. 4 qts. milk @ 57 cents $2.40; $2.28
3. 7 kg flour @ 32 cents $2.10; $2.24
4. 1.95 m fabric at $6.89 $14; $13.44

The unit price may be for a group of items, such as "2 rolls of foil, $2.29," and you may need to find the extension for 12 rolls. To do this, you must first find the number of 2-roll units, then multiply that number by the unit price.

12 divided by 2 = 6 two-roll units

6 × $2.29 = $13.74 total price

**Exercise 3
Oral**

Find the extensions.

1. 6 bottles mineral water at 2 for $1.10 $3.30
2. 12 cans corn @ 3 for $1.25 $5
3. 2 boxes crackers, $1.98 $1.98
4. 10 pkg. tissue @ 5 for $2 $4
5. 6 bags beans at 3 for $1.50 $3
6. 75 ft. wire @ 25 ft. for $3.50 $10.50
7. ½ doz. filters @ 2 for 90 cents $2.70
8. 12 light bulbs @ 4 for $1 $3
9. 150 m rope at 50 m for $10 $30
10. 8 kg pears @ 2 kg for $1.25 $5

**Exercise 4
Written**

For each of these problems, list the items as they would look on a sales slip. Then figure the extensions and find the subtotal.

1. 4 m fabric @ 2 m for $6.19 $12.38   9 pkg. tape @ 49 cents $4.41
   3.5 m lining @ $2.78 $9.73   1 zipper, $2.99 $2.99
   7 spools thread @ 59 cents $4.13   3 pkg. buttons @ 88 cents $2.64 $36.28

2. 3 lbs. butter @ $1.89 $5.67   8 jars of pickles @ 2 for $3.69 $14.76
   3 lbs. franks @ $1.98 $5.94   4 oranges @ 49 cents $1.96
   15 lbs. flour @ 5 lbs for $0.39 $1.17   3 cans sweet potatoes, $1.69 $1.69 $31.19

3. 3 bags charcoal @ $2.88 $8.64   3 cans plant food, $3.99 $3.99
   1 bottle shampoo, $2.95 $2.95   12 apples at 3 for 89 cents $3.56
   8 cards at $1.25 $10   16 skeins yarn @ 2 for $0.87 $6.96 $36.10

Figuring Sales Taxes. Many states, cities, and counties charge a **sales tax** on items other than food. The seller collects the tax and pays it to the government. Sales taxes often range from 3 to 8 percent of the base price, or subtotal, on the sales slip. They are figured in this way:

Sales Tax Rate × Subtotal = Sales Tax

The sales tax is always rounded to the nearest cent. If more than one tax is charged, the tax rates are combined into one rate. A state tax of 5% and a city tax of 3% is shown on the sales slip as an 8% tax.

The buyer pays the sum of the subtotal and the sales tax.

Subtotal + Sales Tax = Total

The sales slip in Illustration 34–1 shows that the sales tax rate is 5% (0.05) of the subtotal, $266.66. The amount of the sales tax, rounded to the nearest cent, is 0.05 × $266.66, or $13.33. The total paid by the buyer is the subtotal, $266.66, plus the tax of $13.33, or $279.99.

As a buyer, you may not need to know the amount of the sales tax. You may only want to know the total you must pay. You can find this by multiplying the base price by the tax rate + 100%. For example, using the amounts above multiply the base price ($266.66) by 105% (100% + 5%): $266.66 × 1.05 = $279.993 or $279.99.

Exercise 5
Oral

1. Find the sales tax.
   a. Subtotal, $40; sales tax rate, 5% $2
   b. Subtotal, $15, sales tax rate, 8% $1.20
   c. Subtotal, $200; sales tax rate, 4% $8
   d. A suit priced at $250; sales tax rate, 6% $15
   e. A ticket priced at $2; sales tax rate, 7% $0.14

2. Find the totals.

	Subtotal	Sales Tax	Total
a.	$ 75	$ 2.25	$ 77.25
b.	$ 18	$ 1.44	$ 19.44
c.	$450	$13.50	$463.50
d.	$ 16.50	$ 1.16	$ 17.66

Exercise 6
Written

1. The subtotal of a sales slip is $49.39, and the sales tax rate is 8%.
   a. Estimate the amount of the sales tax. $4
   b. Find the exact amount of the sales tax. $3.95
   c. Find the total on the sales slip. $53.34

2. Oki Ichiro's subtotal on her sales slip was $94.89 and the sales tax rate was 5%. What was the total on Oki's sales slip? $99.63

3. Find the sales tax and the totals for each.

	Sales Tax Rate	Subtotal	Sales Tax	Total
a.	3%	$85	$2.55	$87.55
b.	6%	$740	$44.40	$784.40
c.	4%	$7	$0.28	$7.28
d.	7%	$9.98	$0.70	$10.68
e.	2%	$149.95	$3.00	$152.95
f.	5%	$0.75	$0.04	$0.79

4. Where Tony lives, state sales tax is 5% and city tax is 2%. What amount of sales tax must he pay on a $78 purchase? $5.46

5. The Moyas want to buy furniture that costs $795. The city sales tax rate is 8%. In a nearby city the sales tax rate is 5%. How much less would the furniture cost if bought in the nearby city? $23.85

**Exercise 7
Written**

Portions of two different sales slips are shown below. Copy each one on your own paper, calculate the extensions, and find the subtotal, sales tax, and total.

1.

Quantity	Description	Unit Price	Amount
3 pair	socks	2.95	8.85
4	shirts	2 for 35.99	71.98
6	ties	3 for 39.99	79.98
2 pair	slacks	59.88	119.76
	Subtotal	—	280.57
	Sales Tax 5%		14.03
	Total	—	294.60

2.

Quantity	Description	Unit Price	Amount
1 doz	printer ribbons	13.89	13.89
5 pkg.	mailing labels	12.58	62.90
12 reams	letterhead paper	2 for 129.99	779.94
6	print wheels	4.75	28.50
15 boxes	paper clips	0.69	10.35
	Subtotal	—	895.58
	Sales Tax 7%		62.69
	Total	—	958.27

Always check your change.

Counting Change. Many cash registers show the amount of the sale, the amount paid by the customer, and the amount of change to be given to the customer. Other registers show only the amount of the sale. In either case, both the clerk and the customer should make sure that the amount of change given back is correct.

Change is usually given in the fewest pieces possible. For example, if a $10 bill is given for a $7.78 purchase, the change given should be two pennies, two dimes, and two, $1 bills.

If the register doesn't show the amount of change, the clerk usually states the amount of the purchase ("$7.78"). The clerk then gives the pennies to the customer saying "$7.78"; then the dimes, saying "$8"; then the two, $1 bills, saying "$10."

Exercise 8
Written

Copy the form below. For each problem, show the number of pieces of each kind of change the clerk should give the customer. Solve Problem 1 in this way:

Think: $3.26 and 4 cents = $3.30 (write 4 in the 1 cent column):
and 20 cents = $3.50 (write 2 in the 10 cent column):
and 50 cents = $4.00 (write 1 in the 50 cent column):
and $1   = $5.00 (write 1 in the $1 column).

	Amount Received	Amount of Sale	Change						
			1¢	5¢	10¢	25¢	50¢	$1	$5
1.	$ 5.00	$3.26	4		2		1	1	
2.	1.00	0.56	4	1	1	1			
3.	1.00	0.29	1		2		1		
4.	5.00	3.09	1	1	1	1	1	1	
5.	10.00	3.49	1				1	1	1
6.	1.00	0.47	3				1		
7.	5.00	1.89	1		1			3	
8.	10.00	3.15			1	1	1	1	1

REVIEW 34

Terms

1. Match the terms with the statements.

extension   sales tax   unit price
sales slip   subtotal

   a.   A tax on items sold   sales tax
   b.   A form showing what was sold   sales slip
   c.   The price of one item or group of items   unit price
   d.   Quantity times unit price   extension
   e.   The sum of the extensions   subtotal

Skills

2.   a.   Multiply: $12\frac{2}{3}$ by $6\frac{1}{2}$ $82\frac{1}{3}$
   b.   Divide: $7\frac{1}{5}$ by $2\frac{1}{4}$ $3\frac{1}{5}$
   c.   56 is what percent of 224?   25%
   d.   Show in liters: 2.6 L − 125 mL   2.475 L

Problems

3. You buy these items: 6 cans of peas @ 3 for $0.99; 2 packages of frozen vegetables, $4.99; 6 bunches of celery @ 3 for $1.19. What is your subtotal? $9.35 [34]

4. The subtotal of a sale is $28.79. A 5% state and 2% city sales tax are charged. What is the correct total on the sales slip? $30.81 [34]

5. Altors, Inc., had sales of $3,250,000 last year. The company spent 75% of its sales on wages and salaries and 5% on advertising. How much was spent by the company on wages and salaries? on advertising? $2,437,500, wages and salaries; $162,500, advertising [33]

6. Sandra Reade wants to carpet the floor of her room. The room is 2.4 m wide, 2.2 m high, and 3.5 m long. If 10% more carpet is needed to allow for waste, how many square meters of carpet must Sandra buy?   9.24 m² [31]

Calculator Clinic

Using Calculators to Check Sales Slips. Sales slips can be checked easily if you use the memory keys on your calculator. For example, to check the sales slip shown in Illustration 34–1, you must multiply each quantity by the unit price and store the result in the memory register. Then multiply the contents of memory by the sales tax rate and add the result to the contents of the memory register.

Follow these steps:

a. Press these keys in order:

b. Store the result, 159.8, in the memory register by pressing M+ .

c. Find the extension of each of the other items on the sales slip. After each time, you must store the result in the memory register by pressing the M+ key.

d. Press MR/C once, and the subtotal, 266.66, will appear in the display.

e. Press these keys in order: × 5 % and the sales tax, 13.333, will appear in the display.

f. Add the sales tax to the subtotal in main memory by pressing M+ .

g. Press MR/C once, and the total, 279.993, will appear in the display.

Now, all you have to do is round off the total.

This procedure won't give you accurate results if one or more of the extensions produced includes fractions of 1 cent. For example, if the extensions for the first two items on the sales slip were 159.803 and

25.894, the subtotal would be 266.667. The difference occurs because the extensions should have been rounded to the nearest cent.

When this happens, don't add the amount 159.803 or 25.894 to the memory register. Instead, key in the rounded amounts, 159.80 and 25.89 first, and then add them to the memory register.

The need to find extensions with parts of a cent usually occurs when the unit price includes a fraction of a cent. For example, 7 bunches of celery @ $37\frac{1}{2}$¢ = $2.625.

Calculator Practice. Apply what you have learned in this calculator clinic to Exercises 4 and 7 in this section, and to any other exercises your teacher may assign.

Section 35
Figuring Extensions

If you are ever a sales clerk at a retail store, you must know how to figure extensions on sales slips. As a buyer, however, you should also know how to figure extensions so you can check the accuracy of your sales slips. Sometimes, sales slips contain:

1. Fractional quantities, such as $\frac{1}{2}$ dozen.

2. Mixed number quantities, such as $3\frac{1}{2}$ yards.

3. Large quantities, such as a hundred or a thousand.

 3 feet = 1 yard

Finding the Cost of a Fraction of a Unit. To find the cost of a fraction of a unit, you must multiply the unit price by the fraction. For example, suppose that computer cable is priced at 63 cents a yard. You want to buy two feet, or $\frac{2}{3}$ of a yard. The cost would be figured by multiplying 63 cents by $\frac{2}{3}$. In this problem, the unit price, 63 cents, is exactly divisible by 3, the denominator of the fraction. So, you first divide by 3, then multiply that answer by the numerator, 2:

$$\text{63 cents divided by 3 = 21 cents, cost of } \frac{1}{3} \text{ yard}$$

$$\text{2} \times \text{21 cents = 42 cents, cost of } \frac{2}{3} \text{ yard}$$

If the price were 64 cents rather than 63 cents, it would be easier to multiply the 64 cents by 2, then divide the product by 3. That way would be easier because 64 cents is not divisible exactly by 3.

$$\text{2} \times \text{64 cents = \$1.28}$$

$$\text{\$1.28 divided by 3 = } 42\frac{2}{3} \text{, or 43 cents, cost of } \frac{2}{3} \text{ yard}$$

Some stores treat any fraction of a cent as an added cent. Other stores round fractions to the nearest cent. They drop fractions of less than $\frac{1}{2}$ cent and raise fractions of $\frac{1}{2}$ cent or more to the next full cent. For example, they treat $42\frac{2}{3}$ cents as 43 cents and $42\frac{1}{3}$ cents as 42 cents.

When you solve problems in this text, round your answers to the nearest cent unless you are told not to.

**Exercise 1
Written**

Round each extension to the nearest cent.

1. Ana Diaz buys the items below. If she pays with two $20 bills, how much change should she receive? $7.21
   $\frac{1}{3}$ roll of baling wire, $4.89 $4.89 $\frac{3}{4}$ roll fencing @ $24.96 $18.72
   $\frac{1}{5}$ length, plastic culvert @ $45.90 $9.18

2. Find the total cost of the purchase. $13.67
   $\frac{1}{2}$ dozen note pads @ $8.49 $4.25 $\frac{1}{3}$ box of folders @ $7.99 $2.66
   $\frac{5}{8}$ box of ribbons @ $10.82 $6.76

3. Fujio Komuro bought 27 inches of cloth at $2.98 a yard.
   a. What fraction of a yard did he buy? $\frac{3}{4}$
   b. What was the total cost of the cloth, including 5% sales tax?
      $2.35

16 oz. = 1 lb

4. Rick Lenoux bought these items at a grocery store: 14 oz. cold meat @ $3.99 per lb.; 8 oz. bacon @ $2.49 a lb.; 6 oz. cauliflower @ $1.49 a lb.; $\frac{2}{3}$ doz. green onions @ $3.99 a doz. What was the total purchase, including a 3% sales tax? $8.20

5. Find the total price of these items, including an 8% sales tax: 75 ft. of field tile @ $63.75 per 100 ft.; 6 hay sleeve covers at $19.88 per doz.; 4 fasteners at $1.69 per doz.; and 12 oz. seed at $6.95 per lb.
   $68.60

Finding the Cost When Quantities or Prices Are Mixed Numbers. The quantity or the unit price on a sales slip may be a mixed number. For example, you may buy $1\frac{1}{2}$ lbs. of potatoes, or $2\frac{1}{3}$ doz. biscuits. Rope may be priced at $21\frac{1}{2}$¢ per ft., floor tiles at $51\frac{1}{4}$ cents each, or screws at $3\frac{1}{4}$ cents each. To figure the cost of these items, you must multiply by a mixed number.

Finding the cost when the quantity or the unit price is a mixed number is a three-step process. First you multiply the price or quantity by the fraction. Then you multiply by the whole number. Then you add the results.

Example

You want to buy $3\frac{1}{4}$ t of sand at $8.89 a t. What is the cost?

Solution

Step 1: $8.89 × $\frac{1}{4}$ ton = 2.22\frac{1}{4}$
Step 2: $8.89 × 3 tons = $26.67
Step 3: Cost of sand = 28.89\frac{1}{4}$, or $28.89 **Ans.**

**Exercise 2
Written**

1. Philip Gotlieb bought the fabrics below. What was the total cost on Philip's sales slip? $38

   $2\frac{2}{3}$ yd. cotton @ $1.99 $5.31 $3\frac{1}{4}$ yd. wool @ $5.89 $19.14

   $3\frac{1}{2}$ yd. muslin @ $2.88 $10.08 $4\frac{5}{8}$ yd. lace @ $0.75 $3.47

2. Cassie Werner bought the items below at a market. How much change did Cassie get from a $20 bill? $3.33

   $3\frac{3}{4}$ lbs. potatoes @ $1.29 $4.84

   $1\frac{7}{8}$ lbs. grapes @ 99 cents $1.86

   $5\frac{1}{8}$ lbs. apples @ $0.59 $3.02

   $2\frac{1}{3}$ lbs. of pecans @ $2.98 $6.95

3. Find the total cost of these materials: 550 ft. of 12 gauge electric wire at $18\frac{3}{4}$ cents per ft.; 146 ft. of 1" × 2" furring strips at 24 cents a yd.; 165 floor tiles measuring 9 sq. in. each @ $73\frac{1}{2}$ cents each; 276 ft. of 2 in. molding @ $28\frac{3}{8}$ cents a yd. $262.20

4. If she had planned ahead, Peggy O'Neal could have bought a single load of 350 foam panels @ 0.68\frac{1}{2}$. Instead, she made four separate purchases: 75 panels @ 79 cents; 80 panels @ 84 cents; 115 panels @ 77 cents; and 80 panels @ 81 cents. How much could Peggy have saved by planning ahead? $40.05

Finding the Cost For Large Quantities. Many items bought in large quantities are priced by the **hundred (C)**, the **thousand (M)**, the **hundredweight** or **hundred pounds (cwt)**, the **ton (T)**, or the **metric ton (t).**

Office supplies such as envelopes and paper, building supplies such as cement and lumber, and farm products such as grain and fertilizer are often bought in large quantities.

To solve problems using large unit prices, you need to know the meaning of special symbols such as C, M, cwt, T, and t. You also need to know some of the shortcuts for easy and fast figuring.

To find the cost of goods priced by the C, M, or cwt, you first divide the quantity by 100 or 1,000 to find the number of hundreds or thousands you are buying. Then you multiply by the unit price.

Example

Find the cost of 2,560 computer diskettes at $89 per C.

Solution

2,560 ÷ 100 = 25.6

25.6 × $89 = $2,278.40   **Ans.**

To find the cost of goods priced by the Customary ton (T) when the weight is given in pounds, divide the weight by 2,000 (the number of pounds in a Customary ton). The answer is the number of tons. Then multiply the number of tons by the price per ton.

Example

Find the cost of 9,000 lbs. of rock at $88 per T.

Solution

9,000 ÷ 2,000 = 4.5 tons
4.5 × $88 = $396   **Ans.**

To find the cost of goods priced by the metric ton (t) when the weight is given in kilograms, divide the weight by 1,000 (the number of kilograms in one metric ton). Then multiply that answer by the price per ton.

Example

Find the cost of 2 500 kg of sand at $8 per t.

Solution

2 500 ÷ 1 000 = 2.5 metric tons
2.5 × $8 = $20   **Ans.**

**Exercise 3
Written**

Find the estimated and exact costs.

1. 450 ties @ $89.78 per 100 $450; $404.01
2. 219 lb. seed @ $36 per cwt $80; $78.84
3. 189 panels @ $83.50 per C $160; $157.82
4. 8,207 tiles @ $571.99 per 1,000 $4,800; $4,694.32
5. 535 clamps at $6 per hundred $30; $32.10
6. 1,550 bricks @ $265 per thousand $600; $410.75
7. 245 boards @ $852 per M $180; $208.74
8. 789 lb. @ $12 per hundredweight $96; $94.68
9. 1,298 lb. @ $48 per T $24; $31.15
10. 12 450 kg @ $9.88 per t $120; $123.01
11. 600 kg @ $7.75 per metric ton $4; $4.65

REVIEW 35

Terms

1. Match the terms with the statements.

   C   cwt   M   T   t

   a. A metric ton   t
   b. By the hundred   C
   c. Hundred pounds   cwt
   d. By the thousand   M
   e. A ton   T

Skills

2. a. 8 250 kg @ $2.50 per t = ? $20.63
   b. $3\frac{1}{4}$ T @ $2.89 per cwt = ? $187.85
   c. 8,150 @ $0.30 per M = ? $2.45
   d. Subtract: 925 mm from 10.6 m.   9.675 m
   e. Divide: 6 by 7, to the nearest hundredth.   0.86

3. Eric Sutton started the day with $32.77 in cash. During the day he received $10.00 from a friend to repay a loan. Eric spent these amounts on the same day: $2.89, $5.15, $0.78, $12.99. How much cash should Eric have at the end of the day? $20.96 [4]

4. Beth bought these items at an office supply store: $1\frac{1}{4}$ doz. pencils @ $1.89; $\frac{2}{3}$ doz. boxes of correction tape @ $6.10; $1\frac{1}{3}$ cartons of envelopes @ $12.73. What was Beth's total bill? $23.40 [35]

5. Ira bought 4,500 lb. of gravel @ $58.78 per T; $1\frac{1}{4}$ M blocks @ $157.88 per M; 350 rods @ $12.25 per C; and 3,500 lbs. of sand @ $8.56 per ton. He paid 6% state and 2% local sales tax. What was Ira's total bill? $418.47 [34; 35]

Section 36
Shortcuts to Figuring Extensions

Fractional Parts of $1. In figuring extensions, you will often find that the unit price is a part of $1. Often the part of $1 is an exact fractional part of $1; that is, the part is contained in $1 an exact number of times, with no remainder. For example 50 cents is $\frac{1}{2}$ of $1; 25 cents is $\frac{1}{4}$ of $1; $12\frac{1}{2}$ cents is $\frac{1}{8}$ of $1.

There also are multiples of exact fractional parts of $1. For example, 75 cents is 3 times 25 cents. Since 25 cents is an exact fractional part ($\frac{1}{4}$) of $1, 75 cents is also an exact fractional part ($\frac{3}{4}$) of $1. In the same way, 20 cents is $\frac{1}{5}$ of $1, and 40 cents, which is twice as much, is $\frac{2}{5}$ of $1.

If you know the exact fractional parts of $1 and can recognize them quickly and accurately, you can use them to find many extensions easily. You first change the unit price to its fractional equivalent based on $1. Then you multiply that fraction and the quantity. Here is an example:

Example

What is the cost of 24 clamps @ $12\frac{1}{2}$ cents?

Solution	Explanation
$\dfrac{\$0.12\frac{1}{2}}{\$1.00} = \dfrac{1}{8}$ $\frac{1}{8} \times 24 = 3$ $3 \times \$1 = \$3$ **Ans.**	1. Change the unit price to its fractional equivalent based on $1. (You must recognize that $12\frac{1}{2}$ cents or $0.12\frac{1}{2}$, is $\frac{1}{8}$ of $1.) 2. Multiply the quantity of items by the fractional equivalent. 3. Multiply that product by $1.

Table of Exact Fractional Parts of $1. The most often used exact fractional parts of $1 are shown in Illustration 36–1. You must be able to recognize or recall these numbers quickly.

$$50¢ = \frac{1}{2} \qquad 20¢ = \frac{1}{5} \qquad 12\frac{1}{2}¢ = \frac{1}{8} \qquad 33\frac{1}{3}¢ = \frac{1}{3}$$

$$25¢ = \frac{1}{4} \qquad 40¢ = \frac{2}{5} \qquad 37\frac{1}{2}¢ = \frac{3}{8} \qquad 66\frac{2}{3}¢ = \frac{2}{3}$$

$$75¢ = \frac{3}{4} \qquad 60¢ = \frac{3}{5} \qquad 62\frac{1}{2}¢ = \frac{5}{8}$$

$$80¢ = \frac{4}{5} \qquad 87\frac{1}{2}¢ = \frac{7}{8}$$

Illustration 36–1. Exact Fractional Parts of $1

Exercise 1
Oral

$\frac{1}{4}, \frac{1}{2}, \frac{3}{4}$. For each of these extensions, explain the solution and give the product. For example, for the extension of 36 @ 25¢:

$$25¢ \text{ equals } \frac{1}{4} \text{ of } \$1.$$

$$36 \text{ times } \frac{1}{4} \text{ equals } 9.$$

9 times $1 equals $9.

	1.		2.		3.	
a.	12 @ 25¢	$3	20 @ 50¢	$10	12 @ 75¢	$9
b.	32 @ 25¢	$8	26 @ 50¢	$13	32 @ 75¢	$24
c.	36 @ $0.25	$9	42 @ $0.50	$21	20 @ $0.75	$15
d.	20 @ $0.25	$5	34 @ $0.50	$17	48 @ $0.75	$36
e.	24 @ $0.25	$6	68 @ $0.50	$34	84 @ $0.75	$63

Exercise 2
Oral

$\frac{1}{8}, \frac{3}{8}, \frac{5}{8}, \frac{7}{8}$. Explain the solutions and give the products.

	1.		2.		3.	
a.	80 @ 12½¢	$10	16 @ $0.62½	$10	96 @ 12½¢	$12
b.	32 @ $0.12½	$4	56 @ 62½¢	$35	80 @ 62½¢	$50
c.	40 @ $0.12½	$5	72 @ 62½¢	$45	32 @ $0.37½	$12
d.	40 @ 37½¢	$15	24 @ $0.87½	$21	72 @ $0.87½	$63
e.	48 @ 37½¢	$18	88 @ 87½¢	$77	48 @ 62½¢	$30
f.	88 @ $0.37½	$33	16 @ $0.87½	$14	320 @ $0.12½	$40

Exercise 3
Oral

$\frac{1}{3}$ and $\frac{2}{3}$. Explain the solutions and give the products for each.

	1.		2.		3.	
a.	18 @ 33⅓¢	$6	54 @ 66⅔¢	$36	45 @ 33⅓¢	$15
b.	33 @ $0.33⅓	$11	30 @ $0.66⅔	$20	66 @ $0.33⅓	$22
c.	42 @ 33⅓¢	$14	60 @ 66⅔¢	$40	21 @ $0.66⅔	$14
d.	24 @ 66⅔¢	$16	36 @ 33⅓¢	$12	54 @ 33⅓¢	$18

e.   48 @ $0.66⅔ $32   72 @ $0.33⅓ $24   78 @ $0.66⅔ $52
f.   27 @ 66⅔¢ $18   12 @ 33⅓¢ $4   96 @ 33⅓¢ $32

**Exercise 4
Oral**

⅕, ⅖, ⅗, ⅘. Explain the solutions and give the products for each.

	1.		2.		3.	
a.	15 @ 20¢	$3	75 @ $0.40	$30	55 @ $0.80	$44
b.	25 @ $0.20	$5	45 @ 60¢	$27	95 @ $0.20	$19
c.	65 @ $0.20	$13	25 @ $0.60	$15	65 @ $0.80	$52
d.	35 @ 40¢	$14	35 @ 80¢	$28	75 @ $0.60	$45

**Exercise 5
Written**

For each of these problems, write the items on your own paper as they would appear on a sales slip. Figure the extensions mentally when you can. Use exact fractional parts of $1, and find the subtotal.

1.   Jay Muir is an agent for United Fruit Distributors. He just bought these items: 4,880 lb. soybean oil @ 12½¢; 2,760 lb. bananas @ 33⅓¢; 600 lbs. grapes @ 62½¢; 1,600 lbs. tomatoes @ 87½¢. $3,305

2.   Century Office Supplies sold these items last week: 84 pkg. cards @ $0.37½; 105 pkg. pencils @ $0.66⅔; 240 bottles correction fluid @ $0.60; 360 boxes erasers @ $0.75; 150 note pads @ $0.80. $635.50

3.   Midwest Farm Supply Co. bought these items last month: 350 pkg. fasteners at $0.50; 275 rolls tape at $0.25; 720 bolts at $0.12½; 54 pkg. tacks at $0.75; 175 tubes glue at $0.40; 275 pkg. brads at $0.20. $499.25

4.   Almeda Markets, Inc., bought these items: 250 candle holders at $0.80; 1,250 pkg. tree lights at $0.87½; 180 boxes lighters at $0.66⅔; 300 mugs at $0.75. $1,638.75

REVIEW 36

Skills

1.   a.   160 @ $0.12½ = ? $20
     b.   320 @ $0.87½ = ? $280
     c.   48 @ $0.66⅔ = ? $32
     d.   4,500 lb. @ $4 per cwt = ? $180
     e.   3% of $2,078 = ? $62.34
     f. $24 is what percent of $75?   32%
     g. $15.50 less 2% of itself = ? $15.19

Problems

2.   Cross Products, Inc., bought these office supplies last week: 1,320 pens @ $0.12½; 1,480 pkg. pencils @ $0.62½; 1,240 boxes of tape @ $0.87½; 1,720 boxes of cards @ $0.80. A 5% sales tax was added. What was the company's total bill? $3,728.55 [36]

3.   Say-Brite, Inc., expects to earn $4,750,000 in sales next year and budgets these percents of sales for expenses: salaries, 65%; rent, 9%; advertising, 6%; power, 8%; other, 12%. What dollar amount should Say-Brite, Inc., budget for each expense?
     $3,087,500, salaries; $427,500, rent; $285,000, advertising; $380,000, power; $570,000, other [33]

4.   Kerry Durr earns a salary plus commission. Her total earnings last year were $23,800, of which $8,400 was salary. If her total sales last

year were $308,000, what rate of commission did Kerry receive?
5% [28]

5. During four days of car washes, a school club used these amounts
   of soap: 5.25 L, 7.5 L, 9.25 L, and 8 L. [32]
   a. Find the estimated amount of liters of soap they used. 30 L
   b. Find the exact number of liters of soap they used. 30 L
   c. How many kiloliters of soap did they use? 0.03 kL

Section 37
Figuring Unit Prices

Many items are packaged and priced in ways that make it difficult to
compare one brand or one size with another. For example, different
brands of crackers may be packaged in $7\frac{1}{2}$ oz., 8 oz., 12 oz., 15 oz., 1 lb.,
or 18 oz. packages. Soap powder may be sold in 12 oz., 1 lb. 2 oz., 24
oz., $2\frac{1}{2}$ lb., or 10 lb. boxes. Baked goods may be packaged in quantities
of 2, 6, 8, 9, 12 or more items to the box. The tendency to label packages as "small," "large," "giant," "economy," "family," or "super" adds to
the problem. These terms cannot be compared.

To help purchasers compare the real costs of goods, many storeowners post unit prices on their shelves. The unit price is the price of one
item or one measure of the item. This may be an ounce, a pound, a quart,
a dozen, a hundred feet, or some other measure. If unit prices are not
posted, the buyer who wants to compare must figure the unit prices.

Finding a Unit Price from a Group Price. Stores may have one price
for a single unit and another price for a group of two or more units.
For example, soup may be sold for 39 cents a can or 3 cans for $1.08. If
you buy 3 cans, you pay only 36 cents a can ($1.08 ÷ 3 = 36¢). In this
way, you are encouraged to buy more of the product.

To compare prices of items priced by the group, you must find unit
prices. You do this by dividing the group price by the number of units
in the group. **If there is a fraction left over, you count it as a whole
cent.** For example, if beans are selling at 3 cans for $1, the price per
can is $1 divided by 3, or 0.33\frac{1}{3}$. That price is rounded to 34 cents.

**Exercise 1
Oral**

What is the cost of one unit of each item?

1. 4 batteries $3.59 $0.90

2. 8 pkg. paper plates   2.39   0.30

3. 3 pkg. crackers   5.89   1.97

4. 4 rolls sausage   5.92   1.48

5. 4 jars olives   8.89   2.23

6.   3 bottles shampoo   5.78   1.93

7.   4 bottles vitamins   5.49   1.38

8.   3 tubes toothpaste   2.59   0.87

9.   3 rolls tape   1.69   0.57

10.   6 boxes candles   9.47   1.58

Finding the Unit Price When the Item Price Is For a Fraction of a Unit. Rolls may be packaged in fractions of a dozen, such as 6 ($\frac{1}{2}$ doz.) or 8 ($\frac{2}{3}$ doz.). Toothpaste may be sold in 3 oz. ($\frac{3}{16}$ lb.) or 5 oz. ($\frac{5}{16}$ lb.) tubes. In these cases, you must find the price of a dozen, a pound, or some other unit.

■ Appendix C lists common units of measure.

To find the unit price, you still divide the price by the quantity even though it is a fraction of a unit. You may first have to show the quantity as a fraction of a unit. For example:

Example

A 5-oz. tube of toothpaste costs $1.50. What is the price per pound?

Solution

5 oz. = $\frac{5}{16}$ lb.

$1.50 divided by $\frac{5}{16}$ =

$$\frac{\overset{0.30}{\cancel{\$1.50}}}{1} \times \frac{16}{\underset{1}{\cancel{5}}} = \$4.80 \quad \textbf{Ans.}$$

Check: $4.80 $\times \frac{5}{16}$ = $1.50

Explanation

Show 5 oz. as $\frac{5}{16}$ of a pound. Then divide the price, $1.50, by the fraction, $\frac{5}{16}$. To divide by the fraction, invert it and multiply $1.50 by $\frac{16}{5}$. The product (answer) is $4.80. Check the answer by multiplying the unit price you found, $4.80, by the fraction, $\frac{5}{16}$. That product is the same as the price, $1.50.

**Exercise 2
Oral**

Write each of these as a fraction of the unit shown.

1.   6 inches, as feet $\frac{1}{2}$ foot

2.   2 feet, as yards $\frac{2}{3}$ yard

3.   5 sq. ft., as square yds. $\frac{5}{9}$ sq. yd.

4.   6 ounces, as pounds $\frac{3}{8}$ lb.

5.   500 pounds, as tons $\frac{1}{4}$ ton

6.   16 fluid ounces, as quarts $\frac{1}{2}$ qt.

7.   1 pint, as quarts $\frac{1}{2}$ qt.

8.   3 quarts, as gallons $\frac{3}{4}$ gal.

9.   4, as dozen $\frac{1}{3}$ doz.

10.   8, as dozen $\frac{2}{3}$ doz.

11.   30, as hundred $\frac{3}{10}$ C

12.   7 ounces, as pounds $\frac{7}{16}$ lb.

**Exercise 3
Written**

In these problems, round each unit to the nearest cent.

1.   Find the prices per pound.
    a.   Biscuit mix at 7 oz. for $0.25 $0.57
    b.   Peanuts at 14 oz. for $3.19 $3.65

c. Yogurt at 11 oz. for $1.39 $2.02
d. Crab meat at 6 oz. for $1.59 $4.24

2. Find the price per dozen for each item listed.
   a. Soap @ 2 bars for 88 cents $5.28
   b. Yarn @ 3 skeins for $2.37 $9.48
   c. Socks @ 7 pairs for $11.67 $20.01
   d. Motor Oil @ 5 qt. for $4.29 $10.30

3. A package of 36 paper plates is marked to sell for $0.33. What is the price of the plates per 100? $0.92

Round the unit price to the nearest cent.

4. A 7-oz. jar of cashews costs $1.61. A 14-oz. jar of the same cashews costs $3.29. Which jar is less expensive to buy, and how much less per ounce is it?   7-oz. jar; $\frac{1}{2}$¢

Finding the Unit Price For Metric Quantities. Some items are sold in metric quantities. To find the unit price of these types of items, you must show the quantity as a decimal value of the unit you want. You then divide the price by the decimal.

Example

A 1 650-gram can of tomato juice sells for $5.99. What is the cost per kilogram?

Solution	Explanation
1 650 g = 1.65 kg	1 650 g is equivalent to 1.65 kg. So, divide the price, $5.99 by the quantity, 1.65 kg. The answer, $3.63 is the price per kg. Check the answer by multiplying the price per kg, $3.63, by 1.65 kg. The product is $5.99.
$5.99 ÷ 1.65 = $3.63 **Ans.**	
Check: $3.63 × 1.65 = $5.99	

**Exercise 4
Written**

Find the unit price to the nearest cent.

1. A bag of pecans weighing 250 g is sold for $1.89. What is the price of the pecans per kilogram? $7.56

2. What is the price of a 240 cm wood board that sells for $0.62 per m? $1.49

3. A 750 mL carton of orange juice that usually sells for $1.78 is on sale for $1.58. What is the price of the juice per liter? $2.11

4. A length of plastic pipe 30 cm long costs $0.99. At that rate, what is the price of the pipe per meter? $3.30

Finding the Unit Price When the Item Price Is For a Mixed Number Quantity. Sometimes the price of an item is for a mixed number quantity, such as $3\frac{1}{4}$ lbs. In this case, you find the unit price as you have before, by dividing the unit price by the quantity.

Example

A $1\frac{1}{4}$ qt. bottle of bleach sells for $2.29. What is the price per quart?

Solution	Explanation
$1\frac{1}{4}$ qt. $= \frac{5}{4}$ qt.	One and one-fourth quarts is equiva-
$\$2.29 \div \frac{5}{4} =$	lent to $\frac{5}{4}$ quarts. Find the price of one
$\$2.29 \times \frac{4}{5} = \$1.83$ **Ans.**	quart by dividing the given price, $2.29,
	by the quantity, $\frac{5}{4}$. To divide, invert the
Check: $\$1.83 \times 1\frac{1}{4} = \$2.29$	fraction and multiply. Check by multi-
	plying the quart price by the quantity.

**Exercise 5
Written**

Find the answers correct to the nearest cent.

1. A carpet that is $18\frac{1}{2}$ sq. yds. in size is priced to sell for $296. What is the price of the carpet per sq. yd.? $16

2. A $2\frac{5}{8}$ lb. box of laundry soap is priced at $2.19. What is the equivalent price per lb.? $0.83

3. A $1\frac{1}{4}$ lb. box of oats sells for $2.19. What is the price of the oats per lb.? $1.75

4. A 28 oz. can of sweet corn sells for $0.59. What is the price of the corn per lb.? $0.34

5. A 24 oz. can of cranberries costs $1.29. What is the price of the cranberries per lb.? $0.86

6. An 18 oz. can of peaches sells for $1.09. What is the price of the peaches per lb.? $0.97

REVIEW 37

Problems

1. a. 45 is what percent of 225?   20%
    b. Divide: 32 by $\frac{3}{4}$ $42\frac{2}{3}$
    c. Show $\frac{2}{15}$ as a percent, to the nearest tenth of a percent.   13.3%
    d. What percent of a kilogram is 400 grams?   40%

2. Find the cost of
    a. $1\frac{1}{2}$ ft. of cloth priced at $1.89 per yd. $0.95 [35]
    b. 8 cartons of yogurt at $6.99 a doz. $4.66 [36]
    c. 946 mL of mouthwash @ $3.79 per L $3.59 [37]

3. Find the unit price of [37]
    a. 1 can of antifreeze @ 3 for $8.59 $2.87
    b. 1 pair of athletic socks @ 4 for $9.79 $2.45
    c. 1 computer diskette @ 50 for $48.99 $0.98

4. Ivy Mitchem works Monday through Friday from 8:30 a.m. to 5:00 p.m., with an hour off for lunch. Last week she worked full time at $5.67 an hour. What were Ivy's total earnings for the week? $212.63 [7]

5. A file cabinet occupies an area of 2 888 cm². [31]
    a. How many cm² would four file cabinets occupy?   11 552 cm²
    b. How many m² would four file cabinets occupy?   1.155 2 m²

‡6. Bart's check register balance on April 1 was $405.58. He found that a check for $8.50 was recorded in his check register as $5.80 and that he had not recorded a service charge of $3.25 or a deposit of $16.37. Find Bart's correct check register balance. $416 [6]

Section 38
Buying Wisely

You can often save money by buying large amounts instead of small amounts. You can also save money by buying products on sale, or by shopping when stores sell items at a discount. In addition you may save money by renting, rather than buying, what you need, especially if you rent items you do not expect to use often.

Buying at Special Prices. You should know how to calculate the amount you can save by buying in large amounts, at sales, or at stores that sell at discounts. Remember, many small savings can add up to a lot of money.

Illustration 38–1. Buying Goods on Sale Saves You Money

**Exercise 1
Written**

1. Kevin can buy compact disks at $7.99 each, or 5 for $35.95. How much would he save by buying five disks now instead of one at a time? $4

2. Eva has found an automatic washer priced at $399.99 and a dryer for $199.99. They are on sale for only $509.99 for the set. How much can Eva save if she buys the items as a set? $89.99

3. Miguel Romano can buy one office floor mat for $219.99 or a set of 3 for $629.85. If Miguel buys the set, how much will he save per mat? $10.04

4. The Calgeris have a 20 m² living room floor. If they buy carpet at a clearance sale, they can get the carpet they want for $48.89 per square meter. The same quality carpet usually sells for $58.89 per square meter. How much money will the Calgeris save if they buy the carpet at the clearance sale? $200

**Exercise 2
Written**

1. At an end of season sale, Vi Carr bought a room air conditioner that was reduced from $298.99 to $259.75 and a fan that was reduced from $49.95 to $37.99. What total amount did she save? $51.20

2. Boxes of 10, $5\frac{1}{4}$-inch computer diskettes regularly priced at $24 are on sale for 3 boxes for $65.85. How much would you save if you bought 6 boxes? $12.30

3. A department store offers senior citizens a courtesy discount of 5% on all items. Bob Vallow, a senior citizen, buys a portable TV priced at $295.99.
   a. What is the estimated amount of Bob's discount? $15
   b. What exact amount does Bob pay for the TV? $281.19

4. At a discount store, Lana Snyder bought a baseball glove for $39.99 and two baseball bats at $29.98 each. The store gave her a 5% discount for paying cash. How much did Lana save by paying cash? $5

5. At a preseason sale, Gil Abramson bought 20 L of kerosene at 15% off the regular price of $0.29 per L.
   a. How much did Gil save by buying the kerosene at the sale? $0.87
   b. How much did Gil pay for the kerosene? $4.93

Comparing Prices. Many of the items you buy come in different sizes and at different prices. To compare and choose the lowest priced item, you must change the price of each item to a price per dozen, ounce, pound, quart, or some other unit.

**Exercise 3
Written**

1. A $1\frac{1}{4}$ lb. box of Brand A cereal sells for $2.49. A $1\frac{1}{2}$ lb. box of Brand B cereal sells for $2.79.
   a. What is the difference in the price per lb.? 13 cents
   b. Which brand costs less per lb.? Brand B

2. A 28 oz. can of Agee pumpkin pie filling sells for $0.79. A $1\frac{1}{4}$ lb. can of Barr pumpkin pie filling sells for $0.59. How much less per lb. is the less expensive of the two cans? 2 cents; Agee

3. A 24 oz. jar of peanuts costs $2.59. A 36 oz. jar costs $3.49. How much less per lb. is the less expensive jar?   18 cents; 36 oz. jar

4. A 2 lb. 10 oz. box of Deli fish sticks costs $4.99. Seaview fish sticks in a 3 lb. 4 oz. box are priced at $6.49. A 3 lb. 12 oz. box of Star fish sticks sells for $6.59.
   a. To the nearest cent, what is the price per lb. of the least expensive brand of fish sticks? $1.76
   b. To the nearest cent, what is the difference in price per lb. of the least expensive and the most expensive brands of fish sticks?   24 cents

5. You can buy a set of 3 computer diskette file cases for $12 from Store A or a set of 6 for $36.96 from Store B.
   a. What is the price per case from Store A? Store B?   A, $4; B, $6.16
   b. How much would you save by buying 12 cases from the lower-priced store? $25.92

6. In a 6 qt. pack, Alwether motor oil sells for $5.40. In a 24 qt. case, it sells for $20.88. How much would you save per qt. by buying the motor oil by the case? $0.03

7. A 2 L bottle of Freshful fruit drink sells for $0.78. Six 350 mL cans of the Weller fruit drink sell for $1.49. Which brand of fruit drink is the cheaper per L, to the nearest cent? How much cheaper per L?   Freshful; $0.32

Renting vs. Buying. Many items that you buy or use can be rented or *leased*. You may find a big difference between the cost of renting and the cost of buying. So, you should know how to compare the expense of renting property with the total cost of buying the same property.

**Exercise 4
Written**

1. A rug cleaner can be rented for $2.50 an hour or $15 per day. If a cleaner is kept for $4\frac{1}{2}$ hours beyond one day, how much will the renter be charged? $26.25

2. Yi Sun wanted to refinish the floors in his home. He rented a floor sander at $25 a day and a floor edger for $20 a day. He used this equipment for $2\frac{1}{2}$ days. He also used 11 sheets of sandpaper for the sander at $1.20 per sheet, and 5 sheets for the edger at 95¢ per sheet. What was Yi's total cost? $130.45

3. Lois tills her garden once each year. She rents a garden tiller for one day at $48 per day to do the job. She pays 5% tax on the rental price and uses 4 gallons of gas at $1.15.
   a. What is her total cost for using the tiller? $55
   b. If a similar tiller costs $264.60, for how many years could Lois rent it before renting would cost more than buying? $5\frac{1}{4}$

4. A homeowner can rent a chain saw from a rental agency at $27 a day. The same saw can be bought new for $189. For how many days could the homeowner rent the saw before renting would cost more than buying?   7

5. A computer can be rented for $174.50 a week or $34.75 a day. If you need the computer for 6 days
   a. At which rate, daily or weekly, would it be cheaper to rent? Weekly rate
   b. How much would you save by renting it at that rate? $34
   c. If a similar computer costs $1,657.75 to buy, for how many weeks could you rent the computer at the weekly rate before renting would cost more than buying? $9\frac{1}{2}$

REVIEW 38

Skills

1. a. $42 is what part greater than $24? $\frac{3}{4}$
   b. What amount is $\frac{1}{3}$% of $2.28? $0.0076
   c. Show $3\frac{3}{5}$ as a decimal. 3.6
   d. What is 25% of 170 m²? 42.5 m²
   e. 2,800 lb. @ $3.50 per cwt. is? $98
   f. 3,978 @ $4.75 per M is? $18.90

Problems

2. Angelo needs a gallon of cleaning fluid and a carpet steamer for one day. He can rent a steamer for $12 a day if he buys the fluid from the rental agency for $6.75 per gallon. He can also rent the steamer at $17 a day and buy the fluid from another store for $2.75 per gallon. How much will Angelo save if he chooses the less expensive way? $1 [38]

3. On June 1, Linda's bank statement balance was $372.57, and her check register balance was $307.65. While comparing the statement and her check register, she found a service charge of $4.23, earned interest of $1.79, and outstanding checks for $17.87, $2.97, $45.33, and $1.19. Prepare a reconciliation statement for Linda. $305.21 [5]

4. Gus Pinsker worked a total of 48 hours in one week. Of that time, 40 hours was at the regular rate of $8.50 an hour and 8 hours was at time and a half for overtime. What was Gus's gross pay for the week? $442 [17]

5. Jake earns an annual wage of $22,750. He estimates his fringe benefits at 28% of his wages. He also estimates that his job expenses are: insurance, 7% of wages; commuting, $345; dues, $275; other, $75. What are Jake's annual net job benefits? $26,832.50 [23]

6. A real estate agent sells a house for $145,800 and the agency receives a commission of $8,748. What is the rate of commission? 6% [28]

7. The Coster's total income last year was $32,500. Next year, they expect to make 6% more than that total. They want to budget next year's income using the percentages below. What amounts should they plan to spend on each budget item? [33]

Food	24%	$8,268	Cars	18%	$6,201
Clothing	6%	2,067	Other	14%	4,823
Housing	30%	10,335	Savings	8%	2,756

8. Delia wants to buy a car that costs $8,788 in a state with a 6% sales tax. How much sales tax will she pay? $527.28 [34]

‡9. In six weeks, Lois drove 1,920 miles in her new car. At the same rate, how many miles will Lois drive in a year?   16,640 [16]

Computer Clinic

Evelyn Franke uses a spreadsheet to find the number of weeks, days, or hours it will take for the rental fees of an item to equal or exceed the item's cost if it were purchased. She is considering renting a snow blower, which costs $350.00, for $70 a week, $25.00 a day, or $10.00 an hour. Follow the steps below to complete the worksheet Evelyn developed.

1. Insert your Spreadsheet Applications Diskette and call up the file "Sec38." After you do, your computer screen should look like Illustration 38–2.

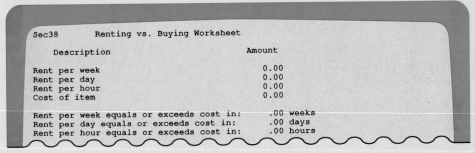

```
Sec38        Renting vs. Buying Worksheet

  Description                              Amount

Rent per week                              0.00
Rent per day                               0.00
Rent per hour                              0.00
Cost of item                               0.00

Rent per week equals or exceeds cost in:   .00 weeks
Rent per day equals or exceeds cost in:    .00 days
Rent per hour equals or exceeds cost in:   .00 hours
```

Illustration 38–2. Using a Spreadsheet to Compare Renting to Buying

2. Enter these data into the template for Evelyn:

   B5 70   B6 25   B7 10   B8 350

3. Answer the questions about Evelyn's completed spreadsheet.
   a. How many weeks will it take the cost of weekly rental fees to equal or exceed the cost of the snow blower?   5 weeks
   b. How many days will it take the cost of daily rental fees to equal or exceed the cost of the snow blower?   14 days
   c. How many hours will it take the cost of hourly rental fees to equal or exceed the cost of the snow blower?   35 hours
   d. If she needs to rent the snow blower for 3 consecutive days, what rental plan do you recommend she choose? Why?
      Weekly; cheaper
   e. If she expects to rent the snow blower for 4 days total throughout the winter season, what rental plan do you recommend? Why?   Daily; cheaper

f. The snow blower goes on sale for $295 at the end of the season and the rental fees are raised to $73.50 weekly, $26.25 daily, and $10.50 hourly next year. In how many
   1. Weeks will the cost of weekly rental fees equal or exceed the sale price of the snow blower, to the nearest whole week?
      4 weeks
   2. Days will the cost of daily rental fees equal or exceed the sale price of the snow blower, to the nearest whole day? 11
   3. Hours will the cost of hourly rental fees equal or exceed the sale price, to the nearest whole hour? 28

Section 39
Checking Energy Costs

Heating, cooling, cooking, lighting, and running appliances all take energy. People use many types of fuels for their home energy needs: natural gas, fuel oil, electricity, kerosene, wood, and even the sun and wind.

Reading the Electric Meter. The amount of electricity you use is measured by an electric meter in kilowatt-hours, or **KWH**, or kw-hr. A kilowatt is 1,000 watts of electric current. A kilowatt-hour is the flow of 1,000 watts of electricity for one hour.

To find the amount of energy you use, someone reads the four dials on your electric meter from left to right. For example, the figures read from each dial in Illustration 39–1 are the last ones the pointer has passed. The last figures passed are:

Last figure passed   8   2   5   1

The reading is 8,251, which means 8,251 kilowatt-hours.

READ THE
LAST NUMBER
PASSED

Illustration 39–1. Electric Meter Dials

Checking the Electric Bill. In many cases, electric bills are based on monthly meter readings. For example, Illustration 39–2 shows an electric bill that has a May 14 meter reading of 4,892 and a June 14 reading of 5,717. The difference, 825, is the number of kilowatt-hours used during the month.

ACCOUNT NO.	DATE DUE	AMOUNT TO BE PAID	
798-334-890	JUL 14		78.12

DETACH HERE   RETURN THIS STUB WITH PAYMENT

- -

KEEP THIS PORTION FOR YOUR RECORDS

Buckeye Power Company
16 Langley Avenue
Lima, OH 45801-2761

Velma Wense
1756 Bridge St.
Lima, OH 45806-8977

ELECTRIC BILL		DAYS
From May 14	To Jun 14	30

METER READINGS		KWH USED	RATE
Past 4892	Present 5717	825	2

```
ENERGY CHARGES
  500 KWH           @ 0.0762      38.10
  300 KWH           @ 0.0986      29.58
   25 KWH           @ 0.1251       3.13
FUEL ADJUSTMENT@ 0.00435          3.59
TOTAL ENERGY CHARGE              74.40
TAXES              @ 0.05         3.72

PLEASE PAY THIS AMOUNT           78.12
```

Illustration 39–2. Electric Bill

To figure the bill, the power company multiplies the number of KWH used in the month by the rate for each amount. For example, the company charges $0.0762 each for the first 500 KWH, and $0.0986 each for the next 300 KWH used. The rate is $0.1251 on all KWH used over 800.

Notice that the company charges a higher rate as more electricity is used. The company does this to encourage people to conserve energy. Some companies charge a *lower* rate as the amount of energy consumed increases.

Some companies charge a lower rate for electric power in the winter than in the summer. For example, you may be charged $0.1183 per KWH in the summer, but only $0.0491 in the winter. Some companies give discounts to senior citizens and charge varying rates to business customers.

Notice the fuel adjustment rate. The total of kilowatt hours used is multiplied by this rate. For example, the total KWH used on this bill is 825 and the fuel adjustment rate is $0.00435. So, the fuel adjustment amount was:

$$825 \times \$0.00435 = \$3.58875, \quad \text{or} \quad \$3.59$$

The **fuel adjustment rate** is used to adjust the rate you pay to changes in the cost of the fuel the company uses to produce electricity. When the cost of the fuel used increases, the company multiplies the KWH by the fuel adjustment rate and *adds* that amount to your bill. When the cost of the fuel used decreases, they *subtract* that amount from your bill.

Notice that Velma Wense had to *pay* the fuel adjustment on her bill. So, the fuel adjustment was *added* to her bill. If she had *received* the fuel adjustment, that amount would have been *subtracted* from her bill.

Velma's total energy charges for the electricity, including the fuel adjustment, are $74.40. This amount is multiplied by the 5% state tax to arrive at the $3.72 tax. The tax is then added to the total energy charges to find the total amount of the bill, $78.12.

**Exercise 1
Written**

1. Find the KWH used, the cost of the KWH, the fuel adjustment amount, the tax, and the total bill for each problem. Use the rates for KWH, fuel adjustment, and tax from the Buckeye Power Company bill in Illustration 39–2. Assume that each customer must pay the fuel adjustment amount.

User	Meter Readings May 10	June 10	KWH Used	Cost of KWH	Fuel Adj.	Tax	Total Bill
a.	278		647	52.59	2.81	2.77	58.17
b.	730	1,940	1,210	118.97	5.26	6.21	130.44
c.	624	1,175	551	43.13	2.40	2.28	47.81
d.	5,308	6,845	1,537	159.88	6.69	8.33	174.90

2. Eda Cesar's electric bill for July shows a reading of 8,124 for June 30 and 7,280 for May 30. Eda pays 8.75¢ per KWH for the first 500 KWH and 12.92¢ for each KWH over 500. She *receives* a fuel cost adjustment of $0.0029 on the total KWH she uses and pays a 6% state sales tax on total energy charges. What amount must Eda pay for her current bill? $90.88

3. Karl Schmidt used 1,230 KWH last month. Because he is over 65, he pays a special senior citizen rate of 7.05¢ per KWH for the first 1,000 KWH and 6.12¢ for each KWH over 1,000 used in one month. He also *pays* a fuel adjustment rate of $0.0143 on the total KWH and a 3% state sales tax on his total energy charges. What amount must Karl pay for his current bill? $105.24

Reading the Gas Meter. Many homes use gas for cooking and heating. Gas is usually measured with a meter in cubic feet. For example, the meter in Illustration 39–3 measures gas in units of 100 cubic feet. The dials are read from left to right, the same as the dials on an electric meter. The reading is 906. This means 906 hundred cubic feet, or 90,600 cubic feet.

Illustration 39–3. Gas Meter Dials

Checking the Gas Bill. Illustration 39–4 shows a gas bill that Mindy Novak received. The bill shows that Mindy's present meter reading is 906. Her reading last month was 802. So, she used 104 hundred cubic feet of gas.

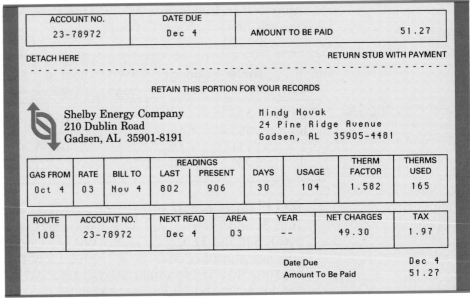

Illustration 39–4. Gas Bill

The amount of heat you get from gas varies. So, many companies charge you for the heat you use instead of the cubic feet of gas you use. The amount of heat in gas is measured in British Thermal Units, or **therms (THMs).**

The gas company finds the amount of heat in the gas by testing it. Using these tests, the company finds a therm factor, which shows the average amount of heat in the gas you bought. To find the cost of gas, you multiply the number of hundred cubic feet of gas you used by the therm factor. The product is the number of therms used, rounded to the nearest whole therm. You then use the company's rate schedule.

For example, Mindy's bill shows that she used 104 hundred cubic feet of gas with a therm factor of 1.582. The number of whole therms she used was:

Hundreds of cubic feet of gas used × therm factor = therms used

104 × 1.582 = 164.5,   or   165 whole therms

The figures for the rest of Mindy's bill are shown in the example below.

Example

Rates:		Computation of Total Bill:	
Shelby Energy's rate schedule is:		Facilities charge	$19.25
		First 90 whole therms	
Facilities charge	$19.25	(90 × $0.2107)	$18.96
First 90 whole therms	$0.2107	Next 75 whole therms	
All therms over 90	$0.1478	(75 × $0.1478)	$11.09
		Subtotal	$49.30
		Sales tax at 4%	1.97
		Total bill	$51.27

Like electric companies, gas companies sometimes sell gas using a graduated rate scale. For example, the rates may be $0.2107 per therm for the first 90 therms, and $0.1478 for each therm over 90. Some companies use a rate that increases with use to discourage waste. Discounts for various types of users are also common. Some electric and gas companies also collect a monthly facilities charge, which is a rental fee for the company's equipment and lines.

Exercise 2
Written

■ Readings are in units of 100 cu. ft.

■ Round off to whole therms.

1. For each user, find the hundreds of cubic feet of gas used, the therms used, the charge for gas, a 5% sales tax, and the total bill. The per therm rates are: first 90 therms, $0.2278; over 90 therms, $0.1568.

	Meter Readings Present	Last	Hundreds of Cubic Feet of Gas Used	Therm Factor	Therms Used	Charge for Gas Used	Sales Tax	Total Bill
a.	380	260	120	1.486	178	$34.30	$1.72	$36.02
b.	784	697	87	1.578	137	27.87	1.39	29.26
c.	189	78	111	1.108	123	25.67	1.28	26.95
d.	573	489	84	1.499	126	26.14	1.31	27.45
e.	205	132	73	1.228	90	20.50	1.03	21.53

2. On Brandon's May gas bill, the present reading is 896 and the last is 784. The therm factor is 1.377. The per therm rates are: first 50 therms, $0.2772; next 50 therms, $0.1798; over 100 therms, $0.1365. Find the amount of his gas bill, including a sales tax of 5%. $31.73

3. Bea's gas meter read 357 hundred cubic feet on May 10 and 496 hundred cubic feet a month later. The therm factor was 1.023. The per therm rates were: first 70 therms, $0.2036; over 70 therms,

$0.2686. There was a facilities charge of $21.97 and a sales tax of 3%. What was Bea's total bill? $57.23

REVIEW 39

Skills

1. a. Show $1\frac{4}{5}$ as a decimal.   1.8
   b. $200 is what part smaller than $320? $\frac{3}{8}$
   c. $98.25 less $66\frac{2}{3}$% of itself is what amount? $32.75
   d. 9,256 @ $0.23 per M $2.13
   e. 32 kg is what percent of 20 kg?   160%
   f. Show $\frac{7}{8}$% as a decimal.   0.00875

Problems

2. Rose's electric meter read 6,361 KWH on May 1 and 6,987 KWH on June 1. She pays 12.7¢ each for the first 100 KWH, 10.5¢ each for the next 100 KWH, and 8.9¢ each for all KWH used over 200. She also pays a fuel adjustment rate of $0.00132 on the total KWH she uses and a sales tax of 4%. What is the total of Rose's electric bill? $64.42 [39]

3. Bell's Sports Center sells 2 racquetball racquets with covers at a sale price of $19.99 for both. At Vito's Outdoor Market, similar racquets are priced at $12.99 each with a manufacturer's rebate of $10. The covers cost an additional $2.89 each. Which store offers the best price for 2 racquets and covers, and how much lower is the price?   Bell's; $1.77 [38]

4. Bud Cross bought these items at the grocery store: $1\frac{1}{4}$ lbs. apples @ $0.45; $\frac{1}{2}$ lb. cream cheese @ $1.19; 2 cans of carrots @ 3 for $1.09. He paid a 5% sales tax. What was the total amount of Bud's bill? $1.98 [37]

Section 40
Reducing Energy Costs

The cost of heating, lighting, cooling, and running appliances is a major expense in operating a home today. Reducing these energy costs and conserving energy are important ways of saving money.

Conserving Home Fuel Costs. There are many ways to save energy in your home. For example, in the winter you can save energy by lowering the thermostat at night or when no one is at home. You can also close off unused rooms, close the fireplace damper, or lower the temperature setting on the hot water heater.

In the summer you can reduce cooling costs by keeping the shades drawn, raising the thermostat on the air conditioner, and opening the windows and doors when there is a breeze at night. You can also serve more cold meals to avoid using the oven, use a fan instead of the air

Illustration 40–1.   Alternate Methods of Heating Save Money

conditioner when possible, dry clothes on a line instead of in a dryer, and use cold water to wash and rinse clothes.

**Exercise 1
Written**

1. During the spring, summer, and fall, you dried your clothes outdoors instead of using the dryer. This reduced your electric power usage by 3,500 KWH. If you pay $0.09 per KWH, how much did you save? $315

2. By lowering the temperature setting on your hot water heater from 180 degrees to 120 degrees, you estimate that your April fuel costs will drop from $175 to $140. What percent of your April fuel costs do you estimate you will save?   20%

3. You usually set your thermostat at 72 degrees. Raising it in the summer may reduce your cooling costs by as much as 3% for each degree it is raised. If you raised your thermostat to 77 degrees
    a. What percent of your fuel costs could you save?   15%
    b. How much could you save if your cooling costs are usually $212 in July? $31.80
    c. How many KWH of electricity could you save if it usually takes 2,100 KWH of energy to cool your house in July?   315 KWH

4. You kept the damper closed on the fireplace, closed off unused rooms, lowered the thermostat setting, and reduced the water heater temperature. By taking these energy-saving steps, you reduced the therms you used in January from 140 to 91.
    a. By what percent did you reduce the therms you used?   35%
    b. At $0.48 per therm, estimate your savings. $25
    c. At $0.48 per therm, exactly how much did you save? $23.52

Figuring Net Savings. You can save energy by buying and installing energy-saving products. Before you buy these kinds of products, however, you should estimate how much you will save with them. That way you can see if what you want to buy will save you enough energy to make it worth buying.

One way to measure the value of energy-saving products is to figure the net savings over a period of time. You find the net savings by subtracting the cost of the product from the gross amount saved for the period of time.

Gross Savings − Cost of Product = Net Savings

For example, you could buy and install storm windows in your home for $750. The windows are estimated to last 20 years and save you $125 a year in heating and cooling costs. Your net savings would be:

20 × $125 = $2,500 total savings

$2,500 − $750 = $1,750 net savings

**Exercise 2
Written**

1. Alice installs a clock thermostat for $59 to adjust the heating and cooling automatically at night and during the day when no one is home. She estimates that this will save her $216 a year. What will be Alice's net savings over ten years? $2,101

2. Haru installs insulation around her hot water pipes and water heater for $12. She estimates that this will save her 7% of her heating oil costs each year. If she spends $900 on heating oil a year, what will be her net savings after 15 years? $933

3. Kip pays $240 to have a whole-house fan installed in his attic to keep his house cool. He estimates that the fan will reduce his air conditioning costs by 15% a year. If his annual air conditioning costs are $960, what will be his net savings over 10 years? $1,200

4. Vicente installs insulation in his attic at a cost of $135. He estimates that this will reduce his heating costs by 9%. If his heating costs average $860 a year, what are his estimated net savings after 15 years? $1,026

Figuring the Payback Period. Another way to measure the value of energy-saving products is to find the payback period. The **payback period** is the number of years it will take for the products to save enough money to pay you back for their cost.

To find the payback period, you divide the cost of the products by the amount of energy costs saved in one year:

Cost ÷ Estimated Savings Per Year = Payback Period

For example, a new heating system was installed at a cost of $1,650. It was estimated that the new system would save $264 a year in heating costs. The payback period would be:

$1,650 divided by $264 = $6\frac{1}{4}$ years

**Exercise 3
Written**

1. John Posek has a solar hot water heating system installed for a total cost of $2,800. He estimates that this will save him $350 each year in fuel costs. What is the payback period for the system?
   8 years

2. Rosa Velez has storm doors installed at a cost of $750. She estimates that the storm doors will save her 3% of her winter fuel bill. If her winter fuel bill averages $870 what is the payback period for the doors to the nearest whole year?   29 years

3. Ted O'Brien buys a portable kerosene space heater for $250. He plans to lower the furnace thermostat and use the space heater to warm the room he is in. He estimates that this will save 12% of his winter heating costs after paying for the kerosene. If his winter heating costs average $1,150, what is the payback period for the heater, to the nearest tenth of a year?   1.8 years

4. Ruth Lucas weather-strips her windows and doors for $27.50. She estimates that this will reduce her annual heating costs by 1.5%. If her annual heating costs are $1,210.
   a. How much will she save each year in heating costs? $18.15
   b. What is the payback period for the weather-stripping, to the nearest tenth of a year?   1.5 years

The Cost of Using Electric Appliances. Many electric appliances are marked to show the number of watt-hours of electricity they use in one hour. An electric light bulb, for example, may be marked "100 WATT." This is the *rating* of the bulb. It means that the bulb uses 100 watts of electricity in one hour.

If a 75-watt bulb burns for 10 hours, it will use 10×75 or 750 watt-hours of electricity. This is equal to 0.75 KWH ($750 \div 1,000 = 0.75$). If the rate is 11 cents per KWH, the cost of the electricity used is $0.75 \times \$0.11$, or 0.0825, or $8\frac{1}{4}$ cents.

Appliances using electric motors are rated in terms of horsepower (HP). One horsepower is equal to 746 watts. So, a 1 HP motor uses 746 watt-hours of electricity in one hour.

Some heating and cooling units are marked with energy guide labels. These labels show the average annual operating cost. The labels also show the unit's EER, or **Energy Efficiency Ratio.** The higher the EER, the more efficient the unit, and the lower the energy cost.

**Exercise 4
Written**

1. Jane uses 10, 100 watt bulbs in her house. She burns these bulbs an average of 5 hours each day.
   a. How many KWH do these bulbs use each day?   5 KWH
   b. At 9 cents per KWH, what do these bulbs cost to use each day? $0.45

2. If Jane, in the previous problem, replaced the 100-watt bulbs with 60-watt bulbs:
   a. How many KWH would she save in one day?   2 KWH
   b. How much money would this save each day? each year?
       $0.18; $65.70

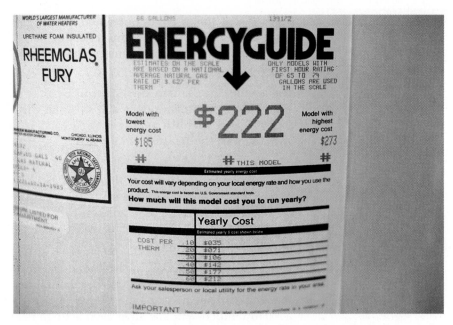

Illustration 40–2. Energy Guide Label for a Hot Water Heater

3. An appliance with a 1 HP electric motor ran 3 hours each day in June.
    a. How many KWH did it use, to the nearest KWH?   67 KWH
    b. At 8 cents per KWH, how much did it cost to use? $5.36
    c. If an appliance with a $\frac{1}{2}$ HP motor had been used, how many KWH would have been saved, to the nearest KWH?   34 KWH
    d. How much money would the smaller motor have saved?
        $2.72

4. The Alaskan room air conditioner, which has an EER of 5, uses 1,200 watts per hour. The Bonner room air conditioner, with an EER of 8, uses 750 watts per hour. At $7\frac{1}{2}$ cents per KWH, how much would you save in 5 hours by using the most efficient unit? $0.17

5. At 8 cents per KWH, find the hourly cost of running these appliances:
    a. Toaster: 1,100 watts   c. Microwave oven: 1,450 watts
        $0.09 $0.12
    b. Clothes dryer: 5,000 watts   d. Hair dryer: 1,000 watts
        $0.40 $0.08

REVIEW 40

Terms

1. Match the terms with the statements.

    Energy Efficiency Ratio (EER)   KWH   therm
    fuel adjustment rate   payback period

    a. A measure of heat in gas   therm
    b. Cost divided by yearly savings   payback period
    c. Adjusts your fuel costs to company fuel costs
        fuel adjustment rate
    d. Kilowatt hours   KWH
    e. The higher the rating, the lower the energy cost   EER

Skills

2. a. Show $8\frac{5}{8}$ as a decimal. 8.625
    b. $320 is what part greater than $200? $\frac{3}{5}$
    c. Give the estimated and exact answers to 4,100 lb. @ $9.89 per ton. $20; $20.27
    d. 45 @ $0.10 = ? $4.50
    e. $3\frac{1}{2} \times 6\frac{2}{3}$ = ? $23\frac{1}{3}$
    ‡f. $2.28 is $\frac{3}{4}$ of what amount? $3.04
    ‡g. $382.50 is 85% of? $450

Problems

3. An electric range uses 12,200 watts per hour and is run an average of 60 hours a year. [40]
    a. On average, how many KWH per year does the range use?
        732 KWH
    b. At 11 cents per KWH, what is the cost of running the range for one year? $80.52

4. Betty had an automatic thermostat installed for $110. On it, she lowered the temperature at night and when the home was empty. She estimates that it saved 18% of her heating costs last year. If her yearly heating costs are usually $800, what were Betty's net savings for the year? $34 [40]

5. Terry's electric meter read 21,308 KWH on June 1, and 21,968 on July 1. He paid the following rates: $15.95 for the first 20 KWH, $0.11 each for the next 150 KWH, and $0.09 each for any amount over 170 KWH. What was Terry's bill, including a 3% tax?
    $78.85 [39]

6. Maura is paid $6.50 an hour and time and a half for all hours worked beyond 8 in any day. Last week she worked these hours: Monday, 8; Tuesday, $7\frac{1}{2}$; Wednesday, $9\frac{1}{4}$; Thursday, 10; Friday, $8\frac{3}{4}$. What was Maura's gross pay for the week? $295.75 [17]

7. Michi is paid $337.50 a week. How much is that a month? a year?
    $1,462.50; $17,550 [7]

8. A real estate agent sold a house for Donna for $135,600. The agent deducted a 6% commission. What net proceeds did Edna receive?
    $127,464 [29]

Computer Clinic

Anne Martin is considering replacing her old central air conditioning unit for a new, energy-efficient one. She estimates that the old unit costs her $648.00 to run in the summer. Landair's unit costs $899 and is estimated to reduce her summer air conditioning energy costs by 15%. Follow the steps on the next page to complete and interpret a payback period analysis chart for Anne.

1. Insert your Spreadsheet Applications Diskette and call up the file "Sec40." After you do, your computer screen should look like Illustration 40–3.

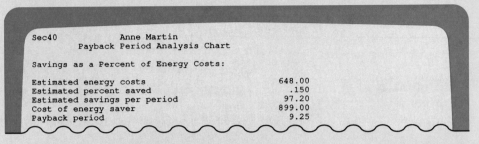

```
Sec40              Anne Martin
          Payback Period Analysis Chart

Savings as a Percent of Energy Costs:

Estimated energy costs                    648.00
Estimated percent saved                     .150
Estimated savings per period               97.20
Cost of energy saver                      899.00
Payback period                              9.25
```

Illustration 40–3. Figuring Energy Savings

Notice how Anne has entered the Landair unit data into cells B7 (estimated percent saved) and B9 (cost of energy saver) of the spreadsheet. The results show that the payback period will be $9\frac{1}{4}$ years.

2. Anne now needs to enter the data about two other units. Belair's unit costs $1,189 and is estimated to save 22%. Sunray's unit costs $1,059 and is estimated to save 19%. Enter the data about the Belair and Sunray units in the same cells of Column B as Anne did. Answer the questions about the completed spreadsheet.
   a. What is the estimated payback period, to the nearest hundredth, for the Landair unit? the Belair unit? the Sunray unit?
      9.25; 8.34; 8.60
   b. How much would Anne save in one summer by buying the Landair unit? the Belair unit? the Sunray unit?
      $97.20; $142.56; $123.12

3. Suppose the cost of energy rose and the old unit would cost $712 to run in the summer. How much would Anne save by buying the unit that would save the most? $156.64

Section 41
Checking and Reducing Water Costs

Water companies measure the water you use by the gallon or cubic foot. The amount used is recorded by a water meter. Someone from the water company usually reads the meter every three, four, or six months and the company then sends you a bill.

The Water Meter. The face of a water meter is shown in Illustration 41–1. The meter reader reads the five dials on the meter clockwise,

Illustration 41–1. Water Meter

starting at the 100,000 dial. The figure read is the last one the pointer has passed. The meter shows a reading of 17,780 cubic feet. The small dial measures parts of a cubic foot and is used only for testing.

If the last reading was 9,280 cubic feet, the amount of water used during the period would be 17,780 − 9,280, or 8,500 cubic feet.

Water Meter Rates. The rates for the Swansea Water Company are shown in Illustration 41–2. The rates are for three months, or one quarter of a year.

Swansea Water Company Quarterly Meter Rates for Water	
Basic quarterly charge......................................	$4.75
First 5,000 cu. ft.	$0.987 per 100 cu. ft.
Next 10,000 cu. ft.	0.863 per 100 cu. ft.
Next 15,000 cu. ft.	0.724 per 100 cu. ft.
All over 30,000 cu. ft................	0.563 per 100 cu. ft.

Illustration 41–2. Water Meter Rate Schedule

The Water Bill. After having your meter read, the water company sends you the water bill. The bill shown in Illustration 41–3 is based on the meter shown in Illustration 41–1. The bill shows the present reading, 17,780 cubic feet; the last reading, 9,280; and the water used, 8,500 cubic feet.

Checking the Water Bill. The charges on Lizbeth Walker's water bill are based on the schedule of rates for the Swansea Water Company shown in Illustration 41–2. The bill was figured this way:

Basic quarterly charge	**$ 4.75**
First 5,000 cu. ft. @ $0.987 per hundred	**49.35**
Next 3,500 cu. ft. @ $0.863 per hundred	**30.21**
Total water bill	**$84.31**

Notice that the basic quarterly charge, $4.75, is added to each bill no matter how much water is used.

RETAIN THIS PART FOR YOUR RECORDS				PLEASE RETURN THIS STUB WITH YOUR PAYMENT

DATE PAID _____ CHECK NO. _____

SWANSEA WATER COMPANY
24 Baron Road
Topeka, KS 66604-1872
913-555-8900

SWANSEA WATER COMPANY
24 Baron Road
Topeka, KS 66604-1872
913-555-8900

DISTRICT	ACCOUNT NO.	LAST DAY TO PAY
4	0829-4913	JULY 31, 19--

PRESENT READING	PREVIOUS READING	CU. FT. USED	AMT. PAST DUE
17780	9280	8500	00.00

FOR WATER USED TO	YOUR NEXT READING	TOTAL AMOUNT
June 30	December 31	84.31

CUSTOMER
Lizbeth Walker
2307 Quail St.
Topeka, KS 66608-3352

DISTRICT	ACCOUNT NO.
4	0829-4913

PRESENT READING	PREVIOUS READING
17780	9280

CU. FT. USED	TOTAL
8500	84.31

Lizbeth Walker
2307 Quail St.
Topeka, KS 66608-3352

Illustration 41–3. Quarterly Water Bill

**Exercise 1
Written**

Use the schedule of rates shown in Illustration 41–2 for Problems 1–4.

1. Find the total water bill for each amount of water used.
   a. 2,170 cu. ft. $26.17
   b. 5,930 cu. ft. $62.13
   c. 17,640 cu. ft. $159.51
   d. 32,590 cu. ft. $263.58

2. Find the total water bill for each problem.
   a. Last reading, 8,920; present reading, 12,220. $37.32
   b. Last reading, 16,000; present reading, 27,740. $112.27
   c. Last reading, 81,090; present reading, 98,370. $156.91

3. Scott's water meter reads 48,170 cu. ft. now. Three months ago it read 35,180 cubic feet. Find Scott's total water bill for the quarter. $123.05

4. Ria's water meter read 72,110 cu. ft. on April 1 and 96,700 cu. ft. on July 1. What was Ria's total water bill for the quarter? $209.83

Reducing Water Costs. In some parts of the country, water is scarce and very expensive. Because water costs money, you should use it carefully wherever you live.

You can save water in many ways. For example, letting the faucet run when you brush your teeth may use 10 gallons. Running the water only to wet the brush and rinse your mouth may use only $\frac{1}{2}$ gallon. A shower may use 25 gallons. Using the shower to wet down and rinse off only may cut that use to 4 gallons. Fixing a dripping faucet may save as much as 20 gallons per day.

**Exercise 2
Written**

1. Frank uses the full cycle of his washing machine to clean two loads of laundry each week. Each load uses 60 gallons of water @ $0.87 per thousand gallons.

Illustration 41–4. Wasting Water Is Expensive

a. How many gallons of water does Frank use a year cleaning clothes? 6,240

b. How much does the water used each year cost him? $5.43

2. If Frank, in the previous problem, used the short cycle of his washing machine, he would use only 27 gallons of water per load.

a. How many gallons per year would Frank save using the short cycle? 3,432

b. How much money per year would Frank save this way? $2.99

3. Sheila takes a 10-minute shower at 9:00 a.m. each day. Her shower uses 4 gallons of 140° water per minute. Water costs $1.182 per thousand gallons.

a. How many gallons per day does Sheila use for her shower? 40

b. What is the yearly cost of the shower water used, to the nearest cent? $17.26

4. If Sheila, in the previous problem, cut her shower to 5 minutes per day

a. How many gallons would she save per year? 7,300

b. How much money would she save in water costs per year? $8.63

5. Vince had a leaking faucet that wasted 18 gallons of water a day in August.

a. Estimate the number of gallons of water Vince wasted in August. 600

b. What is the exact number of gallons Vince wasted in August? 558

c. At $0.98 per thousand gallons, what was the cost of the wasted water? $0.55

REVIEW 41

Skills

1. a. Multiply $1,200 by 0.0415. $49.80
   b. $210 is what percent less than $240? $12\frac{1}{2}$%
   c. Show $7\frac{1}{8}$ as a decimal. 7.125
   d. Estimate the answer: $4\frac{1}{4}$ lb. @ $18.79 = ? $80
   e. 23,450 lb. @ $16 per T = ? $187.60
   f. 248 @ 0.37\frac{1}{2}$ = ? $93
   g. 50 m^2 is what percent greater than 40 m^2? 25%
   ‡h. $48 is $\frac{1}{6}$ less than what amount? $57.60

Problems

2. Nadia's water meter read 42,180 cu. ft. on January 1, and 53,400 on April 1. Using the schedule of rates shown in Illustration 41–2, find the amount of Nadia's water bill for the quarter. $107.78 [41]

3. Alberto runs his automatic dishwasher each day, using the full washing cycle. The full cycle takes 16 gallons. If he used the short cycle, it would only take 7 gallons. At $0.835 per hundred gallons, how much could Alberto save in June by using the short cycle? $2.25 [41]

4. Velma used 231 therms of gas last month. Her gas company charged her $0.86 per therm. The company also charged a fuel adjustment rate of $0.0041 per therm and a state sales tax of 5%. What was Velma's gas bill last month? $209.59 [39]

5. Valgro Company projects their gross sales for next year to be $3,567,200. Of that gross sales, they estimate that 60% will be spent on salaries and wages, 5% on advertising, and 10% on power and utilities. How much do they plan to spend on salaries and wages? on advertising? on power and utilities? $2,140,320; $178,360; $356,720 [33]

6. A salesperson was paid $4,432 commission on sales of $55,400. What was the salesperson's rate of commission? 8% [28]

7. Edgewood Industries' gross sales last year were $514,678,120. They estimate that gross sales this year will be 115% of last year's sales. What are the estimated gross sales for this year? $591,879,838 [25]

8. Tim worked $36\frac{1}{4}$ hours @ $8.50 an hour. His deductions were: federal withholding taxes, $37; state withholding taxes, $6.16; FICA, 7.65%; union dues, $12.50. What was Tim's net pay? $228.90 [21]

9. A holiday light string has lights spaced 1 foot apart. For each white light on the string there are 2 blue lights. How many white and blue lights should there be on a 5-yard light string? 5 white; 10 blue [16]

Checking and Reducing Telephone Costs

Telephone costs depend on where you live, your local phone company and long-distance phone company rates, and the kinds of phone services and equipment you buy or rent. You can usually save money by buying phone equipment instead of renting it and by using phone services carefully.

Local Telephone Bills. You usually buy local phone service from your local phone company. You may buy long-distance service from one or more long-distance companies. So, you may receive more than one phone bill each month. For example, Bella Stein uses the Corbin Telephone Company for local phone service and the NewNet Communications Company for long-distance service. The bill she received last month from the local phone company is shown in Illustration 42–1.

CORBIN TELEPHONE CO.
ALTON, ILLINOIS 62002

DATE OF BILL	PAGE	BILLING NUMBER
5/1/--	1	618-555-3798

LAST AMT. DUE	PAYMENTS	BALANCE
23.77	23.77	0.00

BELLA STEIN
1288 ELM STREET
ALTON, IL 62002

LOCAL SERVICE	10.38
ACCESS CHARGES	2.00
LOCAL CALLS	3.17
U.S. TAX (3%)	.47
STATE TAX (5%)	.78
	AMOUNT DUE
DUE ON OR BEFORE 6/1/--	16.80

CORBIN TELEPHONE CO. ITEMIZED LOCAL CALLS   PAGE 2

DATE	TIME	CALLED PLACE	AREA-NUMBER	RATE	MINS	
4-3	915A	EDWARDSVILLE, IL	618-555-1143	AD	2	.25
4-5	217P	BELLEVILLE, IL	618-555-2819	AD	2	.31
4-19	857P	HIGHLAND, IL	618-555-5829	AE	38	2.61
	TOTAL ITEMIZED CALLS					3.17

RATE: A-DIAL, O-OPERATOR ASSISTED, P-PERSON TO PERSON, D-DAY, E-EVENING, N-NIGHT

Illustration 42–1. Telephone Bill for Local Service

Local Telephone Service. Charges for local phone service depend on the services you rent from your phone company. **Local service** charges may include fees for phone lines, phone equipment, and special phone services. Bella's local service charges are for the one phone line she rents. The total, $10.38, is a flat fee charged to all phone users for one line.

Bella bought her phone from a discount store. Instead of buying her phone, she could have rented a push-button phone for $2.57 a month or a rotary phone for $1.05 a month from Corbin. She could also rent these special services from Corbin at the extra monthly rates shown:

Touch-tone service	$0.73	Three-way calling	$2.50
Call waiting	$3.00	Speed dialing	$2.50
Call forwarding	$2.50		

Touch-tone service lets you use true, push-button phones which are needed to "talk" to computers. **Call waiting** beeps if someone calls you while you are talking to another party. You can put the first party on hold, talk to the other person, and then resume your original call.

Call forwarding automatically transfers calls made to your phone to another phone. Before visiting a friend, you can transfer calls to your friend's phone. That way, you won't miss important calls made to your home while you are away. **Three-way calling** lets you talk to two or three callers at the same time. **Speed dialing** lets you dial frequently-used numbers by touching one or two numbers.

Rental charges for equipment and special services are added to the local service charges. For example, if Bella had rented a rotary phone and call waiting, her local service charges would have been $14.43 ($10.38 + $1.05 + $3).

Telephone Access Charges. Telephone customers must pay charges to access, or use, their local phone company's telephone switches. Corbin customers must pay a $2.00 **access charge** to use Corbin's telephone switches.

Local Telephone Calls. These are charges for calls which are made locally. The costs of these calls may vary with the call length, distance, and the time of day the call is made. Bella was charged $3.17 for local calls.

Telephone Taxes. Federal, state, and local taxes may be charged on your phone bill. The taxes on Bella's bill are shown below. Notice that each tax is figured on each part of the bill separately.

	Charges	U.S. Tax at 3%	State Tax at 5%
Local service	$10.38	$0.31	$0.52
Access charges	2.00	0.06	0.10
Local calls	3.17	0.10	0.16
Totals	$15.55	$0.47	$0.78

**Exercise 1
Written**

Find taxes separately for each service.

Use the service and taxes rates for the Corbin Telephone Company to solve Problems 1–3.

1. Jim paid $10.38 for local phone service plus $0.73 for touch-tone service, $2.57 for a push button set, and $2.50 for call forwarding in May. He also paid $2 for access charges and made $22.45 in local calls that month. What was Jim's total phone bill from Corbin Telephone Company for May, including taxes? $43.89

2. Mario pays a flat fee for one phone line plus two rotary phones. He also pays his $2 access charge and made $17.49 in local calls in March. What was his March phone bill, including taxes? $34.52

3. Darlene pays a flat fee for one line. She also has touch-tone service, 2 push button phones, call waiting, and call forwarding. She pays a $2 access charge. Darlene made local calls costing $37.55 in May. What was her May phone bill, including taxes? $66.22

4. Lynn rents three phones from her phone company at $1.05 per month for each phone. She can buy the same type of phone from a store for $18 each. How much will Lynn save in five years by buying instead of renting? $135

■ Payback
period =
cost ÷ annual
savings

5. Sid rents two push-button phones from the phone company for $2.57 each per month. He can buy similar phones from a store for $30 each. If he buys the phones, what is the payback period to the nearest year? 1 year

Long-Distance Telephone Calls. Long-distance calls are those you make to phone numbers outside the local service area. The cost of these calls depends on the rates of your long-distance company, how far away the other phone is, how long you talk, when you make the call, and the help you need from the operator. It pays to compare the rates charged by all the long-distance companies which serve your area.

The long-distance rates charged by NewNet Communications Co. are shown in Illustration 42–2. These charges are for direct-dial service; that is, when you dial the number yourself instead of asking for operator assistance.

MILEAGE BAND	DAY RATES FIRST MIN.	DAY RATES ADDED MIN.	EVENING RATES FIRST MIN.	EVENING RATES ADDED MIN.	NIGHT RATES FIRST MIN.	NIGHT RATES ADDED MIN.
1–10	0.1960	0.1499	0.1260	0.0829	0.0860	0.0648
11–22	0.2370	0.1898	0.1560	0.1077	0.1070	0.0890
23–55	0.2690	0.2098	0.1560	0.1301	0.1080	0.0980
56–124	0.2760	0.2398	0.1600	0.1487	0.1160	0.1127
125–292	0.2770	0.2597	0.1620	0.1580	0.1270	0.1210
293–430	0.2810	0.2797	0.1640	0.1620	0.1310	0.1300

Illustration 42–2. Long-Distance Rates Charged by NewNet Communications Co.

Day rates are charged for calls made between 8:00 a.m. and 5:00 p.m. on weekdays. Evening rates apply from 5:00 p.m. to 11:00 p.m. on weekdays and Sundays. Night rates apply from 11:00 p.m. to 8:00 a.m. on weekdays and Sundays. Night rates also apply all day Saturdays through 5:00 p.m. on Sunday.

Bella's long-distance charges from NewNet are shown in Illustration 42–3. Her charges for the Peoria call were found by looking at the evening (E) rates for a call to a person between 125–292 miles away. She was charged $0.1620 for the first minute and $0.1580 for each of the other five minutes, or $0.95 — $0.1620 + (5 × $0.1580) = $0.95. Bella's other long-distance calls were computed in a similar manner.

NEWNET COMMUNICATIONS CO., INC.
1280 E. Linden Ave.
Tucson, AZ 85716-1109

ACCOUNT NO.   22-0000397587   APRIL 30, 19--   PAGE 1

	PREVIOUS BALANCE	.00
04/30/--	TOTAL LONG-DISTANCE SERVICE	11.32
04/30/--	FEDERAL TAXES (3%)	.34
04/30/--	STATE TAXES (5%)	.57
	BALANCE DUE UPON RECEIPT	12.23

PLEASE RETURN THIS PORTION WITH YOUR PAYMENT

NEWNET COMMUNICATIONS CO., INC.   PAGE 2

DATE	TIME	# CALLED	DESTINATION		MIN		AMOUNT
03/03	0704P	218-555-3811	PEORIA	IL	6	E	.95
03/12	0148P	309-555-2917	SPRINGFIELD	IL	30	N	3.38
03/28	0413P	518-555-1897	MILWAUKEE	WI	25	D	6.99
		TOTAL LONG-DISTANCE SERVICE					11.32

D-DAY, E-EVENING, N-NIGHT

Illustration 42–3. Long-Distance Telephone Bill

Reducing Long-Distance Telephone Costs. Long-distance costs may be reduced if you call in the evening or on weekends instead of weekdays. You can dial direct instead of using the operator. You can also keep track of how long your call has lasted. Knowing how long your call is taking will help you keep it short.

Asking the operator for help in making a call can be expensive. There are special, higher rates for operator assistance. It is always cheaper to dial the number yourself.

You may need operator assistance for station-to-station and person-to-person calls, long-distance calls from a pay phone, collect calls, credit card calls, calls which are billed to another number, calls from hotels, and calls in which the operator tells you how long you have been calling and how much it has cost (time and charges calls).

Use the rates in Illustration 42–2 to solve the problems.

**Exercise 2
Written**

1. Edna makes a 6-minute, direct-dial call to a friend 100 miles away at 2:00 p.m. on Monday.
   a. What is the cost of the call? $1.48
   b. How much could Edna have saved if she had called at 5:30 p.m.?
      $0.58
   c. How much could she have saved by calling on Saturday?
      $0.80

2. Hector made a 27-minute call to his mother, who lives 300 miles away, at 3:00 p.m. on Friday. He dialed the number himself.
   a. What did Hector's call cost? $7.55
   b. What would have been the cost if Hector had called at 11:01 p.m.?
      $3.51

c. What would have been the cost if he had called at 4:00 p.m. on Sunday? $3.51

3. Find the cost of a 15-minute, direct-dial call to a person 50 miles away
   a. On Wednesday at 9:00 a.m. $3.21
   b. On Wednesday at 6:00 p.m. $1.98
   c. On Sunday at 7:00 p.m. $1.98

4. Find the percent you save, to the nearest whole percent, if you make a 5-minute, direct-dial call to a person 400 miles away at the
   a. Evening rate rather than the weekday rate 42%
   b. Night or weekend rate rather than the weekday rate 54%

REVIEW 42

Terms

1. Match the terms with the statements.

   access charge   call forwarding   call waiting
   local service   speed dialing   three-way calling

   a. You can answer a call while you're talking with someone else
      call waiting
   b. You can talk to more than one person at a time
      three-way calling
   c. You can dial often-used numbers with one or two buttons
      speed dialing
   d. You can transfer calls to another number call forwarding
   e. Local phone lines, equipment, and special services
      local service
   f. A fee charged for use of the phone company switches
      access charge

Skills

2. a. 13,240 ÷ 150,000 to the nearest ten thousandth 0.0883
   b. $540 is what part smaller than $630? $\frac{1}{7}$
   c. Show $9\frac{2}{5}$ as a decimal. 9.4
   ‡d. $3.60 is $37\frac{1}{2}$% less than what amount? $5.76

Problems

3. In June, Hayato's local service charges were $12.50, his access charges were $2, he made 36 local calls totaling $44.23, and he paid 3% federal and 4% state taxes. What was Hayato's total June bill? $62.85 [42]

4. Tom's water meter read 12,880 cu. ft. on April 1 and 18,450 cu. ft. on July 1. He pays $6.34 for the first 500 cu. ft. and $0.79 for each 100 cu. ft. over 500 cu. ft. What is Tom's current quarterly water bill? $46.39 [41]

5. Val worked eight hours daily, Monday through Sunday, producing 698 valves that passed inspection. Her employer paid her a regular-time rate on weekdays, a time-and-a-half rate on Saturday, and a double-time rate on Sunday. Val's regular pay rate was $9 an hour. [17; 21]
   a. What were Val's gross earnings? $612
   b. At 7.65%, find the estimated and exact deduction for FICA taxes. $48; $46.82

Computer Clinic

Tod Kramer now pays for one phone line plus touch-tone service, call waiting, call forwarding, and a touch-tone phone from Corbin Telephone Company. Follow the steps below to complete a telephone service spreadsheet for Tod Kramer.

1. Insert your Spreadsheet Applications Diskette and call up the file "Sec42." After you do, your computer screen should look like Illustration 42–4.

```
Sec42                 TELEPHONE SERVICE SPREADSHEET

                            NUMBER    RATE      TOTAL
Local phone line charge        0      10.38      .00
Touch-tone service             0        .73      .00
Call waiting                   0       3.00      .00
Call forwarding                0       2.50      .00
Speed calling                  0       2.50      .00
Three-way calling              0       2.50      .00
Touch-tone phone               0       2.57      .00
Rotary phone                   0       1.05      .00

TOTAL LOCAL SERVICE CHARGES  -----    -----      .00
ACCESS CHARGE                  0       2.00      .00
CHARGE FOR LOCAL CALLS       -----    -----     0.00
FEDERAL TAXES                -----      .03      .00
STATE TAXES                  -----      .05      .00
TOTAL PHONE BILL             -----    -----      .00
```

Illustration 42–4. Spreadsheet Used to Figure Total Telephone Costs

2. Enter a "1" in these cells: B4, B5, B6, B7, B10, and B14. You have now "told" the spreadsheet that Tod pays for one line, touch-tone service, call waiting, call forwarding, a touch-tone phone, and access charges. Do not enter data into cells which contain -----.

3. Answer the questions about your completed spreadsheet:
    a. What are Tod's total local service charges? $19.18
    b. What is Tod's total telephone bill? $22.88
    c. If Corbin raised their rental fees for touch-tone phones to $2.83, what would be Tod's new local service charges total? $19.44
    d. Suppose that, in addition to the rise in touch-tone costs, state taxes also rose to 8%. How much higher than his original bill would Tod's total telephone bill rise? $0.92

Borrowing Money

Businesses and people borrow money from time to time for many reasons. Often, people borrow money to buy high-priced items such as automobiles, trucks, and equipment, or to build or remodel houses or stores. Money may be borrowed from many sources, including banks and credit unions, and finance, life insurance, and credit card companies.

In this unit, you will learn to solve problems related to borrowing money and paying for the use of it.

After you finish Unit 7, you will be able to:

- Find the number of calendar days between two dates.
- Find the due date of a note.
- Find rate of interest.
- Find interest using exact and banker's methods.
- Find bank discounts.
- Find the proceeds of a discounted note.
- Find the real rate of interest.
- Find the maturity value of a note.
- Find the finance charge on installment loans and purchases.
- Find amounts of monthly installment payments.
- Find annual percentage rates on installment loans and purchases.
- Find the cost of credit card purchases.
- Solve problems that contain more information than you need.
- Estimate answers to problems.
- Read, write, say, and recognize the meanings of the key terms.
- Use a calculator to find exact interest and savings for paying cash.
- Use a computer spreadsheet to figure approximate annual percentage rates (APR).

Section 43
Interest-Bearing Notes

■ **Paying interest is like paying rent to use someone else's money.**

When you borrow money, you usually sign a **promissory note** similar to the one shown in Illustration 43–1. This note is your written promise, or IOU, that you will repay the money to the lender on a certain date. Usually, you also have to pay for using the lender's money. That cost is called **interest**. A note that requires you to pay interest is called an **interest-bearing note.**

Lenders may require a borrower to deposit or pledge property as security for a loan. This property is called **collateral**. Types of collateral that are often used to secure loans are cars, stocks, bonds, and life insurance. If the loan is not repaid, the lender can seize the collateral and sell it to get the borrowed money back.

■ **Equity is the owner's stake in property.**

Many lenders offer **home equity loans** to home owners. Home **equity** is the owner's stake in a home. It is the difference between what the home could be sold for and what is owed on it. To obtain a home equity loan, the borrower pledges the equity in the home as collateral for the loan.

Using a Promissory Note. On April 4, 1990, Bess Baker borrowed $3,500 from her bank to buy a used car, which she used as collateral for the loan. Bess signed the note shown in Illustration 43–1. She was the *maker* of the note. Northport Bank was the *payee*.

Loan No. _230789_   Date _April 4_ 19 _90_

Loan Amount $ _3,500.00_   Maturity Date _April 4_ 19 _91_

One year AFTER DATE _/_ PROMISE TO PAY TO

THE ORDER OF _Northport Bank_

Three thousand, five hundred and no/100 —— DOLLARS

PAYABLE AT _Northport Bank_ with interest at

the rate of _12_ % per annum, for value received, giving said bank a

security interest in this collateral: _1987 Chevrolet I.D. 00780798777_

The rights _/_ (am, are) giving said bank in this property, and the obligations this agreement secures, are defined on the reverse side of this note.

Bess Baker

Illustration 43–1. Interest-Bearing Promissory Note with Collateral

The amount that Bess borrowed, $3,500, is the **face** or **principal**. The day the note was signed, April 4, 1990, is the **date of the note.** The time for which the money was borrowed, one year, is called the **time**. The date the money must be repaid, April 4, 1991, is the **due date** or **maturity date.** The rate of interest that Bess must pay, 12%, is called the **rate of interest.**

Finding the Interest on a Loan for One Year.
In the note, Bess Baker promised to repay the $3,500 "with interest at 12%." This means "with interest at the rate of 12% a year."

Since Bess borrowed the $3,500 for exactly one year, the interest she must pay is 12% of $3,500. Here is how the interest is figured:

Interest for 1 year = $3,500 × 0.12 = $420

Face
+ Interest

Amount due

The total amount Bess must pay on the maturity date is the face of the note, $3,500, plus interest of $420, or $3,920. The total of the face and interest is called the **amount due,** or **amount due at maturity.**

Finding the Interest on a Loan for a Period Other Than One Year.
The interest you pay on a loan is proportional to the time for which you borrow the money. For $\frac{1}{4}$ of a year the interest is $\frac{1}{4}$ of one year's interest. For $1\frac{1}{2}$ years it is $1\frac{1}{2}$ of the interest for 1 year, and so on.

For example, the interest on a loan of $2,000 for $3\frac{1}{2}$ years at 12% would be:

Interest for 1 year = $2,000 × 0.12 = $240

$$\textbf{Interest for } 3\frac{1}{2} \textbf{ years } = 3\frac{1}{2} \times \$240 = \$840$$

**Exercise 1
Written**

1. Find the interest and the amount due at maturity for each note.

3 mo. $= \frac{3}{12} = \frac{1}{4}$ yr.
9 mo. $= \frac{9}{12} = \frac{3}{4}$ yr.
10 mo. $= \frac{10}{12} = \frac{5}{6}$ yr.

	Face of Note	Time	Rate	Interest	Amount Due at Maturity
a.	$500	2 yr.	10%	$100.00	$600.00
b.	300	3 yr.	12%	108.00	408.00
c.	200	$1\frac{1}{2}$ yr.	9%	27.00	227.00
d.	900	3 mo.	8%	18.00	918.00
e.	250	3 mo.	14%	8.75	258.75
f.	450	10 mo.	13%	48.75	498.75
g.	720	$2\frac{1}{4}$ yr.	$8\frac{1}{2}$%	137.70	857.70

2. Terry Wilco borrowed $20,500 to add an addition to her store. She repaid the principal, with 11% interest, 3 years later.
   a. Estimate the interest Terry owed. $6,000
   b. Find the exact amount of interest Terry owed. $6,765
   c. Find the total amount Terry had to repay. $27,265

3. Dorothea borrowed $3,600 at 9% from her credit union for tuition. When she repaid the loan 9 months later, how much did she pay? $3,843

4. To finance the remodeling of his basement, Al borrowed $6,200 on an 8-month home equity loan. He signed a promissory note bearing interest at $10\frac{1}{2}$%. What total amount did Al pay on the due date? $6,634

5. Yong bought a tractor attachment for $6,400. Yong made a down payment of $1,600 and borrowed $4,800 for $1\frac{1}{2}$ years at $13\frac{1}{4}$% interest. What total amount must Yong pay when the note comes due? $5,754

6. Carlotta borrowed $2,000 for a vacation trip. The promissory note she signed was for 3 months at $15\frac{1}{4}$% interest. How much did Carlotta have to pay when the note came due? $2,076.25

7. Charles borrowed $15,000 on a home equity loan to remodel his house. He signed a promissory note for $1\frac{1}{2}$ years at 15% interest.
   a. How much interest did Charles pay? $3,375
   b. What was the total amount he paid when the note came due?
      $18,375

REVIEW 43

Terms

1. Match the terms with the statements.

amount due at maturity	home equity loan
collateral	interest
date of note	interest-bearing note
due date or maturity date	promissory note
equity	rate of interest
face or principal	time

   a. The day the loan is to be repaid   due date or maturity date
   b. The dollar cost of using a lender's money   interest
   c. Written promise to repay, with or without interest
      promissory note
   d. The day the note is signed   date of note
   e. The time for which the money is borrowed   time
   f. The amount borrowed   face or principal
   g. Interest shown as a percent   rate of interest
   h. The total of principal and interest   amount due at maturity
   i. Requires payment of interest   interest-bearing note
   j. Personal property used as security for a loan   collateral
   k. A person's stake in property   equity
   l. A loan using the borrower's equity in a home as collateral
      home equity loan

Skills

2. a. 7% of $350.70 = ? $24.55
   b. 2.4 equals what percent?   240%
   c. $70 is what percent of $280?   25%
   d. $9 is what percent of $7.50?   120%
   e. Show $6\frac{1}{4}$% as a decimal.   0.0625
   f. Find 25% of 2.6 liters.   0.65 L

Problems

3. What is the interest on $4,400 for 9 months at 6%? $198 [43]

4. Alice borrowed $5,000 for tuition, using her equity in her home as collateral. She signed a 3-year promissory note with interest at 15%. [43]
   a. How much interest did Alice pay on the note? $2,250
   b. What total amount was paid when the note came due? $7,250

5. A real estate agent sold property for $157,800 and charged 5% commission and $325 for expenses. What net proceeds did the owner of the property receive? $149,585 [29]

6. Armando Lopez earns $9.50 an hour for a 40-hour work week with time and a half for overtime. Last week he worked $44\frac{1}{4}$ hours. His employer deducted 7.65% for social security and $47 for the federal withholding tax. What was Armando's net pay last week? $359.86 [21]

7. Amy Wright, a farmer, bought these amounts of land during the year: 35 ha, 0.425 km², 0.46 ha, and 12.7 ha. She paid an average of $207 per ha. How much did Amy pay for the land? $18,766.62 [31]

8. On Monday morning, a restaurant had 6 L of milk on hand. During the week, the restaurant owner bought these amounts of milk: 30 L, 45 L, and 60 L. The next Monday, there were 8 L of milk left. How many liters of milk had been used during the week? 133 L [32]

9. For the first 5 months of the year, Tom's monthly sales were $23,890, $21,060, $18,400, $19,780, and $20,700. What must be his sales for the 6th month if he wants his monthly average for the 6 months to be $22,000? $28,170 [10]

‡10. A salesperson's commission is 8% on all sales. How many dollars' worth of goods must be sold to earn $4,500? $56,250 [29]

‡11. Cleo Orr's bank statement showed a balance of $1,342.66 on May 31. Her check register balance on that date was $1,214.15. The outstanding checks were: #86, $15.88; #88, $38.45; #89, $25.18. Cleo also discovered that she had not entered in her register a deposit of $49 made on May 21. Prepare a reconciliation statement for Cleo. $1,263.15 [6]

Section 44
Exact and Banker's Interest

Unless otherwise stated, the rate of interest on a loan is always an **annual rate.** The annual rate shows what percent of interest is charged on the principal for using the money for *one year.*

Interest Formulas. The principal multiplied by the rate is equal to the interest for one year.

$$\textbf{Principal} \times \textbf{Rate} = \textbf{Interest for 1 year}$$

Interest for a period other than one year is found by multiplying the interest for 1 year by the time in years.

P × R × T = I

$$\textbf{P} \quad \times \quad \textbf{R} \quad \times \quad \textbf{T} \quad = \quad \textbf{I}$$

$$\textbf{Principal} \times \textbf{Rate} \times \textbf{Time} = \textbf{Interest}$$

For example, the interest on $1,000 at 12% for 3 years is $360.

$$\textbf{\$1,000} \times \textbf{0.12} \times \textbf{3} = \textbf{\$360}$$

Remember— interest rate is a rate per year.

For $\frac{1}{2}$ of a year, the interest is $60:

$$\textbf{\$1,000} \times \textbf{0.12} \times \frac{\textbf{1}}{\textbf{2}} = \textbf{\$60}$$

**Exercise 1
Oral**

Find the interest.

1. $980 @ 10% for 1 yr. $98
2. $100 @ 7% for 3 yr. $21
3. $300 @ 12% for $\frac{1}{2}$ yr. $18
4. $600 @ 9% for $1\frac{1}{2}$ yr. $81
5. $400 @ 15% for $\frac{1}{4}$ yr. $15
6. $700 @ 11% for 1 yr. $77
7. $300 @ 5% for 2 yr. $30
8. $200 @ 13% for 1 yr. $26
9. $500 @ 9% for 2 yr. $90
10. $800 @ 8% for $1\frac{1}{2}$ yr. $96

Interest for Time in Months. When the time of a note is in months, you must show it as a fraction with a denominator of 12. For example, 3 months is $\frac{3}{12}$, or $\frac{1}{4}$, of a year. So, the interest on $1,000 at 12% for 3 months would be:

$$\textbf{\$1,000} \times \textbf{0.12} \times \frac{\textbf{1}}{\textbf{4}} = \textbf{\$30 interest for 3 months}$$

**Exercise 2
Written**

Find the interest, using the P × R × T formula.

1. $800 @ 10% for 6 months $40
2. $600 @ 12% for 3 months $18
3. $960 @ 8% for 4 months $25.60
4. $400 @ 15% for 9 months $45
5. $1,500 @ 16% for 5 months $100
6. $2,400 @ 7% for 2 months $28
7. $6,900 @ 5% for 8 months $230
8. $3,500 @ 9% for 1 month $26.25
9. $3,000 @ 12% for 10 months $300
10. $4,000 @ $7\frac{1}{2}$% for 6 months $150

Exact Interest for Time in Days. When the time is shown in days, interest is figured by either the **exact interest method** or by the **banker's interest method.** Exact interest uses a 365-day year. Banker's interest uses a 360-day year.

■ The exact interest method uses a 365-day year.

The *exact interest method* is used by the United States government and by many banks and other businesses. To figure exact interest, you use a year of 365 days. So, you show the time as a fraction with 365 as the denominator.

For example, you would show 73 days as $\frac{73}{365}$. The exact interest on $1,000 at 6% for 73 days would be:

$$\$1{,}000 \times 0.06 \times \frac{73}{365} = \$\overset{12}{\cancel{60}} \times \frac{\overset{1}{\cancel{73}}}{\underset{\underset{1}{73}}{\cancel{365}}} = \$12 \text{ interest for 73 days}$$

**Exercise 3
Written**

1. Find the *exact* interest to the nearest cent.
   a. $650 @ 6% for 146 days $15.60
   b. $2,200 @ 12% for 50 days $36.16
   c. $560 @ 10% for 110 days $16.88
   d. $840 @ 15% for 300 days $103.56
   e. $1,450 @ 7% for 100 days $27.81
   f. $500 @ 8% for 90 days $9.86

2. Julie O'Malley borrowed $1,800 at 9% for 270 days through the student loan program at her college. How much exact interest did Julie have to pay on the loan? $119.84

3. Larry Wang borrowed $5,000 for 180 days. He paid exact interest at an annual rate of 12%.
   a. Estimate the interest Larry owed. $300
   b. What is the exact amount of interest he had to pay? $295.89
   c. What total amount did he have to repay? $5,295.89

■ The banker's interest method uses a 360-day year.

Banker's Interest for Time in Days. The *banker's interest* method is used in place of the exact interest method by many businesses. In this method of figuring interest, a year has only 360 days. The 360-day year has 12 months of 30 days each and is known as the *banker's year.* Of course, there really is no such year. It is used because it is easier to calculate with than a 365-day year. In this method, the interest for 30 days is $\frac{30}{360}$, or $\frac{1}{12}$, of the interest for 1 year. The interest for 60 days is $\frac{60}{360}$, or $\frac{1}{6}$ of the interest for 1 year, and so on.

For example, 90 days is $\frac{90}{360}$, or $\frac{1}{4}$ of a year. So, using the banker's year, the interest on $1,000 at 11% for 90 days would be:

$$\$1{,}000 \times 0.11 \times \frac{1}{4} = \$110 \times \frac{1}{4} = \$27.50 \quad \text{interest for 90 days}$$

**Exercise 4
Written**

1. Find the banker's interest on each amount below.
   a. $600 @ 6% for 60 days $6
   b. $360 @ 9% for 30 days $2.70
   c. $200 @ 12% for 120 days $8

d. $400 @ 8% for 180 days $16
e. $960 @ 15% for 270 days $108
f. $1,800 @ 15% for 36 days $27
g. $1,200 @ 8% for 240 days $64
h. $2,400 @ 9% for 45 days $27
i. $1,500 @ 12% for 90 days $45
j. $2,000 @ 7½% for 120 days $50

2. Find the banker's interest on a loan of $900 at 14% for 60 days. $21

The banker's interest method uses 360 days.

3. Dora Lee Avis borrowed $3,840 from her bank for 120 days. She paid banker's interest at an annual rate of 12%. How much interest did Dora Lee pay on the loan? $153.60

4. Rob Tovich signed a 180-day note for $1,825. He repaid the loan when due, with interest at the annual rate of 12%, using a banker's year.
   a. How much interest did Rob pay? $109.50
   b. What total amount did he pay? $1,934.50

5. Sarah Herr needed a loan of $580 to help pay a $750 bill. Her bank required her to sign a 6-month note with banker's interest at 12½%. If she repaid the loan in 90 days, how much interest did Sarah have to pay? $18.13

6. Willie Oranda needs to borrow $8,000 for 135 days. Lender A will loan him the money at 15% exact interest. Lender B will loan him the money at 15% banker's interest.
   a. Find Willie's interest at Lender A. $443.84
   b. Find Willie's interest at Lender B. $450
   c. What is the difference in interest costs? $6.16

Finding the Rate of Exact Interest. If you know the principal and the amount of interest for one year, you can find the rate of interest by dividing the interest by the principal.

$$\text{Rate of Interest} = \frac{\text{Interest for one year}}{\text{Principal}}$$

If the interest given in the problem is not for a year, you must first find how much the interest would be for one year. You then divide that interest by the principal.

For example, Ella Stein paid $30 interest on a loan of $1,000 for 3 months. The interest charge of $30 for 3 months ($\frac{1}{4}$ of a year) is equal to a charge of $120 for one year (4 × $30 = $120, or $30 ÷ $\frac{1}{4}$ = $120). The rate of exact interest she paid was 12%, figured this way:

$$\frac{\$120}{\$1,000} = 0.12 = 12\%$$

Find the rate of exact interest for each problem.

Exercise 5 Written

	Principal	Time	Interest	
1.	$ 400	1 month	$ 4.00	12%
2.	500	2 months	7.50	9%

	Principal	Time	Interest	
3.	$ 300	3 months	$ 10.50	14%
4.	600	4 months	18.00	9%
5.	2,800	6 months	140.00	10%
6.	435	2 months	7.25	10%
7.	1,300	6 months	78.00	12%
8.	1,000	3 months	20.00	8%
9.	800	8 months	80.00	15%
10.	2,000	10 months	150.00	9%
11.	4,000	18 months	600.00	10%
12.	600	15 months	60.00	8%

Exercise 6
Written

1. Tabatha Kerr borrowed $2,400 for 6 months and paid $132 interest. What rate of exact interest did she pay?   11%

2. Evan Cole paid $19.50 in interest on a loan of $2,600 for 1 month. What rate of exact interest did he pay?   9%

3. Ali Ahmed borrowed $6,000 and paid $945 in exact interest when the loan came due $1\frac{1}{2}$ years later. What rate of interest did Ali pay? $10\frac{1}{2}$%

4. Laura Weiss borrowed $1,500 for 21 months. The total interest she paid was $315. What rate of exact interest did Laura pay?   12%

REVIEW 44

Terms

1. Match the terms with the statements.

    annual rate   banker's interest   exact interest

    a. Uses a 360-day year   banker's interest
    b. Uses a 365-day year   exact interest
    c. The percent of the principal that is charged for one year
        annual rate

Skills

2. a. 5.25 equals what percent?   525%
    b. $80 is what percent of $50?   160%
    c. Show $9\frac{7}{8}$% as a decimal.   0.09875
    d. 320 grams is what percent of a kilogram?   32%
    ‡e. $90 is $7\frac{1}{2}$% of what amount? $1,200
    ‡f. $10.64 is 5% less than what amount? $11.20

Problems

3. Jules began the day with $75. During the day he received $25 for mowing a lawn and spent $1.25 for gas, $5 for a movie, $25 for a present, and $3.75 for lunch. How much money did Jules have at the end of the day? $65 [4]

4. Ria Torres paid $27 interest on a loan of $1,800 for 2 months. What rate of exact interest did she pay?   9% [44]

5. Find the exact interest on $4,800 for $1\frac{1}{2}$ years at 14%. $1,008 [44]

6. Ellery Clarke's sales for 5 months were $27,508, $29,686, $29,130, $27,980, and $28,649. What must be his sales next month if he wants his monthly average to be $28,000? $25,047 [10]

7. Edith and Betty share the monthly costs of their apartment in the ratio of 2 to 3, respectively. The total cost of their apartment last year, including rent, heat, and power, was $9,300. What was Betty's share of the costs? $5,580 [16]

8. Karl Obenhous, a secretary, is paid a yearly salary of $10,920. This is equal to how much a week? $210 [10]

9. Anna Bauer works each day from 8:30 a.m. to 4:30 p.m., Monday through Friday, with $\frac{1}{2}$ hour out for lunch. She is paid $6.50 an hour. What were Anna's gross earnings last week if she worked full time except for $1\frac{1}{2}$ hours lost on Wednesday? $234 [7]

10. Henry's sales last week totaled $15,000. His gross earnings for the week were $650, of which $200 was salary and the rest was commission. What percent commission was Henry paid?   3% [28]

11. A collection agency collected 75% of an outstanding bill of $580 and charged 35% commission. What were the net proceeds? $282.75 [29]

12. You bought three crates of berries (16 one-liter baskets to the crate). You had to throw out 7 L that were spoiled. How many liters of berries did you have left?   41 L [32]

‡13. A collection agent who charges 30% commission received $6,600 for collecting an overdue account. What was the amount collected? $22,000 [29]

Calculator Clinic

Finding Exact Interest. Finding exact interest for one year on a calculator is no different from multiplying a number by a percent. You multiply the principal by the rate of interest. For example, to find the exact interest on $100 at 9%:

a. Press these keys in order: ⏄1⏄ ⏄0⏄ ⏄0⏄ ⏄×⏄ ⏄·⏄ ⏄0⏄ ⏄9⏄

b. Press ⏄=⏄ , and the result, 9, will appear in the display.

When the time of the note is for more or less than one year, you must multiply the answer, 9, by the time shown as a fraction of one year. For time in months, the denominator of the fraction will be 12; for time in days, the denominator will be 365.

    For example, to find the exact interest on $100 at 9% for 7 months, you must multiply the interest for one year, $9, by $\frac{7}{12}$.

c.   Press these keys in order: ⊠ 7 ÷ 1 2

d.   Press ⌸ , and the result, 5.25, will appear in the display.

To find the interest on $100 at 9% for $2\frac{1}{2}$ years, you need to multiply the interest for one year, $9, by $2\frac{1}{2}$. To do this, you must convert $2\frac{1}{2}$ to a decimal, 2.5. Then:

e.   Press these keys in order: 9 ⊠ 2 · 5

f.   Press ⌸ , and the result, 22.5, will appear in the display.

Now add the dollar sign and the last zero to arrive at the correct answer, $22.50.

Saving Time. The percent key can shorten your work. The percent key lets you skip converting the rate of interest (9%) to a decimal (0.09). All you do is enter "100 × 9" and press the *percent* key instead of the equals key. Your display will show the same answer as before.

Calculator Practice. Apply what you have learned in this calculator clinic to the problems in Exercises 1–3 in this section, and to any other exercises your teacher may assign.

Section 45
Interest Tables

Figuring Interest by Using an Interest Table. Banks and other businesses may figure interest by using tables like the one shown in Illustration 45–1.

The table shows the interest on $100 for a 365-day year. To find the interest on any amount of money using the table, follow these steps:

1.   Find the interest on $100 for the interest rate and time you want. Do this by reading down the rate column to the point across from the time you want.

2.   Find the number of hundreds of dollars in the principal by dividing the principal by $100. Do this by moving the decimal in the principal two places to the left.

3.   Multiply the interest for $100 by the number of hundreds in the principal.

SIMPLE INTEREST TABLE
Interest on $100 for a 365-Day Year

Time (Days)	8%	8½%	9%	9½%	10%	10½%	11%	11½%	12%	12½%
1	0.0219	0.0233	0.0247	0.0260	0.0274	0.0288	0.0301	0.0315	0.0329	0.0342
2	0.0438	0.0466	0.0493	0.0521	0.0548	0.0575	0.0603	0.0630	0.0658	0.0685
3	0.0658	0.0699	0.0740	0.0781	0.0822	0.0863	0.0904	0.0945	0.0986	0.1027
4	0.0877	0.0932	0.0986	0.1041	0.1096	0.1151	0.1205	0.1260	0.1315	0.1370
5	0.1096	0.1164	0.1233	0.1301	0.1370	0.1438	0.1507	0.1575	0.1644	0.1712
6	0.1315	0.1397	0.1479	0.1562	0.1644	0.1726	0.1808	0.1890	0.1973	0.2055
7	0.1534	0.1630	0.1726	0.1822	0.1918	0.2014	0.2110	0.2205	0.2301	0.2397
8	0.1753	0.1863	0.1973	0.2082	0.2192	0.2301	0.2411	0.2521	0.2630	0.2740
9	0.1973	0.2096	0.2219	0.2342	0.2466	0.2589	0.2712	0.2836	0.2959	0.3082
10	0.2192	0.2329	0.2466	0.2603	0.2740	0.2877	0.3014	0.3151	0.3288	0.3425
11	0.2411	0.2562	0.2712	0.2863	0.3014	0.3164	0.3315	0.3466	0.3616	0.3767
12	0.2630	0.2795	0.2959	0.3123	0.3288	0.3452	0.3616	0.3781	0.3945	0.4110
13	0.2849	0.3027	0.3205	0.3384	0.3562	0.3740	0.3918	0.4096	0.4274	0.4452
14	0.3068	0.3260	0.3452	0.3644	0.3836	0.4027	0.4219	0.4411	0.4603	0.4795
15	0.3288	0.3493	0.3699	0.3904	0.4110	0.4315	0.4521	0.4726	0.4932	0.5137
16	0.3507	0.3726	0.3945	0.4164	0.4384	0.4603	0.4822	0.5041	0.5260	0.5479
17	0.3726	0.3959	0.4192	0.4425	0.4658	0.4890	0.5123	0.5356	0.5589	0.5822
18	0.3945	0.4192	0.4438	0.4685	0.4932	0.5178	0.5425	0.5671	0.5918	0.6164
19	0.4164	0.4425	0.4685	0.4945	0.5205	0.5466	0.5726	0.5986	0.6247	0.6507
20	0.4384	0.4658	0.4932	0.5205	0.5479	0.5753	0.6027	0.6301	0.6575	0.6849
21	0.4603	0.4890	0.5178	0.5466	0.5753	0.6041	0.6329	0.6616	0.6904	0.7192
22	0.4822	0.5123	0.5425	0.5726	0.6027	0.6329	0.6630	0.6932	0.7233	0.7534
23	0.5041	0.5356	0.5671	0.5986	0.6301	0.6616	0.6932	0.7247	0.7562	0.7877
24	0.5260	0.5589	0.5918	0.6247	0.6575	0.6904	0.7233	0.7562	0.7890	0.8219
25	0.5479	0.5822	0.6164	0.6507	0.6849	0.7192	0.7534	0.7877	0.8219	0.8562
26	0.5699	0.6055	0.6411	0.6767	0.7123	0.7479	0.7836	0.8192	0.8548	0.8904
27	0.5918	0.6288	0.6658	0.7027	0.7397	0.7767	0.8137	0.8507	0.8877	0.9247
28	0.6137	0.6521	0.6904	0.7288	0.7671	0.8055	0.8438	0.8822	0.9205	0.9589
29	0.6356	0.6753	0.7151	0.7548	0.7945	0.8342	0.8740	0.9137	0.9534	0.9932
30	0.6575	0.6986	0.7397	0.7808	0.8219	0.8630	0.9041	0.9452	0.9863	1.0274
31	0.6795	0.7219	0.7644	0.8068	0.8493	0.8918	0.9342	0.9767	1.0192	1.0616

Illustration 45–1. Simple Interest Table

Example

Find the interest on $650 for 20 days at 10%.

1. Interest on $100 for 20 days at 10%   = $0.5479
2. The principal, $650, divided by $100   = × 6.5
3. The interest on $100 × number of hundreds = $3.561 or
                                               $3.56 **Ans.**

**Exercise 1
Written**

Use the table in Illustration 45–1 to find the interest to the nearest cent.

1. $800 @ 10% for 10 days $2.19

2. $400 @ 12% for 15 days $1.97

3. $500 @ 8% for 21 days $2.30

4. $100 @ 11% for 7 days   21¢

5. $300 @ $9\frac{1}{2}$% for 12 days   94¢

6. $150 @ 9% for 30 days $1.11

7. $450 @ 12% for 5 days   74¢

8. $1,200 @ $10\frac{1}{2}$% for 10 days $3.45

9. $3,250 @ 9% for 25 days $20.03

10. $75 @ 12% for 20 days   49¢

When the number of days you want is not shown in the table, you must combine figures to get the number you want.

Example

Find the interest on $250 for 45 days at 8%.

Solution

1. Interest on $100 for 30 days at 8%   = $0.6575
    Interest on $100 for 15 days at 8%   = 0.3288
    Interest on $100 for 45 days at 8%   = $0.9863
2. The principal, $250, divided by $100   = × 2.5
3. The interest on $100 × number of hundreds = $2.46575 or
    $2.47 **Ans.**

Interest for a rate not shown on the table can be found in much the same way. For example, the interest on $100 @ $18\frac{1}{2}$% for 20 days is the sum of the amount for 9% ($0.4932) and the amount for $9\frac{1}{2}$% ($0.5205).

$0.4932 + $0.5205 = $1.0137 or $1.01

Exercise 2 Written

1. Use Illustration 45–1 to find the interest on.
    a. $300 @ $9\frac{1}{2}$% for 45 days $3.51
    b. $500 @ 12% for 60 days $9.86
    c. $900 @ 8% for 55 days $10.85
    d. $5,000 @ 10% for 80 days $109.59
    e. $750 @ 9% for 120 days $22.19
    f. $400 @ 19% for 10 days $2.08
    g. $200 @ 16% for 20 days $1.75
    h. $1,800 @ 22% for 30 days $32.55
    i. $2,500 @ 20% for 30 days $41.10
    j. $900 @ 18% for 16 days $7.10

2. Juanita Torres borrowed $700 on a note for 60 days with interest at 12%.
    a. Using Illustration 45–1, what interest did she pay? $13.81
    b. What total amount did she owe when the note was due?
        $713.81

3. You need to borrow $500 for 20 days to help pay a $750 bill due on May 6. You can borrow the money at 17%.
    a. What will be the interest using a banker's year? $4.72
    b. What will be the interest using Illustration 45–1? $4.66

REVIEW 45

Skills

1. a. Show 4.8 as a percent.   480%
    b. $510 is what percent of $340?   150%
    c. Show $8\frac{1}{8}\%$ as a decimal.   0.08125
    d. Show 23.9% as a decimal.   0.239
    e. The cost of 378 pads of paper at $3.50 per 100 = ? $13.23
    ‡f. 180 kL is $\frac{3}{8}$ of ? kL   480 kL
    ‡g. 25% of what amount is equal to $7.20? $28.80
    ‡h. $50.88 is 4% less than what amount? $53
    ‡i. What amount increased by $\frac{2}{5}$ of itself gives $2.10? $1.50

Problems

2. Zeb Crane borrowed $900 for 18 months and paid $121.50 interest. What annual rate of interest did he pay?   9% [44]

3. Alma Scott signed a 120-day, 9% note for $800. What was the amount due at maturity, with exact interest? (Use Illustration 45–1.) $823.67 [45]

4. A sales agent was paid a monthly salary of $910 and a commission on all sales. The agent's sales last year were $112,500. Total earnings, including both salary and commission, were $19,920. Find the [28]
    a. Agent's annual salary $10,920
    b. Agent's annual commission $9,000
    c. Rate of commission the agent earned   8%

5. Eighteen cans of soup are priced at 3 for $0.89.
    a. Estimate the total cost of the cans of soup. $5.40
    b. Find the exact cost of the cans of soup. $5.34 [34]

6. A store sells shirts for $17.80 each, or 3 for $49.95. How much would you save by buying 3 shirts at a time instead of 3 shirts, one at a time? $3.45 [38]

Section 46
Due Dates and Times of Notes

A promissory note usually shows on its face the due date or maturity date of the note. For example, Bess Baker's note in Illustration 43–1 shows a due date of April 4, 1991. In this section you will learn how to find the due dates of notes. You will also learn how to find the number of days between the date of a note and its maturity date.

Finding the Due Date When the Time Is in Months. When the time of a note is in months, you find the due date by counting that number of months forward from the date of the note. The due date is the same day in the month you stop with as the date of the note.

Example

Find the due date of a 6-month note dated May 4.

Solution

May 4 + 6 months =
November 4 **Ans.**

Explanation

The date of the note is May 4. The month the note is due is November, the 6th month after May. So, the due date is November 4.

Sometimes the month in which the note comes due does not have the same date as the date of the note (see Illustration 46–1). In this case, you should use the last date in the month when the note comes due.

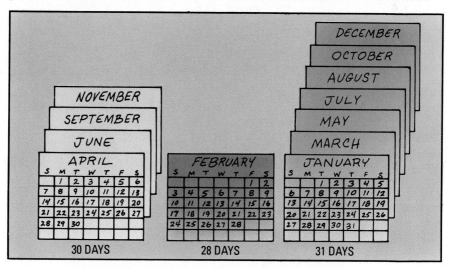

Illustration 46–1. Months Having 28, 30, and 31 Days

Example

Find the due date of a 6-month note dated May 31.

Solution

May 31 + 6 months =
November 30 **Ans.**

Explanation

The date of the note is May 31. The month the note is due is November, the sixth month after May. Since there is no such date as November 31, the due date is November 30, the last date in November.

**Exercise 1
Oral**

■ When working problems, assume that February has 28 days.

Find the due date for each note. Assume that February has 28 days.

	Date	Time			Date	Time	
1.	Feb. 12	1 month	3/12	4.	Mar. 31	4 months	7/31
2.	Jan. 30	1 month	2/28	5.	Mar. 31	3 months	6/30
3.	Nov. 14	2 months	1/14	6.	Apr. 30	1 month	5/30

Finding the Due Date When the Time Is in Days. The time of a note may be shown in days. In this case, you must find the due date by counting, from the date of the note, the number of days shown in the time.

Example

Find the date of maturity of a 90-day note dated May 28.

Solution	Explanation
90 days May $\quad-\;\,3$ $\qquad\quad\overline{87}$ June -30 $\qquad\quad\overline{57}$ July -31 $\qquad\quad\overline{26}$ **Ans.** August 26	Three days are left in May, the date of the note. Subtract 3 days from 90 days, leaving 87 days to carry forward through June. Subtract 30 days for June, leaving 57 days to carry forward through July. Subtract 31 days for July, leaving 26 days to carry forward into August. The due date is August 26.

**Exercise 2
Written**

Find the due date of each note.

	Date	Time			Date	Time	
1.	Mar. 5	30 days	4/4	7.	Oct. 15	30 days	11/14
2.	Jan. 29	60 days	3/30	8.	Dec. 28	80 days	3/18
3.	Nov. 17	90 days	2/15	9.	Aug. 22	90 days	11/20
4.	May 31	30 days	6/30	10.	Feb. 1	30 days	3/3
5.	Jan. 30	45 days	3/16	11.	June 9	120 days	10/7
6.	Apr. 14	75 days	6/28	12.	July 19	45 days	9/2

Finding the Time on Demand Loans. Ordinary loans are payable at the end of fixed periods of time, such as three months or two years. Some loans, however, may be payable "on demand." These loans are called **demand loans,** and the notes are called **demand notes.** Demand loans are usually interest-bearing, and the interest is usually paid monthly or quarterly.

The borrower may repay a demand loan at any time but *must* repay it when the lender demands payment. A demand loan is helpful to a borrower who does not know exactly how long the money will be needed.

Look at the demand note shown in Illustration 46–2. Frank Walker borrowed $2,750 from Shelter Cove Bank on June 14. On that date he

Loan No. *180798*

Date *June 14* 19 *--*

Loan Amount $ *2,750.00*

On demand *I* promise to pay to *Shelter Cove Bank* or order, at the said bank, *Two thousand, seven hundred fifty and no/100* ~~~~~ Dollars, with interest at the rate of *12* % per annum, giving said bank a security interest in this collateral: *200 shares Apex common stock*

The rights *I* (am, ~~are~~) giving said bank in this property, and the obligations this agreement secures, are defined on the reverse side of this note.

Frank Walker

Illustration 46–2. Demand Note with Collateral

signed the note that is payable to the bank on demand. The note bears exact interest at 12%.

The demand note shown in Illustration 46–2 is also a collateral note. It shows that Frank deposited stock that can be sold by the bank if he does not pay the note when the bank demands payment.

Finding the Amount Due on a Demand Note. Frank paid the note on August 23. The amount due was the face of the note ($2,750) plus interest on the face at 12% from the date of the note (June 14) to the date of payment (August 23). The amount due was $2,813.29.

Face of note	**$2,750.00**
Exact Interest at 12% from June 14 to Aug. 23 (70 days)	**63.29**
Amount due on August 23	**$2,813.29**

Finding the Number of Days Between Two Dates. To find the amount due on the date a demand note is paid, you need to find the number of days between two dates.

Example

Find the exact number of days from June 14 to August 23.

Solution		Explanation
	30	Since June has 30 days, there are 16 days
	− 14	left in June after June 14 (30 − 14 = 16).
June	16	The note uses all 31 days in July and
July	31	23 more in August. Adding 16, 31, and
August	23	23 gives 70, the number of days from
	70 **Ans.**	June 14 to August 23.

■ When working problems, assume that February has 28 days.

1. Find the number of days from
   a. Jan. 5 to Mar. 12   66
   b. Nov. 12 to Jan. 29   78
   c. May 6 to Aug. 22   108
   d. June 10 to July 15   35
   e. Sept. 6 to Jan. 4   120
   f. Feb. 23 to May 5   71
   g. Oct. 22 to Jan. 16   86
   h. July 29 to Aug. 8   10

2. On March 5 Suba Jain signed a demand note for $5,000 at 14% exact interest. She paid the note on June 3.
   a. For how many days was interest due?   90
   b. What amount of interest did Suba owe? $172.60
   c. What was the total amount due on June 3? $5,172.60

3. On July 13 Tony Dimato borrowed $8,000 to buy a new car for $12,500. He signed a demand note with exact interest at 8%. If he paid 100% of the note off on September 24, what total amount did he owe? $8,128

Using a Table to Find the Number of Days Between Two Dates. You can use a table like the one shown in Illustration 46–3 to find days between dates. In this table, the days of the year are numbered consecutively, starting with 1 for January 1. The following examples show you how to use the table to find the number of days between two dates.

Example

Find the exact number of days from June 14 to August 23.

Solution		Explanation
The table shows that:		You find the number for the due date, August 23, which the table shows is day 235. Then you find the number for the beginning date, June 14, which is day 165. You subtract 165 from 235 to get 70 days.
Aug. 23 is day	235	
June 14 is day	−165	
Days between dates	70 **Ans.**	

If the due date is in the next year from the date of the note, you find the number of days this way:

Example

Find the exact number of days from October 28 to March 6.

Solution		Explanation
The table shows that:		You find the number of days between the beginning date and the last date of that year, December 31. That number is 64 days. To that number, you add the day number of the due date in the next year, which is 65. The sum of 64 and 65 is 129, the number of days between the dates.
December 31 is day	365	
October 28 is day	301	
Days between	64	
March 6 is day	65	
Total days between dates	129 **Ans.**	

TABLE OF DAYS IN YEAR NUMBERED CONSECUTIVELY

Day of Month	Jan.	Feb.	Mar.	Apr.	May	June	July	Aug.	Sept.	Oct.	Nov.	Dec.
1	1	32	60	91	121	152	182	213	244	274	305	335
2	2	33	61	92	122	153	183	214	245	275	306	336
3	3	34	62	93	123	154	184	215	246	276	307	337
4	4	35	63	94	124	155	185	216	247	277	308	338
5	5	36	64	95	125	156	186	217	248	278	309	339
6	6	37	65	96	126	157	187	218	249	279	310	340
7	7	38	66	97	127	158	188	219	250	280	311	341
8	8	39	67	98	128	159	189	220	251	281	312	342
9	9	40	68	99	129	160	190	221	252	282	313	343
10	10	41	69	100	130	161	191	222	253	283	314	344
11	11	42	70	101	131	162	192	223	254	284	315	345
12	12	43	71	102	132	163	193	224	255	285	316	346
13	13	44	72	103	133	164	194	225	256	286	317	347
14	14	45	73	104	134	165	195	226	257	287	318	348
15	15	46	74	105	135	166	196	227	258	288	319	349
16	16	47	75	106	136	167	197	228	259	289	320	350
17	17	48	76	107	137	168	198	229	260	290	321	351
18	18	49	77	108	138	169	199	230	261	291	322	352
19	19	50	78	109	139	170	200	231	262	292	323	353
20	20	51	79	110	140	171	201	232	263	293	324	354
21	21	52	80	111	141	172	202	233	264	294	325	355
22	22	53	81	112	142	173	203	234	265	295	326	356
23	23	54	82	113	143	174	204	235	266	296	327	357
24	24	55	83	114	144	175	205	236	267	297	328	358
25	25	56	84	115	145	176	206	237	268	298	329	359
26	26	57	85	116	146	177	207	238	269	299	330	360
27	27	58	86	117	147	178	208	239	270	300	331	361
28	28	59	87	118	148	179	209	240	271	301	332	362
29	29	—*	88	119	149	180	210	241	272	302	333	363
30	30	—	89	120	150	181	211	242	273	303	334	364
31	31	—	90	—	151	—	212	243	—	304	—	365

*Add one day after February 28 for leap years.

Illustration 46–3. Table of Days

Exercise 4
Written

1. Using the table in Illustration 46–3, find the number of days from
   a. Feb. 9 to June 13   124
   b. Oct. 21 to Dec. 31   71
   c. Mar. 3 to July 29   148
   d. Nov. 15 to Feb. 5   82
   e. Oct. 1 to Jan. 14   105
   f. Sept. 24 to Feb. 19   148
   g. Aug. 27 to Oct. 20   54
   h. Dec. 28 to Mar. 2   64

2. Vi borrowed $600 on a 12% demand note dated Feb. 9. She paid the note and exact interest on May 5. What amount did Vi pay? $616.77

3. A demand note for $2,500, dated Oct. 4 with exact interest at 15%, was paid in full on Jan. 8. What was the amount paid? $2,598.63

REVIEW 46

Skills

1. a. 3.75 equals what percent? 375%
   b. $\frac{4}{5}$ equals what percent? 80%
   c. $30 is what percent of $250? 12%
   d. What amount is $1\frac{1}{4}$% of $84? $1.05
   e. Find the due date of a 3-month note dated Aug. 31. Nov. 30
   f. Find the due date of a 90-day note dated Feb. 17. May 18
   g. Find the number of days from May 14 to Jul. 4. 51 days

Problems

2. A demand note for $3,200, dated July 14, was paid September 21, with exact interest at 11%. What was the amount paid?
   $3,266.54 [46]

3. The interest on a loan of $4,300 for 3 months is $129. What is the rate of interest? 12% [44]

4. The population of Akins this year was 23,205. Last year, it was 21,000.
   a. Estimate the percent of increase. 10%
   b. What is the exact percent of increase? 10.5% [26]

5. A 60-day note for $500, dated May 4, bears banker's interest at 9%. Find the due date and the amount due at maturity.
   July 3, $507.50 [46,44]

6. A 14 oz. box of Vigor hot cereal costs $0.77. A $1\frac{1}{8}$ lb. box of Wakup hot cereal costs $1.08. Which brand costs less per lb., and how much less? Vigor; 8¢ [38]

7. Edith bought fertilizer for her lawn. Her lot was 25 m wide and 50 m long. Her house took up 100 m² of the lot. If one bag of fertilizer covered 350 m², how many whole bags did Edith need? 4 bags [31]

8. On July 1, Ken Van's balances were: bank statement, $456.70; check register, $333.25. The bank statement included a $1.75 service charge and $1.45 in earned interest. The following checks were outstanding: #678, $56; #682, $23; #683, $44.75. Complete a bank reconciliation statement for Ken. $332.95 [5]

Section 47
Discounted Notes

Banks and other lenders may lend money to businesses and people for short periods of time, such as 30, 60, or 90 days. These loans are called short-term loans.

Discounting a Non-Interest-Bearing Note. When a bank makes a short-term loan, it may require the borrower to sign a note and pay the interest when the loan is made. When interest is collected in advance this way, it is known as **bank discount.** Because the interest is paid in advance, the note itself does not show any interest rate, and it is called a **non-interest-bearing note.**

Face
− Discount
Proceeds

The bank collects the bank discount by deducting it from the face of the note. The amount the borrower gets is the face of the note less the discount. When the loan is due, only the face of the note is paid. Obtaining a loan in this way is known as discounting a note.

The percent of discount charged by the bank is called the **rate of discount.** The amount of money that the borrower gets is called the **proceeds**.

The note shown in Illustration 47–1 is a non-interest-bearing note that Lamont Brown signed when he got a loan from the Beekman State Bank of Kingston, New York.

$ 6,500.00 ____ Kingston, NY _____ June 12 ___ 19 --

Three months _____ AFTER DATE ___/___ PROMISE TO PAY TO

THE ORDER OF Beekman State Bank _____

Six thousand, five hundred and no/100 ~~~~~~~~ DOLLARS

PAYABLE AT Beekman State Bank _____

VALUE RECEIVED WITH INTEREST AT ___14___ %

NO. 3791 ___ DUE September 12 ___ 19 -- ___ Lamont Brown ___

Illustration 47–1. Non-Interest-Bearing Note

The Beekman State Bank discounted Lamont's note at 14% interest for 3 months. The bank subtracted the discount from the face of the note. Lamont actually received only $6,272.50 from the bank as proceeds of the note.

Face of note	**$6,500.00**
Discount at 14% for 3 months	**227.50**
Proceeds	**$6,272.50**

On September 12, the due date, Lamont repaid the face of the note, $6,500.

Exercise 1
Written

1. Find the proceeds and due date of each note. Each note was discounted on the same day as the date of the note.

	Date of Note	Face	Time	Discount Rate	Proceeds	Due Date
a.	May 14	$ 2,000	2 mo.	9%	$1,970.00	July 14
b.	Sept. 3	5,900	3 mo.	15%	5,678.75	Dec. 3
c.	Feb. 22	9,000	4 mo.	10%	8,700.00	June 22
d.	Mar. 6	12,000	6 mo.	12%	11,280.00	Sept. 6
e.	Dec. 15	500	1 mo.	8%	496.67	Jan. 15

2. On April 6, Bea Gardner discounted at her bank, at 13%, her 3-month non-interest-bearing note for $500.
    a. What proceeds did Bea get? $483.75
    b. What was the due date of the note?   July 6
    c. What amount did Bea owe the bank at maturity? $500

3. Ayako Mori signed a 2-month, non-interest-bearing promissory note for $900 at her bank on June 5. The rate of discount that the bank charged her was 18%.
    a. What proceeds did Ayako receive? $873
    b. What was the due date of the note?   August 5
    c. What amount did Ayako owe her bank at maturity? $900

4. On July 22, Al Klein discounted at his bank, at 10%, his 3-month non-interest-bearing note for $995.
    a. Estimate the bank discount. $25
    b. What were the actual proceeds of the note? $970.12
    c. What was the due date?   October 22

Real Rate of Interest. When you discount your own non-interest-bearing note, you pay a rate of interest based on the face of the note. However, you do not get the full face amount because interest is deducted in advance. To find the real rate of interest you paid, you must divide the interest paid by the amount you actually received. The real rate of interest is always higher than the rate stated on the note.

For example, if you borrow $100 for one year on a non-interest-bearing note at 10%, you will pay $10 in interest. If you discount that note, however, you have really borrowed only $90 because the interest is deducted in advance. The rate of interest you paid is not $\frac{\$10}{\$100}$. It is $\frac{\$10}{\$90}$. This is a real rate of 11.1%, rounded to the nearest tenth of a percent.

To find the real rate of interest on Lamont Brown's note shown in Illustration 47–1, find the interest for 1 year:

$$3 \text{ months} = \frac{1}{4} \text{ of a year}$$

$$4 \times \$227.50 = \$910 \text{ interest for 1 year}$$

Then divide the interest for 1 year by the amount borrowed:

$$\$910 \div \$6{,}272.50 = 0.1451, \quad \text{or} \quad 14.5\%$$

So, Lamont really paid a 14.5% rate of interest; not the 14% interest rate shown on the note.

Exercise 2
Written

1. On April 1, Edison, Inc., discounted its two-month, non-interest-bearing note for $2,400 at Capitol Bank. The rate of discount was 12%.
    a. What were the proceeds? $2,352
    b. What was the real rate of interest, to the nearest tenth of a percent?   12.2%

2. On Sept. 23, Eversville Bank discounted Triad Corporation's note for $10,000. The note was dated Sept. 23, due in 3 months, and it carried no interest. The rate of discount was 15%.

    a. What was the amount of the bank discount? $375
    b. What proceeds did Triad Corporation receive? $9,625
    c. What real rate of interest, to the nearest tenth of a percent, did Triad Corporation pay? 15.6%

3. Jed Weeks discounted his 4-month, non-interest-bearing note for $4,500 on August 16. The note was dated August 16 and the discount rate was 11%.
    a. What was the amount of the bank discount? $165
    b. What proceeds did Jed receive? $4,335
    c. What real rate of interest, to the nearest tenth of a percent, did Jed pay? 11.4%

4. To help cover business expenses of $5,000, Rita Esposito discounted her 6-month, non-interest-bearing note for $4,200 at her bank. The rate of discount was 13%.
    a. What was the amount of the bank discount? $273
    b. What proceeds did Rita receive? $3,927
    c. How much did Rita pay her bank on the maturity date? $4,200
    d. What real rate of interest, to the nearest tenth of a percent, did Rita pay? 13.9%

REVIEW 47

Terms

1. Match the terms with the statements.

bank discount   demand note   proceeds
demand loan   non-interest-bearing note   rate of discount

    a. A note that must be paid when the bank asks for payment demand note
    b. A loan payable on demand demand loan
    c. A note without an interest rate non-interest-bearing note
    d. Interest collected in advance bank discount
    e. Face less discount proceeds
    f. Percent charged on a note and paid in advance rate of discount

Skills

2. a. 4 equals what percent? 400%
    b. $4\frac{1}{2}$% of $328 = ? $14.76
    c. $4.80 is what percent of $14.40? $33\frac{1}{3}$%
    d. $2,250 is what percent of $750? 300%
    e. Show $8\frac{1}{4}$% as a decimal. 0.0825
    f. Show 4 108 mL in liters. 4.108 L

Problems

3. A 4-month note for $1,800 with interest at 12% is dated October 8.
    a. What is the due date? February 8 [46]
    b. What is the total interest paid? $72 [43]
    c. What is the amount due at maturity? $1,872 [43]

4. Eva Wall borrowed $1,350 for 18 months at 9% interest. What was the total amount of interest she paid? $182.25 [43]

5. What is the rate of interest charged on a loan of $1,440 for 3 months if the amount of the interest charge is $32.40?   9% [44]

6. Don Reade, a salesperson, is paid a salary of $950 a month, a 4% commission on all sales, and an additional commission of 1% on all monthly sales in excess of $12,500. His sales for June were $15,150. What were Don's total earnings for the month? $1,582.50 [28]

7. Eileen Voss wants to make a dress. Her pattern shows that she needs 2.75 m of fabric of a standard width. The fabric costs $7.50 per m. How much will the fabric cost her? $20.63 [30]

8. On March 25, Al David's bank discounted at 12% his non-interest-bearing, 3-month note for $325.
    a. What were the proceeds of the note? $315.25 [47]
    b. What was the due date of the note?   June 25 [46]
    c. What amount did Al pay at maturity? $325 [47]

9. A 4-month, non-interest-bearing note for $3,000 was discounted at a bank at 8%. [47]
    a. What were the proceeds of the note? $2,920
    b. What was the real rate of interest paid, to the nearest tenth of a percent?   8.2%

‡10. Sue Olney receives a 4% commission on any property she sells. Last week she received a $4,504 commission for selling a house and lot. What was the selling price of the house and lot? $112,600 [29]

Section 48
Installment Loans

Many people like to repay loans in small payments rather than in one large payment. For this reason, many lenders offer **installment loans,** or consumer loans, that are repaid in small part payments. Each part payment, called an **installment**, is usually due each month.

Finance Charge on an Installment Loan. When you borrow on an installment loan, you get the face amount of the loan. You repay the face amount in installments, usually monthly. One month's interest on the unpaid balance is also paid. If the interest rate on the loan is 1.5% a month, this rate is equal to 18% a year (1.5 × 12 = 18).

The amount that you get when the loan is made is known as the **amount financed.** The total of the interest and other charges you pay for the use of the money is called the **finance charge.**

Repayment Schedule. A schedule of monthly installment payments on a $1,000 loan is shown in Illustration 48–1. The loan was repaid in ten monthly payments of $100 on the principal, plus a 1.5% finance charge on the unpaid monthly balance. The payment decreased each month as the finance charge on the unpaid balance decreased.

End of —	Unpaid Balance	Finance Charge: 1.5% of Unpaid Balance	Payment on Principal	Total Payment
1st month	$1,000.00	$15.00	$100.00	$115.00
2d month	900.00	13.50	100.00	113.50
3d month	800.00	12.00	100.00	112.00
4th month	700.00	10.50	100.00	110.50
5th month	600.00	9.00	100.00	109.00
6th month	500.00	7.50	100.00	107.50
7th month	400.00	6.00	100.00	106.00
8th month	300.00	4.50	100.00	104.50
9th month	200.00	3.00	100.00	103.00
10th month	100.00	1.50	100.00	101.50
Totals		$82.50	$1,000.00	$1,082.50

Illustration 48–1. Installment Loan Repayment Schedule

The finance charge due at the end of each month was 1.5% of the unpaid balance. The total payment was the finance charge plus the $100 payment on the principal.

**Exercise 1
Written**

1. For each loan, make a schedule of monthly payments of the finance charges and principal like the one in Illustration 48–1.

		Monthly Repayment Plan		
Amount Financed	Number of Payments	Payment on Principal	Finance Charge on Unpaid Balance	Total Payments
a. $500	5	$100	1%	$515.00
b. 100	10	10	1.5%	108.25
c. 480	6	80	$\frac{3}{4}$%	492.60
d. 800	10	80	1.5%	866.00
e. 350	7	50	$\frac{4}{5}$%	361.20

2. A member of a credit union borrows $720, agreeing to repay it in 6 equal monthly payments plus a finance charge of 1.25% a month on the unpaid balance. What will be the total finance charge? $31.50

3. Kay borrowed $600 from a finance company and repaid it in 6 monthly payments of $100 plus a finance charge of 1.75% on the unpaid balance.

a. What was the total finance charge on the loan? $36.75
b. What was the total amount Kay paid to the finance company?
$636.75

Level Payment Plan. Many lenders figure payments so that each payment is the same amount. This payment method is called the **level payment plan.**

For example, Sol Weintraub borrowed $1,000 from the Payless Credit Company for 12 months. He repaid the loan in 12 monthly payments of $98 each. The total of these payments was 12 × $98, or $1,176. Since the amount financed was $1,000, the finance charge was $176 ($1,176 − $1,000).

The Payless Credit Company gave Sol the book of 12 coupons shown in Illustration 48–2. Each month Sol sent a coupon with his check for $98 to the credit company.

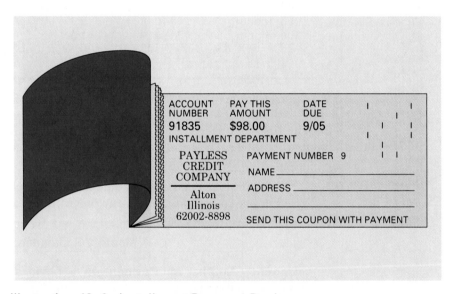

Illustration 48–2. Installment Payment Book

**Exercise 2
Written**

1. For each loan, find the total amount paid and the finance charge.

	Amount of Loan	Monthly Payments		Total Paid	Finance Charge
		Number	**Amount**		
a.	$ 600	12	$ 59.00	$708.00	$108.00
b.	2,000	24	118.00	2,832.00	832.00
c.	500	24	28.75	690.00	190.00
d.	800	18	56.00	1,008.00	208.00
e.	500	6	90.80	544.80	44.80

2. Arlene Kittle borrowed $750 from a consumer finance company and repaid it in 9 monthly payments of $96.44 each. How much was the finance charge? $117.96

3. Juan Delgado traded in his car for $1,500 on another car. He borrowed the balance of $2,500. The loan agreement required Juan to pay $141.66 in 24 monthly payments. How much was the finance charge? $899.84

4. Francine Burroughs borrowed $1,000 from the Marine Finance Corporation. She repaid the loan in 12 monthly installments of $98.50.
   a. Estimate the total amount paid. $1,200
   b. What actual total amount was paid? $1,182
   c. What total finance charge did she pay? $182

5. Dale Barton borrowed $1,500 from a finance company. He repaid the loan in 24 monthly installments of $88.75.
   a. What total amount did Dale pay the company? $2,130
   b. What total finance charge did he pay? $630

6. Paula Kovich borrowed $480 from the Midland Finance Co. Midland required her to repay the loan in 6 monthly installments of $83.60 each.
   a. What total amount did Paula pay the company? $501.60
   b. What total finance charge did she pay? $21.60

REVIEW 48

Terms

1. Match the terms with the statements.

   amount financed   installment   level payment plan
   finance charge   installment loan

   a. A small part payment on a loan   installment
   b. All payments are the same amount   level payment plan
   c. The amount the borrower gets   amount financed
   d. A loan repaid in part payments   installment loan
   e. Interest and other charges paid   finance charge

Skills

2. a. 135% of $95 is what amount? $128.25
   b. What amount is $12\frac{1}{2}$% of $18.80? $2.35
   c. Show $95\frac{1}{2}$% as a decimal.   0.955
   d. Find the number of days from August 24 to November 6.   74
   e. $65.34 is 35% more than what amount? $48.40

Problems

3. Samantha Ali borrowed $400 from a consumer finance company. She repaid the loan in 6 monthly payments of $72.40 each. What was the finance charge? $34.40 [48]

4. Keil Benjamin made sales last year totaling $154,500. His sales this year are expected to be 20% more than last year. What are Keil's expected sales for this year? $185,400 [26]

5. Faith Dumont is paid $8.75 an hour. She works from 9:00 a.m. to 5:30 p.m., Monday through Friday, with 1 hour out for lunch. What were her gross earnings last week if she worked full time except for $2\frac{1}{2}$ hours lost on Monday? $306.25 [7]

6. A 3-month, $5,000 non-interest-bearing note is discounted at the bank at 15%. What are the proceeds? $4,812.50 [47]

7. What is the real rate of interest, to the nearest tenth of a percent, on a 6-month, $3,000 non-interest-bearing note discounted at the bank at 11%?   11.6% [47]

‡8. Keith Corvalis works on a 6% straight-commission basis. How many dollars' worth of goods must he sell to earn $1,200? $20,000 [28]

‡9. An owner wants to receive $110,000 for a house and lot. What is the minimum price, to the nearest $1,000, at which the property must be sold to get that amount if the commission rate is 6%? $118,000 [29]

Section 49
More Installment Loans

Every borrower should know how installment payments, service charges, and annual percentage rates are figured.

Figuring Installment Payments. When you borrow money on an installment loan, you are usually given the face of the loan on the day the loan is made. This amount is called the amount financed. The finance charge is the interest on the amount financed at an *annual rate* for the time you borrow the money. The total of the amount financed and the finance charge is repaid in equal monthly installments.

Example

Twanya Washington wants to borrow $100 and repay it in 10 monthly installments. The loan department of her bank will lend her the money with interest at the yearly rate of 18%. She must repay the face amount and the interest in 10 equal monthly installments.
a. What will be the total of her payments to the bank?
b. What will be the amount of each monthly payment?

Solution

a. Amount financed $100.00
    Finance charge: Int. @ 18% on $100 for 10 months   + 15.00
    Total payments $115.00 **Ans.**

b. $115 ÷ 10 = $11.50   Monthly payment   **Ans.**

**Exercise 1
Written**

For each loan, find the finance charge and add it to the face. Then find the amount of the equal monthly payments.

	Face of Loan	Finance Charge Yearly Rate	Terms of Payment	
1.	$840	12%	12 equal monthly payments	$78.40
2.	$600	14%	10 equal monthly payments	$67.00
3.	$300	8%	6 equal monthly payments	$52
4.	$900	9%	9 equal monthly payments	$106.75

5. A bank loaned Darcy McCall $1,200 on a 12% note to be repaid in 12 equal monthly payments.
   a. What was the finance charge on the loan? $144
   b. What was the total of the payments? $1,344
   c. What was the amount of each monthly payment? $112

Service Charges. Some installment loans have a service charge in addition to interest. **Service charges** may be added to cover the lender's costs of servicing and collecting the loan. Included in the service charges may be the cost of insurance to pay the loan if the borrower dies.

■ Service charges
  + Interest
  ─────────────
  Finance charge

The sum of the interest charge and the service charges is the finance charge.

Example

Bill Hudson borrows $2,400 for 6 months at 9% from his bank. The bank adds a service charge of $15.
a. What is the total finance charge?
b. What will be the amount of each monthly payment?

Solution

a. $2,400 for 6 months at 9% = $108
         Service charge = + 15
         ─────────────────────────
         Finance charge = $123   **Ans.**

b. $2,400 + $123 = $2,523 total of payments
    $2,523 ÷ 6 = $420.50 monthly payment   **Ans.**

**Exercise 2
Written**

1. Ria Carr got a bank loan for $3,240 at 12% and agreed to repay it in 18 equal monthly payments. The bank added a $16.20 service charge.
   a. What was the finance charge on the loan? $599.40
   b. What was the amount of each monthly payment? $213.30

2. Chip Amell got a bank loan for $700 at 10%. He must repay it in 12 equal monthly payments. The bank added a service charge of $7.
   a. What was the finance charge on Chip's loan? $77
   b. Find the amount of each monthly payment? $64.75

3. Tien Wang got a loan for $3,000 at 11%. She must repay it in 6 equal monthly payments. The lender added a $24 service charge.
   a. Estimate the finance charge on this loan. $174
   b. What is the finance charge on this loan? $189
   c. What was the amount of each monthly payment? $531.50

Finding the Installment Finance Charge Rate. To find the rate of interest on a loan for one year, you divide the interest paid by the principal. Finding the rate of finance charges on an installment loan is not so easy. As you know, the cost of borrowing money may include more than interest. It may also include service charges. Also, since you make payments on the loan each month, you are not borrowing the whole principal for the full time of the loan. So, the law makes the lender tell the borrower what annual rate is charged on the loan. The **annual percentage rate** (APR) is a percent that shows the ratio of the finance charges to the amount financed.

The easiest way to find the annual percentage rate is to use tables like the ones shown in Illustration 49–2. To use the tables, you need to know the number of monthly payments for the loan and the finance charge per $100 of the amount financed.

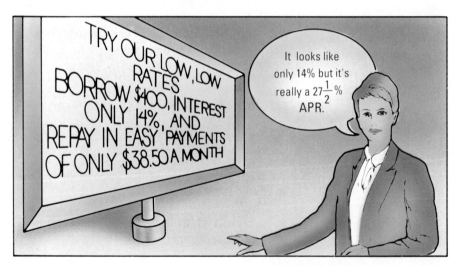

Illustration 49–1. Advertised Interest Rates May Not Be What They Seem

Finding the Finance Charge Per $100 of Amount Financed. To find the finance charge per $100 of the amount financed, you must first multiply the finance charge by 100. You then divide the product by the amount financed.

$$\frac{\textbf{Finance Charge per \$100}}{\textbf{of Amount Financed}} = \frac{\textbf{Finance Charge} \times \textbf{100}}{\textbf{Amount Financed}}$$

For example, if the finance charge on a loan of $400 is $62, the finance charge per $100 of the amount financed is $15.50.

$$\frac{\$62 \times 100}{\$400} = \frac{\$6,200}{\$400} = \$15.50$$

**Exercise 3
Written**

1. Find the finance charge per $100 of amount financed.

	Amount Financed	Finance Charge			Amount Financed	Finance Charge	
a.	$800	$78.00	$9.75	d.	$910	$106.10	$11.66
b.	$250	$41.00	$16.40	e.	$400	$50.00	$12.50
c.	$500	$66.00	$13.20	f.	$760	$89.60	$11.79

2. Opra Meir borrowed $3,500 from a consumer finance company and repaid it in 15 monthly payments of $268.73 each.
    a. What was the finance charge on the loan? $530.95
    b. What was the amount financed? $3,500
    c. What was the finance charge per $100? $15.17

3. Matt Novak needed $4,600 to remodel his store. Matt only had $2,200 that could be spared for this purpose. So, he got a bank loan for $2,400 and repaid it in 12 equal monthly installments of $220.50.
    a. What was the finance charge on the loan? $246
    b. What was the amount financed? $2,400
    c. What was the finance charge per $100? $10.25

Finding the Annual Percentage Rate. To find the annual percentage rate using the tables shown in Illustration 49–2, you must know the

Number of Payments	Annual Percentage Rate										
	$12\frac{3}{4}$%	13%	$13\frac{1}{4}$%	$13\frac{1}{2}$%	$13\frac{3}{4}$%	14%	$14\frac{1}{4}$%	$14\frac{1}{2}$%	$14\frac{3}{4}$%	15%	$15\frac{1}{4}$%
	Finance Charge per $100 of Amount Financed										
3	2.13	2.17	2.22	2.26	2.30	2.34	2.38	2.43	2.47	2.51	2.55
6	3.75	3.83	3.90	3.97	4.05	4.12	4.20	4.27	4.35	4.42	4.49
9	5.39	5.49	5.60	5.71	5.82	5.92	6.03	6.14	6.25	6.35	6.46
12	7.04	7.18	7.32	7.46	7.60	7.74	7.89	8.03	8.17	8.31	8.45
15	8.71	8.88	9.06	9.23	9.41	9.59	9.76	9.94	10.11	10.29	10.47

Number of Payments	Annual Percentage Rate										
	$26\frac{3}{4}$%	27%	$27\frac{1}{4}$%	$27\frac{1}{2}$%	$27\frac{3}{4}$%	28%	$28\frac{1}{4}$%	$28\frac{1}{2}$%	$28\frac{3}{4}$%	29%	$29\frac{1}{4}$%
	Finance Charge per $100 of Amount Financed										
3	4.49	4.53	4.58	4.62	4.66	4.70	4.74	4.79	4.83	4.87	4.91
6	7.95	8.02	8.10	8.17	8.25	8.32	8.40	8.48	8.55	8.63	8.70
9	11.47	11.58	11.69	11.80	11.91	12.03	12.14	12.25	12.36	12.47	12.58
12	15.07	15.22	15.37	15.51	15.66	15.81	15.95	16.10	16.25	16.40	16.54
15	18.75	18.93	19.12	19.30	19.48	19.67	19.85	20.04	20.22	20.41	20.59

Illustration 49–2. Partial APR Tables

number of monthly payments and the finance charge per $100 of the amount financed.

For example, suppose the finance charge per $100 for a 15-payment loan is $18.95. Using the tables, you read across the 15-payment line until you come to the value nearest $18.95. This is $18.93 in the 27% column of the bottom table. So, the annual percentage rate for this loan is 27%.

If the finance charge per $100 falls half way between two columns, you should use the higher percentage rate. For example, on the 3-payment line, $2.45 is half way between $2.43 in the $14\frac{1}{2}\%$ column and $2.47 in the $14\frac{3}{4}\%$ column. So, you would choose $14\frac{3}{4}\%$ as the rate for $2.45.

Exercise 4
Written

1. Use the tables to find the annual percentage rates.

	No. of Payments	Finance Charge per $100	
a.	9	$ 5.75	$13\frac{1}{2}\%$
b.	3	2.50	15%
c.	12	16.36	29%
d.	9	11.98	28%
e.	15	10.26	15%
f.	6	8.39	$28\frac{1}{4}\%$
g.	12	7.13	13%
h.	3	2.20	$13\frac{1}{4}\%$
i.	15	8.85	13%
j.	12	15.19	27%

2. Zeb borrowed $1,300 and repaid it in 12 monthly payments of $116 each.
   a. What was the finance charge on this loan? $92
   b. What was the finance charge per $100 of amount financed? $7.08
   c. What was the annual percentage rate? $12\frac{3}{4}\%$

3. Amy borrowed $400 and agreed to repay the loan in 9 monthly payments of $47 each.
   a. What was the finance charge on this loan? $23
   b. What was the finance charge per $100 of amount financed? $5.75
   c. What was the annual percentage rate? $13\frac{1}{2}\%$

4. Val repaid a loan of $1,600 in 15 monthly payments of $116.40 each. Find the annual percentage rate on this loan. $13\frac{1}{4}\%$

REVIEW 49

Terms

1. Match the terms with the statements.

   annual percentage rate   service charge

   a. A charge in addition to interest   service charge
   b. Ratio of finance charge to amount financed
      annual percentage rate

Skills

2. a. What amount is 265% of $80? $212
   b. $12\frac{1}{2}\%$ of $32 = ? $4
   c. Give the decimal equivalent of $45\frac{1}{4}\%$.   0.4525
   d. Find the exact interest on $1,410 for 1 month at 18%. $21.15
   e. What is $37\frac{1}{2}\%$ of 380 kg?   142.5 kg

Problems

3. You borrow $700 from a finance company and pay it back in 12 monthly payments of $63.50 each. What is your finance charge on this loan? $62 [48]

4. On a loan of $400, there was a finance charge of $32. The total of the loan and finance charge was repaid in 12 equal monthly payments.
   a. What was the finance charge per $100 of amount financed? $8
   b. What was the annual percentage rate? (Use Illustration 49–2.) $14\frac{1}{2}\%$ [49]

5. A 73-day note for $700 with exact interest at 14% is dated June 12.
   a. Find the due date.   August 24 [46]
   b. What will be the amount due at maturity? $719.60 [44]

Computer Clinic

Jay Isen borrowed $2,500 from the Lake Marine Bank. He repaid the bank in 24 monthly payments of $120. Follow the steps below to calculate the approximate annual percentage rate (APR) for Jay's loan.

1. Insert your Spreadsheet Applications Diskette and call up the file "Sec49." After you do, your computer screen should look like Illustration 49–3.

```
Sec49
       Annual Percentage Rate (APR) Approximation
    Original Principal                   0
    Monthly Payments                  0.00
    Number of Payments                   0
    Finance Charges                      0
    Approx. APR as %                   .00%
```

Illustration 49–3. Annual Percentage Rate Approximation Chart

2. Find the finance charges and the approximate annual percentage rate that Jay paid by entering these data into the chart:

B3	2500
B4	120
B5	24

3. Answer the questions about your chart.
   a. What finance charges did Jay pay the bank? $380
   b. What approximate annual percentage rate did he pay?   14.59%
   c. What would be the answers to questions A and B if Jay had made 18 monthly payments of $155? $290; 14.65%
   d. What monthly amount paid over 30 months would make his approximate APR 15.00% (enter 30 in B5; then keep entering different amounts in B4 until B7 displays 15.00%)? $99.48

Section 50
Installment Buying

Boats, cars, TV sets, VCR's, furniture, clothes, and many other items are often bought on an **installment plan.** The installment plan is also called the *time payment plan.* When you buy on the installment plan, you are really borrowing the seller's money and paying it back in part payments.

You may have to make a **down payment** of part of the price at the time you buy something on an installment plan. You may also have to sign an **installment contract** in which you agree to pay the unpaid balance in weekly or monthly payments.

Finding the Installment Price and Finance Charge. The installment price is usually more than the cash price because the seller adds a finance charge to the cash price. This charge pays the seller interest on the money and covers the extra cost of doing business on the installment plan. If there are no other charges, such as insurance, the finance charge is the difference between the installment price and the cash price.

Example

A camcorder has a cash price of $1,300. If you buy it on the installment plan, you must pay $130 down and $75 a month for 18 months. What is the amount of the finance charge?

Solution

a. $75 monthly payment × 18 months = $1,350 total payments
b. $130 down payment + $1,350 total payments = $1,480 installment price
c. $1,480 installment price − $1,300 cash price = $180 finance charge   **Ans.**

**Exercise 1
Written**

Find the (a) installment price and (b) finance charge for each item.

Item	Cash Price	Installment Term
1. Boat	$1,500	$150 down; $67.50 a month for 24 months $1,770; $270
2. Electronic Piano	2,500	$500 down; $115 a month for 20 months $2,800; $300
3. Bicycle	250	$25 down; $26.50 a month for 9 months $263.50; $13.50
4. Garden Tractor	2,400	$250 down; $118.25 a month for 20 months $2,615; $215
5. Microwave Oven	350	$50 down; $26.50 a month for 12 months $368; $18

6. A microcomputer sells for $1,800, in cash. If you buy it on the installment plan, you must pay $180 down and $100.80 a month for 18 months.
   a. Estimate the total amount of the payments. $1,800
   b. Estimate the finance charge. $180
   c. What is the exact amount of the finance charge? $194.40

Finding the Number of Months and Monthly Payment. Sometimes you may know the installment price and the down payment and need to find the amount of the monthly payment or the number of months to pay.

Example

The installment price of a compact disk player is $400. You must pay $40 down and make payments for 20 months. What will be your monthly payments?

Solution

a. $400 installment price − $40 down payment = $360 remainder to pay
b. $360 remainder to pay ÷ 20 months = $18 monthly payment   **Ans.**

Example

The installment price of a compact disk player is $400. You must pay $40 down and make monthly payments of $18. For how many months must you pay?

Solution

a. $400 installment price − $40 down payment = $360 remainder to pay
b. $360 remainder to pay ÷ $18 = 20 months to pay   **Ans.**

1. Find the missing item in each problem.

Item	Installment Price	Installment Terms	
a. Camera	$ 455	$50 down; $33.75 a month for ? months	12 months
b. Vacuum	611	$50 down; ? a month for 20 months	$28.05
c. Jewelry	250	$75 down; $8.75 a week for ? weeks	20 weeks
d. Computer	1,500	$200 down; ? a month for 20 months	$65

2. You can buy a personal computer for the installment price of $1,690. You must pay $250 down and make monthly payments of $120. How many months will it take for you to pay for the computer? 12 months

3. A motorcycle can be bought for $2,300 if you pay $500 down and the rest in 18 equal monthly installments. How much will each of your installments be? $100

Comparing Installment and Cash Prices. A wise buyer will compare the cost of buying an item on the installment plan to the cost of buying the item with cash. The following example shows you how to do this.

Example

A video recorder has a cash price of $400. The installment terms are $100 down and $28 a month for 12 months.
a.   What is the installment price of the recorder?
b.   How much is the finance charge?
c.   By what percent is the installment price greater than the cash price?

Solution

a. $28 monthly payment × 12 months = $336 total of monthly payments
$100 down payment + $336 total monthly payments = $436 installment price
b. $436 installment price − $400 cash price = $36 finance charge

c. $\dfrac{\$36}{\$400}$ = 9%, installment price greater than the cash price

1. Find (1) the installment price, (2) the finance charge, and (3) the percent by which the installment price is greater than the cash price, to the nearest tenth of a percent.

	Article	Cash Price	Installment Terms
a.	Boat	$5,800	$1,000 down; $200 a month for 30 months (1) $7,000 (2) $1,200 (3) 20.7%
b.	Refrigerator	600	$60 down; $18.15 a month for 36 months (1) $713.40 (2) $113.40 (3) 18.9%
c.	Power Saw	360	$36 down; $29.70 a month for 12 months (1) $392.40 (2) $32.40 (3) 9%
d.	Color TV	425	$50 down; $42.50 a month for 10 months (1) $475 (2) $50 (3) 11.8%
e.	Chair	250	$25 down; $39 a month for 6 months (1) $259 (2) $9 (3) 3.6%

2. A hair dryer that sells for $30 cash may be bought for $3 down and $5.76 a month for 5 months. By what percent is the installment price greater than the cash price?   6%

3. You can buy a watch for $150 cash or by paying $30 down and the balance in 12 equal monthly payments of $11.50. By what percent would your installment price be greater than the cash price?   12%

Finding the Annual Percentage Rate. When you buy on the installment plan, you are really borrowing money from the seller. The amount you borrow is the cash price, or the cash price less the down payment if you make a down payment. In any case, the amount you borrow is the amount financed.

The finance charge is the price you pay for the use of the seller's money. The annual percentage rate on the finance charge is found by using tables in the same way you did for an installment loan. A partial table is shown in Illustration 50–1.

Example

The cash price of a mower is $500. The installment price is $572. The terms are $50 down and $21.75 a month for 24 months. What annual percentage rate does the installment buyer pay for the use of the seller's money?

Solution

1. $572 − $500 = $72   finance charge
2. $500 − $50 = $450   the amount of the seller's money the buyer is using. This is the amount financed.
3. $\frac{\$72 \times 100}{\$450} = \$16$ finance charge per $100 of the amount financed.
4. In Illustration 50–1, on the 24-payment line, the value nearest $16 is $16.08, in the 14.75% column. So, the annual percentage rate is 14.75%.

No. of	ANNUAL PERCENTAGE RATE										
Payments	14.00	14.25	14.50	14.75	15.00	15.25	15.50	15.75	16.00	17.00	18.00
	(Finance Charge Per $100 of Amount Financed)										
6	4.12	4.20	4.27	4.35	4.42	4.49	4.57	4.64	4.72	5.02	5.32
12	7.74	7.89	8.03	8.17	8.31	8.45	8.59	8.74	8.88	9.45	10.02
18	11.45	11.66	11.87	12.08	12.29	12.50	12.72	12.93	13.14	13.99	14.85
20	12.70	12.93	13.17	13.41	13.64	13.88	14.11	14.35	14.59	15.54	16.49
24	15.23	15.51	15.80	16.08	16.37	16.65	16.94	17.22	17.51	18.66	19.82
30	19.10	19.45	19.81	20.17	20.54	20.90	21.26	21.62	21.99	23.45	24.92
36	23.04	23.48	23.92	24.35	24.80	25.24	25.68	26.12	26.57	28.35	30.15

Illustration 50–1. Partial Annual Percentage Rate (APR) Table

**Exercise 4
Written**

Use Illustration 50–1 to solve each problem.

1. Find the annual percentage rates.

Item	Cash Price	Installment Terms	
a. Couch	$1,200	$48.50 a month for 30 months	15.5%
b. Car Stereo	350	$12.25 a month for 36 months	15.75%
c. Printer	1,500	$100 down; $126 a month for 12 months	14.5%
d. Canoe	480	$48 down; $75.60 a month for 6 months	17%
e. Disk Drive	800	$80 down; $44.80 a month for 18 months	14.75%

2. You can buy an outboard motor for $2,500 cash or with $500 down and 30 payments of $80 each. What is the annual percentage rate? 14.75%

3. A table selling for $135 is reduced to a cash price of $75 because of low sales during the last 3 months. The credit terms are $5 down and $12.25 a month for 6 months. What annual percentage rate is charged? 17%

4. A computer display screen can be bought for $395 cash, or for $55 down and $30.77 a month for 12 months. What annual percentage rate is paid by the installment buyer of the screen? 15.5%

REVIEW 50

Terms

1. Match the terms with the statements.

down payment   installment contract   installment plan

a. Another name for time payment plan   installment plan
b. Part of price paid at time of buying   down payment
c. Agreement to pay back an unpaid balance periodically
   installment contract

Skills

2. a. Show $350\frac{1}{2}$% as a decimal.   3.505
    b. $4.90 is what percent greater than $4.20? $16\frac{2}{3}$%
    c. What amount is $62\frac{1}{2}$% greater than $88? $143
    d. Multiply 360.05 by 4.3.   1,548.215
    e. 8 km + 625 m = ? m   8 625 m

Problems

3. The cash price of a TV was $120. Dan Herr bought it for $12 down and 12 monthly payments of $9.80. By what percent did the installment price exceed the cash price?   8% [50]

4. Ann bought an audio system on the installment plan for $790. She paid $90 down and the balance in equal monthly installments of $50 each. How many months did it take Ann to pay for the system? 14 months [50]

5. The cash price of a rug is $420. The installment price is $501.60, payable in 30 equal monthly payments of $16.32. What annual percentage rate is paid by the installment buyer? (Use Illustration 50–1.) 14.25% [50]

6. On May 31, Eve Day's balances were: checkbook, $339.11; bank statement, $394.62. A service charge of $1.74 had not been deducted in the checkbook. Checks outstanding were: #24, $41.32; #25, $3.18; #27, $12.75. Prepare a reconciliation statement for Eve. $337.37 [5]

7. A nut mixture is made up of peanuts and cashews in the ratio of 3 to 2, respectively. How many pounds of each are needed to make a 45 lb. mixture?   27 lbs. peanuts; 18 lbs. cashews [16]

Section 51
Credit Cards

There are many types of credit cards. There are bank credit cards, such as MasterCard and Visa, and travel and entertainment credit cards, such as American Express and Diners Club. Many car owners use oil company credit cards to pay for fuel and automobile repairs. Large department and chain stores often provide customers with credit cards, as well.

Credit cards, like the ones shown in Illustration 51–1, are used to identify customers who can be given credit. When you use a credit card, you are really borrowing money from the credit card company.

Finding Net Receipts from Credit Card Sales. Many small firms do not offer credit to their customers directly. Instead, they accept credit cards for the purchase of merchandise or service. There are two major reasons why. When a firm offers credit to a customer through its own

Illustration 51–1. Bank and Store Credit Cards

store account, it does not receive the money from the sale until the customer pays. The firm also must maintain the credit records.

The money from credit card sales, however, is received quickly from the credit card company and firms do not have to do as much bookkeeping.

When the credit card company pays the firm, it deducts a percentage of each sale to cover the cost of providing the credit service. The percentage varies, but usually it is between 3% and 6% of the total sale.

For example, the Super credit card company charges 5% of total sales for its services. If a sale is made for $400 using their card, the net amount that the store receives is $380.

$400 × 0.05 = $20   deducted by the credit card company

$400 − $20 = $380   net amount received from the credit card sale

**Exercise 1
Written**

1. Algon, Inc., accepts MidTown credit cards. Algon, Inc., had total credit card sales last year of $32,800,000. The MidTown card company charges 4% of sales for its services.
   a. How much did Algon pay the credit card company last year?
      $1,312,000
   b. What were Algon's net receipts from credit card sales last year?
      $31,488,000

2. Bolin Stores accepts the National Bank credit card, which deducts 5% of the total sales made with their card before paying Bolin. Last month, Bolin had $2,700,500 of National Bank card sales. How much did Bolin receive from National Bank? $2,565,475

3. Last month, Tyme, Inc., had $385,000 of AmeriCard charge sales and $268,000 of sales using UniCard credit card. If AmeriCard charges 5% and UniCard charges 3% for services, what were Tyme's net receipts from these companies for the month? $625,710

4. A store estimates that its next year's sales will be $740,000 if it does not take credit cards. If it takes General card, sales are estimated to be $980,000, $500,000 of which will be made using the card. The General card company charges 6% for its services. Using these estimates:
   a. What will be the net sales receipts next year with the card? $950,000
   b. What will be the increase in net sales by using the card? $210,000

Saving Money by Paying Cash. When you buy with a credit card, the sales clerk fills out a **credit card sales slip** similar to the one shown in Illustration 51–2.

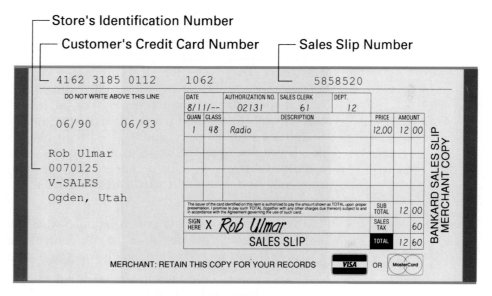

Illustration 51–2. Credit Card Sales Slip

Some firms lower their prices if you pay cash rather than use a credit card. Other firms add a percentage to the cash price if you use a credit card. For example, a service station may charge 3% more if you use an oil company credit card instead of paying cash. If the cash price of the gas you bought was $20, you would have to pay $20.60, or 60¢ more using a credit card.

$20 × 0.03 = $0.60   **extra for using credit card**

$20 + $0.60 = $20.60   **total cost of gas using credit card**

**Exercise 2
Written**

1. Sue bought a chain saw for $275 and received a 4% discount for paying cash instead of using a credit card. What did Sue pay for the saw? $264

2. Jim can buy a compact disk player for $480 cash. If he uses a credit card, the store will add 4% to the price.
   a. How much is the credit-card price of the player? $499.20
   b. How much would Jim save by paying cash? $19.20

3. Teresa can buy stones for a large patio for $785. If she pays cash, the store will give her a 3% discount.
   a. Estimate the discount Teresa will get for paying cash. $24
   b. Estimate the cash price of the stones. $761
   c. What is the actual cash price of the stones? $761.45
   d. How much will Teresa actually save by paying cash? $23.55

4. San-Li can buy a 16 ft. boat originally priced at $5,700 for $3,500 in cash. If he uses a credit card, the store will add 3.5% to the price.
   a. What is the credit card price of the boat? $3,622.50
   b. How much will San-Li save by paying cash? $122.50

Finding the Cost of a Credit Card. Some credit card companies charge an **annual membership fee** ranging from $15 to $25. Other companies may charge a fee for each purchase.

Your credit card company will usually send you a monthly statement. The statement shows your purchases, your payments, the fees you were charged, and the minimum amount that you must pay on the balance.

You are usually given about 25 days to pay your statement balance. If you don't pay the balance, or if you pay only part of it, you will be charged interest. Interest is charged because you are really borrowing money from the credit card company. This interest is called a finance charge.

Exercise 3
Written

1. Angelo's credit card statement balance was $460. He did not pay the balance by the due date, so the credit card firm added a finance charge of 1.5%. How much was the finance charge? $6.90

2. Laura's annual credit card membership fee is $25. She also pays 7¢ per purchase. If she made 90 purchases last year, what was the cost of Laura's card for the year? $31.30

3. SecurCard has an annual fee of $20 and a finance charge of 1.65% per month on the unpaid balance. In May, SecurCard charged Mark the annual fee and a finance charge on his $275 unpaid balance. What was the total on Mark's monthly statement? $24.54

4. Ivy pays a $25 annual membership fee and an 18% finance charge on unpaid balances to Global Card. Belinda pays a $15 annual membership and a 20% finance charge on unpaid balances to Major Card. Both have an average monthly unpaid balance of $40. Who pays the most in yearly membership fees and finance charges? How much more per year? Ivy, $9.20

Borrowing Through Cash Advances. Many credit card firms let members borrow money by using **cash advance** slips or special checks. These firms charge members interest from the date of the loan at a *daily* interest rate.

**Exercise 4
Written**

▪ 0.0628% is a decimal rate of 0.000628.

1. Fess Clark borrowed $300 for 20 days on his credit card using a cash advance. The card company charged him a daily finance charge of 0.0628%. What was the amount of the finance charge? $3.77

2. Bo Dustin borrowed $700 for 35 days from her credit card company using a cash advance check. The company charged her a daily finance charge of 0.0453%. What was the finance charge on Bo's loan? $11.10

3. Ali borrowed $500 on a cash advance for 45 days on his credit card. The finance charge rate was 0.0512% per day. What total finance charge did Ali pay? $11.52

4. CardCo charges a daily finance charge of 0.0722% on all cash advances. How much would your finance charge be if you borrowed $200 for 60 days using the cash advance? $8.66

REVIEW 51

Terms

1. Match the terms with the statements.

annual membership fee   credit card
cash advance   credit card sales slip

a. Identifies a customer who can buy on credit   credit card
b. Money borrowed on a credit card   cash advance
c. Form used to record a credit card sale   credit card sales slip
d. Yearly charge for having a credit card account
   annual membership fee

Skills

2. a. Add $8\frac{1}{2}$ and $1\frac{3}{8}$. $9\frac{7}{8}$
   b. 45 m ÷ 2.4 cm = ? cm   1 875 cm
   c. What is the due date of a 90 day note dated May 5?   August 3

Problems

3. LeBlanc's accepts Premier credit cards. LeBlanc's must pay Premier 3.5% on all credit card sales. If LeBlanc's sells $47,800 this month on the credit card, what net amount will they receive from Premier? $46,127 [51]

4. Midwest Card charges a $22 annual membership fee and a finance charge of 1.3% a month on all unpaid balances. In May, Midwest charged you the membership fee and a finance charge on the $450 unpaid balance in your account. What was the total of your May statement? $477.85 [51]

5. Ben borrowed $360 from a finance company and repaid the loan in 18 monthly payments of $25.40 each. What was the finance charge? $97.20 [48]

6. Dee bought a garden tiller on the installment plan for a total cost of $450. She paid $100 down and the rest in monthly installments of $14 each. How many months did it take Dee to pay for the tiller? 25 [50]

Calculator Clinic

Using the Calculator to Find Your Savings from Paying Cash. You can use a calculator to find the savings you receive for paying cash instead of using your credit card. You follow the same steps you used to multiply a number by a percent. For example, a store which sells an audio tape priced at $6 with a credit card gives you a 4% discount for paying cash. To find the cash price, follow the steps below.

a. Press these keys in order: 6 × · 0 4

b. Press = , and the discount, 0.24, will appear in the display.

c. Press these keys in order: 6 − · 2 4

d. Press = , and the cash price, 5.76, will appear in the display.

If the store *adds* the percent to the store price when you use a credit card, you follow the same steps but use the plus key to add the $0.24 to the price.

Saving Time. On some calculators, you can save time by using the percent key. For example, the cash discount on the audio tape can be found by following these steps:

Press these keys in order: 6 − 4 %

Or, press these keys: 6 × 4 % −

If the store *adds* the percent to the store price, you should follow the same steps but use the plus key instead of the minus key.

Calculator Practice. Apply what you have learned in this calculator clinic to the problems in Exercise 2, and to any other exercises your teacher may assign.

Saving Money

Most of the money you earn will be used to pay for the expenses of everyday living, but you should try to save part of your income every payday. The money you save could be used for emergencies, to take advantage of special sales, or to help you make a large purchase such as a car.

Money that is saved should earn interest until it is needed. As you collect information from companies that offer savings plans, you will find that there are many different ways to save money and to figure interest. Compare the features of the different plans, and figure the interest you could earn before you open an account.

After you finish Unit 8, you will be able to:

- Find the interest and account balances for passbook and time deposit accounts.
- Use compound interest tables to figure interest.
- Figure the effective rate of interest.
- Compare the interest earned on passbook and time deposit accounts.
- Find early withdrawal penalties on time deposit accounts.
- Solve problems that contain more information than you need.
- Estimate answers to problems.
- Read, write, say, and recognize the meanings of the key terms.
- Use a calculator to compound interest.
- Use a computer spreadsheet to compare savings plans.

Passbook Savings Accounts

Many people put money into regular savings accounts at banks, credit unions, and savings and loan associations. Besides keeping their money safe, depositors also earn interest on their money. Money can be put into or taken out of the savings account easily.

■ A passbook is a record of savings.

The Passbook Savings Account. When you open a regular savings account, you are given a **passbook** and an account number that identifies you. The passbook is used to keep a record of your savings.

To open a savings account, you fill out a **signature card** with your name, address, signature, and social security number. This identifies you as the owner of the account. You must also put money into the account. The bank agrees to pay you interest on your money, usually four times a year.

After opening a savings account, you may **deposit** or put money into the account and **withdraw** or take money out of the account. When you do either of these kinds of transactions, either you or the bank teller may write the amount of the deposit or withdrawal into your passbook. The teller may also give you a **receipt**, which is an official record of the transaction.

Study the passbook of Arlene Noles in account with Parkside Bank shown in Illustration 52–1. Notice that the Balance column shows the amount in the account after each transaction.

Date	Withdrawal	Deposit	Interest	Balance
19--				
01-11		300.00		300.00
02-16		400.00		700.00
03-21	150.00			550.00
04-01			4.31	554.31
04-01		70.00		624.31

Date of Transaction

Amount withdrawn is *subtracted* from the balance

The balance tells how much is in the savings account

Deposit and interest amounts are *added* to the balance

Illustration 52–1. Savings Account Passbook

Exercise 1 Written

For each problem, make a form like the passbook in Illustration 52–1. Use only the columns and their headings. Then record the date, withdrawals, deposits, and interest. Figure and write the balance after each transaction.

1. April 2, deposit, $600; April 17, deposit, $400; May 7, withdrawal, $200; June 21, withdrawal, $300; July 1, interest, $6.82. $506.82

2. January 2, deposit, $700; April 1, interest, $9.35; April 25, deposit, $400; May 4, withdrawal, $170; July 2, interest, $10.46. $949.81

3. January 2, deposit, $984.31; April 1, interest, $14.29; April 9, withdrawal, $250; May 30, withdrawal, $97; July 1, interest, $9.86; October 1, interest, $10.01. $671.47

Interest on Savings Accounts. Interest is usually figured on the balance of the account at the end of each quarter. The interest is paid on the first day of the next quarter, or on January 2, April 1, July 1, and October 1. (Since January 1 is a holiday, interest is paid on January 2.) Each quarterly period is one-fourth of a year, or three months. Sometimes interest is figured and paid twice a year, or in semiannual periods. Each semiannual period is six months, or one-half year.

■ A quarter is one-fourth of a year.

■ A semiannual period is one-half of a year.

To find the interest for any interest period, first figure the amount of interest for a full year. Then multiply that amount by the fraction of a year, such as $\frac{1}{4}$ or $\frac{1}{2}$, for which you want to find interest.

Example

If interest is paid at the rate of 6% a year, what is the interest on $270.00 for 1 quarterly period?

Solution

$0.06 \times \$270 = \$16.20$ interest for one year
$\frac{1}{4} \times \$16.20 = \$4.05$ interest for one quarter   **Ans.**

Example

What is the semiannual interest on $400.60 if interest is paid at the rate of $5\frac{1}{2}$% a year?

Solution

$0.055 \times \$400.60 = \$22.033$ interest for one year
$\frac{1}{2} \times \$22.033 = \$11.016$ or $\$11.02$ interest for one semiannual period   **Ans.**

In both examples interest for less than a year is found in two steps. This is the same, though, as using the interest formula $P \times R \times T = I$. So, the first solution is the same as $\$270 \times 0.06 \times \frac{1}{4} = \$4.05$. The second solution is the same as $\$400.60 \times 0.055 \times \frac{1}{2} = \$11.02$.

Note that in this type of interest calculation you round only the *final* answer to the nearest cent.

Exercise 2
Written

1. Find the quarterly interest.
   a. $300 at 5% a year $3.75
   b. $750 at 6% a year $11.25
   c. $400 at $5\frac{1}{2}$% a year $5.50

     d. $628.29 at 7% a year $11
     e. $217.66 at $6\frac{1}{2}$% a year $3.54
     f. $1,400 at $5\frac{3}{4}$% a year $20.13

2. Find the semiannual interest.
     a $700 at 5% a year $17.50
     b. $900 at $6\frac{1}{2}$% a year $29.25
     c. $600 at $5\frac{1}{4}$% a year $15.75
     d. $727 at $5\frac{1}{2}$% a year $19.99
     e. $302.95 at 7% a year $10.60
     f. $612.74 at $5\frac{3}{4}$% a year $17.62

Compounding Interest. At the end of each interest period, the interest due is figured and added to the previous balance in the passbook. The new balance then becomes the principal on which interest is figured for the next period, if no deposits or withdrawals are made.

■ Figure interest on the entire dollar and cents balance.

When you figure and add interest to make a new principal on which to figure interest for the next period, you are **compounding interest.** An example of how this is done is shown below.

Example

On January 2, Peter Monroe deposited $800 in a savings account that pays 6% interest, compounded quarterly. Interest is figured and added to the account on April 1, July 1, October 1, and January 2 of each year. If he made no other deposits or withdrawals, what was Peter's savings account balance on July 1, after the interest was added?

Solution

In account with:	**Peter Monroe**		Account No.	**502176**
Date	**Withdrawal**	**Deposit**	**Interest**	**Balance**
19— JAN 2		800.00		800.00
APR 1			12.00	812.00
JUL 1			12.18	824.18

Explanation

Peter Monroe deposited $800 in his savings account on January 2. Because there were no deposits or withdrawals, the $800 became the principal on which interest was figured at the end of the first quarter. The quarterly interest of $12 ($800 × 6% × $\frac{1}{4}$) paid on April 1 was added to the previous balance of $800 to give a new balance of $812. This balance became the new principal on which interest was figured for the next quarter. Interest of $12.18 ($812 × 6% × $\frac{1}{4}$) paid on July 1 was added to the previous balance of $812, making the balance of July 1 equal $824.18.

    By adding the amounts in the interest column, you can figure the total interest earned ($12.00 + $12.18 = $24.18 total interest).

**Exercise 3
Written**

■ Interest rates
are for one year.

Make a passbook form like the one shown above for each problem. Interest is compounded in all problems.

1. Your savings bank pays 6% interest a year. It figures and adds interest to your account quarterly on January 2, April 1, July 1, and October 1. You deposited $840 on January 2 and made no other deposits or withdrawals.
    a. What was your savings account balance on October 1? $878.37
    b. How much interest did you earn for these nine months?
        $38.37

2. Ying Su's credit union adds interest on January 2, April 1, July 1, and October 1. It pays an interest rate of $6\frac{1}{2}$% on savings. Ying deposited $700 on April 1. If he makes no other deposits or withdrawals for the next 9 months, what will be his account balance on the following January 2? $734.69

3. Jane Eason made a deposit of $1,400 to her savings account on July 1. For the next year she made no other deposits or withdrawals. Interest of 5% a year was added quarterly on January 2, April 1, July 1, and October 1. What was the estimated and actual interest earned by Jane by July 1 of the next year? $70; $71.32

4. Ord Sims has a savings account that adds interest twice a year on January 2 and July 1. His bank pays 7% yearly interest. Ord deposited $510 on January 2 and made no other deposits or withdrawals. What interest did Ord earn for 1 year? $36.32

5. The Village Savings and Loan Association pays interest semiannually on January 2 and July 1. Wanda Galin deposited $900 on January 2 and made no other deposits or withdrawals for the next year. The association pays 6% interest a year. Find Wanda's semiannual interest paid and account balance on
    a. July 1 of the same year $27; $927
    b. The following January 2 $27.81; $954.81

**Exercise 4
Written**

To solve each problem, set up a passbook form like the one used in Exercise 3. For each problem, compound interest is figured and paid quarterly on January 2, April 1, July 1, and October 1. Notice that Problems 1 and 3 have special directions.

1. Lila Malone deposited $400 on April 1 to open an account at the Hiland Savings Bank. The bank pays interest at 6% a year. On July 1, Lila deposited $300 more to her account. She made no other deposits or withdrawals. What was her balance on October 1?
    $716.59

    Hint: For July 1, figure and add the interest on $400 before adding the July 1 deposit of $300. Figure the October interest on $706.00, which is the balance after entering the July 1 deposit.

2. Marv Rowley's credit union pays interest at $6\frac{1}{2}$% a year. He deposited $600 to open an account on January 2 and made another

deposit of $700 on April 1. Marv made no other deposits or withdrawals. What was the balance of Marv's account on July 1? $1,331.03

3. Sonya has an account at a savings bank that pays 7% interest a year. A nearby bank pays $6\frac{1}{4}$% a year. Sonya deposited $800 into her account on April 1 and withdrew $270 on July 1. How much did she have in her account on October 1? $553.52

   Hint: For July 1, figure and enter the interest on $800 before entering and subtracting the July 1 withdrawal. For October 1, figure and enter the interest on $544, which is the balance you get after subtracting the July 1 withdrawal.

4. The County Bank pays a yearly interest of 5%. Felix Reaume made a deposit of $400 on October 1. He withdrew $60 on January 2. What was the balance of Felix's savings account on April 1? $349.31

Figuring Interest on Minimum Balances. Individual banks figure interest on savings accounts in different ways. Some banks pay interest on savings accounts from the date money is deposited until it is withdrawn. The money earns interest for the actual time it is in the bank.

Other banks pay interest only on the minimum or smallest balance on deposit during an interest period. If a bank pays interest quarterly, the principal used to figure interest is the smallest amount in the savings account during the quarter. The passbook for Amanda Pell in account with State Bank in Illustration 52–2 shows interest figured on the minimum balance of each quarter.

Date	Withdrawal	Deposit	Interest	Balance
19-- Oct. 1				968.40
Nov. 23		300.00		1,268.40
19-- Jan. 2			14.53	1,282.93
Feb. 8	470.00			812.93
Apr. 1			12.19	825.12

Second quarter   First quarter   Minimum balance of the quarter

Illustration 52–2. Passbook Showing Minimum Balances

Amanda's savings account pays 6% annual interest that is added on January 2, April 1, July 1, and October 1.

During the first quarter, the minimum or smallest balance in Amanda's account was $968.40. That amount was used to figure interest for the first quarter. The interest, $14.53 ($968.40 × 6% × $\frac{1}{4}$), was added to her account on January 2. In the second quarter, the minimum balance was $812.93. The interest for the second quarter, $12.19 ($812.93 × 6% × $\frac{1}{4}$), was added on April 1.

**Exercise 5
Written**

Figure interest
on minimum
balances.

Set up a passbook form like Illustration 52–2 to do each problem. Figure interest on the smallest balance on deposit for the period.

1. A savings bank pays interest at 5% a year, adding the interest on January 2, April 1, July 1, and October 1. On July 1, Ted Garza had on deposit a balance of $682, including interest added on that date. He withdrew $170 on August 17 and deposited $200 on September 12.
   a. What was Ted's minimum balance during the quarter? $512
   b. How much interest was he paid on October 1? $6.40
   c. How much did Ted have on deposit on October 1? $718.40

2. The Crest Bank adds 6% annual interest to accounts on January 2, April 1, July 1, and October 1. On April 1, Sheila deposited $900 to open an account at the Crest Bank. She withdrew $210 on May 6 and $60 on June 17. What was Sheila's account balance on July 1? $639.45

3. The Millard Credit Union pays interest semiannually on January 2 and July 1 at the rate of $5\frac{1}{2}$% annually. On July 1, Leon Campillo had on deposit a balance of $270, including interest to date. He deposited $140 on November 5 and withdrew $220 on December 9. How much did Leon have on deposit on January 2? $195.23

4. Your local savings and loan association pays 7% annual interest on savings accounts. Interest is figured and added quarterly on January 2, April 1, July 1, and October 1. Your balance on January 2, including interest to date, was $605. You had these transactions: January 17, deposit, $115; February 28, withdrawal, $180; April 12, deposit, $70; June 9, withdrawal, $90; June 25, deposit, $40. On July 15, you expect to withdraw $180 to make a car payment.
   a. What total amount of interest did you get through July 1?
      $18.72
   b. How much did you have on deposit on July 1? $578.72

REVIEW 52

Terms

1. Match the terms with the statements.

   | compounding interest | passbook | signature card |
   | deposit | receipt | withdraw |

   a. Official record of a transaction receipt
   b. To take money out of an account withdraw
   c. Used to keep track of savings account transactions passbook
   d. To put money into an account deposit
   e. Form that identifies a savings account owner signature card
   f. Figuring and adding interest to make a new principal
      compounding interest

Skills

2. a. $30 is what percent less than $120? 75%
   b. What amount is $33\frac{1}{3}$% greater than $145.20? $193.60
   c. $83\frac{1}{4}$% as a decimal is? 0.8325
   d. The banker's interest on $600 at 7% for 120 days is? $14
   ‡e. 7.5% as a fraction in lowest terms is? $\frac{3}{40}$

Problems

3. On January 2, Cecilia Xenon deposited $760 in a savings account that pays interest quarterly at 5% per year. There were no other deposits or withdrawals. Interest was added to the account on April 1 and July 1. What was the balance of Cecilia's account on July 1? $779.12 [52]

4. Aulga Krinitz bought a new car on the installment plan. The cash price was $14,034. She made a down payment of $2,800 and paid the balance, plus a finance charge of $1,582, in 36 equal monthly payments. What was the amount of each monthly payment? $356 [49]

5. A loan of $420 was repaid in 12 monthly payments of $40.67 each. Find the finance charge per $100 of the amount financed. $16.20 [48]

6. A savings bank pays interest at 7% a year on the minimum balance on deposit each quarter. It adds the interest on January 2, April 1, July 1, and October 1. On April 1, Sean Wright deposited $680. He withdrew $190 on May 15. What was his balance on July 1? $498.58 [52]

Calculator Clinic

Using the Calculator to Find Interest. The calculator can be used to find interest for any time period. For example, suppose you want to find the interest for one quarter on $400 at an annual interest rate of 6%. To find this, you set up the problem using the simple interest formula, $I = P \times R \times T$, or $I = \$400 \times 6\% \times \frac{1}{4}$. Then press these keys in order:

Attach a dollar sign to the number in the display and write the answer, $6. This is the amount of the quarterly interest.

Compounding Interest. You may also use your calculator for compounding interest for two or more periods when the interest is added to the principal after each interest period. For example, to find the interest for one year on $543 at an annual interest rate of 5.5%, compounded semiannually, you follow these steps:

a. Add the original balance into the memory register by pressing these

keys in order: 5 4 3 M+

b. Then find the interest for the first semiannual period by pressing these keys in order:

Round the answer, 14.9325, to the nearest cent. Then add the result, 14.93, to the memory register by using the M+ key. The original balance, $543, plus the interest, $14.93, makes a new balance of $557.93.

c. Repeat Step B above to find the interest for the second semiannual period. The answer, 15.343075, should appear in the display. Round that amount to the nearest cent, 15.34, and press M+ to add the interest to the memory register. Press MR/C to recall the new account balance, $573.27. Subtract the original principal, $543, to find the total interest earned for two semiannual periods, $30.27.

Calculator Practice. Apply what you have learned in this calculator clinic to the problems in Exercises 2 and 3.

At 6%, a $10,000 deposit earns this much interest in one year when compounded:
Daily
$627.16
Quarterly
$613.63
Semiannually
$609.00
Annually
$600.00.

Section 53
Compound Interest

Compound Amount and Compound Interest. You have already learned how to compound interest quarterly and semiannually. Interest may also be compounded annually and daily. Regardless of how interest is figured, the total amount of money in the account at the end of the last interest period is called the **compound amount,** assuming that no deposits or withdrawals have been made. The total interest earned, called **compound interest,** is the difference between the original principal and the compound amount.

For example, an $800 deposit will be worth $824.18 if the money is kept on deposit for two quarters and interest is compounded quarterly at an annual rate of 6%. The *compound amount* is $824.18, and the *compound interest* is $24.18 ($824.18 − $800.00).

Compound Interest Tables. When you figure compound interest for several interest periods, you can use a compound interest table like the one in Illustration 53–1. The table shows the value of one dollar ($1) after it is compounded for various interest rates and periods.

The table has two parts. The top part is used to figure annual interest. It may also be used to figure quarterly and semiannual interest. The bottom part is used to figure daily interest.

Figuring Annual Interest. Suppose you want to find the value of a $600 deposit that earns 5% interest for six years. To do so, you first find the

Interest Periods		$1\frac{1}{2}$%	2%	5%	6%	7%	8%	9%
Annual	1	1.015000	1.020000	1.050000	1.060000	1.070000	1.080000	1.090000
	2	1.030225	1.040400	1.102500	1.123600	1.144900	1.166400	1.188100
	3	1.045678	1.061208	1.157625	1.191016	1.225043	1.259712	1.295029
	4	1.061364	1.082432	1.215506	1.262477	1.310796	1.360489	1.411582
	5	1.077284	1.104081	1.276282	1.338226	1.402552	1.469328	1.538624
	6	1.093443	1.126162	1.340096	1.418519	1.500730	1.586874	1.677100
	7	1.109845	1.148686	1.407100	1.503630	1.605781	1.713824	1.828039
	8	1.126493	1.171659	1.477455	1.593848	1.718186	1.850930	1.992563
	9	1.143390	1.195093	1.551328	1.689479	1.838459	1.999005	2.171893
	10	1.160541	1.218994	1.628895	1.790848	1.967151	2.158925	2.367364
	11	1.177949	1.243374	1.710339	1.898299	2.104852	2.331639	2.580426
	12	1.195618	1.268242	1.795856	2.012197	2.252192	2.518170	2.812665
Daily	30	—	—	1.004175	1.005012	1.005850	1.006688	1.007527
	90	—	—	1.012578	1.015112	1.017652	1.020199	1.022752
	180	—	—	1.025313	1.030452	1.035616	1.040806	1.046022
	365	—	—	1.051998	1.062716	1.073544	1.084482	1.095530

Illustration 53–1. Compound Interest Table for $1

value of $1 in the 5% column of the table. The value of $1 compounded for six annual interest periods is $1.340096. So, for the $600 deposit, the *compound amount* is 600 × $1.340096, or $804.06.

The annual *compound interest* on the $600 deposit is $804.06 − $600.00, or $204.06.

■ Round the answer to the nearest cent.

Study how these compound amounts were figured by using annual compounding:

$300 deposit at 6% for 5 years = 300 × $1.338226 = $401.47

$900 deposit at 9% for 8 years = 900 × $1.992563 = $1,793.31

$582 deposit at 8% for 3 years = 582 × $1.259712 = $733.15

Figuring Daily Interest. To find the value of a $500 deposit that earns interest compounded daily at 6% for 30 days, you also can use the compound interest table. Look at the 6% column in the daily interest period section. The amount of $1 compounded for 30 daily interest periods is $1.005012. For the $500 deposit, the compound amount is 500 × $1.005012, or $502.51.

The daily compound interest on $500 is $502.51 − $500.00, or $2.51. Study these examples showing the compound amount for daily compounding of interest:

$700 deposit at 7% for 180 days = 700 × $1.035616 = $724.93

$300 deposit at 9% for 30 days = 300 × $1.007527 = $302.26

$450 deposit at 6% for 90 days = 450 × $1.015112 = $456.80

**Exercise 1
Written**

Use the table in Illustration 53–1 to find the compound amounts and interest.

	Prin-cipal	Rate	Time	Compounded	Compound Amount	Compound Interest
1.	$1,000	5%	4 years	Annually	$1,215.51	$ 215.51
2.	700	9%	11 years	Annually	1,806.30	1,106.30
3.	800	7%	365 days	Daily	858.84	58.84
4.	600	5%	180 days	Daily	615.19	15.19
5.	400	8%	7 years	Annually	685.53	285.53
6.	900	8%	90 days	Daily	918.18	18.18

Figuring Quarterly and Semiannual Interest. When interest is compounded quarterly, you use the figure in the table for *four times* the number of annual periods, and *one fourth* the rate. When interest is compounded semiannually, you use the figure for *twice* the number of annual periods and *one half* the rate.

For example, to find the amount of $1 compounded quarterly for 3 years at 8%, you use the figure for 12 periods (4 × 3 periods) at 2% (8% × $\frac{1}{4}$), or $1.268242.

To find the amount of $1 compounded semiannually for $1\frac{1}{2}$ years at 12%, you use the figure for 3 periods (2 × $1\frac{1}{2}$ periods) at 6% (12% × $\frac{1}{2}$), or $1.191016.

**Exercise 2
Written**

Find the compound amount and compound interest by using the compound interest table shown in Illustration 53–1.

	Principal	Rate	Time	Compounded	Compound Amount	Compound Interest
1.	$1,000	6%	3 years	Quarterly	$1,195.62	$195.62
2.	600	8%	2 years	Quarterly	703.00	103.00
3.	2,500	6%	$1\frac{1}{2}$ years	Quarterly	2,733.61	233.61
4.	800	12%	5 years	Semiannually	1,432.68	632.68

Figuring the Effective Rate of Interest. The **effective rate of interest** is the rate you actually earn by keeping your money on deposit for one year. The annual rate and the effective rate you earn can be different.

For example, assume that Bank A compounds interest annually at a rate of 6%. A deposit of $1,000 in that bank will earn interest of $60 for one year ($1,000 × 0.06 × 1). Bank B also pays interest at 6%, but compounds interest quarterly. A $1,000 deposit in Bank B will earn interest of $61.36 for one year. The interest is found by using the compound interest table. The compound amount is $1,061.36 (1,000 × $1.061364), and $1,061.36 − $1,000 = $61.36, the compound interest amount.

The effective rate of interest paid by both banks is found in this way:

$$\frac{\text{Amount of Interest Earned for One Year}}{\text{Amount of Money on Deposit}} = \frac{\text{Effective Rate}}{\text{of Interest}}$$

Bank A: $60 ÷ $1,000 = 0.06, or 6% effective rate of interest

Bank B: $61.36 ÷ $1,000 = 0.06136, or 6.136% effective rate of interest

**Exercise 3
Written**

For each deposit, find the amount of interest earned for *one year* and the effective rate of interest to the nearest hundredth percent.

	Deposit	Annual Rate	Compounded	Interest Earned	Effective Rate of Interest
1.	$1,000	8%	Quarterly	$ 82.43	8.24%
2.	800	6%	Quarterly	49.09	6.14%
3.	1,400	10%	Semiannually	143.50	10.25%
4.	1,810	14%	Semiannually	262.27	14.49%

5. The Coles Savings Bank pays 8.2% interest compounded annually. The Drew Savings Bank pays 8% interest compounded daily. Assume a deposit of $2,000 is made in each bank and kept there for one year, or 365 days. At which bank will the higher effective rate of interest be paid? What is the effective rate paid by the higher-paying bank, to the nearest hundredth percent?   Drew; 8.45%

REVIEW 53

Skills

1. a. $\frac{2}{5}$ of $170 is ? $68
   b. $1\frac{1}{2}$% of $3,200 is ? $48
   c. $490 is what percent of $560 ? $87\frac{1}{2}$%
   d. $32.80 increased by 60% of itself is ? $52.48
   e. $1.50 is what percent greater than $1.20?   25%
   f. 3.6 L of oil at $1.28 per L is ? $4.61

Problems

2. A $600 note, bearing 14% banker's interest and dated May 10, was paid in full on July 29. What was the amount paid? $618.67 [44, 46]

3. A real estate agent sold a company's unused land for $245,000. The agent charged a 7% commission and $8,400 for expenses. What net proceeds did the company receive? $219,450 [29]

4. On July 1, Nell Griffith deposited $4,000 in a savings account that pays 7% interest per year, compounded quarterly. Interest was added to her account on October 1 and January 2. There were no other deposits or withdrawals. What total amount did Nell have on deposit on January 2? $4,141.23 [52]

5. Daphne is paid a salary of $900 per month, a commission of 5% on all monthly sales over $4,000, and an additional commission of 2% on sales over $7,000 a month. Her sales for April were $8,300, which was 10% greater than last month. What was her total salary and commission for April? $1,141 [28]

6. The cash price of a computer projector is $1,000. It can be bought on the installment plan by making 6 payments of $198 each.
   a. What is the estimated finance charge per $100? $20 [49]
   b. What is the actual finance charge per $100? $18.80 [49]

‡7. Herd Miller is paid a salary of $210 a week plus a commission on all sales over $2,500 in a week. His total sales last week were $4,800. What rate of commission was he paid if his total earnings for the week were $325?   5% [28]

Section 54
Special Savings Plans

In addition to passbook savings accounts, many banks also offer special savings accounts. The rates paid on these special savings accounts vary, but all banks pay a higher rate of interest than the regular passbook account rate.

Time-Deposit Accounts. One of these special savings accounts is the **time-deposit account,** also known as a certificate of deposit or a savings certificate.

To open a time-deposit account, depositors must meet certain requirements. For example:

1. They must deposit a minimum amount. This may be $500, $1,000, $5,000, or $10,000. More than the minimum may be deposited.

2. They must leave the money on deposit for a minimum time. The time may be three months, six months, or in years from one year to ten years. The minimum time may also be called the term. The date that marks the end of the term is the maturity date.

3. They must pay a penalty if money is withdrawn from the account before the end of the term of the deposit. The penalty involves the loss of interest for a certain period of time, figured on the amount of money withdrawn.

Although some government rules apply to time-deposit accounts, the requirements for these accounts vary from bank to bank. Deposits in time-deposit accounts are usually insured.

Comparing the Accounts

Time-Deposit Accounts	**Passbook Savings Accounts**
A place to put money that you won't need until some future date.	**A convenient account that lets you put money in and take money out as needed.**
In return for using your money for a longer period of time, the bank pays you more interest.	**In exchange for the convenience of the account, you are paid less interest.**
You pay a penalty for taking money out of the account before the end of the term.	**There is no penalty for taking money out of the account.**

Comparing Time-Deposit Interest and Passbook Interest. Depositors may need help in choosing the type of savings account they wish to open. One way to choose an account is to figure and compare the interest that could be earned in a time-deposit account and in a passbook savings account. Depositors may decide that the extra interest earned from time-deposit accounts is worth the inconvenience and risk of paying a penalty.

**Exercise 1
Written**

■ Figure your needs and compare the interest before you deposit money into any savings account.

1. Mae Abraham put $8,000 into a regular savings account that paid 6% compound interest. The annual interest earned for one year was $490.91. She could have put her money into a time-deposit account that paid $708 interest for one year. How much more interest could Mae have earned by opening a time-deposit account? $217.09

2. A $3,000 deposit in a passbook savings account at your bank will earn $41.25 interest in 3 months. You can also invest your money in a 3-month certificate account that pays interest at the rate of 9.5% a year, figured and paid each quarter.
   a. How much interest can you earn on the certificate in 3 months? $71.25
   b. How much more interest would you earn in 3 months by investing in the certificate rather than the passbook account? $30

3. Your credit union offers a 6-month time-deposit account that pays interest at the rate of 12% a year. You plan to deposit $2,000 in this account for 6 months and then reinvest the principal and interest for another 6 months at 12% a year. How much interest will you earn in a year? $247.20

4. The Seaport Bank pays 5.2% interest a year, compounded quarterly, on passbook accounts. The bank also offers a 6-month certificate of deposit account that pays $522 interest on a $12,000 investment.
   a. How much interest could you earn in 6 months if you invested the $12,000 in a passbook account? $314.03
   b. How much more interest would you earn on $12,000 in 6 months by opening a certificate instead of a passbook account? $207.97

5. You have $18,000 to invest. In a savings certificate, you can earn $1,125 interest in 6 months. In a passbook account, you can earn interest at the rate of 5% per year, compounded quarterly.
   a. How much interest, compounded quarterly, can you earn in 6 months on the passbook account? $452.81
   b. How much more interest could you earn in 6 months on the savings certificate than on the passbook account? $672.19

6. Chester Bohn had $5,000 on deposit in a regular passbook savings account. He wanted to keep $1,000 in that account and invest the rest, or $4,000, in a time-deposit account that pays 12.25% interest, compounded annually. In one year, the $4,000 would earn $235.02

in a passbook account. How much more interest could Chester earn in 1 year by investing the $4,000 in a time-deposit account? $254.98

7. Your savings and loan association compounds interest quarterly at 5.5% a year on passbook savings. It also pays 8.75% annual interest on time deposits. How much more would you earn in a year on $7,000 invested in a time deposit rather than a passbook account? $219.48

Penalties on Time-Deposit Accounts. There is a penalty for withdrawing money early from a time-deposit account. The penalty is figured on the money withdrawn from the time-deposit account before the end of its term.

Example

Henrietta Fenwick invested $3,000 in a 4-year time-deposit account that paid 8% interest, compounded annually. She withdrew $500 before the end of the 4 years. The penalty for early withdrawal was 6 months' interest. What was the amount of the penalty?

Solution	Explanation
$500 × 8% × $\frac{1}{2}$ = $20 **Ans.**	The penalty for early withdrawal of any part of the principal was the loss of 6 months' interest on the amount withdrawn. The amount of the penalty was found by figuring the simple interest on $500 at 8% for 6 months, or $\frac{1}{2}$ year.

Each bank sets its own interest penalty after allowing for any minimum penalty set by government rules. The exact penalties are written in the contract signed by the depositor.

It is possible for the penalty to be greater than the interest earned. If that happens, the difference is deducted from the money the depositor is withdrawing. The interest earned and part of the principal are used to pay the penalty.

Exercise 2
Written

1. Eli Sarissian has $9,000 on deposit in a 1-year Super Saver Time-Deposit account. His contract with the bank states that he will be penalized 3 months' interest if he withdraws any part of his deposit before the end of 1 year. Find the amount of the penalty if Eli withdraws these amounts early and the penalty is figured at 7% a year:
    a. $2,000 $35
    b. $5,000 $87.50

2. You have invested $4,000 in a savings certificate but have to withdraw part of the money before the certificate is due. The penalty for withdrawing money early is the loss of 6 months' interest at 14% a year. Find the penalty in dollars if you withdraw
    a. $900 $63
    b. $3,000 $210

Interest Earned
– Penalty
Net Interest

3. Tillie Figrel has earned $540 in interest on a $24,000 6-month Money Management Certificate of Deposit she has held for 3 months. She needs the $24,000 now for a down payment on a home. Tillie will have to pay a penalty of 2 months' interest at 9% a year on the $24,000 if she withdraws the money early.
    a. What is the amount of the penalty for early withdrawal? $360
    b. What net interest will she receive after paying the penalty? $180

4. Roman Bushek owns a $12,000 certificate that has earned $1,210 in interest. He is withdrawing the $12,000 before the certificate term ends. The penalty for early withdrawal is 9 months' interest at 11%. What net interest will he receive after he pays the penalty? $220

5. Hannah withdrew the $17,000 she had invested in a 6-year certificate that paid 9.5% interest a year. Her credit union charged a penalty of 12 months' interest. To date, her certificate had earned $942 in interest.
    a. What is the estimated amount of the penalty? $1,700
    b. What was the actual amount of the penalty? $1,615
    c. How much greater was the penalty than the interest? $673

6. Earl Comito invested $4,000 in a time-deposit account. After keeping the account for one month and earning $23.33 in interest, he withdrew all of the money. The bank charged a penalty of 6 months' interest at 7% on the $4,000. What amount did Earl receive? $3,883.33

Money Market Accounts. Like time deposit accounts, **money-market accounts** are special savings accounts that offer higher interest rates than regular passbook accounts. The rate of interest that is paid changes frequently and is usually based on the interest rate that the federal government pays for the money it borrows. Here are some examples of rules that banks may set for money-market accounts:

1. A minimum amount must be deposited for a minimum amount of time.

2. The interest rate paid is fixed for short periods of time, such as 1 month, 3 months, or 6 months.

3. A penalty is applied to early withdrawals.

Some banks may offer accounts that pay a higher interest rate for large deposits. Others will allow some limited withdrawals from the account as long as a minimum balance is maintained. If the minimum balance is not kept, only the passbook rate will be paid.

Exercise 3
Written

1. Gertrude Olkin deposited $3,000 into a 6-month money-market account. For the first 3 months, her account earned interest at the rate of 8.1%. The interest was not added to the account balance. For the next 3 months, interest was paid at the rate of 7.9%. Find the amount of interest she was paid for the
    a. First three months $60.75
    b. Next three months $59.25

2. For the first quarter of the year, the North Hill Savings & Loan Association paid a rate of 7.43% on Money-Market Investment accounts with balances of $1,000 to $5,000. For money-market accounts with a balance of $5,001 to $10,000, North Hill added an extra 0.14% to the rate paid. An extra 0.12% was added for money-market account balances greater than $10,000. Giancomo Pardo's money-market account had a balance of $8,400 during the first quarter. What amount of interest was he paid for the quarter?
$158.97

3. Marian Stevitz's money-market account balance of $2,100 was less than the minimum balance needed to earn the money-market rate of 8.48% paid for the first quarter. So, her account earned interest at the passbook rate of 5.25%. What amount of interest did she earn for the money she had on deposit during the first quarter?
$27.56

REVIEW 54

Terms

1. Match the terms with the statements.

compound amount   money-market account
compound interest   time-deposit account
effective rate of interest

   a. The total in a savings account at the end of the last period
      compound amount
   b. The annual rate actually earned on savings
      effective rate of interest
   c. The difference between the original principal and the compound amount   compound interest
   d. Rate paid is based on the federal government's borrowing rate
      money-market account
   e. Also known as a certificate of deposit account
      time-deposit account

Skills

2. a. $480 is what percent greater than $320?   50%
   b. $0.90 is what percent less than $1.20?   25%
   c. The exact interest on $7,200 at 8% for 4 months is ? $192
   d. 5 000 mg ÷ 2 = ? g   2.5 g
   e. A room 7 m by 5 m = ? m²   35 m²

Problems

3. The Oak Savings Bank compounds interest semiannually at 5% a year on passbook savings accounts. It also pays 8% annual interest on time-deposit accounts. How much more would you earn in one year if you deposited $6,000 into a time-deposit account instead of a passbook account? $176.25 [54]

4. Gilbert Zer has a $7,500 certificate that has earned $437 in interest. If he withdraws the $7,500 before the certificate term ends, he will pay a penalty of 1 month's simple interest at 10%. What net interest will he earn on his investment if he withdraws his money early and pays the penalty? $374.50 [54]

Computer Clinic

Ronald Holrick wants to compare the interest earned from two savings plans when $15,000 is deposited for six months. A passbook savings account pays 6% interest compounded quarterly, or four times a year. A time-deposit account pays 8% interest compounded semiannually, or twice a year. Follow the directions below to compare the passbook savings account with the time-deposit account.

1. Insert your Spreadsheet Applications Diskette and call up the file "Sec54." After you do, your computer screen should look like Illustration 54–1.

```
Sec 54                Comparing Savings Plans
--------------------------------------------------------------
ACCOUNT INFORMATION:              PASSBOOK    TIME DEPOSIT
Interest Rate (%)                   0.00         0.00
Times Compounded in Year             0            0
Periods on Deposit                   0            0
Amount of Deposit                  $.00         $.00
--------------------------------------------------------------
Compound Amount                    $.00         $.00
Less Original Deposit              $.00         $.00
Interest                           $.00         $.00
Amount Time Deposit Greater                                 $.00
  or (Less)
--------------------------------------------------------------
```

Illustration 54–1. Using a Spreadsheet to Compare Savings Plans

2. Enter these data into your template:

B4	6	C4	8
B5	4	C5	2
B6	2	C6	1
B7	15000	C7	15000

3. Answer the questions about your completed savings plan comparison spreadsheet.
   a. What compound amount was in each account at the end of 6 months? Passbook, $15,453.38; Time Deposit, $15,600
   b. How much interest was earned in each account at the end of 6 months? Passbook, $453.38; Time Deposit, $600
   c. In which account was the greatest amount of interest earned? How much greater? Time deposit interest greater by $146.62
   d. Assume that the time-deposit account interest rate was the same as the passbook rate. In which account would Ronald earn more interest? How much more?
   Passbook account would earn $3.38 more interest

Investing Money

As you know, people put money into special savings accounts instead of regular savings accounts to earn more money on the cash they invest. That is one way to make money grow.

Stocks, bonds, and real estate are other types of investments that offer investors a chance to earn a higher return on their investment. In all types of investments, it is important to study the risks involved and make careful investments to avoid losing money.

After you finish Unit 9, you will be able to:

- Find total investment made in bonds, stocks, and mutual funds.
- Read bond, stock, and mutual fund quotation tables.
- Find income and rate of income from bond and stock investments.
- Find net gain or loss from buying and selling stock and redeeming mutual fund shares.
- Find purchase price and redemption value of savings bonds.
- Figure gross and net income from renting real estate.
- Find the rate of income on a real estate investment.
- Figure rent needed to earn given income.
- Figure maximum investment to make in real estate for rate of income wanted.
- Find amount of capital investment in property.
- Solve problems that contain more information than you need.
- Estimate answers to problems.
- Read, write, say, and recognize the meanings of the key terms.
- Use a computer spreadsheet to figure yields of bond investments, find profits on stock investments, figure income earned from rental property, and find monthly rent needed to earn a specific rate of income.

Many people invest in bonds known as U.S. Savings Bonds. Others buy the bonds of corporations. An investment in corporation bonds is fairly safe, it provides regular income, and it may provide a better rate of return than other investments, such as special savings accounts.

■ A bond is a long-term note.

Nature of a Bond. A **bond** is a form of long-term promissory note. Bonds are used by corporations and governments to borrow money. For example, the American Energy Corporation may need to borrow $100,000,000 for ten years. So, it issues 100,000 ten-year bonds, each with a face value of $1,000. An example of a bond issued by the American Energy Corporation is shown in Illustration 55–1.

$1000 — AEC — $1000

AMERICAN ENERGY CORPORATION

FIRST MORTGAGE 9% BOND SERIES H
DUE FEBRUARY 1, 2005

American Energy Corporation an Iowa Corporation (thereinafter called the Company) for value received hereby promises to pay to **Rhonda Finney** or registered assigns, on the first day of February, 2005, the sum of **ONE THOUSAND DOLLARS**

and to pay to the registered owner interest on said sum from the date hereof until said sum shall be paid at the rate of nine percentum (9%) per annum payable semiannually on the first day of February and the first day of August in each year. Both the principal of and the interest on this bond shall be payable at the office or agency of the company in the city of Des Moines, state of Iowa, or at the option of the company in the borough of Manhattan, the city of New York, state of New York, in any coin or currency of the United States of America which at the time of payment is legal tender for the payment of public and private debts.

This bond shall not be entitled to any security or benefit under the mortgage or be valid or become obligatory for any purpose unless and until it shall have been authenticated by the execution of the corporate trustee or its successor in trust under the mortgage of the certificate endorsed herein.

In Witness whereof . . . .

American Energy Corporation has caused this bond to be executed in its name by its president or one of its vice-presidents and has caused its corporate seal to hereto be affixed by its secretary or one of its assistant secretaries as of the first day of February, 19--.

AMERICAN ENERGY CORPORATION

NO. 5001

Illustration 55–1. Corporation Bond

■ Note the promise to repay, with interest.

These bonds are the corporation's written promise to repay the money on the due date and to pay interest on the loan. The interest is usually paid semiannually. Persons who are willing to lend money to the corporation buy one or more of the bonds. Buyers of the bonds are called *bondholders* of the corporation.

Large amounts of money may be borrowed in the same way by the federal government. States, counties, cities, towns, and school districts also sell bonds to borrow money.

Bonds are usually issued with a face value of $1,000. Face value is the value printed on the front of the bond. Sometimes bonds are issued with a face value of $500, or even $5,000 or $10,000.

Corporations often use their property as collateral for the money they borrow. If the loan is not repaid, the bondholders may take over the corporation's land, buildings, or equipment. This guarantee is made between the corporation and a bank or trust company, called the *trustee*. The trustee is appointed by the corporation to represent the bondholders as a group in their dealings with the corporation.

Selling a Bond Issue. When money is borrowed by issuing bonds, the entire issue is often sold to an *investment banking house.* The banking house then sells the bonds to investors at a slight increase in price over what the banking house paid for them.

For example, a corporation may issue 100,000 bonds, each with a face value of $1,000. The banking house may buy them from the corporation at $993 each and sell them to investors at $1,000 each.

Par Value and Market Value of a Bond. Bonds have two kinds of value: par value and market value.

The **par value** of a bond is the same as its face value, or the amount that is printed on the face of the bond. It is the amount that the borrower promises to pay the bondholder on the due date.

The **market value** of a bond is the price at which the bond is now being sold. The market value may or may not be the same amount as the par value. If the market value is greater than the par value, the bond is selling at a **premium**. For example, a $1,000 bond selling at $1,030 is selling at a premium.

If the market value is less than the par value, the bond is selling at a **discount**. A $1,000 bond selling at $920, for example, is selling at a discount.

The amount of the premium or discount is the difference between the market value and the par value.

How the Market Price of a Bond Is Quoted. The market price, or market value, of a bond is quoted as a percent of the par value. For example, a price quotation of 97 means 97% of the par value of the bond.

■ Bond quotes are in percents.

The market price of the bond is found by multiplying the par value by the percent. For example, if the banking house of Miller & Row offers American Energy Corporation bonds at 97, the price of one of the corporation's $1,000 bonds is 97% of $1,000, or $970.

$$0.97 \times \$1,000 = \$970$$

If the quoted price of a bond is $104\frac{1}{2}$, the price of a $1,000 bond would be $104\frac{1}{2}$% of $1,000, or $1,045.

$$1.04\tfrac{1}{2} \times \$1,000 = \$1,045$$

If the quoted price of a $500 par value bond is 102, the market price would be 102% of $500, or $510.

$$1.02 \times \$500 = \$510$$

Exercise 1
Oral

State the market price, in dollars and cents, of one $1,000 bond at each quoted price. Also state if the bond is selling at a discount or at a premium.

1.	98	$980 discount	5.	99	$990 discount	9.	97 $\tfrac{1}{4}$	$972.50 discount	
2.	93	$930 discount	6.	120	$1,200 premium	10.	105$\tfrac{3}{4}$	$1,057.50 premium	
3.	106	$1,060 premium	7.	102$\tfrac{1}{2}$	$1,025 premium	11.	104$\tfrac{1}{8}$	$1,041.25 premium	
4.	101	$1,010 premium	8.	96$\tfrac{1}{2}$	$965 discount	12.	85$\tfrac{7}{8}$	$858.75 discount	

Finding the Total Investment in Bonds When You Know the Market Price and the Number of Bonds Bought. To find the total investment in bonds, you must find the market price of one bond and multiply by the number of bonds bought.

Example

Lenore Walters bought four Zontech Company bonds at 108. What was her total investment in Zontech bonds?

Solution

108% = 1.08
1.08 × $1,000 = $1,080 market price of 1 bond
4 × $1,080 = $4,320 total investment   **Ans.**

Exercise 2
Written

Find the amount of money invested in each of the bond purchases.

1. Forlund County, $1,000 bonds:
    a. 3 @ 92 $2,760   b. 7 @ 89 $6,230   c.   9 @ 107 $9,630

2. Northeast Power Corporation, $1,000 bonds:
    a. 6 @ 98 $5,880   b. 5 @ 95 $4,750   c.   8 @ 104 $8,320

3. Huron Auto Centers, $1,000 bonds:
    a. 2 @ 98$\tfrac{1}{2}$ $1,970   b. 6 @ 92$\tfrac{1}{4}$ $5,535   c.   4 @ 91$\tfrac{3}{8}$ $3,655

4. Rowland Community Schools, $500 bonds:
    a. 4 @ 112 $2,240   b. 8 @ 90 $3,600   c.   12 @ 78$\tfrac{3}{4}$ $4,725

Investing in Bonds. People invest in bonds because they hope to make more money on their investments. However, investing in bonds is riskier than depositing money in a bank, and it requires more study.

For example, these are some of the details you must consider before you buy bonds: price and interest rates, tax laws, ability to resell the bonds, earnings record and credit history of the issuer, and business conditions.

Using a Broker to Buy and Sell Bonds. After a bond issue has been sold by the investment banking house, anyone who wants to buy the bonds must buy them from a bondholder who wants to sell bonds. Likewise, a bondholder who wants to sell must sell to someone who wants to buy bonds.

Bonds are seldom sold directly by the seller to the buyer. Usually, they are handled through a **broker**, who is a dealer in stocks and bonds.

Each buyer and seller places an order with a broker to buy or sell a particular bond. Each broker then sends the order to one of the exchanges, such as the New York Stock Exchange. In the exchanges, orders to buy and sell are received from all over the country. The actual buying and selling takes place when the buy and sell orders are matched.

Broker's Commission. When bonds are bought and sold through a broker, the buyer is charged a **broker's commission** or *brokerage fee*. The commission may be an amount such as $10 each on 1 to 5 bonds, $7.50 each on 6 to 25 bonds, and $5 each on 26 or more bonds.

Finding the Total Investment in Bonds When the Market Price, Commission, and Number of Bonds Are Known. When bonds are purchased through a broker, the amount of the investment is the market price of the bonds plus the broker's commission.

Example

Through a broker, Esteban Velazquez bought 3, $1,000 Tinwell Company bonds at 96 plus $10 commission per bond. What was the amount of his investment?

Solution

$0.96 \times \$1,000 = \$960$ market price of 1 bond

$3 \times \$960 = \$2,880$ market price of 3 bonds
$3 \times \$10 \ = \quad \underline{\quad 30}$ commission on 3 bonds
$\qquad\qquad \$2,910$ total investment   **Ans.**

**Exercise 3
Written**

In these problems, assume the commission is included in the quoted price, unless otherwise stated.

1. Find the total investment in each of the following bond purchases. The par value of each bond is $1,000. The commission in each case is $8 per bond.
   a. 8 @ 85 $6,864
   b. 5 @ 92 $4,640
   c. 4 @ 103 $4,152

d. 12 @ 113 $13,656
e.   6 @ $89\frac{1}{2}$ $5,418
f.   9 @ $105\frac{1}{4}$ $9,544.50
g. 10 @ $93\frac{5}{8}$ $9,442.50
h. 16 @ $112\frac{3}{4}$ $18,168
i.   7 @ $99\frac{1}{2}$ $7,021

2. Adam Edlund invested in 14 bonds with a par or face value of $1,000 each. He paid $1,035 for each bond, and the total brokerage fee was $105. How much did Adam invest? $14,595

3. Simone Mullins bought 8, $1,000 bonds, but she paid only $730 for each of them. If $56 commission was charged, what was her total investment in the bonds? $5,896

4. Otto Bawol bought 4, $1,000 bonds at $87\frac{1}{2}$. Two days ago the price of the bonds was 85. The brokerage fee was $10 on each bond. What was the amount of Otto's investment in the bonds? $3,540

■ Remember—
Bond quotes are
in percents.

5. Marian bought 6, $500 par value bonds at a market price of 93. If the commission fee was $9 a bond, what was the amount of Marian's investment? $2,844

6. Gilbert bought 5, $1,000 bonds at $89\frac{7}{8}$ and 7, $1,000 bonds at $90\frac{1}{8}$. For this purchase of 12 bonds
    a. What was his estimated total investment? $12,000
    b. What was his actual total investment? $10,802.50

7. Theodora Hoffman invested in 2, $1,000 par value bonds at 96 and 14, $500 par value bonds at 123. The total brokerage fee was $125. How much did Theodora invest? $10,655

Daily Bond Quotations. Each day's bond sales on the exchanges are shown the next day on the financial pages of many city newspapers. An example of what a daily bond quotation from the New York Exchange might look like is shown in Illustration 55–2.

Reading the Bond Quotation Table. The sales of Arnold Power Company bonds for a day are shown on the first line of the table.

At the right of the name, the "$9\frac{1}{4}$" means that the bonds pay an interest rate of $9\frac{1}{4}$%. The "07" means that the bonds are due in the year 2007.

The number of bonds sold, 19, appears in the Volume column. In the Close column, the "96" is the last price at which a sale was made that day.

The "$+\frac{1}{2}$" in the Net Change column means that the last price for the day was $\frac{1}{2}$ higher than the closing price yesterday. So, the closing price yesterday must have been $95\frac{1}{2}$, or $955.

Illustration 55–2. Daily Corporation Bond Quotations

**Exercise 4
Written**

Use the information in Illustration 55–2 to answer these questions.

1. What annual rate of interest is paid on the Meldin bonds listed in the bond quotation table? $11\frac{5}{8}\%$

2. In what year are the Zinco bonds due for payment? 2005

3. What was the last, or closing, price, in dollars, of Penlet bonds for the day shown in the table? $925

4. How many Linc bonds were sold for the day? 18

5. What was the last price, in dollars, of Cadco bonds on the day before the day shown in the table? $997.50

Savings Bonds. The United States Government sells Series EE **savings bonds** in these denominations: $50, $75, $100, $200, $500, $1,000, $5,000, and $10,000. The **denomination** is the amount printed on the face of the savings bond.

When you buy a savings bond, you pay one-half of its denomination. So, a $500 savings bond costs $250, a $1,000 bond costs $500, and so on. Bonds may be purchased at most banks and through payroll savings plans offered by employers.

Bonds earn interest at a minimum rate of 6%, but the actual rate earned may be higher when the bond is held five years or longer.

Redeeming Savings Bonds. When you redeem a bond, you exchange the bond for money. The amount you get, which includes the original purchase price and interest, is called the **redemption value.** Illustration 55–3 shows a table of redemption values for a $50 savings bond. Since redemption values change from time to time, the amount you get when you redeem a savings bond will probably be different from the amounts in the table. To find the redemption value of a $100 bond, you can multiply by two, and so on for larger bond denominations.

End of Year	Redemption Value	End of Year	Redemption Value
1	$26.08	5	$38.38
2	28.14	6	41.66
3	30.30	7	45.42
4	32.94	8	49.32

Illustration 55–3. Redemption Table for $50 Savings Bond

Example

Cindy buys a $100 savings bond and holds it for 6 years. Find: (a) The bond's redemption value and (b) the interest earned on the bond.

Solution

a. $100 ÷ $50 = 2   equivalent number of $50 bond units

$41.66   redemption value of $50 bond
$\underline{\times 2}$

$83.32   redemption value of $100 bond   **Ans.**

b. $100 \times \frac{1}{2} =$ $\begin{array}{l} \$83.32 \\ \underline{50.00} \\ \$33.32 \end{array}$ $\begin{array}{l} \text{redemption value of bond} \\ \text{purchase price of bond} \\ \text{interest earned on bond} \quad \textbf{Ans.} \end{array}$

Exercise 5
Written

When necessary, use the redemption values from Illustration 55–3 to solve the problems.

1. What is the purchase price of a $50 savings bond? a $75 savings bond? $25, $37.50

2. If you bought 8, $500 savings bonds, what total amount would you pay for this purchase? $2,000

3. Jean Hertz redeemed 3, $50 savings bonds after holding them for 4 years. What total amount did she receive? $98.82

4. Merilou Hogan has a $200 savings bond. What amount will she receive if she redeems the bond at the end of 2 years? $112.56

5. You hold 3, $500 savings bonds for 3 years and then redeem them.
    a. How much did you pay for the bonds? $750
    b. What is the redemption value of the bonds? $909
    c. How much interest have you earned on the bonds? $159

6. Wesley Henneck owns 10, $50 savings bonds. How much total interest will he have earned if he redeems the bonds after 7 years?
   $204.20

REVIEW 55

Terms

1. Match the terms with the statements.

   bond   discount   premium
   broker   market value   redemption value
   broker's commission   par value   savings bonds
   denomination

   a. The face value of a corporation bond   par value
   b. A selling price above par value   premium
   c. The price on the face of a savings bond   denomination
   d. The fee charged by a broker   broker's commission
   e. The price of a bond after it is issued   market value
   f. A Series EE bond sold by the federal government   savings bond
   g. A long-term promissory note   bond
   h. A selling price below par value   discount
   i. A dealer in stocks and bonds   broker
   j. Amount you get when a savings bond is redeemed
      redemption value

Problems

2. A total of 6 bonds are purchased at 107 plus $7.50 commission per bond. What is the total investment in bonds? $6,465 [55]

3. Kelly Lind borrowed $5,100. Find the due date and the amount due at maturity on this 75-day, 8% note, dated May 16. Use a 360-day year for this note.   July 30 [46]; $5,185 [43]

4. On January 2, Bob deposited $740 in a bank account that paid 5% interest per year, compounded semiannually. Interest was added on July 1 and January 2. What was Bob's balance on January 2 of the next year if he made no other deposits or withdrawals?
   $777.46 [52]

Section 56
Bond Income

When you invest in bonds, the corporation or governmental organization that issues the bonds makes interest payments to you, usually semiannually. These payments are your income from the bonds.

Bond Interest. The interest rate of a bond is based on the par value. Since the par value is the principal, the interest formula is:

$$\textbf{Par Value} \times \textbf{Rate} \times \textbf{Time} = \textbf{Interest}$$

For example, the interest for one year on a $1,000 par value, 8% bond would be $80.

$$\textbf{\$1,000} \times \textbf{0.08} = \textbf{\$80,} \quad \textbf{interest for 1 year}$$

■ Bond interest is based on par value.

If the interest is paid semiannually, the amount of each interest payment for this bond would be $40.

$$\textbf{\$1,000} \times \textbf{0.08} \times \frac{1}{2} = \textbf{\$40,} \quad \textbf{semiannual interest}$$

Finding the Income from an Investment in Bonds. To find your income from bonds, you first find the interest you receive for one bond. You then multiply that result by the number of bonds you own. For example, the annual income from 5, $1,000 bonds paying 13% interest would be $650.

$$\textbf{0.13} \times \textbf{\$1,000} = \textbf{\$130,} \quad \textbf{interest on 1 bond}$$

$$\textbf{5} \times \textbf{\$130} = \textbf{\$650,} \quad \textbf{income from 5 bonds}$$

Exercise 1
Written

1. Find the annual income in each problem.
   a. 4, $1,000, 9% bonds $360
   b. 16, $1,000, 14% bonds $2,240
   c. 7, $1,000, 6% bonds $420
   d. 12, $500, 12% bonds $720
   e. 8, $500, 7% bonds $280
   f. 10, $1,000, $11\frac{1}{2}$% bonds $1,150
   g. 16, $1,000, 7.25% bonds $1,160
   h. 3, $1,000, $14\frac{3}{4}$% bonds $442.50
   i. 9, $1,000, 5.5% bonds $495
   j. 20, $1,000, $9\frac{3}{8}$% bonds $1,875

■ A bond's interest rate is an annual rate.

2. What is the annual income from 4, $1,000, $8\frac{1}{8}$% bonds? $325

3. You own 23 bonds having a par value of $1,000 each and paying 7.75% interest. What annual income do you get from these bonds? $1,782.50

4. How much is each interest payment on a $500, 9% bond if the interest is paid semiannually on June 1 and December 1? $22.50

5. What estimated and actual annual interest would you get from 8, $1,000 par value bonds that pay $6\frac{7}{8}$% interest?
   $560 estimated; $550 actual

For each of these bond investments, find the total investment in the bonds and the total annual income from the investment.

**Exercise 2
Written**

	Bonds Owned	Par Value per Bond	Price Paid	Commission per Bond	Total Investment	Interest Rate	Annual Income
1.	5	$1,000	87	$10.00	$4,400	8%	$400
2.	10	1,000	$92\frac{1}{2}$	7.50	9,325	12%	1,200
3.	30	1,000	$105\frac{1}{4}$	5.00	31,725	$10\frac{1}{2}$%	3,150
4.	45	1,000	96	5.00	43,425	7.6%	3,420
5.	16	500	105	7.50	8,520	14%	1,120
6.	4	500	72	10.00	1,480	6.75%	135

Finding the Rate of Income on Investment. Before you buy bonds, you should find out what rate of income you will receive from them. This will help you compare bonds with other types of investments.

You can find your rate of income by dividing the annual income you receive in interest by your total investment in bonds. By dividing in this way, you are comparing the part with the whole. Your annual income from interest is the part. The amount you invested in bonds is the whole with which you compare the part.

$$\text{Rate of Income} = \frac{\text{Annual Income}}{\text{Investment}}$$

Rate of income is often called **yield**. For example, you may say that your *yield* on an investment is 8.4%, or that an Alpha Cable Company bond *yields* 8.4%. To see how yield is figured, look at the following example:

Example

What is the rate of income, or yield, on a $1,000, 8% Alpha Cable Company bond priced at 94 plus $10 commission?

Solution

$0.08 \times \$1,000 = \$80$ annual income
$0.94 \times \$1,000 = \$940$ amount invested
$\underline{\qquad\quad 10}$ commission
$\qquad\qquad\quad \$950$ amount invested

$\text{Rate of income} = \dfrac{\$80}{\$950} = 0.0842 = 8.4\%$ (to the nearest tenth percent)   **Ans.**

**Exercise 3
Written**

Find the rate of income to the nearest tenth of a percent.

1. For each bond, find the rate of income on the investment.

	Par Value	Interest Rate	Market Price	Commission	Rate of Income
a.	$1,000	16%	91	$ 5	17.5%
b.	1,000	7%	87	10	8.0%
c.	1,000	12%	109	10	10.9%
d.	1,000	8.5%	74	10	11.3%
e.	1,000	$11\frac{1}{2}$%	112	5	10.2%
f.	500	$5\frac{1}{4}$%	95	5	5.5%
g.	500	7.8%	62	5	12.4%

■ Yield equals annual income divided by investment.

2. A $1,000 bond, paying interest at 8%, was bought at $68\frac{1}{2}$, plus $5 commission. What was the rate of income on the investment?   11.6%

3. A $1,000, 18% bond was bought at 124. The previous day the bond sold at 120. What was the rate of income on the investment?   14.5%

When the commission is not stated, you should assume it is included in the quoted price.

4. What is the yield on a $1,000, $4\frac{1}{2}$% bond bought at 104?   4.3%

5. What is the rate of income on a 12% bond bought at 108?   11.1%

When the par value is not given, you should assume it is $1,000.

6. What is the yield on a 9% bond bought at 98?   9.2%

7. Al Horwath bought 7 Nole Company $1,000 par value, 13% bonds at 150 plus a commission charge of $10 per bond. Interest on these bonds is paid semiannually on February 1 and August 1.
    a. What semiannual interest payment will Al receive from this investment in bonds? $455
    b. What annual yield will he earn on this bond investment?   8.6%

**‡Exercise 4
Written**

1. a. How much annual income does an investor receive from 1, $1,000, 6% bond? $60
    b. How many of the bonds must be bought to have an annual income of $720 from the investment?   12

2. What amount must be invested in Bloom County 7% bonds at 80 in order to earn an annual income of $2,800? $32,000

3. Art Products Company $9\frac{1}{2}$% bonds can be purchased at 107. How much money must be invested in the bonds to produce an annual income of $1,520? $17,120

4. Marshall Steel Company 5% bonds can be purchased at 42.
    a. How many of these bonds must Mabel Whiting buy to have an annual income of $750 from the investment?   15
    b. What will be her total investment in the bonds? $6,300

5. Louis Bard can buy 9% mining company bonds at 84, or 7% oil company bonds at 68.
   a. Which bond pays the higher yield?   mining company
   b. What is the rate earned by the bond with the higher yield?
      10.7%

REVIEW 56

Skills

1. a. $15,000 × 0.3482 = ? $5,223
   b. What amount is 35% less than $54? $35.10
   c. $11.84 is what percent smaller than $32?   63%
   d. The exact interest on $1,108 at 14% for 60 days is ? $25.50
   e. $349,459.48 rounded to the nearest hundred is ? $349,500
   f. The estimated product of 19.7 × 105 is ?   2,000

Problems

2. Dora owns 15, $1,000 par value bonds paying $7\frac{1}{2}$% interest. What is her annual income from these bonds? $1,125 [56]

3. Avis Baird owns 20, $500 par value bonds paying 14% interest. He bought the bonds at $105\frac{1}{2}$ and paid $5 commission on each bond. What is the yield from his investment in the bonds, to the nearest tenth of a percent?   13.1% [56]

4. Borg Vesco bought 7, $1,000 bonds at $91\frac{1}{4}$, and 4, $500 bonds at $105\frac{3}{4}$. The commission on each bond was $7.50. What was Borg's total investment in bonds? $8,585 [55]

5. On April 1, Sheila Page deposited $600 in a passbook savings account paying 5% interest, compounded quarterly on the minimum balance on deposit in the quarter. Interest is added on July 1, October 1, and January 2. Sheila withdrew $200 from her account on July 5. How much was in her account on October 1 if she made no other deposits or withdrawals? $412.59 [52]

6. Marvin is paid on an 8-hour day basis with time-and-a-half pay for overtime. Last week he worked these hours: Monday, 8; Tuesday, 11; Wednesday, 10; Thursday, 9; Friday, 7. At a regular-time rate of $6 per hour, what were Marvin's gross earnings for the week? $288 [17]

7. Cora earned $24,000 this year. How much FICA tax at 7.65% should have been deducted from her total earnings? $1,836 [21]

Computer Clinic

Sarah Chaurbon owns two corporation bonds. She wants to find the annual income earned from each bond as well as their yields based on current prices. Follow the steps on the next page to find the annual income and yield of Sarah's bond investments.

1. Insert your Spreadsheet Applications Diskette and call up the file "Sec56." After you do, your computer screen should look like Illustration 56–1.

```
Sec 56                Finding Bond Investment Yield
-----------------------------------------------------------------------
Number of Bonds                              0
Par Value                                   $0
Bond Interest Rate (%)                    0.00
Market Price                             0.000
Commission per Bond                      $.00
-----------------------------------------------------------------------
Total Investment                         $.00
Annual Income                            $.00
Annual Yield (%)                          .00
-----------------------------------------------------------------------
```

Illustration 56–1. Finding Bond Investment Yield

2. Compare Sarah's bond investments by entering these data into the spreadsheet. Enter all the data for Bond A and write down the results, then enter the data for Bond B.

	Bond A	**Bond B**
B3	7	12
B4	1000	500
B5	8.2	9.75
B6	97.5	103.125
B7	6.00	7.50

3. Answer these questions about the completed templates:
    a. What total investment did Sarah make in each bond?
        Bond A, $6,867; Bond B, $6,277.50
    b. What annual income did she earn from each bond?
        Bond A, $574; Bond B, $585
    c. What yield does each bond earn?
        Bond A, 8.36%; Bond B, 9.32%
    d. Which bond has the higher yield?   Bond B
    e. What is the lowest market price, to the nearest quarter, at which both Bonds A and B will yield at least 10%?
        Bond A, 81.25; Bond B, 96

Section 57
Buying Stock

In addition to issuing bonds, a corporation may also raise money by issuing shares of its capital stock. For example, a company may need

$5,000,000 to renovate and expand its factory. It may try to raise money by issuing 100,000 shares of stock and selling them for $50 a share.

Corporation Stock. Investors who buy the shares of a corporation are called the **shareholders** or *stockholders* of a company. Each shareholder gets a **stock certificate** that shows on its face the number of shares it represents. Each certificate is registered with the corporation in the owner's name. A sample stock certificate is shown in Illustration 57–1.

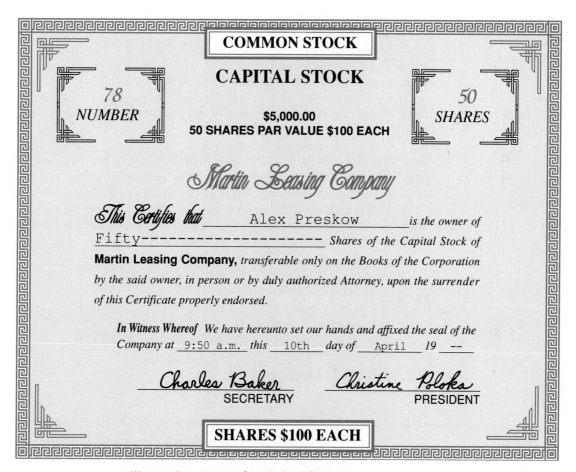

COMMON STOCK

CAPITAL STOCK

78
NUMBER

$5,000.00
50 SHARES PAR VALUE $100 EACH

50
SHARES

Martin Leasing Company

This Certifies that _____Alex Preskow_____ *is the owner of*

Fifty---------------------- *Shares of the Capital Stock of*

Martin Leasing Company, *transferable only on the Books of the Corporation by the said owner, in person or by duly authorized Attorney, upon the surrender of this Certificate properly endorsed.*

In Witness Whereof We have hereunto set our hands and affixed the seal of the Company at _9:50 a.m._ *this* _10th_ *day of* _April_ 19 _--_

Charles Baker
SECRETARY

Christine Poloka
PRESIDENT

SHARES $100 EACH

Illustration 57–1. Stock Certificate

When a corporation raises money by issuing stock, it does not promise to repay the money at some future date as it does when selling bonds. It does not promise to pay interest. Instead, the money it gets from the sale of stock becomes a permanent part of the corporation.

■ A stock certificate shows ownership in a corporation.

When you buy a share of stock, you own a part of the corporation. As a part owner or shareholder, you have a right to share in the profits of the corporation. The profits that the corporation distributes to its shareholders are called **dividends**. Dividends are usually paid quarterly. They may also be paid semiannually or annually.

Selling a Stock Issue. An issue of stock is sold in much the same way as an issue of bonds. The whole issue is usually sold to an investment banking house. The banking house then sells the shares to investors at a somewhat higher price than it paid for them.

Par Value and Market Value of Stock. The *par value* of a share of stock is the value printed on the certificate. This value may be $1, $10, $35, $50, or $100, or any other value that the corporation may want to set. It is seldom more than $100. All the shares of an issue of stock have the same value.

Many corporations issue stock without giving the shares any value. Such stock is called **no-par stock.**

After an issue of stock has been sold the first time, investors buy and sell the shares at any price they agree on. The price at which a stock is sold is called the **market price** or *market value.*

The market price of a stock depends largely on what investors think about the future earnings of the company. The market price changes often.

How the Market Price of a Stock Is Quoted. The trade of 1,000 shares of Weylin International stock may be posted on an electronic screen, as shown in Illustration 57–2. The price at which a stock is sold is its market price. The market price, or market value, of a share of stock is usually quoted in dollars per share. For example, a quotation of "$58\frac{1}{2}$" means that the price of one share is $58.50.

$$WI \ldots \quad 58\frac{1}{2} \ldots \quad 1000$$

Illustration 57–2. Stock Trade

Stockbroker's Commission. After a stock issue has been sold through an investment banking house, purchases and sales of stock are made through brokers in the same way that bonds are sold. The broker charges a commission or brokerage fee for the service.

The amount of a broker's commission depends on the price of the stock and the number of shares bought. A special type of broker, called a *discount broker,* charges lower commissions but also often gives less service and advice to customers.

Finding the Total Cost of a Stock Purchase. When you buy stock through a broker, the total cost of the stock is the market price of the stock plus the broker's commission.

Market Price + Commission = Total Cost

Example

Richard Lim bought 300 shares of Crestone stock at 31. The broker charged him $97 commission. Find the total cost of the stock.

Solution

Market price, 300 × $31	$9,300
Broker's commission	97
Total cost	$9,397 **Ans.**

Exercise 1
Written

Find the total cost of each stock purchase.

	# of Shares	Name of Stock	Market Price	Commission	Total Cost
1.	100	Arcell	28	$ 67.60	$2,867.60
2.	200	Concorp	$20\frac{5}{8}$	86.81	4,211.81
3.	100	Dryer Glass	$15\frac{1}{4}$	50.33	1,575.33
4.	50	General Importers	$64\frac{3}{8}$	73.67	3,292.42
5.	20	IMX	$109\frac{7}{8}$	58.86	2,256.36
6.	80	Montenet	$30\frac{1}{2}$	62.38	2,502.38
7.	400	Nortox	4	46.80	1,646.80
8.	140	Strand	$36\frac{5}{8}$	101.09	5,228.59
9.	30	Tole Instruments	$45\frac{1}{4}$	41.22	1,398.72
10.	150	XOE Computer	$55\frac{1}{4}$	140.60	8,428.10

11. Diane was charged a commission of $50 to buy 20 shares of Stone & Kerr stock at 62. What was her total investment in the stock? $1,290

12. A discount broker offers a 40% discount off the $80 commission charged by another broker to handle the purchase of 30 shares of Eaton at $70\frac{1}{2}$. How much could a buyer save by purchasing from the discount broker? $32

Daily Stock Quotations. Each day's sales on the stock exchanges are shown the next day on the financial pages of many large city newspapers. Some examples of quotations from a stock exchange for one day are shown in Illustration 57–3.

Reading the Stock Table. The sales of Amliss Corporation are shown in the first quotation on the table. The figures at the left of the company name show the highest price paid, $38, and the lowest price paid, $19.25, for the stock during the past 52 weeks.

■ Stock quotations are shown in dollars.

At the right of the company name, the "2.00" is what Amliss is paying its shareholders as a dividend for each share ($2).

The "658" in the Sales in 100s column means that 65,800 shares were sold during the day.

Highest and
lowest prices
for past 52 weeks

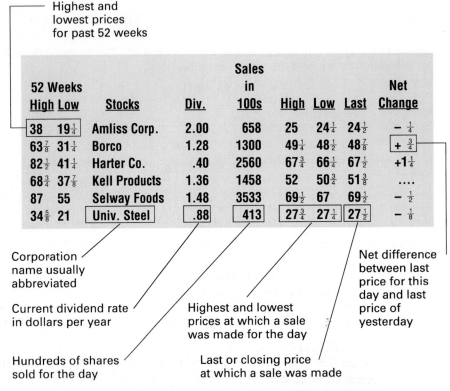

| 52 Weeks | | | | Sales in | | | | Net |
High	Low	Stocks	Div.	100s	High	Low	Last	Change
38	$19\frac{1}{4}$	Amliss Corp.	2.00	658	25	$24\frac{1}{4}$	$24\frac{1}{2}$	$-\frac{1}{4}$
$63\frac{7}{8}$	$31\frac{1}{4}$	Borco	1.28	1300	$49\frac{1}{4}$	$48\frac{1}{2}$	$48\frac{7}{8}$	$+\frac{3}{4}$
$82\frac{1}{2}$	$41\frac{1}{4}$	Harter Co.	.40	2560	$67\frac{3}{4}$	$66\frac{1}{4}$	$67\frac{1}{2}$	$+1\frac{1}{4}$
$68\frac{3}{4}$	$37\frac{7}{8}$	Kell Products	1.36	1458	52	$50\frac{3}{4}$	$51\frac{3}{8}$	....
87	55	Selway Foods	1.48	3533	$69\frac{1}{2}$	67	$69\frac{1}{2}$	$-\frac{1}{2}$
$34\frac{5}{8}$	21	Univ. Steel	.88	413	$27\frac{3}{4}$	$27\frac{1}{4}$	$27\frac{1}{2}$	$-\frac{1}{8}$

Corporation
name usually
abbreviated

Current dividend rate
in dollars per year

Hundreds of shares
sold for the day

Highest and lowest
prices at which a sale
was made for the day

Last or closing price
at which a sale was made

Net difference
between last
price for this
day and last
price of
yesterday

Illustration 57–3. Corporation Stock Quotations

The High column shows the highest price paid for the stock during the day ($25). The Low column shows the lowest price paid for the stock during the day ($24.25). The last column shows the price of the last, or closing, sale of the day ($24.50).

The "$-\frac{1}{4}$" in the Net Change column means that the last price of the day was $\frac{1}{4}$ of $1 or $0.25 lower than the last price yesterday. The last price yesterday must have been $24.75, or $24.50 + $0.25.

**Exercise 2
Written**

1. a. During the past 52 weeks, what stock in the table above sold at the highest price of all?   Selway Foods
   b. What stock sold at the lowest price?   Amliss Corporation

2. a. What stock paid the highest dividend? What amount was paid?   Amliss, $2
   b. What stock paid the lowest dividend? What amount was paid?   Harter Co., $0.40

3. a. How many shares of Borco were sold?   130,000
   b. How many shares of Universal Steel were sold?   41,300

4. a. What stock from the table showed a net change of exactly $0.75 for the day?   Borco
   b. What stock from the table had the greatest net change for the day?   Harter Co.

5. a. For what stock was the last price also the highest price for the day?   Selway Foods

b. What stock had the same closing price as the day before?
Kell Products

REVIEW 57

Terms

1. Match the terms with the statements.

dividends   no-par stock   stock certificate
market price   shareholder   yield

a. A paper showing shares owned   stock certificate
b. Stock without par value   no-par stock
c. Rate of income on bonds   yield
d. Anyone who owns stock   shareholder
e. Profits distributed to shareholders   dividends
f. Selling price of stock   market price

Skills

2. a. $2,800 × 4.09 = ? $11,452
    b. 45 × $4\frac{2}{5}$ = ?   198
    c. 32.8 ÷ 1,600 =   0.0205
    d. $11.20 is what percent less than $16.80? $33\frac{1}{3}\%$

Problems

3. Mark bought 42 shares of Ester Computer stock at $48\frac{1}{2}$ and paid $63.56 commission. What was his total investment? $2,100.56 [57]

4. The total investment in 25, $500, 12% bonds is $12,125. A commission of $125 is paid for this purchase. What is the yield on this investment, to the nearest tenth percent?   12.4% [56]

5. Alicia Paquin borrowed $18,000 to remodel her hardware store. She repaid the principal, with 15% interest, 3 years later. How much did she pay? $26,100 [43]

6. Jack Treblen needs to buy $30 worth of gasoline. If he pays for the gas with a credit card, he will be charged an extra 2.5%. [51]
    a. What is the cost of this purchase using a credit card? $30.75
    b. How much could Jack save by paying cash? $0.75

7. The local electric company charges $0.0762 for each KWH used as well as a fuel adjustment rate of $0.00034 per KWH. What is the total cost of using 520 KWH of electricity? $39.80 [39]

Section 58
Stock Income

Shareholders earn income on their investments in stock through dividends they get. They may receive dividends for as long as they own stock. The amount of dividends paid by a company usually depends on how much profit the company makes.

$ PROFITS $
(DIVIDENDS)

G
O
T
O

SHAREHOLDERS

Classes of Stock. Many corporations issue two classes of stock—common stock and preferred stock. Both types of stock represent ownership. They differ, though, in how they share in profits paid out as dividends.

Preferred stock is stock that has its dividend set by the corporation at the time it is issued. The dividend is set as a specific rate, such as 5%, or $5 a share. **Common stock** is the ordinary stock of a corporation. Common stock does not have a set dividend.

There is no guarantee that dividends will be paid to either class of stock. When dividends *are* paid, they go first to shareholders of preferred stock.

Dividends. When a corporation decides to distribute profits to the shareholders, it *declares a dividend.* The dividend may be shown either as a percent of the par value of the stock or as an amount of money per share.

For example, suppose a corporation declares a dividend of 3.4% of the par value, and the par value of the shares is $100. The amount of the dividend on each share is 3.4% of $100, or $3.40. The corporation may declare either a dividend of 3.4% or a dividend of $3.40 a share.

For stock with no par value, the dividend is always declared as an amount per share.

Finding the Income from an Investment in Stock. When a corporation pays dividends on stock that you own, you earn income. To find the total amount of the dividend payment you get, you multiply the dividend on one share by the number of shares you own. Your yearly income is the total of the dividends you get in one year.

Example

Myrna Wolf owns 70 shares of Antel Computer common stock, par value $100. If the corporation declares a 4.5% dividend, what is the total dividend that Myrna should receive?

Solution

$0.045 \times \$100 = \$4.50$ dividend on 1 share
$70 \times \$4.50 = \$315$ total dividend   **Ans.**

Example

What yearly income will Roy Zern get from an investment in 60 shares of Heritage Furniture stock if a dividend of $0.47 is paid quarterly?

Solution

$60 \times \$0.47 = \$28.20$ dividend for 1 quarter
$4 \times \$28.20 = \$112.80$ yearly income   **Ans.**

**Exercise 1
Written**

Find the total annual dividend received by each shareholder.

	Shares Owned	Par Value per Share	Dividend Rate	Annual Dividend
1.	100	$100	6%, annually	$ 600
2.	80	100	9%, annually	720
3.	35	50	5%, annually	87.50
4.	82	50	$7\frac{1}{2}$%, annually	307.50
5.	50	—	$0.65 per share, quarterly	130
6.	160	—	1.70 per share, quarterly	1,088
7.	200	—	0.48 per share, quarterly	384

Finding the Yield on a Stock Investment. The yield, or rate of income, you receive from any investment is found by dividing your annual income from the investment by the amount you have invested.

For stocks, the investment is the total cost of the stock. The income is the annual dividends. The yield is the annual dividends divided by the total cost.

$$\text{Yield} = \frac{\textbf{Annual Dividends}}{\textbf{Total Cost of Stock}}$$

**Exercise 2
Written**

1. Find the yield on the investment in each of the following stocks. Round all answers to the nearest tenth of a percent.

	Total Cost per Share	Par Value per Share	Dividend Rate	Dividend Payable	Yield
a.	$130	$100	8%	Annually	6.2%
b.	60	100	5%	Annually	8.3%
c.	34	50	4%	Annually	5.9%
d.	90	—	$0.57 per share	Quarterly	2.5%
e.	56	—	1.30 per share	Quarterly	9.3%
f.	12	—	0.17 per share	Quarterly	5.7%

■ Round answers to the nearest tenth of a percent.

2. Nora owns a share of stock that cost $18 and pays a quarterly dividend of 0.31\frac{1}{2}$. To what rate of income is the dividend equal?   7%

3. Casimir owns 160 shares of a stock that cost him $6,840, including commission. He receives quarterly dividends of $1.51 a share. What yield does Casimir earn on his investment?   14.1%

4. Ada Garza bought 50 shares of stock at $47.375 a share. She paid a commission of $62.43 for this purchase. The stock pays an annual dividend of 6% on a par value of $50.
   a. What total dividend does Ada get from these 50 shares? $150
   b. What yield does Ada earn on this investment?   6.2%

5. Regal Paint Company stock sells for $28 and pays an annual dividend of 2.7% on a par value of $100. Esteem Footwear Company has a market price of 8$\frac{1}{4}$ and pays a quarterly dividend of $0.18.

a. Which stock earns the higher yield?   Regal Paint
b. How much higher?   0.9%

REVIEW 58

Skills

1. a. $7.004 \times 0.035 = ?$ 0.24514
   b. $1,800 \div 10.7$, to the nearest tenth, is ?   168.2
   c. $798.72 is what percent of $12,800?   6.24%
   d. $\frac{2}{3}$ of $9.51 = ? $6.34
   e. 84 increased by 22.5% of itself is ?   102.9

Problems

2. Clara Aponte bought 250 shares of Sennett Oil Company stock that pays a quarterly dividend of 37¢ a share. At that rate, what should be her income from the stock for 1 year? $370 [58]

3. Charles bought 120 shares of 7% preferred stock with a par value of $150. What is his annual dividend income? $1,260 [58]

4. Kelly Lynch owns 9.2% preferred stock with a par value of $50 that she bought for $117 a share. What rate of income does she receive on her investment, to the nearest tenth of a percent?   3.9% [58]

5. Bert Lovell bought 15, $500 bonds at 108, including broker's commission. The bonds pay interest at the rate of 5.4%. What was the yield on Bert's bond investment?   5% [56]

6. Ava borrows $900 and agrees to repay the loan in 36 payments of $31 each. How much is the finance charge on the loan? $216 [48]

7. Find the maturity date and amount due on a 4-month, 12% exact interest note for $3,500 dated March 5.   July 5 [46]; $3,640 [43]

‡8. Dominic Avtar wants to buy enough $1,000, 7% bonds to have an annual income of $1,610. How many bonds must he buy?   23 [56]

Section 59
Selling Stock

When shareholders sell their stock, they either make a profit, break even, or take a loss. To find out how they did on their investments, the investors must consider the cost of the stock, its selling price, and the expenses of selling.

Market price less selling expenses equals net proceeds.

Finding the Proceeds from the Sale of Stock. When you sell stock, you must pay a commission and a small Securities and Exchange Commission (SEC) fee. Sometimes, the state in which you sell stock charges a *transfer tax.* When you buy stock, you do not pay a transfer tax or SEC fee.

When you sell stock through a stockbroker, you get the market price less the commission, transfer tax, and SEC fee. The amount you receive is called the **net proceeds.**

Market Price − (Commission + Taxes + Fees) = Net Proceeds

For example, the net proceeds from the sale of 50 shares of stock at 30 with commission, taxes, and fees of $62 is $1,438.

50 × $30 = $1,500 market price

$1,500 − $62 = $1,438 net proceeds

Find the net proceeds from the sales of the stock below.

**Exercise 1
Written**

	Name of Stock	Shares Sold	Selling Price	Commission, Taxes, and Fees	Net Proceeds
1.	Zenwell Mining	100	34	$ 61.34	$3,338.66
2.	Melork Properties	50	$12\frac{1}{4}$	48.22	564.28
3.	Dryson Chemical	230	81	145.57	18,484.43
4.	Harbridge Hospitals	80	$28\frac{1}{8}$	52.68	2,197.32
5.	Atamar Trucking	300	17	75.31	5,024.69

6. Kirk LaBond sold 200 shares of Neal Labs stock at 45 and 300 shares of Wicker Organic Foods Company stock at 17. His commission and other charges amounted to $182.50 on the Neal stock and $124.30 on the Wicker stock. What total net proceeds did Kirk receive from the sale of both stocks? $13,793.20

7. Toni Ulworth sold 100 shares of stock at $19\frac{7}{8}$. Her total expenses from the sale of the stock were $50.11.

    a. What were her estimated net proceeds from the sale? $1,950
    b. What were her actual net proceeds from the sale? $1,937.39

Finding the Profit or Loss on the Sale of Stock. Your profit or loss on a sale of stock is the difference between the total cost of the stock and the net proceeds. If the amount of the net proceeds is greater than your total cost, you have a profit. If it is less than your total cost, the result is a loss.

Net Proceeds − Total Cost = Profit

Total Cost − Net Proceeds = Loss

**Exercise 2
Written**

1. Find the profit or loss in each of these sales, labeling each loss.

Name of Stock	Shares Traded	Selling Price	Commission, Taxes, and Fees on Sale	Total Cost of Stock Purchase	Profit/ Loss
a. UDC Polymers	100	42	$88.04	$3,935.56	$176.40
b. King Theaters	80	$8\frac{1}{2}$	50.73	558.42	70.85
c. Sun Graphics	400	17	97.39	7,003.67	301.06 loss
d. Com-Design	75	$28\frac{1}{4}$	57.58	2,840.31	779.14 loss
e. Euro Shipping	110	37	86.47	3,200.75	782.78
f. Exell Foods	90	$51\frac{1}{8}$	92.25	4,618.66	17.41 loss

■ Net proceeds less total cost of stock equals profit/loss.

2. Gerardo bought 60 shares of stock for a total cost of $2,985. He later sold the stock at $51 a share and had selling expenses of $94. What was his profit or loss from this sale of stock? $19 loss

Finding the Total Gain from Owning Stock. Besides any profit you may make on the sale of stock, you may also earn dividends on stock you own. To find your total gain from owning stock, you must combine the profit or loss from the sale of stock with the dividends received.

**Exercise 3
Written**

1. Ester Howell bought 40 shares of stock for a total cost of $3,757. She kept the stock for 3 years, during which time she received semi-annual dividends of $3.10 per share. She then sold the stock and received net proceeds of $4,211. What was Ester's total gain from owning and selling the stock? $1,198

2. Darian Woods bought 75 shares of stock for a total cost of $1,298. After receiving 6 quarterly dividends of $0.27 per share, he sold the stock and received net proceeds of $1,194. What was his total gain from owning and selling the stock? $17.50

3. Jeannette sold 62 shares of Wexor Van Lines at a profit of $345 and 120 shares of Ark Adhesives at a loss of $490. Before she sold the stock, she received 3 quarterly dividends of $0.90 a share on the Wexor Van Lines stock. Ark Adhesives paid no dividends. What was Jeannette's total gain from owning and selling both stocks? $22.40

**‡Exercise 4
Written**

1. Eastboard Parcel Service Company stock pays an annual dividend of $4 a share. How many shares would you have to own to get an annual income of $360 from the stock?   90

2. Page Alarm Company stock pays a regular annual dividend of $2.50 a share.
   a. How many shares must you buy to get an annual income of $1,000 from the investment?   400
   b. What total investment will you make in the stock if you buy it at 56 and pay $82 per 100 shares for commission? $22,728

3. A $10 par value stock pays a 12% dividend. At a total cost of $20 a share, how much must be invested in the stock in order to receive annual dividends of $960? $16,000

4. A stock paying an annual dividend of $1.40 a share now sells at 34.
    a. How many shares of stock must you buy at that price to get an annual dividend income of $308?   220
    b. What total investment, without figuring commissions, would you have to make to earn the dividend income you want? $7,480

REVIEW 59

Terms

1. Match the terms with the statements.

    common stock   net proceeds   preferred stock

    a. Market price less commission, taxes, and fees   net proceeds
    b. Ordinary stock of a corporation   common stock
    c. Gets paid first when profits are distributed   preferred stock

Skills

2. a. $37,000 × 2.38 = ? $88,060
    b. 5,724 ÷ 12,000 = ?   0.477
    c. 6,350 is what percent of 50,000?   12.7%
    d. How many m^2 are in a lot 22 m by 40 m?   880 m^2
    e. 5 600 m = ? km   5.6

Problems

3. Janet Zurn sold 100 shares of Entinol stock at $32\frac{1}{2}$. By selling the stock through a discount broker, she saved 20% of the $88.20 commission charged by another broker. What were Janet's net proceeds from the sale of this stock? $3,179.44 [59]

4. Sam Nehad bought 150 shares of stock at a total cost of $3,200. The stock paid a quarterly dividend of $0.48 a share. He kept the stock for $\frac{1}{2}$ year, during which he received 2 dividend payments. He then sold the stock and received net proceeds of $3,890. What was Sam's total gain from owning and selling the stock? $834 [59]

5. What is the rate of income on a share of preferred stock that costs $90 and pays a semiannual dividend of $3.60 a share?   8% [58]

Computer Clinic

Two years ago, Rob Lowell purchased 100 shares of stock at a total cost of $2,000.00. He then sold the stock at $34.50 a share, paying selling costs of $78.00. During the two years, Rob received eight quarterly dividend payments of $0.55 for each share of stock owned. Use the following steps to figure Rob's profit or loss from owning and selling the stock.

1. Insert your Spreadsheet Applications Diskette and call up the file "Sec59." After you do, your computer screen should look like Illustration 59–1.

```
Sec 59                   Figuring Gain From Stock Ownership
-----------------------------------------------------------------------
Stock Purchase Cost                        $.00
Sales Data:
    Number of Shares                          0
    Selling Price                         $.000
    Selling Costs                          $.00
Dividend Data:
    Amount per Share                       $.00
    No. of Payments                           0
-----------------------------------------------------------------------
Net Proceeds                               $.00
Net Profit (Loss)                          $.00
Dividends Received                         $.00
Net Gain (Loss)                            $.00
-----------------------------------------------------------------------
```

Illustration 59–1. Stock Ownership Analysis Template

2. Figure the net profit or loss from the sale of stock and the net gain or loss of stock ownership by entering these data into the template.

B3	2000	B7	78
B5	100	B9	0.55
B6	34.50	B10	8

3. Answer the questions about your completed spreadsheet.
   a. Did Rob make a profit or a loss from the sale of stock? What was the amount?   Profit; $1,372
   b. Did a net gain or loss result from Rob's ownership of the stock? What was the amount?   Net gain; $1,812
   c. To the nearest $\frac{1}{8}$ of a dollar, at what selling price would the net proceeds from the sale almost equal the purchase cost? $20.75
   d. To the nearest quarter dollar, at what price must the stock be sold to make the net gain nearest to, but not less than, $1,200? $28.50

Section 60
Mutual Funds

If you make an investment in the stock of only one company, you can make a good profit if the company does well. If the company is not profitable, however, you may lose all or part of your investment. To lessen your risk of making an unwise investment, you may want to invest in many companies by buying shares in a mutual fund.

Nature of Mutual Funds. An investment company, called a **mutual fund,** sells shares of stock to the general public. The mutual fund uses the money it receives to buy stock in a large number of companies. By

A mutual fund buys stock in other companies.

investing in a large number of companies, the mutual fund increases its chances of buying stocks that will be profitable.

Mutual fund shares are traded based on their net asset values. You can figure **net assets** by finding the total value of the mutual fund's investments and subtracting any money owed to others. The **net asset value,** or NAV, is found by dividing the net assets by the number of shares outstanding. For example, a fund with net assets of $10,000,000 and 500,000 shares outstanding will have a net asset value of $20 ($10,000,000 ÷ 500,000).

The net asset value of mutual funds is figured daily and is published on the financial pages of daily newspapers in a form similar to that shown in Illustration 60–1. Following the fund name, the net asset value appears in the NAV column.

Fund Name	NAV	Offer Price
Denton Fund	10.03	10.96
Frontier Growth	39.80	41.03
Kaner High Yield	10.58	11.48
Mark International	6.37	N.L.
Newsome Growth	17.87	N.L.
Payne Hall New Horizon	9.27	N.L.
Randall Explorer	17.54	19.17
Walker A-15 Fund	12.21	N.L.

Illustration 60–1. Mutual Fund Quotations

Types of Mutual Funds. Two types of mutual funds are listed in Illustration 60–1: **no-load funds** and **load funds.** The term *load* means the same as commission. *No-load funds* are sold without a commission being charged. The no-load funds are identified by the abbreviation "N.L." in the Offer Price column.

Some of the funds shown in Illustration 60–1 have two numbers or prices following their names. These funds are called *load funds.* When you buy load funds, you pay the amount shown in the Offer Price column, which includes a commission charge.

Finding the Total Investment in Mutual Fund Shares. The mutual fund investment is figured in two different ways, depending on the type of fund being purchased. For load funds, the total investment is found by multiplying the **offer price** by the number of shares bought. For example, in Illustration 60–1 the offer price of the Kaner High Yield fund is 11.48. So, the cost of 200 shares is $2,296 (200 × $11.48).

For no-load funds, the *NAV* is multiplied by the number of shares to find total investment. In Illustration 60–1, you can see that Newsome Growth has a NAV of 17.87. The total investment in 100 shares would be $1,787 (100 × $17.87).

**Exercise 1
Written**

1. Using the information in Illustration 60–1, find the total investment in the mutual fund purchases.

Mutual Fund	# of Shares	Total Investment
a. Payne Hall New Horizon	40	$370.80
b. Mark International	132	840.84
c. Denton Fund	80	876.80
d. Randall Explorer	260	4,984.20

2. Amy Lester bought these Pacific Trends, no-load mutual fund shares: 50 shares, NAV 13.56; 120 shares, NAV 13.84; 90 shares, NAV 14.05. What was her total investment in Pacific Trends? $3,603.30

3. Foster A-2, a no-load fund, has a net asset value of 16.82. Foster Growth, a load fund, is quoted with a net asset value of 7.50 and an offer price of 8.03. What total investment would be made if 100 shares each of Foster A-2 and Foster Growth were purchased? $2,485

Finding the Number of Shares Purchased When a Fixed Dollar Amount Is Invested. Many people who buy mutual fund shares invest a certain dollar amount, such as $500, instead of buying a certain number of shares. To find the number of shares purchased in this case, you divide the amount of the investment by the price of a mutual fund share. The price of a no-load fund is its net asset value. The price of a load fund is its offer price.

For example, if $500 is invested in a no-load mutual fund with a net asset value of 6.37, the number of shares purchased will be 78.493 ($500 ÷ $6.37). Note that the number of shares is figured to three decimal places to make sure that the entire dollar amount is invested.

Figure shares to the nearest thousandth share in the problems.

**Exercise 2
Written**

1. Antoine LeBaron has $2,500 to invest in Udrell Technology, a no-load fund with a current NAV of 16.20. How many shares of Udrell can Antoine purchase?   154.321

2. Rose invested $5,000 in a load fund that has a current NAV of 16.50 and an offer price of 17.34. How many shares did she buy?   288.351

3. Today's NAV of the Ark-Stone Group, a no-load fund, is 6.73. At that price, how many shares can be bought for $8,000?   1,118.707

4. Cecile owns 804.726 shares of Lorgen New Vision, a load mutual fund. She is investing another $500 in Lorgen shares which are quoted today with a net asset value of 22.60 and an offer price of 24.75.
   a. Estimate the number of shares Cecile can buy today.   20
   b. What is the actual number of shares she can buy?   20.202
   c. After this purchase, how many shares of Lorgen will she own?   824.928

Finding the Rate of Commission. When you buy no-load funds, you are not charged for commission. For load funds, the amount of commission is the difference between the net asset value and the offer price. To find the rate of commission on the purchase of load funds, divide the amount of commission by the offer price.

Offer Price − Net Asset Value = Commission

Commission ÷ Offer Price = Rate of Commission

Example

What is the rate of commission, to the nearest percent, on Frontier Growth funds with a net asset value of 39.80 and an offer price of 41.03?

Solution

$41.03 − $39.80 = $1.23 amount of commission
$1.23 ÷ $41.03 = 0.02997, or 3%, rate of commission   **Ans.**

**Exercise 3
Written**

1. Find the amount of commission and the rate of commission, to the nearest tenth, for each of the mutual fund shares.

Mutual Fund	NAV	Offer Price	Amount of Commission	Rate of Commission
a. Pentel Government	6.29	6.42	$0.13	2.0%
b. Zoll Energy Fund	12.78	13.44	0.66	4.9%
c. Allen Asia Fund	17.75	19.40	1.65	8.5%
d. Will Technology	8.58	8.98	0.40	4.5%

2. Stenwell Growth Fund is quoted at 6.08 NAV, 6.24 offer price. To the nearest tenth of a percent, what commission rate is charged? 2.6%

3. Your broker quotes Leland Air Fund at these prices: NAV, 14.06; offer price, 14.80. What rate of commission is charged?   5%

4. A commission of $0.78 is charged for a mutual fund with an offer price of 10.04.
   a. What is the estimated commission rate?   8%
   b. What is the actual rate, to the nearest tenth percent?   7.8%

Finding the Profit or Loss from Mutual Fund Redemption. When shares are *redeemed*, or sold back to the mutual fund company, the investor is paid the net asset value. The proceeds from the sale are found by multiplying the net asset value by the number of shares redeemed.

Proceeds = Number of Shares × Net Asset Value

The profit or loss from owning mutual fund shares is figured by finding the difference between the proceeds and the total amount invested.

Proceeds − Amount of Investment = Profit

Amount of Investment − Proceeds = Loss

Example

What are the proceeds from the sale of 200 shares of a mutual fund with a net asset value of 12.30? What is the amount of the profit or loss if the total investment in the 200 shares is $1,950?

Solution

200 × $12.30 = $2,460 proceeds
$2,460 − $1,950 = $510 profit   **Ans.**

Exercise 4
Written

1. Lana Willens sold her 810.4 share investment in a mutual fund at a net asset value of 8.84. What proceeds did she get? $7,163.94

2. The Dart Oil & Gas Fund has a current NAV of 11.87. Elmo Nuenfeld redeemed the 320 Dart shares that he had bought for a total cost of $3,198.
   a. What were his proceeds? $3,798.40
   b. What was his profit or loss from owning these shares?
      $600.40 profit

3. A share of Dresden Gold Fund is traded at these prices: NAV, 22.86; offer price, 23.81. When Clarissa Nash sells the 500.271 shares she owns, what profit or loss does she make if her total investment is $12,520? $1,083.80 loss

4. The Odgen Fund had a net asset value of 7.94 and an offer price of 8.10 on the day that Herb Mills invested $4,000 in the fund. Six months later, the fund was quoted at these prices when Herb redeemed his investment in the fund: NAV, 8.11; offer price, 8.28.
   a. What estimated number of shares did Herb buy?   500
   b. What actual number of shares did Herb buy?   493.827
   c. What proceeds did he receive? $4,004.94
   d. What amount of profit or loss did Herb's investment make?
      $4.94 profit

REVIEW 60

Terms

1. Match the terms with the statements.

   load fund   net assets   no-load funds
   mutual fund   net asset value   offer price

   a. A mutual fund that charges a commission on sales   load fund
   b. A type of investment company   mutual fund
   c. A price that includes a commission charge   offer price
   d. Net assets divided by outstanding shares   net asset value
   e. Are sold commission free   no-load funds
   f. Value of a fund's investments less money owed   net assets

Problems

2. Violeta Nieves bought 300 shares of the Virginia Beta Fund on the day it traded at a net asset value of 14.70 and an offer price of 15.62. What was her investment in the fund? $4,686 [60]

3. The TransEuro Fund is trading at these prices: 29.64, NAV; 31.20, offer price. How many shares can you buy for $8,000?   256.410 [60]

4. The Boswenth Americas Fund trades at a net asset value of 17.44 and an offer price of 18.23.
    a. What commission amount is paid per share? $0.79 [60]
    b. To the nearest tenth of a percent, what rate of commission is paid?   4.3% [60]

5. Mark bought 350 shares of Alcan Fund for $7,192.50. Two years later he sold his Alcan shares at a 21.75 NAV. What was his profit or loss on this investment? $420 profit [60]

6. Minola Zurek bought 8, $500 par value bonds at 95. The commission was $7.50 a bond. What was her total bond investment? $3,860 [55]

7. To the nearest tenth of a percent, what is the yield on a $1,000, 6.7% North York municipal bond priced at 85?   7.9% [56]

Section 61
Buying Real Estate

Another way to try to make money is by investing in real estate and then renting the property to others. The real estate may be land that is suitable only for farming or oil exploration. It may also be land on which houses, apartments, condominiums, offices, stores, or factories have been built.

 Gross Income = Annual Rent

 Net Income = Annual Rent Less Expenses

Gross Income and Net Income from a Real Estate Investment. When you invest in real estate, the rent you receive from others is your gross income from the investment. Your net income is the amount that is left after you have paid all the expenses of owning the property.

Even though you may collect rent monthly, you usually figure your income and expenses on an annual basis. For example, assume that you collect rent of $700 a month and have annual expenses of $7,600. Your gross income for the year is 12 × $700, or $8,400. Your net income for the year is $8,400 − $7,600 or $800.

Expenses of Owning Rental Property. As Illustration 61–1 shows, only part of the money you collect as rent is profit. The rest of the money is usually used to pay for taxes, repairs, and insurance. Generally, you will also have to pay interest on a mortgage loan.

Most investors in rental property do not have enough money, or don't want to use all of their own money, to buy the property. So, they borrow money from a bank or other lender by signing a note and giving a **mortgage** on the property. The mortgage gives the lender the

Illustration 61-1. Where Rental Money Goes

right to take the property if payments are not made by the borrower as agreed. The term of mortgage notes is usually 20 to 30 years, but it may run longer.

Most mortgages require monthly payments of interest and part of the principal. In this way, the borrower gradually repays the loan over the term of the mortgage. The mortgage interest on any payment date is the simple interest on the unpaid balance since the last payment date.

As an owner of rental property, you will also have depreciation expense. **Depreciation** is a loss in the value of property caused by aging and use. For example, even though a house may be kept in good repair, it will gradually wear out and become less valuable. Your property may also lose value because it goes out of style or becomes too expensive to heat and cool as energy costs rise. Most housing and business property depreciates slowly at about 2% to 4% of its original value per year.

Finding the Annual Net Income from a Real Estate Investment. The annual net income is the amount left after deducting the annual expenses from the annual rental income.

Annual Rental Income − Annual Expenses = Annual Net Income

Example

Lori Nalin bought a house for $50,000. She made a $10,000 cash down payment and got a $40,000 mortgage for the balance of the purchase price. She rented the house to a tenant for $500 a month. Her annual payments for taxes, repairs, insurance, interest, depreciation, and other expenses totaled $4,700. What annual net income did she earn?

Solution

12 × $500 = $6,000 annual rental income
$6,000 − $4,700 = $1,300 annual net income   **Ans.**

Exercise 1
Written

1. Find the annual net income for each real estate owner.

| | Monthly Rent Income | Annual Expenses | | | | | | Annual Net Income |
		Taxes	Repairs	Insur-ance	Inter-est	Depre-ciation	Other	
a.	$590	$1,720	$470	$500	$2,100	$1,300	$50	$940
b.	310	950	360	380	1,100	560	40	330
c.	840	2,800	210	590	3,000	2,050	90	1,340
d.	540	1,630	840	360	1,870	1,200	75	505

2. Marvin bought a condominium and lot for $72,000. He paid $18,000 in cash and got a mortgage for the balance. He rented the condominium to a tenant for $950 a month. For the first year, Marvin's expenses were:

Mortgage interest, $4,800
3% depreciation on the house valued at $58,000
Taxes, repairs, insurance, and other expenses, $3,750

What was his net income for the year? $1,110

3. Nicole bought an eight-unit apartment building for $170,000. During the first year of ownership, she received $460 a month for the rent of *each apartment unit*. Her expenses for the year were:

Mortgage interest, $20,400
2% depreciation on the building valued at $130,000
Taxes, repairs, insurance, and other expenses, $14,900

What was her net income for the year? $6,260

Finding the Rate of Income on a Real Estate Investment. The rate of income, or yield, is based on the cash investment in the property. It is found by dividing the annual net income by the cash investment.

$$\text{Rate of Income} = \frac{\text{Annual Net Income}}{\text{Cash Investment}}$$

**Exercise 2
Written**

1. Find the rate of income, to the nearest tenth of a percent, that these owners will get on their cash investments.

| | Cash Investment | Monthly Rental Income | Annual Expenses | | Rate of Income |
			Interest on Mortgage	Other	
a.	$21,000	$ 500	$2,400	$1,900	8.1%
b.	38,000	780	1,600	3,300	11.7%
c.	46,000	1,800	9,600	9,300	5.9%
d.	12,000	390	2,200	1,450	8.6%
e.	31,000	640	2,200	2,150	10.7%

▌Rate of income is based on cash investment.

2. Lester Collins took out a $62,000 mortgage on a 2-family house after making a down payment of $11,000 as a cash investment. During the first year, he rented one unit at $560 a month and the other unit at $580 a month. For the year, he paid $8,200 in mortgage interest and $4,400 in other expenses. To the nearest tenth of a percent, what rate of income did Lester earn on his cash investment? 9.8%

3. For $78,000, Bridgette can buy an office building that rents for $920 a month. Taxes, insurance, and repair expenses average $3,900 annually. Depreciation is estimated at $1,200 a year. Bridgette plans to pay $78,000 cash for the property. To the nearest tenth of a percent
   a. Find the rate of income she will make on her cash investment. 7.6%
   b. Find the rate of income Bridgette will make on her cash investment by charging $1,050 monthly rent and keeping the expenses the same. 9.6%

4. Kim Ruiz bought a 6-unit apartment house for $70,000 and made a cash down payment of $20,000. The first year, she rented each of the 6 apartments at $290 a month. Her expenses for the year were:

   Mortgage interest, $9,800
   Depreciation at 4% of the house's value of $55,000
   Taxes, insurance, and other expenses, $6,300

   Find Kim's rate of income on her cash investment, to the nearest percent. 13%

5. Zack Eason made a $7,000 down payment on a house that cost $24,000. He rented the house at $490 monthly for the first year. During the year he had these expenses: taxes, $990; insurance, $270;

interest, $2,400; repairs, $900; depreciation at 2% of the cost of the house. What was Zack's rate of income on his cash investment?
12%

REVIEW 61

Skills

1. a. What amount is 60% more than $4.20? $6.72
   b. $\frac{1}{5}$ less than $6.30 is ? $5.04
   c. To what fraction is $37\frac{1}{2}$% equivalent? $\frac{3}{8}$
   d. $13\frac{1}{2} \div 2\frac{1}{4} = $?   6
   e. $150,000 is what percent of $50,000?   300%
   f. 958.8006 rounded to the nearest thousandth is?   958.801

Problems

2. Last year, Pearline rented a house to a tenant for 1 year at $800 a month. Pearline's expenses were: mortgage interest, $2,780; depreciation, $1,400; taxes, $800; other expenses, $3,650. What was her net income for the year? $970 [61]

3. Xavier bought a house for $22,000 cash and got a mortgage for the rest of the purchase price. He rented the house to a tenant for $900 a month for 1 year. His expenses for the year were: mortgage interest, $5,100; taxes, $1,570; repairs and maintenance, $940; insurance, $800; depreciation, $1,800. What rate of income, to the nearest tenth of a percent, did Xavier earn on his cash investment?
   2.7% [61]

4. Lorna Renseler owns 199.521 shares of a mutual fund that she bought at a total cost of $2,500. The fund currently trades at 11.83 NAV and 12.34 offer price. If Lorna sells all of her mutual fund shares now, what amount of profit or loss will she make?
   $139.67 loss [60]

Computer Clinic

Marie Santoya plans to invest $50,000 in property that rents for $890 a month. She estimates these annual expenses of ownership: taxes, $1,620; repairs, $430; insurance, $500; interest, $2,300; depreciation, $1,100; other expenses, $100. Follow these steps to find the rental income Marie can expect to earn from owning this property.

1. Insert your Spreadsheet Applications Diskette and call up the file "Sec61." After you do, your computer screen should look like Illustration 61–2.

```
Sec 61                        Finding Rental Income
----------------------------------------------------------------------
Cash Investment                         $.00
Monthly Rent                            $.00
Annual Expenses
   Taxes                                $.00
   Repairs                              $.00
   Insurance                            $.00
   Interest                             $.00
   Depreciation                         $.00
   Other                                $.00
----------------------------------------------------------------------
Annual:
   Gross Rental Income                  $.00
   Less Expenses                        $.00
   Net Income (Loss)                    $.00
   Rate of Income (%)                    .00
----------------------------------------------------------------------
```

Illustration 61-2. Using a Spreadsheet to Find Rental Income

2. Find Marie's rental income on property by entering these data into the template:

B3 50000	B6 1620	B8 500	B10 1100
B4 890	B7 430	B9 2300	B11 100

3. Answer the questions about your completed template.
   a. What were the annual gross and net rental incomes?
      $10,680; $4,630
   b. What rate of income did Marie earn on this property investment?
      9.26%
   c. To the nearest dollar, what is the lowest monthly rent that could be charged without showing a net loss? $505
   d. How much net income would be earned if the monthly rent was raised to $935? What would be the rate of income, to the nearest tenth percent?   Net income, $5,170; Rate, 10.3%

Section 62
Real Estate Income

Finding the Rent That You Must Charge to Earn a Given Rate of Income.
When you invest in real estate, you should set a goal for the rate of income that you want to earn on your cash investment. The rent you charge must cover the net income that you want to earn and all expenses of owning the property.

Annual Rental Income = Annual Net Income + Annual Expenses

$$\text{Monthly Rent} = \frac{\text{Annual Rental Income}}{12}$$

Example

Ezra wants to earn 15% annual net income on his $10,000 cash investment in property. His annual expenses of owning the property are $2,700. What monthly rent must Ezra charge?

Solution

0.15 × $10,000 = $1,500   desired annual net income
$1,500 + $2,700 = $4,200   annual rental income
$4,200 ÷ 12 = $350   monthly rent   **Ans.**

**Exercise 1
Written**

1. In each problem, find the monthly rent the owner must charge to make the desired income.

	Cash Investment	Desired Annual Net Income	Annual Expenses	Monthly Rent
a.	$20,000	14% of investment	$3,500	$525
b.	8,000	7% of investment	2,560	260
c.	45,000	12% of investment	9,120	1,210
d.	36,000	9% of investment	8,400	970

2. Elvira Needham bought two lots for $12,000 at a tax sale. She estimates that her yearly expenses of owning these lots will be $540. A nearby factory wants to use the lots for parking trucks overnight. To earn a 15% rate of income on her investment,
   a. What annual rent should Elvira charge? $2,340
   b. What estimated monthly rent should she charge? $200
   c. What actual monthly rent should Elvira charge? $195

3. Brian Mahaney bought a vacant warehouse by making a $12,000 cash down payment. He estimates that his expenses of owning the warehouse will be $4,320 for the first year. Brian's goal is to earn a rate of income of 8% on his investment.
   a. To reach this goal, what monthly rent must he charge? $440
   b. If Brian's annual expenses go up by 5% in the second year, what monthly rent will he have to charge in the second year to reach his investment goal? $458

‡**Finding the Maximum Cash Investment Needed to Give a Desired Rate of Income.** Investors in real estate know the annual net income and the rate of income they want to earn. The cash investment they must make to reach these goals is found by dividing the annual net income by the rate of income.

$$\text{Cash Investment} = \frac{\text{Annual Net Income}}{\text{Rate of Income}}$$

Example

Sandy wants to buy a building from which she can earn annual rental income of $18,000. Annual expenses are $10,800. How much cash should she invest in the building to earn 9% on the investment?

Solution

$18,000 − $10,800 = $7,200   annual net income
$7,200 ÷ 0.09 = $80,000   maximum cash investment   **Ans.**

‡**Exercise 2**
Written

1. Marilyn wants to buy an office building that earns its current owners an average yearly net income of $6,720. What is the greatest amount of cash she can invest in it to earn a 14% rate of income on her investment? $48,000

2. The total annual rental from a building that you are thinking of buying is $8,740. Annual expenses are $3,280. How much cash should you invest in the building to earn 8% on your investment? $68,250

3. A house that Archie Katz wants to buy rents for $640 a month. The annual expenses average $3,080. How much cash should Archie invest in the house to earn $11\frac{1}{2}$% on his investment? $40,000

4. The total monthly income from a 2-family house is $1,140. The annual expenses total $4,560. Ten years ago the property sold for $58,000. To earn $9\frac{1}{2}$% on this investment, what is the most cash a buyer can invest in this house? $96,000

Capital Investment vs. Expenses. If you plan to be a property owner, you will spend money on capital investments and expenses. **Capital investment** is the amount of the original investment plus anything else spent for improvements that make the property more valuable. Adding a room to your house and building a garage are examples of capital investment.

■ Capital
Investment =
Original Cost
+ Improvements
and Additions.

Money spent for repairing and replacing broken items does not increase the value of property, but it is an expense of owning the property. Expenses are deducted from the gross income of property to find net income. The money paid out returns the property to its original condition. Repainting the house, replacing a broken sidewalk, and repairing leaking faucets are examples of expenses.

Exercise 3
Written

1. Cynthia Drexel bought a 5-year old condominium for $68,000 and immediately spent $2,200 to install a deck. She spent $1,600 to paint the interior and make minor repairs. What was her capital investment in the condominium? $70,200

2. Marv can buy a house for $28,000 cash. To make it more appealing to renters, Marv also has to spend $12,000 to improve the property by adding a room and paving the driveway. Marv estimates the total annual expenses of owning the house to be $2,600.
   a. What would be Marv's capital investment in the house? $40,000

b. What monthly rent will he have to charge, after the improvements are made, in order to make a net income of 7% on his total capital investment? $450

3. Rick Weiss plans to buy a vacant 4-unit apartment by paying $26,000 in back taxes due the city. To meet current building and safety codes, he will have to spend $32,000. Rick figures that each unit can be rented for $280 a month and that total annual expenses for all units will be $8,700. If he makes this capital investment, what rate of income will Rick earn, to the nearest tenth of a percent?
    8.2%

‡4. A real estate agent showed Patti a 2-family house that will need some minor improvements before it can be rented. Considering its location, Patti figures that each unit can be rented for $380 a month while total annual expenses will be $5,100. What is the most cash that Patti should invest in the house to earn 12% on her capital investment? $33,500

REVIEW 62

Terms

1. Match the terms with the statements.

    capital investment   depreciation   mortgage

    a. Loss of value caused by wear and tear   depreciation
    b. Gives the lender the right to take property if payments are not made by the borrower   mortgage
    c. Total of original cost and improvements   capital investment

Problems

2. The annual expenses on a house that costs $60,000 cash are estimated to be $3,900. What monthly rent must be charged to earn a net income of $7\frac{1}{2}$% on the cash investment? $700 [62]

3. Susan bought a vacant building and lot for $56,000. During the first year she spent $22,000 to divide the building into smaller spaces. In the first year, her cash expenses of ownership were $8,350. Depreciation was figured at 2% on the $42,000 original worth of the building alone. What was Susan's capital investment?
    $78,000 [62]

4. Jessica withdrew $2,400 from a time-certificate account that paid 8% annual interest. Because she withdrew her money before the end of the term, the bank charged a penalty of 2 months' interest. What was the amount of the penalty? $32 [54]

Computer Clinic

Abe Goodrich plans to invest $40,000 cash in rental property on which he expects to earn a net income of 8% on his investment. Abe figures annual expenses of owning the property to be $3,400. Follow the steps below to find the monthly rent Abe has to charge to cover expenses and earn the rate of income he wants.

1. Insert your Spreadsheet Applications Diskette and call up the file "Sec62." After you do, your computer screen should look like Illustration 62–1.

```
Sec 62                       Finding Monthly Rents
------------------------------------------------------------------------
Cash Investment                          $.00
Desired Income Rate (%)                  0.00
Annual Expenses                          $.00
------------------------------------------------------------------------
Desired Annual Net Income                $.00
Annual Expenses                          $.00
Annual Rental Income                     $.00
Monthly Rent                             $.00
------------------------------------------------------------------------
```

Illustration 62–1. Monthly Rent Template

2. Enter these data into the template to find the monthly rent to be charged:

         B3   40000   B4   8   B5   3400

3. Answer the questions about your completed monthly rent template.
   a. In dollars, what annual net income on his investment does Abe expect to earn? $3,200
   b. What annual rental income must Abe earn to provide the net income he wants and cover the estimated expenses? $6,600
   c. What monthly rent does Abe have to charge to meet his net income goal? $550
   d. Assume that Abe can buy a similar property in another area for $52,000 with annual expenses of $4,151. What monthly rent would he have to charge on that property, to the nearest dollar, to earn an 8% rate of income? $693

Home and Transportation Expenses

The purchase of a home and a car or truck are the largest expenditures that most people make during their lifetimes. As with any purchase, you should shop to compare prices and value to get the most for your money.

Most houses are sold through real estate agents. Before a house is listed for sale, the owner of the house may want it appraised. The **appraised value** is an estimate of the price at which the house may sell. The final selling price, or **market value,** is the price at which the sale takes place.

New cars or trucks are purchased through dealers. If you have an old car or truck, you may keep it, sell it, or use it as a down payment on a new car or truck.

In addition to the initial price, the expense of owning a home, car, or truck must be considered. Renting a home or leasing a car or truck may be cheaper than buying.

After you finish Unit 10, you will be able to:

- Find the down payment and closing costs for a home purchase.
- Figure total payments and total interest paid over the life of a mortgage.
- Find and compare expenses of owning a home to renting it.
- Find the cost of owning and operating a car or truck.
- Figure the amount and rate of depreciation for homes, cars, or trucks.
- Find the cost of leasing a car or truck.
- Compare the cost of owning a car or truck to leasing them.
- Solve problems that contain more information than you need.
- Estimate answers to problems.
- Read, write, say, and recognize the meanings of the key terms.
- Use computer spreadsheets to: figure monthly payments needed to amortize a mortgage, compare costs of buying a home to renting it, figure amount and rate of annual depreciation of a car or truck, and compare costs of buying a car or truck to leasing it.

About 25% of the families in the United States own their own homes. The home may be a single family house, a mobile home, or a condominium. Buying any type of home is a major financial decision for families.

Making the Purchase. Buying a home usually requires a great deal of cash. Most home buyers have to borrow money to pay for the home. They use their savings to make a down payment, which is part of the purchase price paid when the home is bought. The down payment is often between 10% and 25% of the price of the home.

There are also many **settlement** or **closing costs** to pay. These are expenses that must be paid when the property is purchased. These costs include legal fees, insurance, prepaid interest, property taxes, termite inspections, and land surveys. Closing costs often total from 1% to 3% of the purchase price of the home.

■ Closing costs are expenses paid when a home is purchased.

Exercise 1
Written

1. The Greenwalds want to buy a condominium priced at $90,000. They will need to make a down payment of 20% and pay closing costs of 3% of the purchase price.
   a. How much cash will they need for the down payment? $18,000
   b. How much of the purchase price must they borrow? $72,000
   c. How much cash will they need for the closing costs? $2,700

2. Ed and Roberta Rogers bought a house at its market value of $59,000. They made a 25% down payment, and paid these closing costs: legal fees, $180; property survey, $125; insurance, $190; termite inspection, $50; prepaid interest, $393; prepaid taxes, $242.
   a. What was the amount of the down payment? $14,750
   b. What was the total of the closing costs? $1,180
   c. What percent were the closing costs of the purchase price, to the nearest whole percent? 2%

3. Ann Doyle will purchase a house for $53,500 on August 1. The house was appraised at $58,000. On August 1, she must make a down payment of 15% of the purchase price and pay these closing costs: termite inspection, $40; legal fees, $420; land survey costs, $115; insurance, $210; prepaid interest, $401; prepaid taxes, $312.
   a. What total amount of cash must Ann have on August 1 to make the purchase? $9,523
   b. What percent are the closing costs of the purchase price, to the nearest tenth of a percent? 2.8%

Borrowing Money on a Mortgage. When you buy a home, you usually borrow most of the purchase price from a bank or other lender. You do this by signing a note and giving the lender a mortgage on the property. The *mortgage* is security for repayment of the loan. It gives the lender the right to take the property if you do not repay the loan as agreed.

There are many different types of mortgages. Two types often used are fixed rate mortgages and variable rate mortgages. In a **fixed rate mortgage,** you pay the same rate of interest for the life of the loan. In a **variable rate mortgage,** the rate of interest you pay may change every year, every three years, or every five years.

Fixed Rate Mortgages. Most mortgages are repaid gradually, or *amortized*, over the life of the mortgage. Mortgage loans are usually made for 20, 25, or 30 years. Equal monthly payments are usually made just like the level payments for an installment loan. Each payment pays off part of the principal plus the interest due on the unpaid balance.

■ Amortize means to repay gradually over time.

At first, the monthly payment is used mostly to pay interest. Later the amount of the payment used for interest decreases, and the amount that goes to repay the principal increases. Look at Illustration 63–1, which shows how much of a $442.48 equal monthly payment goes for interest during the term of the mortgage. The monthly payment is figured on a $40,000 mortgage taken for 30 years at 13%. A complete amortization table for this mortgage is found in Appendix E.

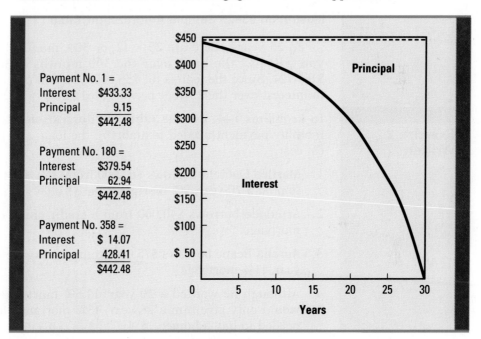

Payment No. 1 =
Interest $433.33
Principal   9.15
           $442.48

Payment No. 180 =
Interest $379.54
Principal   62.94
           $442.48

Payment No. 358 =
Interest $ 14.07
Principal   428.41
           $442.48

Illustration 63–1. Interest and Principal Payments on a Mortgage

Using the Amortization Table. Illustration 63–2 shows the monthly payments needed to amortize mortgage loans over different periods of time using interest rates of 9%, 11%, and 13%.

Let's say you want to buy a home that costs $72,000. You have $17,000 for a down payment and your bank will lend you $55,000 on a 25-year, 11% mortgage.

On the $55,000 line of the table, in the 25-year column under 11%, is the amount, $539.07. This is the monthly payment you must make to pay off the loan in 25 years.

Monthly Payments Needed to Pay a Loan									
Amount of Loan	Interest Rate								
	9%			11%			13%		
	Time of Loan								
	20 yrs.	25 yrs.	30 yrs.	20 yrs.	25 yrs.	30 yrs.	20 yrs.	25 yrs.	30 yrs
$30,000	$269.92	$251.76	$241.39	$309.66	$294.04	$285.70	$351.48	$338.36	$331.86
35,000	314.91	293.72	281.62	361.27	343.04	333.32	410.06	394.75	387.17
40,000	359.90	335.68	321.85	412.88	392.05	380.93	468.64	451.14	442.48
45,000	404.88	377.64	362.09	464.49	441.06	428.55	527.21	507.53	497.79
50,000	449.87	419.60	402.32	516.10	490.06	476.17	585.79	563.92	553.10
55,000	494.85	461.56	442.55	567.71	539.07	523.78	644.37	620.31	608.41
60,000	539.84	503.52	482.78	619.32	588.07	571.40	702.95	676.71	663.72
65,000	584.83	545.48	523.01	670.93	637.08	619.02	761.53	733.10	719.03
70,000	629.81	587.44	563.24	722.54	686.08	666.63	820.11	789.49	774.34
75,000	674.80	629.40	603.47	774.15	735.09	714.25	878.69	845.88	829.65

Illustration 63–2. Sample Amortization Table

In 25 years, there are 25 × 12, or 300, months. The total amount you will pay the bank over the 300 months is 300 × $539.07, or $161,721. Since the loan is for $55,000, you will pay a total of $106,721 in interest over the 25-year period ($161,721 − $55,000 = $106,721).

**Exercise 2
Written**

In Problems 1–4, use the table in Illustration 63–2 to find (a) the monthly payment needed to amortize the loan, and (b) the total interest cost.

1. Marilee Lenfield borrows $60,000 from a savings and loan association on a 20-year, 9% mortgage.   a. $539.84; b. $69,561.60

2. Armondo borrows $40,000 from a credit union on a 25-year, 13% mortgage.   a. $451.14; b. $95,342

3. Aurelia Beane borrows $75,000 from a mortgage company on a 30-year, 11% mortgage.   a. $714.25; b. $182,130

4. Although he wanted a 20-year, 12.5% mortgage, Howard's bank would only give him a 25-year, 13% mortgage for the $45,000 he needed to buy a home.   a. $507.53; b. $107,259

Variable Rate Mortgages. Many lenders offer variable rate mortgage loans on homes. In a variable rate mortgage, the rate of interest changes at certain times depending on the interest rates charged by others.

The terms of these loans differ among lenders. Some lenders offer loans on which the interest rate changes every year, three years, or five years. When the interest rate changes, some lenders will change the monthly payment as well. Other lenders keep the monthly payments the same even though the interest rate changes. When lenders do this, they add more time onto the loan.

Refinancing a Mortgage. When interest rates go down, business firms and property owners often refinance, or replace, their higher interest rate mortgages with lower interest rate mortgages. When you **refinance** a mortgage, you take out a new mortgage and use that money to pay off the old mortgage. When you refinance a mortgage, you may have to pay settlement costs on the new loan. There may also be a *prepayment* penalty charged by the old lender if you pay off the old mortgage before it is due.

For example, the Rowes have a fixed rate mortgage at 16.25% with an unpaid balance of $50,000. The monthly payment on the old mortgage was $845.86. They got a new mortgage at 13% for the amount of the unpaid balance from another lender. Their new monthly payment was $585.79. To get the new mortgage, they had to pay closing costs of $935. To pay off the old mortgage before it was due, they had to pay a prepayment penalty of $500. By getting the new mortgage, they reduced their total payments by $1,685.84 in the first year.

12 × $845.86 = $10,150.32   one year's payment under old mortgage

12 × $585.79 =   7,029.48   one year's payment under new mortgage

$ 3,120.84   difference in yearly payments

1,435.00   closing costs and prepayment penalty ($935 + $500 + $1,435)

$ 1,685.84   net amount payments reduced

■ To refinance, money from a new loan is used to pay off an old loan.

Exercise 3 Written

1. The rate of interest on Sol Retal's variable rate mortgage has changed from 14.5% to 12%. Sol's old monthly payment was $539.75. Sol's new monthly payment is $464.32. How much less does Sol pay in 1 year at the new mortgage rate? $905.16

2. Emily Metarel's monthly payment on her original 14.25% variable rate mortgage is $734.87. The interest rate on her mortgage has been raised to 15.75%, and her new monthly payment is $813.58. How much more will Emily pay in 1 year at the new mortgage rate? $944.52

3. Your old 14.7% mortgage has a monthly payment of $796.69. The monthly payment on a new 11.5% mortgage is $602.41. To refinance, you must pay $990 in closing costs and a $1,005 prepayment penalty. By getting a new mortgage, your total payments in the first year will be reduced by
   a. What estimated net amount? $400
   b. What actual net amount? $336.36

4. The Greens have a fixed rate mortgage at 13.1% with a monthly payment of $614.41. They can refinance their loan with a variable rate mortgage at 10.8% from another lender with a monthly payment of $471.35. The rate of interest on the new mortgage will stay fixed for 3 years. If they refinance the mortgage, they must pay closing costs of $1,630. Find the

a. Total monthly payments under the old mortgage for 3 years
   $22,118.76
b. Total monthly payments under the new mortgage for 3 years
   $16,968.60
c. Net amount paid less in 3 years under new mortgage
   $3,520.16

REVIEW 63

Terms

1. Match the terms with the statements.

   appraised value   refinance
   fixed rate mortgage   settlement or closing costs
   market value   variable rate mortgage

   a. Payment due at time of home purchase   settlement costs
   b. The price at which a home is sold   market value
   c. Interest rate may change at certain times
      variable rate mortgage
   d. Interest rate stays the same for the term of the loan
      fixed rate mortgage
   e. Pay off old mortgage with new mortgage   refinance
   f. Estimated price at which a home may sell   appraised value

Skills

2. a. What percent of $24 is $84?   350%
   b. What is 140% of $85? $119
   c. Find the number of days from March 15 to August 7.   145 days
   d. Find the banker's interest at 12% on $420 for 72 days. $10.08

Problems

3. Shirley buys a house for $85,000. She pays 25% as a down payment and these closing costs: prepaid interest, $799; insurance, $340; legal fees, $280; land survey, $150; city inspection fee, $80. [63]
   a. What down payment did Shirley make? $21,250
   b. What were the total closing costs? $1,649
   c. What percent were the closing costs of the purchase price, to the nearest tenth of a percent?   1.9%

4. Brent Hodge bought a 4-unit apartment for $120,000. He made a down payment of $24,000 and took out a mortgage for the rest. In the first year, he rented each apartment for $420 a month. Total expenses for the year, including interest, were $17,280. What was his rate of income on his cash investment?   12% [61]

5. Pat Reeves paid $1,850 for 40 shares of stock. She kept the stock for 4 years and got regular quarterly dividends of $0.56 a share. She then sold the stock and received $1,690 as net proceeds. What was her gain from owning and selling this stock? $198.40 [59]

Computer Clinic

Ed Zorego plans to buy a house by making a $14,000 down payment and borrowing $30,000 on a 12%, 20-year mortgage. Follow the steps below to find the monthly payment needed to pay off the mortgage and to calculate total interest paid.

1. Insert your Spreadsheet Applications Diskette and call up the file "Sec63." After you do, your computer screen should look like Illustration 63–3.

```
Sec 63              Figuring Mortgage Payments and Interest
---------------------------------------------------------------------
Mortgage:
   Amount                           $.00
   Interest Rate (%)               0.000
   Term (in years)                     0
---------------------------------------------------------------------
Mortgage Factor                 .0000000
Number of Payments                     0
Monthly Payment                     $.00
Total Amount Paid                   $.00
Less Original Mortgage              $.00
Interest Paid                       $.00
---------------------------------------------------------------------
```

Illustration 63–3. Mortgage Record Spreadsheet

2. Figure the monthly mortgage payment and total interest paid on the mortgage by entering these data into the template:

B4   30000   B5   12   B6   20

3. Answer the questions about your completed mortage template.
   a. What is the amount of the monthly mortgage payment? $330.33
   b. What total amount of money will be paid on the mortgage over its life? $79,279.20
   c. What total amount of interest will be paid on the mortgage? $49,279.20

4. Beginning with the original data before each step, make the changes below and answer the questions.
   a. How much more total interest would be paid during the life of the loan if the term is extended to 25 years? $15,511.80
   b. You can get a $30,000 mortgage at 11.5% for 25 years or 11.125% for 30 years. How much more interest would you pay over its term for the more expensive mortgage? $12,388.80 more for the 30-year mortgage

Section 64
Owning a Home

A homeowner has many expenses. Cash has to be paid out for property taxes, repairs, maintenance, insurance, and mortgage interest. Depreciation and the loss of income on the money invested in the home are two other expenses to be figured.

On the other hand, owning a home has some tax benefits. For example, homeowners may be able to deduct from their income the interest they pay on their home mortgage and the property taxes they pay on their property. This will reduce the income tax they pay. For these reasons, owning a home may or may not be less expensive than renting.

Depreciate means to lose value.

Home Depreciation. As a home gets older, it gradually loses value, or depreciates. The loss in value may be caused by the wearing out of parts of the home, such as the roof. It may also occur if home styles change, making the older house less desirable to purchasers.

An actual loss in value cannot be figured until a house is sold. Then the selling price can be compared to the original price of the home to find the depreciation. Until that time, depreciation must be estimated. Estimates of depreciation are often shown as a percent of the original purchase price.

For example, Elvita's home cost her $70,000. She estimates that depreciation each year reduces the value of the home by 3%. The depreciation for one year, then, is 0.03 × $70,000 = $2,100.

**Exercise 1
Written**

1. Tom and Jane Yurko estimate that their home depreciates 2% each year. If the home originally cost them $75,300, how much do they estimate that the home will depreciate this year? $1,506

2. The home of the Collins family is estimated to depreciate at the rate of 3.2% each year. If the home originally cost $52,700, how much will this home depreciate in 1 year? $1,686.40

3. Artie Brouillard bought a condominium. The former owner originally wanted $85,000 for the home before selling it to Artie for $74,900. If the condominium's annual depreciation is estimated at 2.5%, how much will it depreciate this year? $1,872.50

4. Marie Santos bought a house for $55,200 ten years ago. If she estimates that the house depreciates at the rate of 1.8% a year, how much has the house depreciated so far? $9,936

5. Ezra Wilkins bought a mobile home for $32,000 three years ago. He estimates that the home depreciates at a 5% rate each year. How much does Ezra estimate the mobile home has depreciated? $4,800

Income Loss on Money Invested. You may also lose money if you take funds for your cash down payment from an interest-earning investment.

For example, Novella Shafkalis withdrew $20,000 from a time-deposit account to use as a down payment on her home. She had been earning interest at 8% from the certificate. The interest she loses each year, 0.08 × $20,000 = $1,600, is an expense of owning her home.

Exercise 2
Written

1. To buy a home, Po-ling Yang must make a down payment of $17,600. He could also invest that money in a bond that pays 11.3% interest annually. What amount of income will Po-ling lose in 1 year on his down payment if he buys the home? $1,988.80

2. Carol Derko withdrew $8,400 from her savings account to make a down payment on a condominium. If the savings account was paying 5.5% interest compounded annually, how much interest will Carol lose in 1 year on the down payment money? $462

3. Josh Ewald could put $8,987 into a certificate of deposit earning 8.91% annually, or he could use that money to make a down payment on a home. If he buys the home,
   a.   What estimated interest income will Josh lose in one year? $810
   b.   What actual interest income will he lose in one year? $800.74

Estimating the Net Cost of Home Ownership. Before you buy a home, you should estimate the net cost of owning it. To estimate the net cost of home ownership, you must add the expenses of mortgage interest, taxes, insurance, maintenance, repairs, depreciation, and the income you will lose by investing in the home. Then subtract the income tax savings you estimate you will get for owning the home.

Example

The Lingalis want to buy a home. The interest they will pay on their mortgage in the first year will be $4,810. The annual property taxes on the home are $1,350, and an insurance policy on the home will cost $320 a year. They estimate that the home will depreciate $1,240 the first year and that maintenance and repairs will cost $1,450. They will lose $1,270 per year in interest on the money used for the down payment. They estimate that they will save $1,428 in income taxes in the first year because they can subtract mortgage interest and property taxes from their income. What will be the net cost of owning the home for 1 year for the Lingalis?

Solution

$ 4,810	mortgage interest		$10,440	total expenses
1,350	property taxes		− 1,428	tax reductions
320	insurance		$ 9,012	net cost **Ans.**
1,240	depreciation			
1,450	maintenance, repairs			
1,270	lost income			
$10,440	total expense			

Exercise 3
Written

1. The Kerns want to buy a home. Their estimated first-year expenses are: mortgage interest, $7,128; property taxes, $1,800; insurance, $515; depreciation, $1,680; maintenance and repairs, $1,237; lost

income on the down payment, $1,472. They also expect to save $3,112 on their income taxes because of mortgage interest and property taxes. What will be the Kerns' net cost of owning their home the first year? $10,720

2. Kirk and Edna Rowe own a home. They estimate their expenses to be: mortgage interest, $10,180; property taxes, $3,690; insurance, $833; depreciation, $3,800; maintenance and repairs, $900; lost income on cash invested, $2,375. They expect to save $5,700 in income taxes from home expense. What is their net cost of home ownership? $16,078

3. The Sotos want to buy a home that costs $55,000. They must make a 20% down payment. They estimate their expenses for the first year to be: mortgage interest, $4,914; property taxes, $1,208; insurance, $260; depreciation, 2% of the purchase price; maintenance and repairs, $1,050. They are earning 12% interest on the money they would use for the down payment on the home. They expect to save $1,280 in income taxes because of home expenses. What will be the net cost of the home for 1 year? $8,572

4. Trudy Hertz wants to buy a home for $64,800. To make the 25% down payment, she will withdraw savings that are earning 8.5% interest. She estimates her first year expenses to be: mortgage interest, $6,005; property taxes, $850; insurance, $395; depreciation at 2.5% of the purchase price; maintenance and repairs, $1,400. She expects to save $1,847 in income taxes from home expenses. What will the net cost of owning the home be for the first year? $9,800

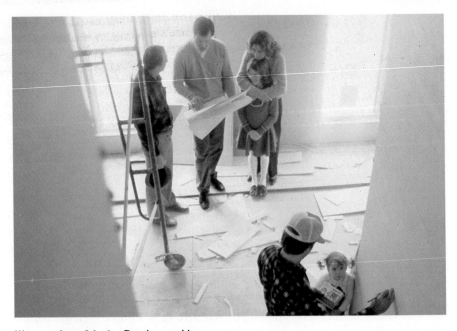

Illustration 64–1. Buying a Home

Comparing Renting and Owning a Home. Whether you should buy or rent a home depends on many factors. For example, you may want the personal satisfaction you get from owning a home and improving the property to suit your tastes. By renting, you gain the convenience of not having to take care of repairs. In addition to these personal reasons that have nothing to do with money, you should also estimate the difference in expenses when deciding to rent or buy.

**Exercise 4
Written**

1. Art Emmons can rent an apartment for $475 a month, or he can buy a home. If he buys the home, he estimates his net annual cost of owning the home will be $7,250. How much will Art save in one year by renting? $1,550

2. Amelia Burgos rents an apartment for $640 a month. She can buy a home with about the same space for $52,000. If she buys the home, she must withdraw $10,400 from a savings account earning 7% interest. Her other home ownership expenses are estimated to be $9,300. She also estimates that she will save $1,428 in income taxes from home expenses.
   a. What is her total rent for the year? $7,680
   b. What is her yearly net cost of owning the home? $8,600
   c. How much less would it be for Amelia to rent for the year?
      $920

3. Nina rents a home for $850 a month. If she bought the home, her estimated yearly expenses would be: mortgage interest, $4,800; property taxes, $1,400; depreciation, $1,980; maintenance and repairs, $900; insurance, $410. She would lose $1,100 in interest on her down payment and save $1,736 in income taxes.
   a. What is her total rent for the year? $10,200
   b. What is her annual net cost of owning the home? $8,854
   c. How much less would it be to buy than to rent for 1 year?
      $1,346

4. The Mills family rents an apartment for $510 a month. They could buy a home with the same space for $44,000. To make the 15% down payment, they would have to withdraw savings earning them 7.5% a year. They estimate that their other expenses would be: depreciation, $570; maintenance and repairs, $1,400; insurance, $290; mortgage interest, $4,516; property taxes, $1,120. They estimate they would save $1,026 in income taxes from home expenses.
   a. What annual income would be lost to make the down payment?
      $495
   b. What would be the Mills family's annual net cost of owning the home? $7,365
   c. How much more would it be to buy than to rent for 1 year?
      $1,245

5. The Jenkins have owned their home for many years. Their expenses last year were: mortgage interest, $1,870; property taxes, $2,800; maintenance and repairs, $2,360; insurance, $570; depreciation, $1,900. They could have earned 9.2% on the $50,000 they have in-

vested in the home. They saved $1,290 in income taxes from home expenses.

  a. What was their net cost of owning the home last year?
    $12,810

  b. If they had sold their home and rented an apartment for $850 a month, how much could they have saved last year? $2,610

REVIEW 64

Skills

1. a. Add: $2\frac{3}{4}$, $5\frac{1}{2}$, $7\frac{5}{6}$ $16\frac{1}{12}$
  b. Subtract: 17.736 from 28.94   11.204
  c. Multiply: $6\frac{1}{4}$ by $8\frac{1}{2}$ $53\frac{1}{8}$
  d. Divide: 24 by $\frac{2}{3}$ 36
  e. Multiply: 5.65 by 0.58   3.277
  f. Find $\frac{1}{2}\%$ of $56,000. $280
  g. Estimate the product of 50.2 × 79.99.   4,000
  h. Round $5,089,764 to the nearest thousand. $5,090,000

Problems

2. The Craine family rents an apartment for $640 a month. If they buy a home instead, they must withdraw $12,000 from a savings account paying 12.5% annual interest. Their estimated annual expenses of owning a home would be: mortgage interest, $5,300; insurance, $380; depreciation, $1,700; repairs, $770; property taxes, $1,460. They expect to save $1,876 in income taxes from home expenses. How much will they save by renting for the year? $1,554 [64]

3. Norma bought a house appraised at $61,000 for $58,000, making an $18,000 down payment and getting a mortgage for the rest. She rented the house to a tenant for $900 a month. Her expenses were: mortgage interest, $4,320; taxes, $1,800; insurance, $650; depreciation, $1,740; other, $400. What rate of income did Norma make on her cash investment, to the nearest whole percent? 11% [61]

4. On June 30, Mark's check register balance was $286.34 and his bank statement balance was $830.28. There was a service charge of $2.60 and earned interest of $0.72 on the bank statement that had not been recorded in the register. Outstanding checks were: #67, $172.13; #70, $292.54, and #72, $81.15. Prepare a reconciliation statement. $284.46 [5]

5. Alvin Beauchamp, an office clerk, is paid $238.50 for a 37.5 hour week. What is his hourly rate of pay? $6.36 [11]

6. Julio is paid a monthly salary of $1,350, plus 4% commission on all sales over $38,000 made in a single month. For March, April, and May, his sales were $35,600, $39,400, $42,800, respectively. What was the amount of his total earnings for the 3 months? $4,298 [28]

7. A lawn mower that sells for $330 cash may be purchased for $47.94 down and 6 monthly payments of $54.16. By what percent is the installment price more than the cash price? 13% [50]

8. Daisy deposited $600 in her credit union on July 1. The credit union adds interest semiannually at an annual rate of 7%. How much did Daisy have in the account 1 year later? $642.74 [52]

Computer Clinic

Louise Ruell has collected data about the expenses of home ownership and rental. Follow the steps below to use that data to compare the cost of owning and renting a home.

1. Insert your Spreadsheet Applications Diskette and call up the file "Sec64." After you do, your computer screen should look like Illustration 64–2.

```
Sec 64              Home Expense: Comparing Renting and Owning
--------------------------------------------------------------------
Monthly Rent                    $0.00
No. of Months Rented                0
Home Purchase Price             $0.00
Mortgage Interest               $0.00
Property Taxes                  $0.00
Depreciation                    $0.00
Maintenance/Repairs             $0.00
Insurance                       $0.00
Lost Interest                   $0.00
Income Tax Saving               $0.00
--------------------------------------------------------------------
Total Cost of Renting           $0.00
Total Cost of Owning            $0.00
--------------------------------------------------------------------
```

Illustration 64–2. Comparing Costs of Home Ownership and Rental

2. Figure the total cost of renting and owning a home by entering these data into the spreadsheet.

B3	420	B7	1200	B10	317
B4	12	B8	600	B11	450
B5	40000	B9	550	B12	980
B6	2300				

3. Answer the questions about the completed home ownership spreadsheet.
   a. What is the total cost of renting the home? $5,040
   b. What is the total cost of owning the home? $4,437
   c. Which costs less, renting or owning? Owning costs less
   d. At what monthly rent, in whole dollars, would the total cost of renting and owning be about equal? $370
   e. If income tax laws change and there is no tax savings from owning a home, would renting or owning be cheaper at the original monthly rent of $420? Renting would be cheaper

Depreciating a Car or Truck

Depreciation on a Car or Truck. When cars or trucks wear out from being used or getting old, they are usually not worth as much as when they were new. This loss of value is called *depreciation*.

For example, a car loses value as it grows older. The total depreciation on a car is the difference between its original cost and its resale, or trade-in, value. **Resale value** is the market value or the amount you get when you sell the car to someone else. The **trade-in value** is the amount you get for your old car when you trade it in to buy a new car.

For example, if you buy a car for $10,500 and four years later trade it in for $4,500, the total depreciation is $6,000.

$10,500	**original cost**
4,500	**trade-in value**
$ 6,000	**depreciation**

Exercise 1
Written

1. Find the total depreciation for each.

	Type of Vehicle	Original Cost	Resale Value or Trade-in Value	Total Depreciation
a.	Delivery Van	$14,500	$3,100	$11,400
b.	Compact Car	$ 7,050	$3,850	$ 3,200
c.	Luxury Car	$28,900	$9,600	$19,300
d.	Pickup Truck	$10,220	$1,850	$ 8,370

2. Manda bought a truck for $14,740. After using the truck, she sold it for $6,790. What was the total depreciation on the truck? $7,950

3. Stuart sold his car for $2,400. If Stuart paid $8,100 for the car 4 years ago, what was the total depreciation on the car? $5,700

4. Yvette Tolbert paid $7,300 for a car 7 years ago. She bought a new car recently at a total cost of $11,100 after deducting the $700 she got as a trade-in for her old car. What was the total depreciation on the 7-year old car? $6,600

Figuring the Average Annual Depreciation on a Car or Truck. The depreciation on a car or truck is usually figured for a year. A year's depreciation, or **average annual depreciation,** can only be estimated because the actual depreciation cannot be known until the car or truck is sold or traded in.

To estimate the average annual depreciation on a car or truck:

1. Estimate the number of years the car or truck will be kept.

2. Estimate the value of the car or truck when it is to be resold or traded in.

3. Subtract the resale or trade-in value from the original cost to find the estimated total depreciation.

4. Divide the total depreciation by the number of years the car or truck will be kept.

The following example shows how average annual depreciation is figured.

Example

A car that cost $14,800 has an estimated trade-in value of $5,900 at the end of 4 years. Find the average annual depreciation.

Solution

$14,800   original cost
  5,900   trade-in value
$ 8,900   total depreciation

$8,900 ÷ 4 = $2,225 average annual depreciation   **Ans.**

This way of estimating the average annual depreciation is called the **straight-line method.** It spreads the total depreciation expense evenly over the time the car is to be kept.

**Exercise 2
Written**

1. Find the average annual depreciation for each.

	Original Cost	Resale or Trade-in Value At end of	Amount	Average Annual Depreciation
a.	$ 9,500	3 years	$6,200	$1,100
b.	$18,500	7 years	$3,800	$2,100
c.	$13,525	2 years	$8,775	$2,375
d.	$ 8,100	5 years	$2,025	$1,215

2. A used dump truck that sells for $20,250 today is estimated to have a resale value of $5,100 in 5 years. What is the average annual depreciation of the truck? $3,030

3. A paint supplier bought a delivery truck for $12,417. After using it for 4 years, the supplier bought a new truck that cost $15,890. A trade-in value of $3,710 was given for the old truck. What was the average annual depreciation of the old truck, to the nearest dollar? $2,177

4. Diedra Neff, the owner of a lawn care company, bought a truck for business use for $17,072. She used the truck for 7 years and then sold it for $2,890.
   a. Estimate the average annual depreciation. $2,000
   b. What was the actual average annual depreciation? $2,026

5. Alphonse Carr bought a car for $8,850 three years ago. Alphonse has been offered $3,825 by a car dealer as the trade-in value, but he

feels he can sell the car for $4,500. What will be the average annual depreciation

a. If he takes the trade-in offer? $1,675

b. If he is able to sell the car at the price he wants? $1,450

Rate of Depreciation. When the straight-line method of figuring depreciation is used, the average annual depreciation is often shown as a percent of the original cost. When finding the **rate of depreciation,** the average annual depreciation is the part, and the original cost is the whole with which the part is compared.

$$\text{Rate of Depreciation} = \frac{\text{Average Annual Depreciation}}{\text{Original Cost}}$$

For example, if the average annual depreciation of a car is $1,800 and the original cost is $12,000, the rate of depreciation is 15%.

$$\text{Rate of Depreciation} = \frac{\$1,800}{\$12,000} = 0.15 = 15\%$$

**Exercise 3
Written**

■ Rate of depreciation is based on original cost.

Round answers to the nearest percent in Problems 1–7.

1. Find the rate of depreciation in each problem.

	Original Cost	Resale or Trade-in Value At end of	Amount	Rate of Depreciation
a.	$14,500	4 years	$5,600	15%
b.	$ 8,100	3 years	$4,200	16%
c.	$ 9,450	6 years	$1,800	13%
d.	$12,680	2 years	$7,700	20%

2. Rex Bell paid $10,400 for a new truck. He estimates that the truck will be worth $4,300 when he trades it in 4 years later. Based on Rex's estimate, what will be the rate of depreciation? 15%

3. Hertha Rogers bought a car for $9,210. If she keeps the car for 3 years, she figures that it can be sold for $4,800. Using Hertha's estimate, what is the rate of depreciation on the car? 16%

4. Jorge Lanell bought a car for $15,300 and used it in his business for 2 years. He then sold it for $8,000. At what rate did Jorge's car depreciate annually? 24%

5. Arlene Norris bought a car for $8,675 and sold it $7\frac{1}{2}$ years later for $725. What was the annual rate of depreciation? 12%

6. A van that costs $13,060 is estimated to be worth $2,900 after 4 years. What will be the rate of depreciation on the van? 19%

7. David Blanton's new car cost $17,380. He estimates the car will be worth $5,200 at the end of 6 years. What will be the rate of depreciation based on David's estimates? 12%

REVIEW 65

Terms

1. Match the terms with the statements.

average annual depreciation   straight-line method
rate of depreciation   trade-in value
resale value

   a. Amount received when car is sold   resale value
   b. Depreciation per year   average annual depreciation
   c. Amount received for old car when buying new car   trade-in value
   d. Spreads total depreciation evenly   straight-line method
   e. Shows depreciation as a percent   rate of depreciation

Skills

2. a. Multiply: $63,000 by 10.5% $6,615
   b. What percent less than 960 is 192?   80%
   c. Find banker's interest at 15% on $500 for 120 days. $25
  ‡d. 48 is $\frac{1}{3}$ smaller than ?   72

Problems

3. Lowell Krygol bought a motor home for $28,000. Six years later he sold the motor home for $12,880. What was the average annual depreciation of the motor home? $2,520 [65]

4. A van that cost $19,000 was traded in for $2,280 after 8 years of use. What was the average annual rate of depreciation?   11% [65]

5. A mutual fund's prices are: 8.54, NAV; 9.08, offer. To the nearest thousandth share, how many shares can $5,000 buy?   550.661 [60]

6. A note dated September 17 for $5,400, bearing 14% exact interest, was paid in full on the following November 29. What was the amount of the payment? $5,551.20 [44, 46]

7. To the nearest tenth percent, what is the yield on a 6%, $500 par value bond selling at 92?   6.5% [56]

Computer Clinic

Herbert Sutton purchased a car for $12,000 and sold it six years later for $3,000. Follow these steps to figure the total depreciation on the car, the average annual depreciation, and rate of depreciation.

1. Insert your Spreadsheet Applications Diskette and call up the file "Sec65." After you do, your computer screen should look like Illustration 65–1.

```
Sec 65                  Figuring Car or Truck Depreciation
----------------------------------------------------------------------
Original Cost                           $.00
Resale/Trade-In Value                   $.00
No. of Years Owned                         0
----------------------------------------------------------------------
Total Depreciation                      $.00
Average Annual Depreciation             $.00
Rate of Depreciation                   .000%
----------------------------------------------------------------------
```

Illustration 65–1. Using a Spreadsheet to Figure Depreciation

2. Figure the depreciation and rate of depreciation on a car by entering these data into the spreadsheet:

   B3   12000   B4   3000   B5   6

3. Answer the questions about your completed depreciation spreadsheet.
   a. What was the total depreciation on the car? $9,000
   b. What amount of depreciation took place, on the average, for
      each year the car was owned? $1,500
   c. What was the rate of the average annual depreciation? 12.5%
   d. If Herbert had kept the car 7 years, its resale/trade-in value
      would have been $500 less. What would have been the amount
      and rate of average annual depreciation?
      Amount, $1,357.14; Rate, 11.310%
   e. Assume the car was worth $6,600 after 2 years of use. What
      was the average annual depreciation and the rate of deprecia-
      tion for the 2 years?
      Average depreciation, $2,700; Rate, 22.500%

4. Suppose that Car A cost $16,000 when new and was traded-in for
   $4,850 at the end of 6 years. Car B cost $9,200 as a new car and
   was sold for $2,675 after being used for 6 years. Which car, A or B,
   had the higher rate of depreciation? What was the rate, to the
   nearest tenth of a percent? Car B had the higher rate, 11.8%

Section 66
Cost of Operating a Car or Truck

In figuring the total cost of operating a car or truck, you need to include expenses such as insurance, gas, oil, license and inspection fees,
tires, repairs, garage rent, parking fees, tolls, taxes, and general upkeep. You also have to allow for the interest that you could have earned
on the money that you have invested in the car, and for depreciation.

Cost of Operating a Car or Truck. The total annual operating cost is the sum of all the annual expenses, including depreciation and loss of interest figured on the original cost of the car or truck.

Example

Kay paid $10,200 for her car. Her annual payments for insurance, gas, oil, repairs, and other expenses total $1,900. The car depreciates 18% a year. Kay could have earned 6% interest on her investment in the car. What was her total annual cost of operating the car?

Solution

Insurance, gas, oil, etc.	$1,900
Depreciation, 18% of $10,200	1,836
Loss of interest, 6% of $10,200	612
Total annual operating cost	$4,348 **Ans.**

**Exercise 1
Written**

1. Find the total annual operating costs.

	Original Cost	Rate of Interest Loss	Depreciation	Other Expenses	Total Operating Cost
a.	$ 9,600	7%	16%	$1,600	$3,808
b.	15,400	12%	20%	1,940	6,868
c.	12,800	10%	15%	2,100	5,300
d.	11,900	9%	21%	1,570	5,140

2. Richard bought a car for $13,500. His expenses for the first year were: gas and oil, $755; repairs, $125; insurance, $562; license plates, $42; loss of interest on investment at 7%; depreciation at 17%. Find the total operating cost for the year. $4,724

3. Before buying a car for $9,800, Rita Romano estimates her first year's car expenses will be: license plates, $46; insurance, $640; gas and oil, $670; loss of interest at 11% of the cost of the car; repairs, $30; depreciation, 23% of the cost of the car. Find Rita's total cost of operating the car for the first year. $4,718

4. The Elliott Flower Shop had these truck expenses last year: gas and oil, $4,120; insurance, $843; license plates, $160; repairs, $710; depreciation, $1,734; loss of interest on investment, $583; other expenses, $170. What was the average weekly cost of operating the truck last year? $160

**Exercise 2
Written**

Your teacher will tell you whether to use Customary or metric measurements, or both, to solve these problems. The metric values in parentheses are only the *approximate* equivalents of Customary values.

1. A car weighs 2,400 pounds (1 080 kilograms). What will be the cost of license plates for the car if the rate is $1.05 per 100 pounds ($2.33 per 100 kilograms)? $25.20 ($25.16)

L = liter
km = kilometer

2. A small car used 14 gallons (54 L) of gas to travel 448 miles (756 km). How many miles (km) did the car average per gallon (per L)?   32 miles (14 km)

3. A truck used 32 gallons (121 L) of gas on a trip of 316 miles (508 km). How many miles (km) did the truck average per gallon (per L) of gas? Show your answer to the nearest mile (km).   10 miles (4 km)

4. On a business trip of 552 miles (882 km), Dave used 24 gallons (90 L) of gas. Gas cost an average of $1.21 per gallon (32.3¢ per L).
   a. How many miles (km) did he average per gallon (per L)? Show your answer to the nearest mile (km).   23 miles (10 km)
   b. What was the total cost of the gas used on the trip? $29.04 ($29.07)
   c. What was the cost of the gas per mile (per km) traveled, to the nearest tenth of a cent? $0.053 ($0.033)

Do not use commas in large metric numbers.

5. Lana Quinn drove her car 14,600 miles (23 500 km) last year. She used 770 gallons (2 918 L) of gas. Her expenses were:

Gas and oil	$ 811.50
Insurance	419.00
Loss of interest	630.00
Depreciation	1,350.00
Repairs and parts	125.00
License and inspection fees	46.00
Garage rent, parking, tolls	271.80

   a. What was the total operating cost for the year? $3,653.30
   b. What was her average operating cost per mile (per km), to the nearest cent? $0.25 ($0.16)
   c. How many miles per gallon (km per L) did she get, to the nearest mile (km)?   19 miles (8 km)

6. Joel Breslin drove 24,318 miles (39 116 km) last year. His car averaged 18 miles per gallon (7.7 km per L). For the year, gas averaged $1.28 per gallon (34¢ per L). How much did Joel spend for gas during the year, to the nearest dollar? $1,729 ($1,727)

Leasing a Car or Truck. When you buy a car or truck, you usually make a down payment and then make monthly payments for the balance of the purchase price. However, instead of buying, you may want to lease a car or truck for a monthly charge.

The monthly charge generally depends on the length of the lease and how much it would cost to buy the car or truck you are leasing. Most leases run for 48 months and limit the number of miles the car or truck can be driven. A per mile charge is made for excess mileage.

If you lease a car, you are responsible for insurance, gasoline, and maintenance. You also have to pay a charge for excess wear and tear.

Exercise 3
Written

Use the leasing charges from the following chart to solve the problems.

A-1 Leasing Company
Monthly Leasing Charges

Type of Car or Truck	Monthly Charge
Two-door compact	$122
Four-door sedan	$190
Convertible	$236
Station wagon	$221
Pickup truck	$170

Monthly charges are based on a 48-month lease. The maximum mileage allowed is 60,000 miles. A charge of 6¢ per mile is made for all miles driven over 60,000 miles.

1. What amount must be paid to the leasing company during a 12-month period for leasing a station wagon? $2,652

2. Tameko wants to lease a pickup truck from A-1 for 4 years. She estimates that insurance, maintenance, and fuel will cost $1,600 a year. She also estimates that she will drive the truck an average of 14,000 miles each year. Including the leasing charges, find
   a. The total cost of operating the truck for 4 years. $14,560
   b. The operating cost per mile for 4 years. $0.26

3. Adam Voleck leased a 2-door compact from A-1 Leasing for 4 years. The total cost of insurance, maintenance, repairs, and gas for 4 years was $4,434. He drove the car for 14,000 miles for the first year, 17,000 miles for the second, 16,000 miles for the third, and 15,000 for the fourth. What was the total cost of operating the car for 4 years? $10,410

4. Joyce Gardner can buy a convertible for a total cost of $15,250. She expects to drive the car 15,000 miles a year for the next 4 years. Joyce estimates that insurance, maintenance, repairs, and fuel will total $6,350 for 4 years and that depreciation will be 60% of the original cost. By paying cash for the car she will lose $3,600 in interest over the 4 years.
   a. What is the total cost of owning and operating the car for 4 years? $19,100
   b. What is the total cost of leasing a similar car from A-1 and operating it for 4 years? $17,678
   c. Is it cheaper for Joyce to buy or lease, and by how much?
      Lease; $1,422

5. Kirk Mandell is comparing the leasing charges for a 4-door sedan and a van that leases for $328.70 a month.
   a. How much more per year would it cost to lease the van?
      $1,664.40
   b. What percent more will it cost to lease the van instead of the 4-door sedan? 73%

6. The owner of the A-1 Leasing Company now wants to charge 6¢ a mile for all miles driven over 15,000 miles each year. What is the total leasing charge in the first year for a 2-door compact car that is driven 18,700 miles? $1,686

**Exercise 4
Written**

Related Problems. Owners of cars and trucks need to be able to figure the savings that can result from wiser buying. They also need to compare costs to help them make buying decisions.

1. The gas station near Harvey's place of work charges $1.15 a gallon for gasoline. A station near Harvey's house charges $1.07 a gallon. If Harvey's car uses 600 gallons of gasoline a year, how much will Harvey save by buying at the station near his house? $48

2. Rhonda drives 24,000 miles a year. A compact car she is considering buying gets 32 miles per gallon of gasoline. She is also considering a sports car that gets 15 miles per gallon. Gasoline prices average $1.25 per gallon. What amount will she save on gasoline annually by buying the compact car? $1,062.50

3. The purchase price of a company's 2-door car is $12,700. The car is expected to be worth $3,556 at the end of 5 years. The 4-door model of another make of car can be bought for $15,800. Its expected resale value 5 years from now is $5,530. Which car, the 2-door or 4-door, has the greatest percent of total depreciation, and what is the rate?   Two-door; 72%

4. A new car is purchased for $14,000. The car's estimated resale value at the end of 1 year is 75% of its purchase price and 60% of the purchase price at the end of 2 years. Using these estimates,
   a. What is the car's resale value at the end of 1 year? $10,500
   b. What is the resale value of the car at the end of 2 years? $8,400
   c. At the end of 2 years, what is the amount of the average annual depreciation? $2,800

5. Matt Richards uses his own car for business. Matt's employer pays him $0.21 for every business mile driven and for all business parking costs. Last week Matt drove these business miles in 5 days: 78, 91, 55, 140, 118. His business parking costs for the week were $12.50. How much will Matt get to cover his car operating costs? $113.72

REVIEW 66

Skills

1. a. $48 is what part smaller than $72? $\frac{1}{3}$
   b. Multiply: 17.8 m by 8 m   142.4 m^2
   c. Divide: 34.8 by 0.04   870
   d. Multiply: $20,000 by 1.05 $21,000
   e. What number is $62\frac{1}{2}$% less than $856? $321

Problems

2. Polly Rhodes bought a car for $9,200. She drove the car 12,000 miles last year. Her car expenses for the year were: insurance, $436; gas and oil, $670; repairs, $28; license plates, $42; loss of in-

terest on original investment, 5%; depreciation, 18%. Find last year's operating cost per mile, to the nearest cent. $0.27 [66]

3. You lease a car for $238 a month and 7¢ for every mile it is driven over 15,000 miles in 1 year. If you drive the car 16,500 miles each year, what amount will you pay for leasing charges in 2 years? $5,922 [66]

4. The trade-in value of a car that cost $11,900 seven years ago is $1,400. The same type of car sells for $15,200 today. What is the average annual depreciation of the 7-year old car? $1,500 [65]

5. The monthly payment on a 20-year, 12%, $45,000 mortgage is $495.49. How much interest will the buyer pay over the life of the loan? $73,917.60 [63]

6. A stock that sells at 60 pays a quarterly dividend of $0.45 a share. What annual rate of income can be earned on this stock?   3% [58]

Computer Clinic

Davina Lewis has collected data about the expenses of buying and leasing one car model. Follow the steps below to compare the costs of leasing and owning the car.

1. Insert your Spreadsheet Applications Diskette and call up the file "Sec66." After you do, your computer screen should look like Illustration 66–1.

```
Sec 66            Comparing Car Leasing and Ownership Costs
-------------------------------------------------------------------
Monthly Lease Charge              $.00
Years Leased                         0
Excess Mileage:
   Number of Excess Miles           0
   Per Mile Charge                $.00
Purchase Price                    $.00
Total Operating Cost              $.00
Total Depreciation                $.00
Total Interest Lost               $.00
-------------------------------------------------------------------
Total Cost of Leasing             $.00
Total Cost of Owning              $.00
Difference (Leasing - Owning)     $.00
-------------------------------------------------------------------
```

Illustration 66–1. Car Leasing/Ownership Comparison Spreadsheet

2. Figure the total cost of leasing and owning a car by entering these data into the spreadsheet:

B3	215		B8	11600
B4	4		B9	5000
B6	2000		B10	7424
B7	0.06		B11	2784

3. Answer the questions about the completed leasing/ownership comparison spreadsheet.
    a. Which costs less: leasing or owning the car? What is the difference?   Owning costs $232 less
    b. If the monthly lease charge was reduced by 5% from $215 monthly to $204.25 monthly, which would be cheaper, leasing or owning? By how much?   Leasing cheaper by $284
    c. Use the original data given in Step 2 and assume that Davina could lease the car and not have to pay excess mileage charges. Would leasing or owning be cheaper? By how much?
        Owning cheaper by $112

Taxes

Individuals and businesses pay many different types of taxes to support the federal government, state government, local government, and schools. In this unit, you will learn how to solve problems about property, sales, social security, and income taxes.

After you finish Unit 11, you will be able to:

- Compute property taxes using rates per $1, $100, and $1,000.
- Compute property tax rates.
- Show property tax rates in mills, cents, and dollars.
- Compute sales taxes using a table and using a sales tax rate.
- Compute excise taxes.
- Compute FICA taxes for employees, employers, and self-employed persons.
- Compute social security retirement benefits.
- Compute federal and state income taxes.
- Solve problems that contain more information than you need.
- Estimate answers to problems.
- Read, write, say, and recognize the meanings of the key terms.
- Use a computer spreadsheet to calculate federal income taxes and to see the effects of increased income on taxes.

Property taxes are taxes on real estate. These taxes are a major expense of owning farm land, business property, or a home. Property taxes are collected by the community in which the property is located. Each year, the local tax office will send a tax bill like the one shown in Illustration 67–1 to each property owner.

		Taxing District	Amount of Tax
Parcel I.D. No.	13-89-47699	COUNTY	$ 390.10
Loan I.D. No.	3870-7798	TOWN	107.00
Market Value	$ 150,000	ROAD & BRIDGE	105.30
Assessment Rate	33⅓%	SCHOOL DISTRICT	1,590.60
Assessed Value	$ 50,000	TOWNSHIP	650.30
Tax Rate per $100	$ 6.20	FIRE DISTRICT	95.95
OTIS & LATONYA JOHNSON 45 SEVENTH STREET		COMMUNITY COLLEGE	160.75
MADISON, IL 62060-1978		TOTAL TAX DUE	$3,100.00

Illustration 67–1. Property Tax Bill

Assessed Value of Real Estate. The amount of property taxes you pay is based on the **assessed value** of your property. This value is figured by local tax assessors. For example, the Johnsons' property in Illustration 67–1 has a fair market value of $150,000. It is assessed at only 33⅓% of its market value, or $50,000.

The Tax Rate. The amount of tax you pay depends on the assessed value of your property and the tax rate. In some communities, the tax rate may be shown as the number of *dollars* for each $100 or $1,000 of assessed value. For example, the Johnsons' tax rate may be shown as $6.20 per $100 or $62 per $1,000 of assessed value.

In other communities, the rate is shown as the number of **mills** or *cents* for each $1 of assessed value. A cent is one hundredth of a dollar ($0.01). A **mill** is one thousandth of a dollar ($0.001). The Johnsons' tax rate may be shown as 6.2 cents per $1, or 62 mills per $1 of assessed value.

■ These tax rates are the same:
$40 per $1,000
$4 per $100
4¢ per $1
40 mills per $1.

Finding the Tax for Rates Shown in Dollars per $100 or $1,000. The Johnsons' tax rate is $6.20 per $100 of assessed value. To find their tax bill, you must follow these steps:

Step 1: **First find the number of $100 units in the assessed value:**

$50,000 ÷ $100 = 500   units of $100

Step 2: **Multiply the number of units by the rate per $100:**

500 × $6.20 = $3,100   amount of tax

If their tax rate was $62 per $1,000, the Johnsons' tax bill would be figured this way:

Step 1: $50,000 ÷ $1,000 = 50   units of $1,000

Step 2:   50 × $62 = $3,100   amount of tax

**Exercise 1
Written**

1. Find the amount of tax due.

	Assessed Value	Tax Rate	Tax Due
a.	$80,000	$5.20 per $100	$4,160
b.	48,500	7.10 per $100	3,443.50
c.	15,000	34 per $1,000	510
d.	20,800	28 per $1,000	582.40
e.	18,000	3.085 per $100	555.30
f.	40,500	25.764 per $1,000	1,043.44

2. The tax rate for Elderton is $3.775 per $100. What is Norma Miranda's tax bill if she owns property in Elderton assessed at $60,500? $2,283.88

3. What tax must Ira Baum pay on his home, assessed for $25,900, if the tax rate is $38.20 per $1,000? $989.38

4. Find the tax on property assessed at $17,500 if the tax rate is $4.155 per $100. $727.13

5. The town of Chester has a tax rate of $45.089 per $1,000. What is the tax bill on property in Chester worth $250,000, assessed at 60% of its value? $6,763.35

6. The tax rate for Amestown is $19 per $1,000. Chi Huang owns property valued at $151,000 in Amestown that is assessed for 50% of its value.
    a. Estimate Huang's tax bill. $1,500
    b. Find Huang's exact tax bill. $1,434.50

Finding the Tax for Rates Shown in Mills or Cents per $1. To find the tax when the tax rate is in mills or cents per $1, you must first change the rate to a rate in dollars. You then multiply the rate in dollars by the assessed value.

A mill is one tenth of a cent, one thousandth of a dollar, or $0.001. There are 10 mills in one cent and 1,000 in a dollar. To change mills to dollars, you divide the number of mills by 1,000. For example:

56.8 mills ÷ 1,000 = $0.0568   (or move the decimal point 3 places to the left: $0.056.8)

To change cents to dollars, you divide the number of cents by 100. For example:

5.68 cents ÷ 100 = $0.0568   (or move the decimal point 2 places to the left: $0.05.68)

Example

Camden's tax rate is 45.9 mills per dollar of assessed value. Find the tax bill on property assessed at $40,000.

Solution

Step 1: Change the tax rate from mills to dollars by dividing the number of mills by 1,000.

45.9 mills ÷ 1,000 = $0.0459

Step 2: Multiply the rate per $1 by the assessed value of the property.

$0.0459 × $40,000 = $1,836 **Ans.**

**Exercise 2
Written**

1,000 mills = $1

1. Find the tax due on each property.

	Assessed Value	Tax rate Per $1	Tax Due
a.	$80,000	35 mills	$2,800
b.	48,500	82.1 mills	3,981.85
c.	15,000	77.3 mills	1,159.50
d.	20,800	9 cents	1,872
e.	18,000	2.7 cents	486
f.	40,500	4.54 cents	1,838.70

2. The tax rate in Datenberg is 48 mills per dollar of assessed value. Find the tax to be paid on property assessed at $35,200. $1,689.60

3. What tax must Barby Tomlin pay on a home assessed at $20,750 if her tax rate is 3.5 cents per $1? $726.25

4. A house with 2,800 sq. feet of living space is worth $125,000. It was assessed this year at 25% of its value. If the tax rate is 72.5 mills per $1, what is the tax bill? $2,265.63

5. Al Busby owns properties worth $70,800 and $140,300 in Bentville. What total tax must he pay if the properties are assessed at 35% of their values and the tax rate is 28.5 mills per dollar? $2,105.72

REVIEW 67

Terms

1. Match the terms with the statements.

   assessed value   mill   property tax

   a. Tax on real estate   property tax
   b. Base for property tax   assessed value
   c. One tenth of a cent   mill

Skills

2. a. Multiply: $28,000 by 0.08076. $2,261.28
   b. $264 is what part less than $440? $\frac{2}{5}$
   c. $480 is what percent of $192?   250%
   d. 250 mL is what percent of 4 L? $6\frac{1}{4}$%

Problems

3. Janice owns property assessed at $25,400. The tax rate in her town is $56.731 per $1,000 of assessed value. What is her tax bill? $1,440.97 [67]

4. You can buy a portable stereo/radio from Ashcroft's Music Store for a down payment of $20 and weekly payments of $2.50 for 1 year. Leneen's Electronics offers the same stereo for $25 down and $10 a month for 1 year. How much will you save by taking the better of the two offers? $5 [50]

5. Riva bought 9, $1,000 bonds at $92\frac{1}{8}$. How much did she invest in the bonds if the brokerage charge was $6 per bond? $8,345.25 [55]

6. Ted paid $760 for a $1,000 bond with interest at $9\frac{1}{2}$%. What is the yield on his investment? $12\frac{1}{2}$% [56]

7. Olive Meade has a mortgage loan of $80,000 on her new home and must repay the principal and interest in payments of $880 a month over 20 years. How much interest will she pay over the life of the mortgage? $131,200 [63]

8. A living room suite that sells for $1,500 cash can be bought for $150 down and $59.99 a month for 24 months. [50]
   a. What is the finance charge? $89.76
   b. What is the amount financed? $1,350

‡9. How many $1,000, 8% bonds must be bought to get an annual income of $10,000 from the investment?   125 [56]

Section 68
Property Tax Rates

Assessed value: the value put on property by tax assessors.

Cities, counties, towns, villages, school districts, and other tax districts provide many services for their citizens. Much of the money for these services comes from property taxes, which are taxes on the value of the real estate in the tax district.

Tax districts must determine what tax rates are needed to collect enough money to pay for the services they provide. They can then multiply the assessed value of each piece of taxable property by the tax rate.

Finding a Decimal Tax Rate. To find the tax rate needed, the tax district estimates its expenses for the coming year and prepares an expense budget. The district also estimates its income from sources other than the property tax, such as licenses, fees, fines, rents, state aid, and so on. The difference between the total budgeted expenses and the income from other sources is the amount that must be raised by the property tax.

The amount to be raised by the property tax is then divided by the total assessed value of all property in the district. The result is a decimal tax rate, which districts may round to 3, 4, or 5 places.

$$\frac{\textbf{Amount to be Raised by Property Tax}}{\textbf{Total Assessed Value of All Property}} = \textbf{Decimal Tax Rate}$$

For example, the Peru School District's total budgeted expenses last year were $6,000,000. The district's estimated income from sources other than the property tax was $1,800,000. The difference of $4,200,000 was the amount to be raised by property tax.

Total budgeted expenses	**$6,000,000**
Income from other sources	**− 1,800,000**
Amount to be raised by property tax	**$4,200,000**

The total assessed value of all taxable property in Peru last year was $39,000,000. So, the amount to be raised by the property tax, $4,200,000, was divided by the total assessed value, $39,000,000. The quotient, 0.107692, rounded to 5 places was Peru's decimal tax rate.

$$\frac{\$\ 4,200,000}{\$39,000,000} = \textbf{0.107692,} \quad \text{or} \quad \textbf{0.10769 decimal tax rate}$$

**Exercise 1
Written**

1. For each problem, find the decimal tax rate correct to 5 places.

	Assessed Value	Amount to be Raised	
a.	$ 8,000,000	$ 507,000	0.06338
b.	6,000,000	483,200	0.08053
c.	2,700,000	158,500	0.0587
d.	9,800,000	889,600	0.09078
e.	1,750,000	100,500	0.05743
f.	5,390,000	125,800	0.02334
g.	725,000	22,750	0.03138
h.	7,400,000	282,500	0.03818
i.	15,320,000	1,279,000	0.08349
j.	24,130,000	2,528,600	0.10479

2. Find the amount to be raised by property tax and the tax rate. Show the rate as a decimal, correct to 3 places.

	Assessed Value	Total Expenses	Other Income	Raised by Property Tax	Tax Rate
a.	$36,000,000	$878,000	$97,500	$780,500	0.022
b.	22,750,000	382,700	68,400	314,300	0.014
c.	7,900,000	396,300	45,600	350,700	0.044

3. The Allis Fire District must raise $583,400 from property taxes. The assessed value of the property in the district is $24,780,000. What is the decimal tax rate needed, to 3 decimal places?   0.024

4. Aspen village has a total assessed property value of $6,800,000. The village must raise $278,000 through property taxes. What must be the decimal tax rate, to 3 decimal places?   0.041

5. Central City plans to spend $2,210,000 next year. Income from sources other than property taxes will be $835,000. The taxable property in the city has a total assessed value of $40,000,000.
   a. Estimate how much the city must raise through property taxes.
   $1,200,000
   b. What is the exact amount the city must raise by property tax?
   $1,375,000
   c. What will be the tax rate, correct to 4 decimal places?   0.0344

6. Property in the Boise School District has a total assessed value of $89,500,000. The school's budget for next year shows expenses totaling $4,000,000 to serve 3,500 students in 7 buildings. The district expects to earn $2,900,000 from sources other than property tax. What decimal property tax rate, to 4 places, will the district use to raise enough money to meet the budgeted expenses?   0.0123

Finding a Property Tax Using a Decimal Rate. To find the tax on a property when you know the decimal rate, you multiply the property's assessed value by the decimal rate. For example, the decimal tax rate in the Boise School District was 0.0123. The tax on a property in Boise, assessed at $96,000, was $1,180.80.

$$0.0123 \times \$96,000 = \$1,180.80$$

Exercise 2 Written

1. Jose's property is assessed at $82,000. The school tax rate in his district is 0.0145. What is Jose's school tax? $1,189

2. Cato Community College's tax rate is 0.04218. What is the tax on property in the college's district assessed at $15,600? $658.01

3. The tax rate in Torrenton is 0.0375. Terri Carr owns 2 pieces of property in Torrenton. One is assessed for $9,900 and the other for $27,300. What is her total tax? $1,395

4. The Eaton Water District must raise $2,100,000 through property taxes. The total assessed value of property in the district is $198,000,000.
   a. Estimate the decimal tax rate.   0.01
   b. What will be the exact tax rate in the district, rounded to 4 decimal places?   0.0106

  c. What will be the district's tax on property assessed at $24,000?
   $254.40

5. Fox County's budget for a year was $6,750,000. Of that, $650,000 was from other income, and the rest was raised through property taxes. The total assessed value of the county's property was $80,000,000.
  a. What amount was raised by property tax? $6,100,000
  b. What was the decimal tax rate, rounded to three places? 0.076
  c. What was the county tax on property assessed at $40,000?
   $3,040

Changing a Decimal Rate to a Rate per $1, $100, or $1,000. Tax district workers often need to change a decimal rate to a rate in cents or mills per $1 or in dollars per $100 or $1,000. The method used to change a decimal rate is shown below.

Decimal Rate	×	Base	= Rate in Other Terms
0.04858	×	$100	= $4.858 per $100
0.04858	×	$1,000	= $48.58 per $1,000
0.04858	×	100 cents	= 4.858 cents per $1 (100 cents = $1)
0.04858	×	1,000 mills	= 48.58 mills per $1 (1,000 mills = $1)

**Exercise 3
Written**

1. Copy and complete the table.

	Decimal Rate	Rate in Dollars per $100	Rate in Dollars per $1,000	Rate in Cents per $1	Rate in Mills per $1
a.	0.03478	3.478	34.78	3.478	34.78
b.	0.01208	1.208	12.08	1.208	12.08
c.	0.10675	10.675	106.75	10.675	106.75
d.	0.08462	8.462	84.62	8.462	84.62
e.	0.01782	1.782	17.82	1.782	17.82

2. Allentown has a total assessed value of $32,000,000 and needs to raise $680,000 from a property tax. What tax rate per $1,000 will be needed? $21.25

3. The Belmont City Library needs to raise $636,000 in property taxes on a total assessed value of $240,000,000. What tax rate per $100 will the library need to charge? $0.265

4. The Eberle school system's budget for next year requires the raising of $4,800,000 through a property tax. The total assessed value in the Eberle District is $64,000,000. Find the school tax rate needed, shown in
  a. Cents per $1 7.5 c. Dollars per $100 $7.50
  b. Mills per $1 75 d. Dollars per $1,000 $75

5. On property assessed at $55,000, Rhonda Cohen paid $2,310 in property tax. What was the tax rate per $1,000? $42

6. Sea Isle City needs $9,500,000 to meet its expenses for next year. It will get $3,000,000 from sources other than property tax. The city's total assessed value is $125,000,000. Find what property tax rate will be needed
    a. Per $100 $5.20
    b. Per $1,000 $52

REVIEW 68

Skills

1. a. Divide: 2,800 by 175,000.   0.016
    b. What amount is 250% of $60? $150
    c. Find the number of days between July 6 and October 19.   105
    d. Find the banker's interest on $6,400 for 120 days at 6%. $128

Problems

2. The budget for Kempler's sewer district for the year was $720,000. Income from fines, fees, and other sources was estimated to be $128,000. The balance was to be raised by a property tax on a total assessed value of $21,000,000. Find the tax rate, to 5 places.   0.02819 [68]

3. The Deere Park District has a decimal tax rate of 0.01182.
    a. What is the rate per $1,000? $11.82
    b. What is the rate in mills per $1?   11.82 mills [68]

4. The tax rate in a village is $82.19 per $1,000 of assessed value. Find the tax to be paid on a property assessed at $16,800. $1,380.79 [67]

5. Brad pays $400 a month to rent a house that he can buy for $52,000 with a down payment of $13,000. The annual expenses are estimated to be $6,240. If Brad could earn 12% interest on his money, which option would be cheaper: buy the house, or keep renting it? How much would Brad save annually?   Rent; $3,000 [64]

Section 69
Sales and Excise Taxes

You have learned how to figure sales taxes by multiplying the subtotal by the sales tax rate. To save time, many businesses find the same information by using sales tax tables.

Figuring Sales Tax with a Table. The sales tax table shown in Illustration 69–1 is used in a city where a 5% sales tax is charged.

Amount of Sale	Sales Tax
$0.01 — $0.10	0
0.11 — 0.25	1 cent
0.26 — 0.45	2 cents
0.46 — 0.65	3 cents
0.66 — 0.85	4 cents
0.86 — 1.10	5 cents
More than $1.10	5 cents on each dollar, plus amount in table for cents

Illustration 69–1. 5% Sales Tax Table

The table shows that the sales tax on a $0.60 sale is $0.03. To find the tax on a sale of $8.60, follow these steps:

Step 1: **Find the tax on $8.00**

(8 × tax on $1, or 8 × 5 cents) .... 40 cents

Step 2: **Find the tax on 0.60**

(from table — $0.46 to $0.65) .... 3 cents

Step 3: **Add both amounts**

Tax on $8.60 .... 43 cents

Exercise 1 Oral

Using the table above, find the tax on each sale.

	Amount of Sale	Sales Tax		Amount of Sale	Sales Tax		Amount of Sale	Sales Tax
1.	$0.81	$0.04	4.	$0.11	$0.01	7.	$1.12	$0.06
2.	$3.47	$0.18	5.	$4.55	$0.23	8.	$3.01	$0.15
3.	$9.16	$0.46	6.	$0.65	$0.03	9.	$6.10	$0.30

Exercise 2 Written

Use the sales tax table in Illustration 69–1.

1. A box of $5\frac{1}{4}$ inch diskettes sells for $10.79. What is the
   a. Sales tax? $0.54
   b. Total price, including tax? $11.33

2. A video is priced at $24.99. What is the sales tax? $1.25

3. An auto seat cover at $99.95 and a floor mat at $10.79 are listed on a sales slip. What is the sales tax on the total sale? $5.54

Figuring Sales Taxes When Some Items Are Not Taxable. Some cities and states do not tax certain items, such as food, prescription drugs, and services.

Example

A service station mechanic spent 4 hours repairing a car @ $35 an hour. The mechanic also replaced the car's fan belt and battery. The fan belt cost $12.98 and the battery, $48.99. The state has a sales tax of 5% that is charged on goods, but not on services. What was the total bill?

Solution

Step 1: Find the subtotal of all the taxable items that were sold.
$12.98 + $48.99 = $61.97   subtotal of taxable items

Step 2: Find the sales tax on that subtotal.
$61.97 × 0.05 = $3.098, or $3.10   tax on subtotal

Step 3: Add the subtotal, the tax, and the cost of the nontaxable items sold.
4 hours × $35 = $140.00   cost of mechanic's services
61.97   cost of taxable items
 3.10   tax on taxable item
$$$205.07   total bill   **Ans.**

**Exercise 3
Written**

1. A carpenter built a bookcase for a customer. The carpenter figured his time to be 3 hours @ $30, and the cost of materials to be $45. The state charges a 6% sales tax on goods but does not tax services. What was the total cost of the bookcase? $137.70

2. Sandra Brown bought these items at a grocery store: 3 cans of soup @ 3 for $1, 2 bunches of celery @ $0.87, 5 lbs. of potatoes @ $0.88, 1 box of dishwasher soap, $2.79, and 2 potholders, $1.29. The state has a 3% sales tax but does not tax food. What was Sandra's total bill? $11.34

3. Find the sales tax and total bill for each sale below. The state has a sales tax of 5% but does not tax all items sold.

	Total of Taxable Items	Total of Nontaxable Items	Sales Tax	Total Bill
a.	$145.70	$103.00	$ 7.29	$255.99
b.	39.39	128.89	1.97	170.25
c.	8.34	201.12	0.42	209.88
d.	378.50	100.08	18.93	497.51
e.	44.67	34.87	2.23	81.77

Excise Taxes. The United States Government charges an **excise tax** on some goods and services such as gasoline, sporting equipment, airline tickets, and telephone service. To find the amount of excise tax, you multiply the price of the good or service by the excise tax rate. You then round the result to the nearest cent.

Some excise taxes are stated in cents per unit of sales. For example, the excise tax on gasoline may be one tenth of one cent ($0.001) per gallon. If you bought 15 gallons of gas, the amount of the excise tax would be 15 × $0.001, or $0.015, or $0.02.

When both sales and excise taxes are charged, you must find the amount of each tax on the bill and round each tax to the nearest cent. For example, Jason bought a fishing reel for $24.79. The purchase was subject to a 6% sales tax and a 10% federal excise tax. The total bill for the reel was $28.76. This is how the total was found:

Step 1:   Find the sales tax.

$24.79 × 0.06 = $1.487, or $1.49

Step 2:   Find the excise tax.

$24.79 × 0.10 = $2.479, or $2.48

Step 3:   Add the price of the reel and the amounts of both taxes.

$24.79 + $1.49 + $2.48 = $28.76

Exercise 4
Written

1. An airline ticket costs $210 plus 8% excise tax. What is the total cost of the ticket? $226.80

2. Eve's phone bill for June showed a charge of $15.75 for regular service and $22.57 for long distance calls. A federal excise tax of 3% and a sales tax of 6% were added to the bill. What was Eve's total bill? $41.77

3. John bought 19 gallons of gas for $18.62. The sale was subject to a 0.1 cent per gallon excise tax and a state sales tax of 6%. What was John's total bill? $19.76

4. Find the total cost of each item.

Item	Cost	Sales Tax	Excise Tax	Total Cost
a. Video tape	$ 6.89	6%	0	$ 7.30
b. 15 gal. gas	13.35	4%	$0.001 per gallon	13.90
c. Airline ticket	274.59	0%	8%	296.56
d. Tackle box	19.99	5%	10%	22.99
e. Telephone service	24.92	7%	3%	27.41
f. Baseball glove	29.89	5%	11%	34.67

‡Exercise 5
Written

1. A store's sales in June totaled $88,620, including a 5% sales tax.
   a. What were the store's sales, without tax? $84,400
   b. How much sales tax did the store collect? $4,220

2. Sue's airline ticket cost $378. That price included an 8% federal excise tax. What amount was Sue charged for
   a. The airline service? $350
   b. Excise tax? $28

REVIEW 69

Skills

Problems

1. a. Show a tax rate of 0.0146 as a rate per $1,000. $14.60
   b. $450 is what part smaller than $540? $\frac{1}{6}$
   c. What amount is $\frac{1}{2}$% of $380? $1.90
   d. 5 m multiplied by 3 is ? centimeters.   1 500
   e. $150 is $\frac{2}{3}$ smaller than ? $450

2. The repair of your TV cost $45.87 for labor and $13.22 for parts. A state sales tax of 5% was charged on goods, but not labor. What was the total bill? $59.75 [69]

3. A bill for $18.56 for telephone service was subject to a sales tax of 6% and an excise tax of 3%. What was the total bill? $20.23 [69]

4. Don started the month with 56 gallons of fuel oil. He bought 100 gallons @ $0.92 during the month. At the end of the month, he had 65 gallons left. How much fuel oil had he used during the month?   91 gal. [4]

5. A 12% exact interest note for $2,000, dated March 17, was paid in full on the following May 29. What was the amount of the payment? $2,048 [44, 46]

6. An agent sold a house for $96,200 and charged a 6% commission.
   a. Estimate the amount of commission. $6,000
   b. What were the exact net proceeds from the sale? $90,428 [29]

7. Jerry's school tax for a year was $1,419.12. His property was assessed at $21,600. What was the tax rate shown in
   a. Dollars per $1,000? $65.70
   b. Dollars per $100? $6.57 [68]

Section 70
Social Security Taxes and Benefits

Employees, employers, and self-employed persons are taxed under the Federal Insurance Contributions Act. This tax is called the *FICA tax* or social security tax. Money from the tax is used to pay for benefits to retired and disabled workers and their dependents.

FICA Tax on Employees. An employer must deduct a certain percent of each employee's earnings for FICA tax. For example, in June the employees at Faber's Designs earned $3,000 in taxable wages. From these wages, FICA taxes of 7.65% were deducted. The owner of Faber's Designs deducted $229.50 (0.0765 × $3,000 = $229.50) from the total wages and paid it to the federal government.

   Employees are taxed on only a certain amount of their yearly wages. For example, if the taxable limit for wages is $45,000, workers are not taxed on any wages they earn beyond $45,000.

FICA Tax on Employers. The employer also is taxed on wages paid to employees. The rate is the same as the rate paid by employees. For example, the owner of Faber's Designs also had to pay $229.50 on the June wages. So, the total of the FICA taxes that Faber's Designs sent to the government for June was 2 × $229.50, or $459.

FICA Tax on Self-Employed Persons. People who work for themselves must also pay a FICA tax on yearly net earnings up to a certain amount. The FICA tax rate for these people is higher than the rate paid by employees. For example, Eleanor Faber, the owner of Faber's Designs, found that her net earnings from her company for the year were $35,000. She paid a **self-employment tax** of 15.3% on those earnings. The amount of the tax was $5,355 (0.153 × $35,000 = $5,355).

The FICA tax rates and the maximum wages on which the taxes are charged are set by Congress and may change from time to time.

**Exercise 1
Written**

1. Find the FICA tax on each of the weekly wages. Each wage is fully taxable. Use a rate of 7.65%, and round the tax to the nearest cent.
   a. Steven Dietz $206.00 $15.76
   b. Wilma Drake   399.70   30.58
   c. Jose Mendoza   516.20   39.49
   d. Marge O'Brien   422.50   32.32
   e. Ying Pai   380.80   29.13
   f. Irving Rosen   295.07   22.57

2. During June, Rayco Toy Co. paid a total of $38,746 in taxable wages to employees. At a rate of 7.65%, what amount of FICA tax did Rayco have to pay as an employer? $2,964.07

3. Sylvia is a self-employed accountant. Last year she paid 15.3% FICA tax on net income of $42,370. What was her self-employment tax? $6,482.61

4. Chris Crouse is paid an annual salary of $58,800. The FICA tax rate is 7.65% on a maximum of $45,000.
   a. What amount of Chris's salary is subject to FICA tax? $45,000
   b. What amount of his salary is not subject to FICA tax? $13,800
   c. Estimate Chris's FICA tax. $4,000
   d. How much FICA tax did he pay? $3,442.50

5. Arlene Pagliano earns an annual salary of $61,500, payable monthly. The FICA tax rate is 7.65% on a maximum of $45,000 per year. How much FICA tax must be deducted from her salary in
   a. January? $392.06
   b. August? $392.06
   c. October? $0.00

Social Security Benefits. Social security benefits for workers include retirement benefits, disability benefits, and **Medicare**. Medicare pays for hospital and medical bills. The dependents of retired or disabled workers, such as a husband, wife, or children, and survivors of deceased workers may also get social security benefits.

Figuring a Worker's Retirement Benefit. Social Security benefits are paid monthly. The amount of your monthly benefits depends on your age, how many years you have worked, how much pay you have earned, the benefit plan in effect when you retire, and other factors.

Social security benefits change often. To figure your exact benefits, you must contact the local office of the Social Security Administration. You can get an idea of how the benefit system works, though, from the partial benefits table shown in Illustration 70–1. The table is taken from detailed tables available from the Social Security Administration.

The table shows the amounts you would receive if you retired at 65. If you plan to retire at 64, the Social Security Administration suggests that you estimate your benefits at $6\frac{2}{3}\%$ less than the table amounts. If you retire at 63, your benefits would be $13\frac{1}{3}\%$ less, and at 62, 20% less.

Average Covered Monthly Earnings	Monthly Benefits At 65
$ 200	$180.00
400	313.00
600	377.00
800	441.00
1,000	505.00
1,200	569.00
1,400	633.00
1,600	697.00
1,800	761.00
2,000	811.70

Illustration 70–1. Partial Table of Social Security Retirement Benefits

To use the benefits table, you must find your "average covered monthly earnings." This amount is the average of your monthly earnings covered by FICA over many years. To find that amount, you must know how many years you have worked and how much of your earnings were subject to FICA tax.

For example, if your average covered monthly earnings are $200 and you retire at 65, your monthly benefit will be $180. If you retire at 62, your monthly benefit will be 20% less than $180, or $144.

Use Illustration 70–1 to solve these problems.

**Exercise 2
Written**

1. Ben Stein's average covered monthly earnings are $1,000. What will his monthly benefits be if he
    a. Retires at 65? $505
    b. Retires at 62? $404

2. Penny Brzinski is considering retiring at 64. She estimates that her average covered monthly earnings at 64 will be $1,400. What will her monthly benefits be? $590.80

3. Trent Oro is 63, and he has average covered monthly earnings of $800.

    a. If he retires at 63, what will be his monthly benefit? $382.20

    b. If he retires at 65, and his covered earnings are the same as at 63, what will be his monthly benefit? $441

4. At 62, Louise Benito's average covered monthly earnings are $1,600. If her covered earnings stay the same, how much more in monthly benefits would she receive at 65 than at 62? $139.40

5. Robert Walkfar plans to retire at 65 with average covered monthly earnings of $1,200.

    a. What will be his total yearly benefit? $6,828

    b. If he retired at 62, with average covered monthly earnings of $1,200, what would be his yearly benefit? $5,462.40

    c. How much greater per year would his benefit be by retiring at 65 rather than at 62? $1,365.60

6. Tien Su is planning to retire at 64. She estimates that her average covered monthly earnings at that time will be $2,000.

    a. What will be Tien's monthly benefit? $757.59

    b. How much more per month would Tien receive if she waited until 65 to retire and her average covered monthly earnings stayed the same? $54.11

REVIEW 70

Terms

1. Match the terms with the statements.

    excise tax   Medicare   self-employment tax

    a. Tax paid by those who work for themselves
        self-employment tax

    b. Pays for hospital and medical bills Medicare

    c. A federal tax on certain goods and services excise tax

Skills

2. a. Find $\frac{1}{4}$% of $3,800. $9.50

    b. $700 is what part greater than $420? $\frac{2}{3}$

    c. Find the banker's interest at 9% on $4,800 for 30 days. $36

    d. Show a tax rate of 67 mills on $1 as a rate on $1,000. $67

    e. $14 is $\frac{1}{3}$ greater than what amount? $10.50

Problems

3. If Victor retires at 65, his monthly social security benefits will be $633. How much would his monthly benefits be if he retired at 62 and his average monthly covered earnings were the same? $506.40 [70]

4. Jill was paid $52,000 for 1 year. Her employer paid FICA tax at 7.65% on a maximum of $45,000 of Jill's wages. How much FICA tax did the employer pay for Jill? $3,442.50 [70]

5. Hortencia is self-employed. Last year she earned $56,000. She paid self-employment tax of 15.3% on a maximum of $45,000. How much tax did she pay? $6,885 [70]

6. A town's total budget for last year was $4,104,670. Income from other sources was $376,800. The balance was raised by a property tax on a total assessed value of $93,600,000. What was the decimal tax rate, correct to 3 places? 0.040 [68]

7. Tony buys a computer originally priced at $1,399 on sale for a total cost of $790. He pays $100 down and the balance in 30 equal monthly payments. What is the amount of each monthly payment? $23 [49]

8. A 90-day note for $1,200, with banker's interest at 12%, is dated March 10. What is the due date and amount due? June 8; $1,236 [44,46]

9. Janice bought 20 shares of stock at a total cost of $1,580. She kept the stock for 3 years and received regular quarterly dividends of $0.65 per share. She then sold the stock and received net proceeds of $1,660. What was Janice's total gain from owning and selling this stock? $236 [59]

‡10. A camera sold for $148.40, including a 6% sales tax. What was the selling price of the camera before the tax was added? $140 [69]

Section 71
Federal Income Taxes

The incomes of U.S. citizens and others are taxed by the federal government. The tax is called the U.S. individual income tax, or **federal income tax.**

If you are an employee, your employer deducts money for the income tax from your pay. This is called a *withholding tax.* If you are self-employed, you must make **estimated tax** payments each quarter. In either case, the amounts withheld or paid are estimates of the tax you will owe when the year ends.

You must figure and report your actual federal income taxes by April 15 of the following year. The report you complete is called an **income tax return.** The completed return will show you how much you actually owe in federal income taxes. If the amount withheld from your wages was larger than what you owe, you claim a refund. If the withholding taxes you paid were less than what you owe, you pay the difference.

To find the tax you owe, you must first figure your adjusted gross income and your taxable income.

Figuring Adjusted Gross Income. *Gross income* includes money from such sources as wages, salaries, commissions, bonuses, tips, interest, dividends, prizes, pensions, rents, gain on sale of property, and profit from a business or profession. Gifts and inheritances are not considered income and are not taxed by the federal government.

From your gross income, you subtract certain kinds of payments, called *adjustments to income.* These include business losses, payments to approved retirement plans, alimony, and penalties on early withdrawal of savings. The amount left after subtracting adjustments to income from gross income is **adjusted gross income.**

Gross Income − Adjustments to Income = Adjusted Gross Income

1. Tina Barr's tax return last year showed gross income of $18,648 and adjustments to income of $1,380. What was Tina's adjusted gross income last year? $17,268

2. On his federal income tax return, Cesar Castillo reported these items of income: wages, $13,820; tips, $5,495; interest earned, $341; gifts, $125. Cesar had these adjustments to income: payments to a retirement plan, $2,000; penalty for early withdrawal of savings, $19.
    a.   What was Cesar's gross income? $19,656
    b.   What was the total of his adjustments to income? $2,019
    c.   What was Cesar's adjusted gross income? $17,637

3. Ed and Ginny Threll's income last year was from these items: net income from business, $45,635.90; dividends, $1,926.12; interest, $4,101.73; rental income, $2,180. Adjustments to income totaled $5,108.33. What was their adjusted gross income? $48,735.42

4. In one year, Felix Gomez's wages totaled $27,850. Marta Gomez had a salary of $26,378 and a bonus of $750. The Gomezes also received $1,610 in interest, $787.35 in dividends, and a $1,500 inheritance. They paid $4,330 into a retirement fund and were penalized $78 for removing money from a savings plan early. What was their adjusted gross income that year? $52,967.35

Figuring Taxable Income. After finding your adjusted gross income, you figure your taxable income. **Taxable income** is the amount of income on which you pay tax. It is adjusted gross income less deductions and exemptions.

Taxable Income = Adjusted Gross Income

− (Deductions + Exemptions)

Deductions are expenses that you claim to reduce the amount of your taxable income. For example, you may deduct interest paid on a home mortgage, property taxes, state and local income taxes, part of your medical and dental expenses, some casualty and theft losses, and contributions to charities.

You may claim a fixed amount, called a *standard deduction*. If your actual deductions are more than the fixed amount, you may list, or *itemize*, them on your return. Either way, you subtract the deductions from your adjusted gross income.

An **exemption** is an amount of income that is free from tax. You can claim one exemption for yourself *unless* you are claimed as a dependent on another person's return. You can also claim an exemption for a spouse, and one for each dependent. For example, a married couple with two dependent children can claim four exemptions. A single person with a dependent parent can claim two exemptions. A child listed as an exemption on the parent's return can claim no exemption.

The amounts allowed for the standard deduction and exemptions change often. In this text, the amount used for the standard deduction will be $3,000 and the amount used for an exemption will be $2,000.

Example

Nora Boone is single and has an adjusted gross income of $30,000. Nora has deductions of $6,400. She has two exemptions. What is her taxable income?
  Alan Roche also has an adjusted gross income of $30,000. Alan takes the standard deduction of $3,000. He has two exemptions. What is his taxable income?

Solutions

	Nora Boone	Alan Roche
Adjusted gross income	$30,000	$30,000
Deductions	6,400	3,000
	$23,600	$27,000
Exemptions (2 × $2,000)	4,000	4,000
Taxable Income	$19,600 **Ans.**	$23,000 **Ans.**

Exercise 2
Written

1. Jan Teel's adjusted gross income last year was $15,354. Jan's itemized deductions were $5,650. She claimed one exemption of $2,000. What was her estimated taxable income? $7,704

2. On Jamal Jackson's return for last year, the adjusted gross income was $32,007. His itemized deductions totaled $4,700, and he claimed 3 exemptions at $2,000 each. What was his taxable income? $21,307

3. In preparing their tax return, the Delgados claimed 4 exemptions at $2,000 each, and itemized deductions of $7,107. Their adjusted gross income was $45,208.
   a. Estimate their taxable income. $30,000
   b. What was their exact taxable income? $30,101

Figuring the Tax with a Tax Table. If your taxable income is less than $50,000, you use a tax table to figure your tax. Parts of a tax table are shown in Illustration 71–1.

To use the tax table, find your taxable income in the "At least ... but less than" columns. Then read across that line to the column that shows your filing status. The amount on that line and in that column is your tax.

For example, if your taxable income is $13,500 and you are single, your tax is $1,957. If you are married and filing a joint return with your spouse, your tax for the same taxable income is $1,909.

A "head of household" is an unmarried or legally separated person who pays more than half the cost of keeping a home for a dependent father, mother, or child.

If your taxable income is:		And your filing status is:			
At least	But less than	Single	Married filing jointly	Married filing separately	Head of household
$13,400	$13,450	$1,942	$1,894	$1,954	$1,914
13,450	13,500	1,949	1,901	1,961	1,921
13,500	13,550	1,957	1,909	1,969	1,929
13,550	13,600	1,964	1,916	1,976	1,936
13,600	13,650	1,972	1,924	1,984	1,944
13,650	13,700	1,979	1,931	1,991	1,951
13,700	13,750	1,987	1,939	1,999	1,959
13,750	13,800	1,994	1,946	2,006	1,966
13,800	13,850	2,002	1,954	2,014	1,974
13,850	13,900	2,009	1,961	2,021	1,981
13,900	13,950	2,017	1,969	2,029	1,989
13,950	14,000	2,024	1,976	2,036	1,996
22,000	22,050	3,911	3,184	4,287	3,204
22,050	22,100	3,925	3,191	4,301	3,211
22,100	22,150	3,939	3,199	4,315	3,219
22,150	22,200	3,953	3,206	4,329	3,226
22,200	22,250	3,967	3,214	4,343	3,234
22,250	22,300	3,981	3,221	4,357	3,241
22,300	22,350	3,995	3,229	4,371	3,249
22,350	22,400	4,009	3,236	4,385	3,256

Illustration 71–1. Partial Tax Table

Exercise 3
Oral

Use Illustration 71–1 to find the tax for each problem below.

	Taxable Income	Filing Status	Tax
1.	$13,980	Single	$2,024
2.	13,411	Head of household	1,914
3.	13,783	Married filing jointly	1,946
4.	13,634	Married filing separately	1,984
5.	22,098	Married filing jointly	3,191
6.	22,365	Single	4,009
7.	22,007	Head of household	3,204

Exercise 4
Oral

Use Illustration 71–1 to solve these problems.

1. Carmen and Angel Diaz are married and file a joint tax return. Their taxable income is $22,378. What is their tax? $3,236

2. Roberta O'Toole is single. Her gross income last year was $19,455 and her taxable income was $13,926. What was her tax? $2,017

3. How much tax does a head of household with taxable income of $22,098 owe? $3,211

4. Rob Duval is married but is filing a separate tax return. His taxable income is $13,624. What is the amount of his tax? $1,984

Figuring the Refund or Amount Owed. If you worked during the year, your employer withheld money for income taxes, or you paid self-employment tax. In either case, the amount of tax you paid was an estimate and is probably more or less than the tax you actually owe.

To find the tax you actually owe, you must complete your tax return. If too much withholding or self-employment tax has been paid, the government will pay back (refund) the difference. If less than the amount of your tax has been paid, you must pay the difference to the government.

**Exercise 5
Written**

1. Carl Breese's tax return for last year shows a total tax of $8,278. Carl's employer had withheld $8,450 from his wages during the year. What refund should Carl get? $172

2. Sara Wickam is a self-employed farmer. Last year she paid $16,118 in self-employment tax. Sara's total tax for the year, as shown on her tax return, was $17,448. What amount of tax did she owe? $1,330

Use Illustration 71–1 to solve Problems 3 and 4.

3. Paul Dimitry is single. On his tax return for last year, his taxable income was $13,532. His employer withheld $2,140.75 from his wages.
   a. What was his actual tax for the year? $1,957
   b. How much refund is due him? $183.75

4. On their joint tax return, the Pavlik's show taxable income of $22,298. Their employers withheld $3,205.46 from their wages. How much more will the Pavliks owe with their tax return? $15.54

REVIEW 71

Terms

1. Match the terms with the statements.

adjusted gross income   federal income tax
estimated tax   income tax return
exemption   taxable income

   a. A federal tax on incomes   federal income tax
   b. A form for figuring taxes   income tax return
   c. Gross income less adjustments   adjusted gross income
   d. An amount of income free from tax   exemption
   e. Adjusted gross income less exemptions and deductions   taxable income
   f. Income taxes paid quarterly by self employed   estimated tax

Skills

2. a. $35 is what part greater than $28? $\frac{1}{4}$
   b. What percent of $90 is $270? 300%

    c. What amount is $\frac{1}{2}$% of $250? $1.25

    d. Find the banker's interest on $500 for 36 days at 6%. $3

    e. 360 m is what percent less than 480 m? 25%

Problems

3. Maude James is single with a taxable income of $22,315. Her employer withheld $4,110 from her wages for income tax during the year. Using the tax table in Illustration 71–1, find how much her refund should be. $115 [71]

4. The Chou's adjusted gross income last year was $32,908. Their itemized deductions were $4,808. They claimed 3 exemptions of $2,000 each. What was their taxable income? $22,100 [71]

5. Vespa County's tax rate is $38.20 per $1,000 of assessed value. What tax must you pay on a property valued at $64,000, which is assessed at 50% of its value? $1,222.40 [67]

Section 72
More Federal Income Taxes

Many students hold part-time jobs or work full time in the summer. They are usually listed as dependents on their parents' tax returns. Their total yearly incomes often are so low that they owe little or no actual federal income tax. However, their employers withhold federal income taxes from their wages. To get a refund on the taxes they have paid, they must complete an income tax return.

Finding the Standard Deduction for a Dependent. Jane Vistal is a senior at Allorton High School. Jane worked five weeks last summer and earned $1,785. Jane also earned $22 in interest on her savings account. Because she had no adjustments to income, the total ($1,785 + $22 = $1,807) was her adjusted gross income.

    Jane wants to claim the standard deduction instead of itemizing her deductions. However, Jane's parents claimed her as a dependent on their tax return. As a dependent, Jane may not be able to claim the full standard deduction of $3,000.

    A dependent's income is grouped into two categories for the federal income tax return: *earned income* and *unearned income*. Earned income is income from the dependent's own labor, such as wages, salaries, and tips. Everything else is unearned income, including interest and dividends.

    A dependent can claim as a standard deduction the higher of these two amounts: $500, or the amount of earned income, up to $3,000. Jane's earned income of $1,785 in wages was more than $500 and not more than $3,000. So, $1,785 was the total standard deduction she could claim.

**Exercise 1
Written**

Find each dependent's standard deduction.

	Earned Income	Unearned Income	Standard Deduction
1.	$ 250	$ 100	$ 500
2.	1,950	600	1,950
3.	0	200	500
4.	0	1,200	500
5.	4,875	300	3,000

Finding the Tax Refund for a Dependent. Since Jane's parents claimed an exemption for her on their return, she could not claim a $2,000 exemption for herself on her tax return.

Jane's taxable income was figured this way:

Wages	**$1,785**
Interest	**22**
Adjusted Gross Income	**$1,807**
Less deductions	**1,785**
Taxable Income	**$ 22**

To find her tax, Jane looked up her taxable income in the tax tables shown in Illustration 72–1. Jane's tax according to the table was only $2. Jane's employer, however, withheld $225 from her wages for federal taxes. So, she was entitled to a refund of $223:

$225 − $2 = $223   Amount of refund

If your taxable income is:		And your filing status is:			
At least	**But less than**	**Single**	**Married filing jointly**	**Married filing separately**	**Head of household**
$ 0	$ 5	$ 0	$ 0	$ 0	$ 0
5	15	1	1	1	1
15	25	2	2	2	2
25	50	4	4	4	4
50	75	7	7	7	7
75	100	10	10	10	10
100	125	12	12	12	12
125	150	15	15	15	15
300	325	34	34	34	34
325	350	37	37	37	37
350	375	40	40	40	40
375	400	43	43	43	43
400	425	45	45	45	45
425	450	48	48	48	48
450	475	51	51	51	51
475	500	54	54	54	54

Illustration 72–1. Part of a Federal Income Tax Table

**Exercise 2
Written**

Use Illustration 72–1 to solve these problems. Assume that each person will claim the standard deduction and that each person was listed on the parents' return as a dependent.

1. Todd earned $2,406 in wages last year as a part-time gardener and $148 in interest. His employer withheld $336 in income taxes from his wages.
   a. What is Todd's taxable income? $148
   b. How much refund will Todd receive? $321

2. Sylvia Wells earned $3,256 last year in part-time wages and $174 in interest. Her employer withheld $420 from her wages for income taxes.
   a. What is Sylvia's taxable income? $430
   b. How much money will she receive as a refund? $372

3. Last summer, Otis Wilson earned $2,855. His employer withheld $384 of his wages for income taxes. What is the amount of Otis' tax refund? $384

4. Luisa Guzman worked part time last year while attending college and earned $3,288. The total withholding taxes she paid were $410. Luisa also earned $78 in interest and $16 in dividends. How much tax refund should she receive? $367

5. Mike Duvalier worked during the summer to earn $1,600 to help pay college expenses. From these earnings, $220 in withholding taxes were deducted. Mike also earned $330 for yard work. No withholding taxes were deducted from these earnings.
   a. What is Mike's taxable income? $0
   b. What amount will he receive as a tax refund? $220

6. Sue Bent's parents subtracted $2,000 from their adjusted gross income when they listed her as an exemption on their tax return. Her taxable income was $148. She paid $277 in withholding taxes. What amount should she expect as a tax refund? $262

REVIEW 72

Skills

1. a. $189 is what percent smaller than $270?   30%
   b. Find $\frac{1}{8}$% of $4,800. $6
   c. 625 grams is what percent of 5 kilograms? $12\frac{1}{2}$%
   ‡d. What amount is 250% greater than $50? $125
   ‡e. $300 is $33\frac{1}{3}$% less than ? $450

Problems

2. Ruby Johnson earned $3,312 for college expenses last summer. Her employer deducted $456 in withholding taxes. Ruby also earned $38 in interest from her checking account. Her father listed her as a dependent on his tax return. Use Illustration 72–1 to find the tax refund she should receive. $416 [72]

3. Rupert is the head of his household. His taxable income last year was $22,278. Find his tax, using the schedule in Illustration 71–1. $3,241 [71]

4.   Wendy bought these gifts for her spouse: a shirt for $19.79, two pairs of socks @ $4.95, and a belt for $28.99. There was a sales tax of 5% on the purchase.
     a.   Estimate the total of the bill. $63
     b.   What was the exact bill? $61.61 [34]

5.   The cash price of a microwave oven is $450. The installment price is $60 down and 10 monthly payments of $42 each. How much money would be saved by buying it for cash? $30 [50]

6.   In a town with property assessed at $16,500,000, a real estate tax of $866,250 must be raised. What tax rate per $1,000 will be needed to collect this amount? $52.50 [68]

Computer Clinic

Will Irons earned $3,178 in wages at a part-time job last year and $126 in interest on his checking account. His employer withheld $444 from his pay for federal income taxes. Will's parents claim him as an exemption on their federal income tax return. Follow the steps below to complete a federal income tax worksheet for Will.

1.   Insert your Spreadsheet Applications Diskette and call up the file "Sec72." After you do, your computer screen should look like Illustration 72–2. (If you are using MicroTools, a short tax table will appear on your screen also.)

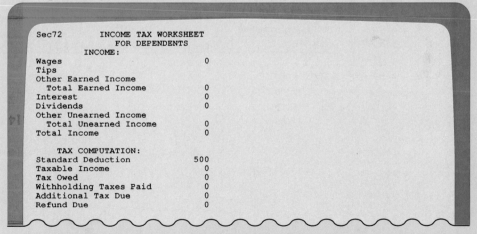

```
Sec72           INCOME TAX WORKSHEET
                  FOR DEPENDENTS
            INCOME:
Wages                            0
Tips
Other Earned Income
   Total Earned Income           0
Interest                         0
Dividends                        0
Other Unearned Income
   Total Unearned Income         0
Total Income                     0

   TAX COMPUTATION:
Standard Deduction             500
Taxable Income                   0
Tax Owed                         0
Withholding Taxes Paid           0
Additional Tax Due               0
Refund Due                       0
```

Illustration 72–2. Using a Spreadsheet to Find Income Taxes

2.   Complete Will's federal tax worksheet by entering these data into the template: B4, 3,178; B8, 126; B18, 444. (If you are using Micro-Tools, press PgDn to determine the amount to enter in B15. Then

refer to the tax table on your screen and enter the correct tax in B17.)

3. Answer these questions about Will's completed tax worksheet:
   a. What amount of income tax did Will owe for last year? $34
   b. What refund did Will receive? $410
   c. What amount of income tax would Will owe if he had earned no interest during the year? $21
   d. What amount of income tax would Will owe if he had earned $3,278 in wages, $89 in interest, and $215 in dividends? $65

Section 73
State and City Income Taxes

Most states and some cities tax the incomes of their residents, but they usually do so at lower rates than the U.S. income tax. The amount of state and city income taxes is often found by taking a percent of your federal taxable income.

Some states and cities use a fixed tax rate no matter how much taxable income a person has. Others use a *graduated* tax rate like the federal government. That is, the tax rate gets larger as taxable income gets larger.

Part of a graduated tax rate schedule that might be used by a state is shown in Illustration 73–1.

For taxable income		
Over– –	**But not over– –**	**The tax is– –**
$ – 0 –	$ 5,000	2% of taxable income
5,000	10,000	$ 100 plus 3% of taxable income over $ 5,000
10,000	15,000	250 plus 4% of taxable income over 10,000
15,000	20,000	550 plus 5% of taxable income over 15,000
20,000	25,000	1,200 plus 6% of taxable income over 20,000
25,000	30,000	1,550 plus 7% of taxable income over 25,000
30,000	35,000	1,950 plus 8% of taxable income over 30,000
35,000	40,000	2,400 plus 9% of taxable income over 35,000
40,000	45,000	2,900 plus 10% of taxable income over 40,000

Illustration 73–1. Partial Graduated Income Tax Table

Using Illustration 73–1, figure your tax this way:

Example

Your taxable income last year was $21,600. What was your state income tax?

Solution

$21,600 − $20,000 = $1,600	amount over $20,000
$1,600 × 0.06 = $96	tax on amount over $20,000
$1,200 + $96 = $1,296	total state income tax **Ans.**

Explanation

Your taxable income of $21,600 is over $20,000 but not over $25,000. The tax rate in the table for that amount is $1,200 plus 6% of the taxable income over $20,000. The taxable income over $20,000 is $1,600. So, the total tax is $1,200 plus 6% of $1,600 ($96), or $1,296.

Use the tax rates in Illustration 73–1 to solve the problems.

Exercise 1
Written

1. Olive Budde's taxable income last year was $15,798. What was her state income tax? $589.90

2. Ana Orestes's state income tax return shows taxable income of $35,470. What is the state income tax on that amount? $2,442.30

3. The Kimura's income on which they must pay state tax is $41,548. What is their state tax? $3,054.80

4. Wynne Odonjo's income subject to state income tax is $12,892. What is his state income tax? $365.68

5. Mr. and Mrs. Simon's gross income for a year was $57,722. From that amount they subtracted $13,230 in adjustments, deductions, and exemptions to find their taxable income.
    a. What was their taxable income? $44,492
    b. What was their state tax? $3,349.20

6. Last year, Amy Rosco's employer withheld $420 from her wages for state income tax. When she prepared her tax return, Amy showed gross income of $12,400 less $3,000 in deductions and $2,000 in exemptions.
    a. What was Amy's taxable income? $7,400
    b. What was her correct state tax for the year? $172
    c. How much refund was due her? $248

Exercise 2
Written

1. In addition to federal and state income taxes, Rob Traub also has to pay a city income tax. The city income tax rate is $2\frac{1}{2}$% of his taxable income. If his taxable income is $18,345, what is his city income tax? $458.63

2. Carsville charges its residents an income tax of $\frac{1}{2}$% of their taxable income. Diana Schmitt lives in Carsville and has taxable income of $23,616. What is her income tax? $118.08

For Problems 3, 4, and 5, use the tax rates shown in Illustration 73–1.

3. Gil Harrick has taxable income of $16,900. He pays a city income tax of 1% on his taxable income, in addition to state and federal taxes.
    a. What is Gil's city tax? $169
    b. What is his state tax? $645
    c. What is Gil's total city and state tax? $814

4. Francis Lange pays a city tax of 2% on her taxable income, in addition to a state income tax. Her taxable income for last year was $22,896. What was her total state and city income tax? $1,831.68

5. Harry Rogers pays a city income tax of $2\frac{1}{4}$% on his taxable income of $42,834. In addition, he pays both state and federal income taxes on the same taxable income. If his federal tax last year was $8,231, what was the total of his federal, state, and city income taxes last year? $12,378.17

REVIEW 73

Skills

1. a. Multiply: 15.3 by 2.4   36.72
    b. Divide: 32.4 by 2.4   13.5
    c. Add: $4\frac{2}{5}$ and $6\frac{1}{2}$ $10\frac{9}{10}$
    d. Subtract: $6\frac{1}{3}$ from $17\frac{1}{4}$ $10\frac{11}{12}$
    e. Multiply: $8\frac{1}{2}$ by $5\frac{1}{3}$ $45\frac{1}{3}$
    f. Divide: $5\frac{1}{3}$ by $1\frac{1}{3}$ 4

Problems

2. The Carr's taxable income last year was $43,780. They paid a state tax of 3.5% and a city tax of 1.25% on that income. What was the total of the state and city taxes they paid? $2,079.55 [73]

3. Ty Wilson works on a piece-rate basis. He completed 140 pieces on Monday, 136 on Tuesday, 148 on Wednesday, and 144 on Thursday. He is paid $0.60 for each piece. How many pieces must he complete on Friday so that his earnings for the 5 days will average $84 a day?   132 [10]

4. Halor Corporation paid 3 workers gross wages of $256.80, $287.77, and $297.89 for working 40 hours each during the week of January 26. Find the total amount of FICA taxes withheld from their gross wages. Use a FICA rate of 7.65%. $64.45 [70]

5. Last year the Pikanos earned $42,800 from their salaries. They also earned $1,280 in interest and $789 in dividends. The Pikanos paid $6,240 into a retirement fund and spent $2,890 for moving expenses. What was their adjusted gross income for the year? $35,739 [71]

6. Vicente is paid 5% commission on all sales up to and including $15,000, and 7% on all sales over $15,000 in any month. Last month Vicente's sales were $25,750. What was the amount of his total commission? $1,502.50 [28]

7. Lucy Dunwood borrowed $400 and must repay the loan in 24 monthly payments of $19.50 each. (a) Estimate the finance charge on the loan. (b) What is the exact finance charge on the loan? (c) What is the amount financed? (d) What is the finance charge per $100 of the amount financed? $80; $68; $400; $17 [48, 49]

‡8. Stock with a par value of $100, paying a 9% dividend, can be bought for 97, including commission. How much money must be invested in the stock to earn a yearly income of $3,600?
$38,800 [59]

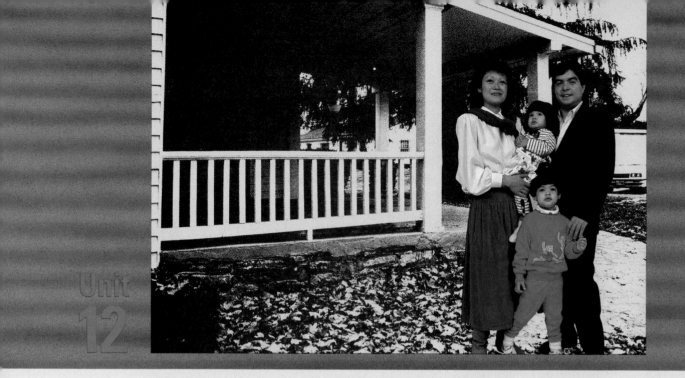

Insurance

You are exposed to risks every day. Health problems may arise at any time, a car you are driving may be involved in an accident, and property you own may be stolen. Insurance is one of the ways that you can protect yourself from the financial costs of these risks.

Individuals and business owners usually buy four types of insurance to provide protection against financial loss. Two types, life, and health, protect individuals and their families. Home and automobile insurance primarily protect property. As you consider buying any type of insurance, you must determine your needs first. Careful shopping will help you get the best price for the insurance you want and need.

After you finish Unit 12, you will be able to:

- Find the annual premiums for life, homeowners, renters, and car insurance policies.
- Use cash value tables to figure life insurance benefits.
- Figure net cost of life insurance.
- Figure benefits of insurance policies that have deductible or coinsurance features.
- Figure amount of refund to be received for canceled home insurance policies.
- Figure how losses are divided among insurance companies.
- Solve problems that contain more information than you need.
- Estimate answers to problems.
- Read, write, say, and recognize the meanings of the key terms.
- Use a computer spreadsheet to find amount of property loss that will be paid by an insurance company.

Buying life insurance is the usual way of protecting your family from financial loss when you die. If you are the main income provider, your family will need money to replace the income it will no longer get. If you are a homemaker, your surviving spouse may need money to pay someone to care for your children. In both cases, money is also needed to pay funeral costs.

Life insurance may also be bought to repay, upon death, money that has been borrowed to buy a home or a car.

Insurance Policies. The money paid to an insurance company for life insurance is the **premium**. The person whose life is insured is called the **insured**. The insurance company is called the **insurer**. The contract between the insured and the insurer is called the **policy**.

A life insurance policy may be canceled at any time by the insured. If premiums are not paid, the policy may be canceled by the insurer.

Types of Life Insurance. There are many types of life insurance that you can buy. One type, term life insurance, offers protection only. The other types offer both protection and a savings feature. You will be learning about these three types of life insurance policies:

1. **Term life insurance:** Offers protection for a fixed period of time, such as 1, 5, or 10 years. It can usually be renewed for its current face value after its fixed term, but at a higher premium.

2. **Whole life insurance:** Insures you for a fixed amount for as long as you live. Premiums must be paid for your whole life in order to keep the original terms of the policy in effect.

3. **Limited-payment life insurance:** Gives you protection for life, but you pay premiums only for a fixed time, such as 20 years.

You will find that individual insurance companies offer slightly different policies. The features, costs, and benefits must be compared to find the policy that is best for your needs.

Premium Rates. Illustration 74–1 shows the premiums an insurance company might charge for each $1,000 of life insurance you buy. The rates are for non-smokers. You can see that the premium you pay will depend on how old you are when you buy the policy and on the kind of policy you buy. For example, if you are a female who buys a $15,000 whole-life insurance policy at the age of 20, your annual premium is $93.30.

$$\$15,000 \div \$1,000 = 15$$

$$15 \times \$6.22 = \$93.30$$

ANNUAL PREMIUMS FOR $1,000 OF LIFE INSURANCE						
Age of Insured	1-Year Term		Whole Life		20-Payment Life	
	Male	Female	Male	Female	Male	Female
20	$1.39	$1.22	$ 7.07	$ 6.22	$25.29	$23.27
25	1.41	1.24	8.37	7.37	27.77	25.54
30	1.45	1.28	10.16	8.94	30.75	28.29
35	1.62	1.43	12.58	11.07	34.15	31.42
40	1.91	1.68	16.30	14.34	38.89	35.78
45	2.45	2.16	20.02	17.62	44.72	41.14

Illustration 74–1. Sample Life Insurance Premiums Per $1,000

The premiums that you will pay when you buy life insurance will be different from those shown in the table. Each insurance company charges different rates based on the kinds of services they offer.

Notice that women pay a lower premium than males do at the same ages. This happens because women as a group live longer than men. Persons who are in good health and lead a life-style found to add to one's life expectancy get the best rates. Those who smoke pay more for life insurance, as do workers in dangerous jobs.

**Exercise 1
Written**

Use the annual premium table in Illustration 74–1 to solve the problems.

1. Find the annual premium for each policy.

	Kind of Policy	Age and Sex	Face of Policy	Premium
a.	Whole Life	25, male	$10,000	$ 83.70
b.	1-Year Term	30, female	80,000	102.40
c.	20-Payment Life	40, male	12,000	466.68
d.	1-Year Term	25, male	40,000	56.40
e.	20-Payment Life	35, female	7,600	238.79
f.	Whole Life	45, female	14,000	246.68

2. How much more is the annual premium on a $20,000, 20-payment life policy for a male, age 45, than the same policy at age 25? $339

3. How much more is the annual premium on a 30-year-old female's 20-payment life policy for $7,000 than on a whole-life policy? $135.45

4. For a male, age 30, how much less is the annual premium on a $45,000, 1-year term policy than on a whole-life policy? $391.95

5. A 20-payment life policy for $9,000 is taken out by a female at age 25. What total amount will she pay in premiums by the end of 20 years? $4,597.20

6. Sam Pontel, age 30, is comparing the total premium cost of a $30,000, 20-payment life policy he may take now and the cost of the same policy at age 35. What will be the difference in total premium costs over 20 years for this policy at the two age levels? $2,040

7. Mary Crane, age 20, wants to invest no more than $600 a year in life insurance. In even thousands of dollars, what is the largest policy she can buy without spending more than $600 annually on a
   a. Whole-life insurance policy? $96,000
   b. 1-year term insurance policy? $491,000

8. Because he smokes, Bert Hoover pays 20% more for life insurance. How much more will Bert pay for $50,000 of 1-year term insurance at age 45 than a non-smoker would pay at the same age? $24.50

9. To the nearest percent, what percent greater is the cost of a whole-life policy taken out by a male at age 45 than at age 35? 59%

REVIEW 74

Terms

1. Match the terms with the statements.

insured	policy	term life
insurer	premium	whole life
limited-payment life		

   a. Amount paid for insurance premium
   b. Insurance contract policy
   c. Person whose life is insured insured
   d. Insurance company insurer
   e. Offers protection only for a fixed period of time term life
   f. Pay premiums for lifetime whole life
   g. Insured for a lifetime; pay premiums for fixed time limited-payment life

Skills

2. a. The city income tax on $36,000 at 2% is ? $720
   b. $15.10 increased by 30% of itself is ? $19.63
   c. 96 reduced by $62\frac{1}{2}$% of itself is ? 36
   d. 16.8 m + 23.9 cm + 1 400 mm = ? m 18.439 m

Problems

3. Use Illustration 74–1 to find the annual premium for a whole life policy bought by a male at age 40 and for a female at the same age. For a $20,000 whole life policy,
   a. estimate the difference in annual premium. $40 [74]
   b. find the actual difference in annual premium. $39.20 [74]

4. The regional park system tax rate in Odell County is 2.3 mills per dollar of assessed value. Find the tax to be paid on property assessed at $70,000. $161 [67]

5. Iris earned $2,500 last year at her part-time job. Her parents claimed her as a dependent on their federal income tax return. What taxable income did Iris have last year? $0 [72]

Life Insurance Benefits

The main benefit of having any life insurance policy is the protection it offers. When the insured dies, *death benefits*, usually equal to the face amount of the policy, are paid to the beneficiary. The **beneficiary** is a person named in the policy to receive the death benefits. Some policies have another benefit, which is their savings feature.

Cash Value. Policies such as whole life and limited-payment life build up a cash value after premiums have been paid for the first few years. **Cash value** is the money that you will get if you cancel one of these policies. If you cancel a term policy, you get nothing.

The terms of the policy usually give you a choice of using the cash value in one of these ways:

1. **Policy Loan.** You can borrow an amount up to the cash value from the insurance company and still keep insurance coverage. You must repay the money you borrow, but you usually pay a lower rate of interest than other lenders would charge.

2. **Paid-Up Life Insurance.** The cash value may be used to make a one-time payment to buy a smaller amount of insurance that covers you until you die. You do not have to pay any more premiums on the insurance.

3. **Extended Term Life Insurance.** You may also trade the cash value for term insurance. You will be covered for the original amount of the insurance for a fixed, shorter period of time.

Table of Cash Values. A policy that builds cash value would have a table much like the one shown in Illustration 75–1.

End of Year	Cash and Loan Values per $1,000	Paid-Up Whole Life per $1,000	Extended Term	
			Years	Days
1	$ 0	$ 0	0	0
5	17.80	119	8	274
10	76.09	403	19	115
15	170.72	716	21	80
20	327.50	1,087	22	107
25	564.33	1,599	22	312

Illustration 75–1. Sample Cash Value Table

This example will show you how to read the table: If you had paid premiums on a $10,000 policy for 20 years, you would get $3,275 in cash if you canceled it.

$$\textbf{\$10,000} \div \textbf{\$1,000} = \textbf{10} \qquad\qquad \textbf{10} \times \textbf{\$327.50} = \textbf{\$3,275}$$

If you chose to, you could borrow up to $3,275 on the policy. You could also buy $10,870 of paid-up life insurance (10 × $1,087 = $10,870). Or, you could buy a $10,000 term insurance policy that would cover you for 22 years and 107 days.

Use the table in Illustration 75–1 to solve the problems.

**Exercise 1
Written**

1. How much cash would you get if you canceled a $50,000 policy after paying premiums for 5 years? $890

2. You have paid annual premiums of $212 on a $25,000 policy for 10 years. What amount could you borrow on your policy? $1,902.25

3. How much paid-up, whole-life insurance could you buy if you canceled a $6,000 policy after making payments for 25 years? $9,594

4. After paying premiums for 5 years, Pam Korper cancels her $125,000 policy. How many years and days of term insurance can Pam buy with the cash value of the policy? 8 years, 274 days

5. Alfred Buckley has made payments for 15 years on a $33,000 policy. If he canceled the policy
   a. What estimated cash payment could he get? $6,000
   b. What actual cash payment could he get? $5,633.76
   c. How much paid-up, whole-life insurance could he buy? $23,628
   d. How many years and days of term insurance coverage could Alfred get? 21 years, 80 days
   e. What amount of insurance would Alfred get if he traded the cash value of this policy for extended term insurance? $33,000

Dividends. After you have had a policy for a few years, your insurance company may return part of your premium to you as a **dividend**. The amount of the dividend is usually shown on the premium notice. You may (1) deduct the dividend from the premium due and pay the difference, (2) leave the dividend with the company to buy more insurance or to earn interest, or (3) take the dividend in cash.

**Exercise 2
Written**

1. Miriam pays a premium of $12.80 per $1,000 for an $8,000 life insurance policy. Her policy has paid a dividend of $18.90, which she uses to reduce her premium. How much should Miriam send to the insurance company when she pays her premium? $83.50

2. Casey McLore's annual premium on a $15,000 policy is $32.64 per $1,000. Casey plans to apply a dividend he has received of $62.46 against his next premium payment. What net amount should he send the company when he makes his next payment? $427.14

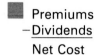 Premiums
−Dividends
Net Cost

3. Zena Omal took out a 20-payment life policy for $40,000 at $21 per $1,000. In 20 years she received total dividends of $621.68. What was the net cost of the policy to Zena over 20 years? $16,178.32

4. Bennie Rose paid annual premiums on a $25,000 whole-life policy at a rate of $17.20 per $1,000. At the end of 10 years he canceled the policy and found that its cash value was $97 per $1,000. Over the 10 years, he received dividends of $318.55. For the time Bennie had the policy, what was the net cost of the insurance? $1,556.45

5. Aaron DeVough has chosen to leave his life insurance dividend of $993 with his insurer to earn interest. How much interest will he earn on this amount for the first year at $4\frac{1}{4}\%$? $42.20

REVIEW 75

Terms

1. Match the terms with the statements.

beneficiary   dividend   paid-up life insurance
cash value   extended term life   policy loan

   a. A return of part of the premium   dividend
   b. Borrowing cash value of life insurance   policy loan
   c. Person to whom policy is paid when you die   beneficiary
   d. Full coverage for limited time   extended term life
   e. Amount you get if you cancel a policy   cash value
   f. Buying insurance for life with no more premiums   paid-up life

Skills

2. a. $248\frac{2}{5}\%$ as a decimal is ?   2.484
   b. The banker's interest at 14% on $8,000 for 180 days is ? $560
   c. $384 plus $12\frac{1}{2}\%$ of itself is ? $432

Problems

3. Roger paid annual premiums on a $35,000 whole-life policy at a rate of $14.76 per $1,000. At the end of 5 years he canceled the policy and received the cash value of $35 per $1,000. Over the 5 years, he had received total dividends of $62. What was the net cost of this policy? $1,296 [75]

4. You want to borrow money on a $60,000 life insurance policy that you have held for 17 years. The loan value of the policy is $175 per $1,000. (a) What is the maximum amount you can borrow? (b) If you borrow the maximum amount at 8%, what will be your interest cost for a year? $10,500; $840 [75]

‡5. Letitia's check register balance on March 31 was $764.20. In making a reconciliation statement, she found that a check for $19 was incorrectly recorded in the register as $91, and she had no record in her register of a service charge of $4.80, earned interest of $1.21, and a deposit of $78.34. What was her correct check register balance? $910.95 [6]

Health and Accident Insurance

When a person has serious health problems, the cost of medical care can add up to thousands of dollars. Instead of using their savings or current income to pay health care bills, most people buy health insurance. The insurance company then pays most of the cost of certain kinds of health care. So, **health insurance,** like other insurance, protects against financial loss.

Employers often provide *group health insurance* for their employees. In some cases, the employer pays for the total cost of the *group policy.* However, employees may have to pay for extra coverage that is not standard or for their dependents.

If you are not covered by a group policy, you may buy *individual health insurance* for yourself and your family.

Older and disabled persons have health insurance through the Medicare programs of the federal government. State governments provide Medicaid health insurance to people with low incomes, regardless of age.

Kinds of Health Insurance. These are the standard kinds of health insurance that you may have:

Hospital Insurance. This pays for the expenses of staying in a hospital, such as the cost of a room, meals, medicine, lab tests, X-rays, and operating room.

Surgical Insurance. This covers the fees of doctors who do surgery or who help with surgery in or out of a hospital.

Medical Insurance. This pays the fees of other doctors and expenses such as physical therapy.

These three kinds of insurance are sometimes called *basic health coverage.* They give limited protection. To protect yourself against the cost of long illnesses or serious injury, you may have to buy two additional kinds of insurance:

Major Medical Insurance. This pays for all or most of the hospital, surgical, medical, or other health care expenses of a major illness or injury not covered by basic health coverage. Thus, major medical coverage is usually bought in addition to basic health coverage.

Disability Income Insurance. This coverage replaces part of the income you lose if you are unable to work for an extended period of time because of illness or accident. Usually, coverage starts after a certain period, such as 30 days. In this case, you receive no disability income insurance benefits for the first 30 days.

Basic Health Insurance. Your basic health insurance policy will state, in writing, your maximum coverage or benefits. The maximums determine how long each service will be provided or give the dollar amount of the coverage.

For example, a limit is usually set on the number of days of hospital care that are paid by the insurance company. A limit may also be set on the amount of money that will be paid for a hospital room per day, for doctors' fees, or for the total cost of a health service. You must pay for the cost of health services above the limits.

**Exercise 1
Written**

1. Lela Zerkin's hospital bill for 6 days was $1,900. Her surgeon's bill was $1,250. Lela's insurance covered $1,740 of the hospital bill and $1,175 of the surgeon's bill.
   a. How much did the insurance company pay? $2,915
   b. How much did Lela have to pay? $235

2. Gerald Brinson's insurance pays all hospital charges except for a maximum limit of $140 a day for a hospital room. Gerald stayed in a hospital for 9 days, and had a private room that cost $210 a day. During his stay, other hospital charges amounted to $738.
   a. What total amount did the insurance company pay? $1,998
   b. What total amount did Gerald pay? $630

3. Despana Stavros needed hospital care after being injured in an accident. Her medical bills for 15 days of care were: room, $3,045; X-rays, $590; medicine, $260; operating room, $520; surgeon, $950. Despana's insurance paid $190 a day for the room; $545 for X-rays, $900 to the surgeon, and the full amount of all other charges. Despana paid the amount not covered by her insurance.
   a. What was the total of Despana's medical bills? $5,365
   b. What amount was paid by the insurance company? $5,075
   c. What amount did Despana pay? $290

4. Ed has disability income insurance that pays him 70% of his regular wages if he can't work because of illness or injury. His insurance starts after he has missed 30 days of work. Due to an accident at home, Ed has lost 39 days of work, and he will be paid disability income insurance by his insurance company. His total medical expenses were $3,200. If Ed's regular daily wage is $148,
   a. What estimated amount of disability income will he get? $900
   b. What actual amount of disability income will he get? $932.40

Major Medical Insurance Payments. Major medical insurance offers more protection by paying higher maximum benefits than basic insurance pays.

Many major medical insurance policies require you to pay a part of health care expenses. This is done through a deductible feature or a coinsurance feature, or both. In a policy with a **deductible** feature, you have to pay a fixed amount each time you get health services. For example, you may have to pay for the first $10 of every X-ray charge. The insurance company pays the rest of the charge.

In a policy with a **coinsurance** feature, you and the insurer share the cost of health care above the deductible amount. For example, if your policy has an 80% coinsurance feature, the insurance company pays 80% of a health care bill after subtracting the deductible amount. You pay the other 20% of the bill and the deductible amount.

Example

Costella Nunez carries a major medical insurance policy that has a $500 deductible feature and an 80% coinsurance feature. Her policy covers the hospital, surgical, and medical expenses of $14,500 that Costella has been charged after being injured in an accident at home. (a) What amount will the insurance company pay? (b) What amount must Costella pay?

Solution		Explanation
Total covered expenses	$14,500	The deductible of $500 is subtracted
Less: deductible amount	500	from the total expenses of $14,500 to
Balance to be shared	$14,000	find the amount to be shared, or $14,000.
a. Company's share:		The company pays $11,200, which is
80% of balance = $11,200 **Ans.**		80% of the balance to be shared. Costella
b. Costella's share:		pays $2,800, which is her 20% share of
20% of balance = $2,800		the balance, plus the deductible amount
Deductible amount	500	of $500. Costella's total share is $2,800 +
	$3,300 **Ans.**	$500, or $3,300.

**Exercise 2
Written**

1. Your major medical policy has an $800 deductible feature and a 90% coinsurance feature. You are injured in a car accident and your health care bills amount to $36,000.
   a. What amount will be paid by your insurance company?
      $31,680
   b. What amount will you pay? $4,320

2. Molly Denard had 6 X-rays taken at a total cost of $260. Under her major medical insurance coverage, the insurance company paid 80% of the cost of X-rays after a $10 deductible was made for each X-ray.
   a. What was the company's share of the cost of the X-rays? $160
   b. What was Molly's share of the cost? $100

3. Daniel Sparks received medical care in the emergency room of a hospital. His bill for this care included these items: emergency room use, $75; doctor's fee, $65; lab tests, $90; medical supplies, $12. For emergency care, Daniel's major medical coverage had a 70% coinsurance feature, with a deductible of $25 for doctors' fees.
   a. How much did the insurance company pay? $151.90
   b. How much did Daniel pay? $90.10

4. Ivy Gould was hospitalized for 17 days. Her total bill for medical care was $24,490. Ivy's major medical coverage pays for 85% of medical expenses above a $750 deductible. Ivy has a disability income insurance policy with another company that pays her $65 each day that she is hospitalized. After using the disability insurance to pay her medical bill, how much will Ivy still owe? $3,206

5. Howard Laird's injury required lengthy hospital and medical care. The fees of his doctors were $8,700 and covered at 100% by his major medical policy. His hospital expenses were $34,460, and the policy covered 90% of the hospital bills beyond a $250 deductible. After Howard left the hospital, a physical therapist made 30 visits

to his home over a 45-day period at $75 a visit. Howard's policy paid 70% of the therapy bills. Of the total expenses, what amount did Howard's insurance company pay? $41,064

Not all expenses are covered.

6. Adele and Jim Emmet's major medical policy pays 90% of covered expenses for *each* of them in any year. A $500 deductible feature applies to each person's claim. The Emmets filed a claim with their insurance company for last year's medical bills. Adele's claim was for $530; Jim's claim was for $950. The insurance company did not allow $70 of Adele's claim as a covered expense. What amount did the insurance company pay for
    a. Adele's covered expenses? $0
    b. Jim's covered expenses? $405

REVIEW 76

Terms

1. Match the terms with the statements.

    coinsurance   deductible   health insurance

    a. Protects you from financial loss due to illness   health insurance
    b. You pay the first part of health care cost   deductible
    c. You share health care costs above the deductible amount with the insurance company   coinsurance

Skills

2. a. $6.65 is what percent greater than $5.32? 25%
    b. 36.2 increased by 75% of itself is ? 63.35
    c. $192 is what percent less than $288? $33\frac{1}{3}\%$
    d. $55,600 decreased by 8% of itself is ? $51,152

Problems

3. Steve went to the hospital emergency room to get medication for his headache. His bill for that visit was $85. Two days later he sprained his ankle and went to the emergency room for X-rays and treatment. On that visit, his bill was $160. The hospital sent both bills to Steve's insurance company for payment. The company did not allow the $85 for the first visit and paid 90% of the other bill. What amount does Steve still owe the hospital? $101 [76]

4. Sabrina Wooten canceled her $25,000 life insurance policy after 8 years and took the cash value of $62 per $1,000. The annual premiums on the policy were $350. While the policy was in effect, she received a total of $187.40 in dividends. What was the net cost of the policy for the 8 years? $1,062.60 [75]

Section 77
Property Insurance

By insuring property, such as a home, you protect yourself against the risks that go along with home ownership. Fire, theft, and lawsuits by

persons who are injured on your property are some of the risks that
may cause you to lose money.

Homeowners Insurance. A policy that covers your home and protects
you against other risks is called **homeowners insurance.** A basic form
of homeowners insurance covers these items:

1. *Dwelling*, which is the home in which you live.

2. *Other structures*, such as a garage.

3. *Personal property*, which includes the contents of a home such as
    clothing, furniture, rugs, and many other items.

4. *Additional living expense*, which pays for the extra costs of living
    when you cannot use your own home because of fire or other damage.

5. *Personal liability*, which protects you in case of lawsuits by persons
    injured on your property.

6. *Medical payments to others*, but not to you or your family, for medi-
    cal expenses in case of injury on your property.

The amount for which your home or dwelling is insured determines
the protection limits for other categories. For example, if your home is
insured for $60,000, personal property is covered for 50% of that amount,
or $30,000. The *coverage* is similar among insurance companies.

Premium Rates. The premiums you pay depend on many things, such
as how much and what kind of coverage you buy, how your house is
built, and where it is located. For example, the premium rates for a
house made of brick that is near a fire department will be less than for
a house made of wood that is far from a fire department.
   Property insurance premium *rates* are usually based on $100 units
of insurance. *The total premium charge is rounded to the nearest dollar.*
For example, Dave Linz insured his house for $79,000 at an annual rate
of $0.51 per $100. His premium was figured this way:

$79,000 ÷ $100 = 790,   the number of $100 units in $79,000

790 × $0.51 = $402.90, or $403,   the premium for one year

**Exercise 1
Written**

For each problem, find the premium to the nearest dollar.

1. Find the premium for 1 year in each problem.

	Face of Policy	Annual Rate/$100				Face of Policy	Annual Rate/$100	
a.	$ 51,000	$0.38	$194	d.	$ 62,000	$0.41	$254
b.	25,000	0.68	170	e.	33,500	0.39	131
c.	109,000	0.35	382	f.	135,200	0.32	433

2. Esther insured her home for $45,000. The rate was $0.87 per $100.
    What was the annual premium of this policy? $392

3. Bill wants to insure his home for $56,000. The Hobarth Company's rate is $0.75 per $100 while the Dexter Company's rate is $0.68 per $100.
   a. What annual premium would be charged by Hobarth? $420
   b. What annual premium would be charged by Dexter? $381
   c. What is the difference between the annual premiums charged by the two companies? $39

4. The Clark family moved to a new home with the same value as their old home, $89,500. Because the new home is located more than 1,000 feet from a fire hydrant, their homeowners insurance rate increased by $0.19 per $100.
   a. What estimated amount more will the Clarks pay each year? $180
   b. What actual amount more will their insurance cost? $170

5. Consuela insures her home for $60,000 and pays insurance at a rate of $0.50 per $100. The average house in the neighborhood is insured for $57,000. Because she has installed smoke detectors, her insurance company will give her a 2% discount on annual premiums. What annual premium will she pay, including the discount? $294

6. The basic annual premium on a house insured for $150,000 is $902. The owner of the house wants to get additional personal property insurance of $12,500 to cover jewelry and watches owned by the family. That coverage will cost $1.20 per $100. What total premium will be paid by the owner? $1,052

Renters or Tenants Policies. If you rent a house or an apartment, you may want to buy a **renters policy.** A renters policy provides nearly the same coverage as a homeowners policy except for loss of the building itself. Annual premiums for a renters policy are based on the amount of insurance on the contents of your home. The table in Illustration 77–1 shows the annual premium charged by one company for a renters policy. Notice that the premiums vary with how much insurance you buy and where the building is located.

Amount	Distance From Fire Station	
Coverage on Contents	Less Than 5 Miles	5 Miles or More
$5,000 or less	$ 61	$ 70
$ 8,000	75	86
10,000	82	94
12,000	94	108
14,000	106	121
16,000	114	130

Illustration 77–1. Renters Policy Annual Premiums

Each renters policy provides coverage for the contents of your home and for personal liability. This policy also provides off-premises coverage. This covers personal property away from home, such as the clothing you take on a vacation. Living expenses charged while damage to your home is being repaired are also covered.

Coverage for contents off the premises is 10% of the amount of the policy. Living expense coverage is figured at 20% of the amount of the policy. For example, if you insure the contents of your home for $8,000, the coverage of those contents off the premises is $800 and your living expense coverage is $1,600.

Use the table in Illustration 77–1 to solve the problems.

Exercise 2 Written

Find the annual premium, the amount of off-premises coverage, and the amount of living expense coverage for each.

	Amount of Policy	Distance From Fire Station	Annual Premium	Off-Premises Coverage (10%)	Living Expense Coverage (20%)
1.	$10,000	8 miles	$ 94	$1,000	$2,000
2.	16,000	2 miles	114	1,600	3,200
3.	5,000	12 miles	70	500	1,000
4.	12,000	1 mile	94	1,200	2,400
5.	14,000	20 miles	121	1,400	2,800

6. Delia Ward has $2,000 of personal property to insure through a renters policy. If she lives 500 feet from a fire station, what annual premium does she pay? $61

Deductible Policies. Insurance policies can be written for different deductible amounts. With a $100 **deductible policy,** you are responsible for the first $100 of the loss. The insurance company will then pay the remainder of the claim up to the face of the policy.

For example, Aretha Carnes had a renters policy with a $100 deductible clause in it. A small fire destroyed $700 worth of her furniture. The insurance company paid her $600 for her loss ($700 loss − $100 deductible = $600 paid.)

Many people get a discount on their homeowners, renters, business, or other property insurance by taking a policy with a higher deductible.

Exercise 3 Written

1. Anita Bergman had a $100 deductible homeowners policy. Her home computer valued at $1,200 was stolen. How much did Anita collect from the insurance company? $1,100

2. Ned Ryan had a fire in his apartment that destroyed his sofa, worth $900. His clothing and drapes, worth $2,800, were damaged by smoke and had to be thrown away. Ned's insurance company paid for the loss, less a $250 deductible. How much did the company pay? $3,450

3. Ricardo Mentos could purchase a homeowners policy from Bristol Insurance Company for $487 with a $100 deductible clause, or for $414 with a $250 deductible clause. How much will Ricardo save by buying the policy with $250 deductible? $73

■ Round
premiums to
nearest dollar.

4. Willa Lengstrom can reduce the annual premium on her renters policy by 35% by increasing the amount of her deductible clause from $100 to $1,000. If her annual premium is $218 now, what will be her new annual premium? $142

5. Ted Levette increases the deductible amount of his homeowners policy from $100 to $250 and saves 18% of the annual premium. If the annual premium was $284, what is the
   a. Estimated new annual premium? $240
   b. Actual new annual premium? $233

6. The owner of an apartment building was charged $1,200 a year for property insurance with a $250 deductible. By taking a $750 deductible, the owner will reduce the policy's cost by 22%. What will be the annual premium on the policy with a $750 deductible? $936

7. By increasing the deductible amount on her property, Rita Malzone saved $85 on her annual premium. If her annual premium was $340, what percent of the premium did she save? 25%

8. Chi Pai increased the deductible amount on his property insurance from $100 to $1,000. This reduced his annual premium of $680 by $238. By what percent did he reduce his annual premium? 35%

Short-Term Policies and Cancellations by the Insured. An insurance policy for less than a year is called a **short-term policy.** The premium is found by taking a percent of the annual premium. Sample short-term rates are shown in Illustration 77–2.

Number of Days Policy Is in Effect	Percent of Annual Premium Charged
1 Day to 30 Days	25%
31 Days to 90 Days	50%
91 Days to 180 Days	75%
More than 180 Days	100%

Illustration 77–2. Sample Short-Term Rates

The short-term rates are used also to find how much you will be refunded if *you* cancel your policy. For example, if you cancel a one-year policy at the end of 98 days, the company will keep 75% of the premium and refund 25% to you. If the premium for the year was $120, the amount of your refund would be 25% of $120, or $30.

Policies Canceled by the Insurance Company. If the insurance company cancels your policy, the refund must be calculated on a *pro rata basis.* This means that the amount of the refund must be in proportion to the time the policy has left to run.

For example, suppose you pay a premium of $80 on a 1-year renters policy and the company cancels the policy at the end of 73 days. The unexpired time is 365 − 73, or 292 days. Since $\frac{292}{365}$ can be simplified to $\frac{4}{5}$, $\frac{4}{5}$ of the premium must be refunded. The refund is $\frac{4}{5} \times \$80$, or \$64.

Exercise 4
Written

Use the rates in Illustration 77–2 to solve Problems 1–3.

1. Millicent Crane paid \$0.62 per \$100 for \$20,000 worth of renters insurance. She canceled the policy after keeping it for 120 days, or about 4 months. How much was her refund? $31

■ **Round premium to the nearest dollar.**

2. Ronald Green canceled a \$4,000 property insurance policy on his sailboat at the end of summer. He had kept the policy for 89 days after paying \$2.45 in premiums per \$100 of value. How much was his refund? $49

3. Due to a family emergency, Gregg Baines had to cancel his apartment lease and renters insurance policy after 15 days. He paid \$60 as a semiannual premium on the policy. How much did the insurance cost Gregg for the time he used it? $30

4. Lottie's insurance company canceled her homeowners policy after 146 days. If she paid an annual premium of \$275 for the policy,
   a. What did the insurance cost her for the 146 days? $110
   b. What amount should Lottie expect as a refund? $165

5. Phil Wilborn paid \$85 for the premium on a 1-year renters policy. After it was in force for 219 days, it was canceled by the insurance company. How much money should the company return to Phil? $34

REVIEW 77

Terms

1. Match the terms with the statements.

   deductible policy   renters policy
   homeowners insurance   short-term policy

   a. Coverage for less than a year   short-term policy
   b. Protects owner and owner's dwelling and other property   homeowners insurance
   c. Property insurance for tenants   renters policy
   d. The owner pays part of the loss   deductible policy

Skills

2. a. Divide: 261 by 58,000   0.0045
   b. \$13 is what part less than \$104? $\frac{7}{8}$
   c. What amount is 60% less than \$76.35? $30.54
   d. Write 12.25 as a mixed number in lowest terms. $12\frac{1}{4}$
   e. Find the exact interest on \$2,000 for 8 days at 14%. $6.14

Problems

3. Max insures his house for $34,700. If the rate is $0.47 per $100, find the amount of the premium. $163 [77]

4. Rahid Niktar's home insurance policy contains a $750 deductible clause. He loses $1,800 worth of personal property in a theft. How much will his insurance company pay Rahid for the loss? $1,050 [77]

5. An insurance company canceled the homeowners policy of Brian Worthy because he abandoned his residence. The policy cost $430 and was in effect for 73 days. What was the amount of the refund? $344 [77]

6. The annual premium on a whole-life policy for a 30-year old male is $10.45 per $1,000, and $7.58 for a female at the same age. What is a male's annual premium on a $24,000 policy? $250.80 [74]

7. The tax rate in Briggs City is $34.70 per $1,000. If property worth $76,000 is assessed for 60% of its value, what will be the amount of the tax bill? $1,582.32 [67]

Section 78
Collecting on Property Insurance

If a fire occurs and your property is damaged, you have to file a claim with your insurance company. The company will send an adjuster to look at the property and decide on the amount of the loss.

Collecting for Loss Under a Basic Policy. If you have a basic policy, the company will pay the full amount of the loss up to the face of the policy. They will not pay more than the amount of your policy.

Exercise 1
Oral

Find the amount the insurance company will pay under a basic policy for the loss in each problem.

	Property Insured for	Fire Loss			Property Insured for	Fire Loss	
1.	$105,000	$ 7,800	$ 7,800	5.	$36,000	$35,400	$35,400
2.	34,500	34,500	34,500	6.	67,000	69,800	67,000
3.	27,000	4,000	4,000	7.	31,000	42,000	31,000
4.	89,000	92,300	89,000	8.	56,500	56,800	56,500

Dividing Loss among Several Companies. Some insurance companies may not want to take the risk of issuing policies for large amounts. So, the owner may have to insure the property with more than one company. When a loss occurs, the amount of the loss is shared among the companies in proportion to the amount of each policy.

Example

A warehouse is insured by the United Insurance Company for $3,000,000 and by the Northern Insurance Company for $5,000,000. How much should each company pay on a fire loss of $64,000?

Solution

$$\$3,000,000 + \$5,000,000 = \$8,000,000 \quad \text{total insurance}$$

$$\frac{\$3,000,000}{\$8,000,000} = \frac{3}{8} \quad \text{proportion of loss chargeable to United Insurance Company}$$

$$\frac{\$5,000,000}{\$8,000,000} = \frac{5}{8} \quad \text{proportion of loss chargeable to Northern Insurance Company}$$

$$\frac{8}{8} \quad \text{total}$$

$$\frac{3}{8} \times \$64,000 = \$24,000, \quad \text{amount paid by United} \quad \textbf{Ans.}$$

$$\frac{5}{8} \times \$64,000 = \underline{\$40,000}, \quad \text{amount paid by Northern} \quad \textbf{Ans.}$$

$$\phantom{\frac{5}{8} \times \$64,000 =} \$64,000, \quad \text{total}$$

Exercise 2
Written

1. Find each insurance company's share of the fire loss.

Amount of Insurance Carried by

	Fire Loss	American Company		General Company	
a.	$ 60,000	$ 2,500,000	$ 20,000	$ 5,000,000	$ 40,000
b.	20,000	12,000,000	20,000	None	
c.	42,000	1,400,000	21,000	1,400,000	21,000
d.	96,000	1,200,000	9,600	10,800,000	86,400
e.	540,000	20,000,000	216,000	30,000,000	324,000
f.	320,000	1,500,000	40,000	10,500,000	280,000

2. A hotel was insured by Lane Insurance for $3,000,000 and by Alb Insurance for $9,000,000. How much should each company pay on a fire loss of $180,000?   Lane, $45,000; Alb, $135,000

3. A fire insurance policy of $12,000,000 was carried on an office building by these companies: Trent Insurance, $1,800,000; Morgan Company, $4,200,000; States Casualty Company, $6,000,000. How much should each company pay on a fire loss amounting to $1,000,000?
Trent, $150,000; Morgan, $350,000; States, $500,000

4. The Branden Company owns a bakery that it has insured for $300,000 with Company A, for $400,000 with Company B, and for $200,000 with Company C. A fire loss of $72,000 occurs. What amount should the Branden Company get from each insurance company?
Company A, $24,000; Company B, $32,000; Company C, $16,000

5. Jack Booth owns a building that has a market value of $20,000,000. Jack has insured the building with the Elgin Company for

$5,000,000, with the Grand Company for $8,000,000, and with the Marlin Company for $7,000,000. A fire loss of $600,000 occurs. What is each company's share of the loss? Elgin Company, $150,000; Grand Company, $240,000; Marlin Company, $210,000

Collecting a Loss with Coinsurance. Most fires cause only partial damage to property. A fire rarely destroys all of a property. For this reason, many owners carry only enough insurance to cover the partial loss they think might happen.

To encourage owners to carry more insurance, insurance companies offer lower rates on policies with a **coinsurance clause.** Under this clause, the company will pay the full amount of any loss up to the face amount of the policy only if the owner has insured the property for a certain percent of its current value. The percent is often 80%, and it is called an 80% coinsurance clause.

Suppose you have a policy with an 80% coinsurance clause and your property is insured for 80% or more of its value. The insurance company will pay you the full amount of any loss up to the face of your policy.

For example, a building you own is valued at $50,000 and is insured under an 80% coinsurance clause for $40,000. This is exactly 80% of the value, so the insurance company will pay you the full amount of any loss up to the face of the policy, $40,000. If the building were insured for $45,000, which is greater than the 80% minimum, the company would pay you the full amount of any loss up to $45,000.

If the face of your policy is less than 80% of the value of the building, the amount paid by the company is figured this way:

$$\frac{\text{Face of Policy}}{80\% \text{ of Property Value}} \times \text{Amount of Loss} = \frac{\text{Amount Paid By}}{\text{the Company}}$$

For example, you insure your building, worth $50,000, for only $35,000 under an 80% coinsurance clause. You should have insured it for at least $40,000 to be fully covered (0.80 × $50,000 = $40,000). If you had a fire loss of $7,200, you would get only $6,300 from the insurance company:

$$\frac{\$35{,}000 \text{ (Face of Policy)}}{\$40{,}000 \text{ (80\% of Value)}} = \frac{7}{8} \qquad \frac{7}{8} \times \$7{,}200 \text{ (Loss)} = \$6{,}300 \text{ paid}$$

Remember, an insurance company will never pay you more than the amount of the loss or more than the face of the policy.

**Exercise 3
Written**

1. Find how much the insurance company will pay in each problem.

	Face of Policy	Amount of Loss	Value of Property	Coinsurance Clause	Amount Paid
a.	$ 63,000	$ 5,600	$ 90,000	80%	$ 4,900
b.	45,000	8,000	75,000	80%	6,000
c.	40,000	13,200	60,000	80%	11,000
d.	45,000	7,000	62,500	80%	6,300
e.	49,000	22,500	70,000	90%	$17,500
f.	32,000	4,620	40,000	80%	4,620
g.	63,000	27,000	70,000	80%	27,000
h.	109,000	35,000	105,000	90%	35,000

2. Joe Dunn's house is valued at $80,000. He insured it for $48,000 under a policy containing an 80% coinsurance clause. If a fire causes a $7,600 loss to the house, how much does Joe get? $5,700

3. An auto repair shop valued at $240,000 is insured for $128,000. The insurance policy contains an 80% coinsurance clause. What amount must the insurer pay in case of a fire loss of $3,870? $2,580

4. Gloria Ruiz owns a building worth $200,000. She insured it for $144,000 under a fire insurance policy with a 90% coinsurance clause. If a fire loss of $16,000 occurs, how much should Gloria collect from the insurance company? $12,800

Collecting a Loss with a Replacement Cost Policy. Because the prices of homes can rise rapidly, many people insure their property under **replacement cost policies.** With this type of policy, the insurance company will pay the cost of replacing your property at *current* prices.

To collect the full amount of the replacement cost, many insurance companies will require you to insure your property for at least 80% of its current replacement cost. As with coinsurance, if you insure for less than 80% the company may pay only part of your loss. The part that the company may pay is the ratio of the amount of insurance carried to 80% of the replacement cost.

$$\frac{\textbf{Insurance Carried}}{\textbf{80\% of Replacement Cost}} \times \frac{\textbf{Amount of Loss at}}{\textbf{Replacement Cost}} = \frac{\textbf{Amount Paid By}}{\textbf{the Company}}$$

For example, if your house would cost $50,000 to replace, you must insure it for at least $40,000 to collect the full replacement cost of any loss (0.80 × $50,000 = $40,000). If you insure it for only $30,000 and you have a loss of $16,000 in a fire, you will receive only $12,000 of the loss:

$$\frac{\$30,000 \textbf{ (Insurance Carried)}}{\$40,000 \textbf{ (80\% of Replacement Cost)}} = \frac{3}{4} \times \$16,000 \textbf{ (loss)}$$

$$= \$12,000 \textbf{ paid}$$

**Exercise 4
Written**

1. Albert insures the contents of his apartment for $7,000 with a replacement cost policy. The policy requires him to insure the property for at least 80% of its replacement cost. To replace the contents at current prices, Albert would have to pay $17,500. If a fire loss of $3,250 occurred, how much would Albert be paid by the insurance company? $1,625

2. After putting on a new roof costing $2,900, Dee Morgan figured her house would cost $70,000 to replace. She insured it for $48,000 with a replacement cost policy that required her to insure the property for at least 80% of its replacement cost. If a fire loss of $21,000 occurred, how much would the insurance company pay? $18,000

3. Maurice insured a barn on his farm for $22,400 with a replacement cost policy that required him to carry insurance for at least 80% of the property's replacement cost. The barn would cost $42,000 to re-

place at current prices. If a loss of $12,000 occurred, how much would Maurice's insurance company pay? $8,000

REVIEW 78

Terms

1. Match the terms with the statements.

   coinsurance clause   replacement cost policy

   a. Requires property to be insured at a minimum percent of its current value   coinsurance clause
   b. Property loss is paid at the amount needed to buy it new or to build it new   replacement cost policy

Skills

2. a. $77 is what part greater than $56? $\frac{3}{8}$
   b. $68.70 minus 40% of itself is what amount? $41.22
   c. Find the number of days from August 15 to October 30.
       76 days
   d. Find the exact interest at 8.4% on $800 for 3 months. $16.80
   e. What percent of $1.20 is $0.54?   45%

Problems

3. Delroy, Inc., has a fire insurance policy on its plant for $540,000 with the Federated Insurance Company and another for $120,000 with the National Insurance Company. A fire in the plant causes a loss of $44,000. How much should be collected from each company?
   Federated, $36,000; National, $8,000 [78]

4. Chi-luan insured his house for $45,000 with a replacement cost policy. The policy required him to carry insurance of at least 90% of the house's current replacement cost. A fire caused a loss of $10,800. The house's replacement cost was $90,000. What amount did his insurance company pay? $6,000 [78]

5. Lucinda reduced the annual premium on her renters policy from $160 to $136 by increasing the deductible amount from $100 to $250. By what percent did she reduce her premium?   15% [77]

6. Suzie bought stock at a total cost of $42 a share. The stock paid an annual dividend of 5.5% on a par value of $60. What rate of income did she receive on the investment, to the nearest tenth of a percent?   7.9% [58]

7. A bookcase is offered by Store A for a down payment of $80, with 12 monthly payments of $19.75 each. Store B offers a similar bookcase for a down payment of $25 with 26 biweekly payments of $10.50 each. How much will the buyer save by taking the better of the 2 offers? $19 [50]

8. Erik began a trip with a full, 64 L tank of gas. During the trip he bought 195 L of gas. When he arrived home, he had 21 L left in his tank. How many liters of gas were used on the trip?   238 L [4, 32]

Computer Clinic

Sarah Hulmich's house, worth $90,000, is insured for $60,000 under an insurance policy that contains an 80% coinsurance clause. She recently filed a property loss claim for $1,200 with her insurer. Follow the steps below to find the amount of property loss that the insurance company will pay.

1. Insert your Spreadsheet Applications Diskette and call up the file "Sec78." After you do, your computer screen should look like Illustration 78–1. (If you are using MicroTools, additional instructions for determining the amount for B9 will appear at the bottom of your computer screen.)

```
Sec 78              Finding Amount of Loss Paid By Insurer
-----------------------------------------------------------------
Value of Property                    $0
Insurance Carried                    $0
Coinsurance Rate (%)                  0
Amount of Loss                       $0
-----------------------------------------------------------------
Required Insurance                   $0
Amount of Loss Insurer Pays          $0
-----------------------------------------------------------------
```

Illustration 78–1. Figuring Insurance Loss Payments

2. Find the amount Sarah's insurance company will pay by entering these data into the template:

   B3 90000   B4 60000   B5 80   B6 1200

3. Answer the questions.*
   a. To meet coinsurance requirements, for what amount must Sarah insure the house? $72,000
   b. How much greater or less was the amount of insurance carried than the amount of required insurance? $12,000 less
   c. Of the total loss, what amount did the insurance company pay, if any? $1,000
   d. Of the total loss, what amount was not covered, if any? $200

4. For extra practice, check the problems in Exercises 3 and 4 in Section 78.

---

*If you are using MicroTools, remember that the amount of loss the insurer pays (B9) cannot exceed the amount of insurance carried (B4). If the amount in B9 is larger than the amount in B4, use B4 as the amount of loss the insurer pays. Do not, however, enter the new amount in B9.

Kinds of Car and Truck Insurance. There are four basic types of insurance for cars and trucks that protect you against the risk of financial loss:

1. **Bodily injury,** which covers your liability for injury to other persons. Coverage of at least $20,000 for injury to one person and a total of $40,000 for injury to two or more persons in one accident is required by law in many states.

2. **Property damage,** which covers damage to other people's property that you cause with a car or truck.

3. **Collision**, which covers damage to your car or truck from an accident. Most people buy deductible collision insurance. If you buy a $100 deductible policy, you pay the first $100 of damages for each accident and the insurance company pays the rest.

4. **Comprehensive damage,** which covers damage or loss to your car or truck from fire, theft, vandalism, falling trees, hail, and other causes.

In some states, bodily injury and property damage coverages are not listed separately but are combined into one minimum limit. The limit applies regardless of whether there is injury to one or more persons or damage to property of others in a single accident.

In addition to the basic types of insurance coverages, states may require additional coverages for which you will be charged.

Car and Truck Insurance Premiums. Premiums for car and truck insurance vary from state to state. Insurance companies base their premiums on the amount of financial risk they have in issuing policies. Premiums are usually higher in large cities than in small cities and rural areas.

Premiums for bodily injury and property damage insurance are higher on cars and trucks used for business than those used for pleasure or only for driving to and from work. Premiums may be higher for drivers under 25 years of age than for drivers over 25.

Premiums for collision insurance are higher for high-cost cars than for low-cost cars. They are also higher for $100 deductible coverage than for $250 deductible coverage.

Sample annual premiums for a car or truck driven by an adult living near a large city are shown in Illustration 79–1. Rates are shown for the four basic types of insurance with different amounts of coverages. To use the table, find the desired coverage and match it with the type of driving done with the car.

Type of Insurance	Limits	Pleasure Only	Used for Driving to Work	Business
Bodily Injury	$20/40,000	$ 82	$ 90	$118
	25/50,000	98	108	140
	50/100,000	114	126	162
Property Damage	$10,000	10	12	16
	25,000	12	14	18
	50,000	14	16	20
Collision	$100 deductible	550	612	796
	250 deductible	386	428	556
	500 deductible	302	336	436
Comprehensive	$ 50 deductible	92	101	132
	100 deductible	68	76	98

Illustration 79–1. Sample Annual Car and Truck Insurance Premiums

**Exercise 1
Written**

In solving Problems 1–7, use Illustration 79–1 to find the cost of insurance. If a coverage is not given, assume it is one of these standard coverages: bodily injury, $20/40,000; property damage, $10,000; collision, $100 deductible; comprehensive, $50 deductible.

1. What is the total premium for standard insurance coverages on a car driven to work? $815

2. Reva Wilson uses her truck for business and insures the truck with standard coverages.
   a. What total annual premium does she pay? $1,062
   b. If she took the highest deductibles, what amount could she save annually on her truck insurance? $394

3. On a truck that he uses to drive to work, Nolan Wyatt carries bodily injury insurance of $50/100,000 and a $250 deductible on collision. Other coverages are standard. What is his annual premium? $667

4. Julia Santos owns 2 cars. One car, used for pleasure driving only, is insured at standard coverage. Her other car is used for business and is insured for the greatest amount of bodily injury and property damage coverage. Because she insures both cars with the same company, she gets a 10% discount from her total premium. What net premium will Julia pay for insuring both cars for 1 year? $1,659.60

5. A truck used on a farm is insured in the Driving to Work category. The truck has standard coverage, with the highest deductibles. Because the truck is seldom driven outside the farm, it can be insured for 70% of the usual rate. What is the annual premium? $359.80

6. Because of the 3 speeding citations he received, Lew Marsh will have to pay an insurance premium of 2.2 times the rates for standard coverage. Lew uses his car to drive to work. What is his premium for $\frac{1}{2}$ year? $896.50

7. Olivia McVey, a 16-year-old owner of a car driven for pleasure, wants to buy insurance. Because of her age she must pay 4 times the usual rate.
   a. What annual premium must she pay with standard coverage?
      $2,936
   b. To reduce the amount she must pay, she is considering not covering her car for collision and comprehensive damage. What would be her annual premium with this reduced coverage?
      $368

REVIEW 79

Terms

1. Match the terms with the statements.

   bodily injury   comprehensive damage
   collision   property damage

   a. Covers damage for others hurt in an accident   bodily injury
   b. Covers damage to other people's property   property damage
   c. Covers damage to own car from accident   collision
   d. Covers damage to own car from causes other than an accident
      comprehensive damage

Skills

2. a. Add: 34.89, 133.9, 4.275, and 1.47   174.535
   b. Divide: $9\frac{1}{2}$ by $\frac{1}{4}$ 38
   c. Round: $23,896.73 to the nearest thousand $24,000

Problems

3. Dan Rhodes has retired and now uses his car only for pleasure driving instead of driving to work. Using Illustration 79–1, find out how much less the new annual premium will be if Dan carries these same coverages: bodily injury, $25/50,000; property damage, $25,000; collision, $250 deductible; comprehensive, $100 deductible. $62 [79]

4. Kay Pollard bought a car for $9,502. Four years later she got $2,850 for the car as a trade-in allowance. What was the average annual depreciation of the car? $1,663 [65]

5. Lloyd Conner's taxable income for last year was $17,200. The state in which he lives charges a tax rate of 2.3% on taxable income. His city tax is 0.5% of taxable income. What is the total of his state and city income tax? $481.60 [73]

Finding and Distributing Business Income and Loss

Business firms keep many types of records. Since no business can survive for very long without making a profit, keeping track of sales, merchandise bought, and expenses of doing business is very important. From time to time, business firms also prepare a balance sheet that shows how much the business is worth.

Depending on the number of owners a business has and the way in which it is organized, a business may distribute net income in a number of ways. In any case, net income that does not need to be kept in the business is distributed to the owners as net profit.

Many businesses fail within a short time after they begin operation. When a business cannot make a profit, it may be declared bankrupt and sold to pay its debts.

After you finish Unit 13, you will be able to:

- Figure capital when given assets and liabilities.
- Prepare simple balance sheets.
- Figure net sales, gross profit, cost of merchandise sold, operating expenses, and net income or net loss.
- Do a percentage analysis of simple income statements.
- Figure merchandise turnover rate.
- Figure each partner's share of net income or loss using several methods.
- Figure rate of corporation dividend in percent or dollars and cents.
- Find total corporation dividend and amount kept in retained earnings.
- Figure total dividends for a cooperative association.
- Figure rate and amount of claims paid to creditors in bankruptcy.
- Solve problems that contain more information than you need.
- Estimate answers to problems.
- Read, write, say, and recognize the meanings of the key terms.

Assets. To start a business and continue its operation, the owners must have many kinds of property. Bookstore owners, for example, may have books, magazines, reading lamps, and related items to sell. They also must have shelving, cash registers, counters, and wrapping supplies. Money in the form of cash is also needed to make change and to pay small expenses. All these things that have value and that are owned by the business are called the **assets** of the business.

■ Assets are things owned.

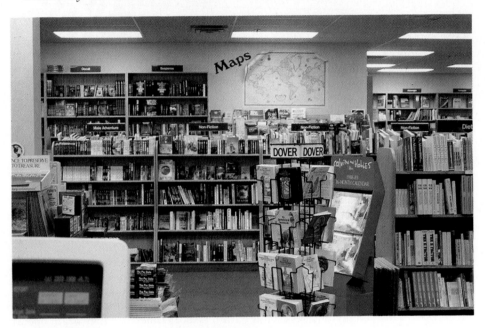

Illustration 80–1. Small Business with Assets

■ Liabilities are amounts owed to others.

Liabilities. A business often gets some of its assets by buying them on credit and promising to pay for them later. The persons to whom the money is owed are called the **creditors** of the business. The amounts owed to creditors are the **liabilities** of the business.

■ Capital is the owners' share of the business.

Capital. If all the assets of a business are owned free of debt, the owners' share of the business is equal to the total value of the assets. If there are liabilities, the value of the owners' share, called **capital**, is found by subtracting the liabilities from the assets.

For example, Lynn Gordon owns a bookstore called Lynn's Book Place. The bookstore owes the Hubbel Book Co. $19,000 and Acril Supply $11,000 for merchandise Lynn has bought on credit. The total liabilities are $19,000 + $11,000, or $30,000. Lynn's Book Place has assets worth $90,000, so Lynn's capital is $90,000 − $30,000, or $60,000.

Assets − Liabilities = Capital

$90,000 − $30,000 = $60,000

1. Vince Regis owns a garden shop with these assets: Cash, $2,100; Merchandise, $51,700; Store Equipment, $7,800; Store Supplies, $930. He owes the Grossel Co. $3,175 and the Tipaloy Supply Co. $1,850 for merchandise bought on credit.
   a. What are Vince's total assets? $62,530
   b. What are his total liabilities? $5,025
   c. What is Vince's capital? $57,505

2. Samantha Merks owns a paint store. She has these assets: Cash, $3,850; Merchandise, $42,000; Store Supplies, $520; Store Equipment, $9,200; Delivery Truck, $8,400; Land and Building, $60,000. She owes the State National Bank $8,600 and the Logan Manufacturing Company $23,800. What is her capital? $91,570

Accounts receivable is the amount owed to a business by customers.

3. David Salamer has a small ceramics business with these assets: Cash, $1,400; Accounts Receivable, $1,600; Merchandise, $23,500; Kilns, $3,700; Storage Shelving, $2,100; Land and Buildings, $25,500. He owes Trek Pottery $7,500, Landon Suppliers $3,300, and Long Lake Bank $9,100. What is David's capital? $37,900

4. Karen Carns owns a delivery company. She has 6 employees whose total annual wages are $94,000. On December 31 last year, her assets were: Cash, $2,620; Office Supplies, $2,875; Delivery Equipment, $29,250. On that date she owed Rondell Office Supply, $580; Steel Oil Company, $2,700; Liberty Finance Co., $17,200; and the Hartley Repair Garage, $1,200. What was Karen's capital? $13,065

The Balance Sheet. At least once a year, a business takes an inventory of its assets and liabilities. An **inventory** is a list of items and their values. For example, a **merchandise inventory** is a list that shows the value of goods on hand for resale.

With this information, the business prepares a balance sheet. A **balance sheet** is a form that shows the assets, liabilities, and capital of the business as of a certain date.

The balance sheet for Lynn's Book Place as of March 31, 19--, is shown in Illustration 80–2.

Lynn's Book Place			
Balance Sheet, March 31, 19--			
Assets		_Liabilities_	
Cash	$ 8,300	Hubbel Book Co.	$19,000
Merchandise Inventory	63,600	Acril Supply	11,000
Store Equipment	16,000	Total Liabilities	$30,000
Store Supplies	2,100		
		Capital	
		Lynn Gordon, Capital	$60,000
Total Assets	$90,000	Total Liabilities and Capital	$90,000

Illustration 80–2. Balance Sheet for Lynn's Book Place

The assets are listed on the left side, and the liabilities and capital are listed on the right side of the balance sheet. In that way, all that is owned is shown on the left side and all claims to the assets are listed on the right side, with the amount of the claim.

Since Lynn Gordon is the owner of the bookstore, the capital account is written in her name. The total capital of $60,000 is Lynn's claim against the assets of the business.

**Exercise 2
Written**

Prepare a balance sheet for each of these problems, using Illustration 80–2 as a guide. Figure the amount of Capital.

1. On December 31 of last year, Clyde Slade, a small engine repair shop owner, had the assets and liabilities listed below:

Cash	$ 2,744	Debts owed to creditors:	
Parts Inventory	40,316	On-Time Distributors	$ 6,230
Shop Supplies	1,650	Do-All Suppliers	2,970
Shop Equipment	18,500	Clyde Slade, Capital	54,010
Total Assets	$63,210	Total Liabilities and Capital	$63,210

2. Jill Grover's business had these assets on December 31, 19--: Cash, $3,842; Accounts Receivable, $4,915; Merchandise Inventory, $97,150; Store Equipment, $21,470; Delivery Equipment, $14,752; Supplies, $1,732. Her liabilities were a debt to the Dren Company of $44,655.   Total Assets, $143,861; Capital, $99,206; Total Liabilities and Capital, $143,861

3. As of March 31, 19--, Bezard Brothers' had these assets: Cash, $15,450; Accounts Receivable, $4,550; Merchandise Inventory, $79,990; Store Equipment, $5,430; Delivery Equipment, $20,450; Supplies, $450. The company owed Roform Supply $5,960; Meldex Inc. $2,670; and Cole Industries $1,010.   Total Assets, $126,320; Capital, $116,680; Total Liabilities and Capital, $126,320

4. Saturn Jewelry Suppliers had these assets on June 30, 19--:

Cash	$ 17,643.10
Accounts Receivable	32,524.65
Merchandise Inventory	234,631.50
Supplies	13,398.00
Equipment	129,463.00
Building	154,770.00

The company owed $325,000 to the Lern County Bank and $140,000 to New Creations, Inc.   Total Assets, $582,430.25; Capital, $117,430.25; Total Liabilities and Capital, $582,430.25

REVIEW 80

Terms

1. Match the terms with the statements.

assets	capital	inventory	merchandise inventory
balance sheet	creditors	liabilities	

a. A list of items and their value   inventory
b. Creditors' claims to assets   liabilities

c.   People to whom money is owed   creditors
d.   A form showing assets, liabilities, and capital   balance sheet
e.   Value of the owner's share of a business   capital
f.   Goods on hand for resale   merchandise inventory
g.   All things of value owned by a business   assets

Skills

2.   a.   Multiply: $4,678 by 0.01 $46.78
     b.   Find the number of days from July 7 to September 22.   77
     c.   Find the exact interest at 15% on $760 for $1\frac{1}{2}$ years. $171
     d.   Multiply: 8 m by 12.4 m   99.2 m^2
     e.   Show a tax rate of 7.5 mills on $1 as a rate on $1,000. $7.50

Problems

3.   The Keepsake Boutique had these assets and liabilities on July 1:
     Cash, $1,015; Merchandise Inventory, $7,125; Land and Build-
     ings, $59,800; Furniture and Equipment, $12,008; debts totaled
     $10,040. [80]
     a.   Estimate the boutique's capital. $70,000
     b.   Find the actual capital. $69,908

4.   The tax rate in Randolph Meadows is $3.23 per $100. What is the
     tax on a property assessed at $41,000? $1,324.30 [67]

5.   Greta Long and Marge Polinari divided their apartment expenses
     in a ratio of 3 to 2. Find the amount each pays if the expenses total
     $840.   Greta, $504; Marge, $336 [16]

6.   Ezra has a taxable income of $25,600. This income is subject to a
     state income tax of 3% on the first $7,000, 4% on the next $10,000,
     and 5% on any taxable income over $17,000. How much state tax
     does Ezra owe? $1,040 [73]

Section 81
Finding Profit and Loss

The main purpose of a business is to make a profit for the owners. To
make a profit, the business must sell much of its merchandise at prices
higher than the cost of the goods plus the expenses of operating the
business. A business that sells much of its merchandise for less than
cost plus expenses will have a loss. A business cannot operate at a loss
for very long.

Figuring whether a business is making a profit or a loss may take
much time, work, and expense. Also, the amount of sales and profit in
a business may change greatly from day to day and week to week. So,
many business owners figure their profit or loss only for longer periods
of time, such as a month, three months, six months, or a year.

To find their profit (net income) or loss, business owners have to
figure their net sales, cost of merchandise sold, gross profit on sales,
and operating expenses.

Figuring Net Sales. A first step in figuring profit or loss is to figure net sales for the period. **Sales**, or gross sales, is the total value of the goods sold in a period of time. But some goods are returned for refunds, and allowances or reductions in price are given for damaged goods. These *sales returns and allowances* decrease sales, so they are subtracted from sales. The amount left is called **net sales.**

Sales − Sales Returns and Allowances = Net Sales

For example, the sales of Lynn's Book Place for March were $25,820. Sales returns and allowances for March were $820. So, the net sales for the month were $25,000.

Sales	**$25,820**
Sales Returns and Allowances	**− 820**
Net Sales	**$25,000**

**Exercise 1
Written**

1. The Cycle Shop's sales for the first quarter of the year were $152,296. Sales returns and allowances for the quarter were $6,450. What were the net sales for the quarter? $145,846

2. During January, a shoe store's total sales were $40,310. Sales returns and allowances for the month were $1,230.40. What were the shop's net sales for January? $39,079.60

3. In a recent year, the Diamond Record Center's sales returns and allowances were $9,975.23. The gross sales for the year were $589,900.04.
   a. What were the store's estimated net sales for the year?
      $580,000
   b. What were the actual net sales for the year? $579,924.81

Gross profit on sales = margin

Figuring Gross Profit on Sales. **Gross profit on sales,** or margin, is the difference between what the business paid for goods (cost of merchandise sold) and the amount received for those goods when they were ·sold (sales). You find gross profit on sales by subtracting cost of merchandise sold from net sales.

Net Sales − Cost of Merchandise Sold = Gross Profit on Sales

For example, merchandise that was sold at Lynn's Book Place for $25,000 in March cost $16,000. So, the gross profit on sales was $9,000.

Net sales	**$25,000**
Cost of merchandise sold	**− 16,000**
Gross profit on sales	**$ 9,000**

**Exercise 2
Written**

1. A store's sales for July were $61,538 and the cost of merchandise sold was $33,740. What was the store's gross profit on sales?
   $27,798

2. Merchandise that cost $20,348 was sold for $39,720. What was the gross profit on sales? $19,372

3. The Ski Shop's sales in March were $38,432. Returns and allowances for the month were $2,812. The cost of merchandise sold in March was $21,792. What was the shop's gross profit on sales for March? $13,828

Finding the Cost of Merchandise Sold. As you have seen, to find gross profit on sales you need to know the cost of merchandise sold. In the problems you have already done, you were given the cost. If you were a business owner, you'd have to figure the cost of merchandise sold.

One way to find the cost of merchandise sold would be to record the cost of every item as it is sold and to total the amounts at the end of the period. That might be hard to do; it might take a lot of time and it might interfere with business. So, another way may be used.

You start with an inventory of merchandise on hand at the beginning of the period. That is called a *beginning inventory.* To the beginning inventory add the *purchases,* which is the cost of all merchandise purchased during the period for resale. The sum of the beginning inventory and the purchases is called *merchandise available for sale.* From that amount, you subtract the inventory of merchandise on hand at the end of the period, called the *ending inventory.* The difference is the **cost of merchandise sold** for that period.

Beginning Inventory + Purchases = Merchandise Available for Sale

Merchandise Available − Ending Inventory = Cost of Merchandise
**   for Sale   Sold**

For example, the merchandise inventory of Lynn's Book Place on March 1 was $71,190. During the month, merchandise was purchased that cost $9,450, so the merchandise available for sale was $80,640. On March 31, the merchandise inventory was $64,640, so the cost of merchandise sold in March was $16,000.

Merchandise inventory, March 1	**$71,190**
Purchases	**+ 9,450**
Merchandise available for sale	**$80,640**
Merchandise inventory, March 31	**− 64,640**
Cost of merchandise sold	**$16,000**

Exercise 3
Written

1. Find the merchandise available for sale and cost of merchandise sold.

Merchandise inventory, May 1	$49,400	
Purchases	32,100	
Merchandise available for sale	?	$81,500
Merchandise inventory, May 31	$58,294	
Cost of merchandise sold	?	$23,206

2. An imported food store's merchandise inventory on September 1 was $42,790. Purchases in September were $18,400. The merchandise inventory on September 30 was $34,782. What was the cost of merchandise sold in September? $26,408

3. On January 1, Gill Hardware had an inventory of merchandise costing $75,070. During the year, merchandise costing $201,500 was bought. The merchandise inventory on December 31 was $50,730. What was the cost of merchandise sold for the year? $225,840

4. On July 1, a store had on hand goods that cost $89,935. On June 30 of the next year, their merchandise inventory was $70,172. During that 12-month period, the store bought merchandise worth $184,725. What was the store's cost of merchandise sold for the 12-month period? $204,488

**Exercise 4
Written**

1. Find the net sales and gross profit on sales.

	Sales	Returns and Allowances	Net Sales	Cost of Merchandise Sold	Gross Profit on Sales
a.	$21,700	$4,008	$17,692	$12,050	$ 5,642
b.	40,180	3,694	36,486	24,630	11,856
c.	58,170	1,132	57,038	48,100	8,938
d.	90,438	6,342	84,096	60,942	23,154

2. A paint store's sales for April were $33,480. Returns and allowances were $1,402. The store's merchandise inventory on April 1 was $52,500. Purchases during the month were $12,950. The merchandise inventory on April 30 was $51,673.
   a. What were the store's net sales for the month? $32,078
   b. What was the cost of merchandise sold? $13,777
   c. What was the gross profit on sales? $18,301

3. The Tech Company's records show these amounts for the quarter ending December 31; merchandise inventory, October 1, $32,475; purchases for the quarter, $82,890; merchandise inventory, December 31, $30,750; net sales for the quarter, $135,720. Find the cost of merchandise sold and the gross profit on sales for the quarter. $84,615; $51,105

Figuring Net Income or Net Loss. Most business owners spend money to cover expenses such as salaries and wages, utilities, advertising, taxes, and insurance in order to operate the business. These business expenses are called **operating expenses,** or *overhead.* Operating expenses decrease the profit of the business.

If the operating expenses are *less* than the gross profit on sales, you subtract the operating expenses from the gross profit on sales. The amount that is left is called **net income,** or *net profit.*

Gross Profit on Sales − Operating Expenses = Net Income

For example, the gross profit on sales of Lynn's Book Place for March was $9,000. The operating expenses were $7,000. So, the net income for March was $2,000.

Gross profit on sales	**$9,000**
Operating expenses	**− 7,000**
Net income	**$2,000**

If the operating expenses are *more* than the gross profit on sales, you subtract the gross profit on sales from the operating expenses. The result, or difference, is a **net loss.**

Operating Expenses − Gross Profit on Sales = Net Loss

For example, suppose that your business had a gross profit of $13,000 for a month, and the operating expenses were $16,000 for that month. You had a net loss of $3,000 for the month.

Operating expenses	**$16,000**
Gross profit on sales	**− 13,000**
Net loss	**$ 3,000**

**Exercise 5
Written**

1. Find the gross profit on sales and the net income or net loss.

	Net Sales	Cost of Merchandise Sold	Gross Profit on Sales	Operating Expenses	Net Income	Net Loss
a.	$ 6,430	$ 4,010	$ 2,420	$ 1,630	$ 790	—
b.	21,235	10,105	11,130	8,920	2,210	—
c.	35,950	26,900	9,050	10,490	—	$1,440
d.	7,800	5,200	2,600	4,007	—	1,407
e.	50,785	30,945	19,840	18,231	1,609	—
f.	70,385	52,174	18,211	23,984	—	5,773

2. Fran Bork owns a trophy shop. She had net sales of $22,500 for the month of August. Operating expenses for the month totaled $7,230 and the cost of merchandise sold was $13,600. Find her gross profit on sales and net income or net loss for the month.
   Gross profit, $8,900; net income, $1,670

3. The records of Rosetta Wills showed these facts for the year ending December 31: merchandise inventory, January 1, $32,000; purchases, $66,000; net sales, $140,000; merchandise inventory, December 31, $30,000; operating expenses, $42,000. Find the cost of merchandise sold, the gross profit on sales, and the net income.
   Cost of merchandise sold, $68,000; gross profit on sales, $72,000; net income, $30,000

4. For 6 months, the records of a business showed these facts: merchandise inventory, July 1, $27,500; merchandise inventory, December 31, $21,700; purchases, $65,000; gross sales, $101,000; sales returns and allowances, $2,500; operating expenses, $33,500. Cash on hand is $20,237. Find the net sales, cost of merchandise sold, gross profit on sales, and net income or net loss.
   Net sales, $98,500; cost of merchandise sold, $70,800; gross profit on sales, $27,700; net loss, $5,800

REVIEW 81

Terms

1. Match the terms with the statements.

cost of merchandise sold   net loss   operating expenses
gross profit on sales   net sales   sales
net income

  a. Margin, or net sales less cost of merchandise sold
      gross profit on sales
  b. Operating expenses less gross profit on sales   net loss
  c. Sales less sales returns and allowances   net sales
  d. Amount of merchandise sold over a period of time   sales
  e. Gross profit on sales less operating expenses   net income
  f. Money spent to operate the business   operating expenses
  g. Amount paid by a merchant for goods sold
      cost of merchandise sold

Skills

2. a. 4% sales tax on a $1,050 purchase is? $42
    b. 0.642 × $33 rounded to the nearest cent is? $21.19
    c. $18.56 ÷ 0.005 = ? $3,712
    d. $\frac{5}{8} + \frac{1}{4} + \frac{1}{8} = ?$ 1

Problems

3. Elena owns a picture frame shop. Her net sales for the year were $199,910. The cost of merchandise sold was $135,107. Her operating expenses were $39,950. [81]
    a. What was her estimated net income for the year? $25,000
    b. What was her actual net income for the year? $24,853

4. To the nearest tenth of a percent, what is the yield on an 8% bond selling at 92?   8.7% [56]

Section 82
The Income Statement

Net sales, cost of merchandise sold, gross profit on sales, and net income or net loss are usually shown in a form called an **income statement.** Income statements are often prepared monthly, quarterly, semiannually, or annually at the same time balance sheets are prepared. An income statement helps an owner see strengths and weaknesses of the business and guide future actions.

The income statement of Lynn's Book Place for the month of March is shown in Illustration 82–1. As you study it, notice the order in which items are listed and used to find net income or net loss.

Lynn's Book Place			
Income Statement			
For the Month Ended March 31, 19--			
Revenue:			
Sales	25,820		
Less Sales Returns and Allowances	820		
Net Sales		25,000	
Cost of Merchandise Sold:			
Merchandise Inventory, March 1	71,190		
Purchases	9,450		
Merchandise Available for Sale	80,640		
Less Merchandise Inventory, March 31	64,640		
Cost of Merchandise Sold		16,000	
Gross Profit on Sales		9,000	
Operating Expenses:			
Salaries and Wages	3,710		
Rent	1,085		
Taxes	590		
Utilities	535		
Advertising	340		
Depreciation of Equipment	210		
Security Alarm Service	110		
Insurance	95		
Other Expenses	325		
Total Operating Expenses		7,000	
Net Income:		2,000	

Illustration 82–1. Income Statement for Lynn's Book Place

Percentage Analysis of an Income Statement. Most businesses use percentages to analyze and compare income statement data. To do this, they find what percentage each major item is of the net sales.

Here is the percentage analysis of the major items on Lynn's income statement for March:

> The base is net sales.

Net sales	$25,000	100%
Cost of merchandise sold	16,000	64%
Gross profit on sales	$ 9,000	36%
Operating expenses	7,000	28%
Net income	$ 2,000	8%

In figuring the percentages, the net sales are always used as the whole, or base, with which the other items are compared. The net sales are always 100%.

**Exercise 1
Oral**

Find the percentages for each of the items below.

	1.		2.		3.	
Net sales	$5,000	100%	$6,000	100%	$8,000	100%
Cost of merchandise sold	3,000	60%	4,500	75%	5,000	$62\frac{1}{2}$%
Gross profit on sales	$2,000	40%	$1,500	25%	$3,000	$37\frac{1}{2}$%
Operating expenses	1,500	30%	1,200	20%	2,000	25%
Net income	$ 500	10%	$ 300	5%	$1,000	$12\frac{1}{2}$%

**Exercise 2
Written**

■ Net sales
equal 100%.

1. JoAnn Booth's business had net sales of $70,000. The cost of merchandise sold was $42,000, and the gross profit was $28,000.
   a. The cost of merchandise sold was what percent of net sales?
      60%
   b. The gross profit on sales was what percent of net sales?   40%

2. The records of the Paulson Company for a recent year showed these data: net sales, $440,000; cost of merchandise sold, $286,000; operating expenses, $105,600.
   a. Find the gross profit on sales and the net income.
      $154,000; $48,400
   b. Find the percent of net sales for cost of merchandise sold, gross profit on sales, operating expenses, and net income.
      65%, 35%, 24%, 11%

3. A store owner had net sales of $180,000 last year. The cost of merchandise sold for the year was $99,000, and operating expenses were $61,200.
   a. Find the gross profit on sales and net income. $81,000; $19,800
   b. Make a percentage analysis for net sales, cost of merchandise sold, gross profit on sales, operating expenses, and net income.
      100%, 55%, 45%, 34%, 11%

4. For the last 6 months of a year, a shop made a gross profit of $55,200 on net sales of $138,000. Operating expenses for the period were $42,780. The net income was what percent of net sales?   9%

Figuring a Merchandise Turnover Rate. The number of times per year that a store replaces, or turns over, its average stock of merchandise is called a **merchandise turnover rate.** Merchandise turnover rates differ greatly among different kinds of businesses, but they are useful for comparing similar businesses.

■ Turnover rate
equals cost of
merchandise sold
divided by
average inventory.

To figure a merchandise turnover rate, divide the cost of merchandise sold for a period by the average merchandise inventory for that period. If that rate is not for a year, then show the rate as a yearly rate.

The merchandise turnover rate for Lynn's Book Place is figured in the following example:

Example

Using figures from Lynn's Book Place income statement for March, find the merchandise turnover rate.

Solution	Explanation
Merchandise inventory, March 1 $71,790 Merchandise inventory, March 31 + 64,640 Total of inventories $136,430	Step 1. Find the total of the merchandise inventories for the period.
$136,430 ÷ 2 = $68,215 average inventory	Step 2. Find the average merchandise inventory for the period by dividing the total of the inventories by the number of inventories.
$16,000 ÷ $68,215 = 0.235 monthly rate	Step 3. Divide the cost of merchandise sold for the period by the average merchandise inventory. Round the result to the nearest thousandth.
12 × 0.235 = 2.82 annual rate **Ans.**	Step 4. Show the rate as a yearly rate, correct to the nearest hundredth.

As shown in the example, Lynn's Book Place sold, or turned over, its average merchandise inventory 0.235 times in March. That monthly rate, multiplied by 12, is equivalent to a rate of 2.82 times a year. A turnover rate of 2.82 is a low rate. Businesses that sell durable goods such as furniture or large appliances often have a low turnover rate. Businesses that sell perishables such as food often have a high turnover rate.

Exercise 3
Written

1. The Sock Place's merchandise inventory on November 1 was $48,200. On November 30 the inventory was $29,800. The cost of merchandise sold for the month was $31,200.
   a. What was the average merchandise inventory for the month? $39,000
   b. What was the merchandise turnover rate for the month? 0.8
   c. What was the equivalent yearly merchandise turnover rate? 9.6

2. From July through December, McDougall's Closet Shop took 3 merchandise inventories: $44,000, $94,100, and $62,300. The cost of merchandise sold during the 6-month period was $300,600.
   a. What was the store's average merchandise inventory? $66,800
   b. What was the merchandise turnover rate for the 6 months? 4.5
   c. What was the equivalent merchandise turnover rate for a year? 9

3. For the second quarter of the year, April through June, a food store's cost of merchandise sold was $121,000. The merchandise invento-

ries for these 3 months were $39,450, $55,800, and $49,950. What was the store's equivalent annual merchandise turnover rate?   10

4. The Copier Supply Company's cost of merchandise sold for a year was $617,400. The 4 merchandise inventories taken during the year were $84,000, $74,800, $111,600, and $82,400. What was the Company's merchandise turnover rate that year?   7

REVIEW 82

Terms

1. Match the terms with the statements.

   income statement   merchandise turnover rate

   a. Shows net income or net loss   income statement
   b. Shows how many times average inventory is sold in a year
      merchandise turnover rate

Skills

2. a. Show 89.2% as a decimal rounded to the nearest hundredth.
      0.89
   b. What amount is 150% of $42? $63
   c. $481.60 is what percent less than $560?   14%

Problems

3. On net sales of $241,000, Jill had a gross profit of $118,090 and operating expenses of $59,045. What percent of net sales, as an estimated rate and actual rate, was the
   a. Gross profit?   estimated, 50%; actual, 49% [82]
   b. Net income?   estimated, 25%; actual, 24.5% [82]

4. For the third quarter of the year, a store's 3 merchandise inventories were $108,400, $87,100, and $155,500. The cost of merchandise sold for the quarter was $292,500. What was the annual merchandise turnover rate?   10 [82]

5. Syl Reiner borrowed $3,000 for 1 month and paid $3,042 on the maturity date. What interest rate did he pay?   16.8% [44]

6. What is Halina's annual income from 340 shares of stock if the stock pays a regular quarterly dividend of $0.42 per share? $571.20 [58]

7. Allen Cole made an 840 km car trip. He averaged 12 km per liter of gas. (a) How many liters of gas did he use? (b) At 35¢ a liter, how much did he spend for gas?   (a) 70 L (b) $24.50 [66]

Section 83
Distributing Partnership Income

A business owned by one person is called a **sole proprietorship**. A business owned by two or more persons is called a **partnership**.

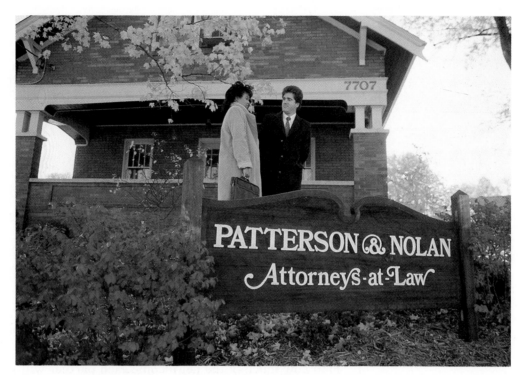

Illustration 83–1. Business Partnership

When you form a partnership, you usually sign a *partnership agreement.*
This agreement often tells how much money the partners invest in the
business and how they will share the net income or net loss.

Ways to Distribute Partnership Net Income. Partners usually agree
on some way to distribute income or loss that seems fair, and they write
it into their agreement. If no way is specified, income or loss is distributed equally.

   Other ways to distribute income or loss are:

1. In proportion to the partners' investments.

2. By paying interest to the partners on their investments.

3. In a fixed ratio.

4. By combining two or more of the above methods.

Net Income Distributed in Proportion to Investments. To find how
much each partner should get when net income is shared in proportion
to investments:

1. Show each partner's investment as a fractional part of the total in-
    vestment in the partnership.

2. Multiply the total partnership net income by each partner's fraction.

Example

Altmon and Baines invest $60,000 and $30,000, respectively, in a partnership. They agree to share net income in proportion to their investments. At the end of the first year, the partnership earns a net income of $63,000. Find each partner's share of the net income.

Solution

Altmon's investment	$60,000
Baines' investment	30,000
Total investment	$90,000

Altmon's share $= \dfrac{\$60,000}{\$90,000} \times \$63,000 = \dfrac{2}{3} \times \$63,000 = \$42,000$

Baines' share $= \dfrac{\$30,000}{\$90,000} \times \$63,000 = \dfrac{1}{3} \times \$63,000 = \$21,000$

Check: $42,000 + $21,000 = $63,000 total net income   **Ans.**

**Exercise 1
Written**

In these problems, the net income is shared in proportion to the partners' investments.

1. Find how much of the net income each partner will get.

	Investments			Net
	Partner X	Partner Y	Partner Z	Income
a.	$ 6,000	$18,000		$ 8,400
	2,100	6,300		
b.	27,000	45,000		5,600
	2,100	3,500		
c.	18,000	36,000		2,925
	975	1,950		
d.	16,000	40,000		8,540
	2,440	6,100		
e.	18,000	27,000	$36,000	12,618
	2,804	4,206	5,608	
f.	8,000	16,000	24,000	17,220
	2,870	5,740	8,610	
g.	7,000	21,000	42,000	36,720
	3,672	11,016	22,032	

2. Ed and Lou, partners, invested $5,000 and $15,000, respectively, in their business. The net income for 1 year was $12,016. For each partner, find the
   a. Estimated net income each gets   Ed, $3,000; Lou, $9,000
   b. Actual net income each receives   Ed, $3,004; Lou, $9,012

3. In the partnership of Dujovny and Ching, Dujovny's investment is $25,000 and Ching's is $30,000. Their net loss for the first year is $8,965. What is each partner's share of the loss?
   Dujovny, $4,075; Ching, $4,890

4. The investments of 3 partners are: Baird, $12,000; Ehardt, $36,000; and Polley, $48,000. Each year the net income is distributed in proportion to the partners' investments. Last year, the firm's net sales were $480,800. The cost of merchandise sold was $312,800, and the operating expenses were $96,960. The partners estimate that the business could be sold for $250,000. How much of last year's net income did each partner get?
Baird, $8,880; Ehardt, $26,640; Polley, $35,520

REVIEW 83

Terms

1. Match the terms with the statements.

   partnership   sole proprietorship

   a. A business owned by two or more persons   partnership
   b. A business owned by one person   sole proprietorship

Skills

2. a. Show 0.007 as a percent.   0.7%
   b. Show 28% as a fraction in lowest terms. $\frac{7}{25}$
   c. The due date of a 70-day note dated March 1 is?   May 9
   d. 36 L ÷ 1.6 = ?   22.5 L

Problems

3. Bower, Caldwell, and Frankel invested $36,000, $48,000, and $60,000, respectively, in a business. Their gross profit for a year was $124,000 and their expenses were $77,900. They share net income and losses in proportion to their investments. How much net income did Bower get? $11,525 [83]

4. Stephanie can buy 1 video tape at $5.79 or a box for 4 tapes for $20.40. How much would she save by buying 4 tapes now instead of 1 at a time? $2.76 [38]

5. Gerard McGhee replaced the windows in his house at a cost of $2,800. He estimates that the new windows will save 15% of his winter heating bill. If his winter heating bill averages $1,200, what is the payback period for the windows to the nearest whole year?
16 years [40]

Section 84
More About Distributing Partnership Income

Net Income Distributed Equally After Paying Interest on Investments. When partners invest different amounts, the partners often are given interest on their investments. Then the rest of the net income is divided equally.

Example

Kirby and Dubois form a partnership, investing $70,000 and $60,000, respectively. They agree to give each partner 9% interest on the investment and to divide the remainder of the net income equally. The net income for the first year is $60,000. Find each partner's share of the net income.

Solution

1. Kirby's interest (9% of $70,000) $ 6,300
   Dubois' interest (9% of $60,000)   5,400
   Total interest $11,700

2. Net income $60,000
   Interest   − 11,700
   Remainder $48,300

3. $48,300 ÷ 2 = $24,150, each partner's share of remainder

4. Kirby's interest $ 6,300   Dubois' interest $ 5,400
   Share of remainder   24,150   Share of remainder   24,150
   Kirby's total share $30,450   Dubois' total share $29,550

Check: $30,450 + $29,550 = $60,000,   total net income   **Ans.**

Exercise 1
Written

1. Find each partner's share of the net income in each problem. Interest is paid on the investments. The rest of the net income is divided equally.

	Investments				Net Income for the
	Partner A	Partner B	Partner C	Interest	Year
a.	$50,000	$30,000		8%	$23,000
	$12,300	$10,700			
b.	22,000	37,000	$46,000	12%	38,100
	11,140	12,940	14,020		
c.	82,000	58,000	69,000	15%	59,010
	21,520	17,920	19,570		

2. Dean and Coliett formed a partnership with investments of $20,000 and $30,000, respectively. In dividing the net income, the partners received 6.5% annually on their investments. The remaining income was divided equally. The net income the first year was $21,780. What amount did each partner receive?
   Dean, $10,565; Coliett, $11,215

3. Healy and Myers are partners with investments of $50,000 and $75,000, respectively. The partners receive 9% annually on their investments. The rest of the net income is divided equally between them. Last year the firm made a net income of $68,428 and a gross profit on sales of $149,750. What is each partner's total share of this net income?   Healy, $33,089; Myers, $35,339

4. Dunn, Rice, and Hardaway formed a partnership. They invested $9,400, $14,000, and $18,500, respectively. For the first year, their gross profit was $82,370, and their expenses were $68,139. The partners got 7% on their investment, and the rest of the net income was shared equally. What was each partner's total share of the net income for the first year?
    Dunn, $4,424; Rice, $4,746; Hardaway, $5,061

5. Jones, Crump, and Young are partners with investments of $150,000, $90,000, and $30,000, respectively. Their partnership agreement shows that from the net income the partners are to get 13% on their investment. The net income that is left is to be divided equally. Last year the partnership sales amounted to $864,000. The business made a net income of 10% of sales. What amount of money should each partner receive?
    Jones, $36,600; Crump, $28,800; Young, $21,000

Net Income Distributed by Fixed Ratio or Fixed Percent. In some partnerships, net income is shared in a fixed ratio, such as 5 to 4. In this case, the net income is divided into nine equal parts, with five parts going to one partner and four parts to the other partner.

In other partnerships, each partner's share may be a certain percent of the net income, such as 55% to one partner and 45% to the other.

You should remember that partnership net income is distributed in the way the partners agreed in their partnership agreement.

Example

Lawrence and Turrell, business partners, agree to divide a net income of $45,000 in the ratio of 5 to 4. What is each partner's share?

Solution

$$\frac{5}{9} \times \$45,000 = \$25,000 \quad \text{Lawrence's share}$$

$$\frac{4}{9} \times \$45,000 = \$20,000 \quad \text{Turrell's share}$$

**Exercise 2
Written**

1. Two business partners, Obiawu and Saeed, divide their net income in a ratio of 3 to 2 in favor of Obiawu. Find the amount of each partner's share of a net income of $80,375.
    Obiawu, $48,225; Saeed, $32,150

2. Daniels and Multon formed a partnership. Their partnership agreement states that Daniels should receive 40% of any net income and Multon should get 60%. The net income for the first year was $82,500. Find each partner's total share of the net income for the first year.   Daniels, $33,000; Multon, $49,500

3. Last year, the partnership of Cade and Purdon had total sales of $524,528. The cost of merchandise sold was $392,500. The operating expenses were $97,028. Cade got 56% of the net income, and Purdon got the rest. What amount of money from the net income did each of the partners receive?   Cade, $19,600; Purdon, $15,400

4. In the Pace-Gibson partnership, Pace invested $35,000 and Gibson invested $42,000. They agreed to divide net income in the ratio of 7 to 4, with Pace receiving the larger share. If last year's net income was $147,400, what was each partner's share?
Pace, $93,800; Gibson, $53,600

REVIEW 84

Skills

1. a. What percent is equal to 7.8?   780%
   b. What percent is equal to $\frac{3}{200}$?   1.5%
   c. Multiply: 4.7 by 0.01   0.047
   d. Divide: 18 by 0.25   72
   e. 500 cm + 34 m = ? m   39 m

Problems

2. Driscoe and Levin invested $46,000 and $87,000, respectively, in a partnership. Of last year's net income of $32,400, each partner received 18% interest on their investment. The rest of the net income was divided equally. Find each partner's total share of the net income for last year.   Driscoe, $12,510; Levin, $19,890 [84]

3. A partnership's net income last year was $121,000. The net income is to be distributed among 3 partners according to these percents: Lee, 34%; Maxwell, 28%; Tyler, 38%. How much should each partner receive?   Lee, $41,140; Maxwell, $33,880; Tyler, $45,980 [84]

4. The FICA tax rate on employees is 7.65% and 15.3% on self-employed persons. What amount of FICA tax will the owner of a car-restoring service pay on her January income of $3,400? $520.20 [70]

5. George Lowe bought a car for $9,460. After using it for 5 years, he sold the car for $3,400. What was the
   a. Average annual depreciation of the old car? $1,212 [65]
   b. Rate of depreciation, to the nearest tenth percent?   12.8% [65]

6. Katrina Roquemore owns a $15,000 time-deposit certificate. She has to withdraw $6,000 before the certificate is due. The penalty for early withdrawal is the loss of 6 months' interest at 9% a year. What amount of interest will she forfeit as a penalty? $270 [54]

Section 85
Distributing Corporate Income

A **corporation** is a business owned by several people who legally act as one person under a *charter*. The charter is usually granted by the state government and tells what kinds of business the corporation can do. It also tells the par value and number of shares of stock that can be issued.

Starting a Corporation. For example, suppose three people own sole proprietorships that produce exercise equipment. After meeting, they decide to put their companies together to form a corporation that will build and sell a broad line of exercise equipment. Because their companies have about the same value, each person will receive the same share of ownership in the corporation.

The three founders of the corporation obtain a charter from the state to incorporate as the Exerco Company. They then issue $750,000 of capital stock, which consists of 15,000 shares of $50 par value stock. **Capital stock** is the total value of the stock issued by a corporation. The capital stock is distributed to the founders in equal shares, each worth $250,000.

As soon as the corporation charter is issued by the state, the Exerco Company may begin doing business. The three original founders now become shareholders of the Exerco Company.

At the end of the first year, the Exerco Company issues a balance sheet, which is shown in Illustration 85–1.

Exerco Company			
Balance Sheet, December 31, 19--			
Assets		**Liabilities**	
Cash	$109,500	Accounts Payable	$147,000
Accounts Receivable	92,800		
Merchandise Inventory	230,400	Capital	
Supplies	8,850		
Office Equipment	29,800	Capital Stock	$750,000
Delivery Equipment	125,650	Retained Earnings	45,000
Land and Buildings	345,000		
Total Assets	$942,000	Total Liabilities and Capital	$942,000

Illustration 85–1. Exerco Company Balance Sheet

Retained Earnings and Dividends. Regularly, such as each month or year, the net income is figured and recorded in an account called **retained earnings.** In the balance sheet in Illustration 85–1, the retained earnings are shown in the capital section as $45,000.

The directors of the corporation then decide how much of the net income is to be distributed to the shareholders and how much is to be kept by the corporation for expansion, improvements, or for emergencies. The net income distributed to the shareholders is called a *dividend.* The **rate of dividend** may be shown as a percent or in dollars and cents.

Finding the Rate of Dividend. To find the rate of dividend as a percent, divide the dividend by the value of the capital stock. To find the rate in dollars and cents per share, divide the dividend by the number of shares.

$$\frac{\text{Dividend}}{\text{Value of Capital Stock}} = \text{Rate of Dividend} \quad \text{(as a percent of capital stock value)}$$

$$\frac{\text{Dividend}}{\text{Number of Shares}} = \text{Rate of Dividend (in dollars and cents per share)}$$

Example

The Exerco Company, with capital stock of $750,000 (15,000 shares at $50 par value per share) has a net income of $60,000 for the second year. What rate of dividend will be declared if all the net income is to be paid to the shareholders as dividends?

Solution

$60,000 ÷ $750,000 = 0.08 = 8%,   rate shown as a percent   **Ans.**

or

$60,000 ÷ 15,000 = $4,   rate in dollars and cents per share   **Ans.**

When the capital stock of a corporation includes both common and preferred shares, figure first the dividend on the preferred shares and subtract that amount from net income. The remainder is the amount of net income that may be paid as a dividend on common shares.

Exercise 1
Written

1. The Kasco Corporation, which has $900,000 of capital stock, has a net income of $108,000 for 1 year. What rate of dividend, shown as a percent, should be declared if all the net income is to be distributed to the shareholders?   12%

2. The capital stock of Zarell Products, Inc., is $460,000. Last year the corporation paid a total dividend of $36,800 to the shareholders. What rate of dividend, shown as a percent, was paid?   8%

3. A corporation with capital stock of $1,500,000 paid a dividend of $210,000 for the year. What was the rate of dividend as a percent?   14%

4. A corporation that has 51,000 shares of capital stock paid an annual dividend of $122,400 after making a net profit of $193,000. What rate of dividend was paid in dollars and cents per share? $2.40

5. The Maxwell Corporation has 8,000 shares of capital stock. The directors voted a dividend of $4,720. In cents per share, what is
    a. The estimated rate of dividend?   60¢
    b. The actual rate of dividend?   59¢

6. The Ranswell Corporation has 30,000 shares of $100 par value stock outstanding. Last year the corporation made a net income of $280,000. The directors voted that 75% of the net income was to be paid as dividends.
    a. What was the dividend rate per share, as a percent?   7%
    b. What was the dividend amount in dollars per share? $7

7. The FSK Company has $120,000 of preferred stock and $480,000 of common stock. The dividend rate on the preferred stock is 6%. The company's net income for 1 year is $50,400. What is the largest percent of dividend that can be paid on the common stock? 9%

8. A corporation has $800,000 of preferred stock and $4,000,000 of common stock outstanding. The preferred stock pays a 12% dividend. What is the largest percent of dividend that can be paid on the common stock from an annual net income of $384,000? 7.2%

Finding the Total Dividend and the Amount Kept in the Retained Earnings Account. Usually only a part of the net income is distributed to the shareholders. The rest is retained by the corporation.

Example

The Exerco Company, with capital stock of $750,000, has a net income of $120,000 for the third year of operation. The directors vote to pay a 4% dividend and to keep the rest of the net income in the retained earnings account. Find (a) the total dividend and (b) the amount kept in the retained earnings account.

Solution

a. 4% of $750,000 =
    $30,000,   total dividend **Ans.**

b. $120,000   net income
    − 30,000   total dividend
    $ 90,000   kept in retained earnings
                                    Ans.

Exercise 2
Written

1. Last year a corporation had a net income of $55,675. The directors voted to pay a dividend of $41,875 to the shareholders and to keep the rest in the retained earnings account. What amount did they keep in the retained earnings account? $13,800

2. Last year, a company that has $780,000 in capital stock earned a net income of $61,568. The directors declared a 5% dividend and voted to keep the rest of the net income in the retained earnings account. What amount was kept in the retained earnings account? $22,568

3. The Devlin Corporation issued 25,000 shares of $100 par value stock. In the current year, the corporation made a net income of $228,400 and declared a 6.75% dividend to shareholders. The rest of the net income was kept in the retained earnings account. What amount was kept as retained earnings? $59,650

4. A corporation has 175,000 shares of capital stock. It earned a net income of $325,000 during the year. During the year, 4 quarterly dividends of 8 cents a share were paid. The rest of the net income was kept in the retained earnings account. How much is kept in the retained earnings account? $269,000

5. A corporation has 5,000 shares of 6% preferred stock (par value $100 per share) and 70,000 shares of common stock ($10 par value

per share). The corporation's net income for last year was $132,720. The directors declared a 6% dividend on the preferred stock and a dividend of 40¢ per share on the common. The net income left was kept in the retained earnings account. How much was kept in the retained earnings account? $74,720

Cooperatives.   A **cooperative** is similar to a corporation, except that its customers are usually the shareholders of the business. The net income is distributed among the shareholders in two parts:

1. A dividend on the capital stock, which is distributed to the shareholders in proportion to the number of shares they own.

2. A patronage or customer dividend, which is distributed to the shareholders in proportion to how much they have bought from the cooperative.

Exercise 3
Written

1. Katarina Pentek is a member of a buying club, organized as a cooperative. At the end of 1 year, the directors of the cooperative declare a 6% dividend on the capital stock and an 8% customer dividend on the sales to the store's customers. Katarina owns 20 shares of the stock, each with a par value of $25. She bought $1,250 from the cooperative during the year. What is the total dividend she should receive from the cooperative? $130

2. At the end of last year, the Farmers' Cooperative declared a 5% dividend on the capital stock and an 8% patronage dividend. Mark Loren owns 30 shares of the capital stock, each with a par value of $60. He bought $1,650 worth of merchandise from the cooperative last year. What total dividend should he receive? $222

3. Tina Perez owns 80 shares of stock in a cooperative (par value of each share, $15). She buys most of her groceries, lawn care products, and office supplies from the cooperative. On December 31, the cooperative declared a 9% dividend on the capital stock and a 2% patronage dividend. What is the total dividend Tina should receive if her purchases from the cooperative totaled $5,470? $217.40

4. A cooperative retail store declared a 4.5% dividend on the capital stock and a 6% patronage dividend on purchases. How much dividend did Roland Johnson receive if he owned 140 shares of the cooperative stock (par value of each share $30) and if his purchases from the cooperative during the year were $2,518? $340.08

REVIEW 85

Terms

1. Match the terms with the statements.

    capital stock   corporation   retained earnings
    cooperative   rate of dividend

    a. Net profit kept by the corporation   retained earnings
    b. Owned by several people under charter by the state
        corporation
    c. Dividend divided by par value   rate of dividend

d. Total value of stock issued by a corporation capital stock
e. Customers are usually its shareholders cooperative

Skills

2. a. Round $107,800 to the nearest $1,000. $108,000
   b. Find the product of $\frac{1}{3}$ × $588. $196
   c. Estimate the quotient of $789 ÷ 0.82. $1,000

Problems

3. The Washburn Corporation, with capital stock of $1,500,000, earned a net income of $206,974 last year. A dividend of 4.5% was paid to the shareholders and the remainder of the net income was put in retained earnings. How much was put in retained earnings? $139,474 [85]

4. Semtel Corporation has issued 5,250 shares of capital stock at a par value of $100. The corporation earned $84,000 in net income last year and declared all of it as a dividend. What was the rate of dividend, as a percent? 16% [85]

5. The assessed value of property in Grand Heights is $19,520,000. To run the city, $947,227 is to be raised by property taxes. What tax rate per $100 is needed to the nearest tenth of a cent? $4.853 [68]

6. The basic annual premium on a house insured for $125,000 is $756. The policyholder wants additional personal property insurance of $14,000 to cover the video and sound recording equipment he uses as a hobby. That coverage will cost $1.35 per $100. What total premium will be paid by the owner? $945 [77]

Section 86
Bankruptcy

When a business keeps operating at a loss, the amounts it owes others may be more than its assets are worth. When this happens, the business is *insolvent* and a court may declare it *bankrupt*. The court then appoints a trustee or receiver to sell all the assets and pay the debts.

■ Creditors file claims for amounts owed to them.

Paying Debts. After selling the assets, the trustee must pay the legal costs of the bankruptcy and any other claims that the law says must be paid first. Then the money that is left is paid to the creditors in proportion to their claims. The percent to be paid to each creditor is found by dividing the total cash available for the creditors by the total of all creditors' claims.

$$\frac{\textbf{Cash Available for Creditors}}{\textbf{Total Creditors' Claims}} = \textbf{Percent Paid on Each Claim}$$

For example, if the total cash available for creditors is $5,000, and the total of creditors' claims is $20,000, each creditor will get 25% of the claim. ($5,000 ÷ $20,000 = $\frac{1}{4}$ or 25%)

Example

A hobby shop was declared bankrupt by the court. The shop's assets were sold by the trustee for $12,000. Legal costs of bankruptcy and other preferred claims totaled $7,000. Creditors' claims totaled $20,000.

    a.   What percent of the creditors' claims can the trustee pay?
    b.   How many cents on the dollar will creditors get on their claims?
    c.   How much will a creditor get who has a claim of $1,200?

Solution

a.	Proceeds from sale of assets	$12,000
	Bankruptcy costs and preferred claims	− 7,000
	Available for creditors	$ 5,000

$\dfrac{\$5,000}{\$20,000} = 0.25 = 25\%$ **Ans.**

b. $0.25 \times 100¢ = 25¢$ **Ans.**

c. $0.25 \times \$1,200 = \$300$ **Ans.**

Exercise 1
Written

1. For each problem, find what percent of the creditors' claims the trustee can pay.

	Total Creditors' Claims	Cash Available for Creditors	Percent of Creditors' Claims Paid
a.	$ 34,000	$ 13,600	40%
b.	18,600	5,580	30%
c.	48,900	17,115	35%
d.	192,000	124,800	65%

2. For each problem, find how many cents on the dollar can be paid to the creditors.

	Total Creditors' Claims	Cash Available for Creditors	Percent of Creditors' Claims Paid
a.	$38,000	$24,320	64¢
b.	55,200	19,320	35¢
c.	98,000	41,160	42¢
d.	18,100	2,896	16¢

3. A luggage store is declared bankrupt. Creditors' claims total $92,000. After the assets are sold and bankruptcy costs are paid, $34,040 is left for creditors' claims. What percent of their claims will the creditors get?   37%

4. A bankrupt company has debts totaling $12,425. The cash available for the creditors is $5,715.50. How many cents on the dollar will creditors get?   46¢

5. The trustee for a bankrupt mobile home builder paid off the builder's debts at the rate of 49¢ on the dollar. A creditor filed a claim with the trustee for $6,994.
    a. What estimated amount will the creditor get? $3,500
    b. What actual amount will the creditor get? $3,427.06

6. The creditors of a bankrupt firm are paid at the rate of 32.6¢ on the dollar. There are 40 creditors with total claims of $34,572. How much will a creditor get on a claim of $1,280? $417.28

7. The New-Day Bakery was declared bankrupt and its assets were sold for $69,600. Legal costs of bankruptcy and other preferred claims totaled $17,800. The total of creditors' claims was $148,000. The Eastern Supply Company had a claim against New-Day of $9,200.
    a. How much money was available for all creditors? $51,800
    b. What percent of each creditor's claim was paid? 35%
    c. How much did Eastern Supply get? $3,220

REVIEW 86

Skills

1. a. Multiply: 23.75 by 14.7   349.125
    b. Divide: 8.6 by 0.04   215
    c. 0.084 ÷ 0.006 = ?   14
    d. Find exact interest on $7,000 at 6.28% for 3 months. $109.90
    e. Round $14,582,589 to the nearest hundred thousand.
        $14,600,000
    f. Round $0.7925 to the nearest tenth of a cent. $0.793
    g. Estimate the product of 4.79 × 30.17.   150
    h. Estimate the quotient of $9,764 ÷ 19.8. $500

Problems

2. A water bed company went bankrupt, owing $150,800. The cash available for the creditors was $57,000. How many cents on the dollar did the creditors get on their claims? $0.38 [86]

3. The A & J Sewing Center went bankrupt, owing $74,600. The net cash available to creditors was $11,190. What amount will be paid to a creditor with a claim of $5,250? $787.50 [86]

4. Julia Morrison's house would cost $60,000 to replace. She insures it for $42,000 with a replacement cost policy that requires her to insure property for at least 90% of its replacement cost. What amount will the insurance company pay if a fire loss of $900 occurs? $700 [78]

5. The monthly payment on a $65,000, 30-year mortgage is $623.50. Over the 30 years of the mortgage,
    a. What will be the total of the mortgage payments? $224,460 [63]
    b. What total amount of interest will be paid? $159,460 [63]

6. The monthly charge for leasing a small car is $129. For all miles driven over 16,000 miles in 1 year, a 7¢ per mile charge is made. What is the yearly cost of leasing the car if it is driven 21,000 miles in a year? $1,898 [66]

7. Dave Shaw borrowed $500 for 23 days on his credit card and paid a daily finance charge of 0.0615%. What was the amount of the finance charge for this cash advance? $7.07 [51]

8. A rental company bought 150 plastic chairs at $12.80, 240 wooden chairs at $16.40, and 320 cushioned chairs at $23.70. What was the average price paid per chair, to the nearest cent? $18.93 [10]

9. Rochelle Springer worked $7\frac{1}{2}$ hours at time-and-a-half pay last week. Her regular-time pay rate was $9.80 an hour. What was Rochelle's total overtime pay for the week? $110.25 [17]

Purchasing for a Business

Owners of retail stores must make careful decisions about the goods they buy for their stores in order to stay in business. In addition to buying the goods customers will want, they also try to get the best quality and service at the lowest price possible. To do this, they check and compare the prices and discounts offered by the wholesalers or manufacturers from whom they buy.

Discounts are given to retailers since they are in the business of reselling goods to others. Retailers also get discounts for paying their bills promptly. A retailer who shops and buys wisely purchases goods for less and stands to make a greater profit.

After you finish Unit 14, you will be able to:

- Figure or check extensions on a purchase invoice.
- Find the due date of an invoice.
- Figure extensions using combinations of fractional equivalents and a base.
- Find net purchases.
- Find the invoice price using single and series trade discounts.
- Find the single discount equivalent to a series of discounts.
- Find cash price when cash discounts are given.
- Figure money saved by borrowing to get cash discount.
- Find the rate of trade and cash discounts.
- Use complements to find single trade discount equivalent.
- Solve problems that contain more information than you need.
- Estimate answers to problems.
- Read, write, say, and recognize the meanings of the key terms.
- Use a computer spreadsheet to figure the cash price of an invoice and the amount saved by borrowing to pay an invoice within the discount period.

When retailers need merchandise, they order it from a wholesaler or a manufacturer. The order may be placed by telephone, mail, or through a salesperson.

Purchase Invoice. When sellers fill an order, they send the retailer an invoice that shows the quantity, description, and price of each item shipped. The retailer calls this form a **purchase invoice.**

The invoice that Jared Lagmeyer received for the shipment of goods he ordered from RADEL Adhesives Company is shown in Illustration 87–1.

1631 Highway 55 Minneapolis, MN 55422-6083			**RADEL** **Adhesives Company**		
SOLD TO: Lagmeyer's Hardware 1575 Arrowhead Road Fargo, ND 58103-2537			**DATE:** June 10, 19-- **TERMS:** n/60		
QUANTITY	**UNIT**	**DESCRIPTION**	**UNIT PRICE**	**AMOUNT**	
72	rolls	Transparent tape	$1.10	$ 79.20	✓
48	bottles	Rubber cement	1.25	60.00	✓
36	rolls	Masking tape	1.50	54.00	✓
24	cans	Wood glue	1.75	42.00	✓
		PAY THIS AMOUNT		$235.20	

Extensions ———

Illustration 87–1. Purchase Invoice

Extension =
Quantity times
Unit Price

Checking the Purchase Invoice. When the goods arrived, Jared Lagmeyer checked the quantity of each item with the invoice to make sure that he got the correct amount. He then checked the extensions and total of the invoice to make sure the arithmetic had been done correctly.

As Jared checked each amount, he put a check mark next to it if it was correct. If the amount was wrong, he wrote the correct amount next to it. The check marks tell you what work you have finished and guard against your doing it again. Check marks are used often by office clerks to show that figures have been checked for accuracy.

Terms of the Sale. When an invoice is to be paid, any discount given for early payment is shown in the terms of sale. The **terms of sale** for the invoice in Illustration 87–1 are "n/60," or net, 60 days. This means that Jared Lagmeyer has 60 days after the date on the invoice to pay it. It also means that he will be given no discount for paying early.

■ n/60 = net amount due 60 days from date of invoice

Wholesalers and manufacturers usually sell to retailers **on account.** They let retailers buy now and pay later. The length of time they give the retailer to pay is usually 30 to 90 days. This is called the **credit period.**

Finding the Due Date of an Invoice. The due date is found by counting ahead, from the date on the invoice, the number of days shown in the terms. For example, the invoice in Illustration 87–1 is dated June 10, and the terms are n/60. The invoice must be paid 60 days after June 10, or on August 9.

■ Always count ahead from the date on the invoice.

60	**days to due date of invoice**
−20	**days left in June**
40	
−31	**days in July**
9	**days in August (August 9, due date)**

**Exercise 1
Written**

1. Find the date on which each invoice must be paid.

	Invoice Date	Terms	
a.	August 16	10 days	Aug. 26
b.	March 5	30 days	April 4
c.	November 14	90 days	Feb. 12
d.	April 24	60 days	June 23
e.	October 28	75 days	Jan. 11
f.	January 7	45 days	Feb. 21

2. Copy the invoice below on a sheet of paper. Check the extensions and total. If an amount is correct, place a check mark next to it. If an amount is wrong, write the correct amount next to it.

12 videotapes	@	$ 3.50	$ 42.00	
16 cassette tapes	@	1.40	22.40	
30 tape storage boxes	@	9.50	280.50	285.00
20 videotape cases	@	0.75	15.00	
18 tape recorders	@	26.25	472.50	
			$832.40	836.90

3. The Leonard Supermarket bought the following items from a wholesaler. The invoice was dated August 16; the terms were net, 45 days:

150 ice cube trays	@	$0.37	$55.50
48 food storage boxes	@	2.25	108.00
115 boxes trash bags	@	2.78	319.70
50 plastic gloves	@	1.45	72.50
18 measuring cups	@	0.81	14.58
			$570.28

You are to (a) copy the invoice, (b) make the extensions, (c) find the total amount of the invoice, and (d) find the due date of the invoice. September 30, due date

Purchases, Returns and Allowances, Net Purchases. The total cost of all the goods you buy in a week, month, or year is called the *purchases* for that period.

You may return some of the goods to the seller. Or, the seller may give you an allowance because the goods are damaged. These returns and allowances decrease the cost of the purchases and should be deducted from the purchases. The amount left is the **net purchases.**

Purchases – Returns and Allowances = Net Purchases

Example

Lagmeyer's Hardware purchases for June were $18,765.92, and the returns and allowances were $405.87. What were the net purchases?

Solution

Purchases	$18,765.92
Returns and Allowances	405.87
Net Purchases	$18,360.05 **Ans.**

Exercise 2
Written

1. For August, the records of The Wood Place showed the purchases and purchases returns in the table on the next page.
   a. Copy and complete the table.
   b. Prove the total net purchases by subtracting the total purchases returns from the total purchases.

Items	Purchases	Purchases Returns	Net Purchases
Shutters	$ 4,418	$135	$ 4,283
Cabinets	12,876	562	12,314
Towel racks	1,317	35	1,282
Picture frames	2,089	172	1,917
Totals	$20,700	$904	$19,796

2. The table below shows the purchases and returns of the Outdoor Shop for 6 months.
    a. Copy and complete the table.
    b. Prove the total net purchases by subtracting the total returns from the total purchases.

Month	Purchases	Returns	Net Purchases
January	$14,618	$ 316	$ 14,302
February	17,830	387	17,443
March	38,512	571	37,941
April	46,984	1,309	45,675
May	53,011	1,470	51,541
June	38,737	698	38,039
Totals	$209,692	$4,751	$204,941

Combinations of Fractional Equivalents. The unit price of an item on an invoice is sometimes a combination of the base and a fractional equivalent.

For example, on the invoice shown in Illustration 87–1, the unit price of the first item is $1.10. The price of $1.10 is equal to $1, the base, + $0.10. Since $0.10 is $\frac{1}{10}$ of $1, $1.10 is equal to $1 + $\frac{1}{10}$ of $1.

In the same way, $1.50 is equal to $1 + $\frac{1}{2}$ of $1. Also, $2.25 is equal to $2 + $\frac{1}{4}$ of $1.

Some commonly used combinations of fractional equivalents are:

$$\$1.10 = \$1 + \frac{1}{10} \text{ of } \$1 \qquad \$1.25 = \$1 + \frac{1}{4} \text{ of } \$1$$

$$\$1.12\frac{1}{2} = \$1 + \frac{1}{8} \text{ of } \$1 \qquad \$1.50 = \$1 + \frac{1}{2} \text{ of } \$1$$

$$\$1.20 = \$1 + \frac{1}{5} \text{ of } \$1 \qquad \$2.50 = \$2 + \frac{1}{2} \text{ of } \$1$$

Multiplication by Combinations of Fractional Equivalents. Multiplication with combinations of a base and a fractional equivalent is done in steps.

Example

Find the cost of 72 rolls of transparent tape at $1.10.

Solution	Explanation
$1.10 = \$1 + \dfrac{1}{10}$ of $1	Step 1. Find the base ($1) and the fractional equivalent ($\frac{1}{10}$ of $1).
$72 \times \$1 = \$72$	Step 2. Multiply the number of items times the base.
$72 \times \dfrac{1}{10} = 7.20,$ or $7.20	Step 3. Multiply the number of items times the fractional equivalent and add a dollar sign to the result.
$72.00 + $7.20 = $79.20 **Ans.**	Step 4. Add the products of Step 2 and Step 3.

**Exercise 3
Oral**

Say the answer and explain how you got it for each problem.

	1.			2.	
a.	13 @ $1.10	$14.30	22 @ $2.50	$55
b.	24 @ $1.12½	27	72 @ $1.12½	81
c.	25 @ $1.20	30	32 @ $1.25	40
d.	28 @ $1.25	35	41 @ $1.10	45.10
e.	14 @ $1.50	21	56 @ $1.12½	63
f.	8 @ $2.50	20	35 @ $1.20	42
g.	16 @ $1.12½	18	44 @ $1.50	66
h.	38 @ $1.50	57	36 @ $1.25	45
i.	33 @ $1.10	36.30	35 @ $1.10	38.50

REVIEW 87

Terms

1. Match the terms with the statements.

credit period   on account   terms of sale
net purchases   purchase invoice

a. Form showing details of what was bought   purchase invoice
b. The time given to pay an invoice   credit period
c. Part that tells when an invoice must be paid and what discounts are given   terms of sale
d. Purchases less returns and allowances   net purchases
e. To buy now and pay later   on account

Skills

2. a. Find the product of $48 \times 4\frac{1}{3}$.   208
    b. Find banker's interest on $4,500 for 90 days at 12%. $135
    c. A tax rate of 45.9 mills on $1 is what rate on $100. $4.59

Problems

3. The extensions and total shown on the next page were taken from an invoice. Check each amount. Place a check mark next to the amount if it is correct. If the amount is wrong, write the correct amount at the right. [87]

A gross is twelve dozen.

6 dozen combs @ $50.40 per gross	$ 302.40	25.20
7 cases toothpaste @ $75.60 per case	529.20	
30 dozen key chains @ $86.40 per gross	216.00	
2,000 batteries @ $49.00 per 100	+ 98.00	980.00
	$1,145.60	1,750.40

4. The Ilson Company had these purchases for the quarter: $67,982; $51,910; $78,295. The total purchases returns and allowances for the quarter were $2,863.
   a. Estimate the company's net purchases for the quarter. $197,000
   b. What were the company's net purchases for the quarter? $195,324 [87]

5. What is the rate of income on a 6% bond bought at 75?   8% [56]

Section 88
Trade Discounts

Many wholesalers and manufacturers sell to retailers at the price listed in their catalog and then give a discount on this price. The price in the catalog is called the **list price** or *catalog price*. The discount is called a **trade discount**. The price the retailer pays is the list price less the trade discount. This price is called the **invoice price**, *net price*, or *invoice cost*.

Finding the Trade Discount and the Invoice Price. A trade discount is usually shown as a percent. This percent is always based on the list price. So, the list price is multiplied by the rate of discount to find the amount of the discount.

$$\textbf{Rate of Discount} \times \textbf{List Price} = \textbf{Trade Discount}$$

The invoice price is found this way:

$$\textbf{List Price} - \textbf{Trade Discount} = \textbf{Invoice Price}$$

Example

> The list price of an outdoor grill in the catalog of the Cook-Rite Company is $200. The discount given to the retailer is 40%. What invoice price will a retailer pay for this grill?
>
> **Solution**
>
> | List price | $200 | |
> |---|---|---|
> | Trade discount | 80 | (40% of $200) |
> | Invoice price | $120 | **Ans.** |
>
> **Check**
>
> 100% of list price = List price
> Subtract   40% of list price = Trade discount
> 60% of list price = Invoice price
> 60% of $200 = $120, invoice price

Why Trade Discounts Are Given. Trade discounts are used by manufacturers and wholesalers who sell by catalog and whose prices change often. The retailer is given a catalog and a discount sheet.

The **discount sheet** shows the discounts that are given on the list prices in the catalog. When a seller wants to change invoice prices, a new discount sheet is given to the retailer. This saves the cost of printing and mailing a new catalog.

In some catalogs, the list price appears as a suggested retail price. Retailers are given a trade discount on this price so that they can make a gross profit. If an item is sold at the list price, catalog price, or suggested retail price, the gross profit is the amount of the trade discount.

Trade discounts are also used to encourage retailers to buy in larger quantities. For example, a discount of 3% may be given if they buy 100 items; 5% if they buy 200; 8% if they buy 300; and so on. These are known as **quantity discounts.**

**Exercise 1
Written**

In each problem, find and check the invoice price by using the method shown in the previous example.

1. Find the amount of the trade discount and the invoice price.

Item	List Price	Rate of Discount	Trade Discount	Invoice Price
a. Golf clubs	$360	40%	$144.00	$216.00
b. Floor lamp	80	30%	24.00	56.00
c. Steel door	280	25%	70.00	210.00
d. Electric drill	38	35%	13.30	24.70
e. Microwave oven	276	$33\frac{1}{3}$%	92.00	184.00
f. Drapery rod	56	15%	8.40	47.60
g. Cookbook	14	45%	6.30	7.70

2. How much would a retailer pay for 30 dozen paint brushes if the wholesaler's price is $54 a dozen, less 28%? $1,166.40

3. Mae Zurn, a store owner, gets prices on rolltop desks from 2 whole-sale firms. The Rinz Company offers a desk for $650, less 30%. The Okemar Company offers the same desk for $800, less 40%.
   a. Which wholesale firm has the lower price?   Rinz Company
   b. How much lower? $25

4. Avetel, Inc., will sell an outdoor furniture set to Mark Giles, the op-erator of a farmers' cooperative, for $570, less 30%. The Hexell Fur-niture Company offers the same set for $700, less 42%.
   a. Which company has the lower price?   Avetel, Inc.
   b. How much is saved by taking the lower price? $7

5. The Reviso Manufacturing Company gives a 5% discount if 200 boxes of computer paper are bought and a 7% discount if 500 boxes are bought. The list price for each box is $11.90. If 200 boxes are bought,
   a. What is the estimated amount of quantity discount? $120
   b. What is the actual quantity discount amount? $119
   c. What is the invoice price? $2,261

6. The Food Place buys frozen mixed vegetables from a wholesaler at 80 cents for a 1-pound package. In July, the store bought 240 pack-ages and got a quantity discount of 4%. In August, they bought 300 packages and got a quantity discount of 7%. How much did The Food Place save by taking these 2 discounts? $24.48

Finding the Rate of Trade Discount. The rate of trade discount is al-ways based on the list price. The rate is found by dividing the amount of the trade discount by the list price.

$$\textbf{Rate of Trade Discount} = \frac{\textbf{Trade Discount}}{\textbf{List Price}}$$

Example

A power saw is listed in a wholesaler's catalog at $80. The saw is sold to retail-ers at an invoice price of $56. What is the rate of trade discount?

Solution

$80 − $56 = $24   Amount of trade discount
$24 ÷ $80 = 0.3,   or   30%   Rate of trade discount   **Ans.**

**Exercise 2
Written**

1. Find the amount and rate of trade discount in each problem.

	Article	List Price	Invoice Price	Trade Discount Amount	Rate
a.	Telephone	$ 40	$ 28.00	$12.00	30%
b.	Filing cabinet	140	105.00	35.00	25%
c.	Postage scale	70	40.60	29.40	42%
d.	Time clock	380	247.00	133.00	35%
e.	Desk	630	420.00	210.00	$33\frac{1}{3}\%$
f.	Wall chart	90	49.50	40.50	45%

2. A catalog lists a tool chest at $96. The same tool chest is billed to the retailer at $64. What is the rate of trade discount? $33\frac{1}{3}\%$

3. A freezer listed at $450 in a wholesaler's catalog is sold to a retailer for $270. What rate of trade discount was given?   40%

‡4. The Weigler Supermarket ordered $760 of various pasta products from Genese Products and got an additional $40 worth free.
   a. What was the total value of the goods received by the Weigler Supermarket? $800
   b. The value of the free goods is what percent of the value of the whole shipment?   5%

‡5. On an order for 15 dozen tape dispensers at $48 a dozen, a store owner got an extra dozen free. What rate of trade discount was this?   6.25%

‡6. A gas station owner is not charged for 1 case of motor oil on a shipment of 20 cases of oil. This is equal to what rate of discount?   5%

REVIEW 88

Terms

1. Match the terms with the statements.

discount sheet   list price   trade discount
invoice price   quantity discount

   a. Catalog price   list price
   b. Discount from list price given to retailers   trade discount
   c. List price less trade discount; net price   invoice price
   d. Shows discounts from list prices   discount sheet
   e. Trade discount based on amount purchased   quantity discount

Skills

2. a. Find $37\frac{1}{2}\%$ of $440. $165
   b. Show $\frac{4}{7}$ as a decimal to the nearest hundredth.   0.57
   c. Subtract: $3\frac{4}{5}$ from $9\frac{1}{4}$. $5\frac{9}{20}$
   d. Estimate the product of 700.97 × 3.01.   2,100
   e. Estimate the quotient of 578 ÷ 18.   30

Problems

3. A dealer bought 40 toaster ovens for $48, less 35%. What was the invoice price? $1,248 [88]

4. A clothes dryer listed at $360 was sold to a retailer at $237.60. What rate of trade discount was given?   34% [88]

5. A retailer had net sales of $200,000 last year. For the year, the cost of merchandise sold was $120,000 and operating expenses were $55,000. About 60% of the expenses went for wages.
   a. What was the gross profit on sales? $80,000 [81]
   b. What was the retailer's net income? $25,000 [81]
   c. What percent of net sales was the net income?   12.5% [82]

6. The Mailen Corporation has 50,000 shares of $100 par value stock outstanding. This year, the corporation made a net income of $285,600 and declared a 2.3% dividend to shareholders. The rest of the net income was kept in the retained earnings account. What amount was kept in retained earnings? $170,600 [85]

7. A delivery truck that cost $12,800 is estimated to depreciate at an annual rate of 14% of the original cost. Find the value of the truck at the end of the fourth year. $5,632 [65]

8. On November 1, a store's merchandise inventory was $45,700. On November 30, it was $34,820. The cost of merchandise sold for the month was $74,481. What was the annual rate of merchandise turnover?   22.2 [82]

Section 89
Series Discounts

Trade Discount Series. A retailer may be given a trade discount that has two or more discounts, called a **series of discounts** or a *discount series.*

For example, the Globe Heating Company makes gas furnaces. The company lists a furnace in its catalog at $1,050 and allows this series of discounts to retailers: 25%, 10%, and 5%.

To find the invoice price, the first discount is based on the list price. The second discount is based on the remainder after deducting the first discount. The third discount is based on the remainder after deducting the second discount, and so on.

Example

The quoted price of a furnace is $1,050, less 25%, 10%, and 5%. Find (a) the invoice price and (b) the amount of the trade discount.

Solution

a. $1,050.00   list price
   − 262.50   first discount (25%, or $\frac{1}{4}$, of $1,050)
   $ 787.50   first remainder
   − 78.75   second discount (10%, or $\frac{1}{10}$, of $787.50)
   $ 708.75   second remainder
   − 35.438   third discount (5%, or $\frac{1}{20}$, of $708.75)
   $ 673.312   third remainder, or invoice price, $673.31   **Ans.**

Check

b. $1,050.00   list price $262.50   first discount
   − 673.31   invoice price   78.75   second discount
   $ 376.69   trade discount   + 35.438 third discount
                                    $376.688

   $376.69   **Ans.**

Explanation

To be accurate to the penny, carry the results to 3 decimal places. Then round the final result to the nearest cent. Note that the third discount is shown as $35.438. Subtracting that amount from the second remainder of $708.75 gives a third remainder of $673.312, which is rounded to $673.31, the invoice price.

The list price of $1,050 less the invoice price of $673.31 gives the amount of the trade discount, $376.69.

The order in which you take the discounts does not change the final result. You can take a series of discounts in any order and get the same result. You may want to change the order to make your work easier, or to check your answer.

Exercise 1
Written

In each problem, check your work by taking the discounts in a different order.

1. Find the invoice price and the amount of trade discount in each problem.

	List Price	Trade Discounts	Invoice Price	Amount of Trade Discount
a.	$ 90	20%, 10%	$64.80	$25.20
b.	36	25%, 10%	24.30	11.70
c.	48	25%, 20%	28.80	19.20
d.	51	$33\frac{1}{3}$%, 20%	27.20	23.80
e.	130	10%, 10%	105.30	24.70
f.	125	20%, 10%, 10%	81.00	44.00
g.	240	20%, 20%, 10%	138.24	101.76
h.	170	25%, 20%, 5%	96.90	73.10
i.	145	30%, 15%, 10%	77.65	67.35
j.	115	10%, 10%, 30%	65.21	49.79

■ Discounts may be taken in any order.

2. The Maldon Company buys a paint sprayer that lists at $280, less 25% and 15%. What is the invoice price? $178.50

3. What is the invoice price of 6 cabinets that list at $130 each, with discounts of 30%, 20%, and 10%? $393.12

4. Eswell Manufacturing sells a ceiling fan for $185, with discounts of 20%, $12\frac{1}{2}$%, and 5%. Find the invoice price. $123.03

5. What would the Home Shop pay for 15 dozen frying pans that list at $107 a dozen, with discounts of 20%, 15%, and 5%? $1,036.83

6. Morland Brothers offers to deliver an order of goods for $1,500 list price, less 25%, 20%, and 10%. Wick Wholesale offers the same goods at the same list price less 30%, 20%, and 5%. How much would be saved by taking the lower offer? $12

Finding the Single Discount Equivalent. When you use the same discount series often, you can find the invoice price faster by using the one discount that is equal to the series of discounts. That one discount is called the **single discount equivalent.**

You find the single discount equivalent this way:

1. Find the invoice price in percent.

2. Subtract the invoice price in percent from the list price, 100%. The difference is the single discount equivalent.

Example

Find the single discount that is equivalent to the series 20%, 10%, and 10%.

Solution

Step 1		Step 2	
100%	list price	100%	list price
20%	first discount	64.8%	invoice price
	(20%, or $\frac{1}{5}$, of 100%)	35.2%	single discount equivalent
80%	first remainder		
8%	second discount		35.2% **Ans.**
	(10%, or $\frac{1}{10}$, of 80%)		**Check**
72%	second remainder		
7.2%	third discount	20%	first discount
	(10%, or $\frac{1}{10}$, of 72%)	8%	second discount
64.8%	third remainder,	7.2%	third discount
	or invoice price	35.2%	total single discount

**Exercise 2
Written**

1. Find the single discount equivalent for each series. Show all your work.
   a. 10%, 10%   19%
   b. 25%, 20%   40%
   c. 20%, 12$\frac{1}{2}$%   30%
   d. 10%, 33$\frac{1}{3}$%   40%
   e. 25%, 20%, 5%   43%
   f. 30%, 20%, 12$\frac{1}{2}$%   51%
   g. 20%, 10%, 33$\frac{1}{3}$%   52%
   h. 20%, 20%, 12$\frac{1}{2}$%   44%

2. Find the single discount that is equivalent to the discount series of each discount plan.
   a. Discount Plan A: 30%, 10%, 10%   43.3%
   b. Discount Plan B: 20%, 10%, 10%   35.2%
   c. Discount Plan C: 20%, 5%, 5%   27.8%

3. The list price of several items that a retailer wants to buy is given below. Use the single discount that you figured in Problem 2 for each discount plan to find the discount amount and the invoice price for each item.

	List Price	Discount Plan	Discount Amount	Invoice Price
a.	$300	C	$83.40	$216.60
b.	140	A	60.62	79.38
c.	90	B	31.68	58.32
d.	160	C	44.48	115.52
e.	70	B	24.64	45.36

Using Tables to Find Invoice Prices. People who work with series of discounts often use tables to make their work easier. These tables show the *invoice price equivalents* after the discounts are taken. Such a table is shown in Illustration 89–1.

Rate	5%	10%	15%	20%	25%	30%
5%	0.9025	0.855	0.8075	0.76	0.7125	0.665
5%, 5%	0.85738	0.81225	0.76713	0.722	0.67688	0.63175
10%	0.855	0.81	0.765	0.72	0.675	0.63
10%, 5%	0.81225	0.7695	0.72675	0.684	0.64125	0.5985
10%, 10%	0.7695	0.729	0.6885	0.648	0.6075	0.567

Illustration 89–1. Invoice Price Equivalents

For example, suppose the list price of a pair of running shoes is $80, and the trade discount series given to the retailer is 20%, 10%, and 10%. You find the 10%, 10% line in the invoice price equivalents table and follow it under the 20% column. The invoice price equivalent you find is 0.648, or 64.8%. Now multiply the list price, $80, by 0.648 and you get $51.84, which is the invoice price of the running shoes.

Find the invoice price for each item using the table in Illustration 89–1.

Exercise 3
Written

	Item	List Price	Trade Discounts	Invoice Price
1.	Work gloves	$ 4.95	20%, 5%	$3.76
2.	Shovel	16.50	30%, 10%	10.40
3.	Garden hose	28.00	10%, 20%	20.16
4.	Grass seed	8.20	25%, 5%, 5%	5.55
5.	Lawn sprinkler	12.40	15%, 10%, 5%	9.01

‡**Using Complements.** You may find it easier to work with the complements of trade discounts than with the discount rates themselves. The **complement** of any discount rate is the difference between that rate and 100%. For example, if the discount rate is 30%, the complement of the discount rate is 70%.

If you multiply the complements of a series of trade discounts and then subtract that product from 100%, you get the single discount equivalent. For example, in a series of discounts, 20%, 10%, 10%, the complements are 80%, 90%, and 90%. To find the single discount equivalent to this series:

1. *Multiply* the complements: $0.8 \times 0.9 \times 0.9 = 0.648$, or 64.8%

2. *Subtract* the product: $100\% - 64.8\% = 35.2\%$

So, 35.2% is the single discount equivalent to 20%, 10%, 10%. Of course, if 35.2% is the rate of discount, then 64.8% must be the percent of invoice price.

‡**Exercise 4**
Written

1. Use complements to find the single discount equivalent to each series. Show all your work.

   a. 10%, 5%   14.5%   f. 30%, 10%, 10%   43.3%
   b. 30%, 5%   33.5%   g. 20%, 5%, 5%   27.8%
   c. 15%, 10%   23.5%   h. 30%, 20%, 10%   49.6%
   d. 10%, 5%, 5%   18.775%   i. 30%, 15%, 10%   46.45%
   e. 25%, 10%, 10% 39.25%   j. 10%, 15%, 25%   42.625%

2. For each of the single discount equivalents in Problem 1, what percent is the invoice price of the list price?   a. 85.5%
b. 66.5%; c. 76.5%; d. 81.225%; e. 60.75%; f. 56.7%; g. 72.2%;
h. 50.4%; i. 53.55%; j. 57.375%

REVIEW 89

Terms

1. Match the terms with the statements.

complement   series of discounts   single discount equivalent

a. One discount that equals a series   single discount equivalent
b. Two or more trade discounts   series of discounts
c. Difference between a discount rate and 100%   complement

Skills

2. a. Divide: 76 by $2\frac{1}{2}$ $30\frac{2}{5}$
   b. 78 × $1.60 = ? $124.80
   c. $154 ÷ $1.10 = ?   140
   d. Find exact interest on $280 for 4 months at 9%. $8.40

Problems

3. What single rate of discount is equivalent to the series 25% and 15%?
   36.25% [89]

4. L & T Electronics will deliver a video camera to a retailer for $1,400 list price, less 35% and 10%. Inex will deliver a similar camera for $1,200, less 20%, 5%, and 5%. How much is saved by taking the lower offer? $47.40 [89]

5. A workbench listed at $125 is sold to a retailer for $80. What is the rate of trade discount?   36% [88]

6. Eve and Loretta, business partners, agree to share net income and loss in the ratio of 5:4, with Eve getting the larger share. If their business earned a net income of $54,000 last year on sales of $612,000, what was Loretta's share of the net income? $24,000 [83]

7. A $200,000 term life insurance policy is sold at a rate of $1.07 per $1,000 of insurance. [74]
   a. What is the estimated annual premium? $200
   b. What is the actual annual premium? $214

Section 90
Cash Discounts

Most wholesalers and manufacturers give retailers a certain amount of time to pay an invoice. They also let retailers deduct some percent from the invoice price if they pay the invoice early. This deduction is called a **cash discount.**

Cash Discount. The cash discount is shown on an invoice after the word "terms." These cash discount terms are used often:

▮ n = net
EOM = end of
month

2/10, n/30. These terms mean that you may deduct 2% if you pay within 10 days of the date on the invoice. Otherwise, you must pay the full invoice price within 30 days after the invoice date.

In the terms "2/10, n/30," the 2 shows the rate of cash discount, 2%. The 10 shows the number of days in the **discount period,** 10 days. The 30 shows the number of days in the *credit period,* 30 days. Both the discount period and the credit period are counted from the date of the invoice.

For example, if the terms are 2/10, n/30 on an invoice dated March 1, the last date on which the discount may be taken is March 1 + 10 days, or March 11. If the invoice is not paid on or before March 11, the full invoice price is due on March 1 + 30 days, or March 31.

2/10, 1/30, n/60. These terms mean that you may deduct 2% if you pay within 10 days or 1% if you pay within 11 to 30 days from the date of the invoice. Otherwise, you must pay the full amount within 60 days.

Sometimes a term such as 3/10 **EOM** is used. This means that you will get a 3% discount if you pay the bill within 10 days after the **end of the month** shown on the invoice.

Exercise 1
Oral

1. Find the last date on which you may take the cash discount in each problem.

	Date of Invoice	Terms	Cash Discount Date
a.	August 15	3/10 EOM	September 10
b.	March 27	2/10, n/30	April 6
c.	November 25	4/15, n/60	December 10
d.	December 30	1/10 EOM	January 10
e.	August 20	3/15, n/90	September 4
f.	January 7	2/20 EOM	February 20

2. What rate of cash discount, if any, may be taken in each problem?

	Date of Invoice	Terms	Date Paid	Rate
a.	March 28	1/10, n/30	April 6	1%
b.	January 23	3/15, n/60	February 7	3%
c.	February 22	3/10, n/90	March 12	none
d.	July 5	2/30, n/60	August 5	none
e.	June 1	2/10, 1/30, n/60	July 1	1%
f.	November 28	4/10, 2/30, n/60	December 6	4%
g.	October 18	3/5, 2/20, n/60	November 8	none
h.	September 24	3/10, 1/30, n/60	October 23	1%
i.	February 25	3/10 EOM	March 10	3%
j.	August 2	4/20 EOM	September 20	4%
k.	March 5	2/10 EOM	May 4	none

Finding the Cash Discount and the Cash Price. When you pay an invoice within the discount period, the amount you pay is the invoice price less the cash discount. This amount is called the **cash price.**

The rate of cash discount is always based on the *invoice price.* So, multiply the invoice price by the rate to find the amount of the cash discount.

Rate of Discount × Invoice Price = Cash Discount

To find the cash price, subtract the cash discount from the invoice price.

Invoice Price − Cash Discount = Cash Price

Example

An invoice for $2,400 is paid within the discount period. If the credit terms are 2/20, what amount should be paid?

Solution

$0.02 \times \$2,400 = \$48$ cash discount

$\$2,400 - \$48 = \$2,352$ cash price, or amount paid   **Ans.**

**Exercise 2
Written**

Find the amount to be paid on each invoice on the date shown.

	Date of Invoice	Amount of Invoice	Terms	Date Paid	Amount
1.	January 24	$758	2/10, n/30	February 3	$742.84
2.	June 28	485	3/10, n/30	July 8	470.45
3.	September 16	920	2/15, n/45	October 1	901.60
4.	August 6	386	2/10, 1/30, n/60	September 5	382.14
5.	November 18	369	5/10, 2/20, n/60	December 8	361.62
6.	March 17	861	2/10, 1/30, n/45	April 25	861
7.	July 14	724	3/10 EOM	August 7	702.28
8.	December 2	580	4/15 EOM	January 15	556.80
9.	February 6	455	2/20 EOM	March 21	455

Trade and Cash Discounts. When both a trade discount and a cash discount are given on an invoice, subtract the trade discount first to get the invoice price. Then subtract the cash discount to get the cash price.

**Exercise 3
Written**

■ Take the trade discount first, then take the cash discount.

1. Find the cash price if the invoice is paid within the discount period.

	List Price	Trade Discount	Terms	Cash Price
a.	$800	25%	3/10, n/60	$582
b.	600	25%, 10%	2/10, n/30	396.90
c.	750	20%, 15%	1/10, n/30	504.90
d.	500	20%, 20%	3/10, n/60	310.40
e.	420	20%, 10%, 5%	5/10, n/60	272.92

2. Peggy Lesner bought merchandise for her store. The list price was $970, less trade discounts of 30% and 10%. The terms were 3/10, 2/30, n/60. The invoice was dated March 17. For what amount should she write a check on April 16 to pay for the merchandise?
$598.88

REVIEW 90

Terms

1. Match the terms with the statements.

   cash discount   cash price   discount period   EOM

   a. Invoice price less cash discount   cash price
   b. End of month shown on invoice   EOM
   c. Number of days to take a cash discount   discount period
   d. Discount given for early payment   cash discount

Skills

2. a. 48 items at $1.25 = ? $60
   b. Multiply: 14.7 by 0.89   13.083
   c. $1.00 is what part smaller than $2.50? $\frac{3}{5}$

Problems

3. An invoice dated November 26 has terms of 4/10, 2/30, n/60. What is the last date on which payment may be made to get the largest cash discount?   December 6 [90]

4. Lexin, Inc., bought goods for $3,600, less 20% and 10%, terms 2/10, n/30. The invoice was dated April 9 and was paid on April 19. What was the amount of cash paid? $2,540.16 [90]

5. What single discount is equivalent to the series discounts of 10% and 5%?   14.5% [89]

Section 91
More About Cash Discounts

Borrowing to Get a Cash Discount. Sometimes retailers do not have the cash they need to pay an invoice within the discount period. If they don't, they may save money by borrowing and taking the discount. The amount they save is the discount less the cost of the interest on the loan.

Cash Discount − Cost of Interest = Amount Saved

Example

Toshi Dazai bought $4,500 worth of goods on July 14 with terms of 3/10, n/30. To pay the bill on July 24 and get the 3% discount, she borrowed the money at her bank for 20 days at 14% banker's interest. How much did she save by borrowing to get the discount?

Solution

Invoice price	$4,500	
Cash discount	135	(3% of $4,500)
Cash price	$4,365	(the amount borrowed)

Banker's interest on $4,365 for 20 days at 14% = $33.95

$135.00	cash discount
33.95	cost of interest
$101.05	amount saved by borrowing to get the discount **Ans.**

**Exercise 1
Written**

Use a 360-day year to figure interest in these problems.

1. Nelson Runnels borrowed $780 for 45 days at 12% to pay cash and get a cash discount of $20 on an invoice. What amount did he save by borrowing the money and taking the discount? $8.30

2. Jackie Drumm can get a $75 cash discount on an invoice by borrowing $3,675 at 8% interest for 30 days. What amount will she save by borrowing? $50.50

■ **Borrow only the cash price.**

3. On June 8, a retailer bought goods worth $9,000; terms 4/10, n/30. To pay for the goods on June 18 and get a discount, the retailer borrowed the money from a bank for 20 days at 15%. How much did the retailer save by borrowing the money to take the cash discount? $288

4. A dealer bought some goods for $23,000 on terms of 3/10, n/60. To get the cash discount, the dealer borrowed the money for 60 days at 16%. How much money did the dealer save by borrowing? $95.07

5. Lori Mechlor received a bill, dated August 3, for $2,400, with terms of 4/20, n/30. To get the cash discount, Lori borrowed enough money to pay the bill on August 23. Her 30-day note carried interest of 13%. How much did she save? $71.04

6. A carpet dealer buys goods on terms of 3% discount for immediate payment upon delivery, net 30 days. On an invoice of $56,000, how much would be saved by borrowing the money at 18% for 45 days to get the cash discount? $457.80

Finding the Rate of Cash Discount. Sometimes the rate of cash discount is unknown and must be found. To find it, remember that the rate of cash discount is always based on the invoice price. So, you find the rate of cash discount by dividing the amount of the cash discount by the invoice price.

$$\text{Rate of Cash Discount} = \frac{\text{Cash Discount}}{\text{Invoice Price}}$$

Example

By taking advantage of a cash discount, a retailer paid $1,261 to settle a $1,300 invoice. (a) What was the amount of the cash discount? (b) What was the rate of cash discount?

Solution

a. $1,300 Invoice price   b. $39 ÷ $1,300 = 3% Rate of discount **Ans.**
    1,261 Cash price
    $ 39 Discount **Ans.**

**Exercise 2
Written**

■ The rate of cash discount is based on the invoice price.

1. Find the missing items in each problem.

	Invoice Price	Cash Price	Cash Discount	Rate of Discount
a.	$ 900	$ 873	$27	3%
b.	750	735	15	2%
c.	800	768	32	4%
d.	1,240	1,178	62	5%
e.	600	582	18	3%
f.	4,200	4,116	84	2%
g.	1,800	1,782	18	1%

2. The owner of a clothing store paid off an invoice of $6,000 with a cash payment of $5,760 made within the discount period.
    a. What was the amount of the cash discount? $240
    b. What percent of the invoice price was the cash discount? 4%

3. A check for $659.60 is used to pay an invoice of $680 within the discount period. The discount period is 15 days. What rate of cash discount is allowed? 3%

4. By paying $855 in cash, a retailer saves $45 on an invoice of oil filters. What is the rate of cash discount? 5%

**‡Exercise 3
Written**

1. The cash discount on an invoice is $11. The rate of discount is 2%. What is the invoice price? $550

2. By taking the 4% cash discount on an invoice, a retailer saved $38. What was the invoice price of the goods? $950

3. A ceramics dealer saved $25.86 by taking a 3% cash discount on an invoice. What was the invoice price of the merchandise? $862

4. After deducting a cash discount of 2%, the cash price of an invoice is $2,548. What is the invoice price? $2,600

5. The cash price of an invoice is $407.68 after deducting a 2% cash discount. What is the invoice price? $416

6. A store owner paid $2,945 to settle an invoice, less a cash discount of 5%. What was the amount of the invoice before the discount was deducted? $3,100

REVIEW 91

Skills

1. a.   180% of $15.50 is ? $27.90
    b.   Find banker's interest on $1,800 for 120 days at 13%. $78
    c.   What part greater than $7 is $9.80? $\frac{2}{5}$
    d.   Round $0.1784 to the nearest tenth of a cent. $0.178
    e.   Write 0.0045 as a percent.   0.45%

Problems

2. Ronwel, Inc., is billed $2,890 for goods it bought. If the bill is paid within 15 days, only $2,774.40 is needed to pay the bill in full. What percent of cash discount is being offered on this bill?   4% [91]

3. On November 17, the Reaume Company bought goods for $16,400 with terms of 2/10, n/60. How much can it save by borrowing for 30 days at 12% banker's interest the amount needed to pay the bill and take the discount on November 27? $167.28 [91]

4. What single discount is equivalent to a series discount of 35% and 5%?   38.25% [89]

5. A photocopier was traded in for $640 after being used for 4 years. The copier cost $4,800 when new. What was the average annual depreciation? $1,040 [65]

6. A field measures 540 meters by 240 meters. Except for a wooded area of 1 800 m², the rest of the field is suitable for planting crops. How many square meters are available for planting?   127 800 m² [31]

Computer Clinic

The Kolmar Company received an invoice for $4,500 with terms of 3/10, n/30, dated March 3. On March 13, the Kolmar Company takes advantage of the 3% cash discount and borrows the money needed to pay the invoice for 20 days at 14% banker's interest. Follow the steps below to find the amount saved by borrowing to take advantage of the cash discount.

1. Insert your Spreadsheet Applications Diskette and call up the file "Sec91." After you do, your computer screen should look like Illustration 91–1.

```
Sec 91        Borrowing to Take a Cash Discount
-------------------------------------------------------------------
Invoice Price                           $.00
Cash Discount Rate (%)                   0.0
Loan Interest Rate (%)                   0.0
Term of Loan in Days                       0
-------------------------------------------------------------------
Amount Borrowed                         $.00
Cash Discount                           $.00
Less Interest                           $.00
Amount Saved                            $.00
-------------------------------------------------------------------
```

Illustration 91–1. Figuring the Cost of Borrowing

2. Find the amount the Kolmar Company saved by borrowing to take a cash discount by entering these data into the template.

   B3 4500   B4 3   B5 14   B6 20

3. Answer the questions.
   a. What was the cash price of the invoice? $4,365
   b. What amount was borrowed to pay the invoice on the discount date? $4,365
   c. What amount was saved by borrowing to take the cash discount? $101.05
   d. For how many days could the money have been borrowed before the cost of borrowing would have been greater than the cash discount? 79 days
   e. For a loan term of 20 days, how high could the interest rate be, to the nearest whole percent, before the cost of borrowing became greater than the cash discount? 55%

4. Use Sec91 to check Problems 3–6 of Exercise 1 in Section 91.

Unit 15

Selling for a Business

This unit presents some of the problems that businesses face when they sell. These problems include keeping sales records, figuring discounts, finding profit on sales, and pricing goods.

After you finish Unit 15, you will be able to:

- Prove cash and find cash short or over.
- Complete cash summary records.
- Record entries in customer accounts and find account balances.
- Find rate of discount on marked price.
- Figure discounts and selling prices.
- Figure gross profit and net income on sales.
- Find rate of markup and net income on sales.
- Figure cost when selling price and rate of markup on selling price are known.
- Find rate of markup based on cost.
- Find selling price needed to get rate of markup on cost wanted.
- Find marked price when selling price and rate of discount are known.
- Figure selling price needed to give desired rate of markup on selling price.
- Figure selling price needed to cover operating expenses and desired rate of net income.
- Find rate of markup on cost equivalent to rate of markup on selling price.
- Find cost when selling price and desired rate of markup on cost are known.
- Solve problems that contain more information than you need.
- Estimate answers to problems.
- Read, write, say, and recognize the meanings of the key terms.
- Use a computer spreadsheet to find cash short or over and to find cost and selling prices for stock.

Cash Registers. **Cash registers** provide a place to keep cash and a means to record cash sales and payments. Employees who use cash registers are called cash register clerks or cashiers.

Modern electronic cash registers are really computer terminals. You have probably seen electronic cash registers in supermarkets. Each checkout counter has a register with a display screen and a scanner that may be connected to a computer. (See Illustration 92–1.) As items pass by, the scanner reads **bar codes** printed on the items. The bar codes tell the computer the department, brand, size, and price of each item bought. This information is shown on the display screen and printed on a cash register receipt so that customers can check their purchases.

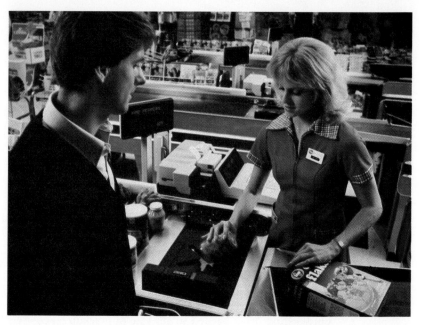

Illustration 92–1. Electronic Cash Register, Bar Code, and Register Receipt

The computer also finds the sales tax, totals the sale, and updates the store's inventory records. When the clerk keys in the amount of money received from the customer, the computer displays the correct change on the screen.

Proving Cash. Cashiers put some money in the cash register drawer when they start work so that they can make change. This money is called a **change fund.** While they work, they take in and pay out cash. At the end of their work period, they have to **prove cash.**

Proving cash means counting the money in the drawer and checking this amount against the cash register readings to see if the right amount is on hand. If you have less cash than you should, you are **cash short.** If you have more cash than you should, you are **cash over.**

For example, suppose Bess Turner worked as a cashier for Tri-County Markets. When she started work on March 16, she put $100 in her cash register drawer as a change fund. At the end of her work period, her register readings showed total cash received, $3,365.75, and total cash paid out, $72.20. When she counted the cash in her drawer, she found $3,395.55. So, she was $2 cash over. In proving cash, she used a **cash proof form** like the one shown in Illustration 92–2.

TCM TRI-COUNTY MARKETS		
803 Blanchester Rd.	Cash Proof	
Augusta, ME 04330-7654		
Date	*March 16, 19--*	
Change Fund	*100*	*00*
+ Register Total of Cash Received	*3,365*	*75*
Total	*3,465*	*75*
− Register Total of Cash Paid Out	*72*	*20*
Cash That Should be in Drawer	*3,393*	*55*
Cash Actually in Drawer	*3,395*	*55*
Cash Short		
Cash Over	*2*	*00*
Cash Register No. *8*		
Cash Register Operator		
Bess Turner		

Illustration 92–2. Cash Proof Form

Exercise 1 Written

1. At the start of the day, July 3, Maude Olaf put $100 in change in the drawer of her cash register. The cash register readings at the end of the day showed total cash received, $2,793.68, and total cash paid out, $29.50. The cash in the drawer at the end of the day was $2,863.38. Prepare a cash proof form, showing cash over or short.   80 cents short

■ Too little cash = cash short

2. When he opened his shop on March 9, Edwin Torinos put $75 in change in his cash register drawer. At the end of the day, the cash register readings showed that $3,812.34 had been taken in, that $213.88 had been paid out in cash refunds, and that Edwin had taken out $50 for his personal use. The cash on hand in the drawer

at the end of the day was $3,624.75. Was the cash short or over? How much?   Over, $1.29

■ **Too much cash = cash over**

3. Ria had $100 in change in her cash register at the start of work on May 6. At the end of her work period, there was $2,988.68 in the cash register. The register totals showed that she received $3,307.43 and paid out $418.75 during the period. How much was the cash over or short?   Not over or short

4. Ron Gaston, a cashier at the Mall Cafeteria, started the day with $100 in change. When he went off duty, he sorted his food receipts and found that he had these:

27 for $2.45	28 for $2.80	3 for $3.05	74 for $3.25
23 for $2.55	11 for $2.85	44 for $3.10	28 for $3.50
34 for $2.60	21 for $2.90	49 for $3.15	55 for $3.75
12 for $2.70	22 for $2.95	36 for $3.20	

Ron had $1,540.90 in the cash drawer. He had made no payments. Was his cash short or over? How much?   Short, 10 cents

Cash Sales Summary Records. Cash sales and cash refunds for goods returned may be recorded using the cash register. Daily totals of cash sales and cash refunds may be summarized for the owner or manager. The summary may show the totals for each department or for each salesclerk.

Exercise 2 Written

1. The table below shows the cash sales and cash refunds for sales returns for the 4 departments of Klein's Drugstore for September 9. You are to:
    a. Copy and complete the table.
    b. Prove total net cash sales by subtracting total cash refunds for sales returns from total cash sales.

Daily Summary — Cash Sales September 9, 19--			
Department	**Cash Sales**	**Cash Refunds for Returns**	**Net Cash Sales**
Prescription Drugs	$1,798.22	$ —	$1,798.22
Nonprescription Drugs	2,666.23	27.89	2,638.34
Cosmetics	902.56	78.12	824.44
Hygiene Items	613.55	43.49	570.06
Totals	$5,980.56	$149.50	$5,831.06

2. The table on the next page shows the cash sales for 6 salespersons who worked at a store on August 17. You are to:
    a. Copy and complete the table.
    b. Prove the total of the Net Cash Sales column by subtracting the totals of the Cash Refunds column from the cash sales column.

Daily Cash Sales Summary August 17, 19--			
Salesperson	Cash Sales	Cash Refunds	Net Cash Sales
Allen	$308.25	$22.87	$ 285.38
Brett	478.29	68.45	409.84
Cruz	511.98	15.77	496.21
Deng	278.41	12.39	266.02
Eaton	645.90	34.85	611.05
Farrell	198.34	5.89	192.45
Totals	$2,421.17	$160.22	$2,260.95

REVIEW 92

Terms

1. Match the terms with the statements.

bar code   cash over   cash register   prove cash
change fund   cash proof form   cash short

a. Keeps track of cash received and paid out   cash register
b. Less cash than you should have   cash short
c. More cash than you should have   cash over
d. Count money and check it against register record   prove cash
e. Money in drawer at start of period   change fund
f. Identifies department, brand, size, price of items   bar code
g. Form used to check cash   cash proof form

Skills

2. a. Add: $9\frac{2}{3}$, $12\frac{3}{4}$, $15\frac{5}{6}$ $38\frac{1}{4}$
    b. Divide: $23\frac{1}{3}$ by $1\frac{5}{9}$ 15
    c. Find exact interest on $3,500 at 12% for 50 days. $57.53
    d. Show 2 107 L in kiloliters.   2.107 kL
    e. Estimate a 21% trade discount on a sale amounting to $2,489.
        $500
    f. Find the exact trade discount for problem 2e. $522.69
    g. Divide: 22.75 by 6.5   3.5
    h. 45.6784 × 1,000 = ?   45,678.4

Problems

3. In the morning, Aldo put $100 in change in the money drawer of his cash register. The readings at the end of the day showed total cash received, $4,107.56, and total cash paid out, $163.88. The cash on hand in the money drawer at the end of the day was $4,044.55. Was the cash short or over? How much?   Over, 87 cents [92]

4. A compact disk system listed at $1,280 is billed to the retailer at $768. What is the rate of trade discount?   40% [88]

5. A sales invoice dated March 25 has terms of 3/10, 2/20, n/30. What is the last date on which payment must be made to get the largest cash discount?   April 4 [90]

6. A building valued at $100,000 was insured for 3 years for $60,000 under an 80% coinsurance clause policy. A 3-alarm fire caused a loss of $12,800. How much did the insurance company pay? $9,600 [78]

Computer Clinic

Betty Tarpey is a cashier for Shopfast Markets. She started her workday on May 5 with a $100 change fund. Her register readings at the end of her workday were: cash received, $2,580.77; cash paid out, $128.22. The cash in her cash register drawer at the end of her workday totaled $2,552.37. Follow the steps below to complete a cash proof form for Betty.

1. Insert your Spreadsheet Applications Diskette and call up the file "Sec92." After you do, your computer screen should look like Illustration 92–3.

```
Sec92                  SHOPFAST MARKETS
                          CASH PROOF

Change Fund                             0.00
 +Register Total of Cash Received       0.00
Total                                    .00
 -Register Total of Cash Paid Out       0.00
Cash That Should Be In Drawer            .00
Cash Actually In Drawer                 0.00
Cash Short                               .00
Cash Over                                .00
```

Illustration 92–3. Spreadsheet Used to Complete a Cash Proof

2. Prepare a cash proof form by entering the correct data into cells B4, B5, B7, and B9 of the template.

3. Answer the questions about the completed cash proof form.
   a. How much cash should have been in the drawer at the end of Betty's workday? $2,552.55
   b. Was the amount of cash on hand at the end of the day the correct amount?   No
   c. Was the cash on hand over or short?   Short
   d. If cash was over or short, by how much was it over or short? $0.18

Customer Invoices. When a seller sells goods to a buyer on credit, the seller sends the customer a sales slip, or sales invoice. A **sales invoice** is a form that lists the goods sold and delivered to the buyer. The buyer calls this form a purchase invoice.

A sales invoice that Technipro Equipment Company, a wholesale computer equipment firm, sent to Computer Station, a retailer, is shown in Illustration 93–1.

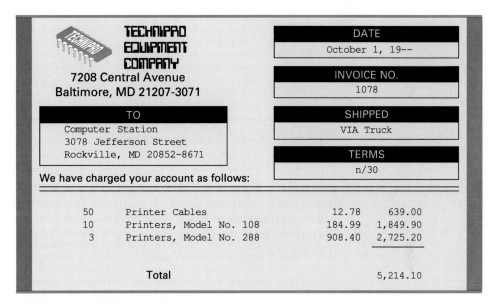

			DATE
			October 1, 19--

TECHNIPRO EQUIPMENT COMPANY
7208 Central Avenue
Baltimore, MD 21207-3071

DATE
October 1, 19--

INVOICE NO.
1078

TO
Computer Station 3078 Jefferson Street Rockville, MD 20852-8671

SHIPPED
VIA Truck

TERMS
n/30

We have charged your account as follows:

50	Printer Cables	12.78	639.00
10	Printers, Model No. 108	184.99	1,849.90
3	Printers, Model No. 288	908.40	2,725.20
	Total		5,214.10

Illustration 93–1. Sales Invoice

The sales invoice may be completed by hand, with a typewriter, or on a computer system. The original invoice is sent to the buyer. Copies of the invoice are kept by the seller.

Credit Memorandums. When merchandise bought on credit is returned, the seller cannot return the buyer's money. After all, the buyer has not paid the seller yet. Instead, the seller reduces the buyer's account balance by the amount of the return. The seller notifies the buyer about the reduction by sending the buyer a credit memorandum, or **credit memo.** For example, when Computer Station returned three defective printer cables from Invoice No. 1078, Technipro sent the credit memo shown in Illustration 93–2.

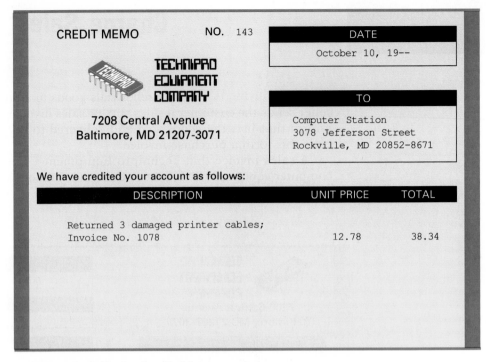

Illustration 93–2. Credit Memorandum

Customer Accounts. When businesses let customers buy on credit, or on account, they must keep records for each customer to show how much each customer owes. A common form of **customer account** is shown in Illustration 93–3. This account shows the transactions between Technipro Equipment Company (the seller) and the Computer Station (the buyer).

Computer Station's Account. On October 1, a new page for Computer Station's account was started. The buyer owed $8,282 from last month, so $8,282 was written in the Balance column of the account.

Also on October 1, the amount of Sales Invoice No. 1078, $5,214.10, was written in the Charges column; and "Invoice No. 1078" was written in the Explanation column. The new balance of $13,496.10 was found by adding $5,214.10 to the old balance.

On October 10, Computer Station returned $38.34 of the merchandise from Invoice No. 1078. Credit Memo No. 143 was sent. The amount of the memo, $38.34, was written in the Credits column; and "Credit Memo No. 143" was written in the Explanation column. The new balance, $13,457.76, was found by subtracting $38.34 from the old balance of $13,496.10.

On October 14, Computer Station paid the balance owed from last month, $8,282. Since Computer Station no longer owed the old balance, $8,282 was written in the Credits column and "Payment" was written in the Explanation column. The new balance of $5,175.76 was written in the Balance column.

■ Charges increase account balances.

■ Sales are charges.

■ Credits decrease account balances.

■ Payments and returns are credits.

NAME	Computer Station			
ADDRESS	3078 Jefferson Street			
	Rockville, MD 20852-8671			

DATE	EXPLANATION	CHARGES	CREDITS	BALANCE
19-- Oct. 1	Balance			8,282.00
1	Invoice No. 1078	5,214.10		13,496.10
10	Credit Memo No. 143		38.34	13,457.76
14	Payment		8,282.00	5,175.76
31	Payment		5,175.76	————

Illustration 93–3. Customer Account

On October 31, Computer Station paid the net amount of the invoice of October 1. The amount due on the invoice was $5,214.10, less the return of $38.34, or $5,175.76. When this was paid, Computer Station no longer owed the $5,175.76, so $5,175.76 was written in the Credits column and "Payment" was written in the Explanation column. Because there was no balance in the account, a short line was drawn in the Balance column.

**Exercise 1
Written**

1. Make an account form like the one in Illustration 93–3. Record these transactions between J. L. Sales, Inc., and a customer, Tenco Products, Inc. Tenco is located at 5302 Post Road, Warwick, RI 02886-9898.

   Aug. 1 The balance of Tenco's account was $2,353.90.
   8 Sold goods to Tenco, $1,685.49; Inv. No. 3369; terms, 30 days.
   16 Tenco returned $45.66 of the goods sold on Aug. 8; Credit Memo No. 388.
   20 Tenco paid the balance on Aug. 1, $2,353.90.
   26 Sold goods to Tenco, $2,275; Inv. No. 3672; terms, 30 days.
   Sept. 9 Tenco paid the invoice of Aug. 8, less Credit Memo No. 388.
   12 Sold goods to Tenco, $1,216; Inv. No. 4180; terms, 30 days.
   15 Tenco returned $120 of the goods sold on Sept. 12; Credit Memo No. 412.
   25 Tenco paid Inv. No. 3672.   Balance, $1,096

2. Make an account form like the one in Illustration 93–3. Record these facts about Sterling Co.'s account with Gorbea Supply Company. Sterling's address is 708 Gower St., Greenville, SC 29611-3381.

June 1   The balance in Sterling's account was $4,116.53.
     3   Sterling paid the June 1 balance.
     5   Sold goods to Sterling, $3,642.39; Inv. No. 9708; terms, n/20.
    17   Sterling returned $488.12 of the goods on Inv. No. 9708; Credit Memo No. 398.
    18   Sold goods to Sterling, $1,785.84; Inv. #9934; terms, n/20.
    25   Sterling paid Inv. #9708, less Credit Memo #398.
    26   Sterling returned $21.72 of the goods on Inv. #9934; Credit Memo #416. Balance, $1,764.12

3. Make and complete an account form like the one in Illustration 93–3 from these facts about Enloe Products Co.'s account with ATV Sales, Inc. Enloe's address is 2278 Cascade St., Bennington, VT 05201-7231. ATV Sales offers no cash or trade discounts and ships its sales by truck. For the last 5 years, Enloe has had an average account balance of about $1,200.

Feb. 1   The balance in Enloe's account was $653.23.
     2   Enloe returned $29.15 of goods; Credit Memo #278.
     5   Sold goods to Enloe, $438.27; Inv. #7451; terms, n/30.
     8   Enloe paid the Feb. 1 balance, less Credit Memo #278.
    17   Enloe returned $8.52 of the goods on Inv. #7451; Credit Memo #302.
Mar. 2   Sold goods to Enloe, $904.72; Inv. #8459; terms, n/30.
     6   Enloe paid Inv. #7451, less Credit Memo No. 302.
    16   Enloe returned $12.83 of the goods on Inv. #8459; Credit Memo #296. Balance, $891.89

REVIEW 93

Terms

1. Match the terms with the statements.

   credit memo   customer account   sales invoice

   a. Describes goods sold and shipped   sales invoice
   b. Shows the balance a buyer owes   customer account
   c. Tells buyer account balance is reduced   credit memo

Skills

2. a. Multiply: $44\frac{1}{2}$ by $6\frac{1}{4}$ $278\frac{1}{8}$
   b. $75.60 is what percent smaller than $108?   30%
   c. Find the number of days from June 15 to October 15.   122
   d. $30 \times \$1.30 = ?$ $39
   e. Estimate the interest on $1,008 at $9\frac{7}{8}\%$ for 1 year. $100
   f. Find the exact interest on $1,008 at $9\frac{7}{8}\%$ for 1 year. $99.54
   ‡g. What amount decreased by $\frac{1}{4}$ of itself equals $8.40? $11.20

Problems

3. Trimer Co.'s account balance with MLR, Inc., was $5,893.11 on July 1. These facts were recorded in the account in July: July 2, Invoice #2977 , $1,007.49; July 9, Credit Memo #125, $23.78; July 21,

payment, $5,000. What was the balance of the account after these items were recorded? $1,876.82 [93]

4. Day Co. bought $1,700 of goods on May 28. Terms were 3/10, n/30.
   a. How much money did Day Co. need to pay the invoice on June 7? $1,649
   b. To pay the bill, Day Co. borrowed the amount needed for 50 days at 9% banker's interest. How much did Day Co. save by borrowing? $30.39 [91]

Section 94
Figuring Discounts and Prices

When you work in retailing, or when you shop, you may need to find the rate of discount, amount of discount, selling price, or marked price of goods.

Marked Price, Discount, and Selling Price. In retail stores, the price marked on an item is called the **marked price** or **retail price.** To sell slow moving items, storeowners may have to reduce prices. The amount prices are reduced is called the *discount* or **markdown.** The price that the customer pays is the **selling price** or **sales price.**

Marked Price − Discount = Selling Price

The discount or markdown is equal to the marked price less the selling price.

Marked Price − Selling Price = Discount

If there is no discount or markdown, the selling price and the marked price are the same.

Finding the Rate of Discount. The rate of discount is based on the marked price. To find the rate of discount, you divide the discount by the marked price.

$$\textbf{Rate of Discount} = \frac{\textbf{Discount}}{\textbf{Marked Price}}$$

Exercise 1
Written

1. Find the amount and the rate of discount in each problem.

Article	Marked Price	Selling Price	Discount Amount	Rate (%)
a. Dinette set	$590.00	$472.00	$118.00	20%
b. Watch	147.90	98.60	49.30	$33\frac{1}{3}$%
c. Microwave oven	199.00	179.10	19.90	10%
d. Log splitter	485.80	412.93	72.87	15%

2. At an electronics store, a compact disk player that regularly sells for $199.99 is reduced to $159.99. What is the rate of discount on the player, to the nearest whole percent?   20%

3. In a shop window, a jogging outfit is marked "$99.45 — was $127.50." At what rate was the price reduced?   22%

4. A basketball backboard, goal, and pole sell separately for $35, $19, and $59. If you buy them as a set, the price is $73.45. What rate of discount are you getting for the set?   35%

5. Miwaku Yoshino bought a dress that was marked at $129. Because she paid cash, she was given a $3.87 discount. What rate of discount did she get?   3%

6. A store sells a line of bikes that are regularly priced at $89.95. At a seasonal sale, the bikes are marked down to $75.95. What is the rate of markdown, to the nearest tenth of a percent?   15.6%

Exercise 2
Written

1. Video tapes priced at $7.50 each are sold at a special sale at 5 for $33. What percent does a customer save by buying 5 video tapes at the sale price?   12%

2. Pine trees that regularly sell for $59.75 each are offered at the special price of 4 for $179.25. What rate of discount is offered?   25%

3. The subscription price of a magazine is $36 for 1 year. A 2-year subscription costs $63, and a 3-year subscription, $91.80.
   a. What is the rate of discount on a 2-year subscription? $12\frac{1}{2}$%
   b. On a 3-year subscription?   15%

4. A hardware store has $\frac{1}{2}$-inch wrenches that sell regularly at $2.99 each. During a 3-week "One Cent Sale," the store sells 2 wrenches for the price of one, plus 1 cent. What is the rate of discount, to the nearest whole percent?   50%

5. A garden center sells 20-10-5 fertilizer bags covering 5,000 sq. ft. for $9.95 and bags covering 10,000 sq. ft. for $16.95. What rate of discount, to the nearest tenth of a percent, do you get if you buy the bag that covers the larger area?   14.8%

Finding the Discount and the Selling Price When the Marked Price and Rate of Discount Are Known. A rate of discount is based on the marked price. So, to find the amount of the discount you multiply the marked price by the rate of discount.

Rate of Discount × Marked Price = Discount

Then you subtract the discount from the marked price to find the selling price.

Marked Price − Discount = Selling Price

Example

A discount of 20% is given on baseball gloves that are marked at $45.
a.   What is the amount of the discount?
b.   What is the selling price?

Solution

1. $20\% = \frac{1}{5}$

$\frac{1}{5} \times \$45 = \$9$ discount   **Ans.**

2. $\$45 - \$9 = \$36$ selling price   **Ans.**

Explanation

1.   The marked price, $45, was multiplied by the rate of discount, 20% or $\frac{1}{5}$, to find the amount of the discount, $9.

2.   The amount of the discount, $9, was subtracted from the marked price, $45, to find the selling price, $36.

**Exercise 3
Written**

1.   Find the discount and the selling price in each problem.

	Item	Marked Price	Rate of Discount	Amount of Discount	Selling Price
a.	Telephone	$259.90	10%	$25.99	$233.91
b.	Roller skates	22.95	20%	4.59	18.36
c.	Camera	170.00	$12\frac{1}{2}\%$	21.25	148.75
d.	Mower	289.00	25%	72.25	216.75
e.	Guitar	370.00	$37\frac{1}{2}\%$	138.75	231.25
f.	Computer	1,599.95	40%	639.98	959.97

2.   How much does a customer pay for a hand-held calculator marked $15.95 if a retail discount of 15% is given. $13.56

3.   Tires priced at $75 are marked down 24%. What is the discount price?
$57

4. During a special sale, the price of a handbag is marked down 20% from $49.99. What is the sale price? $39.99

5. Running shoes, originally priced at $57.95 a pair, are reduced 40% during a sale.
   a. Estimate the amount of discount. $24
   b. How much will the shoes cost at the reduced price? $34.77

‡**Finding the Marked Price When the Selling Price and Rate of Discount Are Known.** Sometimes the seller knows the selling price at which the item should be sold and the rate of discount needed to meet the competition. The seller then needs to find the price at which the item should be marked.

Example

A store wants to sell a fan for $24.80 after deducting a discount of 20% from the marked price. What should the marked price of the fan be?

Solution

$$100\% \times \text{marked price} = \text{marked price}$$
$$-20\% \times \text{marked price} = \text{discount}$$
$$\overline{80\% \times \text{marked price} = \text{selling price} = \$24.80}$$
$$\text{marked price} = \$24.80 \div 80\%$$
$$\$24.80 \div 0.8 = \$31 \quad \textbf{Ans.}$$

Check: Marked Price − Discount = Selling Price
$31 − 20% of $31 = $31 − $6.20 = $24.80

Explanation

The percent of discount (20%) given in the problem is based on the marked price, which is unknown. The problem tells us, however, that if 20% of the marked price is subtracted from the marked price, the remainder is $24.80.

Marked Price − 20% of Marked Price = $24.80

Since the percent is based on the marked price, the marked price is the base, or whole, and so is 100% of itself.

‡**Exercise 4 Written**

1. During a sale, a computer store sold printer stands at 30% off the marked price. The selling price was what percent of the marked price?   70%

2. The Shell Shop sells beach umbrellas for $37.80, which is 16% less than the marked price.
   a. The selling price is what percent of the marked price?   84%
   b. What is the marked price? $45

Marked price = 100%

3. A go-cart sells for $693.75, which is 25% less than the marked price.
   a. What percent of the marked price is the selling price?   75%
   b. How much is the marked price? $925

4. After allowing a retail discount of $12\frac{1}{2}$%, a store sold a tent for $108.50. What was the marked price? $124

5. At what price should a discount store mark a TV set so that the selling price is $270 after allowing an advertised discount of 25% on the marked price? $360

6. The First Lane Auto store wants to sell a car cover for $119.60 after giving a discount of 35% from the catalog price. What should be the catalog price? $184

REVIEW 94

Terms

1. Match the terms with the statements. Be careful — each statement may be matched with more than one term.

markdown   retail price   selling price
marked price   sales price

   a. The price marked on an item   marked price; retail price
   b. A reduction in marked price   markdown
   c. The price a customer pays   sales price; selling price

Skills

2. a. Multiply: $34\frac{3}{8}$ by 26 $893\frac{3}{4}$
   b. The due date of a 90-day note dated June 5 is?   September 3
   c. 125% of $2.80 is? $3.50

Problems

3. At a clearance sale, suits marked $350 were reduced to $245. What was the rate of markdown on these suits?   30% [94]

4. Tom had $100 in change in his cash register at the start of the day. At the end of the day, he had $3,652.12 in the cash register. The register totals showed that he received $3,678.34 and paid out $125.44 during the period. How much was the cash over or short?
Short, $0.78 [92]

5. Tymco's account balance with Belo, Inc., was $9,397.66 on May 1. These facts were recorded in the account in May: May 3, Invoice #1783, $4,798.56; May 8, Credit Memo #238, $89.98; May 25, payment, $8,000. Find the balance of the account. $6,106.24 [93]

6. A service organization sold flowers to motorists at intersections to raise money for a town playground. Their gross sales were $976.50. The flowers cost them $277.50. Other expenses were $28.32. What net amount did they make on the sale? $670.68 [4]

7. An invoice for $1,400 can be fully paid if you pay $1,358 within 20 days from the date of the invoice. What percent of cash discount is allowed?   3% [91]

8. What single discount is equivalent to the series 20%, 25%, and 10%?
46% [89]

‡9. A store wants to sell a copy machine for $893.75 after giving a 35% discount from the marked price. What should be the marked price?
$1,375 [94]

Store owners often want to know how much gross profit and net income they are making on each type of item they sell. They may also want to know the *rate* of profit on each type of item. They can then compare that rate with the rate of profit they find when they analyze their income statements. In this way they can drop unprofitable items and increase their sales efforts on profitable ones.

Finding Gross Profit. You find gross profit by subtracting the cost from the selling price.

■ "Cost" means total cost.

Selling Price − Cost = Gross Profit

The term "cost" means **total cost.** Total cost is the invoice price, or cash price, of the merchandise plus any buying expenses. **Buying expenses** are any costs you had in buying and delivering the merchandise to your business.

Total Cost = Invoice Price (or Cash Price) + Buying Expense

Example

The Racquet Shop bought 100 pairs of tennis shoes for $2,420 and paid $165 to ship them to the shop. During the summer, the shop sold 80 pairs at $49 each. At the end of summer, the rest were closed out at $33 each. What was the shop's gross profit on the shoes?

Solution

1. Find the selling price of the entire lot:

80 pairs @ $49	$3,920
20 pairs @ $33	+ 660
Selling price	$4,580

2. Find the total cost of the purchase:

Invoice price	$2,420
Shipping charges	+ 165
Total cost	$2,585

3. Find the gross profit:

Selling price	$4,580
Cost	+ 2,585
Gross profit	$1,995 **Ans.**

If the cost is more than the selling price, you subtract the selling price from the cost. The result is a **gross loss.**

Cost − Selling Price = Gross Loss

**Exercise 1
Written**

1. The Byte Mart bought 25 computers for $14,750 and paid $275 for shipping charges. The store sold 15 of the computers at $999, 5 at $945, and the rest at $925. What was the store's gross profit on the lot? $9,310

2. The Lilly Pond bought 50 dozen printed T-shirts at $75 a dozen and paid $35 for shipping charges. The store sold 375 of them at $12.95, 150 at $10.95, and the rest at $8.95. What was the store's gross profit on the lot of shirts? $3,385

3. Jenny's Sewing Basket bought 3 dozen scissors for $78 per dozen, less 35%. Jenny's paid $22.40 for delivery charges, and sold the scissors at $7.95 each. What was the gross profit on the scissors? $111.70

4. Tom's Farm-Fresh Stand bought 125 cantaloupes at $0.88 each and paid delivery charges of $4.68. The Stand then sold 90 of them at $1.48 and the rest at $1.25 each. What was the Stand's gross profit on the cantaloupes? $62.27

5. Jaymar Hardware store bought 50 outdoor light kits at $45 each and paid $23 for shipping charges. If the entire lot was sold at $67.88 a kit, what was the gross profit? $1,121

■ Net income means the same as net profit.

Finding Net Income. You find net income, or net profit, by subtracting operating expenses from gross profit.

Gross Profit − Operating Expenses = Net Income

If operating expenses are greater than the gross profit, you subtract the gross profit from the operating expenses. The result is a net loss.

Operating Expenses − Gross Profit = Net Loss

■ Operating expenses are also called overhead expenses.

Operating expenses may also be called overhead expenses. In any case, they are all those expenses needed to run a business. These include salaries, rent, heat, and light.

Finding the exact amount of net income for one type of item sold is hard because you may not know what operating expenses were needed to sell each type of item. In that case, you must estimate the operating expenses for each type of item.

For example, suppose that your income statement shows that your operating expenses average 25% of net sales. If one item sells for $100, operating expenses for that item can be estimated at 25% of $100, or $25.

Example

The Pedal Corner pays $95 for speed bikes and sells them for $180. What is the store's net income on the bikes if operating expenses average 30% of the net sales?

Solution

selling price	$180
− cost	− 95
gross profit	$ 85
− operating expenses	− 54 (30% of $180)
net income	$ 31 **Ans.**

You can also find net income by subtracting the sum of the cost and operating expenses from the selling price.

Selling Price − (Cost + Operating Expenses) = Net Income

Using this method, your solution would be:

Selling price		**$180**
Deduct:		
Cost	**$95**	
Operating expenses, 30% of $180	**+54**	**−149**
Net income		**$ 31**

**Exercise 2
Written**

1. Chang's Auto Store buys wheel cover sets at $29 and sells them at $49. The store figures its operating expenses at 26% of net sales. What is the net income per set? $7.26

2. Lilla Jaworsky, a furniture dealer, bought chairs costing $195 each and sold them for $375 each. She estimated her overhead expenses at 28% of net sales. What was her net income on each chair? $75

3. The Glass Factory bought a line of bay windows that cost $14,750 and sold the line for $22,090. Operating expenses for the purchase and sale of the line were estimated to be $7,394. What was the net income or net loss on this line? $54 net loss

4. A store bought 30 watches for $70 each, less 10% and 10%. It sold 15 of the watches at $135 each, 10 at $120, and the rest at $75. What amount of net income did the store make on the watches if its operating expenses were estimated at 35% of net sales? $639

5. Fred Baum, a retailer, buys can openers at $8 each, less 20% and 10%, plus $0.50 shipping charge on each opener. If he sells them at $12 and his operating expenses are 25% of net sales, what is his net income on each can opener? $2.74

"Based on" means "compared with."

Finding the Rate of Markup (Gross Profit) Based on the Selling Price.

The price a business pays for an item, including any buying expenses, is the business's cost of the item. The price at which the business sells it is the selling price.

The amount by which the selling price is greater than the cost is the **markup**, or gross profit. When shown as a percent, *the rate of markup is usually based on the selling price.*

$$\text{Selling Price} - \text{Cost} = \text{Markup (Gross Profit)}$$

$$\text{Rate of Markup (Gross Profit)} = \frac{\text{Markup (Gross Profit)}}{\text{Selling Price}}$$

Exercise 3 Written

1. The Rawhide Shop pays $98 for a leather case and sells it for $175. The markup is what percent of the selling price?   44%

2. A wholesaler buys truck light bars at $35.20 a set and sells them at $55 a set. What is the percent of gross profit on the selling price?   36%

3. For her farm equipment distributorship, Louisa finds that an average gross profit of $37\frac{1}{2}\%$ of net sales must be made to cover operating expenses and give her the net income she wants.
    a. If fence stakes that can be sold at $47.50 per dozen are bought at $30.40 per dozen from the manufacturer, what percent of gross profit would the store make on the selling price of each dozen?   36%
    b. Is this percent greater or less than the rate the store wants?   Less
    c. What percent greater or less? $1\frac{1}{2}\%$ less

Gross = 12 dozen

4. A retailer buys pens at $74.88 a gross and sells them at 2 for $1.60. What percent of the selling price is the markup?   35%

5. Buy Best buys 20, 7.5 horsepower outboard motors at $348 each and marks them to sell at $750. If the store gives a discount of 20%, what is the rate of markup on the selling price?   42%

Gross profit
− Operating expenses
Net income

Finding the Rate of Net Income Based on the Selling Price.

Net income is the gross profit (or markup) less the operating expenses. If the operating expenses are more than the gross profit, there is a net loss.

You find the rate of net income (or net loss) by dividing the net income (or net loss) by the selling price.

$$\text{Rate of Net Income or Net Loss} = \frac{\text{Net Income or Net Loss}}{\text{Selling Price}}$$

Exercise 4 Written

1. A computer store buys $3\frac{1}{2}$ inch diskettes at $0.69 each and sells them at $18 a dozen. The operating expenses are 38% of net sales. The net income on each diskette is what percent of the selling price?   16%

2. A gift shop buys coffee mugs at $2.79 each and marks them to sell at $4.50. The shop's operating expenses are estimated at 26% of net

sales. What rate of net income does the store make on each mug it sells at the marked price?   12%

3. Goods costing $2,964 are sold for $3,900. The overhead expenses for the sale are $585. What is the percent of net income on the selling price?   9%

4. Goods costing $6,760 were sold for $10,400. Operating expenses averaged 40% of net sales. What was the percent of net loss on the selling price?   5%

5. The Rug Center buys 3 m × 4 m rugs at $87 each and sells them at $145 each. What rate of net income is earned on the selling price if the operating expenses are 30% of net sales?   10%

REVIEW 95

Terms

1. Match the terms with the statements.

    buying expense   gross loss   markup   total cost

    a. Invoice or cash price plus buying expense   total cost
    b. Cost of buying and getting goods to you   buying expense
    c. Total cost less selling price   gross loss
    d. Selling price less cost; gross profit   markup

Skills

2. a. Divide: $16\frac{1}{2}$ by $2\frac{3}{4}$ 6
    b. $4.86 is what percent more than $3.60?   35%
    c. Find exact interest on $3,500 for 2 months at 12%. $70
  ‡d. What number divided by $4\frac{1}{2}$ is 8?   36

Problems

3. A store bought 10 dozen hair driers for $872 delivered. They sold 80 driers at $14 each, 20 at $12 each, and the rest at $8 each. [95]
    a. What was the gross profit on the entire lot? $648
    b. What was the average gross profit per drier? $5.40

4. A grocer pays $0.66 for a box of spaghetti and sells each box for $0.88. Operating expenses are $0.13 per box. [95]
    a. What is the rate of gross profit on the selling price?   25%
    b. What is the rate of net income on the selling price, to the nearest tenth of a percent?   10.2%

5. An invoice for $770 can be fully paid by paying $731.50 within 10 days from the date of invoice. What is the rate of cash discount? 5% [91]

6. A color TV listed at $475 is billed at $308.75.
    a. Estimate the rate of trade discount.   40%
    b. What is the exact rate of trade discount given?   35% [88]

An important decision for businesses is what price to put on the goods they sell. When businesses price goods, the rate of markup (gross profit) they use may be based on the selling price or on the cost of the goods. Most retail stores base their markup on the selling price.

Finding the Cost Price of an Item When the Selling Price and Rate of Markup on Selling Price Are Known. Many businesses sell goods in *price lines*. For example, an auto supply store may stock three price lines of car batteries. One price line sells for $59.99; another line sells for $49.99; a third line sells for $39.99. The different price lines are expected to appeal to different kinds of customers.

When batteries are bought for a price line, the selling price is already known. The problem is to find the highest price that you can pay for the batteries and still get the markup you want. If the cost of the batteries is too high, you will make too little profit in selling them.

Example

Jill Carr owns the Car Shack and has to buy tires for a line she sells for $50. She knows that her markup must be 40% of the selling price to cover expenses and get the net income she wants. What is the highest price she can afford to pay for each tire?

Explanation

The highest price, or cost, is found by subtracting the markup (gross profit) from the selling price. The selling price is 100%, or the base. The markup ($50) is 40% of the selling price.

Solution 1

Selling Price − Markup (Gross Profit) = Cost
$50 − 40% of $50 = cost
$50 − $20 = $30 **Ans.**

Solution 2

100% (selling price) − 40% (markup) = 60% (cost)
0.60 × $50 (selling price) = $30 (cost)

**Exercise 1
Written**

1. Inazo Saga has to buy men's belts for a line that sells for $25. What is the most he can pay for this line if the markup must be 35% of the selling price? $16.25

2. What is the most that a store owner should pay per dozen for scarves that retail for $27.98 each, if the owner must make 34% gross profit on the retail price? $221.60

3. A wholesaler has a line of rugs that sell for $49.50 each. What is the highest price the wholesaler can pay for the rugs and make a markup of 44% of the selling price? $27.72

4. The Shoe Cellar has a 38% markup on the selling price of women's casual shoes that sell for $29.50 a pair.
   a. What is the estimated cost per pair to the store? $18
   b. What is the exact cost per pair to the store? $18.29

‡**Finding the Selling Price That Gives the Rate of Markup on the Selling Price You Want.** If an item is not in a price line, it must be given a selling price. In this case, you know the cost price. The problem is to find the selling price that will give you the rate of markup you want.

Example

RB Computer Sales buys computer screens at $90 each. The manager knows that the markup must be 40% of the selling price to cover expenses and give the business the net income that is wanted. What is the lowest price at which the computers can be sold and still make the rate of markup that is wanted?

Explanation

The percent of markup is based on the selling price, which is unknown. Since the percent is based on the selling price, the selling price is the base, or whole, and is 100% of itself. The problem shows that if 40% of the selling price is subtracted from the selling price, the difference is $90:

Selling Price − 40% of Selling Price = $90

Solution

$$\begin{array}{r} 100\% \times \text{selling price} = \text{selling price} \\ \underline{-40\% \times \text{selling price} = \text{markup}} \\ 60\% \times \text{selling price} = \text{cost} = \$90 \\ \text{selling price} = \$90 \div 60\% \\ = \$90 \div 0.60 = \$150 \end{array}$$

The lowest price at which the computer can be sold is $150. **Ans.**

Check: Selling Price − Markup   = Cost
        $150   − 40% of $150 = $150 − $60 = $90

‡**Exercise 2
Written**

1. Find the retailer's selling price in each problem. The rate of markup is based on the selling price.

	Retailer's Cost	Rate of Markup on Selling Price	Retailer's Selling Price
a.	$93.06	45%	$169.20
b.	72.00	40%	120.00
c.	63.18	35%	97.20
d.	8.20	37½%	13.12

2. For how much must a dealer sell baseball gloves that cost $29 each if the dealer wants a markup of 42% on the selling price? $50

Selling price is the base.

3. Heather Lee bought bracelets from a wholesaler for $28.44 each. She wants to resell them at a gross profit of 40% of the selling price. At what price must she sell each bracelet to make this gross profit? $47.40

4. Trane Office Supply bought 200 boxes of computer paper for $5,850. At what price per box should the store sell the paper to gain 35% of the selling price? $45

5. Klein's Nursery bought pine trees at $480 per dozen, less 25% and 10%. At what price must each tree be sold to make a gross profit of 30% on the retail price? $38.57

6. A store bought 20 above-ground pools, each 15 feet in diameter and 4 feet deep, at $1,248.50 each. At what price must each pool be sold to gain 45% on the retail price? $2,270

Markup equals operating expenses plus net income.

‡Finding a Selling Price to Cover Your Operating Expenses and the Rate of Net Income You Want. Suppose you know your rate of operating expenses and the rate of net income you want, and both are based on the selling price. To find the selling price:

1. Add the percents for operating expenses and net income. The sum is the rate of markup.

2. Follow the steps shown in the **RB Computer Sales** example on the previous page.

‡Exercise 3 Written

1. Find the selling price in each problem. The operating expenses and net income are based on the selling price.

	Seller's Cost	Operating Expenses	Net Income Desired	Seller's Selling Price
a.	$ 60.45	26%	12%	$97.50
b.	125.19	25%	10%	192.60
c.	2.67	25%	15%	4.45
d.	103.60	36%	8%	185.00
e.	1,075.20	33%	11%	1,920.00

2. Ceiling fans cost a store $111 each. If the store's operating expenses are 30% of the sales, at what price must the fans be sold to make a net income of 10% on the selling price? $185

3. V-Mart buys lawn edgers at $38.35 each. If their overhead is 26% of sales, at what price must they sell each edger to make a net income of 9% of the selling price? $59

4. A car stereo is billed to a store at $195. The dealer pays salespeople a 5% commission on sales and estimates the rest of the operating

expenses at 25% of sales. At what price should the stereos be sold to gain a net income of 10% on the selling price? $325

5. A store owner estimates selling expenses at 14%, other operating expenses at 12%, and net income at 9%, all based on the selling price. At what price must an item costing $984.75 be sold to cover expenses and earn the net income the owner wants? $1,515

REVIEW 96

Skills

1. a. Find $3\frac{1}{4}\%$ of $440. $14.30
   b. 150 m² is what percent of 120 m²?   125%
   c. Show $74\frac{3}{8}$ as a decimal.   74.375
   d. $21\frac{7}{8}$ is what part greater than $12\frac{1}{2}$? $\frac{3}{4}$

Problems

2. You must buy sweaters for a line that retails for $59.95. What is the most you can afford to pay for this line if the markup must be 35% of the selling price? $38.97 [96]

3. a. Estimate the annual salary equal to a weekly salary of $288.
      $15,000
   b. A weekly salary of $288 is equal to how much per month?
      $1,248 [10]

4. Vi insured her factory complex for $2,800,000 with Zale Insurance Co., and for $1,200,000 with Filers Insurance Co. A fire loss of $12,400 occurred. How much should Vi collect from each company?
   Zale, $8,680; Filers, $3,720 [78]

5. On June 1, Fred's bank statement balance was $489.47 and his check register balance was $425.60. When he compared his statement and his register, he found a service charge of $5.22, earned interest of $1.78, and these outstanding checks: #35, $28.34; #37, $2.87; #38, $32.12; and #40, $3.98. Prepare a reconciliation statement.
   $422.16 [5]

‡6. A store owner pays $698.75 for a camcorder. At what price must it be sold to make a gross profit of 35% on the selling price?
   $1,075 [96]

‡7. An electric typewriter costs a retailer $147. Operating expenses average 30% of sales. At what price should the typewriter be sold to make a net income of 10% on the selling price? $245 [96]

Computer Clinic

Follow the steps on the next page to use a pricing template for Bella Medina, a buyer for Mackaw's Sports Centers. Mackaw's is a chain of sporting goods stores. Bella uses the template to find the cost and selling prices of the stock she buys for Mackaw's.

1. Insert your Spreadsheet Applications Diskette and call up the file "Sec96." After you do, your computer screen should look like Illustration 96–1.*

```
Sec96                        Selling Price = 100%

                              Cost      Selling
                              Price      Price
                             Missing    Missing

Selling Price in Dollars      0.00        .00
Selling Price in Percent      100         100
Markup in Dollars              .00        .00
Markup in Percent              0           0
Cost in Dollars                .00       0.00
Cost in Percent                0           0
```

Illustration 96–1. Using a Spreadsheet for Pricing

2. Bella needs to find the highest cost price she can pay for a line of weight benches that sell for $89.90. The company uses a markup of 40%, which is based on the selling price.

    Since Bella wants to find the cost price, use Column B, "Cost Price Missing." Notice that 100% has already been entered into Row 8, "Selling Price in Percent."

    Enter these data for Bella into the template: B7, 89.90; B10, 40. Your template should show that the highest cost Bella should pay is 53.94.

3. Use the template to complete or redo Exercise 1 of this section.

‡4. Bella also uses the template to find the price at which stock should be sold when she knows the cost and the markup the company wants. For these stock items, Bella uses Column C, "Selling Price Missing."

    Bella has just bought several two-person, inflatable boats for $32.40 each. She needs to find the selling price at which they should be sold to cover the cost and to give the company a 40% markup based on the selling price.

    Enter these data for Bella into the template: C10, 40; C11, 32.40. Notice that 100% has already been entered into the "Selling Price in Percent" cell. Your template should show that the company must charge at least $54 for the boats.

    Note that if you are using Appleworks Software, data must be entered into cells C10 and C11 in exact order for each problem to be solved.

‡5. Use the template to complete Exercise 2 of this section.

_____

*If you are using MicroTools, *selling price in percent* and *cost in percent* are both shown as 100% until data are entered. Then *selling price in percent* will be shown correctly as 100% and the appropriate *cost in percent* will be calculated.

Many businesses use the selling price as the base for the rate of markup or rate of gross profit. Others use the cost price as the base.

■ **Markup means the same as gross profit.**

Finding the Rate of Markup (Gross Profit) Based on the Cost. When the cost price is used as the base, you find the rate of markup by dividing the markup by the cost.

$$\text{Rate of Markup (Gross Profit)} = \frac{\text{Markup (Gross Profit)}}{\text{Cost}}$$

The term "cost" means the total cost. Total cost is the invoice price, or cash price, plus buying expenses.

**Exercise 1
Written**

1. Find the markup and the rate of markup based on cost for each item.

Item	Cost	Selling Price	Markup	Rate of Markup on Cost
a.	$ 15.00	$ 25.00	$ 10.00	$66\frac{2}{3}\%$
b.	315.00	525.00	210.00	$66\frac{2}{3}\%$
c.	77.25	101.97	24.72	32%
d.	112.80	155.10	42.30	$37\frac{1}{2}\%$

2. A wholesaler buys car air filters for $1.20 and sells them for $1.74. What is the rate of markup based on cost?   45%

**Exercise 2
Written**

1. Find the markup, rate of markup on cost, and the rate of markup on selling price for each item.

Item	Cost	Selling Price	Markup	Rate of Markup On Cost	Rate of Markup On Selling Price
a.	$ 72.00	$ 90.00	$ 18.00	25%	20%
b.	150.00	225.00	75.00	50%	$33\frac{1}{3}\%$
c.	720.00	864.00	144.00	20%	$16\frac{2}{3}\%$
d.	110.25	147.00	36.75	$33\frac{1}{3}\%$	25%

2. A store bought 20 luggage sets for $150 and sold them for $250.
   a. The markup was what percent of the cost? $66\frac{2}{3}\%$
   b. The markup was what percent of the selling price?   40%

3. The wholesale price of a sewing machine is $360. A retailer buys one at the catalog price, less $33\frac{1}{3}\%$ and 10%, and sells it at the catalog price. The gain is what percent of the cost? $66\frac{2}{3}\%$

Finding the Selling Price You Need to Give You the Rate of Markup You Want on the Cost. When the rate of markup is based on the cost, you find the selling price in two steps:

1. Find the amount of the markup. Since the rate of markup is based on the cost, you find the amount of markup by multiplying the cost by the rate.

Rate of Markup × Cost = Markup

2. Find the selling price by adding the markup to the cost.

Cost + Markup = Selling Price

Example

A dealer buys toasters for $5. The dealer uses a markup of 60% of the cost to cover expenses and gain the net income wanted. What is the lowest price at which the toasters can be sold and still earn the rate of markup wanted?

Solution

1. 60% of $5 = 0.60 × $5 = $3, markup
2. cost $5
   markup $3
   selling price $8 **Ans.**

   Check: 100% of cost = cost
              + 60% of cost = markup

              160% of cost = selling price
              160% of $5   = $8 selling price

**Exercise 3
Written**

1. A buyer paid $157.50 for goods and $17.25 for delivery charges. What is the lowest price at which the goods may be sold if a 48% markup, based on cost, is wanted? $258.63

2. A boating store buys boat trailers at $348, less 25% and 10%, plus a shipping charge of $25 on each trailer. At what price should the trailers be marked to gain 40% on the cost? $363.86

3. A farm store is billed $230 each for water pumps, less $37\frac{1}{2}\%$ and 20%, plus a delivery charge of $38. What should be the selling price of the pumps if the store wants a markup of 50% on the cost? $229.50

4. A produce store buys 60 crates of berries (12 baskets to a crate) at $15.50 per crate, delivered. The baskets without the berries weigh $\frac{1}{2}$ ounce each. The store estimates that 24 baskets will spoil and must be thrown away. At what price per basket, to the nearest cent, must the rest be sold to make a markup of 40% on the cost of the 60 crates? $1.87

REVIEW 97

Skills

Problems

1. a. Find the due date of a 45-day note dated March 6.   April 20
    b. What amount is $215\frac{1}{2}$% greater than $8? $17.24
    c. The exact interest at 16% on $700 for 3 months is? $28

2. Radios that cost $34 sold for $54.40. The gross profit was what percent of the cost?   60% [97]

3. You mark goods 55% above the total cost. At what price should you mark a 5-inch TV set that cost you $59 plus shipping charges of $10? $106.95 [97]

4. On July 3, a store buys 50 sunglasses at $5.95 each, less 20% and 5%; terms, 2/10, n/30. [89, 90]
    a. Estimate the cost of the sunglasses *before* any discounts are taken. $300
    b. For what amount should the store write a check to pay for the sunglasses on July 12? $221.58

5. Toddle Office Equipment Co. can buy 20 computers from a local dealer for $1,290 each, less 35% and 10%. An out-of-town dealer sells the same 20 computers for $1,210 each, less 40%. If Toddle buys from the out-of-town firm, $165.88 shipping charges on the lot must be paid. [89]
    a. Which offer is better?   Out-of-town dealer
    b. How much will be saved by taking the better offer? $407.12

6. What single discount is equivalent to 20%, 15%, and 10%?   38.8% [89]

‡7. A dealer needs a gross profit of 42% on the selling price to cover expenses and make enough net income. At what price must the dealer sell an item costing $61.48 to make the markup wanted? $106 [96]

Section 98
Special Pricing Problems

‡**Finding a Rate of Markup Based on Cost That Is Equivalent to a Rate Based on Selling Price.** Suppose that you know a rate of markup based on selling price and you want to find the equivalent rate of markup based on cost. You can find the equivalent rate in two steps:

1. Show the markup and the cost as percents of the selling price.

2. Divide the markup percent by the cost percent, then show the result as a percent.

Example

What rate of markup, based on the cost, is equivalent to a markup of 20% on the selling price?

Solution

1. 100% of selling price = selling price
    − 20% of selling price = markup
    ────────────────────────────────
     80% of selling price = cost

2. Equivalent rate of markup on cost = $\dfrac{markup}{cost}$ = $\dfrac{20\%}{80\%}$ = $\dfrac{1}{4}$ = 25% **Ans.**

For the same amount of markup, the rate of markup based on selling price is always lower than the rate of markup based on cost.

‡Exercise 1
Written

1. For each item, find the rate of markup, based on cost, that is equivalent to the rate of markup based on selling price. Round your answers to the nearest tenth of a percent.

Item	Markup on Selling Price	Markup on Cost	Item	Markup on Selling Price	Markup on Cost
a.	50%	100.0%	d.	45%	81.8%
b.	30%	42.9%	e.	40%	66.7%
c.	15%	17.6%	f.	36%	56.3%

2. To make a gross profit of 55% of the selling price, an item should be marked up what percent of the cost?   122.2%

3. What percent of the cost should an item be marked up to yield 27% markup on the selling price?   37%

4. What rate of markup on cost is equivalent to a markup of $37\frac{1}{2}\%$ on the selling price?   60%

‡Finding the Cost Price When the Selling Price and the Rate of Markup on Cost Are Known.
Suppose that you know the selling price and the rate of markup on cost you need on an item. What you need to find out is the highest cost price you can pay for it. To find the cost price, follow these two steps:

1. Show the selling price as a percent of cost.

2. Divide the selling price by that percent.

Example

A nursery owner has to buy trees for a line that sells for $35. The owner knows that the markup must be 65% of the cost to cover expenses and get the net income that is wanted. What is the highest price that the owner can pay for the trees?

Solution

$$100\% \times cost = cost$$
$$+ \ 65\% \times cost = markup$$
$$\overline{165\% \times cost = selling\ price = \$35}$$
$$cost = \$35 \div 165\%$$
$$= \$35 \div 1.65 = \$21.212 = \$21.21 \quad \textbf{Ans.}$$

Check: $21.21 + 65% of $21.21 = $21.21 + $13.79 = $35

‡Exercise 2
Written

1. In each problem, find the highest price the business can pay and still earn the rate of markup wanted.

	Selling Price	Rate of Markup on Cost	Highest Cost Price
a.	$ 53.80	45%	$37.10
b.	3.85	55%	2.48
c.	134.60	60%	84.13
d.	80.00	70%	47.06
e.	258.90	52%	170.33
f.	15.70	63%	9.63

2. As the buyer for Martin's Clothing Store, you have to buy slacks for a line that sells for $59.98. What is the highest price you can pay for this line if the markup must be 60% of the cost? $37.49

3. A store sells a line of boots at $125 a pair. At what price must the store buy them if its markup on this line is 58% of the cost? $79.11

4. What does an item cost a wholesaler if it is sold for $178.50 and gains 70% on the cost? $105

5. What is the most that a distributor should pay per dozen for 4-liter cans of paint that retail for $16.89 each, if the distributor must make 50% markup on the cost? $135.12

REVIEW 98

Skills

1. a. Subtract: $6\frac{4}{5}$ from $21\frac{3}{4}$ $14\frac{19}{20}$
   b. Estimate the interest on $1,850 at 11% for 6 months. $100
   c. Find the exact interest on $1,850 at 11% for 6 months. $101.75
   d. Find the due date of a 120-day note dated May 4.   September 1
   e. What amount increased by $\frac{1}{8}$ of itself equals $15.75? $14

Problems

2. A gain of 34% on the selling price is equal to what percent gain on the cost, to the nearest tenth of a percent?   51.5% [98]

3. What is the highest price that should be paid for coffee makers that retail at $39 if the store wants to make a profit of 40% on the cost? $27.86 [98]

4. A swing set is billed to a dealer at $124, less 25%. The dealer's operating expenses are 30% of sales. At what price must the dealer sell the swing set to make a net income of 8% on the selling price? $150 [96]

5. Rental income from an apartment building is $115,200 a year. Annual expenses are estimated at $110,400. What is the most you can invest in the property and net 8% on your investment? $60,000 [62]

‡6. By paying an invoice in time to get a 3% cash discount, Julie had to pay only $355.99. What was the amount of the invoice? $367 [91]

‡7. A retailer saved $48.75 by taking a cash discount of 3%. What was the amount of the invoice? $1,625 [91]

‡8. Stock with a par value of $100 pays an annual dividend of 4%. How many shares of this stock must an investor buy to have an annual income of $4,800?   1,200 [59]

‡Computer Clinic

Follow the steps below to use an equivalent markup template for Harold Cobb, a store manager for Allied Merchandising Corporation. Harold uses the template to find the rate of markup on cost that is equivalent to a rate of markup based on the selling price.

1. Insert your Spreadsheet Applications Diskette and call up the file "Sec98." After you do, your computer screen should look like Illustration 98–1.

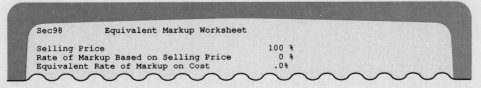

```
Sec98              Equivalent Markup Worksheet

Selling Price                                  100 %
Rate of Markup Based on Selling Price            0 %
Equivalent Rate of Markup on Cost               .0%
```

Illustration 98–1. Using a Spreadsheet to Find Equivalent Markups

2. Harold wishes to find the markup based on an item that costs $350, which is equivalent to a 37% markup based on the selling

price of the item. Harold rounds off the equivalent markup to the nearest tenth of a percent.

To find the equivalent markup, enter these data into the template: B4, 37. The answer, 58.7%, should appear in cell B5.

3. Use the spreadsheet to complete or redo Exercise 1 in this section.

Manufacturing and Office Costs

In this unit you will learn how to solve some of the problems of manufacturers, including figuring costs and expenses, finding break-even points for manufactured goods, figuring shipping costs, and figuring depreciation. You will also learn how to solve business problems concerned with office and computing costs.

After you have finished Unit 16, you will be able to:

* Figure total factory costs.
* Distribute factory expenses to departments by several methods.
* Figure manufacturer's gross and net income.
* Calculate the break-even point.
* Figure cost, sales income, or selling price needed to break even.
* Depreciate property by declining-balance method, sum-of-the-years digits method, and modified accelerated cost recovery system.
* Find total, average, and unit costs of office equipment, supplies, space, and labor.
* Find cost of purchasing, installing, and leasing computer systems.
* Find cost of purchasing and developing computer programs.
* Find cost of computer storage.
* Solve problems that contain more information than you need.
* Estimate answers to problems.
* Read, write, say, and recognize the meanings of key terms.
* Use a computer spreadsheet to compare depreciation methods and to find payroll costs.

Manufacturers make the products they sell. They must keep records of their factory costs so they can control costs and quote selling prices that will produce a net income instead of a net loss.

Kinds of Factory Costs. There are three kinds of factory costs:

1. **Raw materials costs** are the costs of materials that are used in manufacturing and become part of the finished product.

2. **Direct labor costs** are the wages of all the workers who work directly on the products as they go through the factory.

3. **Factory expense** includes the salaries or wages of the factory managers, supervisors, inspectors, and other workers who do not work directly on the manufactured products. It also includes building rent, depreciation of equipment, heat, light, power, insurance, and factory supplies. Factory expense is sometimes called *factory overhead.*

■ **Raw materials plus direct labor plus factory expense equals total factory costs.**

The sum of the costs of raw materials, direct labor, and factory expense is the **total factory cost.**

For example, the costs of manufacturing 1,000 telephone sets are $10,000 for raw materials, $30,000 for direct labor, and $5,000 for factory expense. The total factory cost is $45,000:

Raw materials	**$10,000**
Direct labor	**30,000**
Factory expense	**5,000**
Total factory cost	**$45,000**

**Exercise 1
Written**

1. The records of a leather factory show these costs for the goods produced in the first quarter of a year: raw materials, $316,780; direct labor, $376,300; factory expense, $175,390. What was the total factory cost of the goods produced during the quarter? $868,470

2. In April of last year, the manufacturing costs of Fairmont Products Company were: raw materials, $264,963; direct labor, $378,208; factory expense, $78,672. What was the total factory cost? $721,843

3. A factory owned by Mirafeed Corporation had this overhead for July: supervisory wages, $108,342; rent, $7,278; depreciation, $23,207; power, $7,725; maintenance and repairs, $12,465; other, $3,674. What was the total factory overhead? $162,691

4. The factory records of Kargill Enterprises show these costs for last quarter: raw materials, $478,392.70; direct labor, $610,729.20; supervisory salaries and wages, $56,388.80; rent, $25,825; depreciation and repairs, $31,103.76; power, $15,281.50; factory supplies, $16,950.40; other factory expense, $6,204.86.

a. What was the total factory overhead for the quarter?
    $151,754.32

b. What was the total factory cost? $1,240,876.22

5. To make 150 radios, Techland Manufacturing Co. had these manu-
    facturing costs: materials, $1,282.29; labor, $1,975.26; factory ex-
    pense, $1,234.31. What was the average factory cost of each radio, to
    the nearest whole cent? $29.95

6. For 1 month, Alper Paper Products had these manufacturing costs:
    raw materials, $391,444; direct labor, $1,027,044; overhead, $303,759.
    In that month, Alper manufactured 12,000 units of their product.
    a. Estimate the total factory costs for the company. $1,700,000
    b. What was the average cost per unit, to the nearest cent? $143.52

Distributing Factory Expense. Manufacturers need to know the costs
of running each unit or department. So, factory expense is often distributed or charged to each department. The way it is distributed varies
with the company and the kind of expense. Rent, for example, may be
distributed in proportion to the floor space used by the departments.

Example

Shamrock Company's factory pays monthly rent of $20,000. What amount
should be charged to each of its 3 departments? Department A has 2,000 sq. ft.
of floor space; Department B, 5,000 sq. ft.; and Department C, 3,000 sq. ft.

Solution

2,000 + 5,000 + 3,000 = 10,000 sq. ft. total floor space

Department A: $\frac{2,000}{10,000}$ or $\frac{1}{5}$ of $20,000 = $ 4,000

Department B: $\frac{5,000}{10,000}$ or $\frac{1}{2}$ of $20,000 = $10,000

Department C: $\frac{3,000}{10,000}$ or $\frac{3}{10}$ of $20,000 = $\underline{$ 6,000}$

$20,000

Taxes and insurance on equipment are often distributed on the basis of
the value of the equipment in each department. Other kinds of expenses may be charged in several ways. For example, cleaning expenses
may be distributed on the basis of floor space. Management salaries may
be distributed based on the number of factory workers in a department.

**Exercise 2
Written**

1. The 4 departments of Tensor Electronics, Inc., use this floor space:

    Printers, 3,000 square feet $6,750
    Copiers, 2,000 square feet $4,500
    Assembly, 1,800 square feet $4,050
    Finishing, 1,200 square feet $2,700

The annual maintenance cost of the building is $18,000. It is distributed on the basis of the floor space of each department. How much should each department be charged annually?

2. Nestor, Inc., pays its managers $400,000 a year. This expense is charged to the departments on the basis of the number of workers in each department. The number of workers is:

Department A, 108 $180,000   Department C, 12 $20,000
Department B, 36 $60,000   Department D, 84 $140,000

What amount should be charged to each department?

3. A company uses electric power costing $4,500, which is distributed on the basis of the number of horsepower hours of the equipment in each department. This is found by multiplying the horsepower of each motor by the number of hours it is used. The horsepower hours of each department are:

Department X, 3,000 $900   Department Z, 7,500 $2,250
Department Y, 4,500 $1,350

Find the amount to be charged to each department.

4. The annual sales of EVR, Inc., are $143,000,000. The cost of EVR's insurance on its manufacturing equipment is $2,890, which is 27% of the total insurance costs of the company. The equipment insurance cost is distributed in proportion to the value of the equipment in each department. Those values are:

Department G, $36,125 $722.50
Department K, $21,675 $433.50
Department R, $86,700 $1,734

How much insurance should be charged to each department?

REVIEW 99

Terms

1. Match the terms with the statements.

direct labor cost   raw materials cost
factory expense   total factory cost

a. Cost of materials in finished product   raw materials cost
b. Wages of production workers   direct labor cost
c. Sum of labor, materials, expenses   total factory cost
d. Nonproduction wages, rent, depreciation, heat, light, power
   factory expense

Skills

2. a. $81.20 \div 140\% = ?$ $58
   b. Divide: 10 by $\frac{2}{5}$ 25
   c. Change 60% to a fraction and simplify. $\frac{3}{5}$
   d. 275 cm + 4 m + 720 cm = ? m   13.95 m

Problems

3. To make 300 book covers, the costs were: materials, $3,589.12; labor, $6,128.43; factory overhead, $721.31. What was the average cost of each cover, to the nearest cent? $34.80 [99]

4. Four departments of a factory use this floor space: A, 5,600 sq. ft.; B, 2,400 sq. ft.; C, 4,800 sq. ft.; D, 3,200 sq. ft. The annual rent of the building, $180,000, is distributed on the basis of floor space. How much should be charged to each department?
A, $63,000; B, $27,000; C, $54,000; D, $36,000 [99]

5. Lester Williams bought a car for $12,900 and drove it 15,000 miles in the first year. His expenses that year were: depreciation, 20% of the cost of the car; interest at 12% of the cost of the car; gas, oil, insurance, and other expenses, $1,860. Find the operating cost of the car per mile, to the nearest tenth of a cent.   39.9 cents [66]

6. What single rate of discount is equivalent to the series 20%, $12\frac{1}{2}$%, and 5%? $33\frac{1}{2}$% [89]

Section 100
Finding the Break-Even Point

To stay in business, a manufacturer must produce and sell products for a price that will cover all manufacturing costs and other expenses, and still yield a reasonable net income.

Figuring Gross Profit and Net Income. A manufacturer finds the gross profit on an item by subtracting total factory cost from the selling price.

Selling Price − Total Factory Cost = Gross Profit

Besides the total factory cost, a manufacturer has expenses for salespeople, advertising, office salaries, and other general operating costs. These expenses, called **selling and administrative expenses,** are subtracted from gross profit to find net income.

Gross Profit − Selling and Administrative Expenses = Net Income

Selling and administrative expenses are often shown as a percent of net sales or selling price.

Exercise 1
Written

1. An axle that a manufacturer sells for $88.75 has these manufacturing costs: materials, $19.50; labor, $25.90; factory expense, $8.15. What is the manufacturer's gross profit on each axle? $35.20

2. A manufacturer sells ceiling fans for $47.25. The manufacturing costs are: material, $12.19; labor, $17.71; factory overhead, $5.48. Selling and administrative expenses are figured at 12% of the selling price. What is the manufacturer's net income? $6.20

3. The costs to manufacture an electric motor are these: material, $6.74; labor, $15.25; factory expenses, $3.36. The selling and administrative expenses average 15% of the selling price, which is $39. What is the rate of net income, based on the selling price?   20%

4. Calico, Inc., filled an order for 5,000 party mugs at $1.50 each. The company's manufacturing costs were: materials, $1,849; labor, $3,062; factory overhead, $825. Selling and administrative costs were estimated at 12% of the net sales.
    a. Estimate the company's total factory costs. $6,000
    b. What was the company's net income from this sale? $864

5. A factory makes 3½-inch diskettes that sell for $7.60 a box. There are 10 diskettes in a box. For an order for 1,000 boxes, the factory had these costs: materials, $1,750; labor, $2,800; factory expense, 25% of the total material and labor cost. Selling and administrative costs were estimated at 15% of net sales.
    a. What was the net income on the order? $772.50
    b. What was the rate of net income on net sales to the nearest tenth of a percent?   10.2%

Figuring a Break-Even Point. Manufacturing firms must decide how many units to produce, how much to spend to produce and sell these units, how many units they can expect to sell, and at what price they must sell the units to make the profit they want.

To make these decisions, these firms often calculate or estimate the break-even point. The **break-even point** is the point at which income from sales equals the total cost of producing and selling goods. It is the point at which the business will make no profit or suffer a loss.

To find the break-even point, fixed costs and variable costs are considered. **Fixed costs** are costs such as rent, salaries, heat, insurance, advertising, and other overhead items that remain the same no matter how much is produced and sold. **Variable costs** are costs such as raw materials, direct labor, and energy that vary or change with the amount of goods produced and sold.

For example, Faber Company plans to produce 1,000 units of a new picture frame that will be sold at $10 per unit. Producing 1,000 frames will cost an estimated $12,000 in fixed costs and $28,000 in variable costs. Faber's break-even point is the sum of $12,000 and $28,000, or $40,000. That is, if Faber's sales income from the new product is $40,000, they will "break even." They will make no profit and have no loss.

So, to break even, Faber must sell 4,000 frames at $10 each. (4,000 × $10 = $40,000). If Faber sells more than 4,000 frames, they will make a profit. (See Illustration 100–1.)

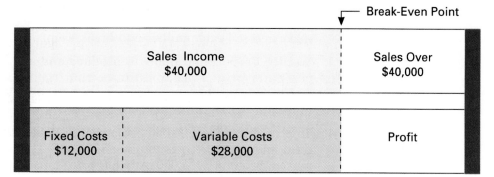

Illustration 100–1. Faber Company's Break-Even Point

Exercise 2
Written

1. Barrin, Inc., manufactured 5,000 football helmets. Their fixed costs of production were $105,000 and their variable costs were $195,000. What was the break-even point at which Barrin's sales income would equal their total cost of production? $300,000

2. To make 200,000 toy trucks, Babyco Corporation's variable costs were $800,000 and their fixed costs were $200,000.
   a. What sales income must Babyco earn from these trucks to break even? $1,000,000
   b. How many trucks must be sold at $20 each to break even? 50,000

3. When planning the production of a new line of chairs, Oramac, Inc., estimated variable costs of $360,000 and fixed costs of $140,000. How many chairs must be sold at $62.50 each for Oramac to break even?   8,000

4. Valley Products makes 10,000 walnut bowls at a total cost of $29,500. The company will sell the bowls to wholesalers at $5 each.
   a. How many bowls must be sold at $5 to break even?   5,900
   b. What will Valley's net income be if all 10,000 bowls sell for $5 each? $20,500
   c. How much will Valley lose if only 4,000 bowls sell for $5 each? $9,500

5. A game company produced and sold 3,000 video games at $10. Their fixed costs were $3 and their variable costs were $5 per game.
   a. What was the total production cost? $24,000
   b. How many games did they have to sell to break even?   2,400
   c. What was the net income from this operation? $6,000

6. Marcor, Inc., plans to make 20,000 wallets that will sell for $4.25 each. The firm estimates that the fixed costs for this operation will be $60,000. What is the maximum amount of variable costs the firm can have and still break even? $25,000

Exercise 3
Written

1. Producing and selling 30,000 pairs of denim jeans will cost a manufacturer a total of $270,000.
   a. What must be the sales income from this operation for the manufacturer to break even? $270,000
   b. At what unit price must each pair be sold to break even? $9

2. Colbert, Inc., plans to make and sell 5,000 mufflers at an estimated total cost of $60,000. What is the minimum price at which they can make and sell each muffler and break even? $12

3. Wordex Corporation plans to produce and sell 50,000 units of a computer printer. They estimate that their fixed costs will be $7,500,000 and their variable costs, $9,800,000. What must be the minimum selling price per unit for Wordex to break even? $346

4. To produce and sell 20,000 books, Sci-Fi Publishers, Inc., will have fixed and variable costs totaling $250,000. The publisher wants to make a profit of $125,000. At what price must the books be sold to break even and make the desired profit? $18.75

5. Hullins, Inc., can produce and sell 30,000 fishing reels at a total cost of $288,000. Hullins wants to make a net profit of 25% on cost. If all units produced can be sold, what
   a. Is the break-even price at which each reel must be sold? $9.60
   b. Selling price per reel is needed to make the net profit wanted? $12

REVIEW 100

Terms

1. Match the terms with the statements.

   break-even point   selling and administrative expenses
   fixed costs   variable costs

   a. Income from sales equals total costs   break-even point
   b. General operating costs   selling and administrative expenses
   c. Remain the same no matter how much is produced   fixed costs
   d. Change with amount produced   variable costs

Skills

2. a. $82 \times 21\frac{1}{2} = ?$ 1,763
   b. $\$4.85 \times 1,000 = ?$ $4,850
   c. Find the due date of a 35-day note dated April 2.   May 7

Problems

3. The costs of manufacturing 400 VCR's were: materials, $11,970; labor, $12,560; factory expense, $5,910. The VCR's were sold at $121.50 each. Selling and administrative expenses were estimated at 40% of total factory cost. What percent of the sales was the net income, to the nearest whole percent?   12% [100]

4. To make a personal computer, a factory has fixed costs of $3,600,000 and variable costs of $10,800,000. How many computers must be sold at $900 to break even?   16,000 [100]

5. Tollen charges a $2,890 yearly equipment insurance premium to each of its departments based on the value of each department's equipment. The Painting Department's equipment is valued at $245,000. If all of Tollen's equipment is valued at $1,750,000, how much should the Painting Department be charged for insurance? $404.60 [99]

6. Chen went bankrupt and owed these creditors: Lehr, $14,000; Rodriguez, $12,000; Amani, $18,000; Kawalski, $31,000. The cash

distributed to the creditors was $24,000. How much money did Amani get? $5,760 [86]

7. You bought a car for $7,500. After using it for 4 years, you bought a new car for $12,000 by trading in the old car and paying $8,900 in cash. What was the average annual depreciation of the old car? $1,100 [65]

8. A retailer buys ring binders at $56 a dozen and sells them for $7 each. What percent of markup is made on the selling price? $33\frac{1}{3}$% [95]

9. On May 5, Sheila discounts at 12% banker's interest a 4-month, non-interest-bearing note for $3,400. Find the proceeds of the note. $3,264 [47]

Section 101
Depreciation Costs

The depreciation of assets that have a life of more than one year is a major expense for business firms. Depreciation may be figured several ways.

Ways to Figure Depreciation. You have already learned how to figure depreciation on cars using the *straight-line method*. In that method, the amount of depreciation is the same for each year.

For example, let's say that you bought a car for $8,500 and planned to keep it five years. You estimated its trade-in value to be $2,500 five years later. The average annual depreciation would be:

$8,500 original cost of car
−2,500 trade-in value

$6,000 total depreciation

$6,000 divided by 5 = $1,200 average annual depreciation

Cars usually lose much more value in the first year than in the fifth year. Office and factory equipment, like cars, usually depreciates more during the early years of use than during later years. Because of this, some businesses use depreciation methods that deduct greater amounts in the early years than in later years. Two of these methods are the declining-balance method and the sum-of-the-years-digits method.

 Original cost minus total depreciation equals book value.

When figuring depreciation, the term **book value** is used. Book value is the original cost of the asset less the total depreciation to date. For example, if a machine that cost $280,000 has been depreciated $40,000, its book value, or present value, is $240,000. ($280,000 − $40,000 = $240,000.)

The Declining-Balance Method. The **declining-balance method** uses a fixed rate of depreciation for each year. Because the rate is applied to a declining or decreasing balance, the amount of depreciation decreases each year.

Example

A truck costing $15,000 is estimated to depreciate 20% each year. What is the estimated book value of the truck at the end of the first and second years?

Solution

0.20 × $15,000 = $3,000	depreciation first year
$15,000 − $3,000 = $12,000	book value at end of first year
0.20 × $12,000 = $2,400	depreciation second year
$12,000 − $2,400 = $9,600	book value at end of second year **Ans.**

Use the declining-balance method to solve these problems.

**Exercise 1
Written**

1. Copy and complete the table below.

	Property	Original Cost	Rate of Depreciation	Book Value End of First Year	Book Value End of Third Year
a.	Drill	$1,500	7%	$1,395	$1,206.54
b.	Press	8,500	8%	7,820	6,618.85
c.	Painter	4,000	9%	3,640	3,014.28
d.	Tools	3,800	12%	3,344	2,589.59
e.	Lift	7,000	14%	6,020	4,452.39
f.	Roller	6,500	15%	5,525	3,991.81

You are using a fixed rate on a declining balance.

2. A machine .hat cost $20,000 decreases in value each year at the rate of 10%. What is the book value of the machine at the end of the fourth year? $13,122

3. Tuxton Foundry buys a press for $5,000. The estimated life is 12 years and the annual depreciation is 8%. How much does the company expect the press to be worth at the end of 6 years? $3,031.77

4. Elsah Box Company buys a splicer for $4,800. The company plans to depreciate the splicer at 20% per year for 4 years and then sell it for scrap.
    a. Estimate the first year's depreciation. $1,000
    b. What do they expect the scrap value will be? $1,966.08

The Sum-of-the-Years-Digits Method. Another way to figure depreciation is the **sum-of-the-years-digits method.** This is a variable-rate method. Like the declining-balance method, the sum-of-the-years-digits method provides the greatest amount of depreciation in the first year and smaller amounts of depreciation after that.

For example, if you estimate that you will use a machine for five years, the amount of depreciation is figured this way:

1. Add the years together: $1 + 2 + 3 + 4 + 5 = 15$ years.

2. Then, depreciate the machine:
   $\frac{5}{15}$ of the total depreciation for the first year.
   $\frac{4}{15}$ of the total depreciation for the second year.
   $\frac{3}{15}$ for the third year.
   $\frac{2}{15}$ for the fourth year.
   $\frac{1}{15}$ for the fifth year.

Example

A machine costing $10,000 is expected to be used for 5 years, then it will be traded in for $4,000. What is the book value of the machine at the end of the second year?

Solution

$10,000	original cost	Sum-of-the-years-digits
− 4,000	trade-in-value	$1 + 2 + 3 + 4 + 5 = 15$
$6,000	total depreciation	

$\frac{5}{15} \times \$6,000 = \$2,000$ depreciation, end of first year
$\$10,000 − \$2,000 = \$8,000$ book value, end of first year
$\frac{4}{15} \times \$6,000 = \$1,600$ depreciation, end of second year
$\$8,000 − \$1,600 = \$6,400$ book value, end of second year   **Ans.**

**Exercise 2
Written**

Use the sum-of-the-years-digits method for these problems.

1. Garmen Products bought a hydraulic winch for $31,700. They plan to use the winch for 6 years and then trade it for $6,500. What will be the book value of the winch at the end of the second year?
   $18,500

2. Diaz Bros. bought a loading machine for $40,000. The firm estimates that the loader will be used for 9 years and then be traded in for $5,000. What will be the book value of the loader at the end of the first and third years?   (1) $33,000; (3) $21,333.34

3. Sheng, Inc., bought a forming machine for $66,500. The company plans to use the machine for 10 years and then sell it. The company estimates the resale value will be $13,500. Find the depreciation for each of the first 3 years.
   (1) $9,636.36; (2) $8,672.73; (3) $7,709.09

4. Tone Fabricators bought 5 items of equipment, weighing 14 metric tons, for $420,000. The company plans to use the equipment for 16 hours daily for 15 years and then scrap it for no value.

a. What will be the book value of the equipment at the end of 3 years of depreciation? $273,000
b. What will be the total depreciation allowed in 3 years? $147,000

‡**The Modified Accelerated Cost Recovery System (MACRS).** For federal income tax purposes, the **modified accelerated cost recovery system (MACRS)** must be used to figure depreciation for most property placed in service after 1986. The MACRS method allows you to claim depreciation over a fixed number of years depending on the class life of the property. The *class life* means how long the Internal Revenue Service (IRS) will let you depreciate the property.

The lives of different types of property are classified into 3, 5, 7, 10, 15, 20, 27.5, or 31.5 years by the Internal Revenue Service (IRS). For example, the IRS puts most office equipment and cars into a 5-year class life.

The rate of depreciation to be used for each year of a property's life is set by the IRS and varies with each class life.

You figure the depreciation deduction for any one year by multiplying the original cost by the rate of depreciation for that year. Trade-in value, or salvage value, is not used in the MACRS method.

The table of depreciation rates for a property with a 5-year class life, bought in the middle of the first year and used until the middle of the sixth year, is shown in Illustration 101–1.

Last Half of First Year	20.0%
Second Year	32.0%
Third Year	19.2%
Fourth Year	11.5%
Fifth Year	11.5%
First Half of Sixth Year	5.8%
Total	100.0%

Illustration 101–1. Table of MACRS Rates for 5-Year Property

For example, Anna Velez bought a new business car for $9,000 on July 1. The car has a 5-year class life. For income tax purposes, Anna can claim these amounts of depreciation on the car:

Last Half of First Year	$0.20 \times \$9,000 =$	**$1,800**
Second Year	$0.32 \times 9,000 =$	**2,880**
Third Year	$0.192 \times 9,000 =$	**1,728**
Fourth Year	$0.115 \times 9,000 =$	**1,035**
Fifth Year	$0.115 \times 9,000 =$	**1,035**
First Half of Sixth Year	$0.058 \times 9,000 =$	**522**
Total Depreciation		**$9,000**

Use the schedule of depreciation in Illustration 101–1 for these problems.

1. Burton Concrete Company paid $4,200 for a laser printer that had a class life of 5 years. They bought the printer on July 5.
   a. What amount of depreciation was allowed on the machine for each year? $840; $1,344; $806.40; $483; $483
   b. What was the book value of the machine at the end of its life? $0.00

2. A machine, bought on July 10, costs $45,000 and has a 5-year class life for MACRS depreciation.
   a. What total depreciation is allowable for the first year's use? $9,000
   b. What is the book value of the machine after the first year? $36,000

3. An asset, bought in July, cost $100,000 and has a 5-year recovery life under MACRS.
   a. What is the total amount of depreciation allowed for the life of the asset? $100,000
   b. What is the book value of the asset after the first year's use? $80,000

REVIEW 101

Terms

1. Match the terms with the statements.

MACRS	declining-balance method
book value	sum-of-the-years-digits method

   a. Depreciation at a fixed rate on a decreasing balance
      declining-balance method
   b. The original cost of property less total depreciation to date
      book value
   c. Figuring depreciation based on the class life of a property
      MACRS
   d. Uses a variable rate which gives decreasing depreciation amounts
      sum-of-the-years-digits method

Skills

2. a. Multiply: $4\frac{1}{2}$ by $3\frac{1}{2}$ $15\frac{3}{4}$
   b. Find exact interest on $600 at 14% for 6 months. $42
   c. Show $\frac{3}{8}$ as a decimal to the nearest hundredth.   0.38
   d. Divide: 534.12 by 100   5.3412

Problems

3. A car costing $12,500 is expected to depreciate 20% per year. Using the declining-balance method of depreciation, what is the estimated book value of the car at the end of the third year? $6,400 [101]

4. Spector, Inc., buys a machine for $12,000. They plan to use it for 5 years and then sell it for $2,500. If they use the sum-of-the-years-digits method of depreciation, what will the book value of the machine be at the end of 2 years? $6,300 [101]

‡5. A machine costing $350,000 has a 5-year class life under MACRS. Use the schedule of depreciation shown in Illustration 101–1 to find the

a. Total depreciation allowed after 3 years' use of the machine $249,200

b. Book value after 3 years' use $100,800 [101]

6. Verdant Products is planning a new line of garden hoses. They estimate that to make 1,000 hoses, fixed costs will be $34,000 and variable costs, $56,000. How many of the hoses must be sold at $20 to break even?   4,500 [100]

7. Two business partners, Earl and Dolly, share profits in the ratio of 3 to 2, respectively. What percent of the profits does Earl get? 60% [16]

8. For the first 5 months of the year, Eiko's monthly sales were $23,890, $21,060, $18,400, $19,780, and $20,700. What must be the sales for the sixth month so that the monthly average for the 6 months will be $22,000? $28,170 [10]

Section 102
Office Costs

An office work station is a place where a worker completes office work.

Office costs result from the use of equipment, supplies, employee time, and space to perform office work. Since office costs reduce profits, they must be watched closely. To do this, you can examine the costs of office work and of office work stations.

Illustration 102–1. Costs of an Office Work Station Include Labor, Equipment, and Supplies

The Cost of Equipment, Supplies, and Labor. *Office equipment* is office furniture and machinery that will last a year or more. For example, a typewriter, word processor, computer, or desk usually lasts more than a year and is treated as office equipment. The cost of office equipment is usually spread out over its useful life. This cost is called depreciation.

Office supplies are items that will not last long or will be used up quickly. For example, computer paper and paper clips are office supplies.

Labor is the largest cost in most offices. The cost of office wages and salaries may be as much as 70% or more of total office costs. The cost of office labor includes more than just the salaries and wages of workers. Total labor cost includes the cost of paid vacations, sick leave, health and life insurance, retirement benefits, and other employee fringe benefits.

**Exercise 1
Written**

1. Word processing paper costs $5.75 per ream (500 sheets). When bought in a case of 10 reams, the same paper costs $42 per case.
   a. What is the cost per ream when buying a case? $4.20
   b. What is the savings per ream when buying a case? $1.55

2. Find the total cost of equipping a word processing secretary's work station with the following equipment.

1 desk	@ $259.75	1 letter tray	@ $	17.50
1 chair	@ 99.50	1 computer system	@	2,595.00
2 file cabinets	@ 187.50	1 calculator	@	59.00
1 supply cabinet	@ 119.95	1 telephone	@	89.85
1 lamp	@ 59.45	1 floor mat	@	29.95

   $3,704.95

3. Emily Weaver is paid $5.50 per hour. Vacation time, sick leave, retirement benefits, and other fringe benefits add another 18% to her total wages. If she is paid for 2,000 hours of work during 1 year,
   a. How much is she paid in straight wages for the year? $11,000
   b. What are her total wages for the year, including straight wages and fringe benefits? $12,980

4. When mailing 5,000 letters to customers, a mail clerk put 33 cents postage on each letter instead of the right amount, 30 cents.
   a. What amount of postage was wasted on this mailing? $150
   b. If the clerk was paid $4 per hour, how many hours of wages could have been paid by this wasted money? $37\frac{1}{2}$ hours

5. A business office uses felt pens that cost $4.50 a dozen. In 1 year, the office uses 120 dozen of those pens. A clerk in the office estimates that 20% fewer pens would be used in a year if better pens costing $5.25 per dozen were used. If this is correct, how much money would be saved per year by using the better pens? $36

6. A manager needed 20 copies of a 30-page report. The copy clerk ran 25 copies of the report so that they would have "extras." The cost of the copy paper was $6.20 per ream (500 sheets).
   a. What was the cost of the paper for the 25 copies? $9.30
   b. How much could have been saved by running only as many copies as were needed? $1.86

7. An office manager studied 15 office workers and found that, on average, each worker spent 1 hour of each 8-hour work day on coffee breaks, personal telephone calls, and other personal business. The average wage of the workers was $52 a day. What was the cost per day to the office of this nonworking time? $97.50

The Cost of Office Space. The cost of office space is a major office expense. The cost of office space may include the cost of renting, lighting, heating, cooling, insuring, cleaning, maintaining, and repairing the space used by the office. (See Illustration 102–2.)

If the office is owned instead of rented, the cost may include depreciation of the building, mortgage interest, and real estate taxes.

Illustration 102–2. Costs of Office Space

**Exercise 2
Written**

1. An office area of 4,500 square feet rents for $42,000 a year. Heating, cooling, lighting, and maintenance are estimated to cost $4,800 a year.
   a. What is the total yearly cost of this office space per square foot? $10.40
   b. If a clerk's work station is 64 square feet, how much does this work station cost per year? $665.60

2. An office in a large building has an area of 3,200 square feet. The office rents for $50,560 a year including heating, cooling, lighting, and maintenance.
   a. What is the annual cost of the office per square foot? $15.80
   b. What is the annual cost of a manager's work station that is 150 square feet in area? $2,370

3. An office manager wants to increase the number of work stations that can be put in a space 43 feet wide by 58 feet long. That space

now contains 6 rows of 10 work stations each. The manager wants to increase floor space by placing every 2 rows of desks together so that the aisle between them is eliminated.

a. How many aisles will be eliminated?   3

b. If the aisles are 3 feet wide, how much floor space, in square feet, is gained?   522 square feet

c. If 2 more rows of 10 work stations are added, by what percent has the manager increased the number of work stations in the same space? $33\frac{1}{3}\%$

d. If the office space rents for $12,420 per year, what is the annual rent per work station with the old arrangement? $207

e. What is the annual rent per work station with the new arrangement? $155.25

The Cost of a Unit of Office Work. Many owners or managers need to know the cost of one job, of a work station, or of a unit of work, such as a letter or report. These cost figures can be compared with similar costs inside and outside the business.

Exercise 3
Written

1. Last year an office spent these amounts on 3 work stations: salaries, $38,325; rent and utilities, $1,100; depreciation of equipment, $1,340; supplies, repairs, postage, and telephone, $4,320.
   a. Estimate the total amount spent on the 3 work stations. $46,000
   b. What was the average annual cost of each work station? $15,028.33

2. Ramon Fuentes works in a typing pool and produces 576 lines of type per day, on average.
   a. In 8 hours, how many lines per minute does he type?   1.2
   b. If he earns $5.40 an hour, what is the labor cost per line? 0.07\frac{1}{2}$

3. An office estimates that a filing clerk can sort and file 180 sales invoices per hour.
   a. How many invoices would the clerk file in a $7\frac{1}{2}$ hour day?   1,350
   b. At a wage rate of $4.50 per hour for the clerk, what does it cost to file each invoice? $2\frac{1}{2}$ cents

4. A computer office manager needs 5 data-entry stations. The cost of *each* station is as follows:

   Wages: 1,950 hours per year @ $5.80
   Fringe benefits: 25% of wages
   Space: 60 square feet @ $16.50 per square foot per year
   Data terminal rental: $50 per month
   Supplies: $275 per year
   Depreciation of other equipment: $1,200 per year

   What is the total yearly cost of the 5 stations? $86,012.50

5. An office manager found that these amounts were spent to produce and mail 100 first-class letters:

Dictator time	$278	Materials	$22
Stenographer time	288	Postage	28
Equipment and space	174	Other	94

What was the average cost per letter? $8.84

6. In a word-processing center, the cost of keying in each line of an original letter averages 13.5 cents. The pages produced in the center average 30 lines in length. What is the average cost per page? $4.05

7. Three workers in a word-processing center produced this number of lines in a week: Tom Komuro, 12,500; Emily Lowell, 11,600; Jose Cruz, 10,300. The total cost of running the center for the week was $1,651.20. How much did each line of type cost, to the nearest cent? 4.8 cents

8. An order center estimates that the costs of work stations for 10 order clerks and a supervisor last year were: wages and fringe benefits, $138,000; space, $8,590; utilities, $890; depreciation, $13,600; supplies, postage, and telephone, $17,098.
    a. What is the average cost of each work station? $16,198
    b. If the office was open 250 days last year, what was the cost of each station per day, to the nearest cent? $64.79
    c. If each clerk usually completed 130 orders each day, what was the cost of each order, to the nearest cent?   50 cents

REVIEW 102

Skills

1. a. Multiply: $16\frac{1}{8}$ by 24   387
    b. Divide: 0.048 by 0.008   6
    c. Show 4.078 as a percent.   407.8%
    d. Find the number of days from May 10 to August 8.   90
    e. Find exact interest on $400 at 15% for 3 months. $15

Problems

2. An office estimated that the costs of materials for 25 sets of a report were: 5 reams of $8\frac{1}{2}'' \times 11''$ copy paper @ $4.50; 25, 1-inch binders @ $4.25; 25 sets of dividers @ $2.45; 25, $2\frac{1}{2}$-inch labels @ 3 cents. What was the cost of the materials per report? $7.63 [102]

3. An insurance office pays a file clerk $5.25 an hour. The clerk can find and pull from the file 95 letters per hour. What would be the labor cost for the clerk to find and pull 3,515 letters? $194.25 [102]

4. Sarah can buy a VCR for $350 cash. On the installment plan, she must make a down payment of $50 and pay $27.25 for 12 months. How much more is the installment price than the cash price? $27 [50]

5. Three departments of a store use this floor space: Jewelry, 400 square feet; Household, 1,500 square feet; Paint, 600 square feet. Cooling costs are charged to departments on the basis of floor space. What should be each department's share of summer cooling costs of $1,200?   Jewelry, $192; Household, $720; Paint, $288 [99]

6. Stock paying quarterly dividends of $1.80 is bought for a total cost
    of $90 per share. What rate of income is earned on the investment?
    8% [58]

7. A building valued at $100,000 was insured for $60,000 under an
    80% coinsurance clause policy. A fire caused a loss of $12,800. How
    much did the insurance company pay? $9,600 [78]

8. Property worth $72,000 is assessed at 45% of its value. The tax
    rate is $52.122 per $1,000 of assessed value. What is the tax on the
    property? $1,688.75 [67]

Section 103
Payroll Costs

The cost of managers, supervisors, clerks, factory workers, and other
employees is often the largest cost of doing business for most firms.
The cost of employees, or payroll costs, includes salaries and wages,
unemployment taxes, social security taxes, and fringe benefits.

Payroll Register. Time cards are often used to show the hours worked
and the earnings of each worker. At the end of each week or other pay
period, data from workers' time cards are transferred to a payroll register. (See Illustration 103–1.)

Faraday Corporation   **Payroll Register**

For Week Ended _____ April 25, 19 – – _____   Date Paid _____ April 25, 19 – – _____

| No. | Name | No. of Allow. | Total Hours | | Rate per Hour | Total Earnings | Deductions | | | | | Net Pay |
			Regular	Overtime			FICA Tax	Fed. Income Tax	Insurance	Other	Total	
1	A. Faro	3	40	0	10.18	407.20	31.15	37.00	22.80	8.85	99.80	307.40
2	B. Garr	1	38	0	6.80	258.40	19.77	40.00	12.68	12.40	84.85	173.55
34	C. Endo	2	40	2	9.76	419.68	32.11	44.00	17.50	8.50	102.11	317.57
		Totals				12299.84	940.94	1371.33	600.44	337.17	3249.88	9049.96

Illustration 103–1. Payroll Register

A **payroll register** shows the total earnings, the deductions, and the net pay for each worker, as well as the totals for all workers. Some payroll registers also show the hours worked each day by each worker.

Exercise 1
Written

1. Copy and complete the payroll register for Miriam, Inc. Time and a half is paid for overtime. Use a FICA rate of 7.65%.

Miriam, Inc.   for the Week Ended June 8, 19--

| | No. of Allow-ances | Total Hours | | Rate per Hour | Total Earn-ings | Deductions | | | | Net Pay |
Employee		Reg.	Over-time			Fed. Inc. Tax	FICA Tax	Other	Total	
a. Sanchez	2	40	2	9.50	408.50	42.00	31.25	10.94	84.19	324.31
b. Tanaka	0	39	0	5.40	210.60	29.00	16.11	8.20	53.31	157.29
c. Unger	1	40	0	4.70	188.00	19.00	14.38	5.00	38.38	149.62
TOTALS					807.10	90.00	61.74	24.14	175.88	631.22

2. Copy and complete the payroll register for Wickham Corporation. Time and a half is paid for overtime. Use a FICA rate of 7.65%.

Wickham Corporation   for the Week Ended May 18, 19--

| | No. of Allow-ances | Total Hours | | Rate per Hour | Total Earn-ings | Deductions | | | | Net Pay |
Employee		Reg.	Over-time			Fed. Inc. Tax	FICA Tax	Hosp. Ins.	Total	
d. Barlow	0	40	0	3.75	150.00	20.00	11.48	00.00	31.48	118.52
e. Boski	0	39	0	5.60	218.40	29.00	16.71	00.00	45.71	172.69
f. Buell	1	40	2	4.80	206.40	22.00	15.79	8.90	46.69	159.71
TOTALS					574.80	71.00	43.98	8.90	123.88	450.92

3. Copy and complete the payroll record for Coastal Line Company. Figure overtime at time and a half. Use a FICA rate of 7.65% and a state income tax rate of 3%.

		Total Hours				Deductions					
Coastal Line Company for the Period Ended October 2, 19--											
Employee	No. of Allow-ances	Reg.	Over-time	Rate per Hour	Total Earn-ings	Fed. Inc. Tax	FICA Tax	State Inc. Tax	Other	Total	Net Pay
g. Carr	3	37½	0	7.36	276.00	17.00	21.11	8.28	15.50	61.89	214.11
h. Levin	4	40	6	9.95	487.55	42.00	37.30	14.63	21.80	115.73	371.82
i. Napoli	2	40	0	10.05	402.00	42.00	30.75	12.06	12.35	97.16	304.84
TOTALS					1,165.55	101.00	89.16	34.97	49.65	274.78	890.77

Employee Earnings Record. Businesses keep a payroll record for each worker. This record is called an **employee earnings record.** An example is shown in Illustration 103–2.

An employee earnings record shows the total earnings, deductions, and net pay of one worker as these amounts build up during the year. The record shows when a worker's total pay exceeds the FICA taxable amount so that the business knows when no more is to be deducted for the year. The record is used also to prepare tax forms for the federal and state governments and the worker.

Name Wynnette Dixon   **Social Security Number** 178-34-8979

Address 84 Herrin Road   **Number of Allowances** 2

City Peoria, IL 61609-8685   **Rate per Hour** 10.48

Department Accounting   **Time Card No.** 207

Week Ended	Gross Pay	Deductions					Net Pay	Total Accumulated Earnings
		With-holding Tax	FICA Tax	State Income Tax	Health Insurance	Total		
1/6	419.20	42.00	32.07	8.38	12.90	95.35	323.85	419.20
1/13	419.20	42.00	32.07	8.38	12.90	95.35	323.85	838.40
1/20	419.20	42.00	32.07	8.38	12.90	95.35	323.85	1,257.60
3/24	419.20	42.00	32.07	8.38	12.90	95.35	323.85	5,030.40
3/31	419.20	42.00	32.07	8.38	12.90	95.35	323.85	5,449.60
Totals First Quarter	5,449.60	546.00	416.91	108.94	167.70	1,239.55	4,210.05	

Illustration 103–2. Employee Earnings Record

**Exercise 2
Written**

1. Copy and complete the employee earnings record below. The employee has one withholding allowance. Use the FICA and income tax withholding tables in Illustrations 21–2 and 21–3 in Section 21.

| Week Ended | Gross Pay | Deductions | | | | | Net Pay | Total Accumulated Earnings |
		With-holding Tax	FICA Tax	State Income Tax	Health Insurance	Total		
1/4	334.60	36.00	25.60	5.02	8.18	74.80	259.80	334.60
1/11	334.60	36.00	25.60	5.02	8.18	74.80	259.80	669.20
1/18	334.60	36.00	25.60	5.02	8.18	74.80	259.80	1,003.80
1/25	334.60	36.00	25.60	5.02	8.18	74.80	259.80	1,338.40
2/1	334.60	36.00	25.60	5.02	8.18	74.80	259.80	1,673.00
2/8	334.60	36.00	25.60	5.02	8.18	74.80	259.80	2,007.60
2/15	334.60	36.00	25.60	5.02	8.18	74.80	259.80	2,342.20
2/22	334.60	36.00	25.60	5.02	8.18	74.80	259.80	2,676.80
3/1	334.60	36.00	25.60	5.02	8.18	74.80	259.80	3,011.40
3/8	334.60	36.00	25.60	5.02	8.18	74.80	259.80	3,346.00
3/15	334.60	36.00	25.60	5.02	8.18	74.80	259.80	3,680.60
3/22	334.60	36.00	25.60	5.02	8.18	74.80	259.80	4,015.20
3/29	334.60	36.00	25.60	5.02	8.18	74.80	259.80	4,349.80
Totals First Quarter	4,349.80	468.00	332.80	65.26	106.34	972.40	3,377.40	4,349.80

2. Prepare an employee earnings record for Alicia Edwards. Use a record with the rows and columns shown below. Start the record as of 1/3 and record a total of 13 weekly wage payments. Find the totals. Alicia earns $435 in gross pay each week. She has one withholding allowance. She pays state income taxes of 4% of her gross pay and $7.15 in health insurance each week. Use the FICA and federal income tax withholding tables in Illustrations 21–2 and 21–3 in Section 21.

| Week Ended | Gross Pay | Deductions | | | | | Net Pay | Total Accumulated Earnings |
		With-holding Tax	FICA Tax	State Income Tax	Health Insurance	Total		
1/3								
Totals First Quarter								

Payroll Taxes. Employers must pay a number of taxes to city, state, and federal agencies based on their payroll. For example, most employers must contribute to the social security system by matching their employees' FICA tax payments. The employer's FICA tax is usually paid quarterly.

Most employers also must pay taxes under the **Federal Unemployment Tax Act (FUTA).** This tax money is used to pay benefits to certain workers who are unemployed. The FUTA tax is figured by taking a percentage of each employee's annual wages up to a maximum amount. For example, the tax rate may be 6.2% of the first $7,000 of each employee's wages.

States also require an employer to make contributions to state unemployment programs. Almost all of the payments made by employers for state unemployment taxes may be deducted from the amount of FUTA tax they owe.

**Exercise 3
Written**

1. On March 31, Trymex Co. had a total gross payroll of $103,789.45. At a rate of 7.65%
   a. What is the company's share of FICA taxes? $7,939.89
   b. Including the employees' shares, what amount of FICA taxes does the company owe? $15,879.78

2. Last year, Intermart, Inc., employed 30 workers, all of whom received at least $7,000 in total wages. The FUTA tax rate was 6.2% on the first $7,000 of each employee's wages. What was the firm's FUTA tax? $13,020

3. Intermart, Inc., (see Problem 2) also had to pay state unemployment taxes of 3.7% on the first $7,000 of each employee's wages.
   a. Estimate the amount of state unemployment taxes due. $8,000
   b. What is the exact amount of state unemployment taxes due? $7,770
   c. If they are able to deduct 90% of the state unemployment taxes from their FUTA taxes, what is the net FUTA taxes they owe? $6,027

4. Last year Bryant Foods, Inc., employed 20 employees who all received at least $7,000 in wages. The total amount of wages paid by Bryant for the year was $520,000. Bryant must match the FICA taxes of 7.65% deducted from employee wages. It also must pay 6.2% of the first $7,000 of each employee's wages for federal unemployment taxes, and 3.7% of the same wages for state unemployment taxes. Bryant may deduct 90% of the state unemployment taxes due from the federal unemployment taxes due.
   a. What is Bryant's share of FICA taxes? $39,780
   b. What is Bryant's state unemployment tax liability? $5,180
   c. What is the net amount of Bryant's FUTA tax liability? $4,018
   d. What is Bryant's total share of payroll taxes? $48,978

REVIEW 103

Terms

1. Match the terms with the statements.

   employee earnings record   payroll register
   Federal Unemployment Tax Act

   a. Shows earnings, deductions, and net pay for all workers
      payroll register
   b. Shows earnings, deductions, and net pay for only 1 worker
      employee earnings record
   c. Pays benefits to unemployed workers
      Federal Unemployment Tax Act

Skills

2. a. Multiply: 1.2078 by 10; 100; 1,000   12.078; 120.78; 1,207.8
   b. Divide: 36.8 by 10; 100; 1,000   3.68; 0.368; 0.0368
   ‡c. 0.08 times ? equals $50.44. $630.50

Problems

3. A firm employs 446 workers for a 40-hour week and has a total weekly payroll of $178,500. How much FICA taxes must it pay to the federal government for both its employees and itself if the rate is 7.65%? $27,310.50 [103]

4. Naperville's tax rate is $4.633 per $100 of assessed value. Find the tax to be paid on property assessed at $24,000. $1,111.92 [67]

5. You insure your $72,000 house for 90% of its value. At a rate of 65 cents per $100, what is your annual premium? $421.20 [77]

6. Statler, Inc., had merchandise inventory on March 1 of $420,300. The inventory on April 1 was $400,600. During the month, they had purchased $135,000 of merchandise. What was the cost of merchandise sold for March? $154,700 [81]

‡7. A salesperson's rate of commission is 5% on the first $3,000 of sales per week, and 6% on sales over $3,000 a week. How much will have to be sold in a week for the salesperson to earn $450? $8,000 [28]

Computer Clinic

Follow the steps below to complete a payroll register for Martin-Allerton, Inc.

1. Insert your Spreadsheet Applications Diskette and call up the file "Sec103." After you do, your computer screen should look like Illustration 103–3.

Sec103				PAYROLL REGISTER SPREADSHEET						
No.Name	No. of Allow.	Reg. Hours	O.T. Hours	Hourly Rate	Total Earn.	FICA Tax	Fed. Inc.Tax	Other	Total	Net Pay
1 A. Orr	0	0	0	0.00	.00	.00	0.00	0.00	.00	.00
2 B. Pike	0	0	0	0.00	.00	.00	0.00	0.00	.00	.00
3 C. Quick	0	0	0	0.00	.00	.00	0.00	0.00	.00	.00
4 D. Ruiz	0	0	0	0.00	.00	.00	0.00	0.00	.00	.00
5 E. Saga	0	0	0	0.00	.00	.00	0.00	0.00	.00	.00
Totals					.00	.00		.00	.00	.00

Illustration 103–3. Using a Spreadsheet for a Payroll Register

2. Complete the payroll register by entering these data:

C5	1	D5	40	E5	0	F5	5.80	I5	27	J5	5.25
C6	0	D6	35	E6	0	F6	4.00	I6	18	J6	5.25
C7	2	D7	40	E7	3	F7	8.50	I7	38	J7	9.75
C8	3	D8	40	E8	2	F8	9.40	I8	37	J8	12.80
C9	1	D9	40	E9	0	F9	7.20	I9	34	J9	8.50

3. Answer the questions about your completed payroll register spreadsheet.
   a. Who received the largest amount of net pay for the week?
      D. Ruiz
   b. Who had the least federal income taxes withheld for the week?
      B. Pike
   c. What was the total net pay for the week? $1,136.55
   d. What was the total gross pay for the week? $1,442.45
   e. What was the total amount deducted for "Other" deductions?
      $41.55
   f. If every employee works 5 hours overtime, what is the total net pay for the firm for the week? $1,316.91
   g. If none of the employees works overtime, what is the total net pay for the firm for the week? $1,075.19

Section 104
Shipping Costs

A firm's shipping costs often include getting the merchandise delivered to its location and delivering goods sold to customers. Three common ways to ship goods are parcel post, express, and freight. Before deciding how to ship, you should consider the speed, distance, and size, weight, and shape of your shipment.

You must also think about other services that you may need, such as insurance, special handling, C.O.D. (collect on delivery), and door-to-door pickup and delivery. All of these services raise the cost of shipping goods.

Who Pays the Transportation Charges. The term **f.o.b.** means free on board. It is often used in price quotations by sellers to tell who will pay the transportation costs, if there are any.

For example, a seller in New York quotes a buyer in St. Louis a price, f.o.b. St. Louis. This means that the *seller* will pay the transportation charges to St. Louis, or that the goods will travel "free on board" to the buyer in St. Louis.

If the seller had quoted a price, f.o.b. New York, the *buyer* would have to pay the transportation costs from New York to St. Louis.

Exercise 1 Written

1. Argos Castings, Inc., a seller in Dover, quotes Barr Foundry in Bensonville a price of $379.85 on a casting, f.o.b. Bensonville. Transportation charges will be $37.80.
   a. Who must pay the transportation charges? Argos Castings
   b. What will be the total cost of the casting to Barr Foundry? $379.85

2. Sno-Town Motors in North Lavelle bought these items from King's Auto Supply Distributors in Carlyle:

   60 battery chargers @ $16.00
   120 battery cables @ $5.95
   120 batteries @ $25.80

   ■ Total cost = invoice price or cash price plus shipping costs

   The shipping charges for the goods sent f.o.b. Carlyle were $85.80. The invoice received by Sno-Town carried terms of 2/10, n/30 and was paid within the discount period.
   a. Did the buyer or the seller pay the shipping costs? Buyer
   b. What was the total cost of the order to Sno-Town? $4,760.40

3. D.B. Veers, Inc., of Seaville, bought 26 portable basketball backstops from Lori Sales, Inc., of Boston at $39 each, less 25% and 20%, f.o.b. Boston. Shipping charges from Boston to Seaville were $35.
   a. What was Veers' total cost of the 26 backstops? $643.40
   b. What was the average total cost per backstop? $24.75

4. Compuland Stores in Elliston ordered 1,000 boxes of $5\frac{1}{4}$-inch disks from Store-Ever Corporation in Moline at $6,000, less 25% and 20%, f.o.b. Moline. Store-Ever prepaid the shipping charges for the shipment, $10.96, and added that amount on the invoice.
   a. What was the total cost of the order? $3,610.96
   b. What was the average total cost of each box? $3.61

5. Jean Wormley can buy a running suit from 4 different manufacturers. She must pay transportation charges from each manufacturer. She makes this list of the costs of buying each manufacturer's product:

Manu-facturer	List Price of Suit	Trade Discounts	Invoice Price of Suit	Transpor-tation Charges	Total Cost of Suit
A	$70	5%	$66.50	$5.15	$71.65
B	80	10%, 10%	64.80	4.75	69.55
C	80	15%, 5%	64.60	6.25	70.85
D	90	20%, 5%	68.40	2.25	70.65

a. Find the invoice price and the total cost for each manufacturer.

b. Which manufacturer offers the lowest total cost?
   Manufacturer B

U. S. Parcel Post Service. **Parcel post** is another name for fourth class mail carried by the U.S. Postal Service. Packages will usually be accepted for delivery anywhere the mail goes.

Parcel post is often used for shipping small packages. Packages may be sent by parcel post if they weigh not more than 70 pounds and are not more than 108 inches in combined length and girth (distance around).

Girth is the measurement around a package at its thickest part. If a package is 30 inches long, 10 inches wide, and 4 inches deep, the girth is 10 + 4 + 10 + 4, or 28 inches. The combined length and girth is 30 + 28, or 58 inches.

Parcel post rates are based on weight and the distance the package is shipped. Distance is shown in zones. The table in Illustration 104–1

Weight, up to but not exceeding- (pounds)	Zones							
	Local	1 and 2	3	4	5	6	7	8
2	1.63	1.69	1.81	1.97	2.24	2.35	2.35	2.35
3	1.68	1.78	1.95	2.20	2.59	2.98	3.42	4.25
4	1.74	1.86	2.10	2.42	2.94	3.46	4.05	5.25
5	1.79	1.95	2.24	2.65	3.29	3.94	4.67	6.25
6	1.85	2.04	2.39	2.87	3.64	4.43	5.30	7.34
7	1.91	2.12	2.53	3.10	4.00	4.91	5.92	8.30
8	1.96	2.21	2.68	3.32	4.35	5.39	6.55	9.26
9	2.02	2.30	2.82	3.55	4.70	5.87	7.17	10.22
10	2.07	2.38	2.97	3.78	5.05	6.35	7.79	11.18
11	2.13	2.47	3.11	4.00	5.40	6.83	8.42	12.14
12	2.19	2.56	3.25	4.22	5.75	7.30	9.03	13.09
13	2.24	2.64	3.40	4.44	6.10	7.78	9.65	14.03
14	2.28	2.69	3.48	4.56	6.27	8.02	9.96	14.50
15	2.32	2.75	3.55	4.67	6.44	8.24	10.24	14.94

Illustration 104–1. Partial Table of Parcel Post Rates*

*Rates in effect when the text was prepared for publication.

shows rates to all zones for packages up to fifteen pounds. *A fraction of a pound counts as a full pound.*

A parcel post package may be insured against loss or damage. The sender pays an insurance fee based on the value of the item shipped. The fee schedule is shown in Illustration 104–2.

Schedule of Parcel Post Insurance Rates	
Coverage	Fee
$ 0.01 to $ 50.00	$0.70
50.01 to 100.00	1.50
100.01 to 150.00	1.90
150.01 to 200.00	2.20
200.01 to 300.00	3.15
300.01 to 400.00	4.30
400.01 to 500.00	5.00

Illustration 104–2. Partial Table of Insurance Fees*

Exercise 2
Oral

1. Which of the packages below may be sent by parcel post?

	Length	Width	Depth	Weight	
a.	23 inches	8 inches	14 inches	16 lb.	Yes
b.	50 inches	12 inches	7 inches	75 lb.	No
c.	30 inches	6 inches	8 inches	$42\frac{1}{2}$ lb.	Yes
d.	60 inches	15 inches	12 inches	50 lb.	No
e.	70 inches	12 inches	14 inches	65 lb.	No

2. Use the table in Illustration 104–1 to find the cost of sending each package by parcel post, without insurance.

	Weight	Destination			Weight	Destination	
a.	5 lb.	Zone 3	$2.24	e.	$6\frac{1}{4}$ lb.	Zone 5	$4
b.	10 lb.	Zone 8	$11.18	f.	$2\frac{1}{2}$ lb.	Local	$1.68
c.	14 lb.	Zone 1	$2.69	g.	3 lb. 4 oz.	Zone 6	$3.46
d.	7 lb.	Zone 7	$5.92	h.	12 lb. 3 oz.	Zone 4	$4.44

3. Use the table in Illustration 104–2 to find the cost of insuring parcels valued at:

a.	$75	$1.50	d.	$195.80	$2.20	g.	$19.89	$0.70
b.	$125	$1.90	e.	$308.99	$4.30	h.	$150	$1.90
c.	$28.75	$0.70	f.	$400	$4.30			

Exercise 3
Written

Use the tables in Illustrations 104–1 and 104–2 to solve the problems.

1. Juan Fuentes sent a 9 lb. package parcel post to a friend who lived in a town in Zone 6. Juan insured the package for $215. What was the cost of shipping the package? $9.02

---

*Rates in effect when the text was prepared for publication.

2. Embers Clothing Store sent a $5\frac{1}{2}$ lb. package to a customer in the same local parcel post zone as the store. The package was insured for $125. What was the cost of the shipment? $3.75

3. Thompson's Outlet, in Maryville, sent 4 packages to customers in Zone 2. Each package weighed 7 lb., 3 oz., had a length of 60 inches, and a girth of 40 inches. Each package was insured for $150. What was the total shipping cost? $16.44

Express Service. Express shipments may be made by airplane, truck, bus, or train. **Express** provides fast delivery of goods that are small and light in weight. Some things that cannot be mailed can be shipped by express. Also, high-value items may be shipped by express because greater amounts of insurance can be purchased than are available by parcel post.

Some express carriers, such as United Parcel Service or Federal Express, offer door-to-door pick up and delivery and C.O.D. service. Some carriers will provide special shipping service for pets, and some will make overnight deliveries to almost any place in the U.S.

Express charges are based on speed, weight, distance, size of package, nature of contents, and the special services used. Rates and services differ among the carriers and are changed often. For charges on a shipment, you should talk with the express agents.

Freight. **Freight** is used most often for shipping heavy, bulky goods. Freight shipments may be sent by airplane, truck, train, or ship. Charges are based on weight, distance, size, nature of the shipment, and special services used. Freight agents will give the rates for shipping specific goods.

**Exercise 4
Written**

1. Merlin Motors sent a motor weighing 120 pounds by express to a customer in Chicago. The express charge was $0.21 per pound plus a $2.50 package fee. What was the cost of shipping the motor?
$27.70

2. A department store ships 2 boxes of porcelain to Tallahassee. Each box weighs 30 pounds. The express rate is $2 per box plus $0.25 per pound. The store also insures each box for $500. Insurance costs are $0.35 per $100 of value. What is the cost of the shipment?
$22.50

3. The cost of shipping a package by parcel post is $7.80; by next-day air express, $62.40. What percent more does it cost to ship the box by next-day air express than by parcel post? 700%

4. An electronic part, worth $300, that was needed to repair a computer system was sent to El Paso by air express for same-day, door-to-door delivery. The air express charges were: basic charges, $45; pick up and delivery, $15.60; and insurance at $0.40 per $100 of value. What was the total shipping cost? $61.80

5. The freight rate to New Orleans on a certain type of goods is $23.88 per 100 pounds, or fraction of 100 pounds, of the weight of the total shipment. A freight customer wants to ship 12 crates weighing 95 pounds each and 9 cartons weighing 21 pounds each.
    a. Estimate the total weight of the shipment.   1,200 lb.
    b. Estimate the shipping charge. $240
    c. What is the exact shipping charge? $334.32

REVIEW 104

Terms

1. Match the terms with the statements.

    express   f.o.b.   freight   girth   parcel post

    a. Free on board   f.o.b.
    b. Fourth class mail   parcel post
    c. Delivery of heavy, bulky shipments   freight
    d. Fast shipping of light packages   express
    e. Distance around   girth

Skills

2. a. Multiply: 28 by $4\frac{1}{4}$ 119
    b. What amount is 140% greater than $34? $47.60
    c. Find the number of days from May 18 to October 5.   140
    ‡d. Show $0.09\frac{1}{4}$ as a fraction, simplified. $\frac{37}{400}$

Problems

3. A firm in Malta offers you goods for $1,000, less 20%, 10%, and 5%, f.o.b. your city. A Vesta firm offers similar goods at $1,000, less 25% and 20%, f.o.b. Vesta. The freight charges from Vesta to your city are $42.75. How much is saved by taking the less expensive offer? $41.25 [104]

4. You ship 8 packages by parcel post to Zone 5. Each package weighs 6 lbs. 7 oz. and is insured for $55. Using the tables in Illustrations 104–1 and 104–2, find the total cost of the shipment. $44 [104]

5. Last year a small business showed these figures on its income statement: Gross Sales, $260,000; Sales Returns and Allowances, $5,200; Merchandise Inventory, January 1, $84,326; Purchases, $158,500; Merchandise Inventory, December 31, $74,746; Operating Expenses, $68,800. What was the firm's net income or loss for the year?   Net income, $17,920 [82]

6. A computer that cost $2,800 is estimated to depreciate 20% each year using the declining-balance method. Find the expected value of the computer at the end of the fourth year. $1,146.88 [101]

Section 105
Computer Costs

The cost of computer systems has decreased rapidly over the last few years. However, the cost of these systems is still an important part of the operating expenses of many businesses.

Purchasing and Leasing Costs. There are two major costs when computer systems are purchased. First, there is the purchase price of the system and all its parts. (See Illustrations 105–1 and 105–2.) These parts, common to nearly every type of computer system, include:

1. The **central processing unit,** or brain of the computer.

2. **Storage devices,** such as disk and tape drives, that store computer programs and data.

Illustration 105–1. Large Computer System

3. **Input devices,** such as computer terminals with keyboards, that are used to enter data into the computer system.

4. **Output devices,** such as printers and terminals with display screens, that are used to get data out of the computer system.

5. **Software**, or a computer program, which is a set of instructions that tell the computer system what to do.

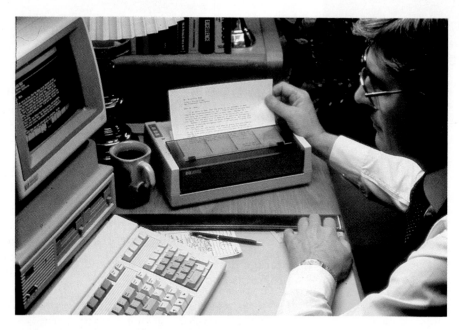

Illustration 105–2. Personal Computer System

Second, there is the cost of installing the computer system. On large computer systems, installation costs may include raised flooring, special electrical wiring, cables, air conditioning, and security systems. Even on small computer systems, special cables may be needed to connect computers to each other, and separate electrical outlets and wiring may be required.

Because large computer systems can be very costly to purchase, many firms lease them. Some firms even lease small computer systems because leasing lets them upgrade to new models easily.

**Exercise 1
Written**

1. The Accounting Department of Milo Manufacturing Co. just bought 20 personal computer systems. Each system has the following parts: central processing unit, $780; disk drives, $600; display screen, $180; keyboard, $75; printer, $300; software, $1,200.
   a. What was the cost of each system? $3,135
   b. What was the total cost of the systems to the department? $62,700

2. The Toy Works purchased a large computer system for $867,000. To install it, the firm paid $30,000 to renovate a large room used by the system. The firm also paid $3,500 for electrical wiring and outlets, $5,000 for additional air conditioning, and $6,300 for cables. What was the total cost to buy and install the system? $911,800

3. Maxell Bros. purchased a computer system. They paid $48,500 for the central processing unit, $5,400 for disk drives, $13,600 each for 2 printers, and $450 each for 10 computer terminals. They also had to install additional cables at $900 to connect the terminals to the system. What was the total cost to buy and install the system? $86,500

4. Kroben, Inc., leases a computer system. The lease costs per month are: central processing unit, $1,200; disk drives, $300; printers, 2 at $350 each; terminals, 15 at $40 each. What is the total yearly cost of leasing the computer system? $33,600

5. Daner, Inc., leases 10 large computer printers for $575 each per month.
   a. Estimate the annual cost of the printers to the firm. $72,000
   b. What is the annual cost of the printers to the firm? $69,000

Software Costs. Computer systems consist of **hardware**, such as terminals, disk drives, and printers, and software, or computer programs.

There are two basic types of computer programs: operating systems, which manage the computer hardware, and application programs. Application programs instruct the computer system to process your data the way you want it processed. Examples of application programs are payroll programs, word processing programs, spreadsheet programs, and computer games.

A firm can buy software in a store, or it can develop programs for its own needs. When a firm develops programs itself, it uses the skills of computer programmers. Large computer programs may be made up of thousands of lines of computer instructions, called "lines of code." A good programmer may produce from 20–40 fully tested and finished lines of computer code in one day.

Exercise 2
Written

1. The owner of a small accounting service firm buys software for her small computer system. She pays $75 for the operating system software, $895 for accounting software, $495 for spreadsheet software, and $375 for a word processing program. What is the total cost of the software? $1,840

2. Jamoco Industries buys software for 25 personal computer systems used by its managers. For each personal computer, it pays $50 for operating system software, $495 for word processing software, $420 for spreadsheet software, and $375 for other software.
   a. What is the software cost per system? $1,340
   b. What is the total cost of the software to Jamoco? $33,500

3. The Data Processing Department of Davis, Inc., assigned 3 programmers the job of developing an inventory management program. Each programmer was paid $15 an hour and spent 640 hours writing and testing the program. What was the cost of labor used to develop the program? $28,800

4. A programmer, paid $14 an hour, took 900 hours to develop a sales management program made up of 3,000 lines of computer instructions. What was the average labor cost per line? $4.20

5. The Data Processing Department of Avery Freight Company has been asked to develop a truck-tracking program. After a detailed study, they estimate that the program will require 2,400 lines of code. They also estimate that they will need to use 2 programmers and that each programmer will produce 25 lines of finished code a day. If the programmers are each paid $72 a day,

a. How many days will the project take? 48
b. What are the estimated labor costs of developing the truck-tracking program? $6,912

Computer Storage Costs. There are many different ways, or "media," on which data can be stored for computer systems. For example, there is internal storage, or storage that is part of the central processing unit. There is also external storage, or storage that is outside the central processing unit. External storage media include floppy disks, hard disks, and tapes. (See Illustration 105–3.) Unlike internal storage, external storage media can be removed from the computer system.

Illustration 105–3. Types of Computer Storage Media

The cost of computer storage is often measured in terms of the number of characters, or **bytes**, of data that can be stored. For example, a floppy disk may be able to store 360,000 characters, or bytes, of data (letters, numbers, and other characters).

People who use computers call 1,000 bytes of data 1 **kilobyte**, or 1 KB. They call 1,000,000 bytes of data 1 **megabyte**, or 1 MB.

**Exercise 3
Written**

■ 1,000 KB
equals 1 MB.

1. You can buy a box of floppy disks, containing 10 disks, for $14.76. Each disk can hold 360 KB of data. What is the cost, per kilobyte, to store data on a single diskette? $0.0041

2. A box of 10, $3\frac{1}{2}$-inch floppy disks, each able to hold 720 KB of data, sells for $25.20. A box of 10, high-density, $5\frac{1}{4}$-inch floppy disks, each able to hold 1.2 MB of data, sells for $36. What is the cost, per kilobyte, to store data on:
a. $3\frac{1}{2}$-inch disks? $0.0035
b. $5\frac{1}{4}$-inch, high-density disks? $0.003

3. A pack of hard disks, costing $320, can store 80 MB of data. What is the storage cost, per megabyte, for the pack of disks? $4

4. A 2,400 foot reel of computer tape, costing $14, can store 140 MB of data. What is the storage cost per megabyte for the reel? $0.10

REVIEW 105

Terms

1. Match the terms with the statements.

bytes   input devices   output devices
central processing unit   kilobyte   software
hardware   megabyte   storage devices

a. Computer equipment   hardware
b. The brain of the computer system   central processing unit
c. 1,000 bytes   kilobyte
d. Where computer programs and data are stored   storage devices
e. Used to put data into a computer system   input devices
f. Used to get data out of a computer system   output devices
g. 1,000,000 bytes   megabyte
h. Computer programs   software
i. Characters stored in a computer system   bytes

Skills

2. a. Subtract: $3\frac{3}{4}$ from $6\frac{1}{8}$ $2\frac{3}{8}$
    b. Multiply: 2.05 by 0.004   0.0082
    c. The number of days between March 30 and June 16 is?   78
    d. 75 m^2 is what percent of 60 m^2?   125%

Problems

3. National Machine Co. bought a computer system. They paid $25,800 for the central processing unit, $4,800 for disk drives, $2,600 for 1 printer and $5,480 for another, and $425 each for 15 computer terminals. They also had to pay $500 for extra wiring and $750 to install cables. What was the total cost of the system?
    $46,305 [105]

4. Computer programmers in a data processing department are paid $480 for a 5-day week and produce 20 lines of finished computer code each day. Using these programmers, what will it cost to develop a program that will have 5,000 lines of code? $24,000 [105]

5. Velma bought a house for $60,000, paying $15,000 down. She rented it out for $700 a month for 1 year. Expenses for the year were: mortgage interest, $5,400; insurance, $355; repairs, $695; taxes, $1,200. What was the yield on her investment?   5% [61]

6. The tax rate in Fenton is 14.5 mills per dollar of assessed value. Find the tax on property assessed at $50,000. $725 [67]

Business Statistics and Graphs

Newspapers, magazine articles, books, and business and government reports frequently use numeric data to make comparisons or to help explain an idea. These data are often shown in tables or graphs to make them more understandable.

Government agencies collect numeric data of all types and use mathematical methods to turn them into statistics. These statistics tell us what is happening to unemployment, the general state of the economy, and the prices we pay for goods and services.

Being able to read graphs and understand basic statistical terms is important to be an informed citizen and an employee in a world that uses numbers at an increasing rate.

After you finish Unit 17, you will be able to:

- Figure the mean, median, mode, and range of a group of numbers.
- Make a frequency distribution table.
- Solve problems using probability.
- Interpret and prepare bar, line, rectangle, and circle graphs of business data.
- Interpret graphs and tables of commonly used economic statistics.
- Read, write, say, and recognize the meanings of the key terms.

You figured simple and weighted averages in Unit 2 by finding the average pay of employees. In this section, you will study three types of averages called the mean, median, and mode. As a group, these averages are called **measures of central tendency.** This is a common term used by people who work with statistics.

Mean. The **mean** is the number you get by adding a group of numbers and dividing the sum by the number of items added. It is the same as a simple or weighted average. The mean is the best known measure of central tendency and the one used most frequently.

Example

During the third quarter, the Surnell Company made these profits: July, $38,000; August, $52,000; September, $33,000. Find the mean profit per month.

Solution

$38,000 + $52,000 + $33,000 = $123,000   total profit for quarter
$123,000 ÷ 3 = $41,000   the mean   **Ans.**

Median. The **median** is the middle number in a group of numbers that is arranged in either ascending or descending order. One-half of the numbers will be on either side of the median.

To find the median, arrange the numbers in order. If the group has an odd amount of numbers, the number in the middle is the median. If the group has an even amount of numbers, add the two middle numbers and divide by 2 to find the median.

Example

a. Find the median of this group of numbers: 12, 18, 17, 10, 15, 22, 13, 23, 9.

Solution

9   10   12   13| 15 |17   18   22   23

one-half   one-half
the numbers   the numbers

b. Find the median of this group of numbers: 7, 0, 1, 9, 5, 4, 6, 2.

Solution

Middle Numbers

0   1   2   4| |5   6   7   9

one-half   one-half
the numbers   the numbers

(4 + 5) ÷ 2 = 4.5   median   **Ans.**

Mode. The **mode** is the number that occurs most frequently in a group of numbers arranged in order. There may be more than one mode in a group of numbers.

Example

Find the mode of this group of numbers showing the ages of officers of a school club: 17, 15, 16, 17, 18, 17, 17, 14

Solution

Mode **Ans.**

14   15   16   17   17   17   17   18

Range. As you work with measures of central tendency, you may also be asked to find the range. The **range** is the difference between the highest and lowest numbers in a group of numbers. So, for the group of numbers in the previous example, the range is 4 (18 − 14 = 4).

**Exercise 1
Written**

1. For each group of numbers, find the mean, median, mode, and range.

Group of Numbers	Mean	Median	Mode	Range
a. 17, 12, 18, 22, 12, 11, 20	16	17	12	11
b. 2, 17, 15, 7, 2, 7, 9, 13	9	8	2, 7	15
c. 16, 25, 19, 29, 18, 25	22	22	25	13
d. 2, 17, 8, 10, 19, 23, 17, 21, 25, 7, 10, 20, 3	14	17	10, 17	23
e. 12, 6, 23, 43, 28, 19, 5, 22, 37, 17, 21, 30, 18, 6	20.5	20	6	38

2. During 1 year, the number of boots produced by the Hasgor Shoe Company for each quarter was: 18,000; 23,400; 45,600; 16,300. What was the mean number of boots produced in a quarter? 25,825

3. Workers at a small restaurant were paid these amounts per hour: $4; $4.25; $4.45; $4.25; $4; $4.40; $4.20; $4; $4.10. Find the median and mode of these hourly wages. $4.20, median; $4, mode

4. Apartments in a certain area rented for these monthly rates: $420; $410; $405; $435; $455; $425; $450; $410; $400; $350; $320; $420; $440; $425; $410; $450; $430.
    a. What were the mean, median, and mode of these apartment rental rates? $415, mean; $420, median; $410, mode
    b. What was the range of rental rates? $135

Frequency Distribution. When you work with larger groups of numbers, it becomes more difficult to arrange them in order by listing them as you have done. Making a **frequency distribution** is a way of arranging numbers into the order you want by using a table.

To make a frequency distribution table, list all the numbers in the group. Then *tally* each number by making a vertical mark next to the number every time it appears in the group of numbers. Make every fifth mark a diagonal mark to separate the marks into groups of five marks to make counting easier.

From the frequency distribution table, you can figure the mean, median, mode, and range.

Example

During a 17-day period, daily sales of electronic typewriters were: 28, 23, 20, 28, 28, 24, 29, 20, 28, 21, 24, 28, 20, 29, 28, 23, 24. Make a frequency distribution table. Then find the (a) mean, (b) median, (c) mode, and (d) range.

Frequency Distribution Table

Number	Tally	Frequency
20	///	3
21	/	1
23	//	2
24	///	3
28	ᵗᴴᴸ /	6
29	//	2
	Total	17

a. Finding the mean:

$20 \times 3 = 60$
$21 \times 1 = 21$
$23 \times 2 = 46$
$24 \times 3 = 72$
$28 \times 6 = 168$
$29 \times 2 = \underline{58}$
              425   Total

$425 \div 17 = 25$ mean **Ans.**

b. The median is the ninth number, or 24 **Ans.**
c. The mode is the most frequent number, or 28 **Ans.**
d. The range is 29 - 20 = 9 **Ans.**

Exercise 2 Written

For Problems 1–4, make a frequency distribution table. Then find the mean, median, mode, and range.

1. During a 10-day period, a school club sold these numbers of magazine subscriptions: 25, 22, 24, 26, 24, 22, 25, 22, 20, 20.
   Mean, 23; median, 23; mode, 22; range, 6

2. The numbers of pages per day entered by a word processing operator in a 2-week period were: 28, 19, 28, 21, 24, 26, 28, 17, 19, 20.
   Mean, 23; median, 22.5; mode, 28; range, 11

3. These numbers of surveys per hour were completed by a researcher during 2 days of interviews at a shopping mall: 15, 14, 11, 16, 18, 14, 17, 12, 9, 10, 12, 14, 16, 11, 17, 10.
   Mean, 13.5; median, 14; mode, 14; range 9

4. During a recent month, a shoe repair shop had these daily numbers of customers: 14, 21, 16, 18, 14, 20, 19, 20, 14, 27, 17, 22, 18, 14, 21, 14, 19, 20, 14, 27, 19, 12, 14.
   Mean, 18; median, 18; mode, 14; range, 15

5. During a year, the Mel-Tran Company bought 15,000 bolts at $0.016; 20,000 bolts at $0.0154; and 5,000 bolts at $0.018. Make a frequency distribution table. Then find the usual price paid per bolt, stated as the

   a. Mean $0.01595
   b. Median $0.0157
   c. Mode $0.0154

REVIEW 106

Terms

1. Match the terms with the statements.

    frequency distribution   median
    mean   mode
    measures of central tendency   range

    a. The middle number in a group   median
    b. Arranging numbers in order with a table
        frequency distribution
    c. Difference between highest and lowest numbers in a group
        range
    d. Sum of the numbers divided by the number of items   mean
    e. The number that occurs most frequently   mode
    f. Averages   measures of central tendency

Skills

2. a. Estimate the product of $23.99 × 12. $240
    b. Estimate the quotient of $5,100,000 ÷ 25. $200,000
    c. Round 0.1896 to the nearest hundredth.   0.19

Problems

3. For 6 days this week, the numbers of defective frying pans pro-
    duced by a factory were: 210, 225, 206, 214, 180, 225. Find the
    mean, median, and mode of defective frying pans.
    Mean, 210; Median, 212; Mode, 225 [106]

4. During a 6-week period, a truck was driven these numbers of miles
    weekly: 1,250; 1,469; 781; 960; 1,351; 1,076. [106]
    a. Shown as a mean, what average number of miles was the truck
        driven weekly, to the nearest mile?   1,148
    b. What was the range of weekly miles driven?   688

5. Laura Byrd has to buy office chairs for a line she sells for $150. She
    knows that her markup must be 45% of the selling price to cover
    selling expenses and provide the net income she wants. What is the
    highest price she can afford to pay for each chair? $82.50 [96]

6. A company produced and sold 7,000 gasoline cans at $5. For each
    can, the company's fixed costs were $1.20 and the variable costs
    were $2. [100]
    a. What was the total production cost? $22,400
    b. How many cans must be sold to break even?   4,480
    c. What net income was earned on this sale? $12,600

Probability is a way of mathematically predicting the chance that an event will occur. This section deals with the basic concepts of probability and how they may be used in everyday and business use.

Chance Events.
You have two marbles that are alike in every way except color. The marbles, one blue and one white, are placed in a bag. Suppose you are asked to pick one of the marbles from the bag without looking. You have no way of knowing which marble is blue and which marble is white. So, you have no way of picking one rather than the other. This will mean that the marble you pick will be a *random choice,* and the outcome will be a **chance event.**

Probability of a Chance Event.
With this bag of marbles, what are the chances that your outcome will be to pick the blue marble? Two outcomes are possible: (1) you pick the blue marble; or (2) you pick the white marble.

Since your pick is a random choice, one outcome is just as likely as the other. The chance that you will pick the blue marble is 1 out of 2, which may be shown as the fraction $\frac{1}{2}$. The probability of the event that you will pick the blue marble is $\frac{1}{2}$. You may also say that the probability is 0.50, or 50%.

Now, suppose that the bag holds 6 blue marbles, 3 white marbles, and 1 red marble, making a total of 10 marbles. Again, the marbles are alike except for color. What are the chances of your picking a blue marble? Since there are 6 blue marbles, there are 6 chances out of 10 that you will pick a blue marble. So the probability of the event that you will pick a blue marble is $\frac{6}{10}$, or $\frac{3}{5}$.

Since 4 of the marbles are not blue, there are 4 chances out of 10 that you will not pick a blue marble. So, the probability of your not picking a blue marble is $\frac{4}{10}$, or $\frac{2}{5}$. Stated formally, the probability of the event that you will not pick a blue marble is $\frac{4}{10}$, or $\frac{2}{5}$.

Certain or Impossible Events.
If a bag holds nothing but 5 yellow marbles, the chances of picking a yellow marble are 5 out of 5, which is $\frac{5}{5}$, or 1. In this case, picking a yellow marble is an event that is certain to happen, because no other outcome is possible. Any event that is certain has a probability of 1.

From a bag holding nothing but yellow marbles, the event that you will pick a white marble is an impossible outcome. The chances of picking a white marble are 0 out of 5, which is $\frac{0}{5}$, or 0. Any event that is impossible has a probability of 0.

Facts About Probability.
From these examples you can see that probability is a fraction that shows the chance that an event will happen. The numerator shows the number of ways the event can happen. The denominator shows the total number of possible outcomes.

The probability of an event can be 0, 1, or any fraction between 0 and 1. It can never be less than 0 or greater than 1.

Probability may be shown as a fraction, a decimal, or a percent.

Exercise 1
Oral

1. If a perfectly balanced coin is flipped and falls freely, it is as likely to turn up heads as tails. What is the probability of its turning up tails? $\frac{1}{2}$

2. A bag holds 3 plastic disks, 1 green, 1 red, and 1 yellow. If one disk is picked at random,
   a. What is the probability that it will be green? $\frac{1}{3}$
   b. What is the probability that it will not be green? $\frac{2}{3}$

3. A drawer holds 5 black socks and four blue socks. If you reach in and pick out one sock without looking,
   a. What is the probability that it will be black? $\frac{5}{9}$
   b. What is the probability that it will not be black? $\frac{4}{9}$
   c. What is the probability that it will be either black or blue? 1
   d. What is the probability that it will be white? 0

4. Forty balls, numbered from 1 to 40, are placed in a drum. What is the probability of your picking a ball that is
   a. Number 4? $\frac{1}{40}$
   b. Numbered with a 1, 11, 21, or 31? $\frac{1}{10}$
   c. Even numbered? $\frac{1}{2}$

5. A box of paper clips holds 20 red clips, 30 blue clips, and 50 yellow clips. One clip is picked at random. What is the probability that it will be
   a. Red? $\frac{1}{5}$
   b. Blue? $\frac{3}{10}$
   c. Green? 0
   d. Either blue or yellow? $\frac{4}{5}$
   e. What is the probability that the clip will not be blue? $\frac{7}{10}$

Probability and Large Numbers. The probability of an event occurring tells you about how many times you can expect the event to happen in a large number of tries.

For example, if a perfectly balanced coin is flipped, it is as likely to come up heads as it is tails. So, you can say that the probability of its coming up heads is $\frac{1}{2}$.

This does not mean that out of 40 slips you are sure to get 20 heads. You may get several more or several less than 20. What it does mean is if you flip the coin many times, say 1,000 times, the number of heads will not be far from $\frac{1}{2}$ of 1,000. The longer you keep flipping, the nearer the number of heads will come to $\frac{1}{2}$ the number of flips. This is called the *principle of large numbers.* It is one of the main concepts of probability. For a large number of tries of the same kind, you can predict the outcome with only a small amount of error.

**Exercise 2
Written**

1. The probability of an event is $\frac{1}{5}$. About how many times would the event happen in 6,000 tries?   1,200

2. Four cards, marked 1, 2, 3, and 4, are put into a hat.
   a. If one card is picked at random, what is the probability that the card picked will be the 4 card? $\frac{1}{4}$
   b. A card is picked and then put back into the hat. This is done 2,400 times. About how many times would the card picked be the 3 card?   600

3. The 6 faces of a small cube are marked 1, 2, 3, 4, 5, and 6. The cube is shaped perfectly. If you toss the cube, there is an equal chance that any one of the 6 numerals will show on top when it comes to rest. In 1 toss of the cube, how many different ways can the cube rest?   6

4. In one toss of the cube in Problem 3, what is the probability of tossing a
   a. 3? $\frac{1}{6}$ d. Numeral greater than a 2? $\frac{2}{3}$
   b. 7?   0   e. Numeral less than a 4? $\frac{1}{2}$
   c. Numeral less than 7?   1   f. Numeral that is not a 6? $\frac{5}{6}$

5. The cube in Problem 3 is tossed 7,200 times. How many times would you expect to toss a
   a. 4?   1,200   c. Numeral less than 4?   3,600
   b. 7?   0   d. Numeral greater than 1?   6,000

Probability Based on Experiment. In all of the examples so far, you could figure in advance the probability of the event from the description of the conditions. In many cases, this information may not be known, and the probability must be based on experiment or experience.

For example, if a coin is worn and out of balance, heads and tails are not equally likely to come up when the coin is flipped. The probabilities for this coin must be found by experiment. That is, we must flip the coin and record the results.

Let's suppose that you got 827 heads and 173 tails in 1,000 flips. If so, you can estimate the chances of a head as $\frac{827}{1000}$, or 0.827. The chances of tossing a tail are $\frac{173}{1000}$, or 0.173. For future flips of this coin, you can predict that about 82.7% will be heads and about 17.3% will be tails.

Factories often test a few samples of the products they make to see what percent are up to standard and what percent are not. If these samples are chosen by chance, they are called **random samples.** For example, suppose we tested 100 random samples of staplers produced in a factory and found that 3 were defective. This represents 3% of the 100 samples. On the basis of this test, you can determine that about 3% of the whole batch of staplers from which the samples were taken will be defective. In a batch of 500 of these staplers, the number of defective staplers will be about 3% of 500, or 15.

Probability Based on Experience. Life insurance companies use records of births and deaths to make mortality tables similar to the one shown in Illustration 107–1. The **mortality table** shows how many persons in a sample group of 100,000 live babies have reached certain ages. The numbers at each age have been rounded to the nearest thousand to make figuring easier.

Age	Number Living
0	100,000
10	98,000
20	97,000
30	96,000
40	94,000
50	90,000
60	82,000
70	65,000
80	39,000

Illustration 107–1. Sample Mortality Table

From the table, you can figure the probability that a person will reach a particular age. For example, the table shows that 94,000 of the sample of 100,000 people born reached the age of 40. So at birth, the probability of living to be 40 is 94,000 ÷ 100,000, or 94%.

Of the 94,000 who were living at age 40, the table shows that 82,000 were still living at age 60. So, the probability that a person who is 40 will live to be 60 is 82,000 ÷ 94,000, or 0.87 rounded to the nearest hundredth.

Exercise 3
Written

Use Illustration 107–1 to work Problems 3 and 4.

1. In a factory, 400 random samples of computer chips were tested. Twelve chips were defective. If 1,200 of these chips are made, how many will be defective?   36

2. During the last 365 days, a weather forecaster's predictions have been right 292 days. They have been wrong 73 days.
   a. What is the probability that the forecaster's prediction of tomorrow's weather will be right? $\frac{4}{5}$
   b. Over the next 30 days, about how many times would you expect the forecast to be right?   24 days

3. What is the probability that a person born today will
   a. Live to be 20?   0.97
   b. Not live to be 20?   0.03

4. To the nearest hundredth, what is the probability that a person 10 years old will live to be
   a. Age 50?   0.92   c. Age 70?   0.66
   b. Age 60?   0.84   d. Age 80?   0.40

REVIEW 107

Terms

1. Match the terms with the statements.

chance event   probability
mortality table   random samples

   a. A few items selected from the whole group by chance
      random samples
   b. The outcome of making a random choice   chance event
   c. A way of predicting the outcome of an event   probability
   d. Shows numbers of people living to certain ages
      mortality table

Skills

2. a. What is $\frac{1}{3}$ of 2,016?   672
   b. 4.2% of 5,000 = ?   210
   c. $45.78 + $332.98 − $189.00 + $23.81 − $1.56 = ? $212.01
   d. Write $\frac{62}{7}$ as a mixed number. $8\frac{6}{7}$
   e. What amount is 20% greater than $48? $57.60

Problems

3. In a group of people, 40 are 20 years old. Using Illustration 107–1,
   a. What is the probability, to the nearest hundredth, that a member of this group will live to be 60?   0.85 [107]
   b. About how many of the 20-year olds will reach age 60?
      34 [107]

4. For about 5 months, the Ekro Company kept track of the number of consecutive days their photocopier worked before it needed service. The days between service calls were: 15, 22, 19, 34, 40, 5, 12. What was the mean number of days between service calls?
21 [106]

5. A vacuum cleaner with a marked price of $160 was sold for $120. [94]
   a. What was the amount of discount? $40
   b. What was the rate of discount?   25%

Section 108
Bar and Line Graphs

Business firms use graphs frequently to show data about their companies or industries. Graph often show facts and trends more clearly than do numbers in tables. Graphs may be produced by hand or by computer programs that use data stored on disk files.

Vertical Bar Graphs. The **vertical bar graph** in Illustration 108–1, with bars running up and down, shows the daily sales of The Home Center for a week. There is one bar for each day, Monday through Saturday. The height of each bar shows the sales for each day. The scale for measuring the bars is on the left side of the graph.

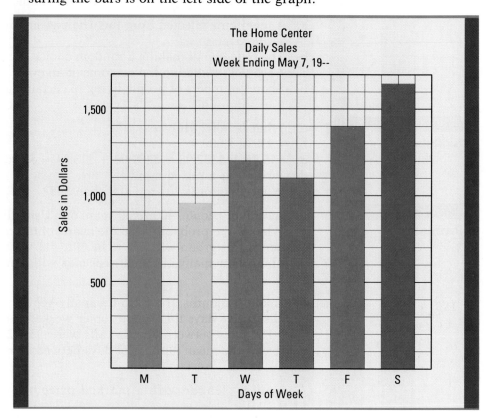

Illustration 108–1. Vertical Bar Graph

Each vertical block on the graph equals $100 of sales. The lines for $500 and multiples of $500 are labeled. The height of each bar is correct to the nearest $50. For example, sales for Monday were $842.20. That amount was rounded to the nearest $50, or $850. The top of the Monday bar was then put halfway between the $800 and $900 lines.

The heading of the graph shows the company name, identifies the data shown, and gives the time period that the graph represents.

Horizontal Bar Graphs. The **horizontal bar graph** in Illustration 108–2, with bars running left to right, shows the sales for four types of goods sold by The Home Center for the quarter ending June 30. It looks like the vertical bar graph except that the bars are horizontal.

Each horizontal block on the graph equals $2,000. The amounts for each bar were rounded to the nearest $1,000 before the graph was made. For example, sales of electrical goods totaled $27,890 but are shown as $28,000.

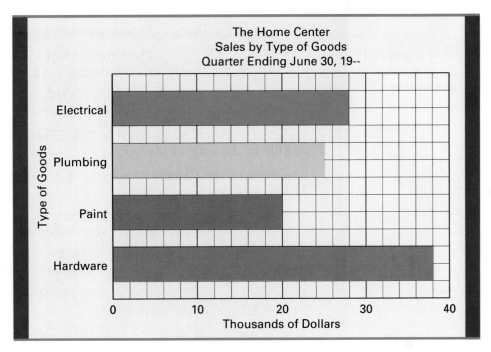

Illustration 108–2. Horizontal Bar Graph

1. The vertical bar graph in Illustration 108–1 shows the daily sales to the nearest $50. Use that graph to answer these questions:
    a. On which day were sales the largest? Saturday
    b. On which day were sales the smallest? Monday
    c. On which days did sales exceed $1,300? Friday, Saturday
    d. On which 2 days was the difference between sales the largest? Monday, Saturday

2. The horizontal bar graph in Illustration 108–2 shows the sales of the 4 types of goods sold by The Home Center for the quarter (April 1 through June 30). Use that graph to answer these questions.
    a. What was the approximate dollar amount of hardware sales during the quarter? $38,000
    b. Which type of good had the lowest sales during the quarter? Paint
    c. For which 2 types of goods were the sales most nearly the same during the quarter? Electrical, Plumbing
    d. How much greater were the sales of hardware than the sales of paint? $18,000

For these problems, use graph paper with 10 blocks, or squares, to the inch. Include a heading for each graph. In all graphs, make the bars 2 blocks wide; leave 2 blocks between bars.

1. Make a vertical bar graph showing these facts:

The Candle Shop
Daily Sales, February 7–12, 19--

Monday	$440	Wednesday	$380	Friday	$460
Tuesday	$340	Thursday	$360	Saturday	$480

Make each vertical block equal to $20 of sales. Label each multiple of $100 in the scale at the left.

2. The sales of the Camera Corner for 6 months are shown below. Make a vertical bar graph with these facts:

Camera Corner
Sales for July–December, 19--

July	$26,000	September	$28,000	November	$32,000
August	$18,000	October	$22,000	December	$46,000

Make each vertical block equal to $2,000 of sales. Label each multiple of $10,000 in the vertical scale.

3. Make a horizontal bar graph with these facts:

Do-It-Yourself Remodeling
Sales, November 16–21, 19--

Paneling	$2,600	Floor Tile	$1,100
Doors	$2,800	Sinks	$1,800
Ceramic Tile	$1,300	Cabinets	$2,200

Make each horizontal block equal to $100 of sales. Mark the scale at the bottom of the graph to show each multiple of $1,000.

4. Make a horizontal bar graph showing last year's sales in 6 selling areas of the Protect-All Company.

Home Alarms	$110,365.20	Locks	$ 58,358.70
Car Alarms	$125,720.10	Steel Doors	$101,395.19
Garage Door Openers	$ 96,359.22	Repairs	$116,682.44

Make each block on the horizontal scale equal to $2,000. Round each sales figure to the nearest $2,000 before entering it into the graph.

Line Graphs. The **line graph** in Illustration 108–3 shows the sales of The Home Center by months from January through December.

The time scale, that runs from left to right, is at the bottom of the graph. The dollar scale, that runs from bottom to top, is at the left.

The monthly sales were rounded to the nearest $1,000. The line was made by first placing dots showing each month's sales. The dots were then joined by drawing a line with a ruler.

To include other items on the same graph, such as operating expenses and net income, different kinds of lines could be used. For example, a solid line could be used for sales, a dotted line for operating expenses, and a dot-and-dash line for net income.

Lines of different colors could be used, also. For example, a red line could be used for sales, a yellow line for operating expenses, and a green line for net income.

Illustration 108–3. Line Graph

Exercise 3
Oral

1. Illustration 108–3 shows the monthly sales of The Home Center to the nearest $1,000. The sales for January were about $28,000; for February, about $22,000; and so on. Use the line graph to answer the questions.

    a. What were the approximate sales for each month from September through December? $36,000; $28,000; $30,000; $18,000
    b. In which month were sales the lowest?   December
    c. In which months did sales fall below $24,000?
        February, December
    d. In which months did sales exceed $35,000?   July, September
    e. Between which 2 consecutive months did sales increase the most? decrease the most?   March, April; November, December

2. In the following graph, sales are shown by a solid line (—), operating expenses by a dotted line (· · · ·), and net income by a dot-and-dash line (· — · —). Use the graph to answer these questions.

    a. In which month were operating expenses lowest?   October
    b. What were the highest operating expenses for a month?
        $12,000
    c. In what month was net income highest?   November
    d. How much was the lowest monthly net income? $2,000
    e. What was the difference between the highest and lowest monthly net income? $8,000

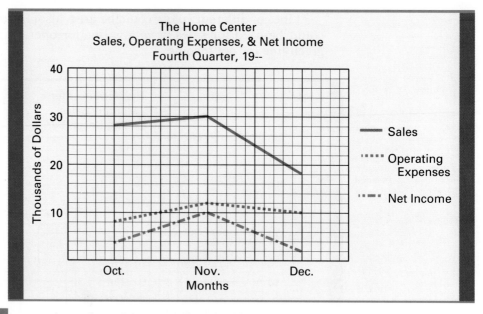

**Exercise 4
Written**

1. Show these facts on a line graph:

The Poster Shop
Sales for May 22–28, 19--

Sunday	$420	Wednesday	$230	Friday	$350
Monday	$270	Thursday	$320	Saturday	$460
Tuesday	$260				

Make each vertical block equal to $10 of sales. Use every fifth vertical line for the days.

2. The table below shows the number of service calls made by a cable company from January through June. Make a line graph.

Merlund Cable Company
6-month Summary of Service Calls

| January | 2,200 | March | 2,700 | May | 2,100 |
| February | 2,900 | April | 2,400 | June | 1,900 |

Make each vertical block equal to 100 calls. Use every fifth vertical line for the months.

3. The monthly sales of the Paper Place for the first 6 months of the last 2 years are shown below. Make a line graph showing the sales for each 6-month period. Show this year's sales with a red line and last year's sales with a black line. If you do not have a red pencil, use a solid line for this year's sales and a dotted line for last year's sales.

Month	This Year	Last Year
January	$68,391	$57,270
February	52,825	50,820
March	66,440	59,630

Month	This Year	Last Year
April	$58,830	$62,004
May	53,904	57,705
June	57,117	51,880

Make each vertical block equal to $2,000, and show each month's sales rounded to the nearest $1,000. Use every fifth vertical line for the months.

REVIEW 108

Terms

1. Match the terms with the statements.

    horizontal bar graph   line graph   vertical bar graph

    a. Bars are drawn up and down the graph   vertical bar graph
    b. Dots show data; lines connect dots   line graph
    c. Bars are drawn left to right on the graph   horizontal bar graph

Skills

2. a. $56 is what part greater than $48? $\frac{1}{6}$
    b. $266.60 is what percent less than $310?   14%
    c. 23.8 L + 1.85 L + 390 mL = ? L   26.04 L
    d. 104 m^2 ÷ 13 m = ? m   8 m

Problems

3. A vertical bar graph is drawn on graph paper that has 8 blocks to an inch. If each block is equal to $200, what is the greatest amount that can be marked on a graph that is 2 inches high? $3,200 [108]

4. Winslow Industries had net sales of $412,000 last month. It began the month with a merchandise inventory of $810,000, bought $285,000 of merchandise during the month, and had an inventory of $862,000 at the end of the month. [81]
    a. What was Winslow Industries' cost of merchandise sold? $233,000
    b. What was the gross profit? $179,000

5. A house valued at $60,000 was insured for $40,000. The policy had an 80% coinsurance clause. If a fire loss of $8,100 occurs, how much of the loss will the insurance company pay? $6,750 [78]

Section 109
Rectangle and Circle Graphs

Rectangle Graphs. A **rectangle graph** is a vertical or horizontal rectangle that is divided into sections. The entire rectangle stands for the whole. The sections stand for parts of the whole. A rectangle graph shows how the parts relate to each other and to the whole.

Each part of a rectangle graph is proportional in size to the whole. For example, suppose that a whole rectangle 5 inches long represents $1,000. To show a part equal to $400 you would mark off $\frac{2}{5}$, or two inches, of the rectangle. ($\frac{\$400}{\$1,000} = \frac{2}{5}$, $\frac{2}{5} \times 5$ inches = 2 inches.)

The values in rectangle graphs are often dollars or percents. In the vertical rectangle graph in Illustration 109–1, the whole rectangle represents the total sales, in dollars, of the Pillow Shop for last year. Parts of the rectangle, also shown in dollars, represent the cost of merchandise sold, operating expenses, and net income.

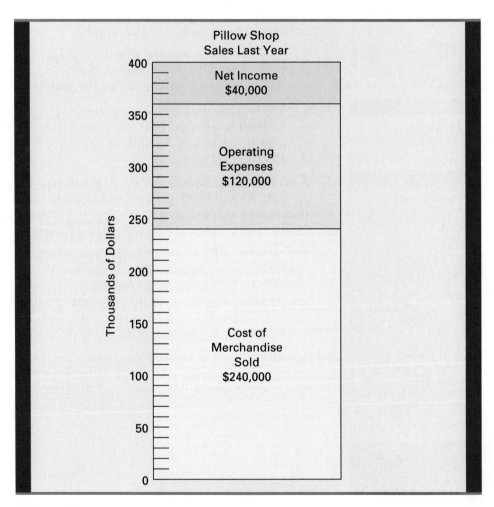

Illustration 109–1. Vertical Rectangle Graph

In the horizontal rectangle graph in Illustration 109–2, the whole rectangle stands for a dollar of sales, or 100% of a sales dollar. The parts of the rectangle stand for cost of merchandise sold, operating expenses, and net income. The parts are shown as percents of a dollar of sales.

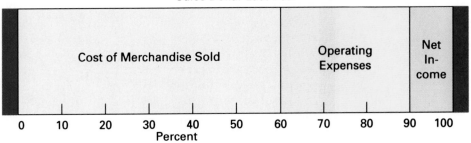

**Pillow Shop
Sales Dollar Last Year**

Illustration 109–2. Horizontal Rectangle Graph

1. In the vertical rectangle graph in Illustration 109–1,
    a. What were the total sales for the year? $400,000
    b. What was the gross profit for the year? $160,000
    c. What percent of sales was the gross profit? 40%
    d. What percent of sales was the net income? 10%

2. In the horizontal rectangle graph in Illustration 109–2,
    a. What percent of each dollar of sales was the cost of merchandise sold? 60%
    b. What percent of each sales dollar were the operating expenses? 30%
    c. Of each dollar of sales, how many cents were for net income? 10¢

For Problems 3 and 4, use graph paper with 10 blocks to the inch.

3. Make a vertical rectangle graph to show the facts below. The table shows the parts of Melron Furniture's sales dollar for last year.

Cost of Merchandise Sold	$0.58
Operating Expenses	0.28
Net Income	0.14
Sales	$1.00

    Make the rectangle an inch and a half wide. Make each vertical block equal to $0.02.

4. Make a horizontal rectangle graph to show these facts taken from the records of the XAC Company. Make each block equal to 2%.

Cost of Merchandise Sold	61%
Operating Expenses	30%
Net Income	9%
Sales	100%

Circle Graphs. A **circle graph** may also be used to show how parts relate to each other and to the whole. The full circle of 360 degrees (360°) is the whole, or 100%. The circle graph in Illustration 109–3 shows in percents the same facts that are shown in the horizontal rectangle graph in Illustration 109–2.

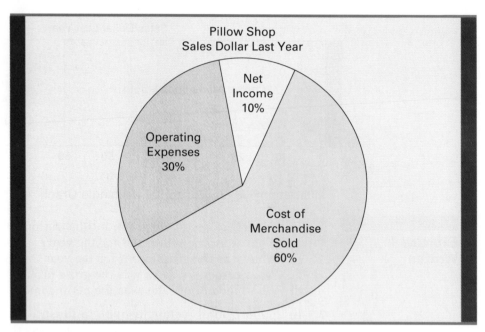

Illustration 109–3. Circle Graph

In making the circle graph, the dollar amounts were first changed to percents, then to degrees. For example, the cost of merchandise sold was 60% of sales ($240,000 ÷ $400,000). The equivalent in degrees was 216° (60% of 360° = 0.60 × 360°, or 216°).

The degrees in the other parts of the circle were found in the same way. Then, a circle was drawn with a compass and the parts were marked off with a protractor.

**Exercise 2
Written**

1. Last year's sales in the 4 departments of the Redi-Solutions Computer Company were:

Hardware	50%	180°		Software	30%	108°
Training	15%	54°		Repair	5%	18°

    a. On a circle graph, how many degrees should be used to show the sales of each department?
    b. Make a circle graph showing the percent for each department.

2. The Teal Company spent $12,000 on advertising last year as shown below. Make a circle graph showing each type of advertising and its percent.

Newspaper........	$3,600	30%		Circulars	$3,000	25%
Radio	2,400	20%		Mailings.............	1,800	15%
Yearbook ads	600	5%		Baseball t-shirts..	600	5%

3. The Robolink Company figures that the $50,000 cost of building a small robot and installing it at the customer's site is divided into these parts: raw materials, $5,000; direct labor, $12,500; overhead, $15,000; delivery and testing; $7,500; training, $10,000. Make a circle graph showing these parts as percents of the total cost of the robot.   10%; 25%; 30%; 15%; 20%

REVIEW 109

Terms

Skills

Problems

1. Match the term with the statements.

    circle graph   rectangle graph

    a. A graph that may be shown vertically or horizontally
        rectangle graph
    b. 100% of this graph is 360 degrees   circle graph

2. a. Divide: 78 by $2\frac{1}{2}$ $31\frac{1}{5}$
    b. What part less than $618 is $515? $\frac{1}{6}$
    c. Find the exact interest at 10% on $7,500 for 4 months. $250
    d. Find the number of days from August 19 to November 8.
        81 days
    e. A tax rate of 23.8 mills on $1 is a rate of ? on $1,000 $23.80

3. An annual salary of $16,380 is equivalent to what
    a. Monthly salary? $1,365
    b. Weekly salary? $315 [10]

4. Selena Krelin bought 150 shares of Crane Tractor preferred stock.
    The stock paid a quarterly dividend of 3% on a par value of $100.
    What was the annual dividend from the stock? $1,800 [58]

5. Richard bought a house for $60,000, paying $12,000 in cash and
    giving a mortgage for the rest. During the first year, he rented the
    house for $600 a month. His expenses were: mortgage interest,
    $4,300; taxes, $1,260; other expenses, $910. What was the rate of
    income on Richard's original cash investment, to the nearest tenth
    of a percent?   6.1% [61]

6. Lila Harris is paid a salary of $250 a week and a commission of 2%
    on net sales. Last week her gross sales were $4,720 and customer re-
    turns were $112. How much did Lila earn last week? $342.16 [28]

‡7. On November 30, Darrell's check register had a balance of $852.07.
    His bank statement balance on the same date was $682.56. Checks
    outstanding were #259, $56.71; #261, $33.78. A slip enclosed with
    the statement showed that the bank charged his account $260 for
    the November car loan payment due the bank. Prepare a reconcilia-
    tion statement. $592.07 [6]

Section 110
Economic Statistics

Government agencies publish many statistics to provide a measure of
how well the economy is doing. These measures also tell us how the
economy affects businesses, families, and individuals. The statistics we
hear most often deal with inflation and unemployment.

Inflation. For consumers, business firms, and the government, **inflation** means that the prices of goods and services they buy are rising. The U.S. Department of Commerce keeps track of prices and publishes a report that tells how much inflation has occurred within the past year. A figure in the report, called the *rate of inflation*, shows the percent increase in prices from the previous year. Illustration 110–1 shows the annual rate of inflation for a ten-year period.

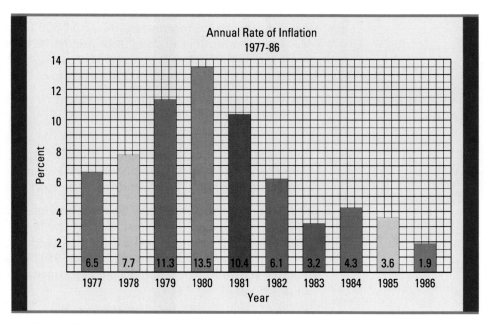

Illustration 110–1. Annual Rates of Inflation*

**Exercise 1
Written**

Use Illustration 110–1 to work the problems in this exercise.

1. What was the rate of inflation for 1978?   7.7%

2. For the years shown, which year had the lowest rate of inflation? What was the rate?   1986; 1.9%

3. In which year was the highest rate of inflation recorded, and what was the rate?   1980; 13.5%

4. During which two consecutive years was the total rate of inflation the greatest? What was the total rate?   1979 and 1980; 24.8%

5. For the 4-year period from 1978 through 1981,
    a. What was the total rate of inflation?   42.9%
    b. What was the average rate of inflation, to the nearest tenth percent?   10.7%

*U.S. Bureau of the Census, *Statistical Abstract of the United States* (Washington, D.C.: U.S. Government Printing Office, 1988), 445.

Purchasing Power of the Dollar. When inflation occurs, each dollar buys less than it did in the past. The **purchasing power of the dollar** is a measure of how much a dollar may now buy compared to what it could have bought during some base period. The **base period** is a period in time, usually a certain year, with which comparisons are made.

Illustration 110–2 shows the purchasing power of the dollar from 1967 to 1987. In the base period, 1967, the dollar was worth its full value of $1.00. In 1968, the dollar was worth $0.96 compared to 1967. The purchasing power of the dollar dropped $0.04 in one year ($1.00 − $0.96). This means that a 1968 dollar could buy only 96¢ worth of the same goods that could have been bought in 1967. The 1968 dollar is worth less because of inflation, and it would take about $1.04 to buy the same goods that could have been bought for $1 in 1967.

Purchasing Power of the Dollar
1967–1987

Year	Purchasing Power	Year	Purchasing Power	Year	Purchasing Power
1967	$1.000	1974	$0.677	1981	$0.367
1968	0.960	1975	0.620	1982	0.346
1969	0.911	1976	0.587	1983	0.335
1970	0.860	1977	0.551	1984	0.321
1971	0.824	1978	0.512	1985	0.310
1972	0.799	1979	0.460	1986	0.304
1973	0.751	1980	0.405	1987	0.289

Illustration 110–2. Annual Purchasing Power, or Worth, of the Dollar*

Exercise 2 Written

Use Illustration 110–2 to work the problems in this exercise.

1. Comparing 1974 to 1967,
   a. What was the purchasing power of the dollar in 1974? $0.677
   b. By what amount did the purchasing power of the dollar drop? $0.323

2. What amount did the purchasing power of the dollar drop from 1967
   a. Through 1973? $0.249
   b. Through 1980? $0.595
   c. Through 1987? $0.711

3. Between which 2 years did the purchasing power of the dollar drop the greatest amount? What was the amount? 1973–74; $0.074

4. What was the first year in which the purchasing power of the dollar dropped to less than $\frac{1}{2}$ of its 1967 value? 1979

5. During which 2-year period did the purchasing power of the dollar show the least amount of change? What was the amount of change? 1985–86; $0.006

*U.S. Bureau of the Census, *Statistical Abstract of the United States* (Washington, D.C.: U.S. Government Printing Office, 1988), 444.

Consumer Price Index. You have already seen how a base period is used to compare the purchasing power of the dollar. Another measure of prices that uses a base period is the Consumer Price Index. The **Consumer Price Index** (CPI) uses a single number, called an index number, to report how much the prices of goods and services typically bought by consumers have changed in comparison to a base period of 1967. The index number for the base period is always equal to 100.

Illustration 110–3 shows index figures for various categories of consumer goods and services. The "all items" column gives an average figure considering all categories, and is the figure commonly used when referring to the CPI.

The CPI may be expressed in several ways. For example, the CPI for 1982 is 292.4. This means that the cost of goods in 1982 was 292.4% of their cost in 1967. The percent increase in prices from 1967 to 1982 is 192.4% (292.4 − 100.0). Looking at the relationship in another way, it cost $292.40 in 1982 to buy the same goods for which you would have paid $100 in 1967.

Historical Report **Consumer Price Index, 1967–1986**							
		Categories of Consumer Goods and Services					
End of Year	**CPI All Items**	**Food and Beverages**	**Housing**	**Apparel and Upkeep**	**Transportation**	**Medical Care**	**Entertainment**	**Other Goods and Services**
1967	100.0	100.0	100.0	100.0	100.0	100.0	100.0	100.0
1970	119.1	115.3	121.7	119.2	116.9	124.2	119.8	119.6
1974	155.4	166.6	157.8	141.9	143.5	159.0	146.7	149.4
1978	202.9	214.1	211.5	163.2	192.6	227.8	180.9	189.1
1982	292.4	279.1	316.3	193.6	294.8	344.3	240.1	276.6
1986	331.1	317.0	362.1	210.9	304.8	446.8	277.4	355.2

Illustration 110–3. Consumer Price Index for Selected Years*

Exercise 3
Written

Use Illustration 110–3 to do the problems in this exercise.

1. a. What was the CPI for all items for 1986?   331.1
    b. By what percent did the CPI increase from 1967 to 1986?   231.1%

2. Which category of goods and services shows the smallest price increase between 1967 and 1986?   Apparel and Upkeep

3. Which 2 categories of consumer goods and services had price increases greater than those of the CPI from 1967 to 1986?
    Medical Care; Housing

*U.S. Department of Labor, *CPI Detailed Report* (Washington, D.C.: U.S. Government Printing Office, 1987), 19.

4. By what percent did prices for Housing increase from 1967 to
   a. 1974? 57.8%
   b. 1986? 262.1%

5. Yvonne earned $10,000 a year and Tom earned $4 an hour in 1967. Since then, they both have received wage increases equal to the increase in the CPI. To the nearest cent, in 1986
   a. Yvonne should have been earning what annual wage? $33,110
   b. Tom should have been earning what hourly wage? $13.24

Unemployment Rate. The **unemployment rate** tells the percentage of the total labor force that is not working. The **labor force** consists of all people who are willing to work and either have a job or are looking for a job.

Illustration 110–4 shows the unemployment rate for different persons for one month as figured by the U.S. Department of Labor.

Unemployment Rates By Marital Status, Race, Age, and Sex **Monthly Report**		
	Unemployment Rate (Percent)	
	Men	**Women**
All persons, 16 years and over	5.1	6.0
Married, spouse present	2.8	4.3
Widowed, divorced, or separated	5.8	6.7
Single (never married)	9.7	8.8
Black, 16 years and over	11.9	12.5
Married, spouse present	5.1	7.4
Widowed, divorced, or separated	9.9	9.9
Single (never married)	20.5	19.1
White, 16 years and over	4.4	5.0
Married, spouse present	2.6	3.9
Widowed, divorced, or separated	5.2	5.9
Single (never married)	8.0	6.7

Illustration 110–4. Unemployment by Various Categories of the Labor Force*

Exercise 4 Written

Use Illustration 110–4 to work the problems in this exercise.

1. Which persons had the highest rate of unemployment? What was the rate? Single black men; 20.5%

2. For *all* single persons (never married), did men or women have a higher unemployment rate? What was the difference in rates? Men; 0.9% higher

*U.S. Department of Labor, *Employment and Earnings* (Washington, D.C.: U.S. Government Printing Office, 1988), 19.

3. For every 1,000 women who are married and have their spouse present, how many would you expect to be unemployed?   43

4. Considering the All Persons category, what is the marital status that has the lowest unemployment rate?   Married, spouse present

REVIEW 110

Terms

1. Match the terms with the statements.

    base period   labor force
    Consumer Price Index   purchasing power of the dollar
    inflation   unemployment rate

    a. A single number used to measure a change in consumer prices
        Consumer Price Index
    b. All persons working or looking for work   labor force
    c. A rise in the prices of goods and services   inflation
    d. The percent of the labor force not working   unemployment rate
    e. Time in the past with which comparisons are made   base period
    f. A measure of how much a dollar will buy
        purchasing power of the dollar

Problems

2. Use Illustration 110–3 to compare the Food and Beverages and the Transportation categories for 1970. [110]
    a. Which category of prices increased faster?   Transportation
    b. What was the difference in price increases?   1.6%

3. August sales of the Dubois Company were $246,172.99. If August's sales were shown on a horizontal bar graph, what amount would be recorded if the sales were rounded to the nearest [108]
    a. $5,000? $245,000
    b. $10,000? $250,000

4. Find the median of this group of numbers: 5, 15, 10, 8, 9, 5, 14, 16, 7, 9, 8.   9 [106]

5. Six cars are parked in a lot. Three of the cars are blue, 2 are white, and 1 is green. What is the probability that the first car leaving the lot will be blue, assuming no other cars enter? $\frac{1}{2}$ [107]

These drills are of two kinds: mental and written.

In a mental drill, all the calculations are done mentally and only the answers are written on an answer paper.

In a written drill, all the calculations and the answers are written on an answer paper.

Drills 1 and 2 are mental drills.

Drills 3 through 17 are written drills.

Drills 18 through 44 are mental drills.

**Mental
Drill 1**

Adding

Place a sheet of paper across the page so that the top edge of the paper is under the sixth item of each column. Then add each column of exposed numbers from the bottom up and write the sum on the sheet of paper. Use combinations when you can. Then repeat the drill, adding the columns from the top down.

Do the same thing with the edge of the paper under the seventh row of numbers, then under the eighth row, and so on.

	a.		b.		c.		d.	
1.	76		456		$ 0.86		$129.35	
2.	94		5,794		0.29		87.29	
3.	81		76,532		0.31		3.50	
4.	27		967		0.42		16.48	
5.	43		87,658		12.95		194.76	
6.	59	380	4,369	175,776	0.87	$15.70	8.95	$440.33
7.	84	464	2,123	177,899	0.64	16.34	69.83	510.16
8.	26	490	35,254	213,153	0.72	17.06	100.00	610.16
9.	29	519	4,683	217,836	0.27	17.33	7.26	617.42
10.	74	593	28,765	246,601	1.46	18.79	35.42	652.84
11.	83	676	5,124	251,725	0.35	19.14	472.19	1,125.03
12.	19	695	71,676	323,401	0.92	20.06	107.24	1,232.27
13.	79	774	3,782	327,183	0.88	20.94	86.28	1,318.55
14.	85	859	52,497	379,680	0.83	21.77	55.24	1,373.79
15.	92	951	870	380,550	5.47	27.24	423.42	1,797.21
16.	67	1,018	3,913	384,463	0.60	27.84	37.68	1,834.89

■ Start with paper edge here →

Subtracting

Place a sheet of paper across the page so that the upper edge of the paper is under the first horizontal row of problems. Then subtract and write the differences on the sheet of paper. Prove each answer by adding the difference to the number subtracted.

Do the same with Problems 2, 3, and 4.

Start with
paper edge here →

	a.	**b.**	**c.**	**d.**
1.	8,965,395	$57,630.00	12,806,638	$877,151.58
	7,360,273	40,534.75	9,707,553	480,561.92
	1,605,122	$17,095.25	3,099,085	$396,589.66
2.	9,789,489	$76,700.00	91,313,904	$120,121.17
	5,608,029	39,410.12	35,296,808	20,250.89
	4,181,460	$37,289.88	56,017,096	$99,870.28
3.	8,437,482	$374,422.08	82,104,006	$105,074.27
	1,105,381	268,370.09	64,008,009	99,257.35
	7,332,101	$106,051.99	18,095,997	$5,816.92
4.	9,491,459	$200,907.00	95,016,102	$121,025.19
	2,441,251	107,358.81	89,067,304	96,865.37
	7,050,208	$93,548.19	5,948,798	$24,159.82

Multiplying Whole Numbers

Multiply and prove the products.

1. 268×341 91,388
2. 722×307 221,654
3. 623×504 313,992
4. 431×208 89,648
5. 822×702 577,044

6. $3,206 \times 2,105$ 6,748,630
7. $4,013 \times 3,402$ 13,652,226
8. $5,204 \times 4,021$ 20,925,284
9. $6,051 \times 5,014$ 30,339,714
10. $7,003 \times 1,008$ 7,059,024

Multiplying Decimals

Multiply and prove the products.

1. 74.1×82 6,076.2
2. 6.32×44 278.08
3. 4.08×67 273.36
4. 6.42×25.4 163.068
5. 8.07×4.23 34.1361

6. 3.61×5.04 18.1944
7. 71.1×30.8 2,189.88
8. 0.406×0.205 0.08323
9. 72.9×0.0301 2.19429
10. 81.5×0.0142 1.1573

Multiplying End Zeros

Written Drill 5

Multiply and prove the products.

1. 264 × 3,800   1,003,200
2. 314 × 1,300   408,200
3. 232 × 4,100   951,200
4. 422 × 2,300   970,600
5. 280 × 76   21,280

6. 94,000 × 570   53,580,000
7. 24,000 × 360   8,640,000
8. 52,000 × 180   9,360,000
9. 1,700 × 4.06   6,902
10. 6.50 × 1,700   11,050

Multiplying Dollars and Cents

Written Drill 6

Multiply and prove the products.

1. $8.50 × 45 $382.50
2. $9.40 × 350 $3,290
3. $6.50 × 1,300 $8,450
4. $0.70 × 1,750 $1,225
5. $0.45 × 180 $81

6. $0.34 × 14,000 $4,760
7. $1.02 × 10,500 $10,710
8. $10.50 × 3,040 $31,920
9. $8,500 × 0.02542 $216.07
10. $12,400 × 0.10205 $1,265.42

Dividing Whole Numbers

Written Drill 7

Divide and prove the quotients.

1. 1,134 ÷ 27   42
2. 1,504 ÷ 32   47
3. 2,294 ÷ 37   62
4. 1,739 ÷ 37   47
5. 7,392 ÷ 84   88
6. 6,322 ÷ 58   109
7. 9,729 ÷ 47   207
8. 11,778 ÷ 39   302

9. 25,920 ÷ 64   405
10. 46,816 ÷ 77   608
11. 94,094 ÷ 143   658
12. 10,032 ÷ 114   88
13. 10,912 ÷ 176   62
14. 22,016 ÷ 128   172
15. 48,222 ÷ 171   282

Dividing Decimals

Written Drill 8

Divide to the correct number of decimal places indicated and prove the quotients.

To 1 decimal place		To 2 decimal places		To 3 decimal places	
1. 500 ÷ 2.2	227.3	6. 70 ÷ 13.2	5.3	11. 7.66 ÷ 2.6	2.946
2. 15 ÷ 6.3	2.4	7. 1.02 ÷ 5.4	0.19	12. 0.892 ÷ 3.9	0.229
3. 84.8 ÷ 1.15	73.7	8. 13.3 ÷ 8.4	1.58	13. 2 ÷ 5.7	0.351
4. 57.1 ÷ 0.09	634.4	9. 6.6 ÷ 0.37	17.84	14. 1.52 ÷ 0.54	2.815
5. 70.7 ÷ 0.87	81.3	10. 2.19 ÷ 0.079	27.72	15. 0.776 ÷ 0.69	1.125

Dividing with End Zeros in the Divisor

Written Drill 9

Divide to the correct number of decimal places indicated and prove the quotients.

To 1 decimal place		To 2 decimal places		To 3 decimal places	
1. $3,815 \div 180$	21.2	5. $2,000 \div 4,700$	0.43	9. $330 \div 7,900$	0.042
2. $2,855 \div 490$	5.8	6. $824.5 \div 3,500$	0.24	10. $21.85 \div 1,500$	0.015
3. $8,325 \div 2,600$	3.2	7. $460 \div 280$	1.64	11. $17,150 \div 17,000$	1.009
4. $4,800 \div 4,400$	1.1	8. $25.9 \div 730$	0.04	12. $200 \div 6,700$	0.03

Adding Fractions and Mixed Numbers

Written Drill 10

Find the sums.

	1.	2.	3.	4.	5.	6.
	$\frac{1}{2}$	$8\frac{1}{4}$	$5\frac{1}{3}$	$12\frac{1}{5}$	$4\frac{1}{4}$	$6\frac{1}{4}$
	$\frac{2}{3}$	$12\frac{1}{2}$	$16\frac{1}{2}$	$7\frac{1}{2}$	$7\frac{2}{5}$	$4\frac{1}{3}$
	$\frac{3}{4}$	$9\frac{1}{3}$	$6\frac{1}{4}$	$9\frac{1}{4}$	$8\frac{1}{8}$	$5\frac{1}{5}$
	$1\frac{11}{12}$	$30\frac{1}{12}$	$28\frac{1}{12}$	$28\frac{19}{20}$	$19\frac{31}{40}$	$15\frac{47}{60}$

	7.	8.	9.	10.	11.	12.
	$12\frac{1}{2}$	$4\frac{1}{4}$	$3\frac{5}{16}$	$10\frac{1}{3}$	$10\frac{2}{3}$	$24\frac{5}{8}$
	$5\frac{5}{6}$	$4\frac{1}{3}$	$6\frac{1}{8}$	$15\frac{5}{9}$	$11\frac{5}{6}$	$5\frac{2}{3}$
	$12\frac{1}{3}$	$19\frac{1}{2}$	$13\frac{3}{4}$	$2\frac{1}{6}$	$4\frac{4}{9}$	$11\frac{1}{4}$
	$20\frac{3}{4}$	$18\frac{5}{6}$	$6\frac{1}{2}$	$7\frac{1}{2}$	$12\frac{1}{2}$	$18\frac{1}{6}$
	$51\frac{5}{12}$	$46\frac{11}{12}$	$29\frac{11}{16}$	$35\frac{5}{9}$	$39\frac{4}{9}$	$59\frac{17}{24}$

	13.	14.	15.	16.	17.	18.
	$6\frac{7}{12}$	$4\frac{2}{3}$	$7\frac{5}{6}$	$8\frac{2}{7}$	$15\frac{3}{4}$	$4\frac{1}{2}$
	$7\frac{3}{4}$	$10\frac{5}{12}$	$12\frac{1}{3}$	$6\frac{3}{4}$	$10\frac{1}{5}$	$16\frac{1}{4}$
	$2\frac{1}{8}$	$11\frac{1}{9}$	$5\frac{4}{9}$	$15\frac{1}{2}$	$22\frac{1}{2}$	$8\frac{1}{8}$
	$11\frac{5}{6}$	$6\frac{1}{4}$	$15\frac{1}{2}$	$3\frac{1}{14}$	$3\frac{7}{10}$	$9\frac{5}{16}$
	$28\frac{7}{24}$	$32\frac{4}{9}$	$41\frac{1}{9}$	$33\frac{17}{28}$	$52\frac{3}{20}$	$38\frac{3}{16}$

Subtracting Fractions and Mixed Numbers

Written Drill 11

Find the differences.

	1.	2.	3.	4.	5.	6.
	$18\frac{7}{12}$	$16\frac{9}{10}$	$27\frac{7}{15}$	$16\frac{1}{2}$	$21\frac{3}{4}$	$19\frac{5}{6}$
	$7\frac{1}{2}$	$\frac{3}{5}$	$9\frac{1}{3}$	$\frac{1}{3}$	$6\frac{2}{3}$	$8\frac{3}{4}$
	$11\frac{1}{12}$	$16\frac{3}{10}$	$18\frac{2}{15}$	$16\frac{1}{6}$	$15\frac{1}{12}$	$11\frac{1}{12}$

	7.	8.	9.	10.	11.	12.
	$24\frac{11}{12}$	$10\frac{7}{15}$	$21\frac{3}{4}$	$10\frac{3}{8}$	$12\frac{3}{4}$	$18\frac{1}{3}$
	$\frac{5}{8}$	$2\frac{3}{10}$	$\frac{4}{5}$	$2\frac{2}{3}$	$\frac{7}{8}$	$4\frac{1}{2}$
	$24\frac{7}{24}$	$8\frac{1}{6}$	$20\frac{19}{20}$	$7\frac{17}{24}$	$11\frac{7}{8}$	$13\frac{5}{6}$

	13.	14.	15.	16.	17.	18.
	$12\frac{1}{2}$	$13\frac{1}{4}$	$10\frac{2}{3}$	$14\frac{1}{2}$	$15\frac{1}{2}$	$28\frac{2}{3}$
	$8\frac{7}{8}$	$\frac{7}{8}$	$3\frac{3}{5}$	$5\frac{5}{8}$	$9\frac{4}{5}$	$5\frac{3}{8}$
	$3\frac{5}{8}$	$12\frac{3}{8}$	$7\frac{1}{15}$	$8\frac{7}{8}$	$5\frac{7}{10}$	$23\frac{7}{24}$

Multiplying Mixed Numbers

Written Drill 12

Find the products.

1. $12\frac{1}{2}$	2. $14\frac{1}{3}$	3. $12\frac{2}{3}$	4. $16\frac{1}{2}$	5. $12\frac{1}{3}$	6. $15\frac{1}{4}$
$16\frac{1}{4}$	$15\frac{1}{2}$	$9\frac{1}{4}$	$5\frac{1}{4}$	$8\frac{1}{2}$	$9\frac{2}{3}$
$203\frac{1}{8}$	$222\frac{1}{6}$	$117\frac{1}{6}$	$86\frac{5}{8}$	$104\frac{5}{6}$	$147\frac{5}{12}$

7. $27\frac{1}{2}$	8. $21\frac{2}{3}$	9. $32\frac{1}{4}$	10. $27\frac{1}{2}$	11. $21\frac{2}{3}$	12. $32\frac{1}{4}$
$22\frac{2}{3}$	$12\frac{1}{3}$	$8\frac{3}{4}$	$15\frac{2}{3}$	$10\frac{1}{3}$	$7\frac{3}{4}$
$623\frac{1}{3}$	$267\frac{2}{9}$	$282\frac{3}{16}$	$430\frac{5}{6}$	$223\frac{8}{9}$	$249\frac{15}{16}$

13. $20\frac{3}{4}$	14. $15\frac{3}{4}$	15. $18\frac{1}{4}$	16. $12\frac{1}{4}$	17. $16\frac{3}{4}$	18. $21\frac{3}{4}$
$9\frac{1}{2}$	$20\frac{2}{3}$	$16\frac{2}{3}$	$13\frac{2}{3}$	$7\frac{1}{2}$	$9\frac{2}{3}$
$197\frac{1}{8}$	$325\frac{1}{2}$	$304\frac{1}{6}$	$167\frac{5}{12}$	$125\frac{5}{8}$	$210\frac{1}{4}$

19. $36\frac{3}{8}$	20. $32\frac{2}{3}$	21. $27\frac{3}{4}$	22. $25\frac{3}{8}$	23. $18\frac{2}{3}$	24. $17\frac{3}{4}$
$24\frac{1}{3}$	$15\frac{1}{8}$	$20\frac{1}{3}$	$16\frac{1}{3}$	$12\frac{1}{8}$	$24\frac{1}{3}$
$885\frac{1}{8}$	$494\frac{1}{12}$	$564\frac{1}{4}$	$414\frac{11}{24}$	$226\frac{1}{3}$	$431\frac{11}{12}$

Dividing Fractions and Mixed Numbers

Written Drill 13

Find the quotients.

1. $47 \div \frac{2}{3}$	$70\frac{1}{2}$	11. $270 \div 9\frac{3}{8}$	$28\frac{4}{5}$	21. $58\frac{11}{12} \div 25\frac{1}{4}$	$2\frac{1}{3}$
2. $28 \div \frac{3}{4}$	$37\frac{1}{3}$	12. $140 \div 11\frac{1}{4}$	$12\frac{4}{9}$	22. $70\frac{5}{16} \div 18\frac{3}{4}$	$3\frac{3}{4}$
3. $42 \div \frac{4}{5}$	$52\frac{1}{2}$	13. $126 \div 13\frac{1}{2}$	$9\frac{1}{3}$	23. $35\frac{8}{15} \div 16\frac{2}{5}$	$2\frac{1}{6}$
4. $92 \div \frac{8}{9}$	$103\frac{1}{2}$	14. $153 \div 15\frac{3}{4}$	$9\frac{5}{7}$	24. $40\frac{5}{8} \div 12\frac{3}{16}$	$3\frac{1}{3}$
5. $39 \div \frac{5}{6}$	$46\frac{4}{5}$	15. $29\frac{3}{8} \div 3\frac{1}{8}$	$9\frac{2}{5}$	25. $48\frac{3}{4} \div 7\frac{7}{8}$	$6\frac{4}{21}$
6. $31\frac{1}{3} \div 4$	$7\frac{5}{6}$	16. $126\frac{2}{3} \div 13\frac{1}{3}$	$9\frac{1}{2}$	26. $37\frac{1}{8} \div 16\frac{1}{2}$	$2\frac{1}{4}$
7. $52\frac{1}{2} \div 6$	$8\frac{3}{4}$	17. $86\frac{1}{4} \div 18\frac{3}{4}$	$4\frac{3}{5}$	27. $154\frac{1}{6} \div 24\frac{2}{3}$	$6\frac{1}{4}$
8. $45\frac{1}{3} \div 8$	$5\frac{2}{3}$	18. $204\frac{1}{6} \div 29\frac{1}{6}$	7	28. $58\frac{1}{3} \div 12\frac{1}{2}$	$4\frac{2}{3}$
9. $69\frac{3}{4} \div 9$	$7\frac{3}{4}$	19. $81\frac{1}{4} \div 43\frac{3}{4}$	$1\frac{6}{7}$	29. $46\frac{2}{3} \div 17\frac{1}{2}$	$2\frac{2}{3}$
10. $124\frac{1}{2} \div 12$	$10\frac{3}{8}$	20. $56\frac{7}{8} \div 16\frac{1}{4}$	$3\frac{1}{2}$	30. $151\frac{2}{3} \div 16\frac{1}{4}$	$9\frac{1}{3}$

Adding Metrics

Written Drill 14

Find the sums in the correct metric units. Prove your answers.

1. $50 \text{ m} + 125 \text{ m} = ? \text{ m}$ 175

2. $460 \text{ cm}^2 + 78 \text{ cm}^2 = ? \text{ cm}^2$ 538

3. $180 \text{ mL} + 540 \text{ mL} = ? \text{ mL}$ 720

4. $460 \text{ g} + 792 \text{ g} = ? \text{ g}$ 1 252

5. $2 \text{ cm} + 1.5 \text{ cm} = ? \text{ cm}$ 3.5

6. $3.5 \text{ km}^2 + 8.7 \text{ km}^2 = ? \text{ km}^2$ 12.2

7. 8.75 kg + 0.5 kg = ? kg   9.25

8. 25.05 m + 0.005 m = ? m   25.055

9. 6.8 m + 50 cm = ? m   7.3

10. 3 km + 1 500 m = ? km   4.5

11. 2.3 L + 75 mL = ? mL   2 375

12. 500 g + 4.5 kg = ? kg   5

Subtracting Metrics

Written Drill 15

Subtract and show your answers in the correct metric units. Prove your answers.

1. 368 kL − 159 kL = ? kL   209

2. 743 mm − 265 mm = ? mm   478

3. 9 046 t − 3 036 t = ? t   6 010

4. 34 ha − 26.5 ha = ? ha   7.5

5. 465 m^2 − 0.75 m^2 = ? m^2 464.25

6. 0.85 m − 0.45 m = ? m   0.4

7. 1.5 L − 0.05 L = ? L   1.45

8. 80 cm − 25 mm = ? mm   775

9. 1 kg − 90 g = ? g   910

10. 2.75 L − 500 mL = ? L   2.25

11. 1 m^2 − 250 cm^2 = ? cm^2 9 750

12. 1 m^2 − 250 cm^2 = ? m^2 0.975

Multiplying Metrics

Written Drill 16

Multiply and show your answers in the correct metric units. Prove your answers.

1. 35 km × 6 = ? km   210

2. 14.5 m × 10 = ? m   145

3. 0.05 km^2 × 50 = ? km^2 2.5

4. 1 640 L × 25 = ? L   41 000

5. 850 mm × 0.5 = ? mm   425

6. 6.5 ha × 20 = ? ha   130

7. 4.5 m × 3.2 m = ? m^2 14.4

8. 2.6 kg × 0.2 = ? kg   0.52

9. 0.5 L × 5 = ? L   2.5

10. 250 mL × 40 = ? L   10

11. 600 g × 0.6 = ? kg   0.36

12. 100 t × 0.625 = ? t   62.5

Dividing Metrics

Written Drill 17

Divide and show your answers in the correct metric units. Prove your answers.

1. 456 m² ÷ 3 = ? m²   152   7. 25 cm² ÷ 6.25 = ? cm²   4

2. 533 ha ÷ 100 = ? ha   5.33   8. 3.6 m ÷ 4 = ? cm   90

3. 2 400 km ÷ 2 = ? km   1 200   9. 4.8 m ÷ 6 = ? m   0.8

4. 45.5 kg ÷ 5 = ? kg   9.1   10. 650 mL ÷ 50 = ? mL   13

5. 37.5 L ÷ 0.5 = ? L   75   11. 3.28 km² ÷ 8 = ? km² 0.41

6. 0.5 kL ÷ 4 = ? kL   0.125   12. 12 468 t ÷ 6 = ? t   2 078

Multiplying by 10, 100, and 1,000

Mental Drill 18

Find the products.

1. 7.38 × 10   73.8   10. 4.2 × 100   420

2. 9.21 × 100   921   11. 3.4 × 1,000   3,400

3. 4.72 × 1,000   4,720   12. 42.7 × 10   427

4. 6.3 × 100   630   13. 0.085 × 100   8.5

5. 3.27 × 10   32.7   14. 0.071 × 10   0.71

6. 0.596 × 1,000   596   15. 4.98 × 1,000 4,980

7. 9.85 × 100   985   16. 5.08 × 100   508

8. 5.345 × 10   53.45   17. 9.76 × 10   97.6

9. 5.63 × 10   56.3   18. 0.021 × 1,000 21

Multiplying by Multiples of 10 and 10¢

Mental Drill 19

Find the costs.

1. 20 @ 65¢ $13   10. 40 @ $0.32 $12.80

2. 60 @ 45¢ $27   11. 70 @ 15¢ $10.50

3. 23 @ $0.30 $6.90   12. 31 @ 80¢ $24.80

4. 30 @ $0.15 $4.50   13. 80 @ $0.45 $36

5. 80 @ $0.35 $28   14. 60 @ 52¢ $31.20

6. 35 @ 40¢ $14   15. 22 @ 70¢ $15.40

7. 20 @ $0.70 $14   16. 20 @ $0.17 $3.40

8. 40 @ $0.35 $14   17. 30 @ 55¢ $16.50

9. 65 @ 60¢ $39   18. 115 @ $0.20 $23

Mental Drill 20

Dividing by 10, 100, and 1,000

Divide.

1. $348 \div 10$ 34.8
2. $1,987 \div 1,000$ 1.987
3. $847 \div 100$ 8.47
4. $7,240 \div 1,000$ 7.24
5. $360 \div 10$ 36
6. $94.3 \div 10$ 9.34
7. $73.8 \div 10$ 7.38
8. $9.2 \div 100$ 0.092
9. $4.7 \div 1,000$ 0.0047
10. $5.63 \div 100$ 0.0563
11. $7.2 \div 10$ 0.72
12. $20 \div 1,000$ 0.02
13. $7.3 \div 100$ 0.073
14. $9.16 \div 10$ 0.916
15. $5.9 \div 1,000$ 0.0059
16. $80 \div 100$ 0.8
17. $7.8 \div 10$ 0.78
18. $30 \div 1,000$ 0.03

Mental Drill 21

Multiplying and Dividing by 10, 100, and 1,000

Multiply or divide as shown.

1. 7.38×10 73.8
2. $0.042 \times 1,000$ 42
3. $348 \div 10$ 34.8
4. $420 \div 1,000$ 0.42
5. 9.20×100 920
6. 0.38×10 3.8
7. $198 \div 1,000$ 0.198
8. $0.38 \div 10$ 0.038
9. $6.47 \times 1,000$ 6,470
10. $6.9 \div 100$ 0.069
11. $0.74 \div 1,000$ 0.00074
12. 56.3×100 5,630
13. $4.7 \div 1,000$ 0.0047
14. 0.069×100 6.9
15. 0.0406×10 0.406
16. $0.21 \div 100$ 0.0021
17. $5.63 \div 100$ 0.0563
18. $0.074 \times 1,000$ 74

Mental Drill 22

Multiplying by 0.1, 0.01, and 0.001

Multiply.

1. 73.8×0.1 7.38
2. 9.2×0.01 0.092
3. 647×0.001 0.647
4. 34.1×0.01 0.341
5. 5.31×0.1 0.531
6. 362×0.001 0.362
7. 83.4×0.1 8.34
8. 3.85×0.01 0.0385
9. 53.4×0.1 5.34
10. 863×0.1 86.3
11. 4.22×0.01 0.0422
12. 713×0.001 0.713
13. 62.4×0.1 6.24
14. $3,420 \times 0.001$ 3.42
15. 4.8×0.01 0.048

Mental Drill 23

Dividing by 0.1, 0.01, and 0.001

Divide.

1. $73.8 \div 0.1$	738	9. $6.456 \div 0.1$	64.56
2. $8.2 \div 0.01$	820	10. $5.74 \div 0.1$	57.4
3. $6.7 \div 0.001$	6,700	11. $4.33 \div 0.01$	433
4. $21.4 \div 0.01$	2,140	12. $6.5 \div 0.01$	650
5. $3.61 \div 0.1$	36.1	13. $33.6 \div 0.1$	336
6. $0.485 \div 0.001$	485	14. $0.706 \div 0.001$	706
7. $72.36 \div 0.1$	723.6	15. $0.263 \div 0.01$	26.3
8. $2.74 \div 0.01$	274		

Mental Drill 24

Multiplying and Dividing by 0.1, 0.01, and 0.001

Multiply or divide as shown.

1. $6.31 \div 0.1$	63.1	9. $3.25 \div 0.001$	3,250
2. $0.042 \div 0.001$	42	10. 7.4×0.01	0.074
3. 348×0.1	34.8	11. 0.9×0.1	0.09
4. 420×0.001	0.42	12. $2.5 \div 0.01$	250
5. $9.20 \div 0.01$	920	13. 8×0.001	0.008
6. $0.27 \div 0.1$	2.7	14. $0.012 \div 0.01$	1.2
7. $183 \div 0.001$	0.183	15. $0.27 \div 0.1$	2.7
8. 0.52×0.1	0.052		

Mental Drill 25

Multiplying and Dividing by 10, 100, 1,000 and 0.1, 0.01, and 0.001

Multiply or divide as shown.

1. $2.6 \div 100$	0.026	11. 0.45×0.1	0.045
2. $0.086 \div 0.01$	8.6	12. 0.073×10	0.73
3. 9.7×10	97	13. 2.6×100	260
4. $0.325 \div 0.001$	325	14. $0.02 \div 10$	0.002
5. $0.55 \times 1,000$	550	15. 0.01×100	1
6. 7.1×0.01	0.071	16. 4.4×0.1	0.44
7. $4.72 \div 10$	0.472	17. $4.3 \times 1,000$	4,300
8. $6.5 \div 0.1$	65	18. $52.4 \div 10$	5.24
9. $3.4 \div 10$	0.34	19. 0.84×0.1	0.084
10. $0.01 \div 10$	0.001	20. $3.6 \div 100$	0.036

21.	$27.8 \div 10$	2.78	26.	0.002×10	0.02
22.	$6.1 \div 0.01$	610	27.	$0.84 \div 0.001$	840
23.	0.021×100	2.1	28.	0.01×0.1	0.001
24.	$0.275 \div 0.01$	27.5	29.	0.045×10	0.45
25.	4.2×100	420	30.	$0.06 \times 1,000$	60

Items Bought in 10's, 100's, or 1,000's

Mental Drill 26

Find the costs.

1.	10 @ $0.16	$1.60	10.	10 @ $0.15	$1.50
2.	100 @ $0.18	$18	11.	100 @ 0.01\frac{1}{4}$	$1.25
3.	1,000 @ $0.12	$120	12.	10 @ $0.06	$0.60
4.	10 @ 0.02\frac{1}{2}$	$0.25	13.	100 @ 0.33\frac{1}{3}$	$33.33
5.	1,000 @ 0.07\frac{1}{2}$	$75	14.	100 @ $0.04	$4
6.	1,000 @ 0.12\frac{1}{2}$	$125	15.	10 @ 0.33\frac{1}{3}$	$3.33
7.	100 @ 0.02\frac{1}{2}$	$2.50	16.	10 @ $0.80	$8
8.	100 @ 0.01\frac{1}{4}$	$1.25	17.	10 @ 0.87\frac{1}{2}$	$8.75
9.	100 @ 0.06\frac{1}{4}$	$6.25	18.	10 @ 0.66\frac{2}{3}$	$6.67

Items priced at 10¢, $1, $10, $100

Mental Drill 27

Find the costs.

1.	65 @ 10¢	$6.50	10.	$1\frac{1}{4}$ @ $10	$12.50
2.	32 @ $1	$32	11.	$6\frac{1}{4}$ @ $10	$62.50
3.	17 @ $10	$170	12.	$3\frac{3}{4}$ @ $10	$37.50
4.	$2\frac{1}{2}$ @ $1	$2.50	13.	$33\frac{1}{3}$ @ $1	$33.33
5.	$37\frac{1}{2}$ @ $10	$375	14.	$3\frac{1}{3}$ @ $1	$3.33
6.	$7\frac{1}{2}$ @ $100	$750	15.	$66\frac{2}{3}$ @ $1	$66.67
7.	$6\frac{1}{4}$ @ $100	$625	16.	$1\frac{1}{4}$ @ 10¢	$0.13
8.	$3\frac{3}{4}$ @ $100	$375	17.	$6\frac{1}{4}$ @ 10¢	$0.63
9.	$8\frac{3}{4}$ @ $100	$875	18.	$3\frac{3}{4}$ @ 10¢	$0.38

Items Priced per C, cwt, M, T, or t

Mental Drill 28

Find the costs.

1.	300 articles @ $9 per C.	$27
2.	125 cans @ $6 per C.	$7.50
3	750 articles @ $4 per C.	$30
4.	150 articles @ $12 per C.	$18

5. 700 pounds @ $3 per cwt. $21

6. 750 pounds @ $4 per cwt. $30

7. 450 pounds @ $2 per cwt. $9

8. 250 pounds @ $4 per cwt. $10

9. 350 pounds @ $6 per cwt. $21

10. 1,400 cans @ $15 per M. $21

11. 1,300 cans @ $9 per M. $11.70

12. 2,500 cans @ $12 per M. $30

13. 9,000 lbs. @ $14 per T. $63

14. 5,000 lbs. @ $18 per T. $45

15. 3,000 lbs. @ $26 per T. $39

16. 6,000 lbs. @ $22 per T. $66

17. 2 000 kg @ $10 per t. $20

18. 1 500 kg @ $30 per t. $45

**Mental
Drill 29**

Adding and Subtracting Fractions

Add or subtract as shown.

1. $\frac{1}{4} + \frac{3}{16}$ $\frac{7}{16}$ 9. $\frac{5}{6} + \frac{1}{8}$ $\frac{23}{24}$ 17. $\frac{7}{12} - \frac{1}{4}$ $\frac{1}{3}$

2. $\frac{1}{3} + \frac{5}{6}$ $1\frac{1}{6}$ 10. $\frac{2}{3} + \frac{3}{4}$ $1\frac{5}{12}$ 18. $\frac{2}{3} - \frac{1}{5}$ $\frac{7}{15}$

3. $\frac{1}{6} + \frac{11}{12}$ $1\frac{1}{12}$ 11. $\frac{3}{4} + \frac{1}{6}$ $\frac{11}{12}$ 19. $\frac{1}{4} + \frac{1}{8} + \frac{1}{2}$ $\frac{7}{8}$

4. $\frac{1}{8} + \frac{15}{16}$ $1\frac{1}{16}$ 12. $\frac{2}{3} + \frac{1}{5}$ $\frac{13}{15}$ 20. $\frac{1}{3} + \frac{1}{6} + \frac{1}{2}$ 1

5. $\frac{7}{8} + \frac{1}{16}$ $\frac{15}{16}$ 13. $\frac{5}{8} - \frac{3}{16}$ $\frac{7}{16}$ 21. $\frac{1}{4} + \frac{3}{8} + \frac{1}{2}$ $1\frac{1}{8}$

6. $\frac{5}{6} + \frac{7}{12}$ $1\frac{5}{12}$ 14. $\frac{2}{3} - \frac{1}{6}$ $\frac{1}{2}$ 22. $\frac{7}{8} + \frac{1}{2} + \frac{3}{4}$ $2\frac{1}{8}$

7. $\frac{5}{6} + \frac{11}{12}$ $1\frac{3}{4}$ 15. $\frac{11}{12} - \frac{1}{4}$ $\frac{2}{3}$ 23. $\frac{1}{3} + \frac{1}{2} + \frac{5}{6}$ $1\frac{2}{3}$

8. $\frac{1}{2} + \frac{2}{3}$ $1\frac{1}{6}$ 16. $\frac{5}{6} - \frac{1}{3}$ $\frac{1}{2}$ 24. $\frac{1}{2} + \frac{1}{4} + \frac{5}{8}$ $1\frac{3}{8}$

**Mental
Drill 30**

Multiplying and Dividing Fractions

Multiply or divide as shown.

1. $\frac{1}{3} \times \frac{2}{3}$ $\frac{2}{9}$ 8. $\frac{2}{3} \times \frac{3}{8}$ $\frac{1}{4}$ 15. $\frac{1}{6} \div \frac{1}{4}$ $\frac{2}{3}$

2. $\frac{1}{2} \times \frac{1}{3}$ $\frac{1}{6}$ 9. $\frac{2}{5}$ of $\frac{15}{16}$ $\frac{3}{8}$ 16. $\frac{3}{8} \div \frac{5}{8}$ $\frac{3}{5}$

3. $\frac{1}{4}$ of $\frac{4}{5}$ $\frac{1}{5}$ 10. $\frac{3}{4} \times \frac{8}{15}$ $\frac{2}{5}$ 17. $\frac{2}{5} \div \frac{4}{5}$ $\frac{1}{2}$

4. $\frac{1}{3} \times \frac{3}{8}$ $\frac{1}{8}$ 11. $\frac{3}{5} \div \frac{9}{10}$ $\frac{2}{3}$ 18. $\frac{1}{9} \div \frac{2}{3}$ $\frac{1}{6}$

5. $\frac{1}{2}$ of $\frac{4}{5}$ $\frac{2}{5}$ 12. $\frac{2}{3} \div \frac{8}{9}$ $\frac{3}{4}$ 19. $\frac{3}{8} \div \frac{1}{2}$ $\frac{3}{4}$

6. $\frac{1}{3}$ of $\frac{15}{16}$ $\frac{5}{16}$ 13. $\frac{1}{3} \div \frac{1}{2}$ $\frac{2}{3}$ 20. $\frac{4}{15} \div \frac{2}{3}$ $\frac{2}{5}$

7. $\frac{2}{3}$ of $\frac{9}{25}$ $\frac{6}{25}$ 14. $\frac{3}{8} \div \frac{2}{3}$ $\frac{9}{16}$

Reviewing Fractions

Add, subtract, multiply, or divide as shown.

1. $\frac{7}{8} - \frac{1}{4}$ $\frac{5}{8}$
2. $\frac{1}{4} \div \frac{1}{3}$ $\frac{3}{4}$
3. $\frac{1}{2} \times \frac{6}{7}$ $\frac{3}{7}$
4. $\frac{4}{5} + \frac{7}{10}$ $1\frac{1}{2}$
5. $\frac{3}{5} \div \frac{3}{4}$ $\frac{4}{5}$
6. $\frac{5}{12} - \frac{1}{3}$ $\frac{1}{12}$
7. $\frac{2}{3} + \frac{1}{4}$ $\frac{11}{12}$
8. $\frac{3}{5}$ of $\frac{15}{32}$ $\frac{9}{32}$
9. $\frac{3}{4} \div \frac{5}{6}$ $\frac{9}{10}$
10. $\frac{2}{5} + \frac{3}{4}$ $1\frac{3}{20}$
11. $\frac{3}{4} \times \frac{16}{25}$ $\frac{12}{25}$
12. $\frac{5}{6} - \frac{1}{12}$ $\frac{3}{4}$
13. $\frac{2}{5} + \frac{5}{6}$ $1\frac{7}{30}$
14. $\frac{5}{9} \div \frac{7}{9}$ $\frac{5}{7}$

15. $\frac{1}{2} - \frac{3}{16}$ $\frac{5}{16}$
16. $\frac{2}{3}$ of $\frac{9}{16}$ $\frac{3}{8}$
17. $\frac{3}{10} \div \frac{9}{10}$ $\frac{1}{3}$
18. $\frac{5}{12} - \frac{1}{6}$ $\frac{1}{4}$
19. $\frac{2}{5}$ of $\frac{15}{32}$ $\frac{3}{16}$
20. $\frac{2}{9} \div \frac{2}{3}$ $\frac{1}{3}$
21. $\frac{3}{4} - \frac{5}{12}$ $\frac{1}{3}$
22. $\frac{4}{5} \div \frac{3}{5}$ $1\frac{1}{3}$
23. $\frac{3}{4} + \frac{1}{6}$ $\frac{11}{12}$
24. $\frac{3}{15} \div \frac{2}{5}$ $\frac{1}{2}$
25. $\frac{5}{6} \times \frac{4}{7}$ $\frac{10}{21}$
26. $\frac{2}{3} - \frac{1}{4}$ $\frac{5}{12}$
27. $\frac{7}{9} \div \frac{2}{3}$ $1\frac{1}{6}$
28. $\frac{3}{5} - \frac{1}{4}$ $\frac{7}{20}$

29. $\frac{2}{3} \div \frac{8}{9}$ $\frac{3}{4}$
30. $\frac{1}{8} + \frac{5}{12}$ $\frac{13}{24}$
31. $\frac{3}{4} + \frac{1}{8} + \frac{1}{2}$ $1\frac{3}{8}$
32. $\frac{1}{4} + \frac{7}{8} + \frac{1}{2}$ $1\frac{5}{8}$
33. $\frac{5}{6} + \frac{1}{2} + \frac{2}{3}$ 2
34. $\frac{3}{4} + \frac{1}{2} + \frac{3}{8}$ $1\frac{5}{8}$
35. $\frac{1}{2} + \frac{1}{6} + \frac{2}{3}$ $1\frac{1}{3}$
36. $\frac{1}{3} \times \frac{3}{4} \times \frac{4}{5}$ $\frac{1}{5}$
37. $\frac{2}{3} \times \frac{3}{8} \times \frac{1}{2}$ $\frac{1}{8}$
38. $\frac{5}{6} \times \frac{2}{3} \times \frac{2}{5}$ $\frac{2}{9}$
39. $\frac{3}{4} \times \frac{2}{3} \times \frac{6}{7}$ $\frac{3}{7}$
40. $\frac{2}{3} \times \frac{7}{8} \times \frac{4}{5}$ $\frac{7}{15}$

Changing Decimals to Percents

Show as percents.

1. 0.25   25%
2. 0.37   37%
3. 0.123   12.3%
4. 0.03   3%
5. 0.004   0.4%
6. 0.003   0.3%
7. 1.25   125%
8. 2.45   245%
9. 3   300%
10. 2   200%
11. 0.4   40%
12. 4.6   460%
13. $1\frac{1}{2}$ 150%
14. $1\frac{1}{3}$ $133\frac{1}{3}\%$
15. 0.20   20%
16. 0.07   7%

Changing Percents to Decimals or Whole Numbers

Show as decimals or whole numbers.

1. 75%   0.75
2. 46%   0.46
3. 3.5%   0.035
4. 0.2%   0.002
5. 175%   1.75
6. 225%   2.25
7. 300%   3
8. 4%   0.04
9. 1%   0.01
10. $\frac{1}{2}\%$ 0.005
11. $\frac{1}{4}\%$ 0.0025
12. $\frac{2}{3}\%$ $0.00\frac{2}{3}$
13. 200%   2
14. 0.125%   0.00125
15. 100%   1
16. 0.15%   0.0015

Mental
Drill 34

Changing Percents to Fractions

Show as simplified fractions.

1. 17% $\frac{17}{100}$	6. 12% $\frac{3}{25}$	11. 2.3% $\frac{23}{1,000}$	16. 0.5% $\frac{1}{200}$
2. 3% $\frac{3}{100}$	7. 5% $\frac{1}{20}$	12. 1.9% $\frac{19}{1,000}$	17. 1.5% $\frac{3}{200}$
3. 6% $\frac{3}{50}$	8. 4% $\frac{1}{25}$	13. 1.3% $\frac{13}{1,000}$	18. 3.5% $\frac{7}{200}$
4. 14% $\frac{7}{50}$	9. 24% $\frac{6}{25}$	14. 1.4% $\frac{7}{500}$	19. 2.8% $\frac{7}{250}$
5. 8% $\frac{2}{25}$	10. 34% $\frac{17}{50}$	15. 0.8% $\frac{1}{125}$	20. 1.2% $\frac{3}{250}$

Mental
Drill 35

Multiplying by Fractional Equivalents of Parts of 100%

Find the products.

1. $12\frac{1}{2}$% of $32 $4	10. $33\frac{1}{3}$% of $129 $43
2. 75% of $28 $21	11. 40% of $80 $32
3. 20% of $40 $8	12. $66\frac{2}{3}$% of $45 $30
4. $66\frac{2}{3}$% of $33 $22	13. 25% of $26 $6.50
5. $87\frac{1}{2}$% of $48 $42	14. $12\frac{1}{2}$% of $65 $8.13
6. $37\frac{1}{2}$% of $64 $24	15. 25% of $29 $7.25
7. $33\frac{1}{3}$% of $36 $12	16. 50% of $43 $21.50
8. $87\frac{1}{2}$% of $72 $63	17. 60% of $40 $24
9. $62\frac{1}{2}$% of $40 $25	18. 80% of $50 $40

Mental
Drill 36

Multiplying by 1%, 10%, 100%, or 1,000%

Find the products.

1. 1% of $40 $0.40	10. 10% of $2.15 $0.22
2. 10% of $82 $8.20	11. 10% of $78 $7.80
3. 100% of $39 $39	12. 1% of $150 $1.50
4. 1,000% of $32 $320	13. 1,000% of $0.90 $9
5. 10% of $24 $2.40	14. 1% of $6.95 $0.07
6. 1% of $76 $0.76	15. 100% of $35.40 $35.40
7. 1% of $120 $1.20	16. 10% of $8.17 $0.82
8. 10% of $65 $6.50	17. 1% of $35.40 $0.35
9. 1% of $125 $1.25	18. 1,000% of $4.60 $46

Mental Drill 37

Multiplying a Percent by $1, $10, $100, $1,000

Find the products.

1.	25% of $1	$0.25		7.	1% of $100	$1
2.	$66\frac{2}{3}$% of $10	$6.67		8.	$87\frac{1}{2}$% of $1	$0.88
3.	$62\frac{1}{2}$% of $100	$62.50		9.	75% of $10	$7.50
4.	20% of $1,000	$200		10.	40% of $100	$40
5.	75% of $100	$75		11.	$12\frac{1}{2}$% of $10	$1.25
6.	$37\frac{1}{2}$% of $10	$3.75		12.	80% of $100	$80

Mental Drill 38

Multiplying by Fractional Parts of 1%

Find the products.

1.	1% of $700	$7		10.	$\frac{3}{4}$% of $600	$4.50
2.	$\frac{1}{2}$% of $600	$3		11.	$\frac{3}{8}$% of $1,600	$6
3.	$\frac{1}{4}$% of $800	$2		12.	$\frac{1}{10}$% of $1,575	$1.58
4.	$\frac{1}{3}$% of $1,200	$4		13.	$\frac{1}{10}$% of $182	$0.18
5.	$\frac{1}{5}$% of $1,000	$2		14.	$\frac{1}{2}$% of $100	$0.50
6.	$\frac{1}{8}$% of $2,400	$3		15.	$\frac{2}{3}$% of $100	$0.67
7.	1% of $525	$5.25		16.	$\frac{3}{4}$% of $520	$3.90
8.	$\frac{2}{3}$% of $1,500	$10		17.	$\frac{3}{4}$% of $100	$0.75
9.	$\frac{1}{2}$% of $1,250	$6.25		18.	$\frac{3}{8}$% of $400	$1.50

Mental Drill 39

Exact Fractional Parts of $1 — $\frac{1}{4}$, $\frac{1}{2}$, and $\frac{3}{4}$

Find the costs.

1.	36 @ 25¢	$9		9.	28 @ $0.25	$7
2.	16 @ 75¢	$12		10.	180 @ $0.50	$90
3.	160 @ $0.50	$80		11.	24 @ $0.75	$18
4.	28 @ $0.75	$21		12.	230 @ 50¢	$115
5.	120 @ $0.25	$30		13.	16 @ $0.25	$4
6.	210 @ 50¢	$105		14.	290 @ 50¢	$145
7.	48 @ $0.25	$12		15.	280 @ 75¢	$210
8.	32 @ 75¢	$24				

**Mental
Drill 40**

Exact Fractional Parts of $1 — $\frac{1}{8}$, $\frac{3}{8}$, $\frac{5}{8}$, and $\frac{7}{8}$

Find the costs.

1. 72 @ 0.12\frac{1}{2}$ $9
2. 24 @ 62$\frac{1}{2}$¢ $15
3. 32 @ 37$\frac{1}{2}$¢ $12
4. 16 @ 0.87\frac{1}{2}$ $14
5. 56 @ 0.37\frac{1}{2}$ $21
6. 72 @ 0.62\frac{1}{2}$ $45
7. 64 @ 12$\frac{1}{2}$¢ $8
8. 32 @ 0.87\frac{1}{2}$ $28
9. 16 @ 62$\frac{1}{2}$¢ $10

10. 24 @ 87$\frac{1}{2}$¢ $21
11. 48 @ 0.37\frac{1}{2}$ $18
12. 32 @ 0.12\frac{1}{2}$ $4
13. 40 @ 0.62\frac{1}{2}$ $25
14. 96 @ 12$\frac{1}{2}$¢ $12
15. 48 @ 0.62\frac{1}{2}$ $30
16. 24 @ 37$\frac{1}{2}$¢ $9
17. 56 @ 0.12\frac{1}{2}$ $7
18. 80 @ 87$\frac{1}{2}$¢ $70

**Mental
Drill 41**

Exact Fractional Parts of $1 — $\frac{1}{3}$ and $\frac{2}{3}$

Find the costs.

1. 27 @ 33$\frac{1}{3}$¢ $9
2. 18 @ 66$\frac{2}{3}$¢ $12
3. 72 @ 0.66\frac{2}{3}$ $48
4. 24 @ 0.33\frac{1}{3}$ $8
5. 21 @ 66$\frac{2}{3}$¢ $14
6. 39 @ 0.33\frac{1}{3}$ $13
7. 36 @ 0.33\frac{1}{3}$ $12
8. 24 @ 66$\frac{2}{3}$¢ $16
9. 42 @ 0.33\frac{1}{3}$ $14

10. 120 @ 66$\frac{2}{3}$¢ $80
11. 48 @ 33$\frac{1}{3}$¢ $16
12. 540 @ 0.66\frac{2}{3}$ $360
13. 45 @ 0.33\frac{1}{3}$ $15
14. 126 @ 0.66\frac{2}{3}$ $84
15. 36 @ 66$\frac{2}{3}$¢ $24
16. 120 @ 0.33\frac{1}{3}$ $40
17. 240 @ 66$\frac{2}{3}$¢ $160
18. 600 @ 0.66\frac{2}{3}$ $400

**Mental
Drill 42**

Exact Fractional Parts of $1 — $\frac{1}{5}$, $\frac{2}{5}$, $\frac{3}{5}$, and $\frac{4}{5}$

Find the costs.

1. 45 @ 20¢ $9
2. 85 @ 40¢ $34
3. 35 @ $0.20 $7
4. 95 @ $0.40 $38
5. 35 @ 60¢ $21
6. 15 @ 80¢ $12

7. 55 @ $0.60 $33
8. 65 @ $0.80 $52
9. 135 @ $0.20 $27
10. 145 @ $0.80 $116
11. 110 @ $0.60 $66
12. 155 @ $0.40 $62

Exact Fractional Parts of $1 — Review

Mental Drill 43

Find the costs.

1. 180 @ $33\frac{1}{3}$¢ $60
2. 48 @ 75¢ $36
3. 185 @ 20¢ $37
4. 160 @ $87\frac{1}{2}$¢ $140
5. 140 @ 50¢ $70
6. 120 @ $0.33\frac{1}{3}$ $40
7. 32 @ $0.62\frac{1}{2}$ $20
8. 128 @ 25¢ $32
9. 360 @ $66\frac{2}{3}$¢ $240
10. 480 @ $37\frac{1}{2}$¢ $180
11. 160 @ $0.40 $64
12. 180 @ $0.66\frac{2}{3}$ $120
13. 64 @ $0.12\frac{1}{2}$ $8
14. 135 @ $0.20 $27
15. 480 @ $0.66\frac{2}{3}$ $320

16. 56 @ $37\frac{1}{2}$¢ $21
17. 350 @ $0.80 $280
18. 600 @ $66\frac{2}{3}$¢ $400
19. 120 @ $0.12\frac{1}{2}$ $15
20. 15 @ $0.60 $9
21. 450 @ $0.33\frac{1}{3}$ $150
22. 240 @ $0.75 $180
23. 155 @ 40¢ $62
24. 240 @ $0.87\frac{1}{2}$ $210
25. 180 @ 50¢ $90
26. 36 @ $0.33\frac{1}{3}$ $12
27. 160 @ $62\frac{1}{2}$¢ $100
28. 240 @ 25¢ $60
29. 540 @ $0.66\frac{2}{3}$ $360
30. 32 @ $0.12\frac{1}{2}$ $4

Combinations of Exact Fractional Parts of $1

Mental Drill 44

Find the costs.

1. 24 @ $1.12\frac{1}{2}$ $27
2. 14 @ $2.50 $35
3. 48 @ $1.25 $60
4. 15 @ $1.10 $16.50
5. 80 @ $1.50 $120
6. 60 @ $1.25 $75
7. 72 @ $1.12\frac{1}{2}$ $81
8. 25 @ $1.10 $27.50
9. 90 @ $1.50 $135
10. 16 @ $2.50 $40
11. 160 @ $1.50 $240

12. 120 @ $1.25 $150
13. 140 @ $2.50 $350
14. 35 @ $1.10 $38.50
15. 96 @ $1.12\frac{1}{2}$ $108
16. 320 @ $2.50 $800
17. 250 @ $1.50 $375
18. 120 @ $1.10 $132
19. 240 @ $1.25 $300
20. 104 @ $1.12\frac{1}{2}$ $117
21. 420 @ $1.50 $630

**Sections 1–6
Unit 1**

1. A cash-and-carry store's cash registers showed these amounts from sales on Friday: Register 1, $5,893.23; Register 2, $6,709.44; Register 3, $1,078.98; and Register 4, $9,101.45. What were the total cash receipts on Friday? $22,783.10 [1]

2. Diana Farley runs errands for local businesses, using her own car. During one week she spent the following amounts: gasoline for car, $54.57; oil for car, $14.79; windshield wiper blade replacement, $15.78; and city sticker for car, $25. How much did Diana spend during the week? $110.14 [2]

3. Mario Torres deposited these items in a bank: (bills) 5 twenties, 6 tens, 5 fives, 61 ones, (coins) 23 halves, 9 quarters, 8 dimes, 21 nickels, 19 pennies, and (checks) $309.78 and $7.24. What was the total deposit? $578.81 [4]

4. Esta Molin's gross power bill for April was $126.89. By paying early Esta was able to take a discount of $2.54. What was the net bill Esta paid? $124.35 [4]

5. Jay Volmer sold bird houses at a homecoming fair for a senior citizen fund. His gross sales were $106.50. The houses cost him $37.50. Other expenses were $24.63. What net amount did he make on the sale? $44.37 [4]

6. A copy center had 138 reams of copy paper on hand on February 1. During February more paper was bought in these amounts: 25, 50, 100, and 75 reams. If 159 reams are on hand at the end of the month, how many reams were used during the month? 229 [4]

7. Clair Weyman started the day with a bank balance of $145.67. During the day she deposited a check for $50 in the automatic teller machine and used her debit card for these purchases: $13.78, $5.50, $26.89, $59.98. What was her new bank balance at the end of the day? $89.52 [4]

8. On April 30 Samantha had a check register balance of $344.05 and a bank statement balance of $504.25. A service charge of $1.95 and interest earned of $1.60 were shown on the bank statement. The outstanding checks were: #21, $24.15; #23, $38.90; #24, $46.50; and #25, $51. Make a reconciliation statement. $343.70 [5]

9. Phil Ford's bank statement on July 1 showed a balance of $539.12. His check register balance on the same date was $412.08. The bank statement listed a service charge of $2.66 and interest earned of $3.02. Outstanding checks were: #156 for $34.41; #157 for $80.33; and #160 for $11.94. Prepare a reconciliation statement. $412.44 [5]

‡10. Brad's bank statement on January 31 showed a balance of $1,165.75. His check register balance was $1,319.05. Checks were

outstanding for $16.60 (#89), $23.10 (#91), and $34.60 (#93). A deposit of $170.50, mailed on January 31, was not recorded on the bank statement. A canceled check for $57.10 had not been recorded in his check register. Prepare a reconciliation statement. $1,261.95 [6]

‡11. Farah's check register showed a balance of $150.77 at the end of last month. Her bank statement balance on the same date was $307.98. A comparison of the statement with the register showed a service charge of $1.02, interest earned of $0.30, and outstanding checks of $28.54 (#101), $19.29 (#102), and $101.10 (#104). A canceled check written for $45.00 had been mistakenly entered in the register as $54. Prepare a reconciliation statement. $159.05 [6]

‡12. On October 31 Wilma Butler received a bank statement showing a balance of $349.82. Wilma's checkbook showed a balance of $210.52 on the same date. When she compared her checkbook with the bank statement, she discovered that she had failed to record a deposit of $50.00 in the checkbook and that there were outstanding checks for $50.80 (#45), $21.15 (#46), and $18.40 (#47). There was also a bank service charge of $2.25 and interest earned of $1.20. Prepare a reconciliation statement. $259.47 [6]

**Sections 7–12
Unit 2**

1. Marva Hiller earns $8 an hour.
   a. What is her gross pay for a 40-hour week? $320
   b. If she earned the same weekly pay for a year, what would be her gross pay for the year? $16,640 [7]

2. Viktor Miller earns a monthly salary of $2,056. What is Viktor's gross pay for one year? $24,672 [7]

3. Samantha works in a factory and is paid $2.40 for every usable chair she produces. Last week she produced these numbers of chairs in five days of work: 40, 37, 35, 41, 44. When the chairs were checked, 5 were found to be unusable. What was Samantha's gross pay for the 5 days of work? $460.80 [7]

4. Piece-rate employees at a factory are paid in this way for the units they make in one work day: $0.70 each for the first 60 pieces, $0.80 each for the next 15 pieces, and $0.95 each for all pieces completed over 75 pieces. On Tuesday Oscar completed 86 pieces. What were his gross earnings for that day? $64.45 [7]

5. Catherine's average sales for the last 9 weeks of last year were $1,138. For the first 4 weeks of this year, her sales were $1,228, $1,875, $1,290, and $1,329. What were Catherine's average sales for the 13 weeks? $1,228 [10]

6. A college student earned $246, $288, $234, and $276 over a 4-week period. How much must he earn during the fifth week to have average earnings of $255 for the five weeks? $231 [10]

7. Mattye Sparks worked 38 hours last week and had gross earnings of $296.40. What was her hourly rate of pay? $7.80 [11]

8. During the first 2 weeks in January, Jerry Melvin earned $250 each week clearing snow from parking lots. In the third week of January he earned $320, and in the fourth week he earned $400. What average amount did he earn per week for those 4 weeks? $305 [10]

Sections 13–20
Unit 3

1. In 1 firm there are 10 office workers, 70 factory workers, and 2 managers. Without simplifying the terms, find the ratio of [16]
   a. Office workers to total workers 10 to 82
   b. Factory workers to managers 70 to 2
   c. Managers to total workers 2 to 82

2. Arlene Block earns $8.20 an hour and is paid double time for any overtime hours she works. Last week she worked 37 regular hours and 6 overtime hours. What were Arlene's gross earnings for the week? $401.80 [17]

3. Alphonse Scanetti is paid $12.70 an hour for regular-time work with time and a half paid for work beyond 40 hours a week. Last week he worked these hours: Monday, 7; Tuesday, 9; Wednesday, 9; Thursday, 10; Friday, 8. What was Alphonse's total pay for the week? $565.15 [17]

4. A worker spent $23\frac{1}{2}$ hours making a part. If the pay was $12.40 an hour, what was the cost of the worker's time to make the part? $291.40 [13]

5. John Czarnota earned $25 last week and $4\frac{1}{2}$ times that much this week. How much did he earn this week? $112.50 [18]

6. A builder bought $32\frac{1}{2}$ acres of land and divided it into lots of $2\frac{1}{2}$ acres each. How many lots were there? 13 [18]

7. Zeline Thomas earned $440 last week. Of that amount, $\frac{1}{8}$ came from a part-time job. What were Zeline's earnings from her part-time job? $55 [15]

8. Patricia Surrell earned $280 last week. That amount is $\frac{7}{8}$ of her usual weekly earnings. What amount does Patricia usually earn? $320 [15]

9. The profit from a business owned by Misek and Brent is shared in the ratio of 5 to 3, with Misek getting the larger share. If last year's profit was $96,000, what amount did Misek get? $60,000 [16]

10. Eve Marsten found a job closer to home that pays $\frac{1}{7}$ less than her old hourly pay rate of $10.50. What is her new hourly pay rate? $9 [19]

Sections 21–29
Unit 4

1. Elroy, Costello, and McMahon earned $672.35, $829.87, and $497.23 respectively last week. Using a FICA rate of 7.65%, find the FICA tax withheld from each worker's pay. $51.43, $63.49, $38.04 [21]

2. Peter Noeltner earns $7.50 an hour for a 40-hour week, with time and a half for overtime. Last week he worked 48 hours. Deduc-

tions from his earnings were: $45 for federal withholding tax, $29.84 for social security tax, $12 for state withholding tax, $5 for a National Fund contribution, and $23.88 for health insurance. What was Peter's take-home pay? $274.32 [21]

3. Piece-rate workers at a factory are paid on this schedule: 60 pieces or less, 50¢; next 15 pieces, 60¢; over 75 pieces, 70¢. If a worker produced 107 pieces and had deductions of $10.60, what was the worker's net pay? $50.80 [7,21]

4. Leona Wunch is paid $1,254 a month. She estimates that her fringe benefits are 28% of her pay. She is offered a new job which pays $995 a month with fringe benefits of 38% of monthly pay. Which job offers more total job benefits per month, and how much more per month does it offer? Old job; $232.02 [23]

5. Wilma Bollini earns an annual wage of $23,589. She estimates her fringe benefits at 0.31 of her wages. She also estimates that her job expenses are: insurance, 0.08 of her wages; transportation, $269; dues, $245; and office birthday fund, $38. What are her annual net job benefits? $28,462.47 [23]

6. Leta Fischer is paid a 5% commission on the first $10,000 of sales she makes and 8% on sales she makes over $10,000. Last week Leta had sales of $35,678. What was her gross pay? $2,554.24 [28]

7. Phan Am Van makes a salary of $650 a month plus a 10% commission on any sales he makes over $5,000. Last month Phan's sales were $8,459. What were his gross earnings? $995.90 [28]

8. Myra Stein gets a monthly salary of $1,100 and is paid commissions of varying rates on sales. Her total earnings, including salary and commissions, were $34,200 for last year. If her sales were $350,000 for the year, what was her average rate of commission, written as a percent? 6% [28]

9. Marlene Sticha was paid 50 cents commission for each box of greeting cards and 40 cents for each box of Mother's Day cards she sold. For one week her earnings were $130. If she sold 72 boxes of greeting cards, how many boxes of Mother's Day cards did she sell? 235 [28]

10. Angela Caragine works in a store selling cosmetics on which she makes a 5% commission and cookware on which she makes an 8% commission. She also gets a base salary of $175 a week. Last week she sold $620.40 worth of cosmetics and $238.50 worth of cookware. What were her gross earnings for the week? $225.10 [28]

11. A real estate agent sold a house for $140,000. The agency's commission was 6% of the selling price. The agent is paid 40% of the commission. How much did the agent get? $3,360 [29]

12. The Aldrich Agency collected 80% of a bill of $2,350 owed to the Bratton Company. If the agency charged 40% commission, what were the net proceeds that Bratton Company received? $1,128 [29]

13. A builder quoted Ramsey a price of $109,782 to build a house using Ramsey's plans. A similar house already built costs $96,300. By what percent does the builder's price exceed the cost of the house already built?   14% [26]

14. A salesperson was paid a salary of $1,200 a month plus a commission on all sales. Last month the salesperson's sales were $30,000, and the total amount earned in salary and commission was $2,700. [28]
    a. How much commission was the salesperson paid? $1,500
    b. What rate of commission was the salesperson paid?   5%

‡15. A real estate agency received a commission of $4,500 on the sale of a house. This was 6% of the selling price of the house. What was the selling price of the house? $75,000 [28]

‡16. A high school class wants to make money by selling magazines. A company offers the class the chance to sell magazines at 40% commission. How many dollars worth of magazines must the class sell to earn a total commission of $3,000? $7,500 [28]

‡17. This year's registration for a typing class in a school is 184 students. This is a decrease of 8% from last year's registration for a typing class at the same school. What was last year's registration in the typing class?   200 [27]

‡18. Last year the Colgeri family saved $4,200, which was 8% of their total income. What was the family's total income last year? $52,500 [27]

‡19. Emerson Mueller has been offered a job paying $2,318 a month. This is 22% more than his current job pays. How much does his current job pay a month? $1,900 [27]

**Sections 30–32
Unit 5**

1. To make orange juice from frozen concentrate, you use 1 part concentrate to 4.5 parts water. Each part is 354 mL. How much orange juice in liters can you make from 1 part concentrate?   1.95 L [32]

2. The heights of 5 members of a basketball team are: 1.97 m, 1.85 m, 2.08 m, 1.81 m, and 1.94 m. What is the average height, in meters, of these basketball players?   1.93 m [10, 30]

3. A bottle of rubber cement weighs 210 g. One gross (12 dozen) of the bottles is being shipped to a store in 2 boxes that weigh 1.1 kg each when empty. What is the total weight in kilograms of the shipment?   32.44 kg [32]

4. You need to carpet a room that measures 4 m by 5.4 m. [31]
    a. How many square meters of carpeting will you need if carpeting is sold only in whole square meters?   22 m^2
    b. How much will the carpeting cost if it is priced at $14 per square meter? $308

5. Danuta Afton is using a stencil to make a sign. She figures that each character will need an average of 20 mm of space. The longest

line will contain 18 characters. Danuta also wants to leave 40 mm of space at each end of the longest line. What exact width must her sign be in centimeters so that her sign will be done as planned?
44 cm [30]

6. Les Wilkins delivers drinking water to his customers in his truck, which holds 9 kL of water. When he began his deliveries on Tuesday, his truck's water tank was 90% full. On that day he delivered these amounts of water: 2 kL, 0.8 kL, 1.3 kL, 1.4 kL, 0.9 kL. How much water was left in the truck after Les's last delivery?
1.7 kL [32]

7. How many kilograms of meat are needed to serve 25 people, if each person is to be served 160 grams of meat?   4 kg [32]

8. A family built a new home on a lot that measures 30 meters wide by 50 meters long. The house and garage take up 210 square meters of the lot. The driveway and sidewalk take up 20% of the lot. If the family decides to plant grass on the remainder of the lot, how much space in square meters will they have to use?   990 m² [31]

Sections 33–42
Unit 6

1. Last year the Jacksons spent their net income this way: 22%, food; 28%, housing; 18%, transportation; 10%, clothing; 15%, other; and 7%, savings. They expect their net income this year to be $37,500. If they spend the same percentage as last year, what amount will they spend on each type of expense?
$8,250, food; $10,500, housing; $6,750, transportation; $3,750, clothing; $5,625, other; $2,625, savings [33]

2. A store's total sales for the year were $745,800. The store's delivery expense was $59,664. What percent of total sales was the delivery expense?   8% [33]

3. What is the cost of 3,600 lbs. of potatoes at $32 per C? $1,152 [35]

4. What is the cost of 6 cans of soup @ 2 for $0.72? $2.16 [34]

5. What is the unit price, to the nearest whole cent, of pens that sell at 8 for $2.99? $0.37 [37]

6. What is the total cost of a VCR that sells for $289.89 plus $5\frac{1}{2}$% sales tax? $305.83 [34]

7. What is the cost of 34,500 lb. of cement at $27.98 per T?
$482.66 [35]

8. Computer diskettes, regularly priced at $15 a box, are reduced to 3 boxes for $39.99. How much would you save by buying 12 boxes at the sale price? $20.04 [38]

9. Find the total cost of this order: 24 yds. @ $0.375, 15 ft. @ $0.60, 18 yds. @ 0.33\frac{1}{3}$, 16 ft. @ $0.75. $36 [34]

10. A camcorder can be rented for $25 a day or $100 a week. If you need it for 6 days [38]

a. How much cheaper would it be to rent it for a week instead of by the day? $50

b. If you could buy the camcorder for $989, what would be the payback period, to the nearest tenth of a week, for buying rather than renting it by the week? 9.9 weeks

11. Bregnev's electric meter read 42,789 on October 1 and 44,885 on January 1. Bregnev's electric company charges $0.1052 for the first 500 KWH and $0.1247 for all KWH over 500. What was Bregnev's electric bill for the quarter if she pays state taxes of 5%? $264.20 [39]

12. Jarret's call to a friend cost $12.76 on Wednesday morning. By waiting until Saturday, he could have saved 55%. What would have been the cost of the call on Saturday? $5.74 [42]

13. Tina bought a space heater for $246. She plans to lower her thermostat and save 20% of her winter heating bills. If Tina's winter heating bills average $820, what is the payback period for the heater? $1\frac{1}{2}$ years [40]

14. Rod used 56 hundred cubic feet of gas last month. The therm factor used on Rod's bill is 1.115. The per therm rates are: first 50 therms, $0.2011; over 50 therms, $0.1892. There is a facilities charge of $15 and a state sales tax of 3%. What was Rod's total bill? $28.15 [39]

15. Becky used 1,200 gallons of water on her last quarterly bill. If she pays $0.895 per 100 gallons of water, what was Becky's water bill for the quarter? $10.74 [41]

Sections 43–51
Unit 7

1. On August 4, you borrow money on a demand note. You repay it on November 2. How many days interest do you pay? 90 [46]

2. On May 12, Vernita borrowed $2,000 for 73 days at 14%, exact interest.
   a. On what date must Vernita repay the loan? July 24 [46]
   b. How much will Vernita owe on the due date? $2,056 [44]

3. On July 19, Genaro signed a $6,000, 12%, 90-day banker's interest note. How much will Genaro pay when the note comes due? $6,180 [44]

4. Vernon signed a $5,900, 4-month note with his bank on October 5. The bank discounted the note at 15%. [47]
   a. What was the due date of the note? February 5
   b. What were the proceeds of the note? $5,605

5. You can buy a snow blower for $250 cash or for $25 down and $12 a month for 24 months. [50]
   a. What is the finance charge on the installment plan? $63
   b. By what percent does the installment price exceed the cash price, to the nearest whole percent? 25%

6. Francine bought an air conditioner for $350. She paid 10% down and the balance in equal monthly installments of $21. [50]

a. What was the amount of Francine's down payment? $35
b. How many months did it take for her to pay for the air conditioner? 15

7. Earl bought a big screen T.V. set on the installment plan for a total price of $1,500. He agreed to make a down payment of $120 and pay the balance in 24 equal monthly installments. [49]
a. What was the amount of each monthly payment? $57.50
b. What percent of the installment price was Earl's down payment? 8%

8. Tracy bought an audio system, with a cash price of $850, on the installment plan. She paid 10% down and the balance in 20 payments of $48.45. [49, 50]
a. What was the down payment? $85
b. What was the installment price? $1,054
c. What was the finance charge? $204
d. What was the finance charge per $100? $26.67

9. Rudy can buy a laser printer for $2,500. If he uses a credit card, the store will add 3% to the price. [51]
a. What is the credit card price of the computer? $2,575
b. How much will Rudy save by paying cash? $75

10. In May, Cherise was charged 1.35% on her unpaid credit card balance of $378. She was also charged $20 for annual membership fees. What was her credit card balance after these charges were made? $403.10 [51]

**Sections 52–54
Unit 8**

1. Mario Healy's savings account had a balance of $501.27 on March 31. On April 1, interest of $5.81 was credited to his account. These were his transactions during the rest of the month: April 8, deposit, $141; April 17, withdrawal, $25; April 22, deposit, $160; April 30, withdrawal, $55. What should be Mario's final savings account balance on April 30? $728.08 [52]

2. On July 1, Beulah Hamel deposited $800 in a savings account that paid 6% annual interest, compounded quarterly on January 2, April 1, July 1, and October 1. She made no other deposits or withdrawals during the rest of the year. What was the balance of her savings account on January 2, after the 2 interest payments made by the bank were added? $824.18 [52]

3. A bank pays 5.5% interest on savings accounts, compounded semi-annually on January 2 and July 1. What amount of interest would be earned on July 1 on a deposit of $1,200 made on January 2, assuming that no additional deposits or withdrawals were made? $33 [52]

4. A credit union pays interest quarterly on January 2, April 1, July 1, and October 1 at a 5% annual rate. On October 1, Angeline had a balance of $630, including interest to date. She deposited $300 on November 14 and withdrew $400 on December 19. What was her balance on January 2 if the credit union figured interest on the minimum balance on deposit in a quarter? $536.63 [52]

5. The value of $1 at 8% annual interest compounded daily for: 30 days = $1.006688; 90 days = $1.020199; and 180 days = $1.040806. Using these values, find how much interest a $700 deposit to a savings account would earn in
   a. 90 days $14.14 [53]
   b. 180 days $28.56 [53]

6. A deposit of $400 earns $38.21 interest when an annual rate of 9% is compounded daily for 365 days. What effective rate of interest is earned on the deposit, to the nearest hundredth percent? 9.55% [53]

7. A savings and loan association pays 6% interest compounded quarterly on passbook savings, and 9% simple interest on savings certificates. How much more would you earn in a year on $8,000 invested in a certificate rather than a passbook account? $229.09 [54]

8. A penalty of 9 months' interest at a rate of 14% on the entire account balance is charged for early withdrawals from time-deposit accounts. What is the penalty for an early withdrawal from a time-deposit account that has a balance of $3,500? $367.50 [54]

9. Russell Del Canto deposited $5,000 in a 6-month money-market account. Compound interest was figured and paid on his account each quarter at these annual rates: first quarter, 8.05%; second quarter, 8.27%. What amount of interest did Russell's account earn for the first quarter? second quarter? $100.63; $105.46 [54]

Sections 55–62
Unit 9

1. Dalton Wade bought 12, $500 par value bonds at 96. Commissions and other expenses were $6.50 per bond. What was the total cost of the bonds? $5,838 [55]

2. Ellen owns 16 bonds that pay interest at an annual rate of 8.5%. If Ellen gets interest on these bonds semiannually, what is the amount of her interest every 6 months? $680 [56]

3. A $1,000 par value, 12% bond was bought at 120. What is the yield on this bond investment?   10% [56]

4. Mark Sun bought 40 shares of stock at $47\frac{3}{4}$, plus commission of $42.50. What was the total cost of the purchase? $1,952.50 [57]

5. Helen Charbonneau owns 80 shares of Pac-Right common stock that pays a quarterly dividend of $0.82 per share. She also owns 140 shares of Pac-Right preferred stock, $100 par value, that pays an annual dividend of 6.8%. What total annual dividend does she get from her
   a. Common stock? $262.40 [58]
   b. Preferred stock? $952 [58]

6. Rico Pirreli bought 70 shares of stock at $51.125 a share and was charged a commission of $64.25. The stock pays an annual dividend of 7.3% on a par value of $50. What rate of income does Rico earn on this investment, to the nearest tenth of a percent? 7.0% [58]

7. Beverly Goraco bought 150 shares of a stock at a total cost of $4,672. She kept the stock for 2 years, during which time she received semiannual dividends of $1.30 a share. She then sold the 150 shares at $33\frac{3}{4}$ and was charged a commission and other costs of $85.
   a. What was her profit or loss from the sale of the stock?
      $305.50 profit [59]
   b. What was her total gain from owning and selling the stock?
      $1,085.50 [59]

8. Henry invested $4,500 in a no-load mutual fund with a net asset value of 8.72. How many shares did he buy?   516.055 [60]

9. To the nearest tenth of a percent, what rate of commission is charged by a fund with a NAV of 14.58 and offer price of 15.78?
   7.6% [60]

10. Arlon Maxwell made a $29,000 down payment on a resort condominium that sold for $85,000. He figures that his average weekly rental income will be $400, while his total annual expenses will be $15,800. If his figures are correct,
    a. What annual net income will this investment earn?
       $5,000 [61]
    b. What rate of income, to the nearest tenth of a percent, will he earn on his cash investment?   17.2% [61]

11. Sue Blakely owns 5 acres of land next to a flower and garden shop. Sue paid $24,000 for the land and figures that her annual expenses of owning the land are $900. The shop is interested in renting Sue's land for only 6 months. If Sue wants to earn an annual rate of 25% on her investment and cover all her expenses for the year, what monthly rent should she ask for? $1,150 [62]

12. Antoine Bergeron made a $15,000 down payment on a vacant auto repair garage and borrowed the rest of the $90,000 purchase price. He installed electric door openers that cost $7,000 and added a revolving sign for another $3,200. He also spent $2,000 to repair the plumbing and heating systems. What was Antoine's capital investment in this property? $25,200 [62]

‡13. The annual rental on a business property is $8,400. Annual expenses are $3,900. What is the highest cash investment you can make in the property if you want a net income of 15% on your investment? $30,000 [62]

**Sections 63–66
Unit 10**

1. Matt Dixon bought a 2-bedroom condominium for $80,000. He paid 35% of the price in cash. He also had to pay $250 to have the property surveyed, $472 to have the title searched, and $320 for the lawyer's fee. What amount of cash did Matt need when he bought the condominium? $29,042 [63]

2. On a 30-year mortgage of $71,400, Nicole Washburn makes monthly payments of $692.37. What total amount of interest will she pay on her mortgage over its 30-year term?   177,853.20 [63]

3. Ralph's mortgage company raised the interest rate charged on his variable rate mortgage from 7.75% to 9%. Ralph's monthly mortgage payment went up from $457.91 to $493.67. What amount more per year will the total of the new monthly payments be? $429.12 [63]

4. Shirley Dressen's old mortgage payment was $683 per month. After refinancing, her new mortgage payment is $571 per month. To refinance the loan, Shirley has to pay $670 in closing costs and $450 in prepayment penalties. What is the net amount less she will pay in the first year with the new mortgage? $224 [63]

5. The Newmans bought a house for $78,000 that was appraised 1 year ago at $90,000. If the house depreciates at the rate of 1.25% of its purchase price, what is the amount of annual depreciation? $975 [64]

6. Helen and Bill Croswell want to buy a home. They estimate that their expenses in the first year will be: mortgage interest, $4,592; real estate taxes, $1,673; insurance, $319; depreciation, $890; maintenance and repairs, $780; lost income on the cash invested, $1,400. They also estimate that they will save $2,300 in income taxes because of home expenses. What is their net cost of owning the home in the first year? $7,354 [64]

7. The Bowdell family rents a house and pays a monthly rent of $735. They can buy the house they are renting for $70,000. If they buy the house, they figure that net annual operating expenses will total $6,300. The Bowdells also would have to withdraw $10,600 from a time deposit account that pays 10.5% annual interest to make the down payment.
   a. Is it cheaper to rent or buy the home?   Cheaper to buy
   b. How much will be saved in 1 year if the Bowdell's choose the less expensive way? $1,407 [64]

8. Beverly bought a car for $10,370. After using it for 5 years, she bought a new car for $12,790, giving her old car as a trade in and $9,590 in cash. What was the
   a. Average annual depreciation of the old car? $1,434 [65]
   b. Rate of depreciation, to the nearest tenth percent?
      13.8% [65]

9. George Caine leases a car for $236 a month and 8¢ for every mile it is driven over 15,000 miles in 1 year. If he drives the car 22,000 miles in a year, what is the total cost of leasing the car for the year? $3,392 [66]

10. Karen drove her car 16,830 miles in 1 year. If she averaged 20.4 miles to the gallon and paid $1.24 per gallon for gas, how much did she spend for gas that year? $1,023 [66]

11. Xavier Delorm paid these amounts to operate his car for 1 year: insurance, $648; gas and oil, $937; inspection fee, $15; license

plates, $51; repairs and maintenance, $293. What average amount was paid monthly for these operating costs? $162 [66]

Sections 67–73
Unit 11

1. The property tax rate in a city is $37.89 per $1,000 of assessed value. What is the property tax on a house and lot assessed at $25,000? $947.25 [67]

2. Tyrone owns property worth $113,000 that is assessed at 50% of its value. If the local tax rate is $2.56 per $100 of assessed value, what is Tyrone's tax bill? $1,446.40 [67]

3. Johnstown's estimated expenses for the year are $1,789,300. Of this amount, $47,140 is to be received from licenses and other income. If the total assessed value of all taxable property in the town is $42,700,000, what tax rate per $100 is needed to raise the rest of the funds? $4.08 [68]

4. A repairman spent 2 hours @ $8.75 an hour fixing a washing machine. The repairman also replaced 2 belts @ $12.50 and an electric motor for $29.95. The state in which the repairs were done has a sales tax of 6% on goods, but not on services. What was the total repair bill? $75.75 [69]

5. Jason's telephone bill included $18.98 for local service and $23.77 for long-distance charges. A 3% excise tax and a 5% sales tax were added to the bill. What was Jason's total bill? $46.17 [69]

‡6. A sweater costs $52, including sales tax of 4%. What is the price of the sweater before the tax is added? $50 [69]

7. During March, Epico Fabrics paid its employees $124,660. At 7.65%, how much FICA taxes did Epico have to pay as an employer? $9,536.49 [70]

8. Phyllis is self-employed and earned $38,895 last year. At 15.3%, how much self-employment tax did she pay? $5,950.94 [70]

9. Rafael Soto is single. On his federal income tax return, he lists adjusted gross income at $29,200. He claims $4,900 in deductions and 1 exemption at $2,000. His return shows that $4,160 has been withheld from his salary by his employer for federal income taxes. Using Illustration 71–1, find if his federal taxes are overpaid or underpaid, and by how much. Overpaid; $165 [71]

10. Ivy worked as a garage attendant during the summer and earned $2,480. Her employer deducted $276 in federal withholding taxes. Her father claimed her as an exemption on his income tax return for the year. If she claimed the standard deduction, how much refund should she receive? $276 [72]

11. Helen has taxable income of $25,789. She must pay a city income tax of $1\frac{1}{2}$% and a state income tax of 3% on her taxable income. Find the total amount of income taxes Helen will pay to the city and state. $1,160.51 [73]

**Sections 74–79
Unit 12**

1. A 20-year old male pays $1.37 per $1,000 of term life insurance. What annual premium will he pay for $150,000 of term insurance? $205.50 [74]

2. The rates per $1,000 for a 20-payment life policy for a female, age 30, follow: smoker, $36.80; non-smoker, $28.40. How much more will a smoker pay for premiums on a $25,000, 20-payment life policy over 20 years than a non-smoker? $4,200 [74]

3. Eloise Hoekstra has a life insurance policy for $15,000 and pays a premium rate of $22.18 per $1,000 annually. The insurance company pays a dividend of $49.80 this year that Eloise deducts from her premium. What is Eloise's net premium for the year? $282.90 [75]

4. The cash and loan value of a $30,000 insurance policy held 10 years is $82.04 per $1,000. How much cash would the policy owner get if the policy was canceled after premiums were paid for 10 years? $2,461.20 [75]

5. Wilbur Lenz spent 5 days in a hospital. His bills were: hospital, $1,580; doctor, $800. Wilbur's insurance paid $1,125 of the hospital bill and $575 of the doctor's bill. What amount did Wilbur pay? $680 [76]

6. Your major medical policy has a $500 deductible feature and a 90% coinsurance feature. Last year you spent $1,600 for medical expenses that were covered under your policy. When you file a claim with your insurer for these medical expenses, how much should you expect the insurer to pay? $990 [76]

7. Wendy Fleitz insured her property, valued at $60,000, for 75% of its value. She paid an annual rate of $0.64 per $100 for homeowners insurance. What annual premium did she pay for this coverage? $288 [77]

8. A renter has $5,000 worth of insurance coverage on the contents of her apartment. With a $100 deductible, the annual premium is $80. If she takes a $300 deductible, the annual premium will be reduced by 20%. What would be her annual premium if she took the higher deductible? $64 [77]

9. Liza Cowles canceled her homeowners insurance policy after it was in effect for 22 days. The insurance company charged her 25% of the $360 annual premium for the time the policy was in effect. What amount of refund should Liza get? $270 [77]

10. Property is insured against fire by the Mutual Company for $2,400,000 and by the Freedom Company for $1,200,000. If the 2 companies agree on a settlement of $48,000 for fire damages, for what amount will the Freedom Company be liable? $16,000 [78]

11. Chuck Bostic's house would cost $55,000 to replace. He insures it for $35,200 with a replacement cost policy that requires him to insure property for at least 80% of its replacement cost. If a fire

loss of $3,300 occurs, what amount will the insurance company pay? $2,640 [78]

12. A house valued at $75,000 was insured for $45,000 under a policy with an 80% coinsurance feature. A fire loss of $12,000 occurred. What amount of money will the insurer pay? $9,000 [78]

13. Arlene Tousley pays these amounts semiannually for truck insurance coverages: property damage, $14; bodily injury, $72; collision, $257; comprehensive, $37. What is the annual premium on her truck insurance policy? $760 [79]

Sections 80–86
Unit 13

1. A store owner has these assets: Cash, $4,760; Merchandise Inventory, $78,200; Equipment, $25,600; Supplies, $1,240. One bill of $15,070 and another bill of $7,213 are owed. How much is the owner's capital? $87,517 [80]

2. A store had net sales of $36,508.72 last month. If the cost of goods sold was $23,810.14 and the operating expenses were $7,834.28, what was the net income? $4,864.30 [81]

3. The records of a shop for the month of August show these amounts: merchandise inventory, August 1, $28,417; merchandise inventory, August 31, $36,982; purchases, $67,118. Find the cost of merchandise sold. $58,553 [81]

4. Aileen Uzin runs a retail store. Her net sales for the year were $162,000. The cost of the merchandise that she sold was $118,500. Her operating expenses were $28,920. Her net income was what percent of the net sales for the year? 9% [82]

5. Last year, a store's cost of merchandise sold was $366,600 and the store's average merchandise inventory was $15,600. What was the annual merchandise turnover rate? 23.5 [82]

6. Larkin and Mazern are partners. Their investments are $50,000 and $30,000, respectively. They share income in proportion to their investments. The net income last year was $53,600. What amount did Larkin receive? $33,500 [83]

7. Crowe, Juliano, and Stevens are members of a partnership with investments of $26,000, $39,000, and $65,000, respectively. The partners have agreed that profits are to be shared in proportion to their investments. In 1 year, the firm had net sales of $318,000. The cost of merchandise sold was $186,200. The operating expenses were $51,700.
   a. What was the net income for the year? $80,100 [81]
   b. How much did each partner receive as a share of the net income?
      Crowe, $16,020; Juliano, $24,030; Stevens, $40,050 [83]

8. Jan Ruell invested $32,000 in a business. She was to receive 5% on her original investment and share equally in any remaining net income. Her share of the remaining net income last year was $10,130. What were her total earnings for the year? $11,730 [84]

9. The Farwell Corporation had capital stock consisting of 300 shares of preferred stock paying 6% dividends and 2,000 shares of common stock. The par value of each type of stock is $100 per share. A dividend of $4,000 is to be paid to the shareholders. After the dividends have been paid to the preferred shareholders, how much will be paid as the dividend on each share of common stock? $1.10 [85]

10. A corporation with capital stock of 100,000 shares at $75 par value had a net income of $360,000 for last year. The directors declared a dividend of $1.18 a share and kept the rest of the income in the retained earnings account. [85]
    a. What amount was kept in the retained earnings account? $242,000
    b. What dividend was received by Greg Flim, who holds 220 shares of the stock? $259.60

11. At the end of a year, a cooperative declared a 5.7% dividend on its stock and a 3% dividend on purchases made during the year. Marge Bayer held 150 shares of the stock, bought at $8 a share, and had purchases totaling $4,280 during the year. What was Marge's total dividend? $196.80 [85]

12. Under a bankruptcy agreement, the firm of Smith and Haynes must pay its creditors $0.57 on each dollar that is due them. How much would a creditor receive on a claim of $3,600? $2,052 [86]

13. When Albert Greer went bankrupt, he had assets of $12,500 and liabilities of $50,000. His bankruptcy filing fee, court costs, and related expenses totaled $3,700. How much money was available to be paid to creditors for outstanding claims? $8,800 [86]

14. A bankrupt company has $28,350 in cash available for creditors. The debts are $90,000. How many cents on the dollar will be paid to creditors?   31.5¢ [86]

15. Bay Road Lumber filed a claim against a bankrupt customer for $12,800. If the trustee paid 21% of all creditors' claims, what amount did Bay Road get? $2,688 [86]

Sections 87–91
Unit 14

1. The list price of an electronic typewriter is $320 less 20% and 20%. What is the invoice price of this typewriter? $204.80 [89]

2. A sewing machine has an invoice price of $364. If this machine had a list price of $520, what percent of discount would there be on the machine?   30% [88]

3. The Paint Store can buy air compressors from the Anders Wholesale Company for $850 each, less a trade discount of 38%. They can buy identical compressors from Westlake Distributing for $720 each, less trade discounts of 20% and 15%. How much will be saved on each air compressor by taking advantage of the lower offer? $37.40 saved by taking Westlake offer [89]

4. Find the total amount of an invoice containing these items: 70 gallons of paint at $10.50 per gallon; 30 drop cloths at $7.42 each; 6 stepladders at $28.60 each. $1,129.20 [87]

5. For the quarter, a company had purchases of $78,210 and purchases returns and allowances of $530.87. Net sales for the quarter were $189,300. What were the net purchases for the quarter? $77,679.13 [87]

6. During an average month, a retailer buys $12,600 worth of goods from 1 supplier, terms 1/10, n/30. How much money does the retailer save in 1 year by taking the cash discount each month? $1,512 [90]

7. A wholesaler offers windshield washer fluid for $0.62 a gallon with a 10% discount when 360 gallons are purchased in 1 order. What total amount of discount will a retailer get by buying 360 gallons of fluid at a time? $22.32 [88]

8. What single percent of discount is equivalent to the series 20%, 15%?   32% [89]

9. What amount of money will be needed to pay an invoice amounting to $712 and dated December 4, with terms of 3/10, 1/20, n/45, if paid on January 2? $712 [90]

10. An invoice for cement mixers bought by the Premier Home Improvement Company was dated March 22, with terms of 3/15, n/45. What is the last day on which the invoice can be paid to take advantage of the cash discount?   April 6 [90]

11. A manufacturer offered a retailer a cash discount of 5% on a $7,400 invoice for computer printers. To take advantage of the cash offer, the retailer borrowed money to pay the invoice. The loan was made for 60 days at 15% banker's interest. How much did the retailer save by borrowing the money and paying cash? $194.25 [91]

12. On October 2, Millicent Torawski ordered printer ribbons for her computer store. The list price of the ribbons was $800, with trade discounts of 30%, 10%. An invoice for the ribbons was prepared and mailed on October 2, with terms of 2/10, n/30. What cash price will Millicent pay if the invoice is paid within the discount period? $493.92 [90]

‡13. If a retailer saved $39 by taking a cash discount of 2%, what was the invoice price of the merchandise purchased? $1,950 [91]

‡14. For every 9 video tapes worth $2.90 each that a retailer orders, 1 video tape is given free as a special promotion by a wholesaler. What rate of trade discount is this?   10% [88]

**Sections 92–98
Unit 15**

1. Felicia Bergen had $100 in change in her cash register at the start of work on July 8. At the end of her work shift, there was $677.46 in the cash register. The register totals showed that she had taken

in $614.86 and paid out $37.50 during her shift. How much cash was short or over? $0.10, cash over [92]

2. Acker's account balance with Sumner, Inc., was $12,308.78 on May 1. These facts were recorded in the account during May: May 3, Invoice #5763, $3,588.98; May 8, Credit Memo #377, $478.33; May 30, payment, $10,000 on account. What was the balance in Acker's account on May 30? $5,419.43 [93]

3. A lamp marked $75 is reduced to $60. What is the rate of discount? 20% [94]

4. What is the amount of gross profit per item on diskette holders that cost $95.88 a dozen and sell for $15.89 each? $7.90 [95]

5. A clothing store bought slacks for $24 each and marked them to sell for $42 each. Later, to increase sales, the slacks were reduced to $35 each.
   a. What was the gross profit per pair at $42? $18
   b. What was the gross profit per pair at $35? $11
   c. What was the rate of markup on selling price, to the nearest tenth of a percent, at the $35 selling price? 31.4% [95]

6. A wholesaler bought goods for $11,595 and sold them for $13,176. Operating expenses were $2,136. What was the wholesaler's net loss? $555 [95]

7. An item that cost a store $22.75 was sold for $35. What was the rate of markup based on the selling price? 35% [95]

8. A service organization bought 50 dozen flowers at $9 per dozen and sold them at a town meeting. They charged $1 for each flower.
   a. What was the rate of markup on the selling price? 25%
   b. What was the total amount of gross profit on the sale?
      $150 [95]

9. A tractor attachment that cost $240 was sold for $336. What was the rate of markup based on cost? 40% [97]

10. Eder, Inc., bought a shipment of 350 personal radios at $8.50 each. Eder sold 160 of them at $15.98 each, 100 at $12.90 each, and the rest at $9.75 each. What rate of gross profit on cost did Eder make on the whole shipment, to the nearest tenth of a percent? 58.8% [97]

11. An office supply store bought 300 calculators at $6.25. The store sold 150 of them at $10.98 each and the rest at $6.98 each. Operating expenses for the calculators were $680. What percent of net income, to the nearest tenth of a percent, based on the cost of the calculators, did the store make? 7.4% [97]

12. Sachi Kato buys cans of tennis balls for $1.90 each. She sells each can for $2.85.
    a. What is Sachi's rate of markup, based on cost? 50% [97]
    b. What is Sachi's rate of markup, based on selling price?
       $33\frac{1}{3}$% [95]

13. Karl Schmidt buys skateboards for $22.80 each and pays shipping charges of $0.80 on each board. How much should he charge for each board to make a gross profit of 45% on the total cost? $34.22 [97]

14. An item costing $486 had to be sold for $388.80. What was the percent of loss, based on the cost?   20% [97]

15. A store bought 6 new camcorders for a total price of $4,500, less $12\frac{1}{2}$%. Shipping charges were $60. At what price should the store sell each camcorder to make a gross profit of 30% on the total cost? $866.13 [97]

16. Alvaro Rios has been buying exercise bicycles for $128 and selling them at $160. The price that Alvaro pays for these bicycles was recently increased to $144. At what price per bicycle must he sell them now to make the same percent of gain on their cost? $180 [97]

17. A wholesaler bought 450 staplers at $3 each. The wholesaler sold 150 of them for $4.50 each. If the wholesaler wants to make a 40% gross profit on the cost of the staplers, at what price must the rest be sold? $4.05 [97]

‡18. What should the selling price be for an item that costs $63 if the store wants to make a gross profit of 30% on the selling price? $90 [96]

‡19. A store buys home computers for $900, less 20% and 10%. The freight charges on each computer are $16. At what price must each computer be sold to make a gross profit of 20% on the selling price? $830 [96]

‡20. Power drills are billed to a retailer at $30, less 25% and 10%. Shipping charges are $0.75 for each drill. The retailer's overhead expenses are 30% of the selling price. At what price should the drills be marked to make a net income of 10% on the selling price? $35 [96]

‡21. A dealer bought an item for $40, less 25% and 10%. The shipping charges were $1.50. The dealer wants to make a markup of 40% on the selling price. What should the dealer's selling price for the item be? $47.50 [96]

‡22. What is the rate of markup on cost, to the nearest tenth of a percent, equivalent to a 24% rate of markup on the selling price? 31.6% [98]

‡23. The gross profit for an item is 26% of the selling price. What is the equivalent rate of gross profit, to the nearest whole percent, based on cost?   35% [98]

Sections 99–105
Unit 16

1. To make 200 motors, Aaron Fabricating Company had these manufacturing costs: materials, $2,978.55; labor, $4,207.23; factory expense, $2,009.43. What was the average factory cost of each motor, to the nearest whole cent? $45.98 [99]

2. The 4 departments of Baylor Insurance Co. use this floor space:

> Property, 1,500 square feet $1,800
> Casualty, 2,400 square feet $2,880
> Health, 2,500 square feet $3,000
> Automotive, 3,600 square feet $4,320

The annual maintenance cost of the building is $12,000. It is distributed on the basis of the floor space each department has. How much should each department be charged annually? [99]

3. A manufacturer sells motor housings for $12.50. The manufacturing costs are: material, $3.40; labor, $4.13; factory overhead, $1.62. Selling and administrative expenses are figured at 12% of the selling price. What is the manufacturer's net income? $1.85 [100]

4. Sytech, Inc., makes 10,000 calculators at a total cost of $17,400. The company will sell the calculators to wholesalers at $4 each. [100]
   a. How many calculators must be sold at $4 to break even?
      4,350
   b. What will be Sytech's net income if all 10,000 calculators sell for $4 each? $22,600
   c. How much will Sytech lose if only 3,000 calculators sell for $4 each? $5,400

5. Equipment that costs $52,000 decreases in value each year at the rate of 15%. Using the declining-balance method, what is the estimated book value of the machine at the end of the second year? $37,570 [101]

6. Davros Industries bought a hoist for $24,500. They plan to use the hoist for 5 years and then trade it for $12,500. Using the sum-of-the-years-digits method, what is the estimated book value of the hoist at the end of the second year? $17,300 [101]

7. A business office uses copy paper that costs $37 a case. Each case holds 10 reams of 500 sheets. The office uses 500 cases of the copy paper each year. The office manager estimates that 10% of the copies made are unneeded or for personal use. If this is correct, how much copy paper money would be saved per year by eliminating the unneeded and personal copies? $1,850 [102]

8. An office area of 800 square feet rents for $6,200 a year. Heating, cooling, lighting, and maintenance are estimated to cost $960 a year.
   a. What is the total yearly cost of this office space per square foot for a year? $8.95
   b. If a data entry clerk's work station is 70 square feet, how much does this work station cost per year? $626.50 [102]

9. Last year, a wholesaler employed 20 workers, all of whom received at least $7,000 in total wages. The FUTA tax rate was 6.2% on the first $7,000 of each employee's wages. What was the firm's FUTA tax? $8,680 [103]

10. Dillon, Inc., in Taylorville, sells Vilex, Inc., in Ashton, equipment for $2,840, f.o.b. Taylorville. Transportation charges are $101.37. [104]
    a. Who must pay the transportation charges? Vilex
    b. What will be the total cost of the equipment to Vilex?
       $2,941.37

11. A store ships 8 boxes of goods to Pine Valley. Each box weighs 52 pounds. The express rate is $3 per box plus $0.28 per pound. The store also insures each box for $200. Insurance costs are $0.30 per $100 of value. What is the cost of the shipment?
    $145.28 [104]

12. Banner Sales, Inc., leases 5 high volume laser printers for $1,100 per month each. What is the annual cost of the printers to the firm?
    $66,000 [105]

13. Balke Motors, Inc., bought 35 personal computer systems. Each system had: central processing unit, $650; disk drives, $450; display screen, $120; keyboard, $50; printer, $250; software, $1,400.
    a. What was the cost of each system? $2,920
    b. What was the total cost of the systems? $102,200 [105]

14. You buy software for your personal computer system. You pay $40 for the operating system software, $275 for spreadsheet software, $375 for a word processing program, and $125 for other software. What is the total cost of the software? $815 [105]

15. Lamery Distributors buys software for 12 personal computer systems. For each computer, it pays $60 for operating system software, $495 for word processing software, $420 for spreadsheet software, and $375 for graphics software. [105]
    a. What is the software cost per system? $1,350
    b. What is the total cost of the software to Lamery? $16,200

16. Four programmers were assigned the job of developing a sales-tracking program. Each programmer was paid $12 an hour. Programmer A spent 120 hours; B, 140 hours; C, 135 hours, and D, 145 hours writing and testing the program. What was the cost of the programming used to develop the program? $6,480 [105]

17. A hard disk drive, costing $2,800, can store 80 MB of data. What is the storage cost per megabyte? $35 [105]

**Sections 106–110
Unit 17**

1. A computer program counted the number of errors it found each day in data sent by users during the first half of a month. The daily totals of errors were: 20, 24, 31, 20, 28, 26, 20, 21, 22, 23, 19, 17, 18, 21, 20. What was the average number of errors per day figured as the [106]
    a. Mean? 22
    b. Median? 21
    c. Mode? 20

2. What was the range of the daily error totals from Problem 1?
    14 [106]

3. In a 365-day year, the months of April, June, September, and November have 30 days. February has 28 days; the rest of the months have 31 days. If you select 1 month at random, what is the probability that it will contain [107]
   a. Exactly 30 days? $\frac{1}{3}$
   b. Less than 31 days? $\frac{5}{12}$
   c. More than 30 days? $\frac{7}{12}$

4. Use Illustration 107–1 to find the probability, to the nearest percent, of a person
   a. Born today living to be 70 years of age   65%
   b. Who is 10 years old today living to be 70 years of age
      66% [107]

5. On a vertical bar graph, a line 1-inch long represents $500. What amount of money would be represented on this graph by a line $5\frac{1}{2}$ inches long? $2,750 [108]

6. The horizontal bar graph below shows the sales by department of the Spencer Hardware Store for the week ending October 12.

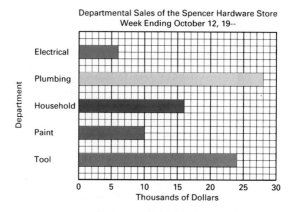

Departmental Sales of the Spencer Hardware Store
Week Ending October 12, 19--

   a. What was the amount of sales of the department that had the largest sales for the week? $28,000
   b. What was the amount of sales of the department that had the least sales for the week? $6,000
   c. If this store is in operation 6 days each week, what are the average daily sales of the Tool Department? $4,000
   d. If the Paint Department is planning a special promotion next week to increase its sales by 15%, what will be the Paint Department's expected sales next week? $11,500
   e. The sales of the Electrical Department for the week of October 12 represented a 20% gain from the previous week's sales. What was the amount of the previous week's sales for that department? $5,000
   f. What were the total sales for all departments for the week?
      $84,000 [108]

7. You are using graph paper that has 10 blocks to the inch. The dollar scale of a rectangle bar graph you are making is to be from $0 to $100,000. Each block represents $2,000. How many inches will you need to draw the dollar scale?   5 [109]

8. The circle graph below represents the income made by a shop from towel sales, bedspread sales, and linen sales. If the income earned by the shop in 1 week was $4,200, how much money was earned from
   a. Bedspread sales? $1,260
   b. Linen sales? $1,050 [109]

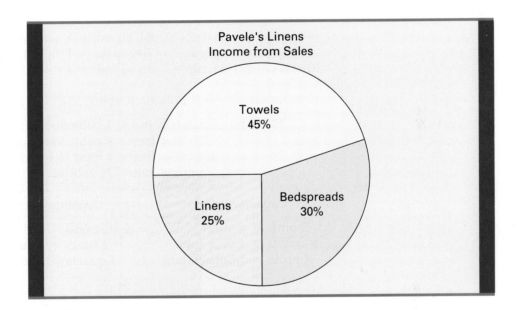

Pavele's Linens
Income from Sales

Towels
45%

Bedspreads
30%

Linens
25%

9. Using Illustration 110–1, find the average rate of inflation, to the nearest tenth percent, for consecutive 3-year periods that had the
   a. Highest total inflation   11.7%
   b. Lowest total inflation   3.3% [110]

10. Using the data in Illustration 110–4, find what number of men you would expect to be unemployed out of a group of 500 widowed, divorced, or separated men.   29 [110]

Some of the measures that have been most commonly used in the United States are these:

Length or Distance (Linear)

12 inches (in.) = 1 foot (ft.)	$16\frac{1}{2}$ feet = 1 rod
3 feet = 1 yard (yd.)	320 rods = 1 mile (mi.)
$5\frac{1}{2}$ yards = 1 rod (rd.)	5,280 feet = 1 mile

Area (Square)

144 sq. in. = 1 sq. ft.	160 sq. rd. = 1 acre (A)
9 sq. ft. = 1 sq. yd.	640 acres = 1 sq. mi. or section
$30\frac{1}{4}$ sq. yd. = 1 sq. rd.	36 sq. mi. = 1 township

Volume (Cubic)

1,728 cubic inches (cu. in.) = 1 cubic foot (cu. ft.)

27 cubic feet = 1 cubic yard (cu. yd.)

128 cubic feet = 1 cord of wood

1 cubic foot = $7\frac{1}{2}$ gallons

Capacity — Dry

2 pints = 1 quart

8 quarts = 1 peck (pk.)

4 pecks = 1 bushel (bu.)

Capacity — Liquid

4 gills (gi.) = 1 pint (pt.)

2 pints = 1 quart (qt.)

4 quarts = 1 gallon (gal.)

Avoirdupois Weight

16 ounces = 1 pound (lb.)

100 pounds = 1 hundred-
weight (cwt.)

2,000 pounds = 1 ton (T)

Time

60 seconds (sec.) = 1 minute (min.)

60 minutes = 1 hour (hr.)

24 hours = 1 day

Counting

12 units = 1 dozen   12 dozen = 1 gross

Account. A record of receipts and payments.

Addend. A number to be added to another.

Addition. A process of combining two numbers to give one number.

Adjusted gross income. A tax term meaning gross income less adjustments.

Agent. A person who legally acts for someone else.

Aliquot part. A number contained in another without a remainder.

Amortization. Gradual repayment of a debt by regular payments of principal and interest.

Amount due at maturity. The amount owed when note is due; the face plus interest on note; maturity value.

Amount financed. The amount of credit given on an installment loan or purchase.

Annual depreciation. A year's depreciation.

Annual percentage rate. A percent that shows the ratio of finance charges to the amount financed.

Annual rate. The rate for one year; the percent of the principal that is charged for one year's interest.

Appraised value. An estimate of the value of property.

Approximate value. A rounded amount; not exact.

Area. An amount of surface. Example: for a rectangle, length times width.

Assessed value. A value put on property as a base for figuring amount of tax.

Assessment roll. A list of property, with assessed valuations.

Assets. Things of value owned by a person or business.

Automatic teller machine. A computer system that lets you withdraw or deposit money in your checking account without a teller's help.

Average. A single number used to represent a group of numbers.

Average annual depreciation. The original cost less scrap value divided by years of use.

Balance. The amount of money in an account; the difference between the two sides of an account.

Balance sheet. A statement showing the assets, liabilities, and capital of a person or business for a certain date.

Bank discount. Interest collected in advance.

Bank statement. A periodic report to a depositor showing deposits, payments, charges, and balance in a checking account.

Banker's interest. Interest based on a 360-day year; ordinary interest.

Bankrupt. Legally insolvent and unable to pay debts.

Bar code. Patterns of printed bars that identify a stock item.

Base. A number with which another is compared; a number that may be multiplied by a fraction or percent; in a numeration system, the number by which a digit is multiplied when moved one place to the left.

Base period. A period in time with which comparisons are made.

Beneficiary. The person to whom life insurance benefits are paid when the insured dies.

Bodily injury insurance. Auto insurance covering liability for injury to other persons.

Bond. A form of long-term promissory note issued by a corporation or government.

Bondholder. One who holds a corporation or government bond.

Book value. Original cost less total depreciation to date.

Break-even point. The point at which income from sales equals total costs.

Broker. A dealer in stocks and bonds or real estate.

Broker's commission. A fee paid to a broker; brokerage fee.

Budget. A plan for using or spending income; an estimate of expenses.

Buying expense. The cost of buying goods.

Byte. A character stored in a computer system.

C. Hundred.

Call forwarding. A phone feature that lets you transfer a call to another number.

Call waiting. A phone feature that lets you interrupt one call to talk to another caller.

Canceled check. A check that has been marked "Paid" by the bank.

Capital. The owner's claim to the assets of a business; proprietorship; owners' equity; investment; net investment; net worth.

Capital investment. The original investment in property plus additions and improvements.

Cash advance. The cash received when money is borrowed on a credit card.

Cash discount. Discount given for early payment of a bill.

Cash over. When there is more cash on hand than there should be.

Cash payments record. A written record of cash spent.

Cash price. Invoice price less cash discount; amount paid when no credit is used.

Cash proof form. A form used to check the amount of cash in a cash register.

Cash receipts record. A written record of cash taken in.

Cash record summary. A review of cash received and paid out, of income and expenses.

Cash register. A device for storing cash and for recording cash received and paid out.

Cash short. When there is less cash on hand than there should be.

Cash value. The value of an insurance policy if it is canceled; cash surrender value.

Catalog price. Same as list price.

Centimeter (cm). One-hundredth of a meter; about 0.3937 inches.

Central processing unit. The brain of a computer system; the part that processes data.

Chance event. The outcome of making a random choice.

Change fund. Money placed in a cash drawer at the start of a period of time.

Charter. A document, issued by a state, that creates a corporation and tells what the corporation can do.

Check. A written order directing a bank to make a payment.

Check register. A record of deposits and checks.

Circle graph. A circle showing how parts relate to the whole and to each other.

Closing costs. Expenses that must be paid when a home is purchased; settlement costs.

C.O.D. Cash on delivery; collect on delivery.

Coinsurance. When the insured and the insurer share losses or costs.

Coinsurance clause. A feature of insurance that requires coverage up to a specified percent of value to recover the full amount of a loss.

Collateral. Personal property deposited or pledged as security for a loan.

Collateral loan. A loan with a note that is backed up or secured by the deposit or pledge of personal property.

Collateral note. A note that is backed up by collateral.

Collision insurance. Auto insurance that covers damage to the insured's car from collision or upset.

Commission. A payment to an agent or salesperson based on the value or quantity of goods bought or sold; broker's or brokerage fee.

Common denominator. Any denominator that is shared by two or more fractions.

Common stock. The ordinary stock of a corporation, paying no specified rate or amount of dividend.

Complement. Applied to trade discounts, the difference between a given trade discount rate and 100 percent.

Compound amount. The total in a savings account at the end of an interest period after compound interest is added.

Compound interest. The difference between the original principal and the compound amount; interest figured on interest after it has been added to the principal.

Compounding interest. Figuring and adding interest to make a new principal.

Comprehensive damage. Insurance that covers damage to the insured's car from causes other than collision or upset.

Consumer loan. Same as an installment loan.

Consumer price index. A single number used to measure a change in consumer prices compared to a base year.

Cooperative. A corporation whose customers are usually shareholders of the business.

Corporation. A business owned by several people legally acting as one under a charter.

Cost of merchandise sold. The amount paid by the seller for the goods sold; cost of goods sold.

Coverage. The amount of insurance carried.

Credit card. A card that identifies a customer who can buy on credit.

Credit memo. A form that tells the buyer that the buyer's account has been reduced.

Credit period. The length of time given to pay an invoice.

Creditor. A person or firm to whom money is owed.

Cross product. The result of multiplying a denominator by a numerator in a proportion.

Customary system. The system of measures used in the U.S.

Customer's account. A record showing a customer's purchases, returns, payments, and balance owed.

cwt. Hundredweight or hundred pounds.

Date of maturity. Same as due date.

Date of note. The date on which the note was signed.

Debit card. A card that lets you pay for purchases using a terminal in a store.

Decimal (or decimal fraction). Represents a fraction with a denominator of 10, 100, 1,000, etc., and written with a decimal point; for example, 0.52 or 7.345.

Decimal point. A point or period indicating the separation of a whole number and a decimal fraction.

Decimal rate. A property tax rate shown as a decimal.

Decimal system. A ten-digit system of numeration; a base-ten system.

Declare a dividend. Distribute corporate profits to shareholders.

Declining-balance method. A way of figuring depreciation at a fixed rate on a decreasing balance; fixed-rate method.

Deductible insurance. A health or casualty insurance policy in which the insured pays the first part of any loss and the company pays the rest.

Deductions. Allowable expenses that may be subtracted from income for tax purposes.

Demand loan. A loan that must be repaid when the bank asks for payment.

Demand note. The note that creates a demand loan.

Denomination. The price on the face of a savings bond; the value on bills and coins.

Denominator. The numeral below the line in a fraction, showing the number of equal parts into which a whole is divided.

Deposit. To put money in a checking or savings account.

Deposit slip. A form used to list all money deposited in a bank.

Depreciation. The decrease in value caused by wear and aging.

Difference. The missing addend that is found by subtracting a known addend from a sum or total.

Digit. Any one of the symbols 0, 1, 2, 3, 4, 5, 6, 7, 8, 9.

Direct labor. The cost of all production workers who work directly on products.

Discount. A reduction in price (markdown) or in the amount of a bill; interest deducted in advance; the difference between market and par value of a bond.

Discount period. The number of days given for a cash discount.

Discount rate. Same as rate of discount; the percent of discount charged by a bank on a discounted loan; the percent of cash or trade discount given.

Discount series. Same as series of discounts.

Discount sheet. A form showing the discounts given from the catalog or list prices.

Discounting a note. Signing a note and paying the interest (discount) immediately.

Dividend. The number that is to be divided by another; earnings distributed to shareholders of a corporation or to holders of insurance policies.

Division. The reverse of multiplication; a process of finding the unknown factor when one factor and the product are known.

Divisor. The number that shows the size or number of groups into which a dividend is to be split.

Double-time pay. Pay that is twice the regular pay.

Double-time rate. A pay rate that is two times the regular rate.

Down payment. The part of a price that is paid at the time of buying on the installment plan.

Due date. The date on which a note must be paid; same as date of maturity.

Effective rate of interest. The annual rate of interest actually earned or paid.

Electronic funds transfer. When funds are withdrawn from one account and deposited into another using computers.

Employee. A person who works for someone else.

Employee earnings card. A form that shows the earnings, deductions, and net pay for one worker.

Employer. A person or company that employs workers.

E.O.M. A term showing that a trade discount will be given on the invoice within a certain number of days after the end of the month.

Energy efficiency rating (EER). A measure of the efficiency of an electric appliance.

Equity. A person's stake in property.

Equivalent fractions. Fractions that name the same number.

Estimate. Find a rough answer.

Estimated tax. Quarterly income tax paid by the self-employed.

Exact interest. Interest based on exact time and a 365-day year.

Exact value. A quotient that is not rounded.

Exchange. A place where stocks, bonds, or commodities are traded.

Excise tax. A federal tax on telephone service, airplane tickets, and some other items.

Exemption. An amount of income that is free from tax.

Expense. Money paid out; the cost of goods or services used up; a decrease in capital caused by the operation of a business.

Express. A shipping service providing fast delivery of goods that are small and light in weight.

Extended coverage. Insurance that adds wind, smoke, and hail coverage to a standard fire policy.

Extended-term life insurance. Provides full coverage for a limited time to an insured person, bought with cash value.

Extension. The total price of each quantity on a sales slip, found by multiplying the quantity by the unit price.

Face. The amount stated on a business paper such as a note, bond, or insurance policy; face value; principal.

Face value. Same as face.

Factor. Each of the numbers in multiplication.

Factory expense. The total cost of items such as rent, depreciation, heat, light, power, insurance, supplies, and indirect labor used in a factory.

Factory overhead. Same as factory expense.

Federal unemployment tax. A payroll tax paid by employers to support the federal unemployment insurance program.

FICA tax. A federal tax on employers, employees, and self-employed persons; social security tax.

Finance charge. The sum of the interest and any other charges on an installment loan or purchase.

Fiscal period. The time for which net income or net loss is figured; financial period.

Fiscal year. A fiscal period of twelve months starting on any date.

Fixed-rate method. Same as declining-balance method.

Fixed-rate mortgage. A loan in which the interest rate stays the same over the life of the loan.

f.o.b. Free on board; a term used in price quotations to tell who will pay transportation costs.

Fraction. A symbol or name, such as $\frac{2}{3}$, $\frac{5}{4}$, $\frac{6}{2}$, standing for the quotient of two numbers or showing the division of the numerator (upper number) by the denominator (lower number); symbol or name for a fractional number; same as fractional numeral.

Fractional equivalent. A fraction that shows what part one number is of another; for example, $\frac{1}{2}$ is the fractional equivalent of 50 cents on a base of $1.

Fractional number. The number that results when one number is divided by another and the quotient is not a whole number.

Fractional numeral. A symbol for a fractional number.

Freight. A service for delivery of heavy, bulky goods.

Frequency distribution. A table of numbers arranged in order and with the frequency, or how often they occur, tallied.

Fringe benefits. Paid vacations, sick leave, retirement plans, insurance, and other benefits beyond the wage or salary.

Fuel adjustment rate. A rate used to adjust your fuel costs to changes in the fuel company's costs for fuel.

Graduated commission. A pay system in which the rate of commission increases as the base increases.

Gram (g). One one-thousandth of a kilogram; $\frac{1}{28}$ of an ounce.

Greatest common factor. The largest number that will divide each term of a fraction without a remainder.

Gross. The total without any deduction, such as gross profit, gross income; twelve dozen.

Gross income. Total income, before adjustments, deductions, or exemptions; total rent received from a tenant.

Gross loss. The opposite of gross income; the amount by which costs exceed the selling price.

Gross pay. The total of all pay earned.

Gross profit on sales. Net sales less cost of merchandise sold; margin.

Hardware. Computer equipment.

Health insurance. Protects policyholder from financial loss due to illness.

Hectare (ha). A square hectometer; about 2.5 acres.

Higher terms. An equivalent fraction in larger terms.

Home equity loan. A loan using the owner's equity or stake in a home for collateral.

Homeowners insurance. Fire and extended coverage on the home, plus theft and liability coverage.

Horizontal addition. Adding across.

Horizontal bar graph. A graph with bars running across.

Hourly rate. An amount of pay for each hour worked.

Improper fraction. A fraction whose numerator is equal to or greater than the denominator.

Income. Revenue; money received.

Income statement. A report showing sales, cost of merchandise sold, gross profit, operating expenses, and net income or loss; a profit and loss statement.

Income tax. A federal, state, or local tax on income.

Income tax return. A form showing how income taxes were figured.

Individual earnings record. A payroll record that is kept for each employee.

Inflation. A rise in the prices of goods and services.

Input device. Equipment used to enter data into a computer system.

Insolvent. A condition in which liabilities exceed assets, so debts cannot be paid.

Installment. A partial payment on a loan or purchase.

Installment loan. A loan repaid in partial payments; a consumer loan.

Installment plan. A way of buying that usually requires a down payment, finance charges, and installment payments; a time-payment plan.

Insured. The party whose life or property is insured.

Insurer. The insurance company.

Interest. The dollar cost of using a lender's money.

Interest-bearing note. A note on which interest is to be paid.

Inventory. A list of things on hand and their values.

Inverting the fraction. A process of "switching" the numerator and denominator.

Investment. Property bought for long-term use or for income or profit; the amount of money invested.

Invoice cost. Same as invoice price.

Invoice price. List price less trade discounts; invoice cost; net price.

Joint return. An income tax return for a husband and wife together.

Kilobyte. One thousand bytes, or characters.

Kilogram (kg). The basic metric unit of weight or mass; equal to about 2.2 pounds.

Kiloliter (kL). One thousand liters.

Kilometer (km). One thousand meters; about $\frac{3}{5}$ of a mile.

Kilowatt-hours (KWH). The flow of 1,000 watts of electricity for one hour.

Labor force. All persons who are working or looking for work.

Lease. A rental agreement; to rent.

Least common denominator. The smallest denominator shared by two or more fractions.

Level payment plan. A loan repayment plan in which all payments are the same amount.

Liabilities. Creditors' claims to assets; debts that are owed.

Like fractions. Fractions having the same denominator.

Limited payment life insurance. Provides coverage for a lifetime, but premiums are paid for a fixed time only.

Line graph. A graph on which lines connect dots to show values.

List price. A price shown in a catalog or price list before trade discounts are deducted; a quoted price; catalog price.

Liter (L). The basic metric measure of capacity; slightly more than a quart.

Load fund. A mutual fund with a commission charge.

Lowest terms. Occurs when no number other than 1 will divide both terms of a fraction.

M. One thousand.

MACRS. A method of figuring depreciation based on the class life of property.

Magnetic ink character recognition. Special characters printed on checks to let computers process the checks.

Maker. One who writes a note and promises to pay.

Margin. Same as gross profit; markup.

Markdown. A reduction in marked or retail price; a discount.

Marked price. The price on an item or attached tag; retail price.

Market price. The price at which a stock or bond is sold; the price or value of an item in the open market.

Market value. The price of a bond after it is issued; market price.

Markup. The amount by which a selling price exceeds the cost; gross profit; margin.

Maturity value. Same as amount due at maturity.

Mean. The sum of the numbers divided by the number of items; arithmetic average; a measure of central tendency.

Measures of central tendency. The mean, median, and mode; averages.

Median. The middle number in a group of numbers arranged in order.

Medicare. A program that pays for hospital and medical bills.

Megabyte. One million bytes, or characters.

Merchandise inventory. A list that shows the cost or market value of goods on hand held for resale.

Merchandise turnover rate. The number of times average inventory is sold in a period.

Meter (m). Basic metric unit of length or distance; equal to 39.37 inches.

Metric system. A system of measures used in most of the world.

Metric ton (t). One thousand kilograms; about 1.1 Customary tons.

Mill. One tenth of a cent.

Milligram (mg). One-thousandth gram.

Milliliter (mL). One-thousandth liter.

Millimeter (mm). One-thousandth meter; 0.03937 inches.

Mixed number. A number having both a whole number and a fraction, such as $3\frac{1}{2}$.

Mode. The number that occurs most frequently in a group of numbers.

Money market account. A special savings account that earns a rate of interest based on the rate the federal government pays.

Monthly benefit. The amount paid each month by social security to a retired or disabled worker and dependents.

Mortality table. A table that shows the number of people who live to certain ages.

Mortgage. A paper signed by a borrower that gives the lender the right to ownership of property if the borrower does not pay the principal or interest.

Multiplication. A short way of adding two or more equal numbers.

Mutual fund. An investment company that buys stocks and bonds of other companies.

Net. The amount left after deductions have been subtracted.

Net asset value. The value of a mutual fund share found by dividing net assets of the fund by outstanding shares.

Net assets. The value of a mutual fund's assets less the money the fund owes to others.

Net income. The amount left after subtracting operating expenses from gross profit; net profit.

Net job benefits. The total value of the benefits received from a job less job expenses.

Net loss. When operating expenses are greater than gross profit, net loss equals operating expenses less gross profit.

Net pay. The remaining pay after deductions have been subtracted from total or gross wages; take-home pay.

Net proceeds. For an agent, gross proceeds or selling price less commission and expenses; in stock sales, market price less commission, taxes, and fees.

Net profit. Same as net income.

Net purchases. Purchases less purchases returns and allowances.

Net sales. Sales less sales returns and allowances.

No-load funds. Mutual funds that sell shares without charging commission.

No-par stock. Stock issued without a stated value on the certificate.

Non-interest-bearing note. A note without interest.

Note. Same as promissory note.

Number sentence. A statement that says two values are equal.

Numeral. A symbol or name for a number.

Numerator. The numeral above the line in a fraction, indicating how many of the equal parts of the fraction are shown.

Offer price. What the buyer pays for a mutual fund share; the net asset value of the share plus commission, if any.

Office equipment. Office furniture and machinery expected to last a year or more.

Office supplies. Items, such as paper and paper clips, that are used up quickly in an office.

On account. A term indicating that payment is to be made at a later date, or describing a partial payment on an amount owed.

Open sentence. A number sentence that has a missing numeral.

Operating expenses. The cost of items such as rent, salaries, and advertising that decrease profits and so must be subtracted from gross profit; overhead.

Output device. Equipment used to get information out of a computer system.

Outstanding check. A check issued but not yet received and paid by the bank.

Overhead. Same as operating expenses.

Overtime. Time worked over or beyond regular time.

Paid-up life insurance. A smaller amount of insurance for life, with no more premiums, bought with cash value.

Parcel post. The common name for fourth-class mail.

Partnership. A business owned by two or more persons, without a charter, who agree to share profits and losses.

Partnership agreement. A written contract between partners that tells who will do what, and how profits and losses will be shared.

Par value. The face value of a bond or stock.

Passbook. A savings account record.

Payback period. The number of years it takes to save enough money to pay back the cost of an item.

Payee. The one to whom a note or check is payable.

Payroll register. A record showing earnings, deductions, and net pay of all workers in a business.

Percent. Per hundred; by the hundred, or out of a hundred; shows the comparison or ratio of any number to one hundred.

Piece. An item produced.

Piece rate. A wage system in which workers are paid by the number of pieces produced.

Place value. The value of a digit determined by its position.

Policy. An insurance contract.

Policy loan. A loan of part or all of the cash value of a policy made by an insurance company to an insured.

Preferred stock. Stock that gets first choice in distributed profits and a stated rate of dividend.

Premium. The amount paid for insurance; a bond selling above par value is selling "at a premium."

Price list. A sheet or booklet that lists the names and prices of items for sale.

Pricing goods. Deciding the price to put on goods to be sold.

Principal. The one for whom an agent acts; the face of a note; the amount on which interest is paid.

Probability. The likelihood that an event will occur; a branch of mathematics concerned with predicting chance events.

Proceeds. The amount the borrower gets on a discounted note; the amount received from a sale.

Product. The result of multiplication.

Profit and loss statement. Same as income statement.

Promissory note. A written promise to repay money at a certain time; a note.

Proper fraction. A fraction in which the numerator is smaller than the denominator.

Property damage insurance. Auto insurance covering damage to property of others.

Property tax. A tax on real estate.

Proportion. A statement showing that two ratios are equal.

Pro rata. In proportion; proportionately.

Prove cash. Count cash on hand and check accuracy against the record of cash received and paid out.

Purchase invoice. An itemized statement showing goods bought, with quantities, descriptions, prices, and charges; called a sales invoice by the seller.

Purchases. The total merchandise bought during a period.

Purchasing power of dollar. A measure of how much a dollar will buy.

Quantity discount. A trade discount based on the amount purchased.

Quarterly. Once very three months or quarter of a year.

Quota. A fixed amount of sales above which commission is paid.

Quotation. The price and terms on which a seller offers to sell; the published market price of a stock, bond, or commodity.

Quotient. The figure that shows how many times the divisor is included in the dividend.

Random sample. A few items selected by chance from the whole group.

Range. The difference between the highest and lowest numbers in a group.

Rate. The percent that is found by dividing the amount of interest, discount, depreciation, dividend, or income by the base.

Rate of depreciation. Depreciation shown as a percent.

Rate of discount. The percent of interest charged on a note and deducted when the loan is made; the percent of price reduction.

Rate of dividend. The amount of dividend divided by the par value.

Rate of interest. Interest shown as a percent.

Ratio. A way of comparing numbers, such as $\frac{2}{3}$, 2 divided by 3, 2:3.

Raw materials. The cost of materials used in manufacturing that are part of the final product.

Real estate. Land and things attached to it, such as buildings and trees.

Receipt. An official record of a transaction.

Reciprocal. The reciprocal of a given number is the number whose product with the given number is 1. For example, the reciprocal of $\frac{3}{2}$ is $\frac{2}{3}$; of 5 is $\frac{1}{5}$; of $\frac{1}{5}$ is 5.

Reconciliation statement. A form showing how the checkbook and bank statement balances are made to agree.

Rectangle graph. A graph that uses vertical or horizontal rectangles to show how parts relate to the whole and to each other.

Redemption value. The amount you receive when a savings bond is turned in for cash.

Refinance. Use a new loan to pay off an old loan.

Regular time. The number of hours of work expected in a regular work day or week; straight time.

Remainder. A leftover in division; the part of the dividend that is left over when the divisor is not contained a whole number of times in the dividend.

Renters policy. Similar to homeowners insurance, but not covering loss of building or apartment.

Replacement cost policy. Insurance that pays the cost of replacing a property at current prices.

Resale value. The amount you receive when you sell an asset, such as a car.

Retail price. Same as marked price.

Retained earnings. Net income that is kept by a corporation rather than distributed to shareholders.

Revenue. An increase in capital resulting from operations of the business.

Reverse addition. A way of checking addition by

adding a column of numbers in the opposite direction of the first addition.

Rounding. The process by which unwanted digits on the right of a number are dropped.

Salary. A fixed amount of pay for a week, month, or year.

Sales. The total amount of merchandise sold over a period of time, expressed in selling prices.

Sales invoice. An itemized statement showing goods sold; called a purchase invoice by the buyer.

Sales price. Same as selling price.

Sales returns and allowances. The dollar amount of goods sold that were later returned for refunds or for which credit was given because of damage; a decrease in sales.

Sales slip. A form showing the details of a sale.

Sales tax. A tax charged by a city, county, or state on the sale of items or services and collected by sellers from buyers.

Savings bond. A series EE bond sold by the federal government.

SEC fee. A fee charged by the Securities and Exchange Commission on stock sold.

Security. Something given to guarantee that a debt will be paid or a promise kept.

Self-employment tax. A social security tax paid by self-employed persons.

Selling and administrative expenses. A manufacturer's costs for salespeople, advertising, office salaries, and other operating costs.

Selling price. The price actually paid by a buyer; the sales price.

Series of discounts. Two or more trade discounts to be applied in succession; a discount series.

Service charge. A bank charge or deduction for handling a checking account; a charge in addition to interest on an installment purchase.

Settlement costs. Same as closing costs.

Shareholder. One who owns shares of corporation stock; a stockholder.

Short-term policy. A property insurance policy issued for less than a year.

Signature card. A bank form that identifies a bank account owner.

Simple average. The sum of the numbers (items) divided by the number of items.

Single discount equivalent. The one discount equal to a series of discounts.

Social security tax. Same as FICA tax.

Software. Computer programs.

Sole proprietorship. A business owned by one person; proprietorship.

Speed dialing. A phone feature that lets you dial a number using only one or two buttons.

Square meter (m^2). The basic unit of area in the metric system; equal to 1.196 square yards.

Standard fire policy. Covers loss by fire and lightning only.

Stock. Goods or supplies on hand; shares of ownership in a corporation.

Stockholder. One who buys and sells stocks for others.

Stock certificate. A paper issued to a shareholder that shows on its face the number of shares it represents.

Stockholder. Same as shareholder.

Stock transfer tax. A tax on stock sold.

Storage device. A computer system component, such as a disk or tape drive, on which data and programs can be kept.

Straight commission. A pay system in which commission is the only pay; there is no other wage or salary.

Straight life insurance. Premiums are paid and the insurance is in force for the whole life of the insured.

Straight-line method. A way of figuring depreciation that spreads the total depreciation evenly over the life of the item.

Straight time. Same as regular time.

Subtotal. On a sales slip, the sum of the extensions before taxes are added.

Subtraction. The reverse of addition.

Sum. The result of addition; the total; an amount of money.

Sum-of-the-years-digits method. A variable-rate way of depreciating that provides decreasing amounts of depreciation as an item ages.

T (Customary ton). Two thousand pounds; equal to 0.91 metric tons.

t (metric ton). One thousand kilograms; equal to 1.102 Customary tons.

Take-home pay. Same as net pay.

Taxable income. The amount used to figure income tax with a tax-rate schedule.

Tax return. A form showing the facts used to figure income tax due; an income tax report.

Tax table income. The amount used to find income tax in a tax table.

Term life insurance. Premiums are paid and insurance is in force for a fixed time only, with no cash values.

Term of discount. The time during which a bank holds a discounted note; date of discount to date of maturity.

Terms. The numerator and denominator of a fraction.

Terms of sale. Tell when an invoice must be paid and what discounts are given.

Therm. A measure of heat.

Three-way calling. A phone feature that enables you to talk to more than one person at a time.

Time. For a note, the length of time for which the money is borrowed.

Time-and-a-half-pay. Pay that is one and a half times the regular pay rate.

Time-and-a-half-rate. A rate that is one and a half times the regular rate.

Time card. A record showing when a worker arrived and left for regular time and for overtime.

Time clock. A device used to stamp a time card.

Time-deposit account. Money in a savings or certificate of deposit account.

Time payment plan. Same as installment plan.

Tips. Money received by employees from customers.

Total. Same as sum.

Total cost. The sum of invoice or cash price and buying expense.

Total factory cost. The sum of the costs of raw materials, direct labor, and factory expense.

Total job benefits. Gross pay plus fringe benefits.

Trade discount. A reduction or discount given from a catalog or list price; a discount given "within the trade."

Trade-in value. The amount you get for your old car or other asset when buying a new car or other asset.

Transit number. A bank identification number shown on a check as the top part of a fraction.

Unemployment rate. The percent of the labor force not working.

Unit price. The price of a single measure, such as $1 per quart or $2 per kilogram.

Unlike fractions. Fractions that have different denominators, such as $\frac{1}{2}$ and $\frac{1}{5}$.

U.S. individual income tax. A federal tax on income.

Variable-rate mortgage. A loan in which the interest rate may change over the life of the loan.

Vertical addition. The usual way of adding up and down.

Vertical bar graph. A graph with bars running up and down.

Wages. The total pay for a day or week of a worker paid on an hourly rate basis.

Weighted average. An average that gives weight to the items in proportion to their frequency or importance.

Whole life. Life insurance that gives coverage for a lifetime, and in which premiums are paid for a lifetime.

Whole numbers. Whole units, such as 1 and 6.

Withdraw. To take money from a bank account, such as a savings or certificate of deposit account.

Withholding allowance. An allowance for a person used to reduce the amount of tax withheld from pay.

Withholding tax. A deduction from pay for income tax.

Yield. The rate of income on an investment, such as 9 percent yield on bonds.

$40,000, 13%, 30-Year Mortgage, with $442.48 Monthly Payment

Payment Number	Balance	Monthly Payment Used for		Payment Number	Balance	Monthly Payment Used for	
		Interest	Principal			Interest	Principal
1	$40,000.00	$433.33	$ 9.15	45	$39,487.86	$427.79	$ 14.69
2	39,990.85	433.23	9.25	46	39,473.17	427.63	14.85
3	39,981.60	433.13	9.35	47	39,458.32	427.47	15.01
4	39,972.25	433.03	9.45	48	39,443.31	427.30	15.18
5	39,962.80	432.93	9.55	49	39,428.13	427.14	15.34
6	39,953.25	432.83	9.65	50	39,412.79	426.97	15.51
7	39,943.60	432.72	9.76	51	39,397.28	426.80	15.68
8	39,933.84	432.62	9.86	52	39,381.60	426.63	15.85
9	39,923.98	432.51	9.97	53	39,365.75	426.46	16.02
10	39,914.01	432.40	10.08	54	39,349.73	426.29	16.19
11	39,903.93	432.29	10.19	55	39,333.54	426.11	16.37
12	39,893.74	432.18	10.30	56	39,317.17	425.94	16.54
13	39,883.44	432.07	10.41	57	39,300.63	425.76	16.72
14	39,873.03	431.96	10.52	58	39,283.91	425.58	16.90
15	39,862.51	431.84	10.64	59	39,267.01	425.39	17.09
16	39,851.87	431.73	10.75	60	39,249.92	425.21	17.27
17	39,841.12	431.61	10.87	61	39,232.65	425.02	17.46
18	39,830.25	431.49	10.99	62	39,215.19	424.83	17.65
19	39,819.26	431.38	11.10	63	39,197.54	424.64	17.84
20	39,808.16	431.26	11.22	64	39,179.70	424.45	18.03
21	39,796.94	431.13	11.35	65	39,161.67	424.25	18.23
22	39,785.59	431.01	11.47	66	39,143.44	424.05	18.43
23	39,774.12	430.89	11.59	67	39,125.01	423.85	18.63
24	39,762.53	430.76	11.72	68	39,106.38	423.65	18.83
25	39,750.81	430.63	11.85	69	39,087.55	423.45	19.03
26	39,738.96	430.51	11.97	70	39,068.52	423.24	19.24
27	39,726.99	430.38	12.10	71	39,049.28	423.03	19.45
28	39,714.89	430.24	12.24	72	39,029.83	422.82	19.66
29	39,702.65	430.11	12.37	73	39,010.17	422.61	19.87
30	39,690.28	429.98	12.50	74	38,990.30	422.39	20.09
31	39,677.78	429.84	12.64	75	38,970.21	422.18	20.30
32	39,665.14	429.71	12.77	76	38,949.91	421.96	20.52
33	39,652.37	429.57	12.91	77	38,929.39	421.74	20.74
34	39,639.46	429.43	13.05	78	39,908.65	421.51	20.97
35	39,626.41	429.29	13.19	79	38,887.68	421.28	21.20
36	39,613.22	429.14	13.34	80	38,866.48	421.05	21.43
37	39,599.88	429.00	13.48	81	38,845.05	420.82	21.66
38	39,586.40	428.85	13.63	82	38,823.39	420.59	21.89
39	39,572.77	428.71	13.77	83	38,801.50	420.35	22.13
40	39,559.00	428.56	13.92	84	38,779.37	420.11	22.37
41	39,545.08	428.41	14.07	85	38,757.00	419.87	22.61
42	39,531.01	428.25	14.23	86	38,734.39	419.62	22.86
43	39,516.78	428.10	14.38	87	38,711.53	419.37	23.11
44	39,502.40	427.94	14.54	88	38,688.42	419.12	23.36

Payment Number	Balance	Monthly Payment Used for		Payment Number	Balance	Monthly Payment Used for	
		Interest	Principal			Interest	Principal
89	$38,665.06	$418.87	$ 23.61	139	$37,109.39	$402.02	$ 40.46
90	38,641.45	418.62	23.86	140	37,068.93	401.58	40.90
91	38,617.59	418.36	24.12	141	37,028.03	401.14	41.34
92	38,593.47	418.10	24.38	142	36,986.69	400.69	41.79
93	38,569.09	417.83	24.65	143	36,944.90	400.24	42.24
94	38,544.44	417.56	24.92	144	36,902.66	399.78	42.70
95	38,519.52	417.29	25.19	145	36,859.96	399.32	43.16
96	38,494.33	417.02	25.46	146	36,816.80	398.85	43.63
97	38,468.87	416.75	25.73	147	36,773.17	398.38	44.10
98	38,443.14	416.47	26.01	148	36,729.07	397.90	44.58
99	38,417.13	416.19	26.29	149	36,684.49	397.42	45.06
100	38,390.84	415.90	26.58	150	36,639.43	396.93	45.55
101	38,364.26	415.61	26.87	151	36,593.88	396.43	46.05
102	38,337.39	415.32	27.16	152	36,547.83	395.93	46.55
103	38,310.23	415.03	27.45	153	36,501.28	395.43	47.05
104	38,282.78	414.73	27.75	154	36,454.23	394.92	47.56
105	38,255.03	414.43	28.05	155	36,406.67	394.41	48.07
106	38,226.98	414.13	28.35	156	36,358.60	393.88	48.60
107	38,198.63	413.82	28.66	157	36,310.00	393.36	49.12
108	38,169.97	413.51	28.97	158	36,260.88	392.83	49.65
109	38,141.00	413.19	29.29	159	36,211.23	392.29	50.19
110	38,111.71	412.88	29.60	160	36,161.04	391.74	50.74
111	38,082.11	412.56	29.92	161	36,110.30	391.19	51.29
112	38,052.19	412.23	30.25	162	36,059.01	390.64	51.84
113	38,021.94	411.90	30.58	163	36,007.17	390.08	52.40
114	37,991.36	411.57	30.91	164	35,954.77	389.51	52.97
115	37,960.45	411.24	31.24	165	35,901.80	388.94	53.54
116	37,929.21	410.90	31.58	166	35,848.26	388.36	54.12
117	37,897.63	410.56	31.92	167	35,794.14	387.77	54.71
118	37,865.71	410.21	32.27	168	35,739.43	387.18	55.30
119	37,833.44	409.86	32.62	169	35,684.13	386.58	55.90
120	37,800.82	409.51	32.97	170	35,628.23	385.97	56.51
121	37,767.85	409.15	33.33	171	35,571.72	385.36	57.12
122	37,734.52	408.79	33.69	172	35,514.60	384.74	57.74
123	37,700.83	408.43	34.05	173	35,456.86	384.12	58.36
124	37,666.78	408.06	34.42	174	35,398.50	383.48	59.00
125	37,632.36	407.68	34.80	175	35,339.50	382.84	59.64
126	37,597.56	407.31	35.17	176	35,279.86	382.20	60.28
127	37,562.39	406.93	35.55	177	35,219.58	381.55	60.93
128	37,526.84	406.54	35.94	178	35,158.65	380.89	61.59
129	37,490.90	406.15	36.33	179	35,097.06	380.22	62.26
130	37,454.57	405.76	36.72	180	35,034.80	379.54	62.94
131	37,417.85	405.36	37.12	181	34,971.86	378.86	63.62
132	37,380.73	404.96	37.52	182	34,908.24	378.17	64.31
133	37,343.21	404.55	37.93	183	34,843.93	377.48	65.00
134	37,305.28	404.14	38.34	184	34,778.93	376.77	65.71
135	37,266.94	403.73	38.75	185	34,713.22	376.06	66.42
136	37,228.19	403.31	39.17	186	34,646.80	375.34	67.14
137	37,189.02	402.88	39.60	187	34,579.66	374.61	67.87
138	37,149.42	402.45	40.03	188	34,511.79	373.88	68.60

| Payment Number | Balance | Monthly Payment Used for | | Payment Number | Balance | Monthly Payment Used for | |
		Interest	Principal			Interest	Principal
189	$34,443.19	$373.13	$ 69.35	239	$29,873.57	$323.63	$118.85
190	34,373.84	372.38	70.10	240	29,754.72	322.34	120.14
191	34,303.74	371.62	70.86	241	29,634.58	321.04	121.44
192	34,232.88	370.86	71.62	242	29,513.14	319.73	122.75
193	34,161.26	370.08	72.40	243	29,390.39	318.40	124.08
194	34,088.86	369.30	73.18	244	29,266.31	317.05	125.43
195	34,015.68	368.50	73.98	245	29,140.88	315.69	126.79
196	33,941.70	367.70	74.78	246	29,014.09	314.32	128.16
197	33,866.92	366.89	75.59	247	28,885.93	312.93	129.55
198	33,791.33	366.07	76.41	248	28,756.38	311.53	130.95
199	33,714.92	365.24	77.24	249	28,625.43	310.11	132.37
200	33,637.68	364.41	78.07	250	28,493.06	308.67	133.81
201	33,559.61	363.56	78.92	251	28,359.25	307.23	135.25
202	33,480.69	362.71	79.77	252	28,224.00	305.76	136.72
203	33,400.92	361.84	80.64	253	28,087.28	304.28	138.20
204	33,320.28	360.97	81.51	254	27,949.08	302.78	139.70
205	33,238.77	360.09	82.39	255	27,809.38	301.27	141.21
206	33,156.38	359.19	83.29	256	27,668.17	299.74	142.74
207	33,073.09	358.29	84.19	257	27,525.43	298.19	144.29
208	32,988.90	357.38	85.10	258	27,381.14	296.63	145.85
209	32,903.80	356.46	86.02	259	27,235.29	295.05	147.43
210	32,817.78	355.53	86.95	260	27,087.86	293.45	149.03
211	32,730.83	354.58	87.90	261	26,938.83	291.84	150.64
212	32,642.93	353.63	88.85	262	26,788.19	290.21	152.27
213	32,554.08	352.67	89.81	263	26,635.92	288.56	153.92
214	32,464.27	351.70	90.78	264	26,482.00	286.89	155.59
215	32,373.49	350.71	91.77	265	26,326.41	285.20	157.28
216	32,281.72	349.72	92.76	266	26,169.13	283.50	158.98
217	32,188.96	348.71	93.77	267	26,010.15	281.78	160.70
218	32,095.19	347.70	94.78	268	25,849.45	280.04	162.44
219	32,000.41	346.67	95.81	269	26,687.01	278.28	164.20
220	31,904.60	345.63	96.85	270	25,522.81	276.50	165.98
221	31,807.75	344.58	97.90	271	25,356.83	274.70	167.78
222	31,709.85	343.52	98.96	272	25,189.05	272.88	169.60
223	31,610.89	342.45	100.03	273	25,019.45	271.04	171.44
224	31,510.86	341.37	101.11	274	24,848.01	269.19	173.29
225	31,409.75	340.27	102.21	275	24,674.72	267.31	175.17
226	31,307.54	339.17	103.31	276	24,499.55	265.41	177.07
227	31,204.23	338.05	104.43	277	24,322.48	263.49	178.99
228	31,099.80	336.91	105.57	278	24,143.49	261.55	180.93
229	30,994.23	335.77	106.71	279	23,962.56	259.59	182.89
230	30,887.52	334.61	107.87	280	23,779.67	257.61	184.87
231	30,779.65	333.45	109.03	281	23,594.80	255.61	186.87
232	30,670.62	332.27	110.21	282	23,407.93	253.59	188.89
233	30,560.41	331.07	111.41	283	23,219.04	251.54	190.94
234	30,449.00	329.86	112.62	284	23,028.10	249.47	193.01
235	30,336.38	328.64	113.84	285	22,835.09	247.38	195.10
236	30,222.54	327.41	115.07	286	22,639.99	245.27	197.21
237	30,107.47	326.16	116.32	287	22,442.78	243.13	199.35
238	29,991.15	324.90	117.58	288	22,243.43	240.97	201.51

Payment Number	Balance	Monthly Payment Used for	
		Interest	Principal
289	$22,041.92	$238.79	$203.69
290	21,838.23	236.58	205.90
291	21,632.33	234.35	208.13
292	21,424.20	232.10	210.38
293	21,213.82	229.82	212.66
294	21,001.16	227.51	214.97
295	20,786.19	225.18	217.30
296	20,568.89	222.83	219.65
297	20,349.24	220.45	222.03
298	20,127.21	218.04	224.44
299	19,902.77	215.61	226.87
300	19,675.90	213.16	229.32
301	19,446.58	210.67	231.81
302	19,214.77	208.16	234.32
303	18,980.45	205.62	236.86
304	18,743.59	203.06	239.42
305	18,504.17	200.46	242.02
306	18,262.15	197.84	244.64
307	18,017.51	195.19	247.29
308	17,770.22	192.51	249.97
309	17,520.25	189.80	252.68
310	17,267.57	187.07	255.41
311	17,012.16	184.30	258.18
312	16,753.98	181.50	260.98
313	16,493.00	178.67	263.81
314	16,229.19	175.82	266.66
315	15,962.53	172.93	269.55
316	15,692.98	170.01	272.47
317	15,420.51	167.06	275.42
318	15,145.09	164.07	278.41
319	14,866.68	161.06	281.42
320	14,585.26	158.01	284.47
321	14,300.79	154.93	287.55
322	14,013.24	151.81	290.67
323	13,722.57	148.66	293.82
324	13,428.75	145.48	297.00
325	13,131.75	142.26	300.22
326	12,831.53	139.01	303.47
327	12,528.06	135.72	306.76
328	12,221.30	132.40	310.08
329	11,911.22	129.04	313.44
330	11,597.78	125.64	316.84
331	11,280.94	122.21	320.27
332	10,960.67	118.74	323.74
333	10,636.93	115.23	327.25
334	10,309.68	111.69	330.79
335	9,978.89	108.10	334.38
336	9,644.51	104.48	338.00
337	9,306.51	100.82	341.66
338	8,964.85	97.12	345.36

Payment Number	Balance	Monthly Payment Used for	
		Interest	Principal
339	$ 8,619.49	$ 93.38	$349.10
340	8,270.39	89.60	352.88
341	7,917.51	85.77	356.71
342	7,560.80	81.91	360.57
343	7,200.23	78.00	364.48
344	6,835.75	74.05	368.43
345	6,467.32	70.06	372.42
346	6,094.90	66.03	376.45
347	5,718.45	61.95	380.53
348	5,337.92	57.83	384.65
349	4,953.27	53.66	388.82
350	4,564.45	49.45	393.03
351	4,171.42	45.19	397.29
352	3,774.13	40.89	401.59
353	3,372.54	36.54	405.94
354	2,966.60	32.14	410.34
355	2,556.26	27.69	414.79
356	2,141.47	23.20	419.28
357	1,722.19	18.66	423.82
358	1,298.37	14.07	428.41
359	869.96	9.42	433.06
360	436.90	4.73	436.90

Notes:

1. The interest payment for a month is figured on the amount shown in the balance column. The interest payment is subtracted from the monthly payment of $442.48 to find the amount to be applied to the principal.

2. When the monthly payment needed to amortize a mortgage is figured, the payment amount is always rounded up to the next highest cent. This is done to ensure that the final payment will be large enough to pay off the mortgage, assuming all the monthly payments are made on time.

3. When the final payment is made, the lender figures the exact amount needed to pay off the mortgage loan. The final payment is rarely equal to the regular monthly payment. In this table, only $441.63 is needed to pay the interest due of $4.73 and the outstanding principal of $436.90.

Index